Illinois Mathematics Assessment Framework

To help increase your knowledge of mathematics and critical thinking, the Illinois Board of Education has established an Assessment Framework to prepare you for the ISAT. Here is an overview of the goals for Number Sense, Measurement, Algebra, and Data Analysis, Statistics, and Probability.

Goal 6: Number Sense

The 18 objectives in this goal (6.8.01 through 6.8.18) cover three topics:
   Representations and Ordering, (6.8.01 through 6.8.08)
   Computation, Operations, Estimation, and Properties, (6.8.09 through 6.8.14)
   Ratios, Proportions, and Percents, (6.8.15 through 6.8.18)

When you have mastered these objectives you will be able to:

♦ Demonstrate knowledge and use of numbers and their representations in a broad range of theoretical and practical settings.

♦ Investigate, represent and solve problems using number facts, operations (addition, subtraction, multiplication, division) and their properties, algorithms and relationships.

♦ Compute and estimate using mental mathematics, paper-and-pencil methods, calculators and computers.

♦ Solve problems using comparison of quantities, ratios, proportions and percents.

What It Means To You

You have learned about fractions, decimals, and whole numbers. These types of numbers are part of the set of *real numbers*. Numbers written with *exponents* (mathematical notation that represents repeated multiplication) or as the square root of a positive number are also real numbers. You will learn to use and simplify expressions with exponents. You will study the square root operation, which is the inverse of squaring.

Goal 7: Measurement

The 6 objectives in this goal (7.8.01 through 7.8.06) cover one topic:
   Units, Tools, Estimation, and Applications, (7.8.01 through 7.8.06)

When you have mastered these objectives you will be able to:

♦ Measure and compare quantities using appropriate units, instruments and methods.

♦ Estimate measurements and determine acceptable levels of accuracy.

♦ Select and use appropriate technology, instruments and formulas to solve problems, interpret results and communicate findings.

SO-AIG-995

Goal 8: Algebra

The 13 objectives in this goal (8.8.01 through 8.8.13) cover three topics:
Representations, Patterns, and Expressions, (8.11.01 through 8.11.05)
Connections Using Tables, Graphs, and Symbols, (8.11.06 through 8.11.10)
Writing, Interpreting, and Solving Equations, (8.11.11 through 8.11.13)

When you have mastered these objectives you will be able to:

♦ Describe numerical relationships using variables and patterns.

♦ Interpret and describe numerical relationships using tables, graphs and symbols.

♦ Solve problems using systems of numbers and their properties.

♦ Use algebraic concepts and procedures to represent and solve problems.

What It Means To You

Many mathematical patterns can be described using formulas and equations. For example, the equation $y = 15x + 45$, where x represents the number of days and y represents the total cost, describes the data in the table.

Just as there are rules for operations with numbers, there are rules for operations involving formulas and equations. Using these rules, you can solve formulas, equations, and inequalities to find an unknown value, such as the number of days you can rent a computer if you can only spend $165.

Cost of Renting a Computer	
Number of Days	Rental Charge
1	$60
2	$75
3	$90
4	$105
5	$120

Goal 10: Data Analysis, Statistics, and Probability

The 8 objectives in this goal (10.11.01 through 10.11.08) cover two topics:
Data Analysis and Statistics, (10.11.01 through 10.11.05)
Probability, (10.11.06 through 10.11.08)

When you have mastered these objectives you will be able to:

♦ Organize, describe and make predictions from existing data.

♦ Formulate questions, design data collection methods, gather and analyze data and communicate findings.

♦ Determine, describe and apply the probabilities of events.

What It Means To You

Real-world data may not be linear. Sometimes, however, the data may follow a trend that is close to a line or a curve. In such cases, you can use a line of best fit to describe a situation and make predictions about the behavior of the data.

As you study data, you will work with a variety of graphs and calculate values that can be used to summarize data, such as the mean and the median.

Prices of Mid-Sized Used Cars

ILLINOIS

PRENTICE HALL MATHEMATICS
PRE-ALGEBRA

PEARSON

Prentice
Hall

Boston, Massachusetts
Upper Saddle River, New Jersey

ISBN 0-13-201595-1
1 2 3 4 5 6 7 8 9 10   10 09 08 07 06

Illinois Mathematics Student Handbook

Illinois Math Program Advisors

Shelly Castans
Math Department Chair
James B. Conant HS
Hoffman Estates, IL

Jane Cotts
Mathematics Instructor
O'Fallon Township HS
O'Fallon, IL

Sandra Graham
Mathematics and
Algebra Instructor
Bloomington Junior HS
Bloomington, IL

Lanis Lenker
Math Chair
Mount Vernon, IL

Michael McGiles
Math Department Chair
Glenwood High School
Jacksonville, IL

Randy Pippen
Assistant Mathematics
Professor
North Central College
Naperville, IL

Frank Sambor
Math Department Chair
East Saint Louis HS
East Saint Louis, IL

Elizabeth Tucker
Math Department Chair
Mendota Township HS
Mendota, IL

Robert Urbain
Math Department Chair
Glenbard West HS
Glen Ellyn, IL

Jamie Wilson
Mathematics Instructor
Lockport Township HS
Lockport, IL

Ishmael Zamora
Mathematics Curriculum
Coordinator
Rich Central HS
Olympia Fields, IL

Table of Contents

This section guides you through the topics that you will be exploring this year. You will find the wording from the state documents, as well as a short explanation of what each standard means to you and an example of how it might be tested.

This section focuses on the Illinois Mathematics Assessment Framework and allows you to monitor your progress in mastering the objectives. It also helps you sharpen your skills so that you will be successful on test day.

Workout for Illinois Standards Mastery

Ready to go after Chapter 1

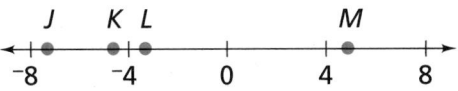 **For help, go to the lesson in green.**

1. An electronics store sells video game memory cards in packages of 3. Each package costs $21.00. Which expression can be used to find the cost, x, of one memory card?
(Lesson 1-1)

A. $x = \frac{21}{3}$ **C.** $x = \frac{21}{3x}$

B. $x = \frac{3x}{21}$ **D.** $x = 21(3)$

2. What is the value of the following expression?
(Lesson 1-2)

$12 + (16 - 6) \div 2$

E. 11   **G.** 17
F. 16   **H.** 25

3. Given: $m = 9$ and $n = 8$
Simplify: $3 \cdot (m - 5) + n$
(Lesson 1-3)

A. 20   **C.** 33
B. 30   **D.** 36

4. Which point represents -5?
(Lesson 1-4)

```
      J    K L          M
    +--•---•-•----+----•---+-->
    -8     -4     0    4    8
```

E. Point J
F. Point K
G. Point L
H. Point M

5. The expression $24 + (-32) + 18$ is equivalent to—
(Lesson 1-5)

A. -26 **C.** 10
B. -8 **D.** 38

6. The average surface temperature on Venus is 464°C. The average surface temperature on Mars is -65°C. What is the difference between the average surface temperatures on Venus and Mars?
(Lesson 1-6)

E. 399°C   **G.** 429°C
F. 409°C   **H.** 529°C

7. Open Response At a park, customers pay $10.00 to rent a canoe for one hour. Each additional hour costs $4.00.
(Lesson 1-3)

A. What would be the cost of renting a canoe for h hours? Write your answer in the form of an expression in which h is the number of hours.
B. What would be the cost of renting a canoe for 4 hours? Show your work.

 Assessment Framework
6.8.09, 6.8.10, 8.8.02, 8.8.05, 9.8.12

Illinois Workout

Workout for Illinois Standards Mastery

Ready to go after Chapter 2

 For help, go to the lesson in green.

1. Which of the following expressions is equal to 0?
   (Lesson 2-1)

   A. $75 \cdot (-32 + 0)$
   B. $-32 \cdot (0 \cdot 75)$
   C. $0 + (-32 \cdot 75)$
   D. $-32 + (75 \cdot 0)$

2. Which of these expressions is equivalent to $32 \cdot 5^2 - 21 \cdot 5^2$?
   (Lesson 2-2)

   E. $5^2(32 - 21)$
   F. $5^2 - (32 \cdot 21)$
   G. $(32 \cdot 5^2) - 21$
   H. $32(5^2 - 21)$

3. Ms. Swenson weighed 153 pounds when holding a puppy and 144 pounds when standing on the scale alone. The equation $153 - w = 144$ can be used to determine w, the puppy's weight in pounds. How much does Ms. Swenson's puppy weigh?
   (Lesson 2-4)

   A. 9 pounds
   B. 11 pounds
   C. 19 pounds
   D. 21 pounds

4. Which statement best describes how the equation $m + 75 = -5$ can be solved for m?
   (Lesson 2-5)

   E. Add 75 to the left side, and subtract 75 from the right side.
   F. Subtract 75 from the left side, and add 75 to the right side.
   G. Add 75 to both sides of the equation.
   H. Subtract 75 from both sides of the equation.

5. What is the solution to $-4x = -64$?
   (Lesson 2-6)

   A. $x = -256$
   B. $x = -16$
   C. $x = 16$
   D. $x = 256$

6. Which inequality is graphed below?
   (Lesson 2-9)

   E. $-1 + d \le -1$
   F. $4 + d \le 2$
   G. $d - (-3) \le 5$
   H. $d - 6 \le -4$

7. In a quiz game, Sarita answered 4 more questions than Helen did. If Helen answered q questions, which expression represents the total number of questions the two girls answered?
   (Lesson 2-3)

   A. $q + 4$ **C.** $5q$
   B. $2q + 4$ **D.** $6q$

8. **Open Response** A marine patrol officer tells a family of 5 that they can catch no more than 75 fish. Write an inequality that best represents m, the number of fish that each person in the family can catch without going over the legal limit.
   (Lesson 2-10)

 Assessment Framework
6.8.11, 8.8.03, 8.8.11, 8.8.12,
8.8.13

Ready to go after Chapter 3

? For help, go to the lesson in green.

1. Which is *closest* to the value of the expression $12.78 + 86.3 - 8.14$?
(Lesson 3-1)

   A. 89   **C.** 91
   B. 90   **D.** 100

2. A computer programmer bought 6 packages of blank CDs for $4.78 each including tax. If the programmer pays with two $20 bills, which is *closest* to the amount of change she should receive?
(Lesson 3-2)

   E. $25.00   **G.** $15.00
   F. $20.00   **H.** $10.00

3. A pebble is thrown off a high bridge and into the water below. The speed of the pebble when thrown is 3 meters per second. The formula $v = 9.8t + 3$ can be used to determine v, the speed of the pebble after t seconds. How fast is the pebble falling 1.5 seconds after it is thrown?
(Lesson 3-4)

   A. 14.7 meters per second
   B. 17.7 meters per second
   C. 44.1 meters per second
   D. 45.9 meters per second

4. Ms. O'Connor deposited $218.32 in her checking account. After the deposit, her balance was $1,086.70. The equation $b + \$218.32 = \$1,086.70$ can be used to determine b, the balance in Ms. O'Connor's account before she made the deposit. What value of b makes the equation true?
(Lesson 3-5)

   E. $850.48   **G.** $1,250.42
   F. $868.38   **H.** $1,305.02

5. What value of p makes the equation $\dfrac{p}{0.068} = 17$ true?
(Lesson 3-6)

   A. 1.156   **C.** 250
   B. 2.5   **D.** 11.56

6. Pierre has a canteen that holds 2 liters of water. If he drinks 600 milliliters, what volume of water will be left?
(Lesson 3-7)

   E. 400 milliliters
   F. 800 milliliters
   G. 1,200 milliliters
   H. 1,400 milliliters

7. Open Response A researcher is testing batteries to determine how long they typically last. The table shows the results of a test of 5 batteries of a particular brand.
(Lesson 3-3)

BATTERY LIFE

Test	Hours
1	2,575
2	2,675
3	2,685
4	1,575
5	2,595

   A. What is the mean life, in hours, of the 5 batteries? Show your work.
   B. Does the mean or the median better represent the number of hours a battery of this brand typically lasts? Explain your reasoning.

Assessment Framework
6.8.13, 7.8.05, 8.8.12, 8.8.13, 10.8.05

Illinois Workout

Workout for Illinois Standards Mastery

Ready to go after Chapter 4

? **For help, go to the lesson in green.**

1. How is the expression $-4 \cdot b \cdot b \cdot b \cdot b$ written using an exponent?
(Lesson 4-2)

    A. $-b^4$ C. $-4b^4$
    B. $-b^8$ D. $(-4b)^4$

2. What is the value of the expression $(0.6)^3$?
(Lesson 4-2)

    E. 0.18 G. 1.8
    F. 0.216 H. 2.16

3. A florist is arranging white roses in glass vases and red roses in ceramic vases. She has 84 white roses and 66 red roses. Each vase must contain the same number of roses. What is the greatest number the florist can put in each vase if no roses are left over?
(Lesson 4-3)

    A. 6 C. 14
    B. 12 D. 25

4. Out of 70 students surveyed, 28 said that they own a cat. What fraction of the students surveyed own a cat?
(Lesson 4-4)

    E. $\frac{1}{6}$ G. $\frac{2}{5}$
    F. $\frac{1}{4}$ H. $\frac{4}{5}$

5. Which of these expressions is equivalent to $5^5 \cdot 5^2$?
(Lesson 4-7)

    A. 5^7 C. 25^7
    B. 5^{10} D. 25^{10}

6. A basketball arena has a seating capacity of 13,570 people. Which of the following shows this number in scientific notation?
(Lesson 4-9)

    E. 13.57×10^4 G. 13.57×10^3
    F. 1.357×10^4 H. 1.357×10^3

7. In one year, light from the Sun can travel about 5.88×10^{12} miles. Based on this information, approximately how far can light from the Sun travel in 3 years?
(Lesson 4-9)

    A. 1.76×10^{12} miles
    B. 1.76×10^{13} miles
    C. 5.88×10^{15} miles
    D. 5.88×10^{36} miles

8. **Open Response** Simplify the expression $\frac{(-3)^6}{(-3)^3}$. Show your work.

    (Lesson 4-8)

Assessment Framework
6.8.04, 6.8.05, 6.8.08, 6.8.09, 6.8.10

Ready to go after Chapter 5

 For help, go to the lesson in green.

1. Which list shows the fractions $\frac{7}{9}$, $\frac{5}{6}$, and $\frac{11}{15}$ in order from least to greatest?
(Lesson 5-1)

A. $\frac{11}{15}, \frac{7}{9}, \frac{5}{6}$

C. $\frac{11}{15}, \frac{5}{6}, \frac{7}{9}$

B. $\frac{5}{6}, \frac{7}{9}, \frac{11}{15}$

D. $\frac{7}{9}, \frac{11}{15}, \frac{5}{6}$

2. A grocery store received a shipment of apples. Of the 35 crates of apples received, 14 contained green apples. Which decimal represents the portion of the shipment that contained green apples?
(Lesson 5-2)

E. 0.35

G. 0.45

F. 0.40

H. 0.60

3. The expression $\frac{4}{9} - \frac{1}{3} + \frac{7}{12}$ is equivalent to —
(Lesson 5-3)

A. $\frac{5}{6}$

C. $\frac{17}{36}$

B. $\frac{5}{9}$

D. $\frac{25}{36}$

4. A recipe for soup calls for $3\frac{3}{4}$ cups of chicken broth. If a cook wants to make only half as much, how many cups of chicken broth should she add?
(Lesson 5-4)

E. $1\frac{3}{8}$ cups

G. $1\frac{7}{8}$ cups

F. $1\frac{5}{8}$ cups

H. $2\frac{1}{8}$ cups

5. What is the solution to the equation $\frac{1}{10}m = \frac{3}{5}$?
(Lesson 5-8)

A. $m = 6$

C. $m = \frac{1}{2}$

B. $m = 2$

D. $m = \frac{1}{6}$

6. The expression $\left(3 \cdot \frac{2}{9}\right)^2$ is equivalent to —
(Lesson 5-9)

E. $\frac{4}{27}$

F. $\frac{4}{9}$

G. $1\frac{1}{3}$

H. 4

7. Open Response A dressmaker shortens a skirt by $\frac{7}{8}$ inch. The final length of the skirt is $28\frac{1}{2}$ inches.

A. Write an equation that can be used to determine *s*, the original length of the skirt in inches.

B. Using the formula written in Part A, find the original length of the skirt.

Assessment Framework
6.8.03, 6.8.06, 6.8.09, 6.8.10,
6.8.18, 8.8.12, 8.8.13

Illinois Workout

Workout for Illinois Standards Mastery

Ready to go after Chapter 6

? For help, go to the lesson in green.

1. The table shows the weight and cost of four brands of salad dressing.

Brand	Weight (ounces)	Cost
A	12	$3.60
B	15	$3.75
C	18	$4.68
D	21	$5.46

Which brand of salad dressing represents the best buy?
(Lesson 6-1)

A. Brand A   **C.** Brand C
B. Brand B   **D.** Brand D

2. If 500 sheets of paper weigh 64 ounces, what is the weight of 20 sheets of paper?
(Lesson 6-2)

E. 1.28 ounces   **G.** 2.56 ounces
F. 1.60 ounces   **H.** 3.20 ounces

3. $\triangle ABC$ is similar to $\triangle DEF$.

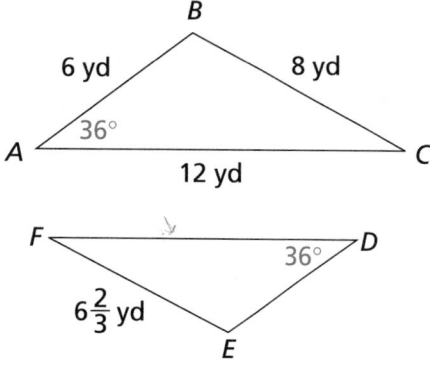

What is the length of $\overline{DF}$?
(Lesson 6-3)

A. $13\frac{1}{3}$ yards   **C.** 10 yards
B. $12\frac{2}{3}$ yards   **D.** 8 yards

4. At a middle school, 144 of the 450 students are in the eighth grade. What percent of students at the school are in the eighth grade?
(Lesson 6-5)

E. 65%   **G.** 48%
F. 59%   **H.** 32%

5. The number of people who attended this week's football game was 120% of the number who attended last week. If 185 people attended the game last week, how many people attended this week?
(Lesson 6-6)

A. 205   **C.** 305
B. 222   **D.** 339

6. Open Response One winter, a mountain had an average snow depth of 40 inches. The following winter, the mountain had an average snow depth of only 38 inches. What was the percent of decrease in the average snow depth between the two winters? Round to the nearest percent and show your work.
(Lesson 6-3)

Assessment Framework
6.8.03, 6.8.15, 6.8.16, 6.8.18, 9.8.11

Ready to go after Chapter 7

 For help, go to the lesson in green.

1. What is the solution to the equation
$8 - \frac{m}{3} = 24$?
(Lesson 7-1)

  A. -96
  B. -64
  C. -48
  D. -16

2. A coach bought 4 jump ropes. She used a coupon for $5.00 off her total purchase and paid a total of $26.84. What is the regular price of each jump rope?
(Lesson 7-1)

  E. $5.46   **G.** $6.71
  F. $6.17   **H.** $7.96

3. In a basketball game, Benjamin scored 5 more points than Alonzo did. Together, they scored 29 points. The equation $p + 5 + p = 29$ can be used to determine p, the number of points Alonzo scored. How many points did Alonzo score?
(Lesson 7-2)

  A. 10 points   **C.** 14 points
  B. 12 points   **D.** 15 points

4. What value of x makes the equation
$\frac{1}{2}x - 7 = 10$ true?
(Lesson 7-3)

  E. 6
  F. 13
  G. 27
  H. 34

5. What is the solution to $-3a + 12 = 2a - 8$?
(Lesson 7-5)

  A. $a = -20$
  B. $a = -4$
  C. $a = 4$
  D. $a = 20$

6. What is the solution to the inequality
$-4x + 5 > -11$?
(Lesson 7-6)

  E. $x > -4$ **G.** $x > 4$
  F. $x < -4$ **H.** $x < 4$

7. Open Response The late fee at a video store is $2.75 for the first day and $0.75 for each additional day. The equation $2.75 + 0.75(d - 1) = f$ can be used to determine the late fee, f, for a video that is returned d days late. If Meredith has a late fee of $5.00, how many days late did she return her video? Show your work.
(Lesson 7-2)

Assessment Framework
8.8.12, 8.8.13

Illinois Workout

Workout for Illinois Standards Mastery

Ready to go after Chapter 8

 For help, go to the lesson in green.

1. The cost of renting a cabin at a campground for one night can be determined by using the equation $c = 5.5p + 30$, where c is the cost in dollars and p is the number of people who will be staying in the cabin. Which table of values could be used to graph this equation?
(Lesson 8-2)

A.
p	2	6	10
c	37.5	41.5	45.5

B.
p	2	6	10
c	40.5	60.5	80.5

C.
p	2	6	10
c	41	63	85

D.
p	2	6	10
c	41	123	205

2.
x	−1	−3	−5	−7
y	0	3	6	9

If the ordered pairs in the table were graphed, what would be the slope of the line connecting them?
(Lesson 8-3)

E. $-\frac{3}{2}$

F. $-\frac{2}{3}$

G. $\frac{2}{3}$

H. $\frac{3}{2}$

3. The scatter plot shows how the number of minutes Ben needs to finish a math quiz depends on the number of hours he spends studying for the quiz.

Based on the trend shown in the scatter plot, which is the best prediction of the number of minutes Ben will need to finish a quiz if he studies for only half an hour?
(Lesson 8-5)

A. 24 minutes   C. 28 minutes

B. 26 minutes   D. 30 minutes

4. **Open Response** Jorge wants to buy a baseball glove. He already has $10 and plans to save an additional $5 each week.
(Lesson 8-3)

A. Write an equation that can be used to determine the total amount of money (y) Jorge will have saved after x weeks.

B. Graph your equation on a coordinate grid. Include a title and appropriate labels for the axes.

C. If the baseball glove that Jorge wants costs $55, how many weeks will it take him to save enough money to buy it? Explain how you determined your answer.

 Assessment Framework
8.8.07, 8.8.09, 10.8.01

Ready to go after Chapter 9

For help, go to the lesson in green.

1. In the figure below, ∠1 measures 48° and ∠2 measures 56°.

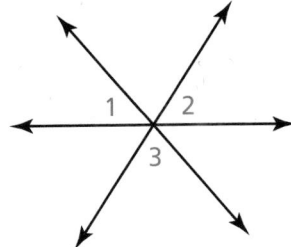

What is the measure of ∠3?
(Lesson 9-2)

A. 48°   **C.** 76°
B. 52°   **D.** 104°

2. The coordinates of point *Q* are (3, −2). If point *Q* is translated left 2 units and down 3 units, what are the coordinates of its translated image?
(Lesson 9-8)

E. (1, −5)
F. (1, 1)
G. (5, 1)
H. (5, −5)

3. What is the circumference of a circle with a radius of 10 inches?
(Lesson 9-6)

A. 5π
B. 20π
C. 100π
D. 200π

4. In the figure below, line *m* is parallel to line *n*.

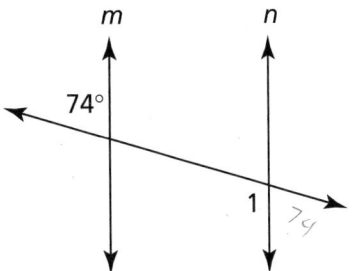

What is the measure of ∠1?
(Lesson 9-2)

E. 114°
F. 106°
G. 96°
H. 74°

5. Open Response A graphic designer is creating a cover for a new book. She begins by using a computer illustration program to draw △*FGH*, shown below. Her next step is to reflect the triangle over the *y*-axis.

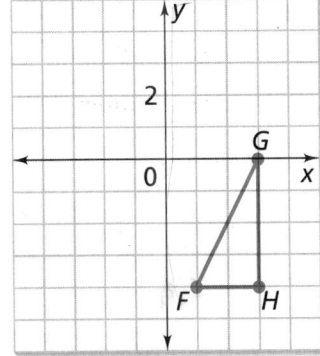

(Lesson 9-9)

A. Draw △*FGH* reflected over the *y*-axis.
B. Label the coordinates of points *F′*, *G′*, and *H′*.

Assessment Framework
7.8.02, 9.8.06, 9.8.08

Illinois Workout

Workout for Illinois Standards Mastery

For help, go to the lesson in green.

1. Penny is covering a rectangular patio with tile. Each tile is a right triangle like the one shown below.

6 in.

4 in.

If the patio has a length of 180 inches and a width of 120 inches, what is the minimum number of tiles that Penny will need?
(Lesson 10-2)

A. 450 tiles   C. 1,800 tiles
B. 900 tiles   D. 2,160 tiles

2. A shipping case has a length of 18 inches, a width of 12 inches, and a height of 18 inches. The case is used to ship boxes of crackers that each have a length of 6 inches, a width of 2 inches, and a height of 9 inches. What is the greatest number of cracker boxes that can fit in the shipping case?
(Lesson 10-7)

$$V = \ell wh$$

E. 12 boxes   G. 32 boxes
F. 27 boxes   H. 36 boxes

3. Khafre's Pyramid in Egypt has a square base with a side length of 216 meters and a slant height of 431 meters. What is the *lateral* surface area of the pyramid?
(Lesson 10-6)

A. 186,192 square meters
B. 232,740 square meters
C. 279,288 square meters
D. 372,384 square meters

4. A park has two swimming pools shaped like rectangular prisms. The volume of the larger pool is 5,280 cubic feet. The dimensions of the smaller pool are $\frac{3}{4}$ of the dimensions of the larger pool. What is the volume of the smaller pool to the nearest cubic foot?
(Lesson 10-7)

E. 2,228 cubic feet
F. 2,970 cubic feet
G. 3,685 cubic feet
H. 3,960 cubic feet

5. **Open Response** A delivery truck carries a cylindrical tank with the dimensions shown below.

40 feet

8 feet

(Lesson 10-5)

A. Write the formulas for finding the surface area and volume of a right circular cylinder.

B. Using the formulas written in Part A, find the surface area and volume of the cylindrical tank shown above. Round answers to the nearest tenth.

Assessment Framework
7.8.02, 7.8.04

Ready to go after Chapter 11

 For help, go to the lesson in green.

1. Nell often takes a shortcut across a rectangular park. How many kilometers *shorter* is the shortcut than the longer path along two sides of the park?
(Lesson 11-2)

A. 0.25 km   **C.** 1.25 km
B. 0.5 km   **D.** 1.75 km

2. A barn is 80 feet south of a house. A shed is 60 feet east of the house. What is the straight-line distance from the barn to the shed?
(Lesson 11-2)

E. 50 feet   **G.** 100 feet
F. 70 feet   **H.** 140 feet

3. Which of these numbers is irrational?
(Lesson 11-1)

A. $-\sqrt{25}$
B. $-3\frac{1}{3}$
C. $4.\overline{09}$
D. $\sqrt{33}$

4. Between what two consecutive whole numbers does $\sqrt{85}$ lie?
(Lesson 11-1)

E. 6 and 7
F. 7 and 8
G. 8 and 9
H. 9 and 10

5. **Open-Ended** Marian wants to determine the distance across Mirror Lake.

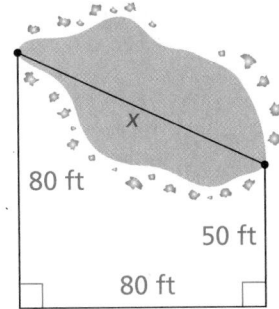

(Lesson 11-2)

A. Write an equation that can be used to find the distance *x*. Explain the process you used to determine your equation.
B. Solve the equation you wrote in Part A to find the distance across Mirror Lake to the nearest foot. Show your work.

Illinois Workout

Assessment Framework
6.8.14, 9.8.03

Workout for Illinois Standards Mastery

Ready to go after Chapter 12

 For help, go to the lesson in green.

1. The histogram shows the daily high temperature in a certain city in February 2005.

DAILY HIGH TEMPERATURES

How many days during February 2005 was the high temperature in this city below 50°F?
(Lesson 12-1)

A. 7 days   **C.** 13 days
B. 17 days   **D.** 24 days

2. A pasta dish comes with a choice of 3 sauces, 3 types of meat, and 6 vegetables. How many different pasta dishes can customers choose from if they pick one sauce, one type of meat, and one vegetable?
(Lesson 12-4)

E. 54   **G.** 18
F. 36   **H.** 12

3. Five runners are competing in a race. In how many different orders can the 5 runners finish the race, assuming there are no ties?
(Lesson 12-6)

A. 15   **C.** 120
B. 25   **D.** 125

4. Monique tosses 3 coins. She repeats this experiment for 50 trials. Her results are shown in the table.

Outcome	Number of Trials
3 heads	7
3 tails	4
2 heads and 1 tail	19
2 tails and 1 head	20

Based on the table, what is the experimental probability of getting at least 2 tails when tossing 3 coins?
(Lesson 12-7)

E. 20%
F. 24%
G. 40%
H. 48%

5. Joel did sit-ups each day for two weeks and recorded his numbers below.
(Lesson 12-2)

40, 42, 45, 45, 49, 55, 57,
57, 58, 60, 60, 60, 62, 65

A. Create a stem-and-leaf plot representing the number of sit-ups Joel did each day.
B. Calculate the mean, median, and mode of the data in the stem-and-leaf plot. Round answers to the nearest tenth, if necessary.

Assessment Framework
10.8.01, 10.8.06, 10.8.07,
10.8.08

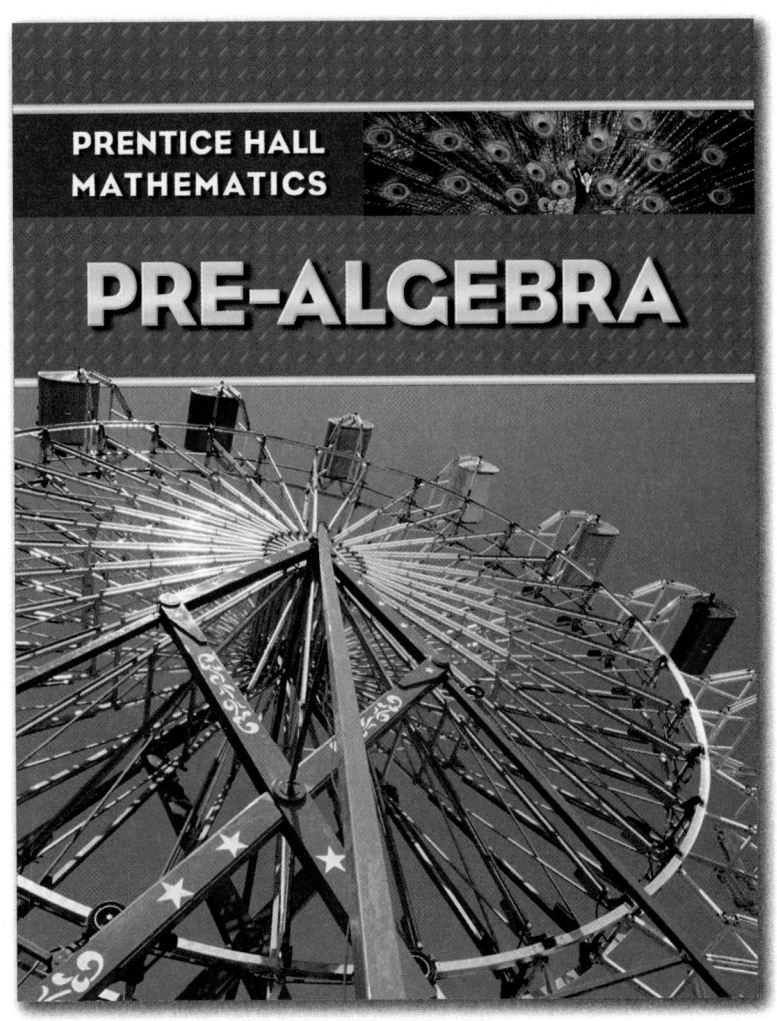

PRENTICE HALL MATHEMATICS

PRE-ALGEBRA

Randall I. Charles

Bonnie McNemar

Alma Ramirez

PEARSON

Prentice Hall

Boston, Massachusetts
Upper Saddle River, New Jersey

ISBN 0-13-133995-8
2 3 4 5 6 7 8 9 10   10 09 08 07 06

Authors

Randall I. Charles, Ph.D., is Professor Emeritus in the Department of Mathematics and Computer Science at San Jose State University, San Jose, California. He began his career as a high school mathematics teacher, and he was a mathematics supervisor for five years. Dr. Charles has been a member of several NCTM committees and is the former Vice President of the National Council of Supervisors of Mathematics. Much of his writing and research has been in the area of problem solving. He has authored more than 75 mathematics textbooks for kindergarten through college.

Bonnie McNemar is a mathematics educator with more than 30 years of experience in Texas schools as a teacher, administrator, and consultant. She began her career as a middle school mathematics teacher and served as a supervisor at the district, county, and state levels. Ms. McNemar was the director of the Texas Mathematics Staff Development Program, now known as TEXTEAMS, for five years, and she was the first director of the Teachers Teaching with Technology (T^3) Program. She remains active in both of these organizations as well as in several local, state and national mathematics organizations, including NCTM.

Alma Ramirez is co-director of the Mathematics Case Project at WestEd, a nonprofit educational institute in Oakland, California. A former bilingual elementary and middle school teacher, Ms. Ramirez has considerable expertise in mathematics teaching and learning, second language acquisition, and professional development. She has served as a consultant on a variety of projects and has extensive experience as an author for elementary and middle-grades texts. In addition, her work has appeared in the 2004 NCTM Yearbook. Ms. Ramirez is a frequent presenter at professional meetings and conferences.

Contributing Authors

David M. Davison, Ph.D.
Professor of Mathematics Education
Montana State University
Billings, Montana

Leah McCracken
Educational Technology Consultant
Billings, Montana

Marsha Landau, Ph.D.
Retired Professor of Mathematics Education
National-Louis University
Evanston, Illinois

Linda Thompson
Consultant
Warrenton, Oregon

Reviewers

Chandler Cox
White Knoll Middle School
West Columbia, South Carolina

Fred Ferguson
Yough High School
Herminie, Pennsylvania

Nancy Hughes
Indian Hills Middle School
Shawnee Mission, Kansas

Dorothy (Dot) Johnson-Manning
Siwell Road Middle School
Jackson, Mississippi

Ellice P. Martin, Ed.D.
Lanier County Middle School
Lakeland, Georgia

Desireé Marcelin McNeal
Susan Miller Dorsey High School
Los Angeles, California

Consultants

Ann Bell
Mathematics
Prentice Hall Consultant
Franklin, Tennessee

Blanche Brownley
Mathematics
Prentice Hall Consultant
Olney, Maryland

Joe Brumfield
Mathematics
Prentice Hall Consultant
Altadena, California

Linda Buckhalt
Mathematics
Prentice Hall Consultant
Derwood, Maryland

Andrea Gordon
Mathematics
Prentice Hall Consultant
Atlanta, Georgia

Eleanor Lopes
Mathematics
Prentice Hall Consultant
New Castle, Delaware

Sally Marsh
Mathematics
Prentice Hall Consultant
Baltimore, Maryland

Bob Pacyga
Mathematics
Prentice Hall Consultant
Darien, Illinois

Judy Porter
Mathematics
Prentice Hall Consultant
Fuquay-Varena, North Carolina

Rose Primiani
Mathematics
Prentice Hall Consultant
Harbor City, New Jersey

Jayne Radu
Mathematics
Prentice Hall Consultant
Scottsdale, Arizona

Pam Revels
Mathematics
Prentice Hall Consultant
Sarasota, Florida

Barbara Rogers
Mathematics
Prentice Hall Consultant
Raleigh, North Carolina

Michael Seals
Mathematics
Prentice Hall Consultant
Edmond, Oklahoma

Margaret Thomas
Mathematics
Prentice Hall Consultant
Indianapolis, Indiana

From the Authors

Dear Student,

Welcome! Mathematics is a powerful tool with far-reaching applications in daily life. We have designed a unique and engaging program that will enable you to tap into the power of mathematics and develop lifelong skills. As you will discover, mathematics is all around us!

Building mathematical skills and an understanding of concepts is an ongoing process—a journey taken both inside and outside of the classroom. This text is designed to help make sense of the mathematics you encounter in class each day.

Your skills will increase through practice and review. The concepts presented in this text will become an integral part of your thinking when you put them to use. Try to work the examples so that you understand the concepts and the processes presented. Then do your homework. Ask yourself how new concepts relate to old ones. Make the connections!

This text will also help you be successful on the tests you take in class as well as on high-stakes tests. The practice problems in each lesson will prepare you for the format and content of these tests. No surprises!

Be sure to use your teacher as a resource. Ask questions! Someone else in your class most likely has the same question in mind and will be grateful that you have the courage to ask it.

We wish you all the best this year as you work through this textbook. The mathematical skills you build and refine will prepare you not only for future success as a student, but also as a member of a vibrant technological society.

Sincerely,

Randy Charles.

Bonnie McNemar   *Alma Beatriz Ramirez*

Contents in Brief

Algebraic Expressions and Integers

Solving One-Step Equations and Inequalities

Chapter 3

Decimals and Equations

Chapter 4

Factors, Fractions, and Exponents

Student Support

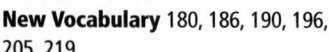

Instant Check System

Check Your Readiness 178

Check Skills You'll Need 180, 186, 190, 196, 201, 205, 209, 214, 219

Quick Check 180, 181, 186, 187, 190, 191, 192, 196, 197, 202, 205, 206, 209, 210, 214, 215, 216, 220, 221, 222

Checkpoint Quiz 199, 218

Vocabulary 🔊

New Vocabulary 180, 186, 190, 196, 205, 219

Vocabulary Tip 181, 191, 196

Vocabulary Builder 184

Vocabulary Review 227

GO Online

Video Tutor Help 186, 222

Active Math 187, 210, 216

Homework Video Tutor 182, 188, 193, 198, 203, 207, 211, 217, 223

Lesson Quizzes 183, 189, 193, 199, 203, 207, 211, 217, 223

Vocabulary Quiz 227

Chapter Test 230

Math at Work 212

Assessment and Test Prep

Chapter 5

Operations With Fractions

Chapter 6

Ratios, Proportions, and Percents

Chapter 7

Solving Equations and Inequalities

Chapter 8

Linear Functions and Graphing

Chapter 9

Spatial Thinking

Chapter 10

Area and Volume

Chapter 11

Right Triangles in Algebra

Data Analysis and Probability

Chapter 13

Nonlinear Functions and Polynomials

Connect Your Learning
through problem solving, activities, and the Web

Applications: Real-World Applications

Animals
Endangered Animals, 450
Horses, 163
Hummingbirds, 216
Insects, 145, 232-233
Pets, 80, 132, 570
Reptiles, 174
Wildlife, 60, 434-435

Careers
Air Traffic Controller, 597
Architecture, 306, 418
Caterer, 341
Choreographer, 467
City Planner, 375
Deep Sea Exploration, 44
Engineering, 113, 437
Geophysicist, 212
Medical Science, 673
Meteorology, 31, 98, 171
Movie Camera Operator, 420
Nurse, 101
Pharmacist, 530
Systems Analyst, 705
Technical Artist, 261
Weaver, 29
Wildlife Statistician, 671
Woodworker, 169
Zoology, 162, 223

Consumer Issues
Car Rental, 482
Cell Phones, 362, 398–399
Comparison Shopping, 141
Consumer Issues, 241, 258
Gas Mileage, 4, 137, 307
Gift Wrapping, 555
Grocery Shopping, 130, 183
Music Sales, 333
Online Shopping, 15, 16
Prices, 684
Purchasing, 7, 15, 16, 90, 300, 322
Renting, 384
Sales Tax, 323, 380
Telephone Service, 131, 362
Unit Cost, 293
Video Rental, 374

Entertainment
Amusement Parks, 106
Art, 364
Concerts, 181
Culture, 120
Fireworks, 713
Literature, 638, 670
Lottery, 600
Television programming, 519
Theaters, 321
Ticket Sales, 76, 98–99, 107, 313, 340, 431

Food
Baking, 624
Cooking, 336, 405, 556
Culinary Arts, 541
Nutrition, 7, 105, 107, 143, 162, 355, 430
Recipes, 336, 556

Money Matters
Account Balances, 32
Banking, 322, 408
Borrowing, 380, 390
Budgeting, 110, 368, 491
Checking Accounts, 151, 152
Commission, 325, 326, 378, 384, 396
Currency, 46, 100
Economics, 331, 384
Exchange Rates, 300
Finance, 28, 152, 173, 256, 302, 354
Fundraising, 139, 607
Home Economics, 297
Income, 84, 427,449, 493
Income Tax, 397
Investing, 48, 388, 390
Jobs, 12, 271
Money, 176–177, 424, 566
Personal Finance, 152, 256, 302, 432, 493
Profits, 323
Royalties, 325, 326
Savings, 42, 96, 100, 354, 386, 389, 700

Recreation
Academic Competitions, 238
Ballet, 611
Bird Watching, 623, 625
Boat Building, 274
Chess, 502, 734
Coin Collections, 100, 394, 448
Computers, 109, 111, 395, 651
Crafts, 250
Creative Writing, 327
Hiking, 97, 248, 260, 378, 595
Hobbies, 732–733
Interior Design, 536
Model Airplanes, 356
Modeling, 7, 86, 87, 252, 465
Photography, 134, 201–202, 379
Physical Fitness, 132, 142, 162, 494, 574
Reading, 270
Recreation, 72, 334, 492, 541
Scuba Diving, 83
Travel, 71, 72, 137, 145, 265, 297, 353, 379, 383, 394, 396, 666, 734
Vacation, 295
Walking, 407
Waterskiing, 617

Sports
Baseball, 301, 609, 638
Basketball, 357, 560, 682
Bicycling, 372
Drill Team, 182
Football, 25, 28, 584–585
Golf, 68
Marathon Training, 85
Soccer, 692-693
Softball, 204, 261
Sports, 168, 236, 326, 426, 429, 528, 679, 714, 725

Applications: **Math at Work**

Applications: **Interdisciplinary Connections**

Problem Solving Strategies

The problem solving lessons included in
Prentice Hall Pre-Algebra progress in depth and
sophistication throughout the course. You will
learn to combine and compare strategies to
solve problems. Throughout the text, a greater
focus on the strategy "Write an Equation"
helps prepare you for success in algebra.

Applications: Chapter Projects

Activities

Activities: Activity Labs

GO Online

Throughout this book you will find links to the Prentice Hall Web site. Use the Web Codes provided with each link to gain direct access to online material. Here's how to *Go Online*:

1. Go to PHSchool.com
2. Enter the Web Code
3. Click Go!

Lesson Web Codes

Lesson Quiz Web Codes: There is an online quiz for every lesson. Access these quizzes with Web Codes ada-0101 through ada-1308 for Lesson 1-1 through Lesson 13-8. See page 85.

Homework Video Tutor Web Codes: For every lesson, there is additional support online to help students complete their homework. Access this homework help online with Web Codes ade-0101 through ade-1308 for Lesson 1-1 through Lesson 13-8. See page 317.

Lesson Quizzes
Web Code format: ada-0204
02 = Chapter 2   04 = Lesson 4

Homework Video Tutor
Web Code format: ade-0605
06 = Chapter 6   05 = Lesson 5

Chapter Web Codes

Chapter	Vocabulary Quizzes	Chapter Tests	Activity Labs	Chapter Projects
1	adj-0151	ada-0152	ade-0153	add-0161
2	adj-0251	ada-0252	ade-0253	add-0261
3	adj-0351	ada-0352	ade-0353	add-0361
4	adj-0451	ada-0452	ade-0453	add-0461
5	adj-0551	ada-0552	ade-0553	add-0561
6	adj-0651	ada-0652	ade-0653	add-0661
7	adj-0751	ada-0752	ade-0753	add-0761
8	adj-0851	ada-0852	ade-0853	add-0861
9	adj-0951	ada-0952	ade-0953	add-0961
10	adj-1051	ada-1052	ade-1053	add-1061
11	adj-1151	ada-1152	ade-1153	add-1161
12	adj-1251	ada-1252	ade-1253	add-1261
13	adj-1351	ada-1352	ade-1353	add-1361
End-of-Course		ada-1354		

Additional Web Codes

Video Tutor Help:
Use Web Code ada-0775 to access engaging online instructional videos to help bring math concepts to life. See page 371.

Data Updates:
Use Web Code adg-2041 to get up-to-date government data for use in examples and exercises. See page 97.

Math at Work:
For information about each Math at Work feature, use Web Code adb-2031. See page 101.

Using Your Book for Success

Welcome to *Prentice Hall Pre-Algebra*. There are many features built into the daily lessons of this text that will help you learn the important skills and concepts you will need to be successful in this course. Look through the following pages for some study tips that you will find useful as you complete each lesson.

Getting Ready to Learn

Check Your Readiness

Complete the *Check Your Readiness* exercises to see what topics you may need to review before you begin the chapter.

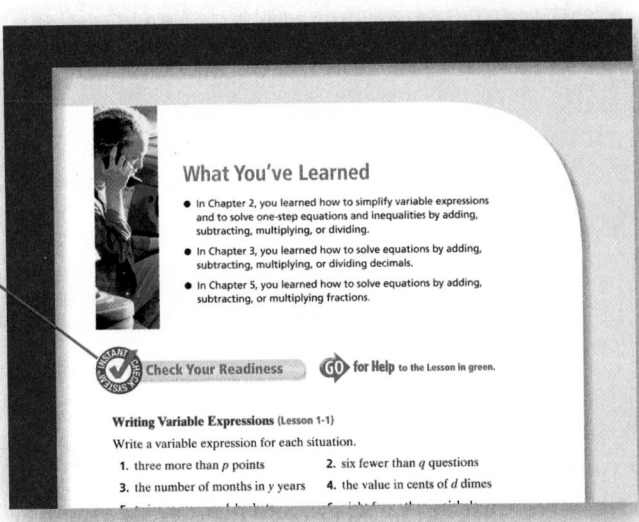

What You've Learned
- In Chapter 2, you learned how to simplify variable expressions and to solve one-step equations and inequalities by adding, subtracting, multiplying, or dividing.
- In Chapter 3, you learned how to solve equations by adding, subtracting, multiplying, or dividing decimals.
- In Chapter 5, you learned how to solve equations by adding, subtracting, or multiplying fractions.

Check Your Readiness   **GO for Help** to the Lesson in green.

Writing Variable Expressions (Lesson 1-1)
Write a variable expression for each situation.
1. three more than p points
2. six fewer than q questions
3. the number of months in y years
4. the value in cents of d dimes

Check Skills You'll Need

Complete the *Check Skills You'll Need* exercises to make sure you have the skills needed to successfully learn the concepts in the lesson.

New Vocabulary

New Vocabulary is listed for each lesson so you can pre-read the text. As each term is introduced, it is highlighted in yellow.

What You'll Learn
- To combine like terms to simplify an equation
- To use the Distributive Property to simplify an equation

. . . And Why
To solve problems involving consecutive integers

Check Skills You'll Need
Simplify each expression.
1. $2x + 4 + 3x$
2. $5y + y$
3. $8a - 5a$
4. $2 - 4c + 5c$
5. $4x + 3 - 2(5 + x)$

GO for Help
Lesson 2-3

New Vocabulary
- consecutive integers

Combining Like Terms

Activity

Simplifying Equations

The tiles below model the equation $2x + 7 + x = 16$.

1. How does this equation differ from others you have seen?
2. a. Group the tiles so that all the x tiles are together. This is the same as combining like terms. Write an equation to represent the tiles once the x tiles are grouped together.
   b. Solve your equation. Check your solution.

Combine like terms to simplify an equation before you solve it.

1 EXAMPLE   Real-World Problem Solving

Model Airplanes Jake and Suki collect model airplanes. Suki has four fewer than twice as many model airplanes as Jake. Together they have 14 models. Solve the equation $m + 2m - 4 = 14$. Find the number of models each person has.

$$m + 2m - 4 = 14$$
$$3m - 4 = 14 \quad \text{Combine like terms.}$$

Built-In Help

Go for Help

Look for the green labels throughout your book that tell you where to "Go" for help. You'll see this built-in help in the lessons and in the homework exercises.

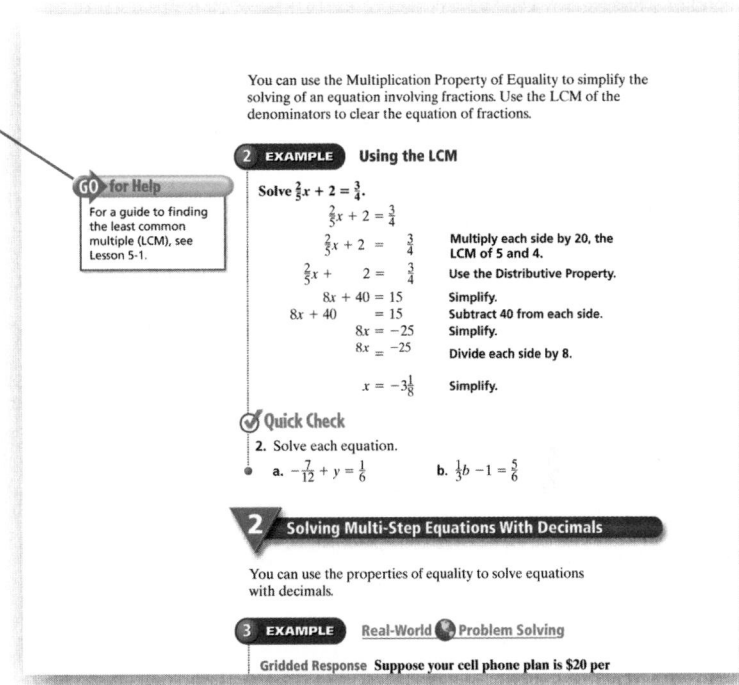

Video Tutor Help

Go online to see engaging videos to help you better understand important math concepts.

Understanding the Lesson

Quick Check

Every lesson includes numerous Examples, each followed by a *Quick Check* question that you can do on your own to see if you understand the skill being introduced. Check your progress with the answers at the back of the book.

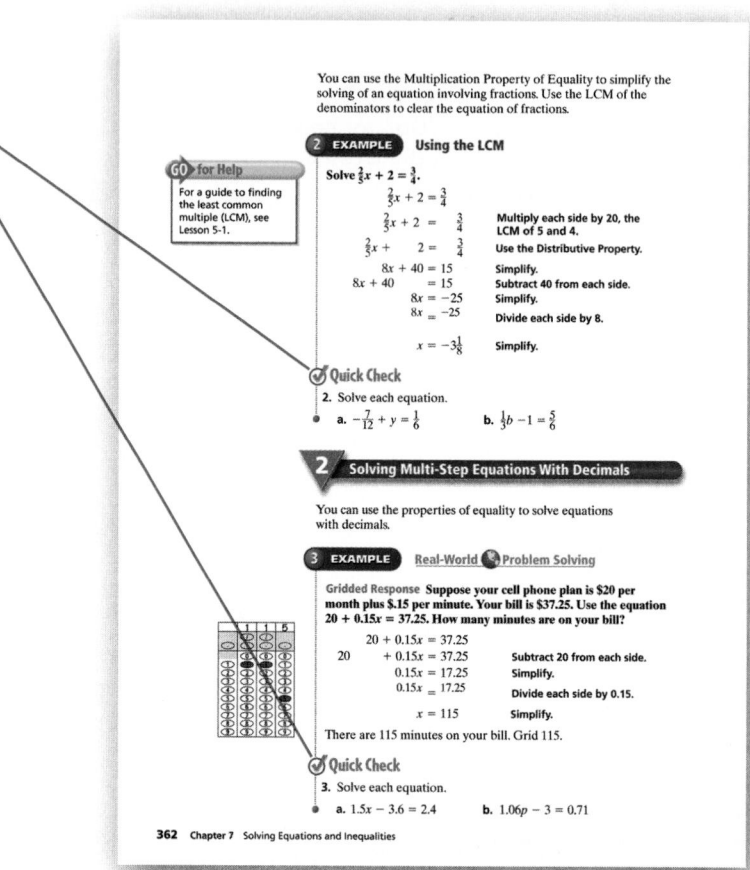

You can use the Multiplication Property of Equality to simplify the solving of an equation involving fractions. Use the LCM of the denominators to clear the equation of fractions.

2 EXAMPLE Using the LCM

GO for Help
For a guide to finding the least common multiple (LCM), see Lesson 5-1.

Solve $\frac{2}{5}x + 2 = \frac{3}{4}$.

$\frac{2}{5}x + 2 = \frac{3}{4}$

$\frac{2}{5}x + 2 = \frac{3}{4}$ Multiply each side by 20, the LCM of 5 and 4.

$\frac{2}{5}x + \quad 2 = \frac{3}{4}$ Use the Distributive Property.

$8x + 40 = 15$ Simplify.

$8x + 40 \quad = 15$ Subtract 40 from each side.

$8x = -25$ Simplify.

$8x = -25$ Divide each side by 8.

$x = -3\frac{1}{8}$ Simplify.

Quick Check
2. Solve each equation.
   a. $-\frac{7}{12} + y = \frac{1}{6}$ b. $\frac{1}{3}b - 1 = \frac{5}{6}$

2 Solving Multi-Step Equations With Decimals

You can use the properties of equality to solve equations with decimals.

3 EXAMPLE Real-World Problem Solving

Gridded Response Suppose your cell phone plan is $20 per month plus $.15 per minute. Your bill is $37.25. Use the equation $20 + 0.15x = 37.25$. How many minutes are on your bill?

$20 + 0.15x = 37.25$

$20 \quad + 0.15x = 37.25$ Subtract 20 from each side.

$0.15x = 17.25$ Simplify.

$\frac{0.15x}{0.15} = \frac{17.25}{0.15}$ Divide each side by 0.15.

$x = 115$ Simplify.

There are 115 minutes on your bill. Grid 115.

Quick Check
3. Solve each equation.
   a. $1.5x - 3.6 = 2.4$ b. $1.06p - 3 = 0.71$

362   Chapter 7   Solving Equations and Inequalities

Understanding Key Concepts

Frequent *Key Concept* boxes summarize important definitions, formulas, and properties. Use these to review what you've learned.

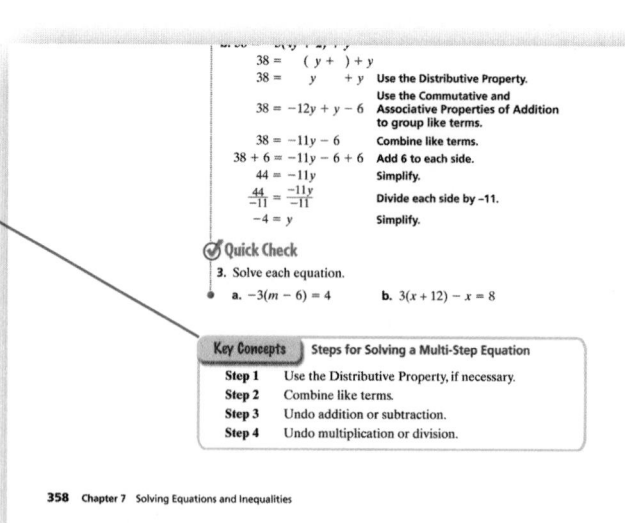

$38 = \quad (y + \quad) + y$

$38 = \quad y \quad + y$ Use the Distributive Property.

$38 = -12y + y - 6$ Use the Commutative and Associative Properties of Addition to group like terms.

$38 = -11y - 6$ Combine like terms.

$38 + 6 = -11y - 6 + 6$ Add 6 to each side.

$44 = -11y$ Simplify.

$\frac{44}{-11} = \frac{-11y}{-11}$ Divide each side by -11.

$-4 = y$ Simplify.

Quick Check
3. Solve each equation.
   a. $-3(m - 6) = 4$ b. $3(x + 12) - x = 8$

Key Concepts   Steps for Solving a Multi-Step Equation

Step 1   Use the Distributive Property, if necessary.
Step 2   Combine like terms.
Step 3   Undo addition or subtraction.
Step 4   Undo multiplication or division.

358   Chapter 7   Solving Equations and Inequalities

Online Active Math

Make math come alive with these online activities. Review and practice important math concepts with these engaging online tutorials.

4. $x + 16 = 4$

5. $b + 6 = -4$

GO for Help
Lesson 2-5

two equal groups.

$x = 2$ Simplify.

To solve a two-step equation, first undo addition or subtraction. Then undo multiplication or division.

1 EXAMPLE Undoing an Operation

Solve $3n - 6 = 15$.

$$3n - 6 = 15$$
$$3n - 6 = 15 \quad \text{Add 6 to each side.}$$
$$3n = 21 \quad \text{Simplify.}$$
$$\frac{3n}{3} = \frac{21}{3} \quad \text{Divide each side by 3.}$$
$$n = 7 \quad \text{Simplify.}$$

Check
$$3n - 6 = 15$$
$$3() - 6 \overset{?}{=} 15 \quad \text{Replace } n \text{ with 7.}$$
$$21 - 6 \overset{?}{=} 15 \quad \text{Multiply.}$$
$$15 = 15 \checkmark \quad \text{Simplify.}$$

352 Chapter 7 Solving Equations and Inequalities

Quick Check

1. Solve each equation.
   a. $15x + 3 = 48$ b. $\frac{t}{4} - 10 = -6$
   c. $\frac{b}{3} + 13 = 11$ d. $9g + 11 = 2$

2 EXAMPLE Negative Coefficients

Solve $5 - x = 17$.

$$5 - x = 17$$
$$5 - x = 17 \quad \text{Add } -5 \text{ to each side.}$$
$$0 - x = 12 \quad \text{Simplify.}$$
$$-x = 12 \quad 0 - x = -x$$
$$-x = 12 \quad \text{Multiply each side by } -1.$$
$$x = -12 \quad \text{Simplify.}$$

Vocabulary Tip

Read "$0 - x = -x$" as "Zero minus x equals the opposite of x."

Quick Check

2. Solve each equation.
   a. $-a + 6 = 8$ b. $-9 - \frac{y}{7} = -12$ c. $13 - 6f = 31$

2 Solving Problems With Two-Step Equations

Vocabulary Support

Understanding mathematical vocabulary is an important part of studying mathematics. *Vocabulary Tips* and *Vocabulary Builders* throughout the book help you focus on the language of math.

Vocabulary Builder   **High-Use Academic Words**

High-use academic words are words that you will see often in textbooks and on tests. These words are not math vocabulary terms, but they are important for you to know to be successful in mathematics.

Words to Learn: Direction Words

Some words tell you what to do in a problem. You need to understand what these words are asking so that you give the correct answer.

Word	Meaning
Determine	Find out by investigating or calculating
Explain	Give facts and details to make an idea easy to understand
Identify	Tell the name of or describe the characteristics of something

EXERCISES

Determine whether each statement is *true* or *false*.

1. The owner's manual for a car explains how to drive.

2. The weatherman determines what kind of storm will arrive.

Practice What You've Learned

There are numerous exercises in each lesson that give you the practice you need to master the concepts in the lesson. Each practice set includes the following sections.

A: Practice by Example

Practice by Example exercises refer you back to the Examples in the lesson, in case you need help with completing these exercises.

B: Apply Your Skills

Apply Your Skills exercises combine skills from earlier lessons to offer you richer skill exercises and multi-step application problems.

C: Challenge

Challenge exercises give you an opportunity to solve problems that extend and stretch your thinking.

Homework Video Tutor

Go online to get help completing your homework! For every lesson, there is a narrated, interactive tutorial to help you review the lesson and understand key concepts.

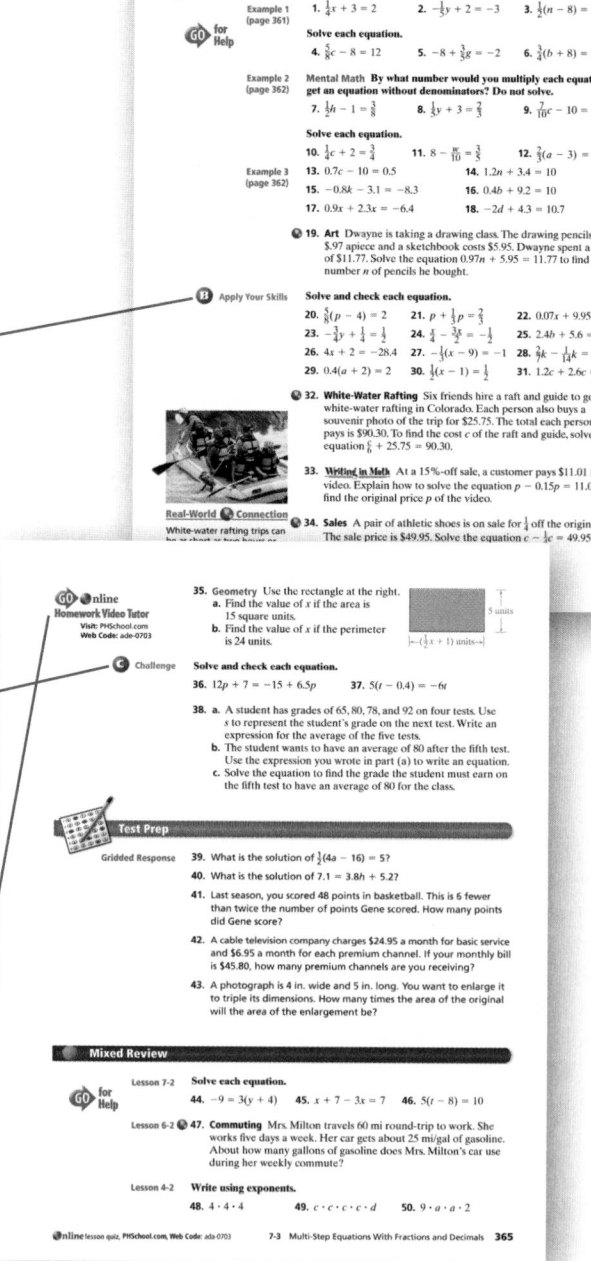

Preparing for Tests

Test-Taking Strategies

Test-Taking Strategies in every chapter teach you strategies to be successful and give you practice in the skills you need to pass state tests and national tests, including the SAT and ACT.

Test Prep

Test Prep pages in every chapter give you more opportunities to prepare for the tests you will have to take.

Test Item Formats

The Standardized Test Prep exercises in your book give you the practice you need to answer all types of test questions.
• Multiple Choice
• Gridded Response, for which you write your answer in a grid
• Short Response, which are scored using a 2-point rubric
• Extended Response, which are scored using a 4-point rubric
• Reading Comprehension

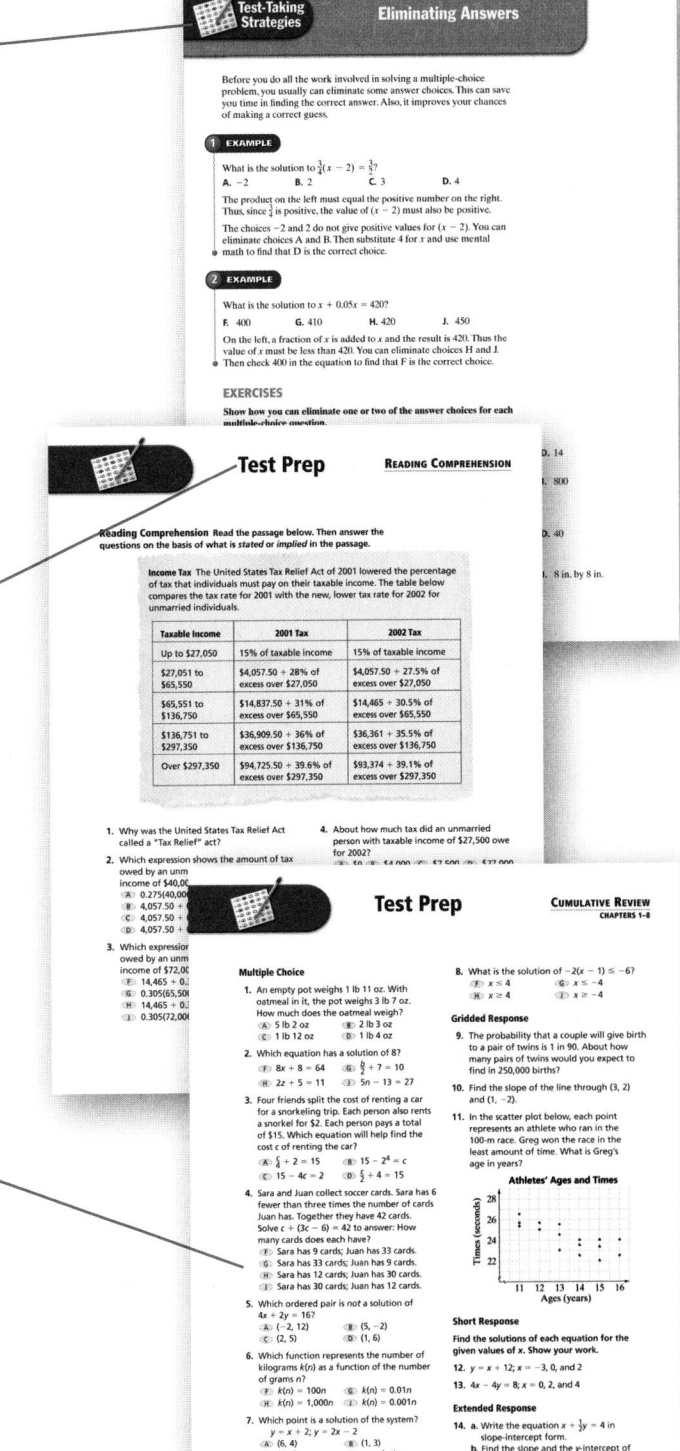

Beginning-of-Course Diagnostic Test

1. Write a decimal for the given words: thirteen and one hundred thirteen ten-thousandths.

2. Write $\frac{25}{70}$ in simplest form.

3. Write 4.032 in words

For Exercises 4–7, write each mixed number as an improper fraction.

4. $2\frac{3}{8}$

5. $12\frac{1}{2}$

6. $3\frac{2}{11}$

7. $5\frac{5}{16}$

For Exercises 8–9, write each improper fraction as a mixed number.

8. $\frac{8}{3}$

9. $\frac{45}{7}$

For Exercises 10–13, use <, >, or = to compare.

10. 1,206 ▨ 121

11. 13,254 ▨ 13,524

12. 1.5234 ▨ 15.234

13. 2.16 ▨ 2.160

For Exercises 14–15, order from least to greatest.

14. 33,457; 34,674; 33,687; 34,328; 32,963

15. 5.013; 5.103; 5.301; 5.310; 5.031

For Exercises 16–19, round to the place value of the underlined digits.

16. 3,2<u>1</u>9

17. 4.<u>1</u>234

18. 3.6<u>9</u>72

19. 14.04<u>7</u>21

For Exercises 20–23, find each sum or difference.

20. 15.623 + 7.3953

21. 12.932 − 3.392

22. 386.7 + 0.85

23. 32.589 − 15.0029

For Exercises 24–33, find each product or quotient.

24. 34×458

25. $341{,}502 \div 346$

26. 1.23×4

27. $1518.75 \div 243$

28. $32.5 \cdot 7$

29. $0.567 \div 10$

30. 0.89×0.6

31. $0.245 \div 0.98$

32. $1.008 \cdot 0.003$

33. $0.0040761 \div 0.063$

For Exercises 34–35, find the missing number.

34. $\frac{11}{3} = \frac{\blacksquare}{39}$

35. $\frac{6}{7} = \frac{18}{\blacksquare}$

For Exercises 36–39, find each sum or difference. Write each answer in simplest form.

36. $\frac{5}{8} + \frac{7}{8}$

37. $\frac{11}{12} - \frac{5}{12}$

38. $2\frac{2}{7} + 1\frac{5}{7}$

39. $5\frac{3}{8} - 1\frac{5}{8}$

For Exercises 40–43, find each product or quotient. Write each answer in simplest form.

40. $\frac{2}{3} \cdot \frac{5}{8}$

41. $\frac{3}{5} \div \frac{7}{10}$

42. $4\frac{2}{5} \cdot 2\frac{1}{2}$

43. $\frac{8}{9} \div 1\frac{1}{3}$

For Exercises 44–47, write an integer for each situation.

44. 8 steps up

45. 7 steps backward

46. 15 degrees above zero

47. a loss of $5

For Exercises 48–50, use <, >, or = to compare.

48. $0 \ \blacksquare \ -2$

49. $-9 \ \blacksquare \ 3$

50. $-7 \ \blacksquare \ -8$

What You've Learned

 Assessment Framework

In previous courses you learned:

- **6.7.09:** How to evaluate expressions using the order of operations.
- **6.7.08:** How to add, subtract, multiply, and divide whole numbers.
- **6.7.05:** How to compare whole numbers.
- **6.7.06:** How to relate numbers to points on a number line.

Check Your Readiness

 for Help to the Lesson in green.

Multiplying and Dividing Whole Numbers (Skills Handbook, pp. 781, 782)

Find each product or quotient.

1. $7 \div 7$	**2.** $99 \div 9$	**3.** $44 \div 4$	**4.** $57 \div 3$
5. $65 \div 5$	**6.** 5×8	**7.** $68 \div 4$	**8.** 11×4
9. 22×8	**10.** 2×14	**11.** 83×2	**12.** 5×15

Comparing Whole Numbers (Skills Handbook, p. 779)

Compare. Use $>$, $<$, or $=$ to complete each statement.

13. $5 \blacksquare 2$ **14.** $1 \blacksquare 0$ **15.** $14 \blacksquare 17$

16. $6 + 12 \blacksquare 7 + 13$ **17.** $10 - 2 \blacksquare 27 - 18$ **18.** $4 \times 7 \blacksquare 2 \times 14$

Multiplying and Dividing Whole Numbers (Skills Handbook, pp. 781, 782)

Find each product or quotient.

19. $36 \div 3$	**20.** 10×3	**21.** $7(4)$	**22.** $25 \div 5$
23. $12 \cdot 8$	**24.** $7\overline{)35}$	**25.** $20 \cdot 10$	**26.** $9\overline{)720}$
27. $124 \div 4$	**28.** $12\overline{)156}$	**29.** $4 \cdot 12 \cdot 10$	**30.** $132 \div 11$

Reading Numbers on a Number Line (Skills Handbook, p. 779)

What is the distance of each point from zero on the number line?

31. A **32.** B

33. C **34.** D

Algebraic Expressions and Integers

Chapter 1

Key Vocabulary

- absolute value (p. 19)
- conjecture (p. 35)
- coordinate plane (p. 52)
- counterexample (p. 37)
- evaluate (p. 14)
- inductive reasoning (p. 35)
- integers (p. 19)
- opposites (p. 19)
- order of operations (p. 8)
- ordered pair (p. 52)
- origin (p. 52)
- quadrants (p. 52)
- variable (p. 4)
- variable expression (p. 4)
- x-axis (p. 52)
- x-coordinate (p. 52)
- y-axis (p. 52)
- y-coordinate (p. 52)

What You'll Learn Next

 Assessment Framework

In this chapter, you will learn how to

- **8.8.02:** Use variables and variable expressions.

- **6.8.10:** Perform operations with integers.

- **9.8.05:** Graph points in the coordinate plane.

- Solve a problem by looking for a pattern.

 Activity Lab Applying what you learn, on pages 64–65 you will solve problems about sunken ships.

3

1-1   Variables and Expressions

 Assessment Framework

8.8.02 Write an expression using variables to represent unknown quantities.

8.8.08 Translate between different representations (table, written, graphical, or pictorial) of whole number relationships and linear expressions.

✓ **Check Skills You'll Need**

Complete each equation.

1. 1 week = ■ days

2. 1 foot = ■ inches

3. 1 nickel = ■ cents

4. 1 gallon = ■ quarts

5. 1 yard = ■ feet

GO for Help
Table 1, p. 798

■)) **New Vocabulary**
• variable
• variable expression

1   Identifying Numerical and Variable Expressions

Gas Mileage How many miles can you drive on ten gallons of gas? The answer depends on the type of vehicle you drive. The table shows some typical data.

Vehicle Type	Miles	Gallons	Miles per Gallon
Subcompact	330	10	$330 \div 10$
Compact	300	10	$300 \div 10$
Mid-size sedan	245	10	$245 \div 10$
Sport utility vehicle	175	10	$175 \div 10$
Pickup truck	160	10	$160 \div 10$

The last column gives a *numerical expression* ↑
for each vehicle's miles per gallon.

If you don't know the number of miles, you can use a *variable* to stand for the number. Then you can write a *variable expression* for miles per gallon.

$$\text{variable} \rightarrow m \leftarrow \text{miles on 10 gallons}$$
$$\text{variable expression} \rightarrow m \div 10 \leftarrow \text{miles per gallon}$$

A **variable** is a letter that stands for a number.
A **variable expression** is a mathematical phrase that uses variables, numerals, and operation symbols.

Online
active math

For: Variable Expressions Activity
Use: Interactive Textbook, 1-1

1 EXAMPLE   **Identifying Expressions**

Identify each expression as a *numerical expression* or a *variable expression*. For a variable expression, name the variable.

a. $5 - 5$
numerical expression

b. $c - 5$
Variable expression; c is the variable.

✓ Quick Check

1. Identify each expression as a *numerical expression* or a *variable expression.* For a variable expression, name the variable.

a. $8 \div x$ **b.** 100×6 **c.** $d + 43 - 9$

2 Writing Variable Expressions

You can translate word phrases into variable expressions.

Word Phrase	Variable Expression
Nine more than a number y	$y + 9$
4 less than a number n	$n - 4$
A number z times three	$z \cdot 3$ or $3z$ or $3(z)$
A number a divided by 12	$a \div 12$ or $\frac{a}{12}$
5 times the quantity 4 plus a number c	$5 \cdot (4 + c)$ or $5(4 + c)$

Writing in Math

You can translate many words for operations into operation symbols.

total	+
more than	+
increased by	+
difference	−
fewer than	−
less than	−
decreased by	−
product	× or · or ( )
times	× or · or ( )
quotient	÷ or —
divided by	÷ or —

A variable expression is an efficient way to express a mathematical relationship.

2 EXAMPLE   Real-World 🌐 Problem Solving

Science The fastest dinosaur may have been *Ornithomimus,* which could run about 60 ft in a second. Write a variable expression for the distance *Ornithomimus* could run in a given time.

Words   60   times   number of seconds

Let s = number of seconds.

Expression   60   · s

The variable expression $60 \cdot s$, or $60s$, describes the distance in feet *Ornithomimus* could run in s seconds.

Real-World 🌐 Connection

Ornithomimus was an ostrich-like oviraptor about 7 ft tall. Its long tail acted as a counterbalance and as a stabilizer during fast turns.

✓ Quick Check

2. a. Bagels cost $.50 each. Write a variable expression for the cost of b bagels.

b. **Measurement** Write a variable expression for the number of hours in m minutes.

EXERCISES

For more exercises, see *Extra Skill and Word Problem Practice*.

Practice and Problem Solving

A Practice by Example

Example 1
(page 4)

GO for Help

Identify each expression as a *numerical expression* or a *variable expression*. For a variable expression, name the variable.

1. $b + 6$ **2.** $80 \div 8$ **3.** $14 - n$

4. 14×14 **5.** $100x$ **6.** $8 + 8 + 8 + 8$

Example 2
(page 5)

Write a variable expression for each word phrase.

7. 16 more than m **8.** 6 divided by z

9. the product of c and 3   **10.** 2 less than p

11. b times 3   **12.** 4 fewer than j

13. n divided by 3   **14.** 3 divided by n

15. x less than 2   **16.** 8 less than z

Write a numerical or variable expression for each quantity.

17. two dozen eggs   **18.** d dozen eggs

19. the value in cents of 7 nickels **20.** the value in cents of n nickels

21. number of quarts in 3 gallons   **22.** number of quarts in g gallons

B Apply Your Skills

Identify each expression as a *numerical expression* or a *variable expression*. For a variable expression, name the variable.

23. $d + 53$ **24.** $12 - 7$ **25.** $\frac{g}{9}$ **26.** $4(5)$

Measurement Write an expression for each quantity.

27. the number of days in 4 weeks

28. the number of days in w weeks

29. number of pounds in 160 ounces

30. number of pounds in z ounces

31. the number of feet in 100 inches

32. the number of feet in i inches

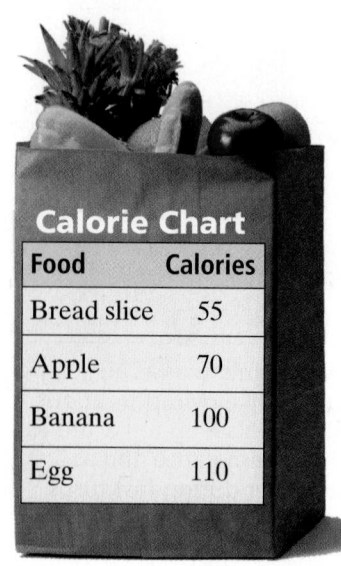

Calorie Chart	
Food	**Calories**
Bread slice	55
Apple	70
Banana	100
Egg	110

33. Mia has $20 less than Brandi. Brandi has d dollars. Write a variable expression for the amount of money Mia has.

Use the calorie chart at the left for Exercises 34 and 35.

34. Write a variable expression for the number of calories in e eggs and one slice of bread.

35. Write a variable expression for the number of calories in a fruit salad made from a apples and b bananas.

6   Chapter 1   Algebraic Expressions and Integers

Modeling In each model, the red line represents a variable expression. Match each model with its expression.

A. $\frac{x}{4}$ **B.** $4 + x$ **C.** $4x$ **D.** $x - 4$

36.

4   x

37.

x   x   x   x

38.

x

4

39.

x

C Challenge

40. Writing in Math How are numerical expressions and variable expressions similar? How are they different?

41. Error Analysis A student wrote the variable expression $n - 5$ for the word phrase *n less than five*. Explain the student's error.

ISAT

Test Prep

Multiple Choice A hot-air balloon is at an altitude of *m* meters. In Exercises 42–44, which expression matches the given word phrase?

42. the balloon's new altitude after rising 34 meters
   A. $m - 34$ **B.** $m + 34$ **C.** $3m$ **D.** $34m$

43. the balloon's new altitude after falling 2,000 meters
   F. $m + 2{,}000$ **G.** $2{,}000 - m$ **H.** $2{,}000m$ **J.** $m - 2{,}000$

44. the balloon's new altitude after tripling its altitude
   A. $m - 34$ **B.** $m + 34$ **C.** $3m$ **D.** $34m$

45. Pam is 15 years old. Which expression gives Pam's age *p* years ago?
   F. $p - 15$ **G.** $p + 15$ **H.** $15 - p$ **J.** $\frac{p}{15}$

Mixed Review

Skills Handbook

for Help

Compute.

46. 9×25 **47.** $3 \times 6 \times 4$ **48.** 8×1

49. $225 \div 3$ **50.** $169 \div 13$ **51.** $25{,}942 \div 12{,}971$

52. Purchasing A customer buys orange juice for $.95 and two apples for $.55 each. She gives the cashier a five-dollar bill. How much change should the cashier give the customer?

53. Nutrition There are seven servings in a box of pita chips. The box weighs 16 oz. About how many ounces are in each serving? Round your answer to the nearest tenth.

The Order of Operations

IL Assessment Framework

6.8.10 Identify and apply order of operations to simplify numeric expressions involving integers (including exponents and roots), fractions, and decimals.

☑ Check Skills You'll Need

Find each quotient.

1. $164 \div 2$ **2.** $344 \div 8$

3. $284 \div 4$ **4.** $133 \div 7$

5. $182 \div 13$ **6.** $650 \div 25$

GO for Help

Skills Handbook, p. 782

🔊 **New Vocabulary**

• order of operations

1 Using the Order of Operations

 ctivity

Experimenting With Order

In most languages, the meaning of words depends on their order. For example, "sign the check" is not the same as "check the sign."

Similarly, order is important in the language of mathematics.

1. **Mental Math** Find the value of the expression $3 + 5 \times 2$.

2. **Analyze** What answer do you get to Question 1 if you multiply before adding? If you add before multiplying?

3. **Reasoning** How does the order in which you do the operations affect your answer?

The order in which you perform operations can affect the value of an expression. To avoid confusion, mathematicians have agreed on an **order of operations.** Multiply and divide first. Then add and subtract.

To *simplify* a numerical expression, you use the order of operations and replace the expression with the simplest name for its value.

GO nline

Video Tutor Help
Visit: PHSchool.com
Web Code: ada-0775

1 EXAMPLE Simplifying Expressions

Simplify $4 + 15 \div 3$.

$$4 + 15 \div 3$$

$$4 + 5 \qquad \text{First divide.}$$

$$9 \qquad \text{Then add.}$$

☑ Quick Check

1. Simplify each expression.

 a. $2 + 5 \times 3$ **b.** $12 \div 3 - 1$ **c.** $10 - 1 \cdot 7$

When operations have the same rank in the order of operations, do them from left to right.

2 EXAMPLE Using the Order of Operations

Simplify $3 \cdot 5 - 8 \div 4 + 6$.

$$3 \cdot 5 - 8 \div 4 + 6$$

$$15 \quad - \quad 2 \quad + \quad 6 \qquad \textbf{Multiply and divide from left to right.}$$

$$13 + 6 \qquad \textbf{Add and subtract from left to right.}$$

$$19 \qquad \textbf{Add.}$$

✓ Quick Check

2. Simplify each expression.

    a. $4 - 1 \cdot 2 + 6 \div 3$ **b.** $5 + 6 \cdot 4 \div 3 - 1$

2 Using Grouping Symbols

Grouping symbols, such as parentheses, ( ), and brackets, [ ], indicate order. A fraction bar also is a grouping symbol, since $\frac{4 + 2}{3} = (4 + 2) \div 3$. Always work inside grouping symbols first.

Key Concepts Order of Operations

  1. Work inside grouping symbols.

  2. Multiply and divide in order from left to right.

  3. Add and subtract in order from left to right.

3 EXAMPLE Simplifying With Grouping Symbols

Multiple Choice **Which procedure is correct for simplifying $24 \div [6 - (2 \cdot 2)]$?**

  Ⓐ $24 \div [6 - (2 \cdot 2)] = 4 - 2 \cdot 2 = 4 - 4 = 0$

  Ⓑ $24 \div [6 - (2 \cdot 2)] = 24 \div 4 \cdot 2 = 24 \div 8 = 3$

  Ⓒ $24 \div [6 - (2 \cdot 2)] = 4 - 2 \cdot 2 = 2 \cdot 2 = 4$

  Ⓓ $24 \div [6 - (2 \cdot 2)] = 24 \div (6 - 4) = 24 \div 2 = 12$

Choice D follows the order of operations by working inside the grouping symbols first. Choice D is correct.

✓ Quick Check

3. Simplify the expression $1 + \frac{10 - 2}{4}$.

You can use the order of operations to find the area of an irregular figure by more than one method.

More Than One Way

Urban Planning Some urban planners specialize in planning entire new towns. These towns are designed for livability, with plenty of open space. The sketch shows the dimensions for a new town called Panorama. Find Panorama's area.

Kevin's Method

Divide the figure into rectangles. Then add their areas.

$$Area = Area① + Area②$$
$$= 4 \cdot 3 + (6 - 3) \cdot 2$$
$$= 4 \cdot 3 + 3 \cdot 2$$
$$= 12 + 6$$
$$= 18$$

Panorama's area is 18 km^2.

Tina's Method

Visualize attaching a small rectangle to complete a large rectangle. Then subtract the small area from the large area.

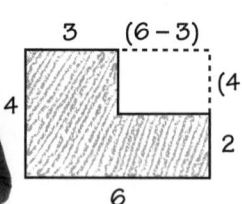

$$Area = \begin{array}{c} \text{Area of large} \\ \text{rectangle} \end{array} - \begin{array}{c} \text{Area of small} \\ \text{rectangle} \end{array}$$
$$= 6 \cdot 4 - (6 - 3) \cdot (4 - 2)$$
$$= 6 \cdot 4 - 3 \cdot 2$$
$$= 24 - 6$$
$$= 18$$

Panorama's area is 18 km^2.

Choose a Method

1. Which method would you use to find the town's area? Explain.

2. Can you think of another way to solve the problem? Explain.

EXERCISES

For more exercises, see *Extra Skill and Word Problem Practice.*

Practice and Problem Solving

 Practice by Example

Examples 1 and 2
(pages 8 and 9)

 for Help

Simplify each expression.

1. $3 + 6 \times 4$ **2.** $35 \div 7 - 2$ **3.** $8 - 2 \cdot 3$

4. $6 - 6 \div 3$ **5.** $21 - 13 + 8$ **6.** $6 \cdot 2 + 4$

7. $12 - 8 \div 2 + 3$ **8.** $21 \div 7 + 14 \times 2$ **9.** $2 \cdot 2 + 0 \cdot 4$

10. $4(4) - 2(5)$ **11.** $2 + 3 \cdot 24 \div 6$ **12.** $4 \div 4 \cdot 4 + 4 - 4$

Example 3
(page 9)

13. $7 + 3 \cdot (8 \div 4)$ **14.** $2(15 - 9) \cdot 9$ **15.** $[2 + (6 \cdot 8)] - 1$

16. $2(6) + \dfrac{7 + 8}{3}$ **17.** $3(7 + 4)$ **18.** $12 \div (3 - 2) + 1$

19. $6 + \dfrac{6 + 2}{4}$ **20.** $\dfrac{21 + 15}{3 + 6}$ **21.** $(21 + 3) \div 4 \div 2$

B **Apply Your Skills**

22. Error Analysis A student found the value of the expression $30 \div 6 - 1$ to be 6. Explain the student's error.

23. Writing in Math Why do we need to agree on an order of operations?

Simplify each expression. Justify your work.

24. $(56 - 5) \div 17$ **25.** $60 \div 4 + 9$ **26.** $2[8 + (5 - 3)] - 8$

27. $12 \div 3 \times 4$ **28.** $36 - 27 \div 9 \div 1$ **29.** $6(4 + 1) - 5$

30. $14 + 5 \times 2$ **31.** $440 \div (2 + 18)$ **32.** $16 \div 8 \times 2$

 for Help

For a guide to solving
Exercise 26, see
page 13.

Compare. Use >, <, or = to complete each statement.

33. $15 \cdot 3 - 2 \ \blacksquare \ 15 \cdot (3 - 2)$ **34.** $18 - 6 \div 3 \ \blacksquare \ (18 - 6) \div 3$

35. $8 + 12 \div 4 \ \blacksquare \ (8 + 12) \div 4$ **36.** $22 - 7 \cdot 2 \ \blacksquare \ (22 - 7) \cdot 2$

37. $12 \div 3 + 9 \cdot 4 \ \blacksquare \ 12 \div (3 + 9) \cdot 4$

38. $(19 - 15) \div (3 + 1) \ \blacksquare \ 19 - 15 \div 3 + 1$

Insert grouping symbols to make each number sentence true.

39. $7 + 4 \cdot 6 = 66$ **40.** $7 \cdot 8 - 6 + 3 = 17$ **41.** $3 + 8 - 2 \cdot 5 = 45$

42. Multiple Choice Insert grouping symbols to make the number sentence $3 + 8 - 2 \cdot 5 = 45$ correct.

   Ⓐ $(3 + 8) - 2 \cdot 5 = 45$ Ⓑ $3 + (8 - 2) \cdot 5 = 45$

   Ⓒ $[3 + (8 - 2)] \cdot 5 = 45$ Ⓓ $3 + [8 - (2 \cdot 5)] = 45$

Write a numerical expression for each phrase. Then simplify.

43. five added to the product of four and nine

44. twenty-one minus the sum of fifteen and five

45. seventeen minus the quotient of twenty-five and five

GO Online
Homework Video Tutor
Visit: PHSchool.com
Web Code: ade-0102

46. On the Job A part-time employee worked 4 hours on Monday and 7 hours each day for the next 3 days. Write and simplify an expression that shows the total number of hours worked.

 Challenge

Write two expressions you could use to find the area of each shaded figure. Find the area.

47.
6 in.
3 in.
5 in.
2 in.

48.
2 m
2 m
6 m
2 m
2 m
6 m

49.
4 ft
1 ft
3 ft
5 ft
3 ft
1 ft
4 ft

50. Open-Ended Write a word problem for the numerical expression $3(4 + 3) + 2$. Then simplify the expression.

51. Number Sense Use the digits 1–9 in order. Insert operation signs and grouping symbols to get a value of 100.

ISAT

Test Prep

Multiple Choice

52. Which expression has a value of 18?
  A. $3 \cdot 2 + 4$
  B. $(18 - 10) \div 4 + 15$
  C. $4 \cdot 2 + 3 - 2$
  D. $27 - 13 \cdot 2 + 17(6 - 5)$

53. Which expression gives the area of the garden?
  F. $4(2 + 5) + 5 \cdot 5$
  G. $(2 + 5 + 2) \cdot (2 + 5 + 2) - 4(2 \cdot 2)$
  H. $(2 + 5 + 2) - (2 \cdot 2)$
  J. $4(2 \cdot 2) + 4(5 \cdot 2) + 5 \cdot 5$

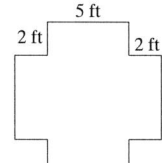
5 ft
2 ft
2 ft

54. Which set of grouping symbols makes the equation true? $2 \cdot 3 + 5 - 2 \cdot 2 = 12$
  A. $(2 \cdot 3) + 5 - (2 \cdot 2)$
  B. $2 \cdot [3 + (5 - 2)] \cdot 2$
  C. $2 \cdot [3 + (5 - 2 \cdot 2)]$
  D. $2 \cdot (3 + 5) - 2 \cdot 2$

55. What is the value of $8 \cdot 5 - 3(24 \div 6)$?
  F. 28
  G. 64
  H. 111
  J. 148

Mixed Review

Lesson 1-1

Write a variable expression for each word phrase.

56. the product of a number n and 8

57. k divided by 20

58. six less than a number h

59. the value, in cents, of d dimes

60. A telephone call costs c cents per minute. Write a variable expression for the cost of a 15-minute call.

Understanding Math Problems Read the problem below. Then let Daria's thinking guide you through the solution. Check your understanding with the exercises at the bottom of the page.

Simplify $2[8 + (5 - 3)] - 8$.

What Daria Thinks

There are two sets of grouping symbols, square brackets and parentheses: $[8 + (5 - 3)]$.

I need to begin by working inside the innermost grouping symbols, the parentheses: $(5 - 3)$.

Now I need to work inside the next pair of grouping symbols, the square brackets, to find $[8 + 2]$.

Multiply before subtracting.

Now subtract.

The simplified expression is 12.

What Daria Writes

$2[8 + (5 - 3)] - 8$

$2[8 + (2)] - 8$

$2[10] - 8$

$20 - 8$

12

EXERCISES

Simplify each expression.

1. $2[(13 - 4) \div 3]$

2. $1 + \frac{10 - 2}{4}$

3. $3[(8 + 4) \div 6]$

4. $\frac{6 + 9}{3} - 2$

5. $4[3 + (2 \cdot 3)]$

6. $16 \div (8 - 4) - 2$

7. $3(8 - 2) + 12$

8. $2[4(7 - 2) + 3]$

9. $6 - \frac{4 - 10}{2}$

10. $25 \div (15 \div 3) \cdot 2$

11. $\frac{17 - 12}{5} + (4 - 2)$

12. $7(12 \div 3 - 3)$

1-3

Writing and Evaluating Expressions

(IL) Assessment Framework

8.8.02 Write an expression using variables to represent unknown quantities.

8.8.05 Evaluate or simplify algebraic expressions with one or more rational variable values.

✓ **Check Skills You'll Need**

Simplify each expression.

1. $6(9 + 1)$

2. $17 - 2 + 3$

3. $9 + 8 \cdot 2 + 4$

4. $[3(5) + 1] \cdot 2$

GO for Help
Lesson 1-2

🔊 **New Vocabulary**

• evaluate

---

1 Evaluating Variable Expressions

To **evaluate** a variable expression, you first replace each variable with a number. Then, you use the order of operations to simplify.

1 EXAMPLE

Evaluate $4y - 15$ for $y = 9$.

$$4y - 15 = 4(9) - 15 \quad \textbf{Replace } y \textbf{ with 9.}$$
$$= 36 - 15 \quad \textbf{Multiply.}$$
$$= 21 \quad \textbf{Subtract.}$$

✓ **Quick Check**

1. Evaluate each expression.

  a. $63 - 5x$, for $x = 7$ **b.** $4(t + 3) + 1$, for $t = 8$

Sometimes expressions have more than one variable.

2 EXAMPLE   **Replacing More Than One Variable**

Evaluate $3ab + \frac{c}{2}$ for $a = 2$, $b = 5$, and $c = 10$.

$$3ab + \frac{c}{2} = 3 \cdot 2 \cdot 5 + \frac{10}{2} \quad \textbf{Replace the variables.}$$
$$= 3 \cdot 2 \cdot 5 + 5 \quad \textbf{Work within grouping symbols.}$$
$$= 6 \cdot 5 + 5 \quad \textbf{Multiply from left to right.}$$
$$= 30 + 5 \quad \textbf{Multiply.}$$
$$= 35 \quad \textbf{Add.}$$

✓ **Quick Check**

2. Evaluate each expression.

  a. $6(g + h)$, for $g = 8$ and $h = 7$
  b. $2xy - z$, for $x = 4$, $y = 3$, and $z = 1$
  c. $\frac{r + s}{2}$, for $r = 13$ and $s = 11$

2 Solving Problems by Evaluating Expressions

You can write and evaluate variable expressions to solve problems.

3 EXAMPLE Real-World Problem Solving

Purchasing Energy drinks come in cases of 24 bottles.
a. Write a variable expression for the number of cases a store should order to get *b* bottles of energy drinks.
b. Evaluate the expression for 120 bottles.

a. *b* bottles

$\frac{b}{24}$ ←bottles wanted
←number in case

b. 120 bottles

$\frac{b}{24} = \frac{120}{24}$ Evaluate for *b* = 120.

$= 5$ Divide.

The store should order five cases to get 120 bottles.

✓ Quick Check

3. The store pays $29 for each case of drinks. Write a variable expression for the cost of *c* cases. Find the cost of five cases.

Real-World Connection

In a case, bottles are often arranged in 4 rows of 6 (or 6 rows of 4).

4 EXAMPLE Real-World Problem Solving

Online Shopping An online music store charges $14 for each CD. Shipping costs $6 per order. Write a variable expression for the cost of ordering CDs. Find the cost of ordering eight CDs.

Table

Number of CDs	Cost of CDs	Shipping ($)	Total Cost ($)
1	1 · 14	6	1 · 14 + 6 = 20
2	2 · 14	6	2 · 14 + 6 = 34
4	4 · 14	6	4 · 14 + 6 = 62

Let *n* = number of CDs.

Expression   14   ·   *n*   +   6

Evaluate the expression for *n* = 8.

$14 \cdot n + 6 = 14 \cdot 8 + 6$ Replace *n* with 8.

$= 112 + 6 = 118$ Multiply. Then add.

It costs $118 to order eight CDs.

Problem Solving Hint
In Example 4, the phrase *for each* implies multiplication. So *$14 for each CD* means "$14 times the number of CDs."

✓ Quick Check

4. Find the cost of ordering ten CDs.

EXERCISES

For more exercises, see *Extra Skill and Word Problem Practice*.

Practice and Problem Solving

 Practice by Example

Example 1
(page 14)

 for Help

Example 2
(page 14)

Examples 3 and 4
(page 15)

Evaluate each expression.

1. $7b$, for $b = 5$ **2.** $5 - c$, for $c = 3$ **3.** $x \div 8$, for $x = 40$

4. $3n + 2$, for $n = 7$ **5.** $41 - 4h$, for $h = 10$ **6.** $5a + 7$, for $a = 20$

Evaluate each expression for $x = 2$, $y = 3$, and $z = 10$.

7. xyz **8.** $8y \div x$ **9.** $\frac{z}{5} + 2$ **10.** $4y - x$

11. $2z + xy$ **12.** $\frac{9 + y}{x}$ **13.** $4xy - z$ **14.** $5(y + z)$

15. Word Processing An office assistant types 55 words per minute.
 a. Write a variable expression for the number of words the office assistant types in m minutes.
 b. Evaluate the expression for 20 minutes.

16. Online Purchasing An online video store charges $24 for each DVD. Shipping costs $4 per order.
 a. Write a variable expression for the cost of ordering DVDs.
 b. Find the cost of ordering 3 DVDs.

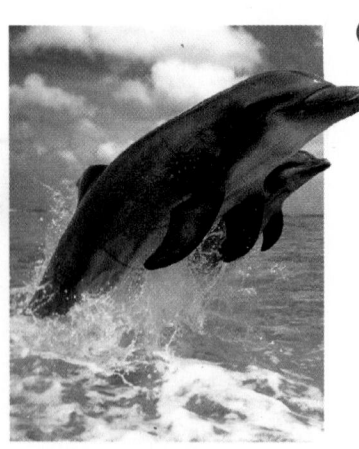

Real-World Connection

By *porpoising* (jumping clear of the water), dolphins can travel as fast as 26 km/h.

B **Apply Your Skills**

Evaluate each expression.

17. $2a + 5$, for $a = 5$ **18.** $105z$, for $z = 7$

19. $6 \div a + 8$, for $a = 2$ **20.** $19 - (a - 4)$, for $a = 8$

21. $13ab$, for $a = 1$ and $b = 7$ **22.** $16 - 4mn$, for $m = 0$ and $n = 3$

23. $j(5 + k)$, for $j = 11$ and $k = 4$ **24.** rst, for $r = 5$, $s = 5$, and $t = 5$

25. $\frac{150}{z + y}$, for $y = 25$ and $z = 50$ **26.** $\frac{x - y}{4}$, for $x = 52$ and $y = 12$

27. Marine Biology Write an expression for the number of kilometers a dolphin travels in d hours swimming at 8 km/h. Then find the number of kilometers the dolphin travels in 3 hours.

28. Data Analysis Use the chart to find how many calories a 100-lb person uses in an hour of moderate walking.
 a. Write an expression for the number of calories a 100-lb person uses in moderate walking for w hours.
 b. Evaluate the expression to find the number of calories a 100-lb person uses in moderate walking for 2 hours.

Calories per Hour Used by a 100-lb Walker	
Type of Walking	Calories
Slow	110
Moderate	153
Brisk	175
Racing	295

SOURCE: www.nutristrategy.com

29. Error Analysis Your friend evaluates $(10 - k) \div 5$ for $k = 5$ and gets 9 for an answer. Explain your friend's error.

Homework Video Tutor
Visit: PHSchool.com
Web Code: ade-0103

C Challenge

30. Evaluate $4a - b + \frac{b}{2}$, for $a = 3$ and $b = 4$.

31. A fitness club requires a $100 initiation fee and dues of $25 each month. Write an expression for the cost of membership for n months. Then find the cost of membership for one year.

32. A carnival charges $5 for admission plus $2 per ride.
    a. Write an expression for the cost of admission plus r rides.
    b. Find the cost of admission plus six rides.
    c. How many rides can you afford if you have $15 to spend?

33. **Writing in Math** Write a word problem that could be solved by evaluating the expression $3x - 5$ for $x = 5$.

ISAT
Test Prep

Multiple Choice

In Exercises 34–37, use the following fact to answer the questions: Every minute, about 145 babies are born in the world.

34. Which expression shows how many babies are born in the world in m minutes?
    A. $60m$ **B.** $145m + 60$
    C. $60m + 145$ **D.** $145m$

35. How many babies are born in the world in 6 minutes?
    F. 360 babies   **G.** 505 babies
    H. 870 babies   **J.** 930 babies

36. How many babies are born in the world in one day?
    A. 3,480 babies   **B.** 86,400 babies
    C. 104,400 babies   **D.** 208,800 babies

37. How many babies are born in the world in one week?
    F. 1,461,600 babies   **G.** 522,000 babies
    H. 60,900 babies   **J.** 10,080 babies

Mixed Review

Lesson 1-2

Simplify each expression.

38. $(60 - 6) \div 9$ **39.** $80 \div 2 + 13$ **40.** $5 \div 5 \cdot 5 - 5$

Lesson 1-1

Write a variable expression for each word phrase.

41. t fewer than 19   **42.** d divided by 20   **43.** the sum of 8 and n

Skills Handbook

44. **Error Analysis** Valerie has test grades of 96, 82, 78, and 76. Using a calculator, she found her average grade to be 275. Is Valerie's answer reasonable? Explain Valerie's error.

1-4 Integers and Absolute Value

 Assessment Framework

6.8.02 Read, write, recognize, model, and interpret integers, including translating numerical expressions.

9.8.12 Relate absolute value to distance on the number line.

☑ **Check Skills You'll Need**

Write an integer for each situation.

1. lose $7

2. find $9

3. 8 steps forward

4. 3 yards gained

5. 5 floors down

GO **for Help**

Skills Handbook, p. 797

◀)) **New Vocabulary**

• opposites
• integers
• absolute value

---

1 Comparing Integers

Antifreeze is mixed with the water in a car's radiator to prevent the water from freezing. Pure water freezes at about 32 degrees Fahrenheit (°F) *above* zero. A mixture of equal parts water and antifreeze freezes at about 32 degrees *below* zero.

Freezing Points

Substance	Freezing Temperature (°F)
Water	32
Antifreeze and water	−32
Seawater	28
Gasoline	−36

You can write 32 degrees above zero as +32°F or 32°F. You can write 32 degrees below zero as −32°F. Read the numbers 32 and −32 as "*positive* 32" and "*negative* 32," respectively.

1 EXAMPLE Representing Negative Numbers

Temperature Write a number to represent the temperature shown by the thermometer.

The temperature of the liquid in the thermometer is 4 degrees Celsius below zero, or −4°C.

☑ **Quick Check**

1. Temperature Seawater freezes at about 28°F, or about 2 degrees Celsius below zero. Write a number to represent the Celsius temperature.

You can graph positive and negative numbers on a number line. A number line helps you compare numbers and arrange them in order.

Numbers increase in value from left to right.

0 is neither positive nor negative.

To compare and order numbers, you can use symbols for "is less than" (<), "is less than or equal to" (≤), "is greater than" (>), and "is greater than or equal to" (≥).

2 **EXAMPLE** **Graphing on a Number Line**

Graph −1, 4, and −5 on a number line. Compare the numbers and order them from least to greatest.

−1 is 1 unit to the left of 0.

−5 is 5 units to the left of 0.

4 is 4 units to the right of 0.

```
◄──┼──┼──┼──┼──●──┼──┼──┼──●──┼──┼──●──┼──┼──┼──┼──►
  −10 −8  −6  −4  −2   0   2   4   6   8   10
```

−5 is to the left of −1, and −1 is to the left of 4, so −5 < −1 < 4. From least to greatest, the numbers are −5, −1, 4.

✓ Quick Check

2. Graph 0, 2, and −6. Compare the numbers and order the numbers from least to greatest.

2 Finding Absolute Value

Numbers that are the same distance from zero on a number line but in opposite directions are called **opposites.**

```
        4 units        4 units
    ◄──┼──┼──┼──┼──┼──┼──┼──┼──┼──┼──►
      −5 −4 −3 −2 −1  0  1  2  3  4  5
```

−4 and 4 are opposites.

Vocabulary Tip

Recall: The <u>whole numbers</u>, 0, 1, 2, 3, 4, . . . , are the counting numbers and zero.

Integers are the whole numbers and their opposites. A number's distance from zero on the number line is called its **absolute value.** You write *the absolute value of 3* as |3|.

3 **EXAMPLE** **Finding Absolute Value**

Use a number line to find |−3| and |3|.

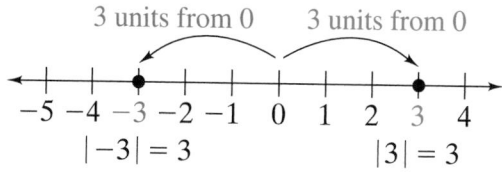

|−3| = 3 |3| = 3

✓ Quick Check

3. Write |−10| in words. Then find |−10|.

EXERCISES

For more exercises, see *Extra Skill and Word Problem Practice.*

Practice and Problem Solving

 A Practice by Example

Example 1
(page 18)

 GO for Help

Write a number to represent each quantity.

1. a profit of $250   **2.** 18°C below zero   **3.** 45 s before launch

4. a deposit of $110   **5.** a debt of $50   **6.** win by 7 points

7. 300 ft below sea level   **8.** a loss of 8 yd   **9.** an elevation of 3,400 ft

Example 2
(page 19)

Write the number represented by each point on the number line.

10. *A*   **11.** *B*   **12.** *C*

Graph each set of numbers on a number line. Then order the numbers from least to greatest.

13. $-2, 8, -9$ **14.** $-3, -12, -9$ **15.** $0, 6, -6$

Example 3
(page 19)

Use a number line to find the absolute values of the integers in each pair.

16. $1, -1$ **17.** $-2, 2$ **18.** $-8, 8$ **19.** $-7, 7$ **20.** $6, -6$ **21.** $-4, 4$

Simplify each expression.

22. $|18|$ **23.** the absolute value of -9

24. $|-3|$ **25.** the absolute value of 6

26. $|-7|$ **27.** the absolute value of -2

B Apply Your Skills

Open-Ended Describe a quantity each integer could represent.

28. $-1,000$ **29.** 28   **30.** -126

Write the integer represented by each point.

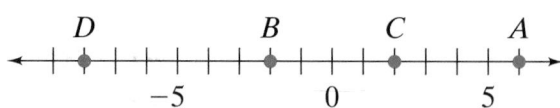

31. *A*   **32.** *B*   **33.** *C*   **34.** *D*

Simplify each expression.

35. $|0|$ **36.** $|-1,000|$ **37.** $-|-13|$

38. $|-56|$ **39.** $-|-23|$ **40.** $-|12|$

Compare. Use >, <, or = to complete each statement.

41. $-8 \blacksquare 0$ **42.** $4 \blacksquare -25$ **43.** $-9 \blacksquare -2$

44. $|-1| \blacksquare |50|$ **45.** $|-6| \blacksquare |-12|$ **46.** $|10| \blacksquare |-10|$

47. Multiple Choice Which expression would you use to represent 10 times your height h in inches?

Ⓐ $10 + h$ Ⓑ $10 - h$ Ⓒ $10h$ Ⓓ $10 \div h$

Write an expression to represent each quantity.

48. a loss of $\frac{1}{3}$ of an investment of d dollars

49. n degrees Fahrenheit above $r°$F room temperature

Read the passage below before doing Exercises 50 and 51.

Finding Famous Ships

Scientist-explorer Robert D. Ballard led the expeditions that found two famous ships deep in the North Atlantic Ocean.

In 1912, the luxury passenger liner *Titanic* struck an iceberg. It came to rest 12,500 ft below sea level. *Titanic* was 882 ft long and 92 ft wide.

In 1941, the mighty warship *Bismarck* sank in battle. *Bismarck* was 823 ft long and 118 ft wide.

Star Hercules, only 269 ft long, towed the underwater camera sled that found *Bismarck* under 15,617 ft of water.

50. Write integers to represent the positions of *Titanic* and *Bismarck*.

51. A friend says that *Bismarck*'s resting place is higher than *Titanic*'s since 15,617 is higher than 12,500. Explain your friend's error.

Complete each sentence with a word that makes it true.

52. An integer is negative, positive, or _?_ .

53. All _?_ integers are less than zero.

54. The opposite of a _?_ number is negative.

55. The absolute value of an integer is never _?_ .

ⓒ Challenge

Open-Ended **Name two consecutive integers between the given integers.**

56. $-6, 2$ **57.** $0, -4$ **58.** $-8, -12$

Record Low Temperatures for Three States

State	Temperature (°C)
California	-45
Nevada	-50
Georgia	-17

SOURCE: *U.S. National Climatic Data Center*

59. a. Data Analysis Use a number line to graph the temperatures in the chart at the left. Label each temperature with the name of the state where it was recorded.
  b. Which state recorded the lowest temperature?

60. Writing in Math How can you use integers to describe elevations above and below sea level?

61. Reasoning Explain why $|x + y|$ and $|x| + |y|$ are not the same. Give examples to show that $|x + y| = |x| + |y|$ for some values of x and y, and $|x + y| \neq |x| + |y|$ for other values of x and y.

Multiple Choice

62. Which list shows the values in order from least to greatest?
    A. 0, 3, −17, −25
    B. −25, −17, 0, 3
    C. 0, −17, −25, 3
    D. −25, 0, 3, −27

63. Which expression has the value −90?
    F. $|-90|$ **G.** 90   **H.** $|90|$ **J.** $-|90|$

64. Which list shows the values in order from least to greatest?
    A. $|-6|$, 6, $|-3|$, 3
    B. -6, $-|-3|$, 3, $|-6|$
    C. $|-6|$, $|-3|$, $|3|$, $|6|$
    D. -3, $-|-6|$, $-|3|$, 6

65. Which two integers are between −5 and 2?
    F. −4, 1   **G.** −3, 3   **H.** −6, 1   **J.** 0, 4

Mixed Review

for
Help

Lesson 1-3

Evaluate each expression.

66. $p - 5$, for $p = 19$ **67.** $3d + 3$, for $d = 7$ **68.** $55y$, for $y = 8$

Lesson 1-2

Compare. Use >, <, or = to complete each statement.

69. $5 + 10 \div 5 \blacksquare (5 + 10) \div 5$

70. $(9 - 6) \div (2 + 1) \blacksquare 9 - 6 \div 2 + 1$

Lesson 1-1

71. Suppose you have c CDs. Your friend has 6 more CDs than you do. Write an expression for the number of CDs your friend has.

Checkpoint Quiz 1
      Lessons 1-1 through 1-4

Write a variable expression for each word phrase.

1. 23 more than f **2.** g divided by 34   **3.** product of 9 and p

Simplify each expression.

4. $17 + 16 - 13$ **5.** $70 \div [5(3 + 4)]$ **6.** $9 \times 6 \div 3 + 1$

Evaluate each expression for $x = 4$, $y = 6$, and $z = 12$.

7. $2x - 8$ **8.** $3(z + y)$ **9.** $4y - z + \frac{z}{x}$

10. Temperature On Monday the average temperature was −10°F. On Tuesday it was −15°F. On Wednesday it was −13°F. On Thursday it was 0°F.
    a. Graph the temperatures on a number line.
    b. Write the days in order from coldest to warmest.

You can use models, such as colored tiles, to represent integers.
Use a yellow tile ☐ to represent a positive integer.
Use a red tile ■ to represent a negative integer.

1 ACTIVITY

Use models to represent the integers 3, −1, and −4.

☐☐☐ 3   ■ −1   ■■■■ −4

An equal number of yellow tiles and red tiles combine to make zero.

These tiles make a zero pair. ⟶ ☐■ represents zero, or ☐ + ■ = 0.

You can remove zero pairs in sets of mixed tiles.

2 ACTIVITY

Write the integer that is represented by ■■■■■☐☐.

Group the zero pairs.
Then remove them.

Write the integer that the remaining tiles represent.

■■■ −3

EXERCISES

Use tiles to model each integer.

1. −3   **2.** 5   **3.** −2   **4.** 7

5. 0   **6.** −6   **7.** 2   **8.** −8

Write an integer for each model.

9. ☐☐

10. ■■■■■

11. ■■

12. ☐☐☐☐☐☐

13. ■■☐☐ ☐☐■■

14. ■■☐☐■☐ ☐

15. ☐■☐☐☐☐ ☐☐■■

16. ■■☐☐☐■■

17. a. Describe how you would model the integers −15 and 25.
b. Reasoning Suppose you combine the models from part (a).
How many zero pairs could you make? How many tiles
would be left after you removed the zero pairs?

1-5 Adding Integers

IL Assessment Framework

6.8.09 Solve problems and number sentences involving addition, subtraction, multiplication, and division using rational numbers, exponents, and roots.

 Check Skills You'll Need

Compare. Use >, <, or = to complete each statement.

1. -6 ■ -3

2. 2 ■ -15

3. -5 ■ $|5|$

4. $|10|$ ■ $|-10|$

5. $|9|$ ■ $|-2|$

6. $|-8|$ ■ $|0|$

GO for Help
Lesson 1-4

1 Using Models to Add Integers

If a car goes forward 20 ft and then backs up 20 ft, it ends where it started. Using opposite integers, you can represent this situation as $20 + (-20) = 0$.

When you add opposites, the sum is zero. So, opposites are also called *additive inverses*.

Key Concepts | **Addition of Opposites**

The sum of an integer and its opposite is zero.

Arithmetic	Algebra
$1 + (-1) = 0$	$x + (-x) = 0$
$-1 + 1 = 0$	$-x + x = 0$

You can use tiles to add integers. One positive tile and one negative tile combine to make a zero pair since ▢ + ■ = 0.

To add integers using tiles, combine tiles and remove the zero pairs.

1 EXAMPLE **Using Tiles to Add Integers**

Modeling **Use tiles to find 2 + (−5).**

$2 + (-5)$ ▢▢ + ■■■ ■■   **Model the sum.**

-3 [▢▢ ■■■] ■   **Group and remove zero pairs. There are three negative tiles left.**
      ■■

$2 + (-5) = -3$

 Quick Check

1. Use tiles to find each sum.

    a. $-1 + 4$ **b.** $7 + (-3)$ **c.** $-2 + (-2)$

A number line provides another model that you can use to add integers, as shown in Example 2.

2 EXAMPLE **Using a Number Line**

Football On two plays, a football team first loses 8 yd and then gains 3 yd. Find $-8 + 3$ to find the result of the two plays.

Start at 0. To represent -8, move left 8 units. To add positive 3, move right 3 units to -5.

$$-8 + 3 = -5$$

The result of the two plays is a loss of 5 yd.

Video Tutor Help
Visit: PHSchool.com
Web Code: ada-0775

✓ Quick Check

2. Use a number line to find each sum.
   a. $2 + (-6)$ **b.** $-4 + 9$ **c.** $-5 + (-1)$

2 Using Rules to Add Integers

You can also use rules to find the sum of two integers.

Key Concepts **Adding Integers**

Same Sign The sum of two positive integers is positive. The sum of two negative integers is negative.

Different Signs To add two integers with different signs, find the difference of their absolute values. The sum has the sign of the integer with the greater absolute value.

3 EXAMPLE **Applying Rules to Add Integers**

Find each sum.

a. $-12 + (-31)$

$-12 + (-31) = -43$ Since both integers are negative, the sum is negative.

b. $7 + (-18)$

$|-18| - |7| = 18 - 7$ Find the difference of the absolute values.

$= 11$ Simplify.

$7 + (-18) = -11$ Since -18 has the greater absolute value, the sum is negative.

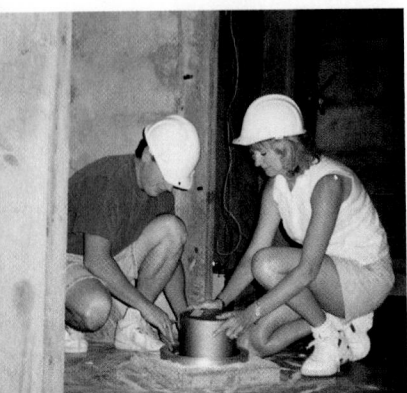

Real-World Connection

A worldwide network of monitors keeps track of earthquake activity. Here technicians check the monitor in Albuquerque.

✓ Quick Check

3. Find each sum.

    a. $-22 + (-16)$ **b.** $60 + (-13)$ **c.** $-125 + 35$

---

4 EXAMPLE   Real-World 🌐 Problem Solving

Earth Science The earthquake monitor in Hockley, Texas, is located in a salt mine at an elevation of -416 m. The elevation of the monitor in Albuquerque, New Mexico, is 2,156 m higher than the one in Hockley. Find the elevation of the monitor in Albuquerque.

$-416 + 2,156$	Write an expression.
$\lvert 2{,}156 \rvert - \lvert -416 \rvert = 2{,}156 - 416$	Find the difference of the absolute values.
$= 1{,}740$	Simplify.
$-416 + 2{,}156 = 1{,}740$	Since 2,156 has the greater absolute value, the sum is positive.

The elevation of the monitor in Albuquerque is 1,740 m.

✓ Quick Check

4. The elevation of a monitor in Piñon Flat, California, is 1,696 m higher than the monitor in Hockley, Texas. Find the elevation of the monitor in Piñon Flat.

To add several integers, use the order of operations.

---

5 EXAMPLE   **Using the Order of Operations**

Find $-12 + (-6) + 15 + (-2)$.

$-12 + (-6) + 15 + (-2)$	Add from left to right.
$-18 \quad + \quad 15 + (-2)$	The sum of two negative integers is negative.
$-3 \quad + \quad (-2)$	$\lvert -18 \rvert - \lvert 15 \rvert = 3$. Since -18 has the greater absolute value, the sum is negative.
-5	The sum of two negative integers is negative.

$-12 + (-6) + 15 + (-2) = -5$

✓ Quick Check

5. Find each sum.

    a. $1 + (-3) + 2 + (-10)$ **b.** $-250 + 200 + (-100) + 220$

EXERCISES

For more exercises, see *Extra Skill and Word Problem Practice.*

Practice and Problem Solving

A Practice by Example

Examples 1 and 2
(pages 24 and 25)

GO for Help

Modeling Write an expression for each model. Find the sum.

1.

2.

3.

4.

Draw a model and find each sum.

5. $2 + (-5)$ 6. $-5 + 2$ 7. $5 + (-2)$ 8. $-5 + (-2)$

9. $-6 + 1$ 10. $-3 + (-6)$ 11. $-3 + 2$ 12. $-3 + 4$

Example 3
(page 25)

Find each sum.

13. $14 + (-11)$ 14. $0 + (-9)$ 15. $-6 + (-7)$

16. $-18 + 4$ 17. $-40 + 93$ 18. $-26 + (-39)$

19. $450 + (-350)$ 20. $100 + (-100)$ 21. $235 + (-420)$

Example 4
(page 26)

22. **Geography** The highest peak at Mt. Ellsworth in Montana is 3,275 m lower than the highest peak of Mt. Kilimanjaro in Kenya, at 5,895 m. Find the elevation of the highest peak at Mt. Ellsworth.

Example 5
(page 26)

Find each sum.

23. $19 + (-9) + 45 + (-32)$ 24. $-3 + 2 + (-7) + 7 + 13$

25. $-94 + 68 + (-22) + (-13)$ 26. $-20 + (-89) + 112 + 9$

B Apply Your Skills

Reasoning Without adding, tell whether each sum is positive, negative, or zero. Explain how you found your answer.

27. $-4 + (-10)$ 28. $11 + (-3)$ 29. $6 + (-6)$ 30. $-4 + (-2)$

Mental Math Find each sum.

31. $-5 + 20$ 32. $9 + (-9)$ 33. $10 + (-3)$ 34. $-5 + 5 + 16$

35. **Multiple Choice** One winter day the temperature starts at $-12°F$, warms 10 degrees, and then drops 2 degrees. What is the temperature at the end of the day?

   Ⓐ $-32°F$ Ⓑ $-4°F$ Ⓒ $-2°F$ Ⓓ $0°F$

Compare. Use >, <, or = to complete each statement.

36. $-6 + 1 \blacksquare 5 + 1$ 37. $0 + 3 \blacksquare -2 + 0$

38. $10 + (-2) \blacksquare -4 + 12$ 39. $-1 + 1 \blacksquare -2 + 0$

40. $49 + (-21) \blacksquare |-18|$ 41. $|-20| + (-7) \blacksquare -11 + (-11)$

Online
Homework Video Tutor
Visit: PHSchool.com
Web Code: ade-0105

Evaluate each expression for $n = -15$.

42. $n + (-7) - n$ **43.** $15 + n + (-8)$ **44.** $n + (-15) + n$

Write a numerical expression for each of the following. Then find the sum.

45. You borrow $20, and then pay back $18.

46. You save $200, and then spend $75.

47. A man deposits $120, and then writes a check for $25.

48. A submarine at 35 ft below sea level moves up 10 ft.

Use the order of operations to find each sum.

49. $4 + (-6) + 3$ **50.** $-1 + 1 + (-3)$

51. $-72 + 36 + (-6) + (-18)$

52. Football A football team gained 4 yd, lost 2 yd, gained 11 yd, lost 8 yd, and then lost 9 yd. Find the net gain or loss.

53. Finance Maria had $123. She spent $35, loaned $20 to a friend, and received her $90 paycheck. How much does she have now?

54. Error Analysis A friend says that the value of $-17 + 5$ is -22. Explain how your friend may have made this error.

55. Writing in Math A friend is having trouble finding the sum of -84 and 28. What explanation would you give to help your friend?

C Challenge

Reasoning For Exercises 56–59, use the number line and tell whether the value of each expression is positive or negative.

56. $a + b$ **57.** $b + c$ **58.** $a + a$ **59.** $|a + b + c|$

ISAT

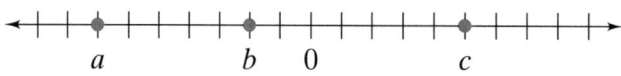

Test Prep

Multiple Choice

60. The temperature starts at $-10°F$, drops 2°, drops 5°, and rises 1°. Which expression gives the current temperature?
 A. $(-10) + 2 + 5 + 1$ **B.** $-10 + (-2) + (-5) + 1$
 C. $10 + 2 + 5 + (-1)$ **D.** $10 + 2 + 5 + 1$

61. A stock price starts at $6, rises $3, falls $1, and falls $1 again. What is the current price of the stock?
 F. $1   **G.** $5   **H.** $7   **J.** $11

62. Which statement shows an example of additive inverses?
 A. $xy = yx$ **B.** $x[(y + (-y)] = x(0)$
 C. $x + y = y + x$ **D.** $x\left(\frac{y}{y}\right) = x(1)$

63. Refer to the map at the right. The lowest temperature recorded in South America is 54 degrees higher than the lowest temperature recorded in North America. What is the lowest temperature recorded in South America?

F. −135°F   **G.** −27°F
H. −17°F   **J.** −138°F

Lowest Recorded Temperatures

SOURCE: *The World Almanac*

Lesson 1-4 **GO for Help**

Compare. Use >, <, or = to complete each statement.

64. −90 ■ −6   **65.** −2 ■ −7   **66.** |−15| ■ −15

67. 0 ■ −8   **68.** −45 ■ −44   **69.** 100 ■ |−101|

70. Write a numerical expression for the phrase *one hundred thirty added to the difference of one hundred sixteen and eight.* Then simplify the expression.

Lesson 1-3 **71. Repairs** A repair center charges a $25 flat fee plus $10 per hour for labor. Write an expression for the cost of a repair that takes *n* hours. Then evaluate the expression to find the cost of an oven repair that takes 3 hours.

Math at Work

Weaver

Weaver A sturdy four-shaft floor loom, a 10-dent reed, a ski shuttle, two boat shuttles—these are some of the tools and terms of the ancient craft of weaving. Weavers use yarn, ribbon, and thread. They design and make colorful, unique items such as rugs, tapestries, and handbags. Like a pattern in algebra, each design has rules that must be followed for the desired result.

Go Online
PHSchool.com   **For:** Information about weavers
Web Code: adb-2031

1-6 Subtracting Integers

IL Assessment Framework

6.8.09 Solve problems and number sentences involving addition, subtraction, multiplication, and division using rational numbers, exponents, and roots.

 Check Skills You'll Need

Find each sum.

1. $8 + (-9)$

2. $-11 + (-18)$

3. $-4 + (-6)$

4. $14 + (-3)$

5. $6 + (-6)$

6. $-13 + (-10)$

GO for Help
Lesson 1-5

1 Using Models to Subtract Integers

You can use tiles to help you understand subtraction of integers.

1 EXAMPLE Using Tiles to Subtract Integers

Find $-6 - (-2)$.

Start with 6 negative tiles.

Take away 2 negative tiles.
There are 4 negative tiles left.

$-6 - (-2) = -4$

✓ Quick Check

1. Use tiles to find each difference.

   a. $-7 - (-2)$ **b.** $-4 - (-3)$ **c.** $-8 - (-5)$

You can use zero pairs to subtract an integer from a smaller integer.

2 EXAMPLE Using Zero Pairs to Subtract Integers

Find $3 - 5$.

Start with 3 positive tiles.

There are not enough positive tiles to take away 5. Add 2 zero pairs.

Take away 5 positive tiles.
There are 2 negative tiles left.

$3 - 5 = -2$

✓ Quick Check

2. Use tiles to find each difference.

   a. $4 - 8$ **b.** $-1 - 5$ **c.** $-2 - (-7)$

You can use models to show the relationship between adding and subtracting integers.

5 + (−4)

5 − 4

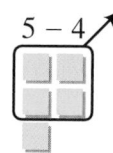

5 − 4 = 1

5 + (−4) = 1

Both 5 + (−4) and 5 − 4 equal 1. So, 5 + (−4) = 5 − 4.

The models suggest the following rule for subtracting integers.

Key Concepts | **Subtracting Integers**

To subtract an integer, add its opposite.

Arithmetic	**Algebra**
$2 - 5 = 2 + (-5) = -3$	$a - b = a + (-b)$
$2 - (-5) = 2 + 5 = 7$	$a - (-b) = a + b$

3 **EXAMPLE** **Real-World 🌎 Problem Solving**

Weather In January, 1916, the temperature in Browning, Montana, dropped 100 degrees overnight. The initial temperature was 44°F. What was the final temperature?

$44 - 100$ **Write an expression.**

$44 - 100 = 44 + (-100)$ **To subtract 100, add its opposite.**

$= -56$ **Simplify.**

The final temperature was −56°F.

✓ Quick Check

3. Find each difference.
   a. $32 - (-3)$ **b.** $-40 - 66$ **c.** $2 - 48$
   d. The lowest temperature ever recorded on the moon was about −170°C. The lowest temperature ever recorded in Antarctica was −89°C. Find the difference in the temperatures.

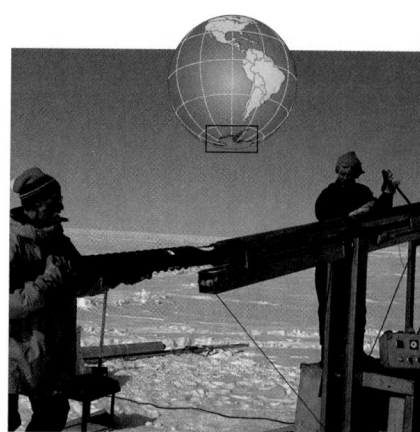

Real-World 🌎 Connection

The lowest temperature ever recorded on Earth was −129°F (−89°C) in Vostok, Antarctica. Scientists there are taking ice-core samples to depths of −3,600 m.

EXERCISES

For more exercises, see *Extra Skill and Word Problem Practice*.

Practice and Problem Solving

 Practice by Example

Examples 1 and 2
(page 30)

Write a number sentence for each model.

1. [model] **2.** [model]

Modeling Use tiles to help you find each difference.

3. $-7 - (-3)$ **4.** $-15 - (-7)$ **5.** $-5 - (-6)$

6. $-9 - (-7)$ **7.** $-7 - (-9)$ **8.** $-16 - (-9)$

9. $-8 - (-3)$ **10.** $-1 - (-3)$ **11.** $10 - (-5)$

12. $9 - (-8)$ **13.** $-14 - (-8)$ **14.** $-7 - (-7)$

15. $2 - 3$ **16.** $-2 - 3$ **17.** $-10 - 2$

Example 3
(page 31)

Write each difference as a sum. Then simplify.

18. $6 - 2$ **19.** $6 - (-2)$ **20.** $-6 - 2$ **21.** $2 - 6$

22. $2 - (-6)$ **23.** $-2 - 6$ **24.** $5 - 11$ **25.** $75 - (-25)$

26. $22 - (-7)$ **27.** $87 - (-9)$ **28.** $35 - 15$ **29.** $100 - (-91)$

🌐 **30. Account Balances** Terry has $43 in a checking account. If Terry writes a check for $62, what is the new account balance?

🌐 **31. Scores** Suppose you have a score of 35 in a game. You get a 50-point penalty. What is your new score?

B **Apply Your Skills**

Find each difference.

32. $-49 - 75$ **33.** $-65 - 15$ **34.** $16 - (-3)$

35. $120 - (-50)$ **36.** $989 - 76$ **37.** $-35 - 25$

38. $-92 - (-9)$ **39.** $-81 - (-13)$ **40.** $36 - 88$

Simplify.

41. $-90 - (-80) - 20$ **42.** $810 - 30 - (-70)$

43. $23 - (-15) - 28$ **44.** $-17 + 25 - (-58)$

Open-Ended Use positive and negative integers to write two different subtraction number sentences for each difference.

SAMPLE   ■ − ■ = −5 $17 - 22 = -5$
                             $-20 - (-15) = -5$

45. ■ − ■ = 0   **46.** ■ − ■ = 10   **47.** ■ − ■ = −6

48. ■ − ■ = −15   **49.** ■ − ■ = $|-3|$ **50.** ■ − ■ = $|11|$

Altitude	Temperature (°C)
9,000 m	−20°
7,500 m	−12°
6,000 m	−4°
4,500 m	4°
3,000 m	12°
1,500 m	20°
0 m	28°

🌐 **Meteorology** The graph at the left shows how temperature changes with altitude. Use this graph for Exercises 51–53.

51. As the altitude increases, what happens to the temperature?

52. What is the change in temperature from 1,500 m to 6,000 m?

53. Multiple Choice Find the change in temperature for every 1,500-meter increase in altitude.

   Ⓐ 12°C   Ⓑ 8°C   Ⓒ −8°C   Ⓓ −12°C

Mental Math Simplify each expression.

54. $-6 - (-8)$ **55.** $-45 - 15$ **56.** $-7 - (-7) + (-7)$

57. $100 - (-50)$ **58.** $20 - (-10) - 20$ **59.** $-11 + 22 - (-55)$

60. $3 - (-3) + 6$ **61.** $-32 + 2 + (-10)$ **62.** $-87 + (-3) + 90$

63. $6 - (-6) + 6$ **64.** $0 + (-15) - 15$ **65.** $-13 - 17 + 10$

Write a numerical expression for each phrase. Then simplify and answer the question.

66. You are $2 in debt. You borrow $4 more. What is the total amount of your debt?

67. An airplane takes off, climbs 3,000 ft, and then descends 600 ft. What is the airplane's current height?

68. From 0°F, the temperature increases 15 degrees and then drops 25 degrees. What is the current temperature?

ⓒ Challenge

Estimation Round each number. Then estimate the sum or difference.

SAMPLE $-2,216 - 488 \approx -2,200 - 500 = -2,700$

69. $-41 - (-86)$ **70.** $-227 - 49$ **71.** $-398 - 67$

72. $-86 - 22$ **73.** $288 - 59$ **74.** $63 - (-21)$

75. a. Writing in Math A thermometer is like a vertical number line. Use the one at the right to write a subtraction problem.

    b. Write and simplify a numerical expression for your problem.

76. a. Patterns Copy and complete. The first one is done for you.

    $8 - (-4) = 12$
    $12 - (-4) = ■$
    $16 - (-4) = ■$
    $20 - (-4) = ■$
    $24 - (-4) = ■$

    b. If you begin at 8 and subtract −4 five times, the result is ■.
    c. Begin at 0 and subtract −4 six times. What is the result?

77. Reasoning For what values of a is each statement true? Give an example, if possible.

    a. $|a - 5| = |a| - 5$ **b.** $|a - 5| > |a| - 5$ **c.** $|a - 5| < |a| - 5$

In each number square, the rows, columns, and diagonals have the same sum. Copy and complete each number square.

78.

5	−9	■
■	−1	■
−3	■	−7

sum = ■

79.

−2	■	■
−9	−5	■
−4	■	■

sum = ■

80.

■	−5	■	6
■	4	3	■
2	0	■	5
−3	■	■	−6

sum = ■

81.

−6	4	5	−9
2	■	−1	−3
−5	1	■	0
■	−7	−8	■

sum = ■

ISAT

Test Prep

Multiple Choice

82. Three of the four expressions have the same value. Which one has a different value?
   A. 6 + (−4)   **B.** 6 − 4   **C.** |4 − 6| **D.** −6 − 4

83. Suppose you have a score of 25 in a game. You get a penalty that lowers your score by 60 points. What is your new score?
   F. −85   **G.** −40   **H.** −35   **J.** 15

84. How many degrees warmer is a temperature of 20°C than a temperature of −7°C?
   A. −27°C   **B.** −13°C   **C.** 13°C   **D.** 27°C

85. What is the value of −23 + −(−15) + |−17| + (−35)?
   F. −56   **G.** −26   **H.** |−26| **J.** 56

Mixed Review

GO for Help

Lesson 1-5   **Find each sum.**

86. −17 + 12   87. −8 + 15   88. −9 + (−4) + 7

Lesson 1-4   **Open-Ended Complete each statement with an integer.**

89. −5 > ■   90. ■ < 6   91. |−1| > ■   92. |■| < 8

Lesson 1-1   93. Write an expression for the phrase *one hundred plus the product of six and nine.* Simplify the expression.

Inductive Reasoning

1 Writing Rules for Patterns

Inductive reasoning is making conclusions based on patterns you observe. A conclusion you reach by inductive reasoning is a **conjecture**.

1 EXAMPLE Reasoning Inductively

Visual Patterns Use inductive reasoning. Make a conjecture about the next figure in the pattern. Then draw the figure.

Observation: The shaded triangle is rotating clockwise around the square.

Conjecture: The next figure will have a shaded triangle in the bottom-right corner.

✓ Quick Check

1. Make a conjecture about the next figure in the pattern at the right. Then draw the figure.

For a number pattern, a conjecture can be a rule that explains how to make the pattern. The three dots in a pattern tell you that the pattern continues.

2 EXAMPLE Writing Rules for Patterns

Number Patterns Write a rule for each number pattern.

a. 30, 25, 20, 15, . . . Start with 30 and subtract 5 repeatedly.

b. 2, −2, 2, −2, . . . Alternate 2 and its opposite.

c. 1, 3, 4, 12, 13, . . . Start with 1. Alternate multiplying by 3 and adding 1.

✓ Quick Check

2. Write a rule for each pattern.

   a. 4, 9, 14, 19, . . .   **b.** 3, 9, 27, 81, . . .   **c.** 1, 1, 2, 3, 5, 8, . . .

What You'll Learn

- To write rules for patterns
- To make predictions and test conjectures

. . . And Why

To use inductive reasoning in finding patterns and in making conjectures about economic data

✓ Check Skills You'll Need

Find each difference.

1. $-3 - 4$ **2.** $-7 - 4$

3. $-11 - 4$ **4.** $-15 - 4$

 for Help
Lesson 1-6

🔊 New Vocabulary

- inductive reasoning
- conjecture
- counterexample

3 EXAMPLE · Extending a Pattern

Number Patterns Write a rule for the number pattern
640, 320, 160, 80, . . . Find the next two numbers in the pattern.

640,　　320,　　160,　　80
　　÷2　　÷2　　÷2

The first number is 640. The next
numbers are found by dividing by 2.

The rule is *Start with 640 and divide by 2.* The next two numbers
in the pattern are $80 \div 2 = 40$ and $40 \div 2 = 20$.

✓ Quick Check

3. Write a rule for the pattern 1, 3, 5, 7, . . . Find the next two
numbers in the pattern.

2 · Predictions and Counterexamples

With sufficient information, you can make predictions based on
reasonable conjectures. Such predictions will probably—but not
necessarily—turn out to be accurate.

4 EXAMPLE · Real-World 🌐 Problem Solving

Statistics See the graph below. Is a conjecture that average hourly
earnings in the year 2005 will be about $15.75 reasonable?

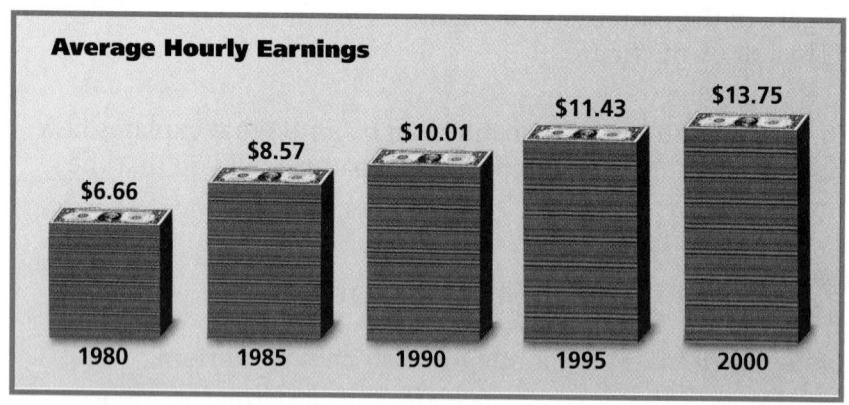

Average Hourly Earnings

				$13.75
			$11.43	
		$10.01		
	$8.57			
$6.66				
1980	1985	1990	1995	2000

Average hourly earnings appear to increase by $1.50 to $2.50
every five years. The conjecture of $15.75 in 2005 is reasonable,
since it is about $2.00 more than the earnings for 2000.

✓ Quick Check

4. You toss a coin four times, and it comes up heads each time. Is
the conjecture *The coin will come up heads on every toss*
reasonable? Explain.

An example that proves a statement false is a **counterexample.**
You need only one counterexample to prove that a conjecture
is incorrect.

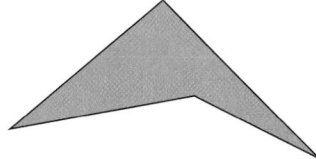 **EXAMPLE** Analyzing Conjectures

Inductive Reasoning Is each conjecture correct or incorrect? If it
is incorrect, give a counterexample.

a. **Every four-sided figure is a rectangle.**
   The conjecture is incorrect. The figure below has four sides, but
   it is not a rectangle.

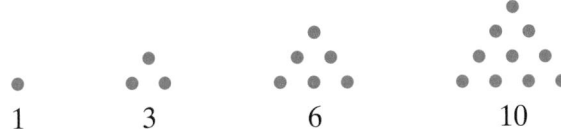

b. **The absolute value of any integer is positive.**
   The conjecture is incorrect. The absolute value of zero is zero,
   which is neither positive nor negative.

c. **The next figure in the pattern below has 15 dots.**

   The conjecture is correct. The diagram below shows the next
   figure in the pattern.

✓ Quick Check

5. Is each conjecture correct or incorrect? If it is incorrect,
   give a counterexample.

   a. The last digit of the product of 5 and a whole number is
      either 0 or 5.
   b. A number and its absolute value are always opposites.
   c. The next figure in the pattern has 25 dots.

A Practice by Example

Example 1
(page 35)

Visual Patterns Describe the next figure in each pattern. Then draw the figure.

1.

2.

Examples 2 and 3
(pages 35 and 36)

Write a rule for each pattern. Then find the next two numbers in each pattern.

3. $100, 85, 70, 55, \ldots$ 4. $5, 20, 80, 320, \ldots$ 5. $2, 7, 12, 17, \ldots$

6. $-10, -4, 2, 8, \ldots$ 7. $1, 4, 7, 10, \ldots$ 8. $1, 2, 5, 6, 9, \ldots$

Example 4
(page 36)

9. Mario caught a cold on each of his last three visits with his cousin. Is it reasonable for Mario to conclude that his catching a cold is the result of visiting his cousin? Explain.

Example 5
(page 37)

Is each conjecture correct or incorrect? If it is incorrect, give a counterexample.

10. All birds can fly.

11. Every square is a rectangle.

12. The product of two numbers is never less than either of the numbers.

B Apply Your Skills

Visual Patterns Describe the next figure in each pattern. Then draw the figure.

13.

14.

Write a rule for each pattern. Then find the next three numbers in each pattern.

15. $1, 1.5, 2, 2.5, 3, \ldots$ 16. $-1, 1, -2, 2, -3, 3, \ldots$ 17. $6, 4, 2, 0, \ldots$

Reasoning Is each conjecture correct? If incorrect, give a counterexample.

18. Every clover has three leaves.

19. The sum of two numbers is always greater than either of the two numbers.

20. A whole number is divisible by 3 if the sum of its digits is divisible by 3.

 Challenge **Write a rule for each pattern. Then find the next three numbers.**

21. $1, 4, 10, 22, 46, 94, \ldots$

22. $1, -2, 4, -5, 7, -8, \ldots$

23. a. Writing in Math Use the graph at the right. Write a conjecture about the unemployment rate in 2001. Justify your reasoning.

b. How could you test your conjecture?

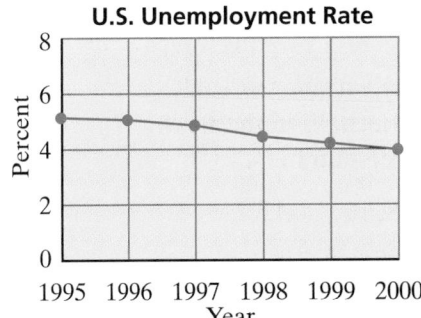

U.S. Unemployment Rate

ISAT

Test Prep

Multiple Choice

24. What are the next three numbers in this pattern? 11, 22, 12, 23, ...
   A. 13, 23, 14   **B.** 13, 24, 15   **C.** 13, 24, 14   **D.** 32, 43, 33

25. Which best describes the rule for this pattern?
   1, −12, 12, −1, ...
   F. subtract 24, then add 13   **G.** subtract 13, then add 24
   H. subtract −24, then add 13   **J.** subtract −13, then add 24

26. Which letter continues this pattern of letters in the alphabet?
   B, E, I, N, ■
   A. R   **B.** S   **C.** T   **D.** U

Mixed Review

Lesson 1-6 **Find each difference.**

27. $1 - 8$ **28.** $-4 - (-9)$ **29.** $86 - (-17)$

Lessons 1-3, 1-5 **Evaluate each expression for $x = -1$ and $y = -3$.**

30. $x + y$ **31.** $y + x + 2$ **32.** $24 + x + y$

Lesson 1-3 **33. Science** The water in a stream flows at the rate of 1,500 gal/h. Write a variable expression for the amount of water that flows in n hours. Evaluate your expression for $n = 24$.

1-8 Problem Solving — Look for a Pattern

What You'll Learn

• To find number patterns

...And Why

To use patterns to solve real-world problems involving communication

 Check Skills You'll Need

Write a rule for each pattern. Find the next three numbers.

1. 8, 11, 14, 17, ...

2. 1, 5, 4, 8, 7, ...

3. 3, 5, 10, 12, 24, ...

4. 1, 4, 7, 10, ...

GO for Help
Lesson 1-7

1 Finding Number Patterns

Math Strategies in Action
What do songs on the radio, computer code, and your body's DNA have in common?

All are based on patterns. Radio uses patterns of electromagnetic waves. Computer code consists of patterns of numbers. Your DNA is made up of molecules that repeat in special patterns.

You can solve many types of problems by finding and using patterns. Making predictions from patterns is a form of inductive reasoning.

1 EXAMPLE   Real-World Problem Solving

Information News spreads quickly at Riverdell High. Each student who hears a story repeats it 15 minutes later to two students who have not yet heard it and then tells no one else.

Suppose one student hears some news at 8:00 A.M. How many students will know the news at 9:00 A.M.?

Understand the Problem

1. How many students does each student tell?

2. How long does the news take to reach the second and third students?

Make a Plan

Make a table to organize the numbers. Then look for a pattern.

3. How many *new* students will hear the news at 8:15 A.M.?

4. How many 15-minute periods are there between 8:00 A.M. and 9:00 A.M.?

The pattern is to add the number of new students to the number who already know.

$1 + 2 = 3$ **the number who know at 8:15**
(**One student talks to 2.**)

$3 + 4 = 7$ **the number who know at 8:30**
(**Two students talk to 4.**)

Make a table and extend the pattern to 9:00.

Time	8:00	8:15	8:30	8:45	9:00
Number of new students told	1	2	4	8	16
Number of students who know	1	$1 + 2 =$ 3	$3 + 4 =$ 7	$7 + 8 =$ 15	$15 + 16 =$ 31

By 9:00 A.M., 31 students will know the news.

Check the Answer

One way to check whether a solution is reasonable is to solve the problem by another method. You can use a *tree diagram* to show the pattern visually.

Time	New Students	Students Who Know
8:00	1	1
8:15	2	3
8:30	4	7
8:45	8	15
9:00	16	31

5. Describe two ways to find the number of students who will know the news at 9:15 A.M.

6. Suppose you want to continue the pattern beyond 9:15. Which would work better, a table or a tree diagram? Explain.

7. There are 251 students at Riverdell High. By what time will every student know the news?

✅ Quick Check

8. Suppose each student who hears the story repeats it in 10 minutes. How many students will know the news at 9:00 A.M.?

EXERCISES

For more exercises, see *Extra Skill and Word Problem Practice*.

Practice and Problem Solving

A Practice by Example

Example 1
(page 40)

GO for Help

Look for a Pattern to help you solve each problem.

1. **Data Analysis** Caroline is training for a swim meet. The graph shows the number of laps per day she swims each week. If she stays with this training pattern, how many laps per day will Caroline swim in week 8?

2. Students are to march in a parade. There will be one first grader, two second graders, three third graders, and so on, through the twelfth grade. How many students will march in the parade?

🌐 3. **Savings** Suppose that every day you save twice as many pennies as you saved the day before. You start by saving one penny on January 1. How much money will you have in all on January 10?

4. An old clock started to lose one minute each day. It was too fragile to fix, but too beloved to stop. How slow was the clock after one year of this? After two years?

B Apply Your Skills

Strategies

- Act It Out
- Draw a Diagram
- Guess, Check, Revise
- Look for a Pattern
- Make a Model
- Make a Table
- Simulate the Problem
- Solve by Graphing
- Use Multiple Strategies
- Work a Simpler Problem
- Work Backward
- Write an Equation
- Write a Proportion

Solve using any strategy.

5. **Geometry** You can cut a pizza into two pieces with one straight cut. With two cuts you can get four pieces. Three cuts give a maximum of seven pieces. What is the maximum number of pieces with four cuts? With five cuts?

6. a. **Number Sense** Complete. Then look for a pattern.

$$2 \cdot 2 = \blacksquare \qquad 3 \cdot 3 = \blacksquare$$
$$1 \cdot 3 = \blacksquare \qquad 2 \cdot 4 = \blacksquare$$
$$\text{Difference} = \blacksquare \qquad \text{Difference} = \blacksquare$$

$$4 \cdot 4 = \blacksquare \qquad 5 \cdot 5 = \blacksquare$$
$$3 \cdot 5 = \blacksquare \qquad 4 \cdot 6 = \blacksquare$$
$$\text{Difference} = \blacksquare \qquad \text{Difference} = \blacksquare$$

   b. Which is greater, $10 \cdot 12$ or $11 \cdot 11$? What is the difference?
   c. **Reasoning** Suppose you know that $47 \cdot 47 = 2,209$. Use this to find $46 \cdot 48$.
   d. Suppose you know that $64 \cdot 66 = 4,224$. Use this to find $65 \cdot 65$.

7. For a buffet dinner, a restaurant charges $10 for one person, $20 for two, $29 for three, $37 for four, $44 for five, and so on.
    a. How much does a buffet dinner for 8 cost? How much does a group of 8 save by eating together rather than separately?
    b. The buffet costs the restaurant $6 per person. How large a group can the restaurant serve without losing money?

 Challenge

8. A woman jogging at 6 mi/h passes a man biking in the opposite direction at 12 mi/h. If they maintain their speeds, how far from each other will they be 10 minutes after passing?

ISAT

Test Prep

Multiple Choice

9. One edition of *Alice's Adventures in Wonderland* has 352 pages. How many 4s were used in its page numbers?
    A. 38   B. 52   C. 75   D. 88

10. Jayne has 3 quarters, 2 dimes, a nickel, and 2 pennies in her pocket. How many different amounts of money can she make using three of these coins?
    F. 24   G. 20   H. 17   J. 14

11. Assuming one yeast cell "buds" into two cells (the original cell and one new cell) at a rate of once every hour, how many yeast cells will be present from one yeast cell after 8 hours?
    A. 128   B. 256   C. 512   D. 1,024

Mixed Review

 GO for Help

Lesson 1-7   **Visual Patterns** Describe the next figure in each pattern. Then draw the figure.

12.

13.

Lesson 1-5   14. **Weather** At midnight, the temperature was −5°F. By dawn, the temperature had risen 14°. What was the temperature at dawn?

Lesson 1-3   **Evaluate each expression for $m = 1$ and $n = 4$.**

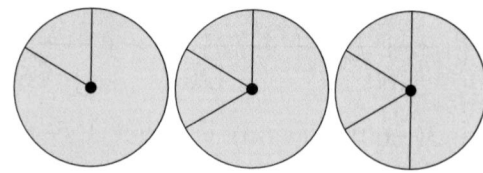

15. $4m - n$ 16. $mn + 13$ 17. $4(n + 2) + m$

1-9 Multiplying and Dividing Integers

 Assessment Framework

6.8.09 Solve problems and number sentences involving addition, subtraction, multiplication, and division using rational numbers, exponents, and roots.

 Check Skills You'll Need

Simplify each expression.

1. $5 \cdot 4$ **2.** $3 \cdot 8$

3. $5 \cdot 5$ **4.** $14 \cdot 2$

5. $6 \cdot 5$ **6.** $20 \cdot 7$

GO for Help
Skills Handbook, p. 781

1   Multiplying Integers

(A)ctivity

Preparing to Multiply Integers

1. Copy and complete the table. The first row is done for you.

Multiplication	Repeated Addition	Sum
$3 \cdot (-5)$	$-5 + (-5) + (-5)$	-15
$5 \cdot (-4)$	■	■
$2 \cdot (-8)$	■	■
$4 \cdot (-10)$	■	■

2. What do you notice about the signs of the sums?

3. Inductive Reasoning What does the pattern suggest about the product of a positive integer and a negative integer?

You can think of multiplication as repeated addition.

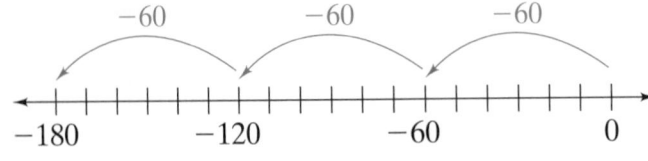

1 EXAMPLE   **Real-World Problem Solving**

Deep-Sea Exploration **After it is launched from a boat, *Deep Rover* descends 60 ft/min. Where is it in relation to sea level 3 minutes after its launch?**

Use a number line to show repeated addition.

$$3(-60) = (-60) + (-60) + (-60) = -180$$

Deep Rover is at -180 feet, or 180 feet below sea level.

Quick Check

1. Simplify each product.

    a. $2(-6)$ **b.** $4(-3)$ **c.** $7(-2)$

Real-World Connection

Scientists explore the deep waters of the Pacific Ocean in *Deep Rover*, a submersible designed for research.

You can use patterns to simplify the product of a negative number and a positive number, or the product of two negative numbers.

2 EXAMPLE Using Patterns to Multiply Integers

Patterns Use a pattern to find each product.

a. −2(5)

2(5) = 10	**Start with products you know.**
1(5) = 5	
0(5) = 0	
−1(5) = −5	**Continue the pattern.**
−2(5) = −10	

b. −2(−5)

2(−5) = −10

1(−5) = −5

0(−5) = 0

−1(−5) = 5

−2(−5) = 10

> **Vocabulary Tip**
>
> Symbols for multiplication:
> | × | −2 × 2 |
> |---|---|
> | · | −2 · 2 |
> | ( ) | −2(3) |
> | * | −2 * 3 |

✓ Quick Check

● **2. Patterns** Use a pattern to simplify −3(−4).

By inductive reasoning, the patterns from Example 2 suggest rules for multiplying integers.

> **Key Concepts** **Multiplying Integers**
>
> The product of two integers with the same sign is positive.
> The product of two integers with different signs is negative.
> The product of zero and any integer is zero.
>
> **Examples**
> | 3(4) = 12 | 3(−4) = −12 |
> |---|---|
> | −3(−4) = 12 | −3(4) = −12 |
> | 3(0) = 0 | −4(0) = 0 |

3 EXAMPLE Using Rules to Multiply Integers

Multiple Choice Which procedure is correct for multiplying −3 · 5(−4)?

Ⓐ −3 · 5(−4) = 15(−4) = −60

Ⓑ −3 · 5(−4) = −3(1) = −3

Ⓒ −3 · 5(−4) = −3(−1) = 3

Ⓓ −3 · 5(−4) = −15(−4) = 60

Multiply from left to right. The product of a negative integer and a positive integer is negative. The product of two negative integers is positive. The product is 60. The answer is D.

> **Test-Taking Tip**
>
> Eliminate any choices that cannot be correct. Since 3 · 5 · 4 > 3, you can eliminate choices B and C.

✓ Quick Check

3. Simplify each product.

● **a.** −4 · 8(−2)   **b.** 6(−3)(5)   **c.** −7 · (−14) · 0

Dividing Integers

The rules for dividing integers are similar to those for multiplying.

Key Concepts | **Dividing Integers**

The quotient of two integers with the same sign is positive.
The quotient of two integers with different signs is negative.
Remember that division by zero is undefined.

Examples
$$12 \div 3 = 4 \qquad 12 \div (-3) = -4$$
$$-12 \div (-3) = 4 \qquad -12 \div 3 = -4$$

---

4 EXAMPLE | **Real-World Problem Solving**

Currency Find the average of the differences in the values of a Canadian dollar and a U.S. dollar for 1999–2003.

Value of Dollars (U.S. Cents)

Year	Canadian Dollar	U.S. Dollar	Difference
1999	67	100	−33
2000	67	100	−33
2001	65	100	−35
2002	64	100	−36
2003	71	100	−29

SOURCES: Bank of Canada; *The World Almanac*

$$\frac{-33 + (-33) + (-35) + (-36) + (-29)}{5}$$ **Write an expression for the average.**

$$= \frac{-166}{5}$$ **Use the order of operations. The fraction bar acts as a grouping symbol.**

$$= -33.2$$ **The quotient of a negative integer and a positive integer is negative.**

For 1999–2003, the average difference was −33¢. The Canadian dollar was worth an average of 33¢ less than the U.S. dollar.

✓ Quick Check

4. Simplify each quotient.

    a. $-32 \div 8$ **b.** $-48 \div (-6)$ **c.** $-56 \div (-4)$
    d. Find the average of $4, -3, -5, 2,$ and $-8.$

EXERCISES

For more exercises, see *Extra Skill and Word Problem Practice*.

Practice and Problem Solving

 Practice by Example

Example 1
(page 44)

GO for Help

1. Write a number sentence for the product shown on the number line.

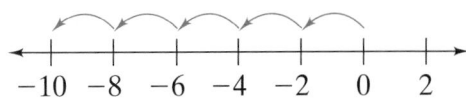

Write each sum as a product. Simplify the product.

2. $(-9) + (-9) + (-9) + (-9)$

3. $(-5) + (-5) + (-5) + (-5) + (-5)$

🌐 **4. Weather** The temperature dropped 5 degrees each hour for 7 h. Use an integer to represent the total change in temperature.

Simplify each product.

5. $3(-3)$	**6.** $4(-11)$	**7.** $3(-8)$
8. $5(-10)$	**9.** $6(-3)$	**10.** $2(-15)$
11. $9(-9)$	**12.** $3(-24)$	**13.** $8(-6)$

Examples 2 and 3
(page 45)

14. $-5(-3)$	**15.** $-6 \cdot 10$	**16.** $-10 \cdot 0$
17. $-9(-8)(-5)$	**18.** $0(-12) \cdot 4$	**19.** $8 \cdot 3(-4)$

Example 4
(page 46)

Find each quotient.

20. $24 \div (-24)$	**21.** $18 \div (-1)$	**22.** $-120 \div 12$
23. $56 \div (-8)$	**24.** $-72 \div 12$	**25.** $-100 \div (-10)$
26. $-38 \div (-2)$	**27.** $-72 \div 6$	**28.** $-33 \div 11$

For each group, find the average.

29. temperatures: $-9°C, -12°C, 9°C, 4°C, -2°C$

30. football yardage: 10 yd, -5 yd, 7 yd, 9 yd, -11 yd

31. golf scores: $-3, 4, 2, 1, -4, -1, 3, -2$

32. bank balances: $325, -\$150, \$130, \$200, -\$45$

 Apply Your Skills

Mental Math Without computing, tell whether each product or quotient is *positive* or *negative*. Explain your reasoning.

33. $-6(-20)$ **34.** $7(-83)$ **35.** $39 \div (-3)$ **36.** $-3(8)(-24)$

Name the point on the number line that is the graph of each product.

$$D \quad F \quad C \qquad A \qquad B \qquad E$$
$$-8 \quad -6 \quad -4 \quad -2 \quad 0 \quad 2 \quad 4 \quad 6 \quad 8$$

37. $-2 \cdot 0$ **38.** $4(-2)$ **39.** $2(-2)$ **40.** $|-2| \cdot |-2|$

Homework Video Tutor
Visit: PHSchool.com
Web Code: ade-0109

Use repeated addition, patterns, or rules to simplify each product or quotient.

41. $225 \div (-15)$ **42.** $|-2| \cdot (-7)$ **43.** $-59(-79)$

44. $243(-88)$ **45.** $-200 \div -25$ **46.** $-18(-12)$

47. $38(-2)$ **48.** $1{,}000 \div (-50)$ **49.** $24(-16)(-32)$

50. Investing The price of one share of a stock fell \$3 each day for 12 days.
   a. Write an integer to represent the total change in price of a share of the stock.
   b. The original stock price was \$76 per share. What was the price after the drop?

Compare. Use >, <, or = to complete each statement.

51. $(-9)(-6) \blacksquare 8(-10)$ **52.** $5(-2) \blacksquare (-6)(-1)$

53. $-10 \div (-2) \blacksquare 25 \div (-5)$ **54.** $-|-28| \div 7 \blacksquare -28 \div (-7)$

55. $|-25| \div |-5| \blacksquare |-25 \div (-5)|$ **56.** $-(-15 \div 5) \blacksquare -100 \div (-20)$

Number Sense Use integer rules and other math facts to answer each question.

57. What integer and -8 have the product -96?

58. What integer and 9 have the product -135?

59. What integer and -3 have the quotient 9?

60. What two integers have a sum of negative ten and a product of negative seventy-five?

 Challenge

Open-Ended Simplify each pair of expressions. Then write an integer that is between the values of the expressions.

61. $-2 \cdot (-2)$ and $2 \cdot 4$ **62.** $10 + (-7)$ and $10 \div (-5)$

63. $50 + (-48)$ and $80 \div (-20)$ **64.** $121 \div (-11)$ and $|-7| - |7|$

65. a. Inductive Reasoning Will the sign be positive or negative for the product of three negative integers? Of four negative integers? Of five negative integers?
   b. Writing in Math Use inductive reasoning to write a rule for the sign of the product of more than two negative integers.

66. Reasoning If a and b are positive integers, and x and y are negative integers, what is the sign of $\frac{a + b}{x + y}$? Explain.

67. Investing Jerry owns 20 shares of stock valued at \$23 each. One day, the price of the stock rose \$2. It fell \$1 on each of the next three days. The stock price rose \$4 on the next day. What was the average daily gain or loss for a share of the stock over this time period? What was the total value of Jerry's stock at the end of this time period?

Test Prep

Multiple Choice

68. A scuba diver descended to a depth of 50 feet in 25 seconds. Which integer indicates the average number of feet per second the diver traveled?

A. −50   **B.** −25   **C.** −2   **D.** −1

69. Which of the following is the simplest form of $\frac{-1,225}{35}$?

F. −35   **G.** −25   **H.** −25   **J.** 35

In Exercises 70 and 71, what is the average for each group of data?

70. bank balances: $200, −$85, $120, $200, $280

A. $97   **B.** $119   **C.** $143   **D.** $177

71. feet above and below sea level:

135 ft, −56 ft, 92 ft, −29 ft, −88 ft, −60 ft

F. −31 ft   **G.** −1 ft   **H.** 19 ft   **J.** 76 ft

Mixed Review

GO for Help

Lesson 1-8

72. Reasoning How many whole numbers from 10 to 200 have exactly two identical digits?

Lessons 1-5 and 1-6

Compare. Use >, <, or = to complete each statement.

73. $-3 + (-8) \blacksquare 12 - (-6)$

74. $-9 + 13 \blacksquare 24 - 30$

75. $|-6| - |12| \blacksquare -8 + |-12|$

Lesson 1-1

Write a variable expression for each word phrase.

76. 50 decreased by a number n **77.** the product of y and 60

78. the sum of x and y **79.** the quotient of d divided by 5

Checkpoint Quiz 2   **Lessons 1-5 through 1-9**

Simplify each expression.

1. $3 + (-11)$ **2.** $12 - (-8)$ **3.** $-9 \cdot 5$

4. $-64 \div (-8)$ **5.** $|3| \cdot 8 \div (-2)$ **6.** $-8(-3)(3)$

Open-Ended Use integers to complete each equation.

7. $\blacksquare + \blacksquare = -7$ **8.** $\blacksquare - (-20) = \blacksquare$ **9.** $\blacksquare \cdot \blacksquare = -40$

Patterns Find the next three numbers in each pattern.

10. $-7, -2, 3, 8, \ldots$ **11.** $1, 3, 9, 27, \ldots$

Studying Math Definitions

You can learn new vocabulary by building your own index-card word list.
- Write the term. Then write the definition.
- Include any math symbols related to the term.
- Give an example that shows how the term is used.
- Give a nonexample showing how the term might *not* apply.

EXAMPLE

Make an index card for the vocabulary term *variable expression.*

Variable Expression	**Write the term.**
Definition: A variable expression is a mathematical phrase that uses variables, numerals, and operation symbols.	**Write the definition.**
Example: $h + 5$ $f - 7$ $3a$ $\frac{x}{2}$	**Give examples.**
Nonexamples: 5 $25 - 4$ 13 -21	**Give nonexamples.**

EXERCISES

Make an index card like the one shown above for each vocabulary term.
Include any helpful everyday meanings.

1. variable

2. order of operations

3. evaluate

4. opposites

5. integers

6. absolute value

7. conjecture

8. inductive reasoning

9. counterexample

10. Error Analysis A student wrote the definition of *integers* at the right. Which parts are correct? Which parts are incorrect? Explain.

Integers

Definition: Integers are all the counting numbers and their opposites.

Examples: $-8, 4, -1, 5, 10, -12$

Nonexamples: $\frac{1}{2}, 0, -\frac{3}{4}, -1.5$

You can analyze data presented in a graph. A bar graph usually compares quantities. The bar graph below shows boys' participation in high school baseball in several states for a recent year.

1 ACTIVITY

Use the bar graph.

1. About how many boys played high school baseball in Texas?

2. About how many boys played high school baseball in Illinois?

3. About how many more boys played high school baseball in Texas than in Illinois?

4. In which two states is the combined number of boys who played high school baseball about equal to the number who played in Pennsylvania?

A line graph usually shows change over time. The line graph shows girls' participation in high school baseball over several years.

2 ACTIVITY

Use the line graph.

5. Between what two school years did girls' participation in high school baseball increase the most?

6. In what two school years was girls' participation in high school baseball about the same?

7. Between what two school years did girls' participation in high school baseball decrease by about 500?

8. In what school year was girls' participation in high school baseball about 1,275?

9. **a.** Estimate the change in participation from 1994–1995 to 2003–2004.
   b. If the trend continues, how many girls will participate in high school baseball in 2014–2015?

1-10 The Coordinate Plane

IL Assessment Framework

9.8.05 Graph points and identify coordinates of points on the Cartesian coordinate plane (all four quadrants).

1 Naming Coordinates and Quadrants

A **coordinate plane** is formed by the intersection of two number lines. The horizontal number line is called the **x-axis** and the vertical number line is called the **y-axis.**

The *x*- and *y*-axes divide the coordinate plane into four **quadrants.**

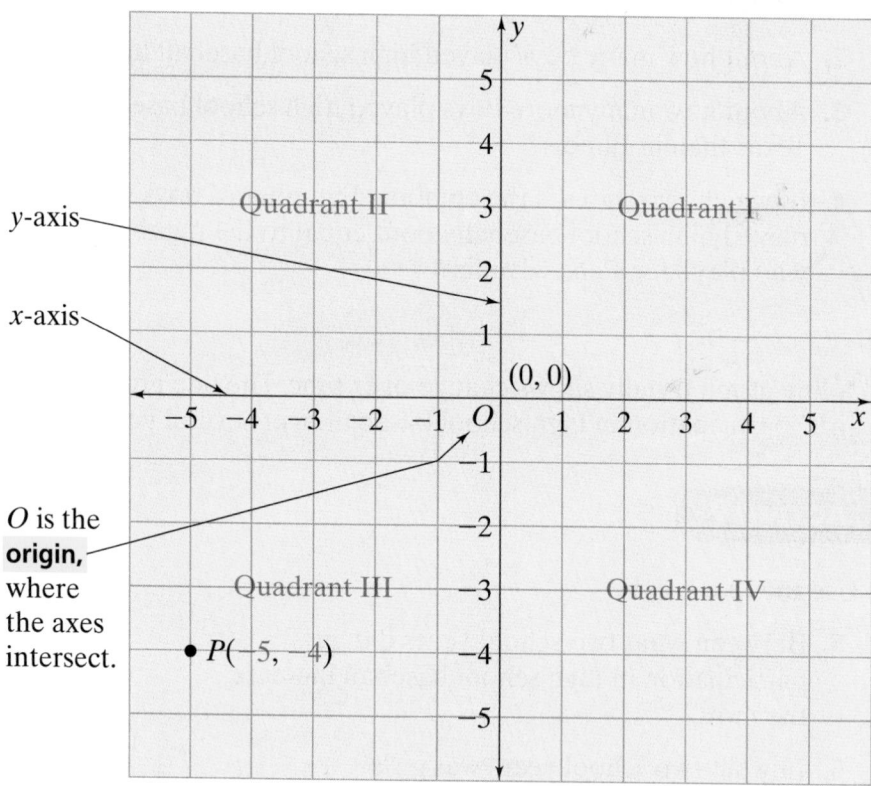

✓ Check Skills You'll Need

Graph the numbers on a number line.

1. $-2, 1, -5$

2. $0, 2, -4$

3. $-3, 3, -2$

4. $-1, -5, -8$

 for Help
Lesson 1-4

◀))) New Vocabulary

• coordinate plane
• *x*-axis
• *y*-axis
• quadrants
• origin
• ordered pair
• *x*-coordinate
• *y*-coordinate

An **ordered pair** gives the coordinates and location of a point. The ordered pair $(-5, -4)$ identifies point P in Quadrant III above.

$$(-5, -4)$$

The **x-coordinate** shows the position right or left of the *y*-axis.

The **y-coordinate** shows the position above or below the *x*-axis.

Online active math

For: Coordinate Plane Activity
Use: Interactive Textbook, 1-10

1 EXAMPLE Naming Coordinates and Quadrants

Write the coordinates of point A. In which quadrant is point A located?

Point A is located 2 units to the left of the y-axis. So the x-coordinate is -2. The point is 1 unit above the x-axis. So the y-coordinate is 1.

The coordinates of point A are $(-2, 1)$. Point A is located in Quadrant II.

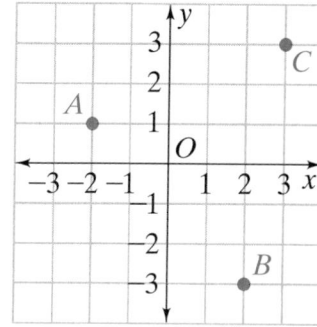

✓ Quick Check

1. a. Use the graph in Example 1. Write the coordinates of B and C.
  b. Identify the quadrants in which B and C are located.

---

2 Graphing Points

To graph a point $A(x, y)$ in a coordinate plane, you graph the ordered pair (x, y).

2 EXAMPLE Graphing Points

Graph point $R(3, -4\frac{1}{2})$.

Step 1
Start at the origin.

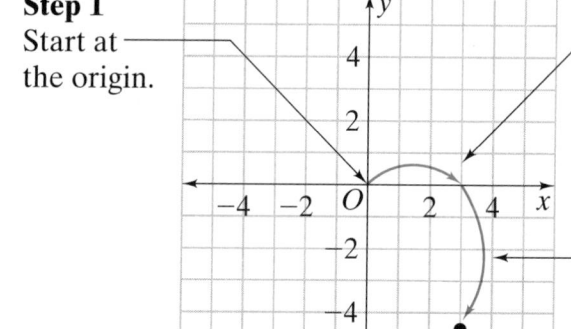

Step 2
For 3 in R $(3, -4\frac{1}{2})$, move 3 units to the right.

Step 3
For $-4\frac{1}{2}$ in R $(3, -4\frac{1}{2})$, move $4\frac{1}{2}$ units down. Draw a dot. Label it R.

North Pole

South Pole

Real-World Connection

Latitude and longitude are measurements in a coordinate system that locate every point on Earth's surface.

✓ Quick Check

2. a. Graph these points on one coordinate plane: $K(3, 1)$, $L(-2\frac{1}{2}, 1)$, and $M(-2, -4)$.
  b. Geometry Draw lines to connect points K, L, and M. Describe the figure that results.

EXERCISES

For more exercises, see *Extra Skill and Word Problem Practice*.

Practice and Problem Solving

A Practice by Example

Example 1
(page 53)

GO for Help

In which quadrant does each point lie?

1. J 2. V 3. M

4. K 5. P 6. Q

Write the coordinates of each point.

7. T 8. G 9. R

10. Q 11. P 12. M

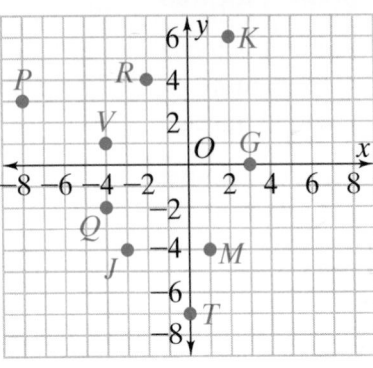

Example 2
(page 53)

Draw a coordinate plane. Then graph each point.

13. $A(-1, 3)$ 14. $B(-4, -1)$ 15. $C(2, 5)$ 16. $D(2, -2)$

17. $E(0, 6)$ 18. $F(-3, 2)$ 19. $G(6, 0)$ 20. $H(1, 7)$

21. $K(5, -6)$ 22. $L(0, 0)$ 23. $M(-5, -2)$ 24. $N(7, 0)$

25. $P(-1, -3)$ 26. $Q(1, 1)$ 27. $R(0, -4)$ 28. $S(-3, 4)$

B Apply Your Skills

29. What ordered pair names the origin?

Name the point with the given coordinates.

30. $(3, 2)$ 31. $(0, -5)$

32. $(2, 3)$ 33. $(-2, -3)$

Write the coordinates of each point.

34. A 35. B

36. C 37. D

Test-Taking Tip

You can tell in which quadrant to graph an ordered pair by looking at the signs of the coordinates.
$(+, +)$ goes in Q I.
$(-, +)$ goes in Q II.
$(-, -)$ goes in Q III.
$(+, -)$ goes in Q IV.

Mental Math Write the coordinates of each point.

38. the point 5 units to the left of the y-axis and 2 units below the x-axis

39. the point on the y-axis 4 units below the x-axis

40. **Multiple Choice** Which coordinates describe the point on the x-axis 3 units to the right of the origin?
    Ⓐ $(0, 3)$ Ⓑ $(3, 0)$ Ⓒ $(3, -3)$ Ⓓ $(3, 3)$

GO **Online**
Homework Video Tutor
Visit: PHSchool.com
Web Code: ade-0110

Mental Math In which quadrant does $P(x, y)$ lie?

41. x is positive, y is negative.   42. x is positive, y is positive.

43. x is negative, y is positive.   44. x is negative, y is negative.

In which quadrant or on which axis does each point lie?

45. $V(13, 25)$

46. $W(x, y)$ if $x = 0, y > 0$

47. $X(-17, -2)$

48. $Z(x, y)$ if $x > 0, y < 0$

49. $B(0, |-2|)$

50. $R(x, y)$ if $x < 0, y > 0$

Geometry **Graph and connect the points in the order given. Connect the last point to the first. Name the figure.**

51. $(-4, 1), (1, 1), (-3, -1)$

52. $(2\frac{1}{2}, 2), (2\frac{1}{2}, -1), (-5, -1), (-5, 2)$

53. $(-1, 2), (1, 5), (7, 5), (5, 2)$

54. $(2, -4), (7, -1), (4, 4), (-1, 1)$

Geometry **$PQRS$ is a square. Find the coordinates of S.**

55. $P(-5, 0), Q(0, 5), R(5, 0), S(\blacksquare, \blacksquare)$

56. $P(-1, 3), Q(4, 3), R(4, -2), S(\blacksquare, \blacksquare)$

Geography **On a map, coordinates are given in degrees of longitude and latitude. Use the map below for Exercises 57–60.**

SAMPLE
Austin, Texas:
Longitude:
about 98° W
Latitude:
about 30° N

57. Find the longitude and latitude of Jackson, Mississippi.

58. Find the longitude and latitude of Topeka, Kansas.

59. What city is located near $85°$ W, $38°$ N?

60. What city is located near $106°$ W, $35°$ N?

Geometry **Use one coordinate plane for Exercises 61–63.**

61. Graph the points $(-2, 1), (-2, 3), (1, 3)$, and $(1, 1)$. Connect them in the order given. Connect the last point to the first.

62. Change the coordinates of Exercise 61 as described below. Graph and connect the points for each new set of coordinates. Use a different color for each set.
   a. Multiply each x-coordinate by -1.
   b. Multiply each y-coordinate by -1.
   c. Multiply each coordinate by -1.
   d. Multiply each coordinate by 2.

63. **Writing in Math** Compare each figure in Exercise 62 to the figure in Exercise 61. Write a short paragraph describing your results.

Challenge

Writing in Math

Describe how to graph $Q(4, 23)$ and four other points, each 1 unit from Q.

64. Open-Ended Draw a dot-to-dot picture on a coordinate grid. Write the coordinates of the points in order. Exchange coordinates with a classmate and draw the other's picture.

65. Reasoning Assume that $a \neq b$. Do (a, b) and (b, a) describe the same point? Explain.

66. Write the coordinates of four points in the coordinate plane that are 3 units from the origin. Graph the points.

ISAT

Test Prep

Multiple Choice

67. $P(a, b)$ is in Quadrant III. Which word pair makes the following sentence true?

The value of a must be __?__ and the value of b must be __?__.

- **A.** positive; positive
- **B.** positive; negative
- **C.** negative; positive
- **D.** negative; negative

68. $C(x, y)$ is in Quadrant IV. Which ordered pair could be the coordinates of C?

- **F.** $(-3, -7)$
- **G.** $(0, 2)$
- **H.** $(-8, 0)$
- **J.** $(5, -6)$

69. To graph point R, start at the origin, move 10 units to the right, 4 units down, and 6 units to the left. What are the coordinates of point R?

- **A.** $(4, -4)$
- **B.** $(10, 2)$
- **C.** $(6, 10)$
- **D.** $(-4, -6)$

70. $P(a, b)$ is located on the x-axis. Which statement is true for all nonzero values of a?

- **F.** $a > b$
- **G.** $b > a$
- **H.** $|a| > b$
- **J.** $|b| > a$

71. $T(a, b)$ is located in Quadrant II. Which statement is *never* true?

- **A.** $a > b$
- **B.** $b > a$
- **C.** $|a| > b$
- **D.** $|b| > a$

Mixed Review

GO for Help

Lesson 1-9   **Find each product or quotient.**

72. $-11 \cdot 11$ **73.** $-432 \div 48$ **74.** $\dfrac{0}{-56}$

Lesson 1-5 **75. Submarines** A submarine at sea level dives 800 ft and then another 125 ft. Find the submarine's final depth.

Lesson 1-4   **Write the value of each expression.**

76. $|-8|$ **77.** $-|-95|$ **78.** the opposite of 12

79. $|16| + 4$ **80.** $|-6| - 2$ **81.** the opposite of -3

Graphing Ordered Pairs

You can use a graphing calculator to display ordered pairs on a coordinate plane.

ACTIVITY

Graph these ordered pairs: $(-6, 2), (-5, 6), (-4, -1), (-3, -5),$ $(-2, 4), (0, 9), (1, 5), (2, -4), (2, 0), (3, 6), (5, 2), (7, -5), (8, 4)$.

Step 1 Enter the ordered pairs into list L_1 for the x-coordinates and list L_2 for the y-coordinates.

Press **LIST** . To clear old entries in L_1, select **L_1**

and press **CLEAR** **ENTER** . (Clear old entries in other columns in a similar way.) Enter all the x-coordinates into list L_1. Enter all y-coordinates into list L_2. Check L_1 and L_2 to make sure the coordinates align as they should.

Step 2 In **PLOT,** enter 1 and select **On.** Select the **Type** as shown below, and check that **Xlist** and **Ylist** show L_1 and L_2, respectively.

Step 3 Press **ZOOM** 6 to graph the data with the standard viewing window. Then press **GRAPH** .

EXERCISES

Graph each group of ordered pairs.

1. $(-5, -1), (-2, 4), (-1, 3), (0, 4), (1, 6), (3, 0), (4, 2), (5, -3)$

2. $(-5, 7), (4, 6), (9, 2), (-2, -8), (0, 3), (-3, -1), (-6, 1), (5, 5),$ $(1, -6), (-1, -3), (3, -2), (-4, 9), (-8, 4), (2, -5), (6, 0), (7, -4)$

Graph the ordered pairs. Adjust the window settings to see all the points.

3. $(-5, 2), (-6\frac{1}{2}, 5), (-5, -5\frac{1}{2}), (3, -5), (-5\frac{1}{2}, -4), (-4, -3\frac{1}{2}), (4, 5), (-5\frac{1}{2}, -5)$

4. $(-10, -5), (-8, -9), (-6, 2), (-5, 8), (7, -3), (9, -6), (10, 4), (12, 9)$

Graph the ordered pairs. Describe the pattern you see.

5. $(7, 3), (-3, -2), (1, 0), (-5, -3), (9, 4), (3, 1), (5, 2), (-7, -4)$

6. $(0, -5), (-2, -3), (4, -5), (0, -1), (2, -3), (-4, -5)$

Writing Gridded Responses

Some tests require you to enter a number answer on a grid. You must find the answer and also show it in a form that you can fit on the grid. For example, you can enter an improper fraction on the grid, but not a mixed number.

1 EXAMPLE

What is the sum of -0.5 and 2?

$-0.5 + 2 = 1.5, \frac{3}{2},$ or $1\frac{1}{2}$.

For the grid, you can use 1.5 or $\frac{3}{2}$, but not $1\frac{1}{2}$. You write the answer in the spaces at the top of the grid and fill in the corresponding bubbles below.

• The grids at the right are correct for 1.5 and $\frac{3}{2}$, respectively.

Here are things to remember as you grid your responses:
• You must begin in the left column OR end in the right column.
• You cannot have blanks in the middle of a response.
• Always write a mixed number as an improper fraction or a decimal.
• You do not have to simplify fractions.

2 EXAMPLE

The surface of a lake is 29.8 ft below sea level. What is the elevation in feet of a street that is 35 ft above the surface of the lake?

$(-29.8) + 35$ **Write an expression.**

$|35| - |-29.8|$ **Find the difference of the absolute values.**

5.2 **Simplify. Since 35 has the greater absolute value, the sum is positive.**

The street is 5.2 feet above sea level. Enter 5.2 on the grid as shown.
• You do not enter the units.

EXERCISES

Write what you would grid for each answer.

1. Simplify $12 \div [12 - (4 \cdot 2)]$.

2. What is the next number in the pattern $0.4, 0.8, 1.3, 1.9, 2.6, \ldots$?

3. What is the next number in the pattern $0, \frac{1}{2}, 1, 1\frac{1}{2}, 2, \ldots$?

Chapter Review

Vocabulary Review

absolute value (p. 19)
conjecture (p. 35)
coordinate plane (p. 52)
counterexample (p. 37)
evaluate (p. 14)
inductive reasoning (p. 35)

integers (p. 19)
opposites (p. 19)
order of operations (p. 8)
ordered pair (p. 52)
origin (p. 52)
quadrants (p. 52)

variable (p. 4)
variable expression (p. 4)
x-axis (p. 52)
x-coordinate (p. 52)
y-axis (p. 52)
y-coordinate (p. 52)

Go Online
PHSchool.com
For: Vocabulary quiz
Web Code: adj-0151

Choose the vocabulary term that correctly completes the sentence.

1. The ordered pair $(0, 0)$ represents the location of the __?__ .

2. A letter that stands for a number in an expression is a(n) __?__ .

3. The vertical axis in the coordinate plane is known as the __?__ .

4. The coordinate plane is divided into four __?__ .

5. All whole numbers and their opposites are __?__ .

6. In the ordered pair $(-5, 2)$, the number -5 is the __?__ .

7. The distance that a number is from zero on a number line is the __?__ of the number.

Skills and Concepts

1-1 Objectives

▼ To identify variables, numerical expressions, and variable expressions (p. 4)

▼ To write variable expressions for word phrases (p. 5)

A **variable** is a letter that stands for a number. A **variable expression** uses variables, numerals, and operation symbols.

Write a variable expression for each word phrase.

8. twenty-five less than x

9. the product of n and 3

10. ten decreased by t

11. a number x divided by 4

12. a number n increased by 5

13. two more than y

1-2 Objectives

▼ To use the order of operations (p. 8)

▼ To use grouping symbols (p. 9)

To simplify a numerical expression, follow the **order of operations.**

1. Work inside grouping symbols.

2. Multiply and divide in order from left to right.

3. Add and subtract in order from left to right.

Simplify each expression.

14. $3 \cdot 7 + 6 \div 2$

15. $(4 + 8) \div 2 \cdot 2$

16. $9 \cdot 5 - 4(12 \div 6)$

1-3 Objectives

▼ To evaluate variable expressions (p. 14)

▼ To solve problems by evaluating expressions (p. 15)

To **evaluate** a variable expression, substitute a number for each variable. Use the order of operations to simplify.

Evaluate each expression.

17. $3x + 4$, for $x = 5$

18. $15 + 10 \div n$, for $n = 5$

19. $(y - 6)2$, for $y = 16$

20. $4(4 + m)$, for $m = 6$

21. $15t \cdot 10$, for $t = 3$

22. $z + [15 - (z - 1)]$, for $z = 4$

1-4 Objectives

▼ To represent, graph, and order integers (p. 18)

▼ To find opposites and absolute values (p. 19)

Integers are the set of whole numbers and their **opposites.** The **absolute value** of an integer is its distance from zero on a number line. On a number line, the integer farther to the right is the greater integer.

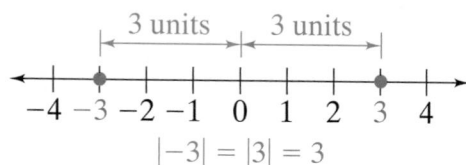

$|-3| = |3| = 3$

Simplify each expression.

23. the opposite of 17

24. $|-1,000|$

25. the absolute value of negative 9

26. the opposite of the absolute value of 12

Compare. Use >, <, or = to complete each statement.

27. $-7 \blacksquare -9$ **28.** $0 \blacksquare -3$ **29.** $-6 \blacksquare 2$ **30.** $|-5| \blacksquare |5|$

🌐 **31. Water Slides** A slide at a water park is 30 ft high. What integer represents your change in elevation when you go down the slide?

1-5 and 1-6 Objectives

▼ To use models to add integers (p. 24)

▼ To use rules to add integers (p. 25)

▼ To use models to subtract integers (p. 30)

▼ To use a rule to subtract integers (p. 31)

To add integers with the *same* sign, add their absolute values. The sum has the same sign. To add integers with *different* signs, find the difference of their absolute values. The sum has the sign of the integer with the greater absolute value. To subtract an integer, add its opposite.

Simplify each expression.

32. $8 + (-15)$ **33.** $-9 + 21$ **34.** $9 - (-5)$

35. $14 + (-9) + (-20)$ **36.** $-62 - (-59) - 24$

37. $-7 - 4$ **38.** $-4 + 12 + (-3) + (-6)$

🌐 **39. Wildlife** An eagle leaves her nest on the side of a cliff. She soars upward 60 ft and then dives 80 ft. What is her change in elevation after leaving the nest?

1-7 Objectives

▼ To write rules for patterns (p. 35)

▼ To make predictions and test conjectures (p. 36)

Inductive reasoning is making conclusions based on patterns you observe. A conclusion reached by inductive reasoning is a **conjecture**.

Write a rule for each pattern. Find the next three numbers in the pattern.

40. $0, 6, 12, 18, \ldots$ **41.** $-18, -9, 0, 9, \ldots$ **42.** $\frac{1}{2}, 1, 1\frac{1}{2}, 2, \ldots$

1-8 Objectives

▼ To find number patterns (p. 40)

You can use patterns to solve problems.

43. Suppose you plan to save $12 per week. You have already saved $7.50. In how many weeks will you have saved at least $100?

44. A four-line classified ad costs $28 for a week. Each additional line costs $10.50. What is the weekly cost of a 12-line ad?

1-9 Objectives

▼ To multiply integers using repeated addition, patterns, and rules (p. 44)

▼ To divide integers using rules (p. 46)

To multiply or divide integers, multiply or divide the absolute values of the integers. If the integers have the same sign, the product or quotient is positive. If the integers have different signs, the product or quotient is negative.

Multiply or divide.

45. $7(-6)$ **46.** $250 \div (-50)$ **47.** $(-9)(-8)$

48. $-56 \div (-8)$ **49.** $-120 \div 40$ **50.** $-15(11)$

51. $\frac{-64}{8}$ **52.** $(-5)(-7)$ **53.** $(-6)(-17)$

1-10 Objectives

▼ To name coordinates and quadrants in the coordinate plane (p. 52)

▼ To graph points in the coordinate plane (p. 53)

A **coordinate plane** is formed by the intersection of two number lines. The **x-axis** and the **y-axis** divide the coordinate plane into four **quadrants**. An **ordered pair** gives the coordinates of a point. The **x-coordinate** shows the position right or left of the y-axis. The **y-coordinate** shows the position above or below the x-axis.

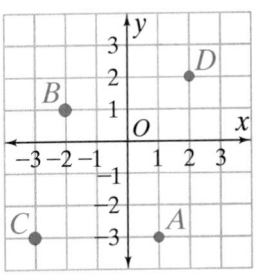

Write the coordinates of each point.

54. A **55.** B **56.** C **57.** D

Chapter Test

Go Online
PHSchool.com
For: Online chapter test
Web Code: ada-0152

Write an expression for each phrase.

1. a number n increased by nineteen

2. ten less than negative three

3. the product of x and negative five

4. 5 more than the opposite of y

Evaluate each expression for the given values of the variables.

5. $3a + 5$, for $a = -5$

6. $5m + 9 + 7n$, for $m = 8$ and $n = 1$

7. $3|x - y| + x$, for $x = 1$ and $y = 8$

8. $20 - 2(a - b)$, for $a = 3$ and $b = 2$

Simplify each expression.

9. $|-5|$

10. opposite of -9

11. opposite of 7

12. $|15|$

Use >, <, or = to complete each sentence.

13. $-6 \blacksquare -5$

14. $8 \blacksquare -10$

15. $-3 \blacksquare 3$

16. $0 \blacksquare -7$

Simplify each expression.

17. $15 + (-7)$

18. $-8 - (-12)$

19. $-9(-7)$

20. $54 \div (-6)$

21. $-6 \cdot 48$

22. $\frac{-56}{-7}$

23. $119 - (-24)$

24. $-47 + (-21)$

25. $-83 + 17$

26. $5(-12)(-3)(-1)$

27. $2 \cdot |14 - (-9)|$

28. $8 \cdot 6 \div (2 + 1)$

29. $4 + 7 \cdot 2 + 8$

30. $16 - 2 \cdot (5 + 3)$

In which quadrant or on which axis does each point lie?

31. $(-5, 7)$

32. $(0, -4)$

33. $(-8, -6)$

Write the coordinates of each point.

34. F

35. G

36. H

37. J

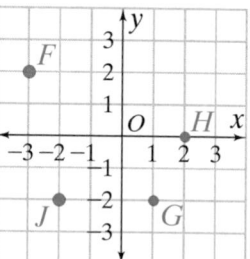

38. A shirt costs \$15 and jeans cost \$25.
   a. Write an expression for the cost of j jeans and s shirts.
   b. Evaluate the expression to find the cost of three pairs of jeans and five shirts.
   c. How many pairs of jeans can you buy for \$60?

39. Which statement is *always* true?
   A. The absolute value of an integer is equal to the opposite of the integer.
   B. The absolute value of an integer is greater than zero.
   C. An integer is greater than its opposite.
   D. A positive integer is greater than a negative integer.

40. A submarine was 250 m below sea level. It rose 75 m. Use an integer to describe the new depth of the submarine.

41. Write a rule for the pattern below. Find the next three numbers in the pattern.
   $100, 90, 85, 75, 70, 60, \ldots$

42. You are in an elevator on the seventh floor. You go down 4 floors and then up 8 floors. Then you go down 3 floors and up 9 floors. The elevator goes down again 2 floors, and you get off. According to the pattern, on which floor are you now?

43. **Writing in Math** Describe how to order the integers $2, -6, 9, 0$, and -13 from least to greatest.

Reading Comprehension Read each passage below. Then answer the questions on the basis of what is *stated* or *implied* in the passage.

> **Numbers in Nature** Numbers appear everywhere in the patterns of nature. For example, the numbers of petals on flowers form patterns. Find some flowers and count their petals. You will find, with few exceptions, the number of petals to be one of 3, 5, 8, 13, 21, 34, and so forth. Also, although all snowflakes are different, each one has 6-fold symmetry. Put 20 pennies on a table and push them as close together as you can. Notice that all the pennies in the middle are surrounded by 6 others. This is an example of 6-fold symmetry.

1. What is true about the pattern for numbers of petals on flowers?
   - (A) The numbers are all odd.
   - (B) The increases from one to the next are always the same.
   - (C) The increases from one to the next suggest a pattern you've seen before.
   - (D) The number of petals on any flower has to be a number in the pattern.

2. Describe the pattern for the numbers of petals in flowers.

3. What number would follow 34 in the pattern for the numbers of petals on flowers?
   - (E) 34
   - (F) 35
   - (G) 55
   - (H) 68

4. What do patterns in snowflakes and pennies pushed close together have in common?

> **Wings or Wheels?** The Arctic tern, a small sea bird, is the animal that migrates the longest distance each year. It can fly from a latitude of 84°N in the Arctic to 78°S in the Antarctic, and back. For some terns, this journey may be about 25,000 mi, which is about the distance around Earth at the equator. By contrast, the average number of miles a vehicle in the United States travels each year is about 14,000. Some Arctic terns live 25 years, which means they pile up an impressive number of miles traveled in a lifetime.

5. About how far does an Arctic tern fly in one migration south?
   - (A) 162 mi
   - (B) 14,000 mi
   - (C) 12,500 mi
   - (D) 25,000 mi

6. On average, how far does a vehicle in the United States travel each year?
   - (E) 14,000 mi
   - (F) 14,000 km
   - (G) 25,000 mi
   - (H) 25,000 km

7. Which travels farther in a year, an Arctic tern in its annual migration or a vehicle that's driven the average number of miles? About how much farther?

8. About how far could an Arctic tern fly in its migrations over 25 years? Justify your answer.

Locating Sunken Ships

Applying Integers Marine archeologists are scientists who study sunken ships. They use scanning devices to locate objects on the ocean floor. When they find a "hot spot," divers take a closer look. If they find a sunken ship, the divers take underwater photographs and record the ship's latitude and longitude, identifying a specific point on Earth's surface.

Ancient World
This globe includes latitude (lines that run east–west) and longitude (lines that run north–south) rings.

Activity

Which part of Earth's coordinate globe corresponds to the indicated part of a coordinate plane?

1. the *x*-axis   **2.** the *y*-axis   **3.** the origin

Write and simplify an expression to show how the depth of a submersible robot changes.

4. from the *Edmund Fitzgerald* to the *Andrea Doria*

5. from the *Titanic* to the *Atocha*

6. from the water's surface to the *Atocha*

7. Estimation About how many times the depth of the *Atocha* is the depth of the *Andrea Doria*? Write an equation to model this relationship.

8. Research Pick one of the ships discussed here or another sunken ship. What factors led to its sinking? Explain.

Prime Meridian
0° Longitude

Titanic
41° N 49° W
−12,600 ft

Edmund Fitzgerald
47° N 85° W
−530 ft

Equator
0° Latitude

Atocha
24° N 82° W
−55 ft

Andrea Doria
40° N 69° W
−240 ft

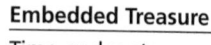

Embedded Treasure
Time and water pressure pushed these coins into a piece of wood.

Sunken World
Scientists explore shipwrecks in submersible vehicles such as Alvin (above) when the ship is too deep for scuba gear (worn by the diver).

Go Online
PHSchool.com
For: Information about sunken ships
Web Code: ade-0153

65

What You've Learned

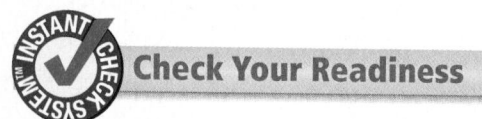 **Assessment Framework**

In Chapter 1, you learned:

● **6.8.10:** How to apply the order of operations to evaluate numerical expressions.

● **8.8.02:** How to evaluate expressions with variables.

● **6.8.09:** How to add, subtract, multiply, and divide integers.

Check Your Readiness   **GO for Help** to the Lesson in green.

Related Equations (Skills Handbook, pp. 786–791)

Complete the related equations.

1. $2.0 - \blacksquare = 0.9$ $0.9 + \blacksquare = 2.0$ **2.** $2 + \blacksquare = 2.3$ $2.3 - \blacksquare = 2$

3. $2.0 - \blacksquare = 1.3$ $1.3 + \blacksquare = 2.0$ **4.** $\blacksquare + 1.2 = 7$ $7 - \blacksquare = 1.2$

5. $3 \cdot \blacksquare = 7.5$ $7.5 \div \blacksquare = 3$ **6.** $7.2 \div \blacksquare = 1.2$ $1.2 \cdot \blacksquare = 7.2$

7. $3.6 \div \blacksquare = 6$ $6 \cdot \blacksquare = 3.6$ **8.** $\blacksquare \cdot (10) = 0.7$ $0.7 \div \blacksquare = 10$

Comparing Numbers (Lessons 1-5, 1-6, and 1-9)

Compare. Use $>$, $<$, or $=$ to complete each statement.

9. $6 \ \blacksquare\ 16$ **10.** $5 \ \blacksquare\ -5$ **11.** $-52 \ \blacksquare\ -21$

12. $0 \ \blacksquare\ -8$ **13.** $-7 \ \blacksquare\ 3$ **14.** $12 + 3 \ \blacksquare\ 19 - 4$

15. $-2 \cdot 6 \ \blacksquare\ 4 \cdot (-3)$ **16.** $27 \div 9 \ \blacksquare\ 6 \cdot 2$ **17.** $18 - 27 \ \blacksquare\ -34 + 12$

18. $8(-5) \ \blacksquare\ 100 - 65$ **19.** $6 \div (10 - 8) \ \blacksquare\ 1 + 5$ **20.** $3(-2)(-4) \ \blacksquare\ 4(-3)(2)$

Order of Operations With Integers (Lesson 1-2)

Simplify each expression.

21. $5 \cdot 2 + 5 \cdot 3$ **22.** $7(6 - 2)$ **23.** $10 \cdot 3 - 5 \cdot 3$

24. $-(34 + 76)$ **25.** $4(6) + 4(3)$ **26.** $-4(12 - 16)$

27. $7(8) - 10(8)$ **28.** $11 \cdot 9 - 6 \cdot 9$ **29.** $-2 \cdot 3 - 2 \cdot 7$

30. $6 \cdot (-9) - 3(-9)$ **31.** $-5(3) - (-5)(2)$ **32.** $(72 - 81)(5)$

Solving One-Step Equations and Inequalities

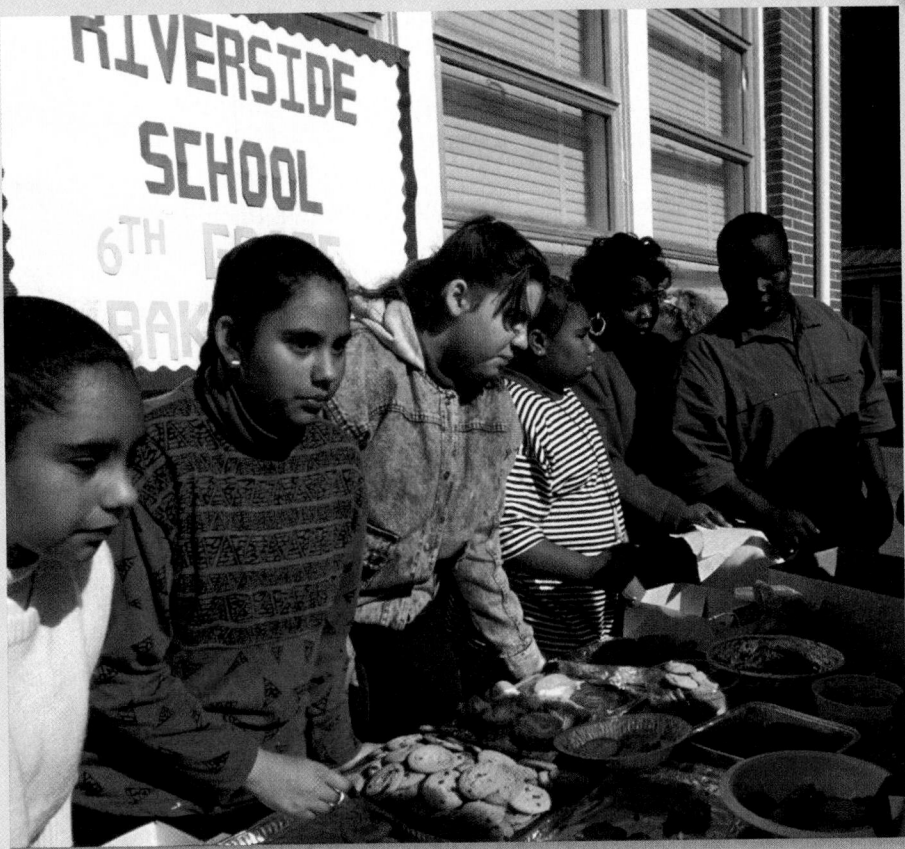

What You'll Learn Next

 Assessment Framework

In this chapter, you will learn how to

● **6.8.11:** Use the Distributive Property.

● **8.8.12:** Write and solve equations.

● **8.8.12:** Write, solve, and graph inequalities.

● Solve a problem by Try, Test, Revise.

 Activity Lab Applying what you learn, on pages 124–125 you will solve problems about a school fair.

Key Vocabulary

- coefficient (p. 78)
- constant (p. 78)
- deductive reasoning (p. 79)
- equation (p. 82)
- inequality (p. 104)
- inverse operations (p. 88)
- like terms (p. 78)
- open sentence (p. 82)
- solution of an equation (p. 83)
- solution of an inequality (p. 104)
- term (p. 78)

67

2-1 Properties of Numbers

IL Assessment Framework

6.8.11 Identify and apply the following properties of operations with rational numbers: the commutative and associative properties for addition and multiplication; the distributive property; the additive and multiplicative identity properties; the additive and multiplicative inverse properties; and the multiplicative property of zero.

✓ Check Skills You'll Need

Simplify.

1. $-18 + (-7)$

2. $32 - (-3)$

3. $(-13) + 6$

4. $2 - 48$

GO for Help

Lessons 1-5 and 1-6

🔊 New Vocabulary

- Commutative Properties
- Associative Properties
- additive identity
- multiplicative identity
- Identity Properties

---

1 Identifying Properties

The sum of 6 and 4 is the same as the sum of 4 and 6. Similarly, the product of 9 and 5 is the same as the product of 5 and 9. These suggest the following properties.

> **Key Concepts** | **Commutative Properties of Addition and Multiplication**
>
> Changing the order of the values you are adding or multiplying does not change the sum or product.
>
> | Arithmetic | Algebra |
> |---|---|
> | $6 + 4 = 4 + 6$ | $a + b = b + a$ |
> | $9 \cdot 5 = 5 \cdot 9$ | $a \cdot b = b \cdot a$ |

You can also change the grouping of the values before you add or multiply them.

> **Key Concepts** | **Associative Properties of Addition and Multiplication**
>
> Changing the grouping of the values you are adding or multiplying does not change the sum or product.
>
> | Arithmetic | Algebra |
> |---|---|
> | $(2 + 7) + 3 = 2 + (7 + 3)$ | $(a + b) + c = a + (b + c)$ |
> | $(9 \cdot 4)5 = 9(4 \cdot 5)$ | $(ab)c = a(bc)$ |

---

1 EXAMPLE **Real-World** 🌐 **Problem Solving**

Golf Carlos rented a set of golf clubs for $7 and a golf cart for $12. He paid a greens fee of $23. Find his total cost.

You can use the Associative Property of Addition to find the total cost in two different ways.

$(7 + 12) + 23 = 19 + 23 = 42$ **Add 7 and 12 first.**
$7 + (12 + 23) = 7 + 35 = 42$ **Add 12 and 23 first.**

Carlos's total cost was $42.

✅ Quick Check

1. You spend $6 for dinner, $8 for a movie, and $4 for popcorn. Find your total cost. Explain which property or properties you used.

When you add a number and 0, the sum equals the original number. The **additive identity** is 0. When you multiply a number and 1, the product equals the original number. The **multiplicative identity** is 1.

Vocabulary Tip

In mathematics, an <u>identity</u> leaves the value of other numbers unchanged.

Key Concepts | **Identity Properties of Addition and Multiplication**

The sum of any number and zero is the original number. The product of any number and 1 is the original number.

Arithmetic	Algebra
$12 + 0 = 12; 10 \cdot 1 = 10$	$a + 0 = a; a \cdot 1 = a$

2 EXAMPLE Identifying Properties

Name each property shown.

a. $5 \cdot 7 = 7 \cdot 5$ Commutative Property of Multiplication

b. $c \cdot 1 = c$ Identity Property of Multiplication

c. $7 + a = a + 7$ Commutative Property of Addition

d. $5(xy) = (5x)y$ Associative Property of Multiplication

✅ Quick Check

2. Name each property shown.

a. $3 + 6 = 6 + 3$ **b.** $8 = 1 \cdot 8$ **c.** $(3z)m = 3(zm)$

2 Using Properties

When numbers are easy to compute mentally, you can use properties and mental math to find sums.

3 EXAMPLE Using Mental Math With Addition

Use mental math to simplify $(81 + 6) + 9$.

$(81 + 6) + 9$

$= (6 + 81) + 9$ Use the Commutative Property of Addition.

$= 6 + (81 + 9)$ Use the Associative Property of Addition.

$= 6 + 90$ Add within parentheses.

$= 96$ Add.

Test-Taking Tip

Look for combinations that equal 10 or a multiple of 10, since they are easier to use in calculating mentally.

✓ Quick Check

3. Use mental math to simplify each expression.

a. $6 + 7 + 14$ **b.** $8 + 0 + 2 + (-7)$
c. $5 + 12 + 18 + 5$ **d.** $19 + (-30) + 21$

$.85

$.35

$1.65

4 **EXAMPLE**   <u>Real-World</u> 🌐 **Problem Solving**

School Supplies **Suppose you buy the school supplies shown at the left. Use mental math to find the cost of the supplies.**

$1.65 + 0.85 + 0.35$

$= 0.85 + 1.65 + 0.35$ **Use the Commutative Property of Addition.**

$= 0.85 + (1.65 + 0.35)$ **Use the Associative Property of Addition.**

$= 0.85 + 2.00$ **Add within parentheses.**

$= 2.85$ **Add.**

The cost of the school supplies is $2.85.

✓ Quick Check

GO **for Help**

For a guide to adding decimals, see Skills Handbook, page 786.

4. Use the supermarket receipt and mental math to find the cost of the groceries.

```
       SOUTH STREET
          MARKET

DATE 08.03.03      THU
1 GALLON MILK    $2.30
BREAD            $1.80
APPLES           $2.20
```

You can also use mental math to help you find products.

5 **EXAMPLE**   **Using Mental Math With Multiplication**

Use mental math to simplify $(4 \cdot 9) \cdot 5$.

$(4 \cdot 9) \cdot 5 = (9 \cdot 4) \cdot 5$ **Use the Commutative Property of Multiplication.**

$= 9 \cdot (4 \cdot 5)$ **Use the Associative Property of Multiplication.**

$= 9 \cdot 20$ **Multiply within parentheses.**

$= 180$ **Multiply.**

✓ Quick Check

5. Use mental math to simplify each expression.

a. $25 \cdot (3 \cdot 4)$ **b.** $3 \cdot 1 \cdot -5 \cdot 8$
c. $2(-8)(-15)$ **d.** $5 \cdot 9 \cdot 6 \cdot (-2) \cdot (-1)$

70   Chapter 2 Solving One-Step Equations and Inequalities

EXERCISES

Practice and Problem Solving

 A Practice by Example

Example 1
(page 68)

 GO for Help

Use the Associative Property to write two different expressions that you could use to find each sum.

1. Add 1, 3, and 25.

2. Add 5, 91, and 11.

3. Travel On a road trip, your family spends $120 for gas, $15 for bottled water, and $80 for food. Find your family's total cost. Explain which property or properties you used.

Example 2
(page 69)

Name each property shown.

4. $7 + 6 = 6 + 7$

5. $0 + 8 = 8$

6. $(6 \cdot 15)2 = 6(15 \cdot 2)$

7. $(12r)s = 12(rs)$

8. $999 \cdot 1 = 999$

9. $ab = ba$

Example 3
(page 69)

Mental Math Use mental math to simplify each expression.

10. $(5 + 23) + 65$

11. $(3 + 62) + 7$

12. $9 + (14 + 1)$

13. $-8 + 35 + 15$

14. $31 + 0 + (-2)$

15. $15 + 13 + (-25)$

Example 4
(page 70)

16. $(0.50 + 34) + 3.50$

17. $(4.55 + 27) + 5.45$

18. $1.50 + (3.17 + 6.50)$

19. $-0.25 + 4.88 + 3.25$

20. $7.02 + 3.40 + 1.98$

21. $8.39 + (-2.00) + 1.61$

22. Mental Math Loryn is flying roundtrip from Dallas, Texas, to Minneapolis, Minnesota. The fare for her ticket is $308. Each airport charges a $16 airport fee. There is also a tax of $12 on the fare. What is the total cost of Loryn's ticket?

Example 5
(page 70)

Mental Math Use mental math to simplify each expression.

23. $6 \cdot 3 \cdot 5$

24. $5 \cdot 7 \cdot (-2)$

25. $25 \cdot 4 \cdot 8$

26. $8 \cdot 4 \cdot (-10)$

 B Apply Your Skills

GO Online
Homework Video Tutor
Visit: PHSchool.com
Web Code: ade-0201

Name each property shown.

27. $8(3 \cdot 2) = (8 \cdot 3)2$

28. $5 + 8 = 8 + 5$

29. $(6x)y = 6(xy)$

30. $6 \cdot 1 = 6$

31. $999 + 0 = 999$

32. $a \cdot 1 = 1 \cdot a$

Simplify each expression.

33. $25 + 157 + (-75)$

34. $140 + 17 + (-60)$

35. $5 \cdot 50 \cdot 20 \cdot (-2)$

36. $125 + 18 + 75 + 162$

$15.20

$7.65

$1.35

37. Gardening Lance has purchased some supplies to start his new garden. Use the prices shown at the left and mental math to find the cost of the supplies.

38. Writing in Math Which two numbers would you combine first to simplify $3 + 6 + 27$? Explain.

C Challenge

Mental Math **Evaluate each expression.**

39. $x(y \cdot z)$, for $x = 4$, $y = 27$, and $z = 5$

40. $t(u)(-v)$, for $t = 3$, $u = 20$, and $v = 8$

41. $a + b + c$, for $a = 14$, $b = 252$, and $c = 26$

42. $d(v)(d)$, for $d = 5$ and $v = 24$

43. **Reasoning** Can you use $4 + 2 = 6$ as your first step in simplifying $3 \cdot 4 + 2 \div (-2)$? Explain.

ISAT

Test Prep

Multiple Choice **44.** Which equation shows the Associative Property of Addition?
A. $8 + 6 + 7 = 8 + 7 + 6$ B. $(10 + 5) + 15 = 10 + (5 + 15)$
C. $9 + 0 + (-1) = 9 + (-1)$ D. $(-2) \cdot 1 \cdot 9 = (-2) \cdot 9$

Read the passage below before doing Exercises 45 and 46.

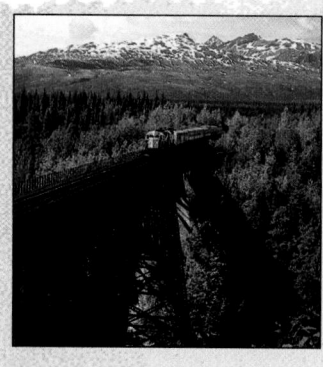

A Fair Fare in Alaska

Railroads are a popular means of transportation in Alaska. One scenic train route travels 356 miles from Anchorage to Fairbanks. It includes a stop in Denali Park, where you can see the tallest mountain in the United States, Mount McKinley. A one-way fare for the 12-hour trip is $154 in the summer and $120 in the spring and fall. A one-way fare for the 7.5-hour trip from Anchorage to Denali Park is $102 in the summer, and $84 in the spring and fall. Children's fares are half the fares for adults.

45. Two adults and two children plan to travel round trip from Anchorage to Fairbanks. How much will the trip cost in the summer?
F. $360   G. $462   H. $720   J. $924

46. Three adults and two children plan to travel round trip from Anchorage to Denali Park. How much will the trip cost in the fall?
A. $672   B. $504   C. $336   D. $252

Mixed Review

Lesson 1-10   **In which quadrant does the graph of each ordered pair lie?**

47. $(-6, -3)$ **48.** $(8, -1)$ **49.** $(-4, 17)$ **50.** $(-1, 4)$

Lesson 1-9 🌐 **51.** **Recreation** Lin worked 4 hours per day for 3 days to build a model bridge. How many hours did she spend on the project?

Lesson 1-2   **Simplify each expression.**

52. $3 \cdot 5 + 3 \cdot 15$ **53.** $4 \cdot 7 + 4 \cdot 11$ **54.** $5 \cdot 22 - 5 \cdot 2$

The Distributive Property

 Assessment Framework

6.8.11 Identify and apply the following properties of operations with rational numbers: the commutative and associative properties for addition and multiplication; the distributive property; the additive and multiplicative identity properties; the additive and multiplicative inverse properties; and the multiplicative property of zero.

1 Numerical Expressions

Activity

Exploring the Distributive Property

You can find the total area of two rectangles by two methods.

1. **Method 1:** Find the area of each rectangle. Then find the sum of the areas.

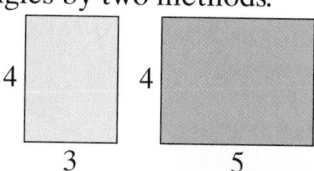

2. **Method 2:** Combine the two rectangles into one large rectangle. Find its length. Find its width. Then find its area.

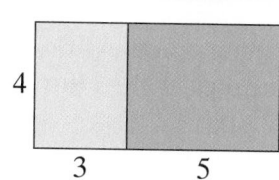

3. On a piece of paper, draw two rectangles with the same width, and lengths different from those above. Label the dimensions. Repeat Method 1 and Method 2 with your pair of rectangles. What do you notice about your results?

✓ **Check Skills You'll Need**

Simplify each expression.

1. $3 \cdot 7 - 9$

2. $(9 - 5)6$

3. $8 + 2 \cdot 6$

4. $2(6 - 3)$

5. $4 \cdot 5 - 4 \cdot 3$

6. $3 \cdot 2 - 1 \cdot 2$

 for Help
Lesson 1-2

🔊 **New Vocabulary**
• Distributive Property

The Activity above shows different ways to find the sum of the areas of two rectangles. It suggests the *Distributive Property*, which combines multiplication with addition and subtraction.

Key Concepts | **Distributive Property**

To multiply a sum or difference, multiply each number within the parentheses by the number outside the parentheses.

Arithmetic	Algebra
$3(2 + 6) = 3(2) + 3(6)$	$a(b + c) = ab + ac$
$(2 + 6)3 = 2(3) + 6(3)$	$(b + c)a = ba + ca$
$6(7 - 4) = 6(7) - 6(4)$	$a(b - c) = ab - ac$
$(7 - 4)6 = 7(6) - 4(6)$	$(b - c)a = ba - ca$

You can use the Distributive Property to multiply mentally.

1 EXAMPLE **Using the Distributive Property I**

Use the Distributive Property to find 20(102) mentally.

$$20(102) = 20(100 + 2)$$ **Write 102 as (100 + 2).**

$$20(100 + 2) = 20 \cdot 100 + 20 \cdot 2$$ **Use the Distributive Property.**

$$= 2,000 + 40$$ **Multiply.**

$$= 2,040$$ **Add.**

Quick Check

1. Find the product $9 \cdot 199$ mentally.

2 EXAMPLE **Real-World Problem Solving**

Multiple Choice At the annual Pancake Breakfast, 397 people ate 4 pancakes each. How many pancakes were served?

(A) 1,600 (B) 1,588 (C) 401 (D) 397

$$(397)4 = (400 - 3)4$$ **Write 397 as (400 − 3).**

$$= 400 \cdot 4 - 3 \cdot 4$$ **Use the Distributive Property.**

$$= 1,600 - 12$$ **Multiply.**

$$= 1,588$$ **Subtract.**

1,588 pancakes were served. The answer is B.

Quick Check

2. Your club sold calendars for $7. Club members sold 204 calendars. How much money did they raise?

3 EXAMPLE **Using the Distributive Property II**

Simplify 8(15) − 8(5).

$$8(15) - 8(5) = 8(15 - 5)$$ **Use the Distributive Property.**

$$= 8(10)$$ **Subtract within parentheses.**

$$= 80$$ **Multiply.**

Test-Taking Tip

You can use the Distributive Property with mental math.

99×2
$= (100 - 1) \times 2$
$= (100 \times 2) - (1 \times 2)$
$= 200 - 2$
$= 198$

Quick Check

3. Simplify each expression.

a. $7(21) + 7(9)$ **b.** $12(52) - 12(62)$ **c.** $(16)7 - (11)7$

You can use algebra tiles to model the Distributive Property with variable expressions.

4 EXAMPLE **Using Tiles to Multiply**

Use algebra tiles to multiply $3(2x + 5)$.

Model three groups of $2x + 5$.

Group like tiles.

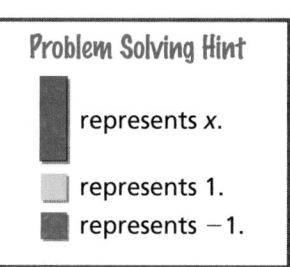
So, $3(2x + 5) = 6x + 15$.

✓ Quick Check

4. Use algebra tiles to multiply.

   a. $4(2x - 3)$ **b.** $3(x + 4)$ **c.** $(3x + 1)2$

In Example 4, notice that 3 multiplies both $2x$ and 5.
That is, $3(2x + 5) = 3(2x) + 3(5)$.

5 EXAMPLE **Using the Distributive Property III**

Multiply.

a. $-5(4x - 3)$

$$-5(4x - 3) = -5(4x) - (-5)(3)$$ **Use the Distributive Property.**

$$= -20x - (-15)$$ **Multiply.**

$$= -20x + 15$$ **Simplify.**

b. $(2x + 5)7$

$$(2x + 5)7 = (2x)7 + (5)7$$ **Use the Distributive Property.**

$$= 14x + 35$$ **Multiply.**

> **Vocabulary Tip**
>
> When you distribute papers in class, you give some to each classmate. Similarly, when you <u>distribute</u> a number over a sum or difference, you multiply each value within the parentheses by that number.

✓ Quick Check

5. Multiply.

   a. $2(7 - 3d)$ **b.** $(6m + 1)(3)$ **c.** $-3(5t - 2)$

Practice and Problem Solving

 Practice by Example

Examples 1 and 2
(page 74)

 for Help

Mental Math Use the Distributive Property to simplify.

1. 6(23)   **2.** 5(18)   **3.** 7(48)   **4.** 13(101)

5. (104)(9)   **6.** 6(52)   **7.** 8(98)   **8.** (208)4

9. Ticket Sales A theater sold out its evening performances four nights in a row. The theater has 294 seats. How many people attended the theater in the four nights?

Example 3
(page 74)

Simplify each expression.

10. 7(3) + 7(5)   **11.** 2(9) − 3(9)   **12.** 6(4) + 6(8)

13. 9(3) − 2(3)   **14.** (12)27 − (12)24   **15.** (3)5 + (27)5

Example 4
(page 75)

Write an expression using parentheses for each model. Then multiply.

16.

17.

Multiply. Use algebra tiles as needed.

18. 2(t − 5)   **19.** (v − 3)4   **20.** 3(2h − 1)   **21.** −2(7z + 3)

Example 5
(page 75)

Multiply.

22. 7(b − 3)   **23.** 12(a + 3)   **24.** (2 + 3d)5   **25.** −5(m + 6)

26. 3(5 − 3w)   **27.** −7(t − 4)   **28.** 4(b + 5)   **29.** (y − 6)2

B **Apply Your Skills**

Mental Math Use the Distributive Property to simplify.

30. 5(1,005)   **31.** (8) · 11 + (−13) · 11

32. 13 · (−3) − 7 · (−3)   **33.** −32 · 6 + 29 · 6

34. 4 · 19 − 4 · (11)   **35.** (−8) · 10 + 3 · (−8)

Mental Math Solve using mental math.

36. Every day, Lila eats a bowl of cereal that has 193 calories. What is the total number of calories from cereal that Lila eats in a week?

37. The trip from Roberto's house to his aunt's house is 896 miles. How long is the round trip?

Use the Distributive Property to multiply.

38. $-3(2t + 6)$ **39.** $-7(-3n + 2)$ **40.** $(4 - t)(-7)$

41. $-5(-m + 6)$ **42.** $-8(6 - c)$ **43.** $(5y + 8)(-3)$

44. **Writing in Math** Explain how to use the Distributive Property to multiply $6(3r + 4s)$.

45. **Error Analysis** Suppose your friend wrote $7(2m + t) = 14m + t$. What error did your friend make?

 Challenge

Mental Math Use the Distributive Property to simplify.

46. $(-4)(70) + (-4)(-90)$ **47.** $3(9) - 3(5) + 3(6)$

Name each property shown.

48. $m[t + (-t)] = mt + m(-t)$ **49.** $m[t + (-t)] = m(-t + t)$

50. $m[t + (-t)] = [t + (-t)]m$ **51.** $m + [t + (-t)] = (m + t) + (-t)$

 Test Prep

Multiple Choice

52. According to the map, if you drive from Atlanta to Los Angeles (L.A.) and back, how many miles would you travel?
A. 7,776 mi   **B.** 3,888 mi
C. 1,944 mi   **D.** 1,888 mi

53. Which equation correctly illustrates the Distributive Property?
F. $18(100 + 4) = (18 \cdot 100) + 4$
G. $18(100 + 4) = (18 + 100) \cdot (18 + 4)$
H. $18(100 + 4) = (18 + 100) \cdot 4$
J. $18(100 + 4) = (18 \cdot 100) + (18 \cdot 4)$

54. You rent three videos for $2.95 each. What do you pay?
A. $6.95   **B.** $8.85   **C.** $9.00   **D.** $9.15

Mixed Review

 for Help

Lesson 2-1

Name the property shown.

55. $3(6 \cdot 2) = 3(2 \cdot 6)$ **56.** $8 = 8 + 0$ **57.** $4(8 \cdot 3) = (4 \cdot 8)3$

Lessons 1-5 and 1-6

58. You have $120 in your checking account. In one month, you deposit $30, write a check for $21, withdraw $20, and deposit $45. Find your balance at the end of the month.

Lesson 1-3

Evaluate each expression.

59. $7 - m$, for $m = 6$ **60.** $6t + 1$, for $t = -2$ **61.** $c \div 3 - 5$, for $c = 6$

Simplifying Variable Expressions

 Assessment Framework

8.8.03 Simplify algebraic expressions.

 Check Skills You'll Need

Simplify each expression.

1. $5(b + 4)$

2. $-3(2x + 5)$

3. $4(-8 - 3q)$

4. $-6(2b - 7)$

GO for Help
Lesson 2-2

🔊 **New Vocabulary**

• term
• constant
• like terms
• coefficient
• simplify a variable expression
• deductive reasoning

1 Identifying Parts of a Variable Expression

The diagram shows the possible parts of a variable expression.

A **term** is a number or the product of a number and variable(s).

$$7a + 4a + 3b - 6 \leftarrow \text{A \textbf{constant} is a term that has no variable.}$$

Like terms have identical variables.

A **coefficient** is a number that multiplies a variable.

When you have a variable expression that includes subtraction, you can rewrite the expression using only addition. This will help you find the coefficient(s) and constant(s).

$5x - 3y + z - 2$
$= 5x + (-3y) + z + (-2)$ **Rewrite subtraction as adding opposites.**
$= 5x + (-3y) + 1z + (-2)$ **Identity Property of Multiplication**

Rewriting the expression using addition shows that the coefficients are 5, −3, and 1. The constant is −2. Notice that the sign between terms in the original expression determines whether a coefficient or constant is positive or negative.

1 EXAMPLE   Identifying Parts of an Expression

Name the coefficients, the like terms, and the constants in $3m - 2n + n - 4$.

Coefficients: $3, -2, 1$ Like terms: $-2n$ and n Constant: -4

✓ **Quick Check**

1. Name the coefficients, the like terms, and the constants.

    a. $6 + 2s + 4s$ **b.** $-4x$ **c.** $9m + 2r - 2m + r$

2 Simplifying Variable Expressions

You **simplify a variable expression** by replacing it with an equivalent expression that has as few terms as possible. Algebra tiles can help you model this process.

2 EXAMPLE **Using Tiles to Simplify**

Simplify $2x + 4 + 3x$.

$$2x \quad + \quad 4 \quad + \quad 3x \quad \longrightarrow \quad 5x \quad + 4$$

✓ Quick Check

2. Use tiles to simplify $3a + 2 + 4a - 1$.

You can also use the Distributive Property to combine like terms.

3 EXAMPLE **Combining Like Terms**

Simplify $5y + y$.

$5y + y = 5y + 1y$ **Use the Identity Property of Multiplication.**

$\quad\quad = (5 + 1)y$ **Use the Distributive Property.**

$\quad\quad = 6y$ **Simplify.**

GO ⏺nline

Video Tutor Help
Visit: PHSchool.com
Web Code: ada-0775

✓ Quick Check

3. Simplify each expression.

   a. $3b - b$ **b.** $-4m - 9m$ **c.** $p + 6p - 4p$

Deductive reasoning is the process of reasoning logically from given facts to a conclusion. As you use properties, rules, and definitions to justify the steps in a problem, you are using deductive reasoning.

4 EXAMPLE **Using Deductive Reasoning**

Simplify $4g + 3(3 + g)$. Justify each step.

$4g + 3(3 + g) = 4g + 9 + 3g$ **Use the Distributive Property.**

$\quad\quad\quad\quad = 4g + 3g + 9$ **Use the Commutative Property of Addition.**

$\quad\quad\quad\quad = (4 + 3)g + 9$ **Use the Distributive Property to combine like terms.**

$\quad\quad\quad\quad = 7g + 9$ **Simplify.**

✓ Quick Check

4. Simplify each expression. Justify each step.

   a. $6y + 4m - 7y + m$ **b.** $4x + 3 - 2(5 + x)$

EXERCISES

For more exercises, see *Extra Skill and Word Problem Practice*.

Practice and Problem Solving

A Practice by Example

Example 1
(page 78)

Name the coefficients, the like terms, and the constants.

1. $3x + 5y - 3$ **2.** $2x - 7$ **3.** $4x - 7x + 3x$

4. $6xy - 5xy$ **5.** $-3x$ **6.** $a + 2a + 3a - 4a$

Example 2
(page 79)

Use tiles to simplify each expression.

7. $x + 2 + 3x + 5 + x + 3 + 2x$

8. $2x + 1 + x - 4 + 4x + 1$

9. $x + 2 + 3x$ **10.** $2x + 1 + 6x - 4$

Example 3
(page 79)

Simplify each expression.

11. $12a + a$ **12.** $5a + 8a$ **13.** $-2b + b$

14. $7w - w$ **15.** $2r - 5 + 6r$ **16.** $4a - 3 + 5a$

Example 4
(page 79)

Simplify each expression. Justify each step.

17. $2g + 3(g + 5)$ **18.** $-3z + 8(z + y)$

19. $4m + 3d - 5m + d$ **20.** $t - 3 + 2(t + 2)$

B Apply Your Skills

Simplify each expression.

21. $8z + 8y + 3z$ **22.** $t - 3t + 2t + 4$ **23.** $18 + 6(9k - 13)$

24. $r + 3 - 6r + r$ **25.** $-4(a + 3) - a$ **26.** $4m + 3 - 5m + m$

27. $3(g + 5) + 2g$ **28.** $2b - 6 + 3b - b$ **29.** $-5 + 3x + 3 + 2$

30. $4(w + 2x) + 9(-4w)$ **31.** $3(2n + 4) - 2(3n + 6)$

🌐 **32. Pet Supplies** Juan bought supplies for his new gecko. He bought four plants for p dollars each. He also bought a 10-gallon tank for $10 and a water dish for $3. Write an expression Juan could use to find the total cost of the supplies.

33. Error Analysis Your friend simplified $x + y + xy$ to $2xy$. What error did your friend make?

34. Open-Ended Use the variables r and s to write a variable expression. Evaluate your expression for $r = 2$ and $s = -5$.

**Online
Homework Video Tutor**
Visit: PHSchool.com
Web Code: ade-0203

35. Writing in Math The expression $10bc$ has two variables. Explain why $10bc$ is not two terms.

C Challenge

Simplify each expression. Justify each step.

36. $12 - 4(-8v + 17)$

37. $6(2x + y) + 2y - 12x$

38. $(2t + 4)3 + 6(-5t) - (-8)$

39. $-12(5x) + 3(-7x) - x$

40. $w + 3w + 4(5 + w - 3w)$

41. $18u - 6(9k - 7 - 10u) + 4k$

ISAT

Multiple Choice

42. Which expression has exactly two like terms?
   A. $3t + 1 - t$ **B.** $7 + 2m$ **C.** $8q + 3p$ **D.** $6r + r - 9r$

43. Which expression simplifies to $3x + 4z + 6$?
   F. $3(x + 6) + 4z$ **G.** $7(x + z) + 6$
   H. $7z + 3(x + 2) - 3z$ **J.** $3 + x + 4 + z + 6$

44. Jaleesa bought three folders for b cents each and two report covers for c cents each. She also bought a binder for $1.89. Which expression could Jaleesa use to find the total cost?
   A. $b + c + 189$ **B.** $3b + 189$
   C. $3b + 2c + 189$ **D.** $189 - 2b - 3c$

Mixed Review

Lesson 2-2

Mental Math Use the Distributive Property to find each product.

45. $8(102)$ **46.** $54 \cdot 6$ **47.** $19(30)$ **48.** $(41)(9)$

Lesson 1-8 ● **49. Rock Climbing** A pair of rock climbers start up a 1,000-ft cliff. After one hour, they have gone up 160 ft. After two hours, they have gone up 320 ft. If they continue at this rate, how far up will they have gone after five hours?

✓ Checkpoint Quiz 1   **Lessons 2-1 through 2-3**

Name each property shown.

1. $3 \cdot (-6) = -6 \cdot 3$

2. $(3a)b = 3(ab)$

3. $17 \cdot 1 = 17$

4. $6 + 0 = 0 + 6$

5. $(3 + 2)(4) = (4)(3 + 2)$

6. $4(3 - 2) = 4(3) - 4(2)$

Simplify each expression.

7. $3(a + 2a)$ **8.** $9y - 3y + 12y$ **9.** $7(2w) + 2(w - 3)$

2-4

Variables and Equations

 Assessment Framework

8.8.11 Represent and analyze problems with linear equations and inequalities.

 Check Skills You'll Need

Write a variable expression for each phrase.

1. the sum of x and 46

2. four less than g

3. t decreased by five

4. the quotient of z and 26

GO for Help
Lesson 1-1

🔊 **New Vocabulary**

• equation
• open sentence
• solution of an equation

---

1 Classifying Types of Equations

An **equation** is a mathematical sentence with an equal sign. Here are three of the ways you will see equations in this book.

$9 + 2 = 11$	a numerical expression equal to a numerical expression
$x + 7 = 37$	a variable expression equal to a numerical expression
$a + (-3) = 2a + 5$	a variable expression equal to a variable expression

An equation with a numerical expression equal to another numerical expression is either *true* or *false*. An equation with one or more variables is an **open sentence.**

1 EXAMPLE Classifying Equations

State whether each equation is *true, false,* or an *open sentence.*

a. 6 + 12 = 18   true, because $18 = 18$

b. 6 = 4 + 3   false, because $6 \neq 7$

c. 6y = −3 + 5y   an open sentence, because there is a variable

✓ Quick Check

1. State whether each equation is *true, false,* or an *open sentence.* Explain.

    a. $9 - 7 = 3$ **b.** $8 + x = 2$ **c.** $4 \cdot 5 = 20$

You can write a mathematical word sentence as an equation.

2 EXAMPLE Writing an Equation

Vocabulary Tip

The verb <u>is</u> between two quantities suggests writing the equal sign.

Write an equation for
Nine times the opposite of five is forty-five.
State whether the equation is *true, false,* or an *open sentence.*

The equation is false. $9 \cdot (-5) = -45$, and $-45 \neq 45$.

✅ Quick Check

2. Write an equation for *Twenty minus x is three.*
Is the equation true, false, or an open sentence? Explain.

---

2 Checking Equations Using Substitution

A **solution of an equation** is a value for a variable that makes an equation true. You substitute a number for a variable to determine whether the number is a solution of the equation.

3 EXAMPLE Substituting to Check

Is 30 a solution of the equation $170 + x = 200$?

$$170 + x = 200$$
$$170 + 30 \stackrel{?}{=} 200 \quad \textbf{Substitute 30 for } x.$$
$$200 = 200$$

Yes, 30 is a solution of the equation.

✅ Quick Check

3. Is the given number a solution of the equation?

  a. $8 + t = 2t; 1$ **b.** $9 - m = 3; 6$

---

4 EXAMPLE Real-World 🌐 Problem Solving

Scuba Diving A diver's equipment weighs 35 lb. The diver plus the equipment weighs 165 lb. Can the diver's weight be 200 lb?

Words   weight of diver   plus   weight of equipment   is   165 lb

Let d = weight of diver.

Equation d +   35   =   165

$$d + 35 = 165$$
$$200 + 35 \stackrel{?}{=} 165 \quad \textbf{Substitute 200 for the variable.}$$
$$235 \neq 165$$

No, the diver's weight cannot be 200 lb.

✅ Quick Check

4. A tent weighs 6 lb. Your backpack and the tent together weigh 33 lb. Use an equation to find whether the backpack weighs 27 lb.

Vocabulary Tip

$\neq$ shows that two values are not equal.
$\stackrel{?}{=}$ asks whether two values are equal.

Real-World 🌐 Connection

A scuba tank can hold 63 ft³ of compressed air. It weighs 29 lb when full.

EXERCISES

For more exercises, see *Extra Skill and Word Problem Practice*.

Practice and Problem Solving

Ⓐ Practice by Example

Example 1
(page 82)

GO for Help

State whether each equation is *true, false,* or an *open sentence.* Explain.

1. $5 + 9 = 14$

2. $4x - 8 = 25$

3. $15 = 3 \cdot 5$

4. $x - 10 = 22 - x$

5. $6 + 1 = 5 + 3$

6. $4c - 12 = 20$

7. $20 = 2 \cdot 10$

8. $20 + 3x = 42$

9. $3 \cdot 9 = 30$

Example 2
(page 82)

Write an equation for each sentence. State whether the equation is *true, false,* or an *open sentence.* Explain.

10. Four times the opposite of five equals negative twenty.

11. Twenty-five equals a number v plus fifteen.

Example 3
(page 83)

Is the given number a solution of the equation?

12. $c + 5 = 3; -2$

13. $24 = c + 29; -2$

14. $4 + d = 6; 2$

15. $20 - c = 12; 8$

16. $8 = a + 3; 10$

17. $3 + 2t = 7; 4$

18. $3 = 12 - a; 6$

19. $2m = m + 6; 4$

20. $5q - 1 = -1; 0$

Example 4
(page 83)

Write an equation. Is the given value a solution?

21. Weight A veterinarian weighs 140 lb. When she steps on a scale while holding a dog, the scale shows 192 lb. Let d represent the weight of the dog. Does the dog weigh 52 lb?

22. Income A family's expenses are $1,200. One parent makes $850. Must the other earn $400 for both incomes to equal expenses?

Ⓑ Apply Your Skills

Determine whether each statement is true or false. Explain.

23. An equation can be false.

24. $3w - 7$ is an open sentence.

25. An open sentence must contain a variable.

26. Some open sentences are true for all variable values.

State whether each equation is *true, false,* or an *open sentence.* Explain.

27. $18 = -3(-6)$

28. $-24(-2) = 18(4 + 2)$

29. $-9 + x = 50 \div 10 + 3$

30. $-2(3 - 8) = 2[-3 - (-8)]$

31. $6[-3 - (-5)] = 2(-4 + 10)$

32. $4[2 + (-6)] = 2[x - (-12)]$

Write an equation for each sentence. State whether each equation is *true, false,* or an *open sentence.* Explain.

33. The product of negative twenty and nine is negative eleven.

34. The sum of fifteen and a number n is fifty.

35. Forty-eight divided by twelve equals three.

36. **Writing in Math** Equations can be true or false. Can an expression be true or false? Explain.

Is the given number a solution of the equation? Explain.

37. $\frac{c}{2} - 8 = 3(-3); -2$

38. $14 = 28 \div x; 14$

39. $-x - 5 = 6; 1$

40. $3b \div 18 = 2; 12$

 Challenge **Language Arts** Some word sentences are similar to equations. Exercises 41–43 are about word sentences.

41. The sentence *Abraham Lincoln was an American president* is true. Write two other true sentences.

42. The sentence *Eleanor Roosevelt was an American president* is false. Write two other false sentences.

43. The sentence *He is a professional baseball player* is open. It is not clear to whom the word *he* refers. Write two other open sentences.

ISAT

Test Prep

Multiple Choice

44. Which equation is false?
   A. $3 + (-7) = 10$
   B. $6 \div 2 = 3$
   C. $8 \cdot 2 - 15 = 1$
   D. $7w = 3w + 12$

45. Together Mike and Amy weigh 350 pounds. Amy weighs 150 pounds and Mike weighs m pounds. Which equation represents this situation?
   F. $m + 350 = 150$
   G. $m = 350 + 200$
   H. $m - 200 = 150$
   J. $m = 350 - 150$

46. A recipe calls for 4 c of flour. You have 20 c of flour. Let r represent the flour you have left after making the recipe. Which equation represents this situation?
   A. $r - 20 = 4$
   B. $20 - 4 = r$
   C. $r - 4 = 16$
   D. $r - 4 = 20$

Mixed Review

Lesson 2-3 **Simplify each expression.**

47. $6m + 7 - 2m$

48. $-8t + 4t - 19$

49. $3w + 5k - 4w + k$

Lesson 1-8 50. **Marathon Training** Larissa ran 15 mi per week before she decided to train for a marathon. The first week of training she ran 17 mi. The second week she ran 19 mi. If she continued her pattern, how far did she run the fifth week?

Lesson 1-3 **Evaluate each expression for $a = 3$ and $b = 2$.**

51. $a - b + 15$

52. $(3b - 2a) \div 4$

53. $3(b + 2) - 4$

You can model an equation using algebra tiles. Use a green rectangular tile to represent the variable. Here are two examples.

Equation 1

$x + 3 = 4$

Equation 2

$x + 3 = -3$

Model each equation.

1. $x + 3 = 5$

2. $z + 2 = -6$

3. $y + 1 = 4$

4. $-3 = a - 4$

5. $2b + 2 = 8$

6. $3 + 3x = -6$

To solve an equation, get the variable alone on one side of the equal sign. To do this, remove the same number of tiles from each side.

Here's how to solve $x + 3 = 7$.

Model the equation.

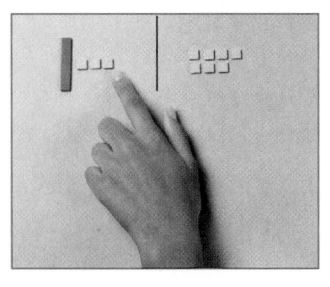

Solve by removing 3 tiles from each side.

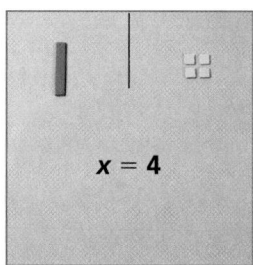

$x = 4$

Check $x + 3 = 7$

$4 + 3 \stackrel{?}{=} 7$ **Replace x with 4.**

$7 = 7$ ✔

Model and solve each equation. Check your result.

7. $x + 3 = 6$

8. $m + 2 = 8$

9. $1 = 1 + d$

10. $-4 + y = -7$

11. $-1 + p = -5$

12. $w - 2 = -3$

Modeling   **Write and solve the equation for each model.**

13.

14.

15.

Sometimes you cannot remove the same number of tiles from each side. You may need to add tiles to form zero pairs. Here's how to solve $x + 2 = -4$.

$x + 2 = -4$

Model the equation.

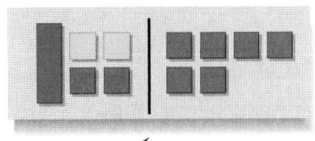
Add −2 to each side.

Remove zero pairs.

$x = -6$

Check $x + 2 = -4$

$-6 + 2 \stackrel{?}{=} -4$ Replace x with −6.

$-4 = -4$ ✔

Model and solve each equation. Check your result.

16. $y + 2 = -2$ **17.** $x + 5 = 2$ **18.** $n + 7 = 1$

19. $-1 = k + 3$ **20.** $x - 4 = 5$ **21.** $2 = z - 3$

Modeling **Write and solve the equation for each model.**

22.

23.

24.

25. Open-Ended Write two different equations that have the solution modeled at the right.

26. Number Sense Give an example of an equation model that has the same color unit squares on each side but still requires zero pairs to solve. Explain why zero pairs are needed.

2-5

Solving Equations by Adding or Subtracting

 Assessment Framework

8.8.12 Solve linear equations and inequalities in one variable over the rational numbers.

8.8.13 Solve word problems involving unknown quantities.

✓ Check Skills You'll Need

Simplify each expression.

1. $3 + 4 - 4$

2. $7 + 9 - 7$

3. $8 - 2 + 2$

4. $6 + 2 - 2$

 for Help
Lesson 2-1

🔊 **New Vocabulary**

• inverse operations

---

1 | Using Subtraction to Solve Equations

Solving an equation is like keeping a barbell balanced. If you add weight to or subtract weight from one side of the bar, you must do the same on the other side.

Subtract 5 lb from each side.

As you can see in the photos, you keep the barbell balanced when you remove the same weight from each side.

In previous math courses, you used related equations like $3 + 5 = 8$ and $8 - 3 = 5$. These equations show that addition and subtraction undo each other.

When you solve an equation, your goal is to get the variable alone on one side of the equation. The value on the other side tells you the solution of the original equation. You use **inverse operations,** which undo each other, to get the variable alone.

Key Concepts | **Subtraction Property of Equality**

You can subtract the same number from each side of an equation.

Arithmetic	Algebra
$10 = 2(5)$	If $a = b$,
$10 - 5 = 2(5) - 5$	then $a - c = b - c$.

After you solve an equation, use your result in the original equation (as shown in Example 1) to check that your solution is correct.

1 EXAMPLE Subtracting to Solve an Equation

Solve $x + 6 = 4$.

Method 1

$$x + 6 = 4$$ **Subtract 6**
$$x + 6 - 6 = 4 - 6$$ **from each side.**
$$x = -2$$ **Simplify.**

Method 2

$$x + 6 = 4$$
$$\underline{ - 6 - 6}$$
$$x = -2$$

Check $x + 6 = 4$
$$-2 + 6 \overset{?}{=} 4$$ **Replace x with −2.**
$$4 = 4 \checkmark$$

✓ Quick Check

1. Solve each equation.

   a. $x + 8 = 3$ **b.** $5 = d + 1$ **c.** $c + (-4) = -5$

You can write and solve equations describing real-world situations. To help check, decide whether your solution is correct using the original problem.

2 EXAMPLE Real-World Problem Solving

Health Fred's target heart rate is 130 beats/min. This is 58 beats/min more than his resting heart rate. Find his resting heart rate.

Words | target rate | is | 58 | more than | resting rate |

    Let r = resting heart rate.

Equation   130   =   58   + r

$$130 = 58 + r$$
$$130 = r + 58$$ **Use the Commutative Property of Addition.**
$$130 - 58 = r + 58 - 58$$ **Subtract 58 from each side.**
$$72 = r$$ **Simplify.**

Fred's resting heart rate is 72 beats per minute.

Check The resting heart rate plus 58 beats per minute should be 130 beats per minute.
$$72 + 58 = 130 \checkmark$$

Real-World **Connection**

Here is one method for estimating your target heart-rate range: Begin by subtracting your age from 220. Then multiply the result by 0.6 and 0.8 to find the lower and upper limits of your heart-rate range.

✓ Quick Check

2. Cora measures her heart rate at 123 beats per minute. This is 55 beats per minute more than her resting heart rate r. Write and solve an equation to find Cora's resting heart rate.

2 Using Addition to Solve Equations

When you solve an equation involving subtraction, *add* the same number to each side of the equation.

> **Key Concepts** | **Addition Property of Equality**
>
> You can add the same number to each side of an equation.
>
> | Arithmetic | Algebra |
> |---|---|
> | $8 = 2(4)$ | If $a = b$, |
> | $8 + 3 = 2(4) + 3$ | then $a + c = b + c$. |

Online
active math

For: Equations Activity
Use: Interactive Textbook, 2-5

3 EXAMPLE   Adding to Solve an Equation

Solve $b - 12 = -49$.

$$b - 12 = -49$$
$$b - 12 + 12 = -49 + 12 \quad \textbf{Add 12 to each side.}$$
$$b = -37 \quad \textbf{Simplify.}$$

✓ Quick Check

3. Solve each equation.

   a. $y - 5 = 8$ **b.** $p - 30 = 42$ **c.** $98 = x - 14$

4 EXAMPLE   Real-World Problem Solving

Purchasing Your friend's VCR cost $328 less than her TV. Her VCR cost $179. About how much did her TV cost?

  Ⓐ about $175   Ⓑ about $300
  Ⓒ about $325   Ⓓ about $500

$$\$328 \approx \$325$$
$$\$179 \approx \$175 \quad \textbf{Round to numbers that are easy to compute.}$$
$$175 \approx t - 325 \quad \textbf{Write an equation.}$$
$$175 + 325 \approx t - 325 + 325 \quad \textbf{Add 325 to each side.}$$
$$500 \approx t \quad \textbf{Simplify.}$$

Your friend's TV cost about $500. The answer is D.

✓ Quick Check

4. A used book costs $17 less than the same book new. The used book costs $9. About how much does the new book cost?

Test-Taking Tip

When you go from words to an equation, the order of the math symbols may be different from the order of the words:

- ten fewer than $n \rightarrow$
  $n - 10$
- eight less than $r \rightarrow$
  $r - 8$
- n times $5 \rightarrow 5n$

EXERCISES

For more exercises, see *Extra Skill and Word Problem Practice*.

Practice and Problem Solving

A Practice by Example

GO for Help

Example 1
(page 89)

Solve each equation.

1. $a + 8 = 12$ **2.** $t + (-3) = 8$ **3.** $3 = n + 4$

4. $d + (-4) = -7$ **5.** $c + 9 = 37$ **6.** $q + (-10) = -25$

7. $b + 24 = 19$ **8.** $65 = n + 24$ **9.** $40 = w + (-5)$

Example 2
(page 89)

10. Astronomy The average distance from the sun to Jupiter is 778 million km. This distance is 550 million km greater than the average distance from the sun to Mars. Write and solve an equation to find the average distance d that Mars is from the sun.

GO for Help

For a guide to reading and solving Exercise 11, see page 93.

11. Physics The speed of sound through steel is 5,200 meters per second (m/s). This is 2,520 m/s faster than the speed of sound through silver. Write and solve an equation to find the speed of sound s through silver.

Example 3
(page 90)

Solve each equation.

12. $d - 4 = -7$ **13.** $c - 34 = 20$ **14.** $a - 4 = -18$

15. $r - 3 = 8$ **16.** $z - 100 = 100$ **17.** $5 = d - 1$

18. $40 = g - 20$ **19.** $34 = c - 19$ **20.** $-54 = q - 9$

Example 4
(page 90)

21. Astronomy Venus's average distance from the sun is 108 million km. This distance is 42 million km less than the average distance from the sun to Earth. Write and solve an equation to find Earth's average distance d from the sun.

B Apply Your Skills

Copy and complete the steps for solving each equation.

22.
$$35 + b = -90$$
$$35 - \blacksquare + b = -90 - \blacksquare$$
$$b = \blacksquare$$

23.
$$y - 86 = -322$$
$$y - 86 + \blacksquare = -322 + \blacksquare$$
$$y = \blacksquare$$

Solve each equation.

24. $54 + x = 98$ **25.** $e - 43 = -45$ **26.** $47 = 7 + y$

27. $450 = a - 325$ **28.** $h + 35 = 15$ **29.** $298 + n = 294$

30. $x - 366 = -415$ **31.** $89 + y = 112$ **32.** $-27 = w - 14$

33. Multiple Choice In 1996, 487 million people across the world spoke English. This was 512 million people fewer than the number who spoke Mandarin Chinese. Which equation could you use to find the number of people n who spoke Mandarin Chinese?

Ⓐ $487 = n - 512$ Ⓑ $487 = n \times 512$

Ⓒ $487 = 512 - n$ Ⓓ $487 = 512 \div n$

34. Open-Ended Write a word problem that can be solved using the equation $x + 15 = 18$.

35. This year, the Tigers won six more games than the Panthers. What other fact would you need to know in order to use the equation $p + 6 = 22$ to find the number of games, p, that the Panthers won?

Mental Math **Use mental math to solve each equation.**

36. $b + 15 = -5$ **37.** $130 = 30 + s$ **38.** $x + 800 = 500$

39. Error Analysis A student solved the equation $x - 6 = -6$. His solution was -12. What error did the student make?

40. Writing in Math To solve $x + 25 = -22$, one student subtracted 25 from each side. Another student added -25 to each side. Will both methods work? Explain.

 Challenge **Solve each equation.**

41. $-45 = x + (-3) + 50$ **42.** $-215 + e + (-43) = -145$

43. $n - 29 - 16 = 246$ **44.** $34 + p + 112 = 78 - 7$

45. $183 + k - 20 = -15$ **46.** $328 = z - 31 + 219$

ISAT

Test Prep

Gridded Response **Solve the equation given by each sentence.**

47. Negative six plus y equals eighteen.

48. Twelve equals 23 subtracted from n.

49. Negative five equals x minus eight.

50. The number a plus 5 is 18.

51. Negative 8 plus y equals 13.

52. Negative seventeen is 32 less than y.

Mixed Review

 GO **for Help**

Lesson 2-4

State whether each equation is *true*, *false*, or an *open sentence*. Explain.

53. $x + 2 = 4$ **54.** $4 = 6 - 2$ **55.** $5 - 3 = 7 - 4$

Lesson 1-8

56. Patterns Deric studied 30 min for his first math test. He studied 45 min for the second test and 60 min for the third test. If he continues this pattern, how long will he study for the fifth test?

Understanding Word Problems Read the problem below. Then let Tom's thinking guide you through the solution. Check your understanding with the exercise at the bottom of the page.

Physics The speed of sound through steel is 5,200 meters per second (m/s). This is 2,520 m/s faster than the speed of sound through silver. Write and solve an equation to find the speed of sound s through silver.

What Tom Thinks

I'll read the problem and write down the important information.

Where to start? Well, it's always helpful to look for a relationship in the problem.

The speed is greater through steel. I will either have to subtract from the speed through steel to get the speed through silver, or add to the speed through silver to get the speed through steel. I'll add.

Since I know the speed through steel, I have to name only one variable.

Now I can write the equation.

I can solve the equation by using the Subtraction Property of Equality.

I have to state what was asked for in the problem.

What Tom Writes

Speed of sound through steel = 5,200 m/s. The speed through steel is 2,520 m/s faster than the speed through silver.

The speed through steel is 2,520 m/s faster than the speed through silver.

Steel speed = silver speed + 2,520

Let s = speed of sound through silver.

$$5,200 = s + 2,520$$

$$5,200 - 2,520 = s + 2,520 - 2,520$$
$$2,680 = s$$

The speed of sound through silver is 2,680 m/s.

EXERCISE

1. Pamela can run the 300-m hurdles in 52.3 s. Elaine takes 2.8 s more than Pamela to make the same run. How long does it take Elaine to run the 300-m hurdles?

2-6

Solving Equations by Multiplying or Dividing

IL Assessment Framework

8.8.12 Solve linear equations and inequalities in one variable over the rational numbers.

8.8.13 Solve word problems involving unknown quantities.

 Check Skills You'll Need

Simplify each quotient.

1. $\frac{18}{18}$ 2. $\frac{-7}{7}$

3. $\frac{21}{-21}$ 4. $\frac{-13}{-13}$

GO for Help
Lesson 1-9

---

1 Using Division to Solve Equations

Division and multiplication are inverse operations. You can solve an equation that involves multiplication by using the Division Property of Equality.

Key Concepts **Division Property of Equality**

If you divide each side of an equation by the same nonzero number, the two sides remain equal.

Arithmetic	Algebra
$6 = 3(2)$	If $a = b$ and $c \neq 0$,
$\frac{6}{3} = \frac{3(2)}{3}$	then $\frac{a}{c} = \frac{b}{c}$.

---

1 EXAMPLE   **Real-World** **Problem Solving**

Statistics The United States population in 1998 was twice the population in 1943. Find the 1943 population in millions.

Words

1998 population	was	twice	1943 population

Let p = population in 1943.

Equation   270   =   2 · p

$270 = 2p$

$\frac{270}{2} = \frac{2p}{2}$ **Divide each side by 2.**

$135 = p$ **Simplify.**

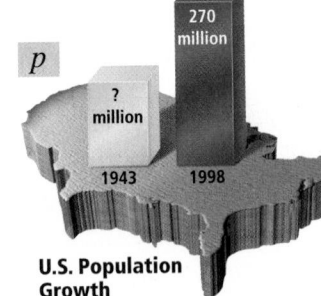

U.S. Population Growth

The United States population in 1943 was 135 million people.

Check Is the answer reasonable? Twice the 1943 population should be the 1998 population. Since $135 \cdot 2 = 270$, the answer is reasonable.

 Quick Check

1. Solve each equation.

a. $4x = 84$ b. $91 = 7y$ c. $12w = 108$

2 EXAMPLE   Dividing to Solve an Equation

Solve $5r = -20$.

$$5r = -20$$

$$\frac{5r}{5} = \frac{-20}{5}$$ Divide each side by 5.

$$r = -4$$ Simplify.

Check $5r = -20$

$5 \cdot (-4) \stackrel{?}{=} -20$ Replace r with −4.

$-20 = -20$ ✔

Video Tutor Help
Visit: PHSchool.com
Web Code: ada-0775

✅ Quick Check

2. Solve each equation.

   a. $-3b = 24$ **b.** $96 = -8n$ **c.** $-4d = -56$

---

2 Using Multiplication to Solve Equations

When you multiply each side of an equation by the same number, the two sides remain equal.

Key Concepts	Multiplication Property of Equality

You can multiply each side of an equation by the same number.

Arithmetic	Algebra
$12 = 3(4)$	If $a = b$,
$12 \cdot 2 = 3(4) \cdot 2$	then $ac = bc$.

---

3 EXAMPLE   Multiplying to Solve an Equation

Solve $\frac{x}{-9} = -3$.

$$\frac{x}{-9} = -3$$

$$-9\left(\frac{x}{-9}\right) = -9(-3)$$ Multiply each side by −9.

$$x = 27$$ Simplify.

✅ Quick Check

3. Solve each equation.

   a. $\frac{r}{-5} = 10$ **b.** $\frac{s}{6} = 54$ **c.** $-30 = \frac{t}{20}$

EXERCISES

For more exercises, see *Extra Skill and Word Problem Practice*.

Practice and Problem Solving

A Practice by Example

Examples 1 and 2
(pages 94 and 95)

GO for Help

Solve each equation.

1. $6x = 96$ **2.** $108 = 9x$ **3.** $8y = 112$

4. $45 = 9a$ **5.** $5w = 95$ **6.** $15c = 90$

7. $125 = 25d$ **8.** $180 = 45s$ **9.** $20b = 2,000$

10. $8x = -48$ **11.** $4a = 28$ **12.** $-60 = 12m$

13. $-2b = 30$ **14.** $-10d = 100$ **15.** $162 = -18t$

16. $-75 = -15x$ **17.** $-5x = -115$ **18.** $-60y = -360$

19. Earnings Carol earns $8/h. How many hours must she work to earn $288?

20. Savings Raul saves $15 each month. At this rate, how many months will he take to save $135?

Example 3
(page 95)

Solve each equation.

21. $6 = \frac{a}{7}$ **22.** $\frac{w}{12} = 2$ **23.** $\frac{n}{15} = 7$ **24.** $\frac{b}{-6} = 20$

25. $-2 = \frac{d}{8}$ **26.** $\frac{v}{3} = -4$ **27.** $-\frac{m}{20} = -2$ **28.** $\frac{r}{-5} = -4$

B Apply Your Skills

Solve each equation.

29. $39 = c \cdot 3$ **30.** $25x = -125$ **31.** $\frac{v}{3} = 14$ **32.** $\frac{m}{-4} = 13$

33. $-50 = \frac{n}{-6}$ **34.** $72 = 8n$ **35.** $22p = 110$ **36.** $\frac{r}{-9} = -18$

37. Reasoning You can divide each side of an equation by the same nonzero value. Explain what would result from the equation $4 \cdot 0 = 5 \cdot 0$ if you could divide each side by zero, and if $\frac{0}{0} = 1$.

Mental Math Is -3 a solution of each equation? Explain.

38. $\frac{b}{-3} = 1$ **39.** $\frac{-18}{k} = -6$ **40.** $3t = 9$

Write an equation for each sentence. Solve the equation.

41. The product of negative twenty and y is one hundred.

42. The value n divided by ten is one hundred.

43. Seven multiplied by k is negative one hundred sixty-eight.

GO **Online**
Homework Video Tutor
Visit: PHSchool.com
Web Code: ade-0206

44. Multiple Choice One of the world's tallest office buildings is in Malaysia. The building has 88 stories. The height of the 88 stories is 1,232 ft. What is the height of one story?

Ⓐ 9 ft high   Ⓑ 11 ft high   Ⓒ 14 ft high   Ⓓ 88 ft high

U.S. School Enrollment

Grades	Millions of Students
Kindergarten	■
1–8	30
9–12	14

SOURCE: U.S. Department of Education.
Go to **www.PHSchool. com** for a
data update. Web Code: adg-9041

45. Use the table at the left. The number of students in grades 9–12 is 4.7 times the number of students in kindergarten. Write and solve an equation to find the number of students s in kindergarten. Round to the nearest million.

46. **Writing in Math** How are the procedures to solve $3x = 9$ and $x + 3 = 9$ alike? How are they different?

47. Open-Ended Write a question that can be solved using the equation $5x = 45$.

Mental Math Solve each equation.

48. $75m = -7{,}500$ **49.** $\frac{v}{-50} = 300$ **50.** $3{,}823 = \frac{s}{100}$

 Challenge

For what values of x is each equation true?

51. $|x| = 7$ **52.** $-3|x| = -9$ **53.** $\frac{|x|}{3} = 2$

54. $x - a = b$ **55.** $a + x = b$ **56.** $ax = b$

ISAT

Test Prep

Multiple Choice

In Exercises 57–60, which equation matches the given sentence?

57. Negative six multiplied by q equals one hundred eight.
  A. $-6 + q = 108$ **B.** $-6q = 108$
  C. $108q = -6$ **D.** $q = -6 + 108$

58. Thirteen equals the quotient of x divided by three.
  F. $13 = \frac{x}{3}$ **G.** $\frac{x}{13}$ **H.** $13 = 3x$ **J.** $\frac{13}{3} = x$

59. Forty-two is the product of some number and 6.
  A. $6(42) = x$ **B.** $\frac{6}{x} = 42$ **C.** $\frac{x}{42} = 6$ **D.** $42 = 6x$

60. Some number divided by eight equals four.
  F. $\frac{8}{x} = 4$ **G.** $\frac{8}{4} = x$ **H.** $\frac{x}{8} = 4$ **J.** $\frac{4}{8} = x$

Mixed Review

 GO for Help

Lesson 2-5 **Solve each equation.**

61. $-4 = a + 7$ **62.** $n - 5 = 12$ **63.** $t - (-4) = -15$ **64.** $y + 10 = 12$

Lesson 1-5 🌐 **65. Hiking** Suppose you start hiking from a point 92 ft below sea level and break for lunch on a hilltop that is 1,673 ft above sea level. What is your change in elevation?

Lesson 1-1 **Write a variable expression for each phrase.**

66. three less than a **67.** 7 times a number n

Guess, Check, Revise

What You'll Learn

- To solve a problem using the Guess, Check, Revise strategy

. . . And Why

To solve real-world problems involving money

 Check Skills You'll Need

Simplify.

1. $158 + 20$

2. $158 + 30$

3. $158 + 25$

4. $158 + 22$

5. In Exercises 1–4, which result came closest to 181?

GO for Help
Lesson 1-5

Math Strategies in Action Did you know that meteorologists use weather balloons to collect data? They use the temperature, humidity, and other data in mathematical models to bring you the daily weather forecast. As more data become available—from weather balloons and satellites, for example—the models, and therefore the weather reports, become more accurate.

Similarly, in math problems, you can make an initial conjecture. You can test your conjecture. If it is not the right answer, you can use what you learn from your first conjecture to make a better, second conjecture.

Real-World Connection

Each day, weather balloons make more than 1,000 measurements of conditions in the upper atmosphere around the world.

1 EXAMPLE Real-World Problem Solving

Ticket Sales The theater club at school put on a play. For one performance, the club sold 133 tickets and raised $471. Tickets cost $4 for adults and $3 for students. How many student tickets and how many adult tickets did the club sell?

Understand the Problem

Look at the given information to make an informed conjecture.

1. How much does each type of ticket cost?

2. How many tickets did the club sell for the performance?

3. How much money did the club raise from ticket sales for this performance?

Make a Plan

Make a conjecture, and then test it. Use what you learn from your conjecture to make a better, second conjecture.

4. When you make a conjecture for how many adult tickets were sold, how can you use your conjecture to find how many student tickets could have been sold?

5. By what number do you multiply your conjecture of adult tickets sold to find how much money was made on adult tickets?

Carry Out the Plan

You can organize conjectures in a table. As a first conjecture, try making about half the tickets adult tickets.

Adult Tickets	Student Tickets	Total Money (in dollars)	
60	$133 - 60 = 73$	$60(4) + 73(3) = 240 + 219$ $= 459$	The total is too low. Increase the number of adult tickets.
80	$133 - 80 = 53$	$80(4) + 53(3) = 320 + 159$ $= 479$	The total is too high. Decrease the number of adult tickets.
70	$133 - 70 = 63$	$70(4) + 63(3) = 280 + 189$ $= 469$	The total is very close. Increase the number of adult tickets.
72	$133 - 72 = 61$	$72(4) + 61(3) = 288 + 183$ $= 471$	The total is correct.

There were 72 adult tickets and 61 student tickets sold.

Check the Answer

To check the answer for reasonableness, solve the problem another way. Consider using logical reasoning.

- The less expensive ticket is $3. So the theater club would get $133 \cdot \$3 = \$399$ if all the tickets sold were student tickets.
- $\$471 - \$399 = \$72$. The theater club actually raised $72 more than if they had sold only student tickets.
- Since adult tickets are $1 more than student tickets, there must have been 72 adult tickets sold.
- $133 - 72 = 61$. There were 61 student tickets sold.
- Since $72 \cdot 4 + 61 \cdot 3 = 471$, the solution 72 adult tickets and 61 student tickets is correct.

✓ Quick Check

6. Suppose the club sold the same number of tickets, but raised $452. How many tickets of each type did the theater club sell?

EXERCISES

For more exercises, see *Extra Skill and Word Problem Practice*.

Practice and Problem Solving

A Practice by Example

Example 1
(page 98)

Use the *Guess, Check, Revise* strategy to solve each problem.

1. **Coin Collections** Bonnie has 16 coins in her pocket worth $1.50. What are two different combinations of coins she could have in her pocket?

2. **Currency** A cashier's drawer has some $5 bills, some $10 bills, and some $20 bills. There are 15 bills worth a total of $185. How many $5 bills, $10 bills, and $20 bills are there?

3. The Smiths have two children. The sum of their ages is 23. The product of their ages is 132. How old are the children?

4. The sum of Mr. and Mrs. Bergen's ages is 100. The difference between their ages is 10. How old are Mr. and Mrs. Bergen?

B Apply Your Skills

Solve using any strategy.

Strategies

- Act It Out
- Draw a Diagram
- Guess, Check, Revise
- Look for a Pattern
- Make a Model
- Make a Table
- Simulate the Problem
- Solve by Graphing
- Use Multiple Strategies
- Work a Simpler Problem
- Work Backward
- Write an Equation
- Write a Proportion

5. **Geometry** A rectangular vegetable garden has a length of 5 ft and a width of 8 ft. The length is increased by 2 ft. By how many square feet does the area increase?

6. Trains leave New York for Boston every 40 min. The first train leaves at 5:20 A.M. What departure time is closest to 12:55 P.M.?

7. Lovell is 16 years old. Lovell's age is the same as Rafi's age divided by three. How old is Rafi?

8. **Number Theory** A number multiplied by itself and then by itself again gives $-1,000$. What is the number?

9. **Coin Collections** In a group of quarters and nickels, there are four more nickels than quarters. How many nickels and quarters are there if the coins are worth $2.30?

10. The sum of the page numbers on two facing pages is 245. The product of the numbers is 15,006. What are the page numbers?

11. **Shopping** A student bought some compact discs for $12 each and some books for $5 each. She spent $39 in all on five items. How many of each item did she buy?

12. **Relay Races** Two runners ran as a team in a 5,000-m relay race. The first runner ran 500 m farther than the second runner. How many meters did each run?

C Challenge

13. **Savings** Ron puts three pennies in a jar. His father offers to triple the total amount of money in Ron's jar at the end of each day. How much is in the jar at the end of one week?

14. **Biology** A certain bacteria doubles the number of its cells every 20 min. A scientist puts 50 cells in a culture dish. How many cells will be in the culture dish after 2 h?

GO Online
Homework Video Tutor
Visit: PHSchool.com
Web Code: ade-0207

100 Chapter 2 Solving One-Step Equations and Inequalities

Multiple Choice

15. A photograph is 6 in. × 4 in. If you make a copy of the photograph with double the length and width, what is the area of the copy?
  A. 96 in.²   **B.** 48 in.²   **C.** 24 in.²   **D.** 20 in.²

16. Cara's age is 4 times Laura's age. If Cara is 16, how old is Laura?
  F. 4 years   **G.** 12 years   **H.** 20 years   **J.** 64 years

17. On a recent test, the lowest score was one fourth the highest score. If the lowest score was 25, how much higher was the highest score?
  A. 4   **B.** 25   **C.** 75   **D.** 100

Mixed Review

GO for Help

Lesson 2-6

(Algebra) **Solve each equation.**

18. $\frac{m}{4} = 52$ **19.** $3x = -18$ **20.** $63 = \frac{t}{-3}$ **21.** $-32 = -16y$

Lessons 2-1 and 2-2

Identify each property shown.

22. $8 + (6 + 17) = (8 + 6) + 17$ **23.** $1{,}879 \cdot 1 = 1{,}879$

24. $8(5 - 3) = 8(5) - 8(3)$ **25.** $-1 + 7 - 3 = -1 - 3 + 7$

Lesson 1-9 **26. Weather** The sound of thunder travels about one mile in five seconds. Suppose a bolt of lightning strikes 3 mi away. How long does it take for the sound of the thunder to reach you?

Math at Work

Nurse

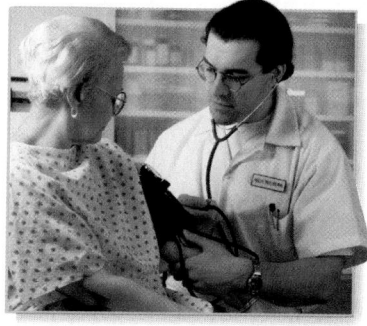

Anyone who has been in a hospital knows that nurses are patients' principal caregivers. Nurses dispense medication, monitor patients' progress, and tend to patients' daily medical needs.

Mathematics is important in a nurse's duties. Nurses compare a patient's blood pressure reading against established norms and make a conclusion about the result. They also solve math problems when they convert one unit of measure of medication to another, and then calculate the total amount of various medications needed for a patient in their care.

Go **O**nline
PHSchool.com   **For:** Information about nurses
                Web Code: adb-2031

Sometimes a graph will help you analyze data. You can use a spreadsheet program to create different types of graphs. First, enter the data in a spreadsheet. Then use a graphing tool to draw an appropriate graph.

1 EXAMPLE

The spreadsheet gives the voting-age populations in thousands for two states. Graph the data in the spreadsheet.

	A	B	C
1	Year	Arizona	Georgia
2	1992	2,812	5,006
3	1994	2,923	5,159
4	1996	3,245	5,420
5	1998	3,405	5,620
6	2000	3,764	6,017

Row 3 contains voting-age populations of both states in 1994.

Cell B3 contains the voting-age population of Arizona in 1994.

Column B contains the voting-age population of Arizona.

Choose an appropriate type of graph from your spreadsheet program. Line graphs are often useful to display changes in data over a period of time. Since the data show changes over time for two states, use a double line graph.

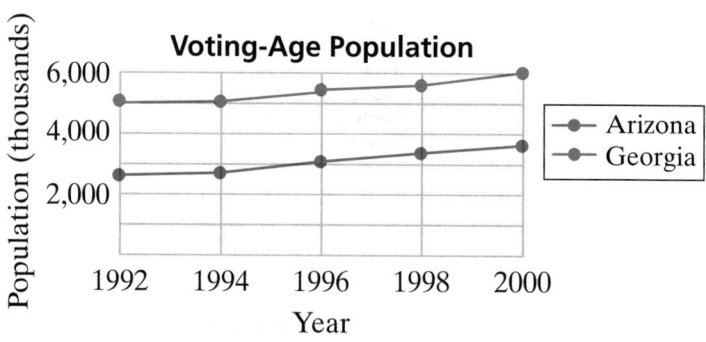

1. Use a spreadsheet to graph the data below.

Average Prices Farmers Received

Year	1996	1997	1998	1999	2000	2001	2002	2003
Price for Turkey (¢/lb)	43.3	39.9	38.0	40.8	40.6	39.0	36.5	36.0
Price for Chicken (¢/lb)	38.1	37.7	39.3	37.1	33.6	39.3	30.5	34.6

SOURCE: U.S. Department of Agriculture.
Go to **www.PHSchool.com** for a data update.
Web Code: adg-9041

EXAMPLE

The spreadsheet gives population data (in thousands) for five states. Graph the data in the spreadsheet.

	A	B	C
1		Age 25 to 34	Age 75 to 84
2	California	5,297	1,357
3	Florida	2,112	1,068
4	Illinois	1,805	544
5	New York	2,671	896
6	Texas	3,284	741

Bar graphs are often useful in comparing amounts. Since the data in the spreadsheet show populations for two age ranges, use a double bar graph.

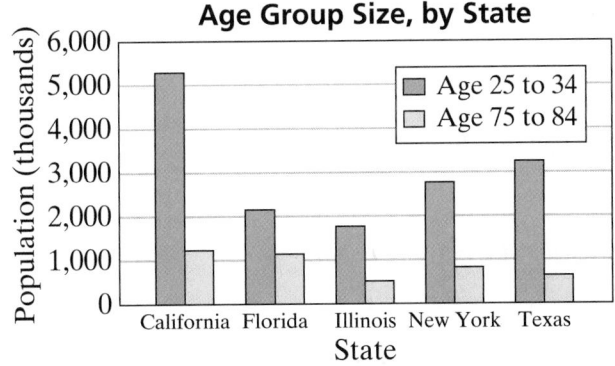

2. a. Use a spreadsheet to make a double bar graph of the postage rate data below.

Postage Rates

Sent From the United States to	First Class 1-oz Letter (¢)	Postcard (¢)
United States	39	24
Canada	60	50
Mexico	60	50
All other countries	80	70

SOURCE: U.S. Postal Service. Go to **www.PHSchool.com** for a data update. Web Code: adg-9041

b. Data Analysis Use the graph you made in part (a). Which bar is tallest? Explain.

3. Writing in Math Explain when you would use a line graph and when you would use a bar graph to display a data set.

2-8 Inequalities and Their Graphs

IL Assessment Framework

8.8.10 Identify, graph, and interpret up to two inequalities with a single variable on a number line.

8.8.11 Represent and analyze problems with linear equations and inequalities.

✓ **Check Skills You'll Need**

Graph each set of numbers on a number line. Order the numbers from least to greatest.

1. $-3, 7, -9$

2. $-2, -10, -8$

3. $0, 3, -5$

4. $3, -6, 10$

GO **for Help**

Lesson 1-4

1 | Graphing Inequalities

An **inequality** is a mathematical sentence that contains $>$, $<$, $\geq$, $\leq$, or $\neq$. Some inequalities contain a variable. Any number that makes an inequality true is a **solution of the inequality.** For example, -4 is a solution of $y \geq -5$ because $-4 \geq -5$.

You can graph the solutions of an inequality on a number line.

1 EXAMPLE **Graphing Solutions of Inequalities**

Graph the solutions of each inequality on a number line.

a. $y < 3$

An open dot shows that 3 is *not* a solution.

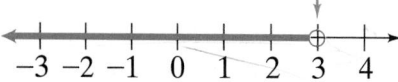

Shade all the points to the left of 3.

b. $x > -1$

An open dot shows that -1 is *not* a solution.

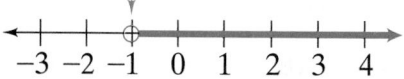

Shade all the points to the right of -1.

c. $a \leq -2$

A closed dot shows that -2 *is* a solution.

Shade all the points to the left of -2.

d. $-6 \leq g$

A closed dot shows that -6 *is* a solution.

Shade all the points to the right of -6.

✓ **Quick Check**

1. Graph the solutions of each inequality.
   a. $z < -2$ **b.** $4 > t$ **c.** $a \geq -5$ **d.** $2 \geq c$

2 Writing Inequalities

You can write an inequality for a graph.

2 EXAMPLE **Writing Inequalities to Describe Graphs**

Write the inequality shown in each graph.

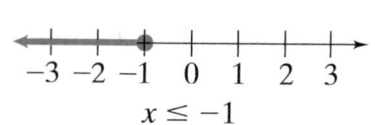

a.

$$-3 \ -2 \ -1 \ \ 0 \ \ 1 \ \ 2 \ \ 3$$
$$x > 0$$

b.

$$-3 \ -2 \ -1 \ \ 0 \ \ 1 \ \ 2 \ \ 3$$
$$x \leq -1$$

> **Vocabulary Tip**
>
> Read > as "is greater than."
>
> Read < as "is less than."
>
> Read ≥ as "is greater than or equal to."
>
> Read ≤ as "is less than or equal to."

✓ Quick Check

2. Write an inequality for the graph below.

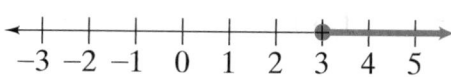

$$-3 \ -2 \ -1 \ \ 0 \ \ 1 \ \ 2 \ \ 3 \ \ 4 \ \ 5$$

You can write an inequality to describe a real-world situation. Keep in mind that *at most* means "no more than," and hence, "less than or equal to." *At least* means "no less than," and hence, "greater than or equal to."

3 EXAMPLE **Real-World 🌐 Problem Solving**

Nutrition Food can be labeled *low sodium* only if it meets the requirement established by the federal government. Use the table to write an inequality for this requirement.

Label	Definition
Sodium-free food	Less than 5 mg per serving
Very low sodium food	At most 35 mg per serving
Low-sodium food	At most 140 mg per serving

Words

| a serving of low-sodium food | has at most | 140 mg sodium |

Let s = number of milligrams of sodium in a serving of low-sodium food.

Inequality

$$s \qquad \leq \qquad 140$$

✓ Quick Check

3. Use the table in Example 3. A certain food is labeled *sodium free*. Write an inequality for n, the number of milligrams of sodium in a serving of this sodium-free food.

EXERCISES

For more exercises, see *Extra Skill and Word Problem Practice*.

Practice and Problem Solving

A Practice by Example

Example 1
(page 104)

GO for **Help**

Graph the solutions of each inequality on a number line.

1. $x < 7$ **2.** $y > 2$ **3.** $a < 3$ **4.** $c < 1$

5. $-3 < z$ **6.** $x > 1$ **7.** $m \leq -4$ **8.** $b \geq 6$

9. $4 \leq p$ **10.** $a \geq -2$ **11.** $j \geq -1$ **12.** $-5 < w$

Example 2
(page 105)

Write an inequality for each graph.

13. ◄—+——●——+——+——+——+——+——►
−3 −2 −1   0   1   2   3

14. ◄—+——+——+——●——+——+——►
−1   0   1   2   3   4

15. ◄——+——+——+——○——+——+——►
−3 −2 −1   0   1   2

16. ◄—+——○——+——+——+——+——►
−5 −4 −3 −2 −1   0

Example 3
(page 105)

Write an inequality for each situation. Use the variable given.

17. Let t be truck weight in tons.   **18.** Let s be speed in mi/h.

B Apply Your Skills

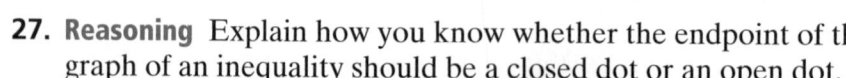

Write an inequality for each sentence. Graph the solutions of each inequality on a number line.

19. x is less than 5.   **20.** y is greater than -3.

21. A number c is at least 12.   **22.** r is not greater than five.

23. The total t is greater than 7.   **24.** p is not more than 30.

25. b is less than or equal to 8.   **26.** A number n is positive.

27. Reasoning Explain how you know whether the endpoint of the graph of an inequality should be a closed dot or an open dot.

28. The sign at the amusement park (left) tells you how tall you must be to ride. Write an inequality for this situation. Let h be height in feet.

Write an inequality for each graph.

Real-World 🌐 **Connection**

Amusement parks make rules for safety.

29.

30.

31.

32.

106 Chapter 2   Solving One-Step Equations and Inequalities

33. Reasoning Explain why graphing the solutions of an inequality is more efficient than listing all the solutions of the inequality.

34. Writing in Math Describe a situation that you could represent with an inequality. Then write the inequality.

35. Movie Tickets Write an inequality to describe this situation. A student pays for three movie tickets with a twenty-dollar bill and gets change back. Let t be the cost of a movie ticket.

36. Nutrition High-fiber foods have at least 5 g of fiber per serving. Write an inequality to represent this situation. Let f be the number of grams of fiber per serving of high-fiber food.

C Challenge

37. Compare. Use $>$ or $<$ to complete each statement.
 a. If $a < b$, then b ▇ a.
 b. If $x > y$ and $y > z$, then x ▇ z.

38. Number Sense No more than 50 students walked in a walkathon. Let s be the number of students. Determine which numbers are reasonable values for s: $40, 45\frac{1}{2}, 50$, and 55.

ISAT

Test Prep

Multiple Choice

39. Which inequality best represents the following sentence?
A number t is greater than or equal to -8.
 A. $-8 \le t$ **B.** $t > -8$ **C.** $t \le -8$ **D.** $-8 \ge t$

40. Which graph matches the inequality $x < -4$?
 F.
$$-5\ -4\ -3\ -2\ -1\ \ 0$$
 G.
$$-5\ -4\ -3\ -2\ -1\ \ 0$$
 H.
$$-5\ -4\ -3\ -2\ -1\ \ 0$$
 J.
$$-5\ -4\ -3\ -2\ -1\ \ 0$$

41. A game-board designer has to design a board that is at least 5 feet wide. Let w be the width of the board. Which inequality describes this situation?
 A. $w < 5$ **B.** $w > 5$ **C.** $w \le 5$ **D.** $w \ge 5$

Mixed Review

Lessons 2-5 and 2-6

GO for Help

Lesson 2-3

Lesson 1-1

Solve each equation.

42. $x - 5 = 29$ **43.** $7y = 35$ **44.** $t \div 12 = 6$

Simplify each expression.

45. $6 - 5s + 4s + 3$ **46.** $n + (n + 2) + (n + 4)$

47. Write a variable expression for the number of weeks in y years.

2-9 Solving One-Step Inequalities by Adding or Subtracting

 Assessment Framework

8.8.12 Solve linear equations and inequalities in one variable over the rational numbers.

8.8.13 Solve word problems involving unknown quantities.

✓ **Check Skills You'll Need**

Solve each equation.

1. $m + 7 = 5$

2. $k - 8 = 11$

3. $12 + h = 21$

4. $6 = n - 23$

 for Help
Lesson 2-5

---

1 Solving Inequalities by Subtracting

Solving an inequality is similar to solving an equation. You want to get the variable alone on one side of the inequality.

You can see from the number line that if you subtract 2 from each side of the inequality $-1 < 2$, the resulting inequality $-3 < 0$ is still true.

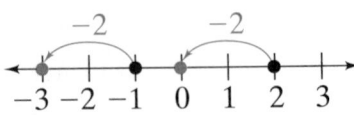

Key Concepts **Subtraction Property of Inequality**

You can subtract the same number from each side of an inequality.

Arithmetic	Algebra
$7 > 4$, so $7 - 3 > 4 - 3$	If $a > b$, then $a - c > b - c$.
$6 < 9$, so $6 - 2 < 9 - 2$	If $a < b$, then $a - c < b - c$.

---

1 EXAMPLE **Subtracting to Solve an Inequality**

Solve each inequality. Graph the solutions.

a. $n + 8 \geq 19$

$$n + 8 \geq 19$$
$$n + 8 - 8 \geq 19 - 8 \quad \text{Subtract 8 from each side.}$$
$$n \geq 11 \qquad\qquad \text{Simplify.}$$

b. $-26 > y + 14$

$$-26 > y + 14$$
$$-26 - 14 > y + 14 - 14 \quad \text{Subtract 14 from each side.}$$
$$-40 > y \text{ or } y < -40 \quad \text{Simplify.}$$

✓ **Quick Check**

1. Solve each inequality. Graph the solutions.

    a. $m + 3 > 6$ **b.** $8 + t < 15$ **c.** $-3 \leq x + 7$

2 EXAMPLE <u>Real-World</u> **Problem Solving**

Computers Nearly 768 megabytes (MB) of memory are available for running your computer. If its basic systems require 512 MB, how much memory is available for other programs?

Words | memory for basic systems | plus | memory for other programs | is less than | total memory |

Let m = memory available for other programs.

Inequality   512   + m <   768

$$512 + m < 768$$
$$512 - 512 + m < 768 - 512 \quad \textbf{Subtract 512 from each side.}$$
$$m < 256 \quad \textbf{Simplify.}$$

Less than 256 MB of memory is available for other programs.

Real-World Connection

You can increase the memory of a computer by adding more memory chips. These chips have extra memory in multiples of 128 megabytes.

✓ Quick Check

2. An airline lets you check up to 65 lb of luggage. One suitcase weighs 37 lb. How much can another suitcase weigh?

---

2 Using Addition to Solve Inequalities

To solve an inequality involving subtraction, use addition.

Key Concepts **Addition Property of Inequality**

You can add the same number to each side of an inequality.

Arithmetic	Algebra
$7 > 3$, so $7 + 4 > 3 + 4$	If $a > b$, then $a + c > b + c$.
$2 < 5$, so $2 + 6 < 5 + 6$	If $a < b$, then $a + c < b + c$.

3 EXAMPLE **Adding to Solve an Inequality**

Solve $n - 15 < 3$.

$$n - 15 < 3$$
$$n - 15 + 15 < 3 + 15 \quad \textbf{Add 15 to each side.}$$
$$n < 18 \quad \textbf{Simplify.}$$

✓ Quick Check

3. Solve each inequality.
   a. $m - 13 > 29$ b. $v - 4 \leq 7$ c. $t - 5 \geq 11$

Online active math

For: Inequalities Activity
Use: Interactive Textbook, 2-9

EXERCISES

For more exercises, see *Extra Skill and Word Problem Practice*.

Practice and Problem Solving

A Practice by Example

Solve each inequality. Graph the solutions.

Example 1
(page 108)

1. $w + 5 < 12$ 2. $2 > 9 + a$ 3. $x + 6 \geq 7$ 4. $2 + m \leq 2$

5. $18 \leq 20 + w$ 6. $-7 < 5 + x$ 7. $30 \geq t + 45$ 8. $p + 22 \geq -10$

Example 2
(page 109)

9. **Transportation** The total weight limit for a truck is 100,000 lb. The truck weighs 36,000 lb empty. What is the most that the truck's load can weigh?

10. **Budgeting** You are saving to buy a bicycle that will cost at least $120. Your parents give you $45 toward the bicycle. How much money will you have to save?

Example 3
(page 109)

Solve each inequality.

11. $x - 5 \geq 6$ 12. $n - 12 \leq 3$ 13. $r - 4 \leq 3$

14. $x - 7 < 15$ 15. $c - 9 > 5$ 16. $h - 10 \geq 6$

17. $w - 8 < 3$ 18. $12 \geq y - 5$ 19. $4 \geq y - 4$

B Apply Your Skills

What do you do to the first inequality to get the second inequality?

20. $x + 8 \leq 11; x \leq 3$ 21. $x - 3 > 9; x > 12$

Solve each inequality. Graph the solutions.

22. $x - 8 > -2$ 23. $6 < y + 19$ 24. $3 \leq y - 5$

25. $-8 \geq k - 3$ 26. $-3 + y > 4$ 27. $a - 0.5 < 2.5$

28. $7 + r > 11$ 29. $9 < b + 4$ 30. $u - 3 \geq 9$

Homework Video Tutor
Visit: PHSchool.com
Web Code: ade-0209

Write an inequality for each sentence. Then solve the inequality.

31. Thirteen plus a number n is greater than fifteen.

32. The sum of a number w and 3 is less than or equal to ten.

33. **Shopping** Jim has $87. He spends $6 for socks and at least $32 for shoes. How much does he have left to spend for shirts?

34. A store's dressing room has a limit of 10 garments per customer. If Carol has at least 3 garments below the limit, how many garments does she have in her dressing room?

C Challenge

Reasoning Justify each step.

35. $4 + a + 3 > 16$
$4 + 3 + a > 16$
$7 + a > 16$
$7 - 7 + a > 16 - 7$
$a > 9$

36. $m - 2(8 - 5) \leq -9$
$m - 2(3) \leq -9$
$m - 6 \leq -9$
$m - 6 + 6 \leq -9 + 6$
$m \leq -3$

37. Writing in Math Which of the inequalities $m > -2, m < -2,$ $-2 < m,$ and $-2 > m$ are solutions to $m + 4 > 2$? Explain.

ISAT

Multiple Choice

38. If x and y are positive, and $x > y$, which is true?

A. $x > \dfrac{x + y}{2}$ B. $y > \dfrac{x + y}{2}$ C. $x = \dfrac{x + y}{2}$ D. $x < \dfrac{x + y}{2}$

For Exercises 39 and 40, use the table at the left. Assume that your computer's basic systems use at least 12 MB of memory.

Computer Memory

Application	Memory Requirement
Word processor	11 MB
Spreadsheet	5 MB
Web browser	9 MB
E-mail	4 MB

39. You want to have your e-mail active while you work on a paper with your word processor. How much memory must your computer have?

   F. at most 13 MB   **G.** at least 14 MB

   H. at least 27 MB   **J.** at most 32 MB

40. If you search the Web for data at the same time that you have your e-mail active, how much memory must your computer have?

   A. at most 41 MB   **B.** at least 25 MB

   C. at most 20 MB   **D.** at least 15 MB

Mixed Review

Lesson 2-8

Graph the solutions of each inequality.

41. $x < 2$ **42.** $x \geq -5$ **43.** $y \leq 4$ **44.** $m > 0$

Lesson 2-3

Simplify each expression.

45. $4x + 6 - 2x + 6$ **46.** $-4 - 5t + t - 10$

Lesson 1-4   **47.** Write an integer to represent a debt of $35.

✓ Checkpoint Quiz 2   Lessons 2-4 through 2-9

State whether the equation is *true, false,* or an *open sentence.* Explain.

   1. $4 + 15 = 27 - 8$ **2.** $-30 = 9w$ **3.** $|9 - 10| = 8 - 9$

Solve each equation or inequality.

   4. $y - 3 = -7$ **5.** $x + 4 = 8$ **6.** $7t = 42$ **7.** $m \div 8 = -4$

   8. $-90 = 10f$ **9.** $9 \leq 3 + a$ **10.** $r - 12 < 7$ **11.** $m + 15 > -4$

   12. You have some quarters, dimes, and pennies—eight coins worth $.77 altogether. How many of each type of coin do you have?

Solving One-Step Inequalities by Multiplying or Dividing

 Assessment Framework

8.8.12 Solve linear equations and inequalities in one variable over the rational numbers.

8.8.13 Solve word problems involving unknown quantities.

 Check Skills You'll Need

Solve each equation.

1. $6x = 24$

2. $63 = -7v$

3. $\frac{x}{-2} = 10$

4. $\frac{t}{6} = 48$

GO for Help
Lesson 2-6

1 Solving Inequalities Using Division

Activity

Solving Inequalities

Explore what happens when you divide each side of an inequality by a number.

1. Simplify each expression at the right. Replace each ■ with $>$ or $<$.

2. **Patterns** Does the direction of the inequality symbol stay the same as you divide each side of an inequality by the given numbers? Explain your reasoning.

$6 \div 3$ ■ $12 \div 3$
$6 \div 2$ ■ $12 \div 2$
$6 \div 1$ ■ $12 \div 1$
$6 \div (-1)$ ■ $12 \div (-1)$
$6 \div (-2)$ ■ $12 \div (-2)$
$6 \div (-3)$ ■ $12 \div (-3)$

You can solve an inequality that involves multiplication by dividing each side of the inequality by a nonzero number.

Key Concepts — Division Properties of Inequality

If you divide each side of an inequality by a positive number, you leave the inequality symbol unchanged.

Arithmetic	Algebra
$3 < 6$, so $\frac{3}{3} < \frac{6}{3}$	If $a < b$ and c is positive, then $\frac{a}{c} < \frac{b}{c}$.
$8 > 2$, so $\frac{8}{2} > \frac{2}{2}$	If $a > b$ and c is positive, then $\frac{a}{c} > \frac{b}{c}$.

If you divide each side of an inequality by a negative number, *you reverse the inequality symbol.*

Arithmetic	Algebra
$6 < 12$, so $\frac{6}{-3} > \frac{12}{-3}$	If $a < b$ and c is negative, then $\frac{a}{c} > \frac{b}{c}$.
$16 > 8$, so $\frac{16}{-4} < \frac{8}{-4}$	If $a > b$ and c is negative, then $\frac{a}{c} < \frac{b}{c}$.

Engineering An elevator can carry up to 2,500 lb. Suppose the weight of an average adult is 150 lb. At most how many average-sized adults can safely ride the elevator at the same time?

Words | the number of adults | times | 150 lb | is less than or equal to | 2,500 lb

Let x = the number of adults.

Inequality | x | · | 150 lb | ≤ | 2,500

$$150x \leq 2,500$$

$$\frac{150x}{150} \leq \frac{2,500}{150}$$ **Divide each side by 150.**

$$x \leq 16.\overline{6}$$ **Simplify. Round the answer down to find a whole number of people.**

At most 16 average adults can safely ride the elevator at one time.

Check Is the answer reasonable? The total weight of 16 average adults is 16(150) = 2,400 lb. This is less than 2,500 lb but so close that another adult could not ride. The answer is reasonable.

✓ Quick Check

1. Solve each inequality.

   a. $4x > 40$ **b.** $-21 > 3m$ **c.** $36 > -9t$

STATE INSPECTION CERTIFICATE
Department of Public Safety
Certificate for Use of Elevator

LOCATION: 221 Pat Street
SPEED: 150 ft. per min.
CAPACITY: 2,500 lb.
ISSUED ON: 08/06/03
EXPIRES: 08/06/04

---

2 | **Solving Inequalities Using Multiplication**

You can solve inequalities that involve division.

Key Concepts | **Multiplication Properties of Inequality**

If you multiply each side of an inequality by a positive number, you leave the inequality symbol unchanged.

| **Arithmetic** | **Algebra** |

3 < 4, so 3(5) < 4(5)   If $a < b$ and c is positive, then $ac < bc$.

7 > 2, so 7(6) > 2(6)   If $a > b$ and c is positive, then $ac > bc$.

If you multiply each side of an inequality by a negative number, *you reverse the inequality symbol.*

| **Arithmetic** | **Algebra** |

6 < 9, so 6(−2) > 9(−2)   If $a < b$ and c is negative, then $ac > bc$.

7 > 5, so 7(−3) < 5(−3)   If $a > b$ and c is negative, then $ac < bc$.

Online *active math*

For: Inequalities Activity
Use: Interactive Textbook, 2-10

2 EXAMPLE **Multiplying to Solve an Inequality**

Solve $\frac{t}{-4} \geq 7$.

$$\frac{t}{-4} \geq 7$$

$$-4\left(\frac{t}{-4}\right) \leq -4(7) \qquad \text{Multiply each side by } -4 \text{ and reverse the inequality symbol.}$$

$$t \leq -28 \qquad \text{Simplify.}$$

✓ Quick Check

2. Solve each inequality.

    a. $\frac{m}{4} \geq 2$ **b.** $\frac{t}{-3} < 7$ **c.** $5 < \frac{r}{7}$

More Than One Way

Solve $-3x < 12$.

Roberto's Method

Divide each side by -3 and reverse the inequality symbol.
$$-3x < 12$$
$$\frac{-3x}{-3} > \frac{12}{-3}$$
$$x > -4$$

Michelle's Method

Rewrite the inequality so the coefficient of the variable is positive.

$$-3x < 12$$
$$-3x + 3x < 12 + 3x$$
$$0 < 12 + 3x$$
$$0 - 12 < 3x + 12 - 12$$
$$-12 < 3x$$
$$\frac{-12}{3} < \frac{3x}{3}$$
$$-4 < x, \text{ or } x > -4$$

Choose a Method

1. Which method would you use to solve this inequality? Explain.

2. Solve $18 < -6x$ using Roberto's Method or Michelle's Method.

EXERCISES

For more exercises, see *Extra Skill and Word Problem Practice*.

Practice and Problem Solving

A Practice by Example

Example 1
(page 113)

Solve each inequality.

1. $3t > 21$ **2.** $-2x < 14$ **3.** $8 > -4x$ **4.** $6m > 24$

5. $9x \le 27$ **6.** $18 < -2m$ **7.** $64 \le -8k$ **8.** $7m > 28$

9. $3x < 21$ **10.** $81 > -9y$ **11.** $5f \ge -15$ **12.** $-3x < 0$

13. Earnings Paul earns $9 per hour. How many hours must Paul work to earn at least $645?

Example 2
(page 114)

Solve each inequality.

14. $\frac{x}{-6} > 3$ **15.** $\frac{m}{6} \le -18$ **16.** $\frac{x}{3} \ge 5$ **17.** $\frac{y}{4} > 3$

18. $\frac{r}{-4} > 2$ **19.** $6 > \frac{q}{-3}$ **20.** $20 < \frac{v}{6}$ **21.** $\frac{b}{4} \ge 3$

22. $\frac{v}{-5} < 9$ **23.** $\frac{x}{4} \le 12$ **24.** $\frac{x}{-3} < 0$ **25.** $8 > \frac{h}{10}$

B Apply Your Skills

What happens to the inequality symbol when you do the following to each side of an inequality?

26. subtract a negative number   **27.** multiply by a positive number

28. divide by a negative number   **29.** multiply by a negative number

Solve each inequality.

30. $-4x < -16$ **31.** $-r \ge 21$ **32.** $\frac{1}{2}x \ge -3$ **33.** $\frac{b}{3} \ge -31$

34. $-3 \ge \frac{g}{-7}$ **35.** $3 > \frac{b}{-6}$ **36.** $4x > -8$ **37.** $-6x \le -24$

38. Budgeting Marnie pays $.06 per kilowatt-hour for electricity. She has budgeted $72 for her electricity. What is the greatest number of kilowatt-hours Marnie can use and stay within her budget?

$3x > -12$
$\frac{3x}{3} < \frac{-12}{3}$
$x < -4$

39. Error Analysis Your friend solved $3x > -12$ as shown at the left. What error did your friend make?

40. Multiple Choice Sue worked at least 13 hours last week. She earns $5.75 per hour. What is the least amount she earned?
   Ⓐ $75   Ⓑ $74.75   Ⓒ $65   Ⓓ $7.50

Write an inequality for each sentence. Then solve the inequality.

41. A number t multiplied by seven is less than or equal to 21.

42. A number b divided by 4 is greater than or equal to 3.

43. The quotient of a number v divided by -5 is less than 9.

44. Reasoning The rules for multiplying and dividing both sides of an inequality do not mention zero. Discuss why.

GO Online
Homework Video Tutor
Visit: PHSchool.com
Web Code: ade-0210

45. Writing in Math Explain how solving $-4t < 32$ is different from solving $4t < -32$.

Reasoning Justify each step.

46. $2g \geq -18$
$\dfrac{2g}{2} \geq \dfrac{-18}{2}$
$g \geq -9$

47. $-7m \leq -28$
$\dfrac{-7m}{-7} \geq \dfrac{-28}{-7}$
$m \geq 4$

48. $\dfrac{a}{3} > 12$
$\left(\dfrac{a}{3}\right)(3) > 12(3)$
$a > 36$

49. Open-Ended Write a problem that you would solve using the inequality $5m \leq 15$.

50. Day Care In Georgia, for every 18 four-year-old children in day care there must be at least one teacher. At one day-care center, 56 four-year-olds are signed up for next year. At least how many teachers must the center have to teach four-year-olds next year?

ISAT

Test Prep

Multiple Choice

51. What is done to $\frac{1}{3}x \leq 18$ to get $x \leq 54$?
A. Multiply each side by 3.
B. Divide each side by 3.
C. Multiply each side by $\frac{1}{3}$.
D. Multiply each side by 3x.

52. Which number is a solution of $-2x \leq -4$?
F. -2
G. 0
H. 1
J. 10

53. Which inequality has the same solutions as $\frac{a}{4} < -20$?
A. $4d > 80$
B. $\frac{m}{-4} < -40$
C. $-2r < -40$
D. $\frac{z}{-2} > 40$

54. Which inequality best represents the following sentence?
A number x divided by 7 is greater than -13.
F. $\frac{7}{x} > -13$
G. $\frac{x}{7} > -13$
H. $\frac{7}{x} < -13$
J. $\frac{x}{7} < -13$

Mixed Review

GO for Help

Lesson 2-9

Solve each inequality.

55. $6 + t > 17$
56. $-9 \geq r + 5$
57. $11 > v - 12$

Lessons 2-1 and 2-2

Name each property shown.

58. $-12(100 - 3) = -12(100) - (-12)(3)$

59. $102 + 34 + 98 = 102 + 98 + 34$

60. $(80 + 321) + 109 = 80 + (321 + 109)$

Lesson 1-6 **61. Weather** The high temperature one day in January was 34°F, and the low temperature was 27°F. What was the difference between the high and the low temperatures that day?

High-use academic words are words that you will see often in textbooks and on tests. These words are not math vocabulary terms, but they are important for you to know to be successful in mathematics.

Words to Learn: Direction Words

Some words tell you what to do in a problem. You need to understand what these words are asking so that you give the correct answer.

Word	Meaning
Determine	Find out by investigating or calculating
Explain	Give facts and details to make an idea easy to understand
Identify	Tell the name of or describe the characteristics of something

EXERCISES

Determine whether each statement is *true* or *false*.

1. The owner's manual for a car explains how to drive.

2. The weatherman determines what kind of storm will arrive.

3. This week's supermarket flyer identifies items that are on sale.

Identify each property shown.

4. $7 + a = a + 7$

5. $3(x - 4) = 3x - 12$

Explain how to use zero pairs to solve each equation.

6.

7.

8. a. **Word Knowledge** Think about the word **justify**. Choose the letter for how well you know the word.
   A. I know its meaning.
   B. I have seen it, but I do not know its meaning.
   C. I do not know it.
   b. Look up **justify** in a dictionary or online. Write its definition.
   c. Write a sentence involving mathematics and using the word **justify**.

Test-Taking Strategies

Writing Short Responses

Short-response questions are often worth 2 points. To get full credit you need to give the correct answer and either give a good explanation, justify your thinking, or show your work.

⬤ EXAMPLE

Jenna had a coupon for $15 off the price of a graphing calculator. She used it to buy a calculator for $89 before tax. **(a)** Write an equation to find the original price. **(b)** Solve your equation.

Here is a *scoring rubric* to help assess different types of answers.

Scoring Rubric

[2] The original price of the calculator is correct. The equation and the solution are correct with all work shown.

[1] The original price is correct, but no work is shown, OR the original price is incorrect, but the work shown has minimal errors.

Here are three responses with the points each received.

2 points	1 point	0 points
x is the original price. $$x - 15 = 89$$ $$x - 15 + 15 = 89 + 15$$ $$x = 104$$ The original price was $104.	x is the original price. $$x + 15 = 89$$ $$x + 15 - 15 = 89 - 15$$ $$x = 74$$ The original price was $74.	The original price was $74.

EXERCISES

Use the scoring rubric to explain the score given for each response.

1. the 2-point response   **2.** the 1-point response   **3.** the 0-point response

Write and solve an equation to solve each problem. Then score your answer using the scoring rubric above.

4. Your grandfather gives you a share of stock that is currently worth $62. He tells you that it has increased in value by $17 since he purchased it. How much did he pay for the stock?

5. The height of a multistory building is 135 ft. It has 15 stories. What is the height of each story?

Chapter Review

Vocabulary Review

additive identity (p. 69)
Associative Properties of Addition and Multiplication (p. 68)
coefficient (p. 78)
Commutative Properties of Addition and Multiplication (p. 68)
constant (p. 78)

deductive reasoning (p. 79)
Distributive Property (p. 73)
equation (p. 82)
Identity Properties of Addition and Multiplication (p. 69)
inequality (p. 104)
inverse operations (p. 88)
like terms (p. 78)

multiplicative identity (p. 69)
open sentence (p. 82)
simplify a variable expression (p. 78)
solution of an equation (p. 83)
solution of an inequality (p. 104)
term (p. 78)

For each numbered definition given below, write the letter of the word or phrase being defined.

1. a value that makes an equation true

2. a term that has no variable

3. a number or the product of a number and variable(s)

4. the number that multiplies a variable

5. the number zero

6. terms with identical variables

7. an equation with one or more variables

8. a mathematical sentence with an equal sign

9. the number one

10. a mathematical sentence with $>, <, \geq, \leq,$ or $\neq$

a. coefficient

b. constant

c. additive identity

d. solution of an equation

e. term

f. equation

g. multiplicative identity

h. like terms

i. inequality

j. open sentence

Go Online
PHSchool.com
For: Online vocabulary quiz
Web Code: adj-0251

Skills and Concepts

2-1 Objectives

▼ To identify properties of addition and multiplication (p. 68)

▼ To use properties to solve problems (p. 69)

Use the **Commutative Property** to change order. Use the **Associative Property** to change grouping. Adding zero to an expression does not change its value. Multiplying an expression by 1 does not change its value.

Simplify each expression. Justify each step.

11. $58 + 16 + 2 + 4$ **12.** $4 \cdot 7 \cdot 25 \cdot 1$ **13.** $125 + 347 + 75$

14. $(20 \cdot 65) \cdot 5$ **15.** $10 \cdot 15 \cdot 2$ **16.** $37 + 0 + (5 + 63)$

2-2 Objectives

▼ To use the Distributive Property with numerical expressions (p. 73)

▼ To use the Distributive Property with algebraic expressions (p. 75)

Use the **Distributive Property** to multiply a number outside parentheses by each term of a sum or difference.

Mental Math **Use the Distributive Property to simplify.**

17. $9(96)$ **18.** $8(62)$ **19.** $(43)(9)$

Use the Distributive Property to multiply.

20. $4(w + 9)$ **21.** $(2 + 4a)12$ **22.** $-7(6 - 2m)$

23. Explain why $5x + 15 = 5(x + 3)$.

2-3 Objectives

▼ To identify parts of a variable expression (p. 78)

▼ To simplify expressions (p. 78)

To **simplify** a variable expression, replace it with an equivalent expression with as few terms as possible.

Simplify each expression.

24. $8a + 7 - 11a$ **25.** $3(w + 3) + 4w$

26. $6 + x - 4x + 3$ **27.** $19 - 4(5n + 1) - 4n$

28. $10 + 7k - 2(3k + 5)$ **29.** $-7(2r - 1) + 3(8 - r)$

30. Explain how to determine whether terms are like terms.

2-4 Objectives

▼ To classify types of equations (p. 82)

▼ To check equations using substitution (p. 83)

You can write an **equation** to model a situation. An equation with numerical expressions is true or false. An equation with at least one variable is an **open sentence**. A **solution** of an open-sentence equation is a value of a variable that makes the equation true.

Write an equation for each sentence. Is each equation *true, false,* or an *open sentence*?

31. Thirty-two plus five equals the product of six and six.

32. A number t divided by seventeen equals the opposite of three.

33. The product of four and twenty equals eighty.

34. **Culture** The admission price to an art museum increased by $1.75 to $6.50. Let p be the original admission price. Write an equation to model the situation.

2-5 and 2-6 Objectives

▼ To solve one-step equations using subtraction (p. 88)

▼ To solve one-step equations using addition (p. 90)

▼ To solve one-step equations using division (p. 94)

▼ To solve one-step equations using multiplication (p. 95)

To solve an equation, use an **inverse operation** and the **properties of equality** to get the variable alone on one side of the equation.

Solve each equation.

35. $6 + y = 17$ **36.** $-2 = a - 10$ **37.** $3x = -15$

38. $\frac{m}{9} = 3$ **39.** $\frac{w}{4} = 32$ **40.** $40 = -5b$

2-7 Objectives

▼ To solve a problem using the Guess, Check, Revise strategy (p. 98)

You can solve some problems by trying an answer. Use each incorrect conjecture to make a better conjecture.

41. School Supplies Marcella and Danilo went to a bookstore. Marcella bought 2 notebooks and 3 pens for $14.50. Danilo bought 1 notebook and 2 pens for $7.50. How much does 1 notebook cost?

2-8 Objectives

▼ To graph inequalities (p. 104)

▼ To write inequalities (p. 105)

To graph an **inequality,** use a number line. Use an open dot for $>$ and $<$. Use a closed dot for $\geq$ and $\leq$.

Graph the solutions of each inequality.

42. $m > -13$ **43.** $t \geq -2$ **44.** $0 < r$ **45.** $w \leq 6$

Write an inequality for each sentence.

46. The temperature t is less than zero degrees.

47. The height h is greater than twelve feet.

2-9 and 2-10 Objectives

▼ To solve one-step inequalities using subtraction (p. 108)

▼ To solve one-step inequalities using addition (p. 109)

▼ To solve one-step inequalities using division (p. 112)

▼ To solve one-step inequalities using multiplication (p. 113)

To solve a one-step inequality, use inverse operations and the **properties of inequality** to get the variable alone on one side of the inequality. When multiplying or dividing each side of an inequality by a negative number, *reverse* the direction of the inequality symbol.

Solve each inequality.

48. $n - 4 > 10$ **49.** $-5 \leq k - 7$ **50.** $6s \leq 18$

51. $\frac{m}{3} < -2$ **52.** $-d > 14$ **53.** $\frac{c}{-4} \geq -9$

Chapter Test

Go Online
PHSchool.com
For: Online chapter test
Web Code: ada-0252

Is each equation *true*, *false*, or an *open sentence*? Explain.

1. $24 = 3(-8)$

2. $5x + 28 = 153$

3. $18(-7 \div 7) = (-2)(9)$

4. $-6 + 15 = (120 \div 20) - (5 - 8)$

Simplify. Use the Commutative and the Associative Properties.

5. $50 \cdot 38 \cdot 2$

6. $45 + 62 + 55$

7. $2 \cdot 27 \cdot 5$

8. $99 + (-7) + 101$

9. **Open-Ended** Write a number sentence that illustrates the Associative Property of Addition.

Simplify each expression.

10. $2(x + y) - 2y$

11. $5a + 2b + 3a - 7b$

12. $3(2r - 5) + 8(r + 2)$

13. $(-2c + 3d)(-5) + 3(-2c) - (-8d)$

Solve each equation.

14. $k - 23 = 17$

15. $\frac{t}{-5} = 15$

16. $y \div 12 = -3$

17. $7w = -217$

18. $-9 + a = 11$

19. $n - 2 = 13$

20. $120 = 38 + p$

21. $w \cdot (-2) = 14$

22. $r + 6 = 30$

23. $m - 7 = -3$

24. $9t = 18$

25. $-3f = -42$

26. $5 = \frac{s}{-7}$

27. $\frac{h}{12} = 12$

For Exercises 28 and 29, write and solve an equation.

28. **Fencing** Thirty-six sections of fencing, all the same length, are joined to form a fence 180 m long. How long is each section of fencing?

29. Brian bought a used bike for $25 less than its original price. He paid a total of $88 for the bike. What was the original price of the bike?

30. **Writing in Math** How are the rules for solving inequalities similar to those for solving equations? How are they different?

Write an inequality for each situation. Graph the solutions.

31. The total t is greater than 5.

32. The perimeter p is less than 64.

33. The number of passengers p on the bus is no more than 45.

34. The number of students s that ran in the road race was not less than 55.

35. The number of questions q answered correctly is at most 49.

Solve each inequality.

36. $5 \leq x + 1$

37. $\frac{a}{3} > 4$

38. $y - 6 < 9$

39. $-2n \leq 10$

40. $3b \geq 3$

41. $\frac{p}{-2} < -5$

42. $r + 8 > 12$

43. $j - 7 \leq 24$

44. $h - 5 \geq -16$

45. $8 + b < -3$

46. $3k \leq -27$

47. $\frac{h}{4} > 16$

48. $9 < \frac{a}{6}$

49. $-7z < 21$

Multiple Choice

Choose the best answer.

1. You make $8.00 per hour. Each week you work *n* hours. Which expression describes your weekly pay?
   - Ⓐ $\frac{n}{8}$
   - Ⓑ $8 - n$
   - Ⓒ $n + 8$
   - Ⓓ $8n$

2. Which equation shows the Associative Property of Addition?
   - Ⓔ $9 + 7 + 8 = 9 + 8 + 7$
   - Ⓕ $(8 + 3) + 13 = 8 + (3 + 13)$
   - Ⓖ $12 + (-4) + 0 = 12 + (-4)$
   - Ⓗ $19 \cdot (-3) \cdot 1 = 19 \cdot (-3)$

3. Mara ordered 5 bags of seed for $7 each and 3 wildflower seed kits for $9 each. She also paid a $13 shipping fee. Which expression shows the total cost?
   - Ⓐ $5 + 7 + 3 + 9 + 13$
   - Ⓑ $(5 \cdot 7) + (3 \cdot 9) + 13$
   - Ⓒ $(5 + 3)16 + 13$
   - Ⓓ $(5 \cdot 7 + 13) + (3 \cdot 9 + 13)$

4. What is the solution of $r + 43 = -45$?
   - Ⓔ -88
   - Ⓕ -2
   - Ⓖ 2
   - Ⓗ 88

5. What is the value of $5(n + m)$ for $n = 12$ and $m = 6$?
   - Ⓐ 30
   - Ⓑ 66
   - Ⓒ 90
   - Ⓓ 810

6. Which integer is *not* a solution of $p + 12 < 16$?
   - Ⓔ 4
   - Ⓕ 3
   - Ⓖ -4
   - Ⓗ -28

7. Which numbers are in order from least to greatest?
   - Ⓐ $4, 2, -2, -4$
   - Ⓑ $|-3|, |-4|, -5, 6$
   - Ⓒ $-7, 1, 4, |-12|$
   - Ⓓ $-3, 4, -5, 6, -7$

8. What is the value of $-23 + (-12)$?
   - Ⓔ 35
   - Ⓕ 11
   - Ⓖ -11
   - Ⓗ -35

9. Which symbol makes the statement true?
   $11 - (-4) \blacksquare -6 - 12$
   - Ⓐ $>$
   - Ⓑ $<$
   - Ⓒ $=$
   - Ⓓ $\leq$

10. Which product equals $3t - 12$?
    - Ⓔ $4(t - 3)$
    - Ⓕ $3(t - 4)$
    - Ⓖ $(4 - t)3$
    - Ⓗ $(3 - t)4$

11. Which equation is an open sentence?
    - Ⓐ $8(8 \div 2) = 32$
    - Ⓑ $18 = (2 \cdot 7) + 6$
    - Ⓒ $5x = 3 + 2x$
    - Ⓓ $15 - 1 = 52 \div 4$

12. What is the value of $-(2 \cdot 7) + 6 \cdot 2$?
    - Ⓔ 26
    - Ⓕ -2
    - Ⓖ -16
    - Ⓗ -26

Short Response

Simplify each expression. Show your work.

13. $3c - 4c + 1$

14. $6(t + 7) + t$

15. $-5(n + 9) - n$

16. $8 - 4(s + 2) - s$

Solve each inequality. Show your work.

17. $24 > b + 17$

18. $x - 9 < -14$

19. $\frac{r}{13} \geq 3$

20. $-4s \geq -56$

21. **a.** How are the rules for solving inequalities with addition and subtraction similar to those for solving inequalities with multiplication and division?
    b. In part (a), how are they different?

22. Simplify $25 \cdot 7 \cdot 4$. Explain how you can use the Commutative and Associative Properties to multiply mentally.

For Exercises 23 and 24, (a) write an expression for total cost and (b) simplify the expression.

23. Lana bought juice for $3.25 and some fruit for $5.25. She also bought five beach passes for *x* dollars each.

24. Chung bought 6 brushes for *b* dollars each, 2 paint tubes for *p* dollars each, 5 more brushes later in the day, and paper for $12.

Gridded Response

Simplify each expression.

25. $7(58)$

26. $6(92)$

27. $5(1,002)$

Solve each equation.

28. $b - 7 = 21$

29. $18 + n = 37$

30. $\frac{c}{7} = 8$

31. $-9r = 108$

Activity Lab

A Profitable Fair

Applying Equations Many schools hold fairs and other events to raise money for extracurricular activities. To make a profit, you must begin with an idea of what your expenses and your income will be. At your school fair, your student council will rent school tables and sell tickets, hot dogs, and juice. The student council makes plans for this year's fair based on last year's fair.

Activity

Copy the chart. Write and solve equations to fill in the blanks.

1. Find the profit P from renting yard-sale tables.

   > **Profit = Income − Cost**

Treasurer's Chart

Item	Last Year	This Year	Income	Profit
Tables (yard sale)	45 tables	■	$35/table = ■	■
Tickets	320 sold	■	■	$800
Hot dogs (and buns)	200 sold	■	■	$280
Juice boxes	200 sold	■	■	$100
Total	N/A	N/A	■	■

2. Suppose you make the tickets. Find the price T to charge for each ticket to make the planned profit.

3. You calculate that you will have to pay an average of $.35 per hot dog, bun, and toppings. How much will this cost in all?

4. Juice boxes cost you $.25 each. How much will they cost in all?

5. How much, h, should you charge for each hot dog?

6. How much, j, should you charge for each juice box?

7. You could sell a hot dog and juice box only as a combination. If you do, how much, c, should you charge for each "combo"?

8. **Open-Ended** How could you improve the Treasurer's Chart?

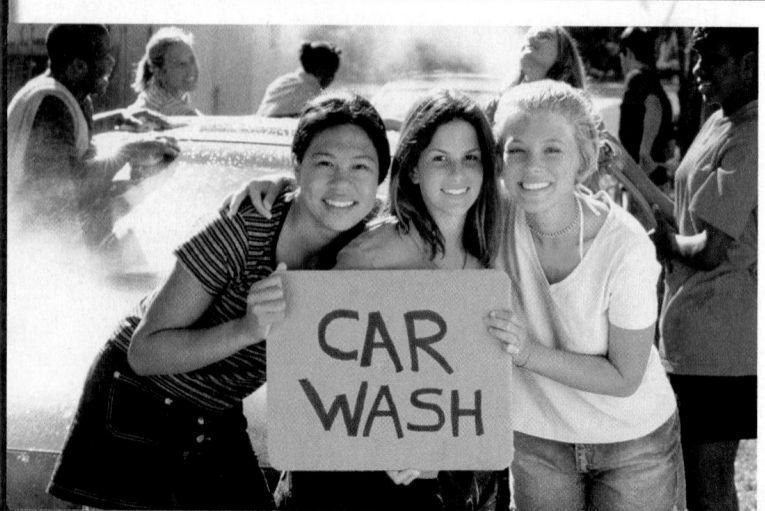

Clean Machines
Some schools use donated supplies for their fundraising car washes.

A Little Goes a Long Way

Middle-school students in Maynard, Massachusetts, are collecting 1 million pennies as their school fundraiser.

Painting Faces

Kids of all ages love having their faces painted! But be warned: Small children can't sit still for long, so know what you're going to paint before you begin.

Go Online
PHSchool.com

For: Information about school fairs
Web Code: ade-0253

What You've Learned

(IL) Assessment Framework

- **6.8.10:** In Chapter 1, you learned how to add, subtract, multiply, and divide integers.
- **8.8.12:** In Chapter 2, you solved equations by adding or subtracting.
- **8.8.12:** In Chapter 2, you also solved equations by multiplying or dividing.

 Check Your Readiness   **for Help** to the Lesson in green.

Rounding Numbers (Skills Handbook, p. 780)

Round each number to the nearest ten.

1. 37 **2.** 9 **3.** 2 **4.** 602 **5.** 834 **6.** 6,009

Comparing and Ordering Decimals (Skills Handbook, p. 784)

Compare. Use >, <, or = to complete each statement.

7. 0.96 ■ 1.32 **8.** 7.641 ■ 7.593 **9.** 6.3 ■ 6.38

10. 5.001 ■ 5.02 **11.** −9.871 ■ −10.3 **12.** −27.619 ■ −27.7

Order each group of decimals from least to greatest.

13. 8.35, 8.349, 8.351, 9.25 **14.** 0.02, 0.017, 0.201, 0.0201

15. −1.4, −1.04, −1.401, −14.1 **16.** −2.3, −3.2, −3.19, −2.8

Operations With Decimals (Skills Handbook, pp. 786–792)

Simplify.

17. 3.4 + 8.09 **18.** 8 − 4.93 **19.** 0.59 + 3.06 **20.** 2.19 − 0.984

21. (1.001)(6.7) **22.** 40.02 ÷ 5.8 **23.** 10.4 · 5.3 **24.** $\frac{77.38}{7.3}$

Multiplying and Dividing by Powers of 10 (Skills Handbook, p. 790)

Simplify.

25. 9.87 · 10 **26.** 5.32 · 100 **27.** 0.3 · 1,000 **28.** 15.407 · 10,000

29. 0.8 ÷ 10 **30.** 8.42 ÷ 100 **31.** 16.1 ÷ 1,000 **32.** 12.09 ÷ 10,000

Decimals and Equations

Chapter

3

LESSONS

3-1 Rounding and Estimating

3-2 Estimating Decimal Products and Quotients

3-3 Mean, Median, and Mode

3-4 Using Formulas

3-5 Solving Equations by Adding or Subtracting Decimals

3-6 Solving Equations by Multiplying or Dividing Decimals

3-7 Using the Metric System

3-8 Problem Solving: Act It Out

◀)) **Key Vocabulary**

- compatible numbers (p. 135)
- formula (p. 145)
- mean (p. 139)
- measures of central tendency (p. 139)
- median (p. 139)
- mode (p. 139)
- outlier (p. 140)
- perimeter (p. 146)
- range (p. 139)

What You'll Learn Next

IL **Assessment Framework**

In this chapter, you will learn how to

- **6.8.13:** Estimate with decimals.

- **8.8.12:** Solve equations with decimals.

- **7.8.05:** Convert metric units of measure.

- **8.8.12:** Solve a problem by simplifying the problem.

 Activity Lab. Applying what you learn, on pages 176–177 you will solve problems about price comparisons.

Writing and Comparing Decimals

Each digit in a decimal has both a place and a value. The value of any place is one-tenth the value of the place to its left. A place-value chart like the one at the right can help you read and write decimals.

ones	.	tenths	hundredths	thousandths	ten thousandths
0	.	4	2	6	

1 EXAMPLE

a. Express 0.426 using words.

The last digit, 6, is in the thousandths place. So, 0.426 ends with the word *thousandths*.

0.426 is four hundred twenty-six thousandths.

b. Write *two and three hundredths* as a decimal.

And represents the decimal point. The hundredths place is the second place to the right of the decimal point.

Two and three hundredths is 2.03.

You can use decimal squares to model and compare decimals.

2 EXAMPLE

a. Model 0.6.

b. Model 0.58.

c. Model 1.05.

d. Compare 0.6 and 0.58. The models show that 0.6 > 0.58.

EXERCISES

Express each decimal using words.

1. 0.23   **2.** 0.624   **3.** 3.081   **4.** 58.36

Write each as a decimal.

5. three and two tenths   **6.** five and forty-one hundredths   **7.** fourteen ten-thousandths

Model and compare each pair of decimals.

8. 0.2 and 0.12   **9.** 0.89 and 0.9   **10.** 0.53 and 0.5   **11.** 1.35 and 1.4

Rounding and Estimating

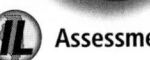 Assessment Framework

1 Rounding Decimals

ctivity

Estimating in the Real World

Some real-world problems require only an estimate for an answer. Others require an exact answer. Decide whether each situation needs an estimate or an exact answer. Explain your reasoning.

1. a headline noting the number of people living in China

2. the amount of money a baby sitter charges per hour

3. the width of a window screen

4. the distance from Earth to the moon

5. the hours at soccer practice in one month

6. the number of tickets to sell for a play

6.8.13 Select, use, and justify appropriate operations, methods, and tools to compute or estimate with rational numbers. Verify solutions and determine the reasonableness of results.

☑ Check Skills You'll Need
Use the number 27.3865. Write the value of the given digit.

1. 2   **2.** 3

3. 8   **4.** 6

GO for Help
Skills Handbook, p. 783

You can round decimal numbers when you don't need exact values.

1 EXAMPLE   Rounding Decimals

a. Round 4.2683 to the nearest tenth.

┌─ tenths place

4.2683

└─ 5 or greater

⬇

┌─ Round up to 3.

4.3

b. Round 4.2683 to the nearest one.

┌─ ones place

4.2683

└─ less than 5

⬇

┌─ Do not change.

4

Online active math

For: Comparing Decimals Activity
Use: Interactive Textbook, 3-1

☑ Quick Check

1. Identify the underlined place. Then round each number to that place.

   a. 38.4̲1   **b.** 0̲.7772   **c.** 7,098.5̲6

   d. 274.94̲34   **e.** 5.0̲25   **f.** 9.85̲1

2 Estimating Sums and Differences

Vocabulary Tip

Read the symbol ≈ as "is approximately equal to."

You can estimate a result before you calculate. Then, if your answer is close to your estimate, you know that it probably is correct.

Write $126   ≈ $130

Read $126 is approximately equal to $130.

One way to estimate is to round all numbers to the same place.

2 EXAMPLE   Rounding to Estimate

Problem Solving Hint

After you have rounded to a place greater than the ones place, write zeros from that place to the decimal point. Do not write zeros after the decimal point.

Estimate to find whether each answer is reasonable.

a. Calculation   Estimate

$$
\begin{array}{rcr}
\$135.95 & ≈ & \$140 \\
\$15.90 & ≈ & \$20 \\
+ \$24.05 & ≈ & + \$20 \\
\hline
\$275.90\ \textbf{✗} & & \$180 \\
\end{array}
$$

The answer is not close to the estimate. It is *not* reasonable.

b. Calculation   Estimate

$$
\begin{array}{rcr}
464.90 & ≈ & 460 \\
- 125.73 & ≈ & - 130 \\
\hline
339.17\ \textbf{✓} & & 330 \\
\end{array}
$$

The answer is close to the estimate. It is reasonable.

✓ Quick Check

2. Estimate by rounding.

    a. 355.302 + 204.889   **b.** 453.56 − 230.07

A *front-end estimate* is often closer to the exact sum than an estimate you find by rounding. First add the front-end digits. Round to estimate the sum of the remaining digits. Then combine estimates.

3 EXAMPLE   Real-World 🌐 Problem Solving

$1.73

$1.10

$2.71

Grocery Shopping Carrots cost $2.71, peppers cost $1.73, and broccoli costs $1.10. Estimate the total cost of the vegetables.

$$
\begin{array}{llcl}
\text{Add the} & 2.71 & \longrightarrow & .70 \\
\text{front-end digits.} \longrightarrow & 1.73 & \longrightarrow & .70 \quad \Big\}\ \text{Estimate by} \\
& + 1.10 & \longrightarrow & + .10 \quad \text{rounding.} \\
\hline
& 4 & + & 1.50 = 5.50 \\
\end{array}
$$

The total cost is about $5.50.

✓ Quick Check

3. Estimate using front-end estimation.

    a. 6.75 + 2.2 + 9.58   **b.** $1.07 + $2.49 + $7.40

You can also use *clustering* to estimate the sum of several numbers that are all close to the same value.

4 EXAMPLE <u>Real-World</u> 🌐 <u>Problem Solving</u>

Telephone Service Estimate the total long-distance charge for the months of May, June, July, and August shown at the right.

four months
↓
The values cluster around $15. ⟶ 15 · 4 = 60

The total long-distance charge is about $60.00.

☑ **Quick Check**

4. Estimate using clustering.

   a. $4.50 + $5.20 + $5.55
   b. 26.7 + 26.2 + 24.52 + 25.25 + 23.9

In this lesson, you have seen several methods for finding a reasonable estimate. Here are two methods used for the same situation.

More Than One Way

Estimate the total cost of four items priced at $4.39, $3.75, $4.96, and $2.40.

Nicole's Method

Round each price to the nearest dollar. Then add.

$4.39 + $3.75 + $4.96 + $2.40
$4   + $4   + $5   + $2   = $15

Eric's Method

Use front-end estimation.

$4.39	⟶	$.40
3.75	⟶	.80
4.96	⟶	1.00
+ 2.40	⟶	+ .40
$13	+	$2.60 = $15.60

Choose a Method

1. Which method would you use to estimate the cost of the items? Explain.
2. Find the exact cost. Which estimate is nearer the exact cost?

EXERCISES

For more exercises, see *Extra Skill and Word Problem Practice*.

Practice and Problem Solving

A Practice by Example

Example 1
(page 129)

GO for Help

Identify the underlined place. Then round each number to that place.

1. 27.3856　　**2.** 0.9122　　**3.** 1,045.98　　**4.** 74.879

Round to the underlined place.

5. 345.678　　**6.** 3.14159　　**7.** 214.76　　**8.** 2.9437

Example 2
(page 130)

Estimate by rounding.

9. $37.99 − $27.32　**10.** 1.58 + 17.0244　**11.** 172.98 − 128.301

12. $4.89 + $3.87　　**13.** $16.81 + $11.49　**14.** $565 − $225

Example 3
(page 130)

Estimate using front-end estimation.

15. $6.04 + $3.45 + $4.43　　**16.** $5.92 + $4.07

17. 9.89 + 2.43 + 8.37　　　　**18.** 14.39 + 79.12

19. Fitness Kim ran 2.76 miles on Monday, 2.34 miles on Tuesday, and 1.97 miles on Wednesday. Use front-end estimation to estimate the total distance Kim ran.

Example 4
(page 131)

Estimate using clustering.

20. 44.87 + 42.712 + 43.5　　**21.** $9.50 + $8.45 + $9.08

22. $21.37 + $22.99 + $22.15　**23.** 15.4 + 16 + 15.9 + 16.25 + 15.7

24. Pets Rico's dog has a litter of four puppies. The puppies weigh 2.33 lb, 2.70 lb, 2.27 lb, and 2.64 lb. Use clustering to estimate the total weight of the puppies.

B Apply Your Skills

Estimate. Use a method of your choice.

25. 8.974 + 2.154　　**26.** 102.44 + 48.35　　**27.** 600 − 209.52

28. $38.59 + $15.28　**29.** $50.00 − $28.89　**30.** $412.44 + $72.23

31. 800 + 810.5 + 807.3 + 791.1　**32.** 54.23 + 56.12 + 57.98 + 55.55

Lake Erie

Lake Superior

33. Geography Lake Superior, the largest of the Great Lakes, has an area of about 31,760 mi^2. Lake Erie, the smallest of the Great Lakes, has an area of about 9,920 mi^2. About how much larger is Lake Superior than Lake Erie?

Estimate. State the method you used.

34. $8.99 + $8.01　　**35.** 2.3 + 2.3 + 4.56　　**36.** $89.90 − $49.29

37. 102.54 − 74.75　　**38.** 20.55 − 1.48　　　**39.** 78.87 + 11.49

Homework Video Tutor
Visit: PHSchool.com
Web Code: ade-0301

40. Weather Mobile, Alabama, has an average annual rainfall of 63.96 in. The average annual rainfall in San Francisco, California, is 19.70 in. About how much more rain falls each year in Mobile than in San Francisco?

41. Open-Ended Describe a situation in which a rounded answer is appropriate. Describe one in which an exact answer is necessary.

C Challenge

42. Writing in Math You have $11.50 to buy two presents. You find one item that costs $7.43. Another item costs $4.41. What estimation strategy will help you decide whether you have enough money to buy both? Explain.

43. Error Analysis You used a calculator to find $383.8 - 21.9$. Your estimate was 360, but your display reads 164.8. How could you have gotten 164.8 on your calculator?

ISAT

Test Prep

Multiple Choice

44. Which phrase best completes the statement?
The sum of $12.75 and $7.65 is __?__.
A. less than $20.00
B. greater than $20.00
C. an integer
D. greater than $25.00

45. When you estimate $320.18 + 46 + 8.68$ by rounding to tens, what value do you get?
F. 370
G. 374.9
H. 375
J. 380

Short Response

46. In 2000, the population of the state of Georgia was about 8.19 million. In 1950, the population was about 3.44 million.
a. About how much greater was Georgia's population in 2000 than in 1950?
b. Explain how you found your answer for part (a).

Mixed Review

for Help

Lesson 2-10   **Solve each inequality.**

47. $9x \le 27$ **48.** $4x < 16$ **49.** $-3y \le 0$ **50.** $-6k > -24$

Lesson 2-7 **51. Collections** Ming's model vehicle collection contains 4-wheeled trucks and 2-wheeled bikes. She owns an even number of vehicles, and they have 26 wheels in all. If Ming has a little more than twice as many bikes as trucks, how many of each does she own?

Lesson 1-9   **Simplify.**

52. $(-2)(-2)$ **53.** $4(-3)$ **54.** $-8 \div 2$ **55.** $6(-5)$

3-2

Estimating Decimal Products and Quotients

6.8.13 Select, use, and justify appropriate operations, methods, and tools to compute or estimate with rational numbers. Verify solutions and determine the reasonableness of results.

✓ Check Skills You'll Need

Round to the nearest one.

1. 145.89   2. 199.27

3. 101.06   4. 28.45

GO for Help
Lesson 3-1

🔊 **New Vocabulary**

• compatible numbers

---

1   Estimating Products

You can use mental math to estimate products and quotients. It is a good idea to estimate answers to check your calculations.

1 EXAMPLE   Estimating the Product

Estimate 7.65 · 3.2.

$7.65 \approx 8$ $3.2 \approx 3$ **Round to the nearest one.**

$8 \cdot 3 = 24$ **Multiply.**

$7.65 \cdot 3.2 \approx 24$

✓ Quick Check

1. Estimate each product.

   a. 4.72 · 1.8   **b.** 17.02 · 3.78   **c.** 8.25 · 19.8

2 EXAMPLE   Real-World 🌐 Problem Solving

Quilting Arlene bought 6 yd of fabric to make this Lone Star quilt. The fabric cost $6.75/yd. The sales clerk charged Arlene $45.90 before tax. Did the clerk make a mistake? Explain.

$6.75 \approx 7$ **Round to the nearest dollar.**

$7 \cdot 6 = 42$ **Multiply 7 times 6, the number of yards of fabric.**

The sales clerk made a mistake. Since $6.75 < 7$, the actual cost should be less than the estimate. The clerk should have charged Arlene less than $42.00 before tax.

✓ Quick Check

2. **Photography** You buy 8 rolls of film for your camera. Each roll costs $4.79. Estimate the cost of the film before tax.

2 Estimating Quotients

When dividing, remember these names for the parts of a division sentence.

$$6 \div 3 = 2$$

dividend
quotient
divisor

When dividing, you can use *compatible numbers* to estimate quotients. **Compatible numbers** are numbers that are easy to divide mentally. When you estimate a quotient, first round the divisor, and then round the dividend to a compatible number.

3 EXAMPLE   Real-World ⊕ Problem Solving

Measurement A bowling ball has a mass of 5.61 kg. Each bowling pin has a mass of 1.57 kg. How many bowling pins are about equal to the bowling ball in mass? Estimate $5.61 \div 1.57$.

$1.57 \approx 2$	Round the divisor.
$5.61 \approx 6$	Round the dividend to a multiple of 2 that is close to 5.61.
$6 \div 2 = 3$	Divide.

The mass of three bowling pins is about equal to that of the bowling ball.

✓ Quick Check

3. Estimate each quotient.

    a. $38.9 \div 1.79$ **b.** $11.95 \div 2.1$ **c.** $82.52 \div 4.25$

Real-World ⊕ Connection

The masses of ten-pin bowling balls range from 3.63 kg to 7.26 kg.

5.61 kg
1.57 kg

You can estimate to determine the reasonableness of results.

4 EXAMPLE   Estimating to Determine Reasonableness

Number Sense Is 2.15 a reasonable quotient for $17.931 \div 8.34$?

$8.34 \approx 8$	Round the divisor.
$17.931 \approx 16$	Round the dividend to a multiple of 8 that is close to 17.931.
$16 \div 8 = 2$	Divide.

Since 2.15 is close to the estimate 2, it is reasonable.

✓ Quick Check

4. Use estimation. Is each quotient reasonable? Explain.

    a. $1.564 \div 2.3 = 0.68$ **b.** $26.0454 \div 4.98 = 52.3$

Test-Taking Tip

You can sometimes use estimation to eliminate answer choices on a multiple choice test.

What is $8.19 \div 2.1$?

   Ⓐ 39   Ⓑ 4.1

   Ⓒ 3.9   Ⓓ 0.41

If you estimate $8 \div 2 \approx 4$, then you know you can eliminate choices A and D.

EXERCISES

For more exercises, see *Extra Skill and Word Problem Practice*.

Practice and Problem Solving

A Practice by Example

Example 1
(page 134)

Estimate each product.

1. 4.56 · 7.02   **2.** 11.15 · 4.44   **3.** 6.3 · 9.2

4. 24.5 · 4.2   **5.** 3.29 · 58   **6.** 0.08 · 40.05

Example 2
(page 134)

Estimate the cost of each purchase.

7. Food Tom bought 6 hamburgers for $2.89 each.

8. Sports Equipment The athletic director bought 5 soccer balls for $12.29 each.

Example 3
(page 135)

Estimate each quotient using compatible numbers.

9. 3.9 ÷ 2.1   **10.** 3.86 ÷ 1.95   **11.** 19.56 ÷ 0.71

12. $585 ÷ 11.75   **13.** 18.2 ÷ 3.4   **14.** 57.1 ÷ 7.2

15. Unit Pricing Marshall buys a sack of peaches for $5.98. If the peaches weigh 2.77 pounds, about what price per pound did Marshall pay?

Example 4
(page 135)

Use estimation. Is each quotient reasonable? Explain.

16. 102.6 ÷ 22.5 = 45.6   **17.** $32.40 ÷ 4.80 = $67.50

18. Number Sense Explain how you would find a reasonable estimate for 14.90 ÷ 4.56.

B Apply Your Skills

Estimate each product or quotient.

19. 193.7 · 1.78   **20.** 7.95 ÷ 2.1   **21.** 9.392 ÷ 2.9

22. 876.66 · 39.64   **23.** $75.45 ÷ 12.48   **24.** 16.33 · 3.5

Data Analysis Use the table below for Exercises 25–27.

Selected Wages (40-h week)

Occupation	Detroit, MI	Lincoln, NE
Elementary School Teacher	$1,820.80	$1,298.00
Secretary	$723.20	$508.00
Truck Driver	$685.20	$636.80

SOURCE: U.S. Department of Labor

25. Estimate the hourly wage for each staff position.

26. Estimate the yearly (52 weeks) salary for each staff position.

27. How much more per hour does a secretary in Detroit, Michigan, make than a secretary in Lincoln, Nebraska?

136 Chapter 3 Decimals and Equations

Use estimation. Is each product or quotient reasonable? Explain.

28. $-46.82(-1.5) = 702.3$

29. $-71.5071 \div (-11.9) = 6.009$

 30. Gas Mileage Shari is planning a 450-mi car trip. Her car can travel about 39 mi on a gallon of gasoline. Gasoline costs $1.89/gal. About how much will the gas cost for her trip?

C Challenge

Estimate each quotient.

31. $-483.09 \div 7.29$

32. $-362{,}400 \div (-4.2)$

33. Health Humans breathe about 15 breaths in a minute. The average breath at rest contains 0.76 liter of air. About how many liters of air will you breathe while at rest for 25 minutes?

34. Writing in Math You estimate $21.2 \div 3.75$ to be 5. Your friend estimates the quotient to be 7. Explain how the two estimates can be different and yet both be reasonable.

ISAT

Test Prep

Multiple Choice

35. Greta ran the 400-m dash in 49.07 s. If Greta ran at a constant rate, how many meters did she run in one second?
 A. between 8 m and 9 m   **B.** between 9 m and 10 m
 C. between 10 m and 11 m   **D.** between 11 m and 12 m

36. A shrew, the world's smallest mammal, has a heart rate of 790 beats per minute. About how many times does a shrew's heart beat in 5 minutes?
 F. 3,500   **G.** 4,000   **H.** 4,500   **J.** 4,790

Short Response

37. Two people estimate the product $1.99 · 8.5.
 a. Will they necessarily get the same estimate?
 b. Explain your answer.

38. You review your sales slip after buying 4 CDs that cost $14.95 each. Before tax, the total was $77.80. Is this total correct? Explain.

Mixed Review

Go for Help

Lesson 3-1

Estimate each sum or difference.

39. $2.99 + $6.01   **40.** $25.90 - $5.79   **41.** $12.3 + 12.3 + 14.56$

42. $1{,}242.24 - 24.05$ **43.** $18.95 - 7.48$ **44.** $7.47 - $5.50

Lesson 1-10

In which quadrant or on which axis of a coordinate plane does each point lie?

45. $(2, 4)$ **46.** $(-5, 0)$ **47.** $(8, -6)$ **48.** $(0, 8)$ **49.** $(-5, -3)$

Lesson 1-8 **50. Travel** A bus trip from Sacramento to Los Angeles takes 7 h 40 min. You depart at 11:40 A.M. At what time will you arrive in Los Angeles?

Read the exercise below and then read how the needed data are found in the table. Follow along as the problem is solved. Check your understanding by solving the exercise at the bottom of the page.

Use the table. How much more per hour does a registered nurse in Washington, D.C., make than a registered nurse in Dallas, Texas?

The title of the table tells you that the table entries are wages for a 40-h week.

Occupations: Look down for registered nurse.

Cities: Look across for Dallas and Washington.

The table tells you that in a 40-h week:

A registered nurse in Dallas makes $997.60.

A registered nurse in Washington makes $1,114.00.

Selected Wages (40-h week)

Occupation	Dallas, TX	Washington, DC
Registered Nurse	$997.60	$1,114.00
Radiology Technician	$909.60	$1,025.20
Orderly	$381.60	$452.00

SOURCE: U.S. Department of Labor

Estimate:

A Washington registered nurse makes about $1,120 − $1,000 = $120 more in a 40-h week.

That's about $120 ÷ 40 = $3 more per hour.

Calculate — Method 1

1,114.00 − 997.60 = 116.40   **Subtract to find the difference in weekly wages.**

116.40 ÷ 40 = 2.91   **Divide to find the difference in hourly wages.**

Calculate — Method 2

1,114.00 ÷ 40 = 27.85   **Divide to find the Washington hourly wage.**

997.60 ÷ 40 = 24.94   **Divide to find the Dallas hourly wage.**

27.85 − 24.94 = 2.91   **Subtract to find the difference in hourly wages.**

A Washington registered nurse makes $2.91/h more than one in Dallas.

This is close to the estimate of $3/h.

EXERCISES

1. How much less per hour does an orderly in Dallas make than an orderly in Washington?

2. How much less per hour does a radiology technician in Dallas make than a nurse in Dallas?

Mean, Median, and Mode

1 | Finding Mean, Median, Mode, and Range

Mean, *median*, and *mode* are **measures of central tendency** of a collection of data. Consider the data 2, 3, 4, 5, 8, 8, and 12.

The **mean** is the sum of the data values divided by the number of data values.

$$\text{mean} = \frac{2 + 3 + 4 + 5 + 8 + 8 + 12}{7}$$
$$= \frac{42}{7} = 6 \quad \underset{\text{data values}}{\llcorner \text{number of}}$$

The **median** is the middle number when data values are written in order and there is an odd number of data values. For an even number of data values, the median is the mean of the two middle numbers.

2 3 4 5 8 8 12
         ↑
      median

The **mode** is the data item that occurs most often. There can be one mode, more than one mode, or no mode.

2 3 4 5 <u>8 8</u> 12
              mode

The **range** of a set of data is the difference between the greatest and least values in the data set.

range = 12 − 2 = 10
greatest ⌐   ⌐ least
value   value

Assessment Framework

10.8.05 Analyze and apply measures of central tendency in problem–solving situations.

✓ **Check Skills You'll Need**
Write the numbers from least to greatest.

1. 8, 6, 4, 9, 3, 5, 6

2. 72, 68, 69, 71, 72

3. 112, 101, 98, 120, 101

4. 3.74, 3, 3.7, 3.3, 37

GO for Help
Skills Handbook, p. 779

◀)) **New Vocabulary**
• measures of central tendency
• mean   • median
• mode   • outlier
• range

1 EXAMPLE   Real-World 🌐 Problem Solving

Fundraising Use the **Readathon graph.** Find the **(a)** mean, **(b)** median, **(c)** mode, and **(d)** range.

a. Mean: $\dfrac{\text{sum of data values}}{\text{number of data values}}$

$$= \frac{40 + 45 + 48 + 50 + 50 + 59}{6}$$

$$= \frac{292}{6}$$

$$= 48.666 \ldots \approx 48.7$$

b. Median: 40 45 48 50 50 59   **Write the data in order.**

$\frac{48 + 50}{2} = 49$ **Find the mean of the two middle numbers.**

c. Mode: Find the data value that occurs most often. The mode is 50.

d. Range: Greatest value − least value = 59 − 40 = 19.

Video Tutor Help
Visit: PHSchool.com
Web Code: ada-0775

✓ Quick Check

● **1.** Find the mean, median, mode, and range: 2.3 4.3 3.2 2.9 2.7 2.3

For: Central Tendency Activity
Use: Interactive Textbook, 3-3

2 EXAMPLE Identifying Modes

How many modes, if any, does each have?

a. **$1.50 $2.00 $2.25 $2.40 $3.50 $4.00**
No values are the same, so there is no mode.

b. 2 3 6 <u>8</u> <u>8</u> 10 11 12 <u>14</u> <u>14</u> 18 20
Both 8 and 14 appear the same number of times, and most often.
There are two modes.

**c. grape, grape, banana, nectarine, <u>strawberry, strawberry,</u>
<u>strawberry,</u> orange, watermelon**
Strawberry appears most often. There is one mode.

✓ Quick Check

2. Find the number of modes.

  a. 11 9 7 7 8 8 13 11   **b.** 38.5 55.4 45.3 38.5 68.4

An **outlier** is a data value that is much greater or less than the other data values. An outlier can affect the mean of a group of data.

3 EXAMPLE Real-World 🌐 Problem Solving

**Approximate Land Areas
That Can Be Farmed in
Central American Countries**

Guatemala
5,000 mi²   Belize
                      200 mi²

                          Honduras
                          6,500 mi²

                      Nicaragua
                      4,500 mi²

El Salvador
2,200 mi²

      Costa Rica
      1,200 mi²   Panama
                          2,100 mi²

Source: *The New York Times Almanac*

Geography Use the map of Central America at the left.

a. Which data value is an outlier?
The data value for Honduras, 6,500 mi², is an outlier. It is an outlier because it is 1,500 mi² away from the closest data value.

b. How does the outlier affect the mean?

$\frac{21,700}{7} = 3,100$ Find the mean with the outlier.

$\frac{15,200}{6} \approx 2,500$ Find the mean without the outlier.

$3,100 - 2,500 = 600$
The outlier raises the mean by about 600 mi².

✓ Quick Check

3. Find an outlier in each group of data below and tell how it affects the mean. Round to the nearest tenth.

  a. 9 10 12 13 8 9 31 9   **b.** 1 17.5 18 19.5 16 17.5

Choosing the Best Measure

One measure of central tendency may be better than another to describe data. For example, consider the eight hourly wage rates shown at the right. Here are the measures of central tendency.

Mode: $5.50
Mean: $7.50
Median: $6.10

Employees' Hourly Wages	
$5.50	$6.20
$5.50	$6.30
$5.50	$8.00
$6.00	$17.00

The mode is the lowest wage listed. So the mode does not describe the data well.

The mean is above the hourly wage of all but two workers. The mean is influenced by the outlier, $17.

The median is the best measure of central tendency here since it is not influenced by the size of the outlier.

4 EXAMPLE   Identifying the Best Measure

Which measure of central tendency best describes each situation? Explain.

a. **the favorite movies of students in the eighth grade**

Mode; since the data are not numerical, the mode is the appropriate measure. When determining the most frequently chosen item, or when the data are not numerical, use the mode.

b. **the daily high temperatures during a week in July**

Mean; since daily high temperatures in July are not likely to have an outlier, mean is the appropriate measure. When the data have no outliers, use the mean.

> **Vocabulary Tip**
>
> To help you recall that <u>median</u> means "middle number," think of the green, grassy median strip in the middle of a divided highway.

c. **the distances students in your class travel to school**

Median; since one student may live much farther from school than the majority of students, the median is the appropriate measure. When an outlier may significantly influence the mean, use the median.

✓ Quick Check

4. a. **Comparison Shopping** Toshio found the following prices for sport shirts:
$20, $26, $27, $28, $21, $42, $18, and $20.
Find the mean, median, and mode for the shirt prices.
   b. **Reasoning** Which measure of central tendency best describes the data? Justify your reasoning.

EXERCISES

For more exercises, see *Extra Skill and Word Problem Practice*.

Practice and Problem Solving

A Practice by Example

Example 1
(page 139)

GO for Help

Find the mean, median, mode, and range of each group of data. If an answer is not a whole number, round to the nearest tenth.

1. 47 56 57 63 89 44 56

2. 4 5 2 3 2 3 3 3 1 1 3

3. 1 2 4 5 5 6 9

4. 2.8 3.6 3.8 4.1 2.8 3.7 4.3

5. Fitness Mia's workouts lasted 1.0 h, 1.5 h, 2.25 h, 1.5 h, 2.4 h, and 2.1 h. Find the mean, median, and mode of these times. If the answer is not an integer, round to the nearest tenth.

Example 2
(page 140)

How many modes, if any, does each group of data have?

6. 31 44 44 31 38

7. 4.3 4.9 4.9 5.2

8. 64 68 64 65 68 65 72 61

9. Bob, Ana, Ron, Bob, Kay

Example 3
(page 140)

Find the outlier in each group of data and tell how it affects the mean.

10. 37 4 7 3 11 9 13 5

11. 126 123 115 125 123

12. Grades Rita's quiz scores are 72, 96, 74, 80, and 79. Find the outlier and tell how it affects Rita's mean quiz score.

Example 4
(page 141)

Which measure of central tendency best describes each situation? Explain.

13. numbers of apples in 2-lb bags

14. favorite brands of jeans of 14-year-olds

15. ages of students in a fifth-grade classroom

Which measure of central tendency best describes each group of data? Explain.

16. minutes on the Internet
50 63 59 85 367 48

17. heights of students in inches
51 45 47 48 50 50 50 52

B Apply Your Skills

For Exercises 18–22, find mean, median, mode, and range. Which measure of central tendency best describes each group of data? Explain.

18. 3,456 560 435 456

19. 5.6 6.8 1.2 6.5 7.9 6.5

20. 33 76 86 92 86

21. 8 2 4 9 16

22. resting heart rate in beats per minute: 79 72 80 81 40 72

Which measure of central tendency best describes each situation? Explain.

23. shoe colors in a classroom

24. widths of computer screens at a bank

25. numbers of pets owned by classmates

Challenge

For Exercises 26–28, use the table at the left. Round answers to the nearest tenth.

Fat and Calorie Content
(per 2-tablespoon serving)

Seed or Nut	Fat (g)	Calories
Peanut	8.9	104
Pecan	9.1	90
Pistachio	7.9	92
Pumpkin	7.9	93
Sunflower	8.9	102
Walnut	7.7	80

26. Data Analysis You make a mixture using the same amount of each kind of seed and nut.
   a. What is the mean number of grams of fat in a 2-tablespoon serving of the mixture?
   b. What is the mean number of Calories in a 2-tablespoon serving of the mixture?

27. Writing in Math Describe two mixtures that each use a total of 8 tablespoons. Do the two parts of Exercise 26 for your mixtures.

28. Nutrition A mixture of equal amounts of pumpkin seeds, sunflower seeds, and pistachios contains 12 tablespoons in all. How many grams of fat and how many Calories does the mixture have?

ISAT

 Test Prep

Multiple Choice

29. The average cost of a meal at the Grand Plaza is $20. Which one of the following statements *cannot* be true?
   A. The cost of four meals is greater than $20.
   B. Some meals cost less than $10.
   C. Each meal costs exactly $20.
   D. Each meal costs more than $20.

30. Kayla's first three quiz scores are 90, 85, and 88. Which score on her next quiz will raise Kayla's mean quiz score to 90?
   F. 97   **G.** 95   **H.** 92   **J.** 90

31. Ten out of 20 students score a perfect 100 on a math test. Which of the following describes the score of 100 for the 20 students?
   A. mean   **B.** median   **C.** mode   **D.** outlier

Short Response

32. In a neighborhood with 46 homes, two are more than 6,000 ft² in area, and the rest are less than 2,500 ft² in area.
   a. Would the mean or the median provide a better measure of the typical home size?
   b. Explain your reasoning.

Mixed Review

GO for Help

Lesson 3-2 **Estimate each product or quotient.**

33. $9.01 ÷ $1.42   **34.** 7.5 · 89.1   **35.** 12.6 · $2.99

Lesson 2-7 **36. Retail Sales** Karen sells children's hats for $4 and adults' hats for $7. On Saturday, she sold 120 hats, and she collected $720. How many adults' hats did she sell?

Lesson 2-3 **Simplify each expression.**

37. $6x + 8 + 2$ **38.** $5z + 4x + 3z$ **39.** $x - 4t + 2t + 5$

You can use a graphing calculator to find means and medians.

ACTIVITY

Find (a) the mean and (b) the median number of acres in Ohio zoos.

Zoos in Ohio

Zoo	Number of Acres	Number of Species
Cincinnati Zoo	75	3,500
Cleveland Metroparks Zoo	168	579
Columbus Zoo and Aquarium	588	758
Toledo Zoo	62	700

SOURCE: *The World Almanac*

a. Use the mean function. Use LIST to enter 75, 168, 588, and 62 for **L1**. In **STAT**, select **MATH** and **mean**, then ENTER. Using **STAT** again, select **L1**. Press ENTER twice to find the mean.

The mean is about 223 acres.

b. Use the median function. Use LIST to enter 75, 168, 588, and 62 for **L1**. In **STAT**, select **MATH** and **median**, then ENTER. Using **STAT** again, select **L1**. Press ENTER twice to find the median.

The median is 121.5 acres.

EXERCISES

Use a calculator to find the mean and median.

1. number of species in Ohio zoos

2. 85°F, 79°F, 80°F, 75°F, 82°F

3. $3.75, $4.50, $9.25, $4.70, $5.90

4. 100, 95, 82, 102, 78, 76

5.

Miles of Atlantic Coastline by State

State	DE	FL	GA	ME	MD	MA	NH	NJ	NY	NC	RI	SC	VA
Miles	28	580	100	228	31	192	13	130	127	301	40	187	112

SOURCE: National Oceanic and Atmospheric Administration, U.S. Dept. of Commerce

Using Formulas

1 Substituting Into Formulas

A **formula** is an equation that shows a relationship between quantities that are represented by variables.

An important formula in math and science is $d = rt$, where d is the distance, r is the rate or speed, and t is the time spent traveling.

1 EXAMPLE   Real-World 🌐 Problem Solving

Travel Suppose you travel 162 miles in 3 hours. Use the formula $d = rt$ to find your average speed.

$$d = rt \qquad \text{Write the formula.}$$
$$162 = (r)(3) \qquad \text{Substitute 162 for } d \text{ and 3 for } t.$$
$$\frac{162}{3} = \frac{3r}{3} \qquad \text{Divide each side by 3.}$$
$$54 = r \qquad \text{Simplify.}$$

Your average speed is 54 mi/h.

✓ Quick Check

1. Use the formula $d = rt$. Find d, r, or t.

    a. $d = 273$ mi, $t = 9.75$ h   **b.** $d = 540.75$ in., $r = 10.5$ in./yr

2 EXAMPLE   Real-World 🌐 Problem Solving

Insects You can estimate the temperature outside using the chirps of a cricket. Use the formula $F = \frac{n}{4} + 37$, where n is the number of times a cricket chirps in one minute, and F is the temperature in degrees Fahrenheit. Estimate the temperature when a cricket chirps 100 times in a minute.

$$F = \frac{n}{4} + 37 \qquad \text{Write the formula.}$$
$$F = \frac{100}{4} + 37 \qquad \text{Replace } n \text{ with 100.}$$
$$F = 25 + 37 \qquad \text{Divide.}$$
$$F = 62 \qquad \text{Add.}$$

The temperature is about 62°F.

7.8.02 Solve problems involving perimeter/ circumference and area of polygons, circles, and composite figures using diagrams, models, and grids or by measuring or using given formulas (may include sketching a figure from its description).

✓ Check Skills You'll Need

Evaluate each expression for $x = 3$ and $y = 4$.

1. $2x + 2y$ **2.** $2x + y$

3. $2(x + y)$ **4.** $\frac{x + y}{2}$

GO for Help
Lesson 1-3

🔊 New Vocabulary

• formula

• perimeter

✓ Quick Check

2. Use the formula $F = \frac{n}{4} + 37$ to estimate the temperature in degrees Fahrenheit for each situation.

   a. 96 chirps/min   **b.** 88 chirps/min   **c.** 66 chirps/min

2   Using a Perimeter Formula

> **Vocabulary Tip**
>
> Think of pe**RIM**eter as the distance around the "rim" of a figure.

The **perimeter** of a figure is the distance around the figure. You can find the perimeter of a rectangle by adding the lengths of the four sides, or by using the formula $P = 2\ell + 2w$, where ℓ is the length, and w is the width. For rectangles, it does not matter which dimension you choose to be the length or the width.

3 EXAMPLE   Finding Perimeter

> **Test-Taking Tip**
>
> Read and solve the problem before looking for the correct answer.

Multiple Choice Use the formula for the perimeter of a rectangle, $P = 2\ell + 2w$. What is the perimeter of the rectangle?

  Ⓐ 60 ft   Ⓑ 61 ft   Ⓒ 62 ft   Ⓓ 64 ft

12.5 ft

18.5 ft

$P = 2\ell + 2w$	**Write the formula.**
$P = 2(18.5) + 2(12.5)$	**Replace ℓ with 18.5 and w with 12.5.**
$P = 37 + 25$	**Multiply.**
$P = 62$	**Add.**

The perimeter of the rectangle is 62 ft.

✓ Quick Check

3. Find the perimeter of each rectangle.

a. 27.3 cm   16.8 cm

b. 17.4 in.   8.6 in.

EXERCISES

For more exercises, see *Extra Skill and Word Problem Practice*.

Practice and Problem Solving

 Practice by Example

Example 1
(page 145)

Use the formula $d = rt$. Find d, r, or t.

1. $r = 38.5$ m/h, $t = 12.5$ h

2. $d = 2{,}730$ mi, $t = 9.75$ h

3. $d = 596.39$ cm, $r = 2.3$ cm/s

4. $d = 10.2$ ft, $r = 0.5$ ft/h

Example 2
(page 145)

Use the formula $F = \frac{n}{4} + 37$ to estimate each temperature.

5. 120 chirps/min

6. 80 chirps/min

7. 92 chirps/min

8. 64 chirps/min

Example 3
(page 146)

Use the formula $P = 2\ell + 2w$. Find the perimeter of each rectangle.

9.

11.2 mm

16.5 mm

10.

6.2 m

7.3 m

 Apply Your Skills

Given that C is the temperature in degrees Celsius, use the formula $F = 1.8C + 32$ to find each temperature F in degrees Fahrenheit.

11. $C = 58$ **12.** $C = -4$ **13.** $C = 72$ **14.** $C = 56$ **15.** $C = -89$

GO Online

Homework Video Tutor

Visit: PHSchool.com
Web Code: ade-0304

Geometry Use the formula $P = 2\ell + 2w$. Find the perimeter of each rectangle. Then use the formula $A = \ell w$ to find each area.

16.

3.7 m

7.3 m

17.

11.2 cm

25.8 cm

18. Multiple Choice The area of the rectangle is 27.8 square feet. Which is the best estimate of the length of the rectangle?

4 ft

Ⓐ 5 ft Ⓑ 6 ft
Ⓒ 7 ft Ⓓ 8 ft

C Challenge

19. The top surface of a world-record rectangular strawberry shortcake was 175.33 ft long and 48 in. wide. Use the formula for perimeter. Find the approximate perimeter of the cake.

20. Find the approximate area of the top of the cake in Exercise 19.

21. The state of Colorado is nearly rectangular in shape. Use the formula for area. Find the approximate area of Colorado.

22. Use the formula for perimeter. Find the approximate perimeter of Colorado.

Online lesson quiz, PHSchool.com, Web Code: ada-0304

Test Prep

ISAT

Multiple Choice

23. What is the perimeter of a rectangle that measures 32 cm by 11 cm?
    A. 352 cm   **B.** 86 cm   **C.** 54 cm   **D.** 43 cm

24. Suppose you travel 320 mi in 5 h. What is your average speed?
    F. 58 mi/h   **G.** 60 mi/h   **H.** 64 mi/h   **J.** 75 mi/h

25. A giant tortoise travels about 0.17 mi/h on land. If a tortoise travels at a constant speed, how far can it travel in 2.5 h?
    A. 0.0425 mi   **B.** 0.267 mi   **C.** 0.425 mi   **D.** 4.25 mi

Short Response

26. A rectangular yard has width w and length ℓ. **(a)** What is a formula for its perimeter, P? **(b)** Find P when w is 16.4 m and ℓ is 28.2 m.

27. The pronghorn antelope can run 0.73 mi/min. **(a)** At this speed, how far can this animal travel in 30 seconds? **(b)** In 1.5 minutes?

Mixed Review

GO for Help

Lesson 3-3

Find the mean, median, and mode. Round to the nearest whole number where necessary. Which measure of central tendency best describes the data?

28. minutes of homework
    8   125   154   120   105   125

29. milliliters per container
    250   250   355   355   375   250

Lesson 2-5

Solve each equation.

30. $c + 8 = 41$ **31.** $b + 32 = 19$ **32.** $98 = n + 42$

Lesson 1-7

33. Patterns Which equation, $n = 2t$ or $t = n \cdot 2$, describes the relationship between the variables in the table? Explain.

n	14	16	18	20
t	7	8	9	10

✓ Checkpoint Quiz 1

Lessons 3-1 through 3-4

Round each number to the underlined place value.

  1. 15.6<u>5</u>71   **2.** 0.89<u>1</u>4   **3.** 7,0<u>2</u>2.56   **4.** 345.<u>6</u>78

Estimate.

  5. $3.7 \cdot 8.06$ **6.** $17.25 + 6.66$ **7.** $8.7 - 9.6$ **8.** $11.7 \div 1.8$

Find the mean, median, and mode.

  9. $47, 56, 58, 63$ **10.** $1, 4, 1, 3, 1, 2, 3, 2, 1, 2$

  11. Jennifer drives at an average speed of 54 mi/h. At this rate, how long does it take Jennifer to drive 459 miles?

Understanding Math Problems Read the problem below. Then let Joe's thinking guide you through the solution. Check your understanding with the exercises at the bottom of the page.

3.7 m

7.3 m

Geometry Use the formula $P = 2\ell + 2w$. Find the perimeter of the rectangle. Then use the formula $A = \ell w$ to find each area.

What Joe Thinks	What Joe Writes
First I need to use the formula for perimeter.	$P = 2\ell + 2w$
Substitute 7.3 for ℓ and 3.7 for w.	$P = 2(7.3) + 2(3.7)$
I can use the Distributive Property to make the work easier.	$P = 2(7.3 + 3.7)$
Add within parentheses.	$P = 2(11)$
Now multiply.	$P = 22$
Next, I need to use the formula for area.	$A = \ell w$
Substitute 7.3 for ℓ and 3.7 for w and multiply.	$A = 7.3(3.7) = 27.01$
Now I need to write the units. Don't forget that area is in square units.	Perimeter is 22 m. Area is 27.01 m².

EXERCISES

Geometry Use the formula $P = 2\ell + 2w$. Find the perimeter of the rectangle. Then use the formula $A = \ell w$ to find each area.

1.

2.4 cm

4 cm

2.

$1\frac{1}{2}$ in.

9 in.

3.

2 ft

15 ft

3-5

Solving Equations by Adding or Subtracting Decimals

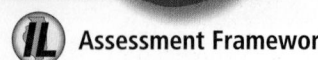
Assessment Framework

8.8.12 Solve linear equations and inequalities in one variable over the rational numbers.

8.8.13 Solve word problems involving unknown quantities.

 Check Skills You'll Need

Simplify.

1. $2.8 + 7.06$

2. $0.65 + 1.8$

3. $4.52 - 2.48$

4. $3.7 - 0.62$

GO for Help
Skills Handbook, 786

1 Using Subtraction to Solve Equations

In Lesson 2-5, you used the Subtraction Property of Equality to solve equations involving integers. You can also use this property to solve equations with decimals. Remember to subtract the same number from each side of the equation.

1 EXAMPLE Subtracting to Solve an Equation

Solve $n + 4.5 = -9.7$.

$$n + 4.5 = -9.7$$
$$n + 4.5 - 4.5 = -9.7 - 4.5 \quad \text{Subtract 4.5 from each side.}$$
$$n = -14.2 \quad \text{Simplify.}$$

Check $\quad n + 4.5 = -9.7$
$$-14.2 + 4.5 \stackrel{?}{=} -9.7 \quad \text{Replace } n \text{ with } -14.2.$$
$$-9.7 = -9.7 ✔$$

Quick Check

1. Solve each equation.

　　a. $x + 4.9 = 18.8$　　　　**b.** $14.73 = -24.23 + b$

2 EXAMPLE Real-World Problem Solving

Astronomy Use the diagram below. A communications satellite is circling Earth. About how far is the satellite from the moon?

22.3 thousand miles
x
Satellite
239.9 thousand miles
Earth
Moon
Not drawn to scale

$$22.3 \approx 22 \quad \text{Round to numbers that are}$$
$$239.9 \approx 240 \quad \text{easy to compute.}$$

$$22 + x \approx 240$$
$$22 + x - 22 \approx 240 - 22 \quad \text{Subtract 22 from each side.}$$
$$x \approx 218 \quad \text{Simplify.}$$

The satellite is about 218 thousand miles from the moon.

GO Online

Video Tutor Help
Visit: PHSchool.com
Web Code: ada-0775

✓ Quick Check

2. **Analyzing Markup** A store's cost plus markup is the price you pay for an item. Suppose a pair of shoes costs a store $35.48. You pay $70. Write and solve an equation to find the store's markup.

GO for Help

For help with adding and subtracting decimals, see Skills Handbook, page 786.

2 Using Addition to Solve Equations

You can also use the Addition Property of Equality to solve an equation involving decimals. Remember to add the same number to each side of the equation.

3 EXAMPLE Adding to Solve an Equation

Solve $k - 14.4 = -18.39$.

$$k - 14.4 = -18.39$$
$$k - 14.4 + 14.4 = -18.39 + 14.4 \quad \textbf{Add 14.4 to each side.}$$
$$k = -3.99 \quad \textbf{Simplify.}$$

Online active math

For: Decimal Equations Activity
Use: Interactive Textbook, 3-5

✓ Quick Check

3. Solve each equation.

   a. $n - 5.85 = 15.25$ b. $-10 = c - 2.6$

4 EXAMPLE Real-World Problem Solving

Gridded Response Danzel wrote a check for $76.85. His new account balance is $235.15. What was his previous balance?

| **Words** | previous balance | minus | check | is | new balance |

Let p = previous balance.

| **Equation** | p | $-$ | 76.85 | $=$ | 235.15 |

$$p - 76.85 = 235.15$$
$$p - 76.85 + 76.85 = 235.15 + 76.85 \quad \textbf{Add 76.85 to each side.}$$
$$p = 312 \quad \textbf{Simplify.}$$

Danzel's previous balance was $312.

Test-Taking Tip

On gridded items, you cannot grid the units. Here, the correct number to grid is 312.

✓ Quick Check

4. **Shopping** You spent $14.95 for a new shirt. You now have $12.48. Write and solve an equation to find how much money you had before you bought the shirt.

EXERCISES

For more exercises, see *Extra Skill and Word Problem Practice*.

Practice and Problem Solving

A Practice by Example

Examples 1 and 2
(page 150)

GO for Help

Solve each equation.

1. $c + 9 = 3.7$

2. $b + 7.6 = 23$

3. $43.6 = n + 17.5$

4. $6.35 + b = 9.89$

5. $12.13 = n + 1.4$

6. $x + 0.35 = 9.15$

7. Astronomy The planet Mars takes 599.01 days longer than Mercury to orbit the sun. In all, the Mars orbit takes 686.98 days. Write and solve an equation to find about how long it takes Mercury to orbit the sun.

8. Car Sales Julia trades in her small car for a large pickup truck that weighs 1,855.3 lb more than the car. If the truck weighs 4,360.3 lb, what is the weight of the car?

Examples 3 and 4
(page 151)

Solve each equation.

9. $d - 4.9 = 18.8$

10. $c - 19.2 = 24$

11. $-2.5 = q - 1.7$

12. $-5.6 = y - 8$

13. $4.3 = g - 1$

14. $a - 108.8 = -203$

15. Personal Finance You spent $13.50 for movie tickets. You now have $26.50. Write and solve an equation to find out how much money you had before buying the tickets.

16. Rachel wrote a check for $161.15. Her new account balance is $423.28. What was her previous account balance?

B Apply Your Skills

GO Online
Homework Video Tutor
Visit: PHSchool.com
Web Code: ade-0305

Complete the steps for each equation. Justify each step.

17.
$$x + 1.2 = 15$$
$$x + 1.2 - \blacksquare = 15 - \blacksquare$$
$$x = \blacksquare$$

18.
$$y - 3.33 = 12.42$$
$$y - 3.33 + \blacksquare = 12.42 + \blacksquare$$
$$y = \blacksquare$$

19. Running Michael Johnson's world record in the 200-m sprint is 19.32 s. His 400-m world record is 23.86 s slower than his 200-m record. Write and solve an equation to find Johnson's 400-m record.

20. Biology A hare travels about 17.83 mi/h faster on land than a giant tortoise. A hare can hop at about 18 mi/h. Write and solve an equation to find about how fast a giant tortoise can travel on land.

Solve each equation.

21. $4.035 = a - 3.25$

22. $h - (-1.5) = 1.5$

23. $e + (-7.8) = -6.7$

24. $r - 0.832 = 8.67$

25. $b - (-1.5) = -9$

26. $-32 = x + (-8.05)$

Real-World Connection

Giant tortoises can weigh up to 500 lb.

Mental Math Use mental math to solve each equation.

27. $1.60 = 0.40 + s$

28. $x + 8.8 = 9.9$

29. $5.5 = x - 5.5$

$$x - 1.6 = -6$$
$$x - 1.6 + 1.6 = -6 - 1.6$$
$$x = -7.6$$

30. Error Analysis A student solved an equation as shown at the left. Explain the student's error.

31. Writing in Math Explain how you would use the Addition (not Subtraction) Property of Equality to solve $x + 1.8 = -4.7$.

 Challenge

Solve each equation.

32. $143.587 + x - 22.96 = 156.4$ **33.** $-924.87 - 1{,}237 + b = 86.125$

34. Reasoning Without solving, tell how the solutions of the equations $x + 14 = 15, x + 1.4 = 1.5,$ and $x + 0.14 = 0.15$ compare. Explain.

Multiple Choice   **35.** Which statement describes how to solve $x + 0.042 = 0.826$?
  A. Add 0.042 to each side.   **B.** Subtract 0.042 from each side.
  C. Add 0.826 to each side.   **D.** Subtract 0.826 from each side.

Short Response   Read the cartoon below before doing Exercises 36 and 37.

Dilbert by Scott Adams

SOURCE: ©1993 United Features Syndicate, Inc.

36. How much money does the clerk owe Dilbert?

37. Dilbert does not want any pennies. What other amount of money could Dilbert have given the cashier? Justify your answer.

Mixed Review

 GO for Help

Lesson 3-4   **Use the formula $A = \ell w$. Find A.**

38. $\ell = 23.4$ in., $w = 15.8$ in.   **39.** $\ell = 5.5$ cm, $w = 7$ cm

Lesson 2-6   **Solve each equation.**

40. $6a = 24$ **41.** $-2b = 60$ **42.** $-81 = 9a$

Lesson 2-2   **43.** A large juice costs \$.83. A small juice costs \$.57. Ida buys one juice each school day. If Ida buys small juices instead of large juices, how much money will she save each week?

3-6

Solving Equations by Multiplying or Dividing Decimals

 Assessment Framework

8.8.12 Solve linear equations and inequalities in one variable over the rational numbers.

8.8.13 Solve word problems involving unknown quantities.

✓ **Check Skills You'll Need**

Find each product.

1. 2.6(4.5)

2. 3.2(0.15)

3. 11.03(0.6)

4. 8.003(0.6)

GO for Help
Skills Handbook, p. 787

---

1 Using Division to Solve Equations

In Lesson 2-6, you used the Division Property of Equality to solve equations involving integers. You can also use this property to solve equations with decimals. Remember to divide each side of the equation by the same nonzero number.

1 EXAMPLE Dividing to Solve an Equation

Solve $0.9r = -5.4$.

$$0.9r = -5.4$$

$$\frac{0.9r}{0.9} = \frac{-5.4}{0.9} \quad \text{Divide each side by 0.9.}$$

$$r = -6 \quad \text{Simplify.}$$

Check $\quad 0.9r = -5.4$

$$0.9(-6) \stackrel{?}{=} -5.4 \quad \text{Replace } r \text{ with } -6.$$

$$-5.4 = -5.4 ✓$$

✓ **Quick Check**

1. Solve each equation.

  a. $0.8x = -1.6$ **b.** $1.15 = 2.3x$ **c.** $-81.81 = -0.9n$

2 EXAMPLE Real-World 🌐 Problem Solving

GO for Help

For help with dividing decimals, see Skills Handbook, page 791.

Petroleum An oil field produces an average of 16.8 thousand barrels of crude oil per day. About how many days will it take to produce 200 thousand barrels?

Words | daily barrel production | times | number of days | equals | 200 thousand barrels

Let d = number of days.

Equation   16.8   · d =   200

$$16.8d = 200$$

$$\frac{16.8d}{16.8} = \frac{200}{16.8} \quad \text{Divide each side by 16.8.}$$

$$d = 11.904 \ldots \quad \text{Simplify.}$$

$$d \approx 12 \quad \text{Round to the nearest whole number.}$$

It will take about 12 days to produce 200 thousand barrels.

Quick Check

2. Postage You paid $7.70 to mail a package that weighed 5.5 lb. Write and solve an equation to find the cost per pound.

---

2 Using Multiplication to Solve Equations

To solve an equation involving division, multiply each side by the same nonzero number.

3 EXAMPLE Multiplying to Solve an Equation

Solve $\frac{m}{-7.2} = -12.5$.

$$\frac{m}{-7.2} = -12.5$$

$$\frac{m}{-7.2}(-7.2) = -12.5(-7.2)$$ **Multiply each side by −7.2.**

$$m = 90$$ **Simplify.**

Quick Check

3. Solve each equation.

a. $\frac{r}{-6.0} = 0.5$ **b.** $\frac{s}{2.5} = 5$ **c.** $-80 = \frac{t}{4.5}$

4 EXAMPLE Real-World Problem Solving

Multiple Choice The 1923 baseball season was one of Babe Ruth's best. He was at bat 522 times and had a batting average of 0.393, rounded to the nearest thousandth. The batting average formula is $a = \frac{h}{n}$, where a is the batting average, h is the number of hits, and n is the number of times at bat. How many hits did Babe Ruth make?

Ⓐ 522 hits Ⓑ 393 hits Ⓒ 206 hits Ⓓ 205 hits

$$a = \frac{h}{n}$$

$$0.393 = \frac{h}{522}$$ **Replace a with 0.393 and n with 522.**

$$(0.393)(522) = \frac{h}{522}(522)$$ **Multiply each side by 522.**

$$h = 205.146$$ **Simplify.**

$$h \approx 205$$ **Since h (hits) represents an integer, round to the nearest integer.**

Babe Ruth made 205 hits. The answer is D.

Quick Check

4. Suppose your batting average is 0.222. You have batted 54 times. How many hits do you have?

Real-World Connection

During his professional career, Babe Ruth was at bat 8,399 times and had a batting average of 0.342.

EXERCISES

For more exercises, see *Extra Skill and Word Problem Practice.*

Practice and Problem Solving

A **Practice by Example**

Examples 1 and 2
(page 154)

GO **for Help**

Solve each equation.

1. $0.8s = -6.4$

2. $0.8x = 0.48$

3. $-0.5y = -0.73$

4. $2x = -4.88$

5. $-0.3y = 7.53$

6. $2.21 = 1.7w$

7. $1.92 = 1.6s$

8. $3.2n = 27.52$

9. $0.7x = 2.8$

10. Manufacturing A factory produces an average of seven thousand televisions per day. About how many days will it take to produce 63.5 thousand televisions?

11. Postage You paid $5.30 to mail a package that weighed 2.5 lb. Write and solve an equation to find the mailing cost per pound.

Examples 3 and 4
(page 155)

Solve each equation.

12. $\frac{n}{2.3} = -4.8$

13. $0.97 = \frac{c}{-2}$

14. $\frac{h}{7} = -8$

15. $\frac{n}{1.7} = 0.22$

16. $\frac{k}{2.01} = 0.04$

17. $120 = \frac{v}{3.8}$

18. $9 = \frac{a}{1.5}$

19. $\frac{m}{7.08} = -100$

20. $-200 = \frac{f}{4}$

21. Batting Averages During the 1954 baseball season with the New York Yankees, Yogi Berra was at bat 584 times and had a batting average of 0.307. Use the batting-average formula in Example 4 to find the number of hits Berra made.

B **Apply Your Skills**

Solve each equation.

22. $6.4x = 0.2816$

23. $-5.1z = -11.73$

24. $0.004m = 0.12$

25. $4.5 = m \div (-3.3)$

26. $-33.04 = \frac{z}{-0.03}$

27. $-0.45 = x \div 12$

28. a. Error Analysis Harry found 324.8 as a solution for the equation $4x = 81.2$. What was Harry's error?
  b. Estimation How could Harry have used estimation to check whether his answer was reasonable?

Write an equation for each sentence. Solve for the variable.

29. The product of a number n and -7.3 is 30.66.

30. The quotient of a number n divided by -4.5 equals 200.6.

31. A number n divided by -2.35 equals 400.9.

GO **Online**
Homework Video Tutor
Visit: PHSchool.com
Web Code: ade-0306

32. a. Batting Averages Your batting average is 0.244, and you have been at bat 82 times. How many hits do you have?
  b. Writing in Math Why is it necessary to round your answer in part (a) to the nearest integer?

156 Chapter 3 Decimals and Equations

33. **Utilities** Jan pays $.08 per kilowatt-hour for electricity. Her electric bill is $59.22. Write and solve an equation to find how many kilowatt-hours of electricity Jan used.

34. **Number Sense** The weight of a record-setting onion was 12.25 lb. An average-sized onion weighs 0.5 lb. About how many average-sized onions have a total weight equal to the record-setting onion?

C Challenge

35. **Measurement** If you know a length ℓ in meters, you can multiply the length by 3.28 to find the length in feet f.
    a. Write an equation to model this situation.
    b. A tree is 7.5 m tall. Use your equation to find this height in feet.
    c. A bookshelf is 6 ft tall. What is this height in meters?
    d. A room is 12 ft long and 15 ft wide. Use your equation and the formula for the area of a rectangle to find the area of the room in square meters. Round to the nearest tenth.

36. **Reasoning** Find values for x and y that satisfy $xy = 0.42$ and $x + y = 1.3$.

37. **Batting Averages** About how many hits did Babe Ruth have during his professional career? (*Hint:* See page 155.)

ISAT

Test Prep

Multiple Choice

38. A group of friends goes out for dinner. The bill is $36.81. If they share the cost equally and each person's share is about $7.35, how many people are in the group?
    A. 4   **B.** 5   **C.** 6   **D.** 7

39. Which equation has 3.2 as its solution?
    F. $20x = 6.4$ **G.** $6.4 = 2x$ **H.** $\frac{x}{2} = 6.4$ **J.** $\frac{x}{6.4} = 2$

Short Response

40. A barber gave enough haircuts in one day to earn $337.50. Each haircut cost $12.50.   **(a)** How many haircuts did the barber give that day? **(b)** Estimate the amount of money the barber can make in a week.

Mixed Review

for Help

Lesson 3-5   **Solve each equation.**

41. $c + 9 = 3.7$ 42. $-5.6 = y - 8$ 43. $4.035 = a - 3.25$

Lesson 2-4   **Is the given number a solution of the equation? Show why.**

44. $20 - c = 12; c = 8$ 45. $8 = 2a + 3; a = 0$

Lesson 1-7   46. a. **Patterns** Multiply $99 \cdot 24, 99 \cdot 25$, and $99 \cdot 26$.
    b. Describe the pattern you found in part (a).
    c. Use the pattern to evaluate $99 \cdot 27$.

3-7 Using the Metric System

 Assessment Framework

7.8.05 Solve problems involving unit conversions within the same measurement system for length, weight/mass, capacity, square units, and measures expressed as rates.
7.8.03 Compare and estimate length using referents.

✓ **Check Skills You'll Need**

Find each product or quotient.

1. 5×100

2. $14.06 \div 1,000$

3. 0.294×10

4. $0.9 \div 100$

 for Help
Skills Handbook, p. 790

1 Identifying Appropriate Metric Measures

Knowing the approximate size of each metric unit of measure will allow you to choose an appropriate unit.

Key Concepts Metric Units of Measurement

	Unit	Reference Example
Length	millimeter (mm)	about the thickness of a dime
	centimeter (cm)	about the width of a thumbnail
	meter (m)	about the distance from a doorknob to the floor
	kilometer (km)	a little more than one half mile
Capacity	milliliter (mL)	about 5 drops of water
	liter (L)	a little more than a quart of milk
Mass	milligram (mg)	about the mass of a speck of sawdust
	gram(g)	about the mass of a paper clip
	kilogram (kg)	about one half the mass of this math book

1 EXAMPLE Choosing an Appropriate Unit

Choose an appropriate metric unit. Explain your choice.

a. height of a classroom chalkboard

Meter; the height of a chalkboard is about twice the distance from the floor to a doorknob.

b. mass of a backpack filled with books

Kilogram; the mass of a backpack filled with books is many times the mass of this textbook.

c. capacity of a birdbath

Liter; several quart bottles of water would fill a birdbath.

✓ **Quick Check**

1. Choose an appropriate metric unit. Explain your choice.

   a. length of a broom   **b.** the mass of an energy bar

   c. mass of a horse   **d.** capacity of a car's gas tank

2 EXAMPLE Estimating With Metric Units

Estimation Choose a reasonable estimate. Explain your choice.

a. capacity of a juice box: 200 mL or 200 L

200 mL; the juice box holds less than a quart of milk.

b. length of a new pencil: 15 cm or 15 m

15 cm; the length of a pencil would be about 15 widths of a thumbnail.

c. mass of a small tube of toothpaste: 100 g or 100 kg

100 g; the mass is about the same as a box of paper clips.

☑ Quick Check

2. Choose a reasonable estimate. Explain your choice.

   a. distance between two cities: 50 mm or 50 km
   b. amount of liquid that an eyedropper holds: 10 mL or 10 L

2 Converting Metric Units

The metric system uses a decimal system to relate different units to each other. Look at the metric-units chart below. The units highlighted in yellow are the units most often used. From left to right, each unit is 10 times the size of the unit before it.

	milli-	centi-	deci-	UNIT	deka-	hecto-	kilo-
Length	millimeter (mm)	centimeter (cm)	decimeter (dm)	meter (m)	dekameter (dam)	hectometer (hm)	kilometer (km)
Capacity	milliliter (mL)	centiliter (cL)	deciliter (dL)	liter (L)	dekaliter (daL)	hectoliter (hL)	kiloliter (kL)
Mass	milligram (mg)	centigram (cg)	decigram (dg)	gram (g)	dekagram (dag)	hectogram (hg)	kilogram (kg)

You can convert from one unit to another by multiplying or dividing by 10; 100; 1,000; and so on.

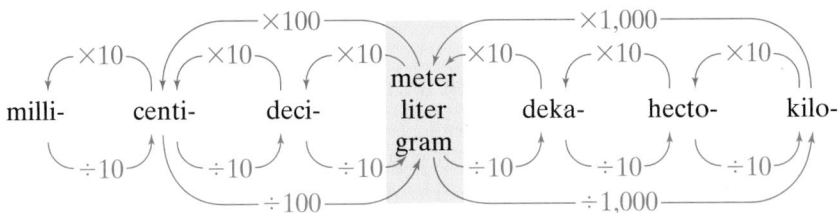

Vocabulary Tip

The prefixes, such as *milli, centi,* and *deci,* denote the relative sizes of the units.

To convert from one unit to another in the metric system, find the relationship between the two units.

Remember:
- Multiply if you are going from a larger unit to a smaller unit since there will be more of the smaller units.
- Divide if you are going from a smaller unit to a larger unit since there will be fewer of the larger units.

GO for Help

For a guide to multiplying and dividing decimals by powers of ten, see Skills Handbook, page 790.

3 EXAMPLE   **Converting Between Metric Units**

Mental Math Complete each statement.

a. 4.35 L = ■ mL

$4.35 \cdot 1{,}000 = 4{,}350$ To convert liters to milliliters, multiply by 1,000.

$4.35 \text{ L} = 4{,}350 \text{ mL}$

b. 914 cm = ■ m

$914 \div 100 = 9.14$ To convert centimeters to meters, divide by 100.

$914 \text{ cm} = 9.14 \text{ m}$

✓ Quick Check

3. Complete each statement.

   a. $35 \text{ mL} = ■ \text{ L}$ **b.** $■ \text{ g} = 250 \text{ kg}$ **c.** $■ \text{ cm} = 60 \text{ m}$

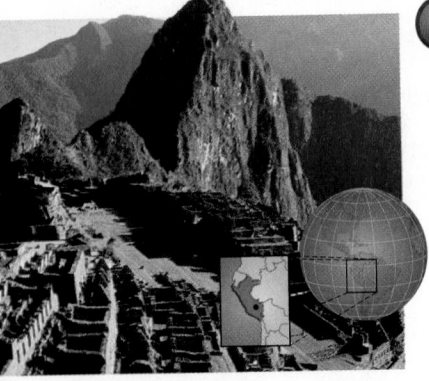

Real-World 🌐 Connection

The ancient city of Machu Picchu (c. 1450–1550) is located in Peru's Andes Mountains. It is one of the few major pre-Columbian sites found nearly intact.

4 EXAMPLE   **Real-World 🌐 Problem Solving**

Geography The ancient Incan city of Machu Picchu is located in Peru. Its altitude is about 2,300 m above sea level. What is Machu Picchu's altitude in kilometers?

Words	altitude in meters	÷	meters per kilometer	=	altitude in kilometers
Equation	2,300	÷	1,000	=	2.3

Machu Picchu is about 2.3 km above sea level.

✓ Quick Check

4. **a.** The record for the highest a kite has flown is 3.8 km. Find the height of the kite in meters.

   b. Number Sense You have a recipe that requires 0.25 L of milk. Your measuring cup is marked only in milliliters. How many milliliters of milk do you need?

EXERCISES

For more exercises, see *Extra Skill and Word Problem Practice*.

Practice and Problem Solving

A Practice by Example

Example 1
(page 158)

GO for Help

Match each quantity with an appropriate metric unit. Explain your choice.

1. length of your thumb
2. mass of a book
3. length of a soccer field
4. amount of water in a fishbowl
5. mass of an eraser
6. amount of fluid in a straw

A. gram
B. meter
C. centimeter
D. milliliter
E. liter
F. kilogram

Example 2
(page 159)

Choose a reasonable estimate. Explain your choice.

7. the mass of a small dog: 5 g or 5 kg
8. amount of liquid you should drink daily: 2,000 mL or 2,000 L
9. the mass of a box of cereal: 350 mg or 350 g

Example 3
(page 160)

Mental Math Complete each statement.

10. $54 \text{ m} = \blacksquare \text{ cm}$
11. $\blacksquare \text{ L} = 234 \text{ mL}$
12. $12 \text{ g} = \blacksquare \text{ kg}$
13. $\blacksquare \text{ m} = 3.01 \text{ km}$
14. $0.25 \text{ m} = \blacksquare \text{ cm}$
15. $\blacksquare \text{ mL} = 7.3 \text{ L}$
16. $595 \text{ g} = \blacksquare \text{ kg}$
17. $35 \text{ m} = \blacksquare \text{ km}$
18. $\blacksquare \text{ mg} = 0.27 \text{ g}$

Example 4
(page 160)

19. **Geography** Elgin Street, in Bacup, England, is the shortest street in the world. It is 518 cm long. How many meters long is it?

20. **Biology** A shrew, the mammal with the fastest metabolism, has a mass of only 0.004 kg. What is its mass in grams?

B Apply Your Skills

Choose an appropriate metric unit of measure. Explain your choice.

21. mass of a banana
22. depth of Lake Michigan
23. length of a small calculator
24. mass of a car
25. width of a highway
26. quantity of water in a spoon

27. **Error Analysis** One of the world's largest pearls had a mass of 6,392 g. Camille wrote in her report that the pearl had a mass of 6,392,000 kg. What was her error?

28. **Multiple Choice** The world's longest model train has 650 cars and is 0.695 km long. Which expression could you use to find how many meters long the train is?
    Ⓐ $650 \div 0.695$
    Ⓑ $0.695 \div 650$
    Ⓒ $0.695 \times 1,000$
    Ⓓ $695 \times 1,000$

Write the metric unit that makes each statement true.

29. $9.03 \text{ m} = 9,030 \blacksquare$
30. $890 \text{ cm} = 8.9 \blacksquare$
31. $130,000 \blacksquare = 1.3 \text{ km}$

🌐 **32. Earth Science** The flow of water over Niagara Falls averages 6,008,835,000 mL/s.
   a. On the average, about how many liters of water flow over Niagara Falls each second?
   b. About how many liters flow over the falls in a minute?

Estimation **Choose a reasonable estimate. Explain your choice.**

33. the width of a sidewalk: 150 cm or 150 m

34. the length of 24 city blocks: 2 m or 2 km

35. the mass of a thumbtack: 1 mg or 1 g

Mental Math **Complete each statement.**

36. 90,050 mL = ▦ L   **37.** ▦ m = 875 cm   **38.** 620 m = ▦ km

39. 9,120 mg = ▦ g   **40.** 900 km = ▦ m   **41.** 5 g = ▦ kg

42. ▦ cm = 13 km   **43.** 301 kg = ▦ mg   **44.** ▦ km = 562,300 cm

🌐 **45. Nutrition** A world-record grapefruit had a mass of 3,068 g. What was its mass in kilograms?

🌐 **46. Zoology** A hippopotamus is so large that it has a stomach 304.8 cm long, yet it is agile enough to outrun a human. How long is the stomach of a hippopotamus in meters?

Number Sense **Match each measurement with its equivalent measurement from the table.**

47. 0.015 km   **48.** 1,500 cm   **49.** 150,000 mg

50. 0.15 L   **51.** 15 L   **52.** 1,500 g

A. 15,000 mL	**B.** 150 cm	**C.** 150 g
D. 1.5 kg	**E.** 15 m	**F.** 150 mL
G. 150 kg	**H.** 0.15 mL	**I.** 1,500 mm

🌐 **53. Marine Biology** The blue whale is the largest of all known animals. The largest known blue whale measured 33.58 meters in length.
   a. How many millimeters long was this whale?
   b. How many kilometers long was this whale?

C Challenge 🌐 **54. Writing in Math** The prefix kilo- means "one thousand," and the prefix milli- means "one thousandth." What do the prefixes tell you about kilometer and kilogram, and milliliter and milligram?

🌐 **55. Physical Fitness** You walk about 3 mi/h.
   a. Approximately how many kilometers can you walk in an hour?
   b. How many meters can you walk in an hour?

ISAT

Test Prep

Gridded Reponse

56. The albatross has a wingspan of 3,350 mm, the largest wingspan of any bird. What is the wingspan of an albatross in meters?

57. How many milliseconds are in one second?

58. A worm is about 143 mm long. What is the length of the worm in centimeters?

59. A pitcher threw a baseball 95 mi/h at a baseball game. Rounded to the nearest foot, how many feet per second is this?

60. Sean tries to drink $2\frac{1}{2}$ qt of water every day. How many gallons does he average in a week?

Mixed Review

Lesson 3-6 **61. Knot Tying** Clinton Bailey, Sr., holds the record for knot tying. He tied six different rope knots in 8.1 s. Write and solve an equation to find his average time per knot.

Lesson 3-2 **Estimate each product or quotient.**

62. $28.134 \div 3.75$ **63.** $8.517 \cdot 9.82$ **64.** $101.49 \div 9.51$

Lessons 2-9 and 2-10 **Solve each inequality.**

65. $a - 5 \geq 16$ **66.** $n + 8 < -7$ **67.** $-3r \leq 21$

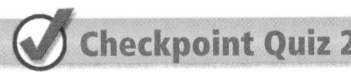

Checkpoint Quiz 2   **Lessons 3-5 through 3-7**

Solve each equation.

1. $0.5m = 0.125$ **2.** $d \div 0.3 = 28.5$ **3.** $y - 135.43 = -5.43$

4. $12.2 = 4x$ **5.** $29.25 = 4.5w$ **6.** $k + 870.9 = 1,000.5$

Choose the most reasonable estimate. Explain your choice.

7. height of a standard house window: 1.5 cm or 1.5 m

8. capacity of a shampoo bottle: 500 mL or 500 L

Complete each statement.

9. $95 \text{ mL} = \blacksquare \text{ L}$ **10.** $\blacksquare \text{ cm} = 76.5 \text{ km}$

11. $\blacksquare \text{ km} = 675 \text{ m}$ **12.** $7.1 \text{ kg} = \blacksquare \text{ g}$

13. Horses The world's smallest horse had a mass of only 9.1 kg. What was the mass of the horse in grams?

Precision and Significant Digits

The pin at the right measures about 5 cm. A more precise measurement is 4.5 cm. An even more precise measurement is 46 mm. The smaller the units on the scale of a measuring instrument, the more precise the measurement is.

1 EXAMPLE

Choose the more precise measurement.

a. 5 g or 8 mg
Since a milligram is a smaller unit of measure than a gram, 8 mg is more precise than 5 g.

b. 2.72 m or 3.5 m
A hundredth of a meter is a smaller unit of measure than a tenth of a meter. So 2.72 m is more precise than 3.5 m.

A calculation will be only as precise as the least precise measurement used in the calculation. So, round your results to match the precision of the least precise measurement.

2 EXAMPLE

Add the lengths 6.31 m, 5.447 m, and 2.8 m.

$6.31 + 5.447 + 2.8 = 14.557$ **The least precise measurement is 2.8 m. Round the sum to the**
Rounded to tenths ≈ 14.6 m   **nearest tenth of a meter.**

Digits that represent an actual measurement are *significant digits*. Nonzero digits (1–9) are always significant. The rules below will help you decide whether a zero is a significant digit.

Type of Number	Which Zeros Are Significant	Example
decimal numbers between 0 and 1	Zeros to the left of *all* the nonzero digits are not significant. All other zeros are significant.	significant digits 0.006040 not significant digits
positive integers	Zeros to the right of *all* the nonzero digits are not significant (unless specifically known to be). Zeros between nonzero digits are significant.	significant digits 203,400 not significant digits
noninteger decimal numbers greater than 1	All zeros are significant.	significant digits 350.07050

3 EXAMPLE

How many significant digits are in 0.0504 m?

The 5 and the 4 are significant. The zero between them is significant. The other zeros are not significant. There are three significant digits.

When you multiply or divide measurements, round your answer to match the least number of significant digits in the problem.

4 EXAMPLE

A plot for a new house measures 152.6 m by 121 m. What is the area of the plot? Use significant digits.

┌───── **3 significant digits**

$152.6 \cdot 121 = 18{,}464.6$ ◄──── **Multiply.**

└───── **4 significant digits**

The area is 18,500 m². ◄──── **Round the area to 3 significant digits.**

EXERCISES

Choose the more precise measurement.

1. 3 m or 5.2 m   **2.** 8 mL or 9.5 L   **3.** 1.89 km or 8.7 cm   **4.** 1.9 kg or 1.87 kg

5. Error Analysis Your friend says that 4.35 km is more precise than 5.2 cm because a hundredths unit is a smaller unit than a tenths unit. What mistake did your friend make?

Find each sum or difference. Round to the place value of the less precise measurement.

6. 5.6 g + 8 g   **7.** 8.35 kg + 6.2 kg   **8.** 8.2 km − 1.75 km   **9.** 9 cm − 2.3 cm

Determine the number of significant digits in each measurement.

10. 0.069 m   **11.** 100.5 L   **12.** 3,400 kL   **13.** 5.2100 km

Find each product or quotient. Use significant digits.

14. 1,234 in. · 31 in.   **15.** 0.0702 ft · 227 ft   **16.** 16,250 m ÷ 14.5 s   **17.** 132.5 cm · 43.2 cm

3-8 Problem Solving **Act It Out**

What You'll Learn

- To solve problems by acting them out

...And Why

To solve real-world problems involving motion

 Check Skills You'll Need

Write a rule for each number pattern. Find the next three numbers in the pattern.

1. $0, 6, 12, 18, \ldots$

2. $-18, -9, 0, 9, \ldots$

3. $0, 2, 1, 3, 2, 4, 3, \ldots$

4. $7, 6, 8, 7, 9, 8, 10, \ldots$

GO for Help
Lesson 1-7

1 Simplify the Problem

Math Strategies in Action
Have you ever wondered how public speakers manage to talk to large audiences in a relaxed manner? Many public speakers brainstorm their topic ahead of time. Then they act

out their speech by practicing in front of a mirror. You can *Act It Out* to solve math problems. Here is a well-known problem that can be solved by acting it out.

1 EXAMPLE **Real-World** **Problem Solving**

A snail is trying to escape from a well 10 ft deep. The snail can climb 2 ft each day, but each night it slides back 1 ft. How many days will the snail take to climb out of the well?

Understand the Problem

A snail needs to climb 10 ft to escape from a well. It can climb 2 ft per day. At night the snail slides back 1 ft.

1. How far up the well will the snail be after the first day and the first night?

2. How far up the well will the snail be after the second day?

3. How far up the well will the snail be after the second day and the second night?

Make a Plan

At first you might think that the snail progresses 1 ft each day and will therefore take 10 days to escape. This answer is wrong, however, because it leaves out an important part of the problem.

To act out the problem, stand up and follow these steps:

- Move forward two steps to *simulate*, or model, the snail's climb during the day.
- Then move backward one step to simulate the snail's slide back during the night.

Carry Out the Plan

Act out the problem, keeping track of your progress in a table like the one below.

Time	Progress
Day 1	Up 2 ft from bottom
Night 1	Up 1 ft from bottom
Day 2	Up 3 ft from bottom

4. Copy and complete the table, acting out the rest of the problem. How many days will it take for the snail to make it out of the 10-ft well?

Check the Answer

You can check whether your answer is reasonable by drawing a diagram.

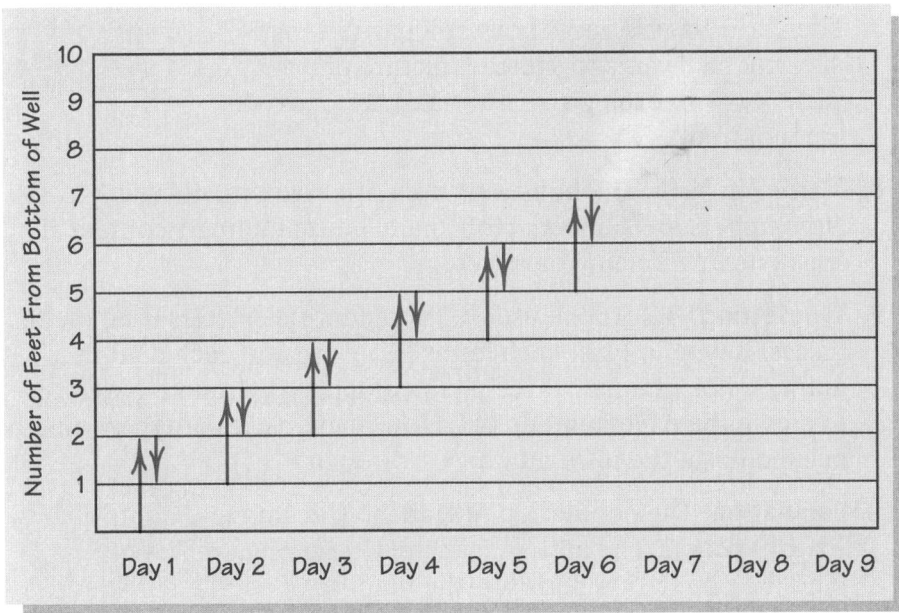

✓ Quick Check

5. Copy and complete the diagram to check your answer.

EXERCISES

For more exercises, see *Extra Skill and Word Problem Practice*.

Practice and Problem Solving

A **Practice by Example**

Example 1
(page 166)

GO for Help

Solve by acting out each problem.

1. Sports In a tennis tournament, each athlete plays one match against each of the other athletes. There are 12 athletes scheduled to play in the tournament. How many matches will be played?

2. Fencing A rancher wants to build a fence for a square lot with dimensions of 50 yd by 50 yd. He wants to install a fence post every 5 yd with a post at each corner. How many fence posts will he need?

3. Elections Four candidates run for president of the student council. Three other candidates run for vice-president. In how many different ways can the two offices be filled?

B **Apply Your Skills**

Strategies

- Act It Out
- Draw a Diagram
- Guess, Check, Revise
- Look for a Pattern
- Make a Model
- Make a Table
- Simulate the Problem
- Solve by Graphing
- Use Multiple Strategies
- Work a Simpler Problem
- Work Backward
- Write an Equation
- Write a Proportion

Solve using any strategy.

4. The school store buys pencils for $.20 each. It sells the pencils for $.25 each. How much profit does the store make if it sells five dozen pencils?

5. Construction To accommodate a wheelchair, a builder installed countertops that are 0.75 ft lower than the original ones. The new countertops are 2.5 ft high. How high were the original countertops?

6. What is the total number of squares in the figure at the right?

7. There are 10 girls and 8 boys at a party. A cartoonist wants to sketch a picture of each boy with each girl. How many sketches are required?

8. Writing in Math The houses on your street are numbered 1 to 120. No numbers are skipped. How many house numbers contain at least one 5? Explain your strategy.

9. Typesetting Before the use of computers, typesetters used metal pieces of type to print each letter in a word and each digit in a number. For example, three pieces of type—1, 4, and 8—were used to create the page number 148. How many pieces of type would be needed to set the page numbers 1 through 476?

C **Challenge**

10. Population The population of Rancho Cucamonga, California, is 151,640 people. The area of Rancho Cucamonga is 37.4 mi^2. Find the population density—the number of people per square mile. Show your work.

11. Seating Arrangements Ana, Brian, Carla, David, and Eric are friends. They go to a movie but cannot find five seats together. They have to split up into a group of three and a group of two. How many different ways can the friends organize themselves into these two groups?

GO Online

Homework Video Tutor

Visit: PHSchool.com
Web Code: ade-0308

Multiple Choice What is the solution of each equation?

12. $x - 8 = -4.8$

    A. -12.8 **B.** -3.2 **C.** 3.2 **D.** 12.8

13. $8 + c = -2.3$

    F. -10.3 **G.** -5.7 **H.** 5.7 **J.** 10.3

14. $7.53 = -0.3y$

    A. 25.1 **B.** 2.26 **C.** -2.26 **D.** -25.1

Short Response **15.** A corral is ringed by 60 ft of fencing with posts every 4 ft. How many fence posts are there? Show your work.

Mixed Review

Lesson 3-7 **Measurement Complete each statement.**

    16. $27 \text{ cm} = \blacksquare \text{ m}$ **17.** $5{,}200 \text{ km} = \blacksquare \text{ m}$ **18.** $2{,}000 \text{ mg} = \blacksquare \text{ g}$

    19. $0.5 \text{ L} = \blacksquare \text{ mL}$ **20.** $3 \text{ m} = \blacksquare \text{ cm}$ **21.** $6 \text{ kg} = \blacksquare \text{ mg}$

Lesson 3-3 **22. Test Scores** Your test scores so far this semester are 100, 90, 82, 96, and 78. You have one more 100-point test to take. Including the last test, what is your highest possible average?

Lesson 3-1 **Estimate using front-end estimation.**

    23. $\$9.54 + \$1.25$ **24.** $\$6.72 + \$5.28$ **25.** $\$12.19 + \$5.66$

Math at Work

Woodworker

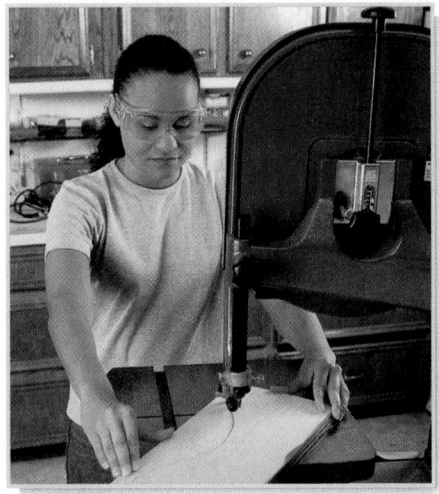

Woodworkers cut, shape, assemble, and finish wood to create tables, chairs, and other types of furniture. To create these items, woodworkers must plan and carry out many individual steps in sequence.

Machines used in professional woodworking shops cut and shape wood with great precision. The most sophisticated machines are controlled by computer programs. Woodworkers can enhance their skills by taking mathematics and computer courses that develop their ability to think three-dimensionally.

Go Online
PHSchool.com   **For:** Information about woodworkers   **Web Code:** adb-2031

Writing Extended Responses

An extended-response question can be worth as many as four points. It often has multiple parts. To get full credit, you need to answer each part and show all of your work or justify your thinking.

EXAMPLE

To get a 90 for this grading period, Jerilyn needs a test average of 94.5. She had a 93.2 average on her first three tests and scored 97 on the fourth test. **(a)** Explain in words how to find the next score she needs. **(b)** Write an equation to find the fifth test score. **(c)** Solve your equation.

Here are three responses with the points each received.

4 points	3 points	1 point
There are 5 tests. For a test average of 94.5, the sum of the test scores must be 5 times 94.5, or 472.5 points.	There are 5 tests. For a test average of 94.5, the sum of the test scores must be 5 times 94.5, or 472.5 points.	Let g = grade on fifth test.
Let g = grade on fifth test.	Let g = grade on fifth test.	$93.2 + 97 + g = 90$
$3(93.2) + 97 + g = 472.5$	$3(93.2) + 97 + g = 472.5$	$190.2 + g = 90$
$376.6 + g = 472.5$	$276.9 + 97 + g = 472.5$	$g = 90 - 190.2$
$g = 472.5 - 376.6$	$373.9 + g = 472.5$	$g = 100.2$
$g = 95.9$	$g = 472.5 - 373.9$	
Jerilyn must score 95.9 or higher on her fifth test.	$g = 98.6$	
	Jerilyn must score 98.6.	

The 4-point response shows the work and gives a written answer to the problem. Note that it identifies the variable before writing the equation. The 3-point response contains a computational error, but the student completed all parts. The 1-point response shows an incorrect equation, and it does not explain the process.

EXERCISES

Use the Example above to do each exercise.

1. **Error Analysis** What is the error in the 3-point response?

2. Write a possible 2-point response for the problem. Explain why it is worth 2 points.

Chapter Review

Vocabulary Review

compatible
  numbers (p. 135)
formula (p. 145)

mean (p. 139)
measures of central
  tendency (p. 139)

median (p. 139)
mode (p. 139)
outlier (p. 140)

perimeter (p. 146)
range (p. 139)

Choose the vocabulary word that completes each sentence.

1. The sum of a group of data items divided by the number of data items is the   ? .

2. Numbers that are easy to divide are called   ? .

3. The data item that occurs most often in a group is the   ? .

4. A data item that is much greater or much less than the rest of the data items in a group is a(n)   ? .

5. When an odd number of data items are written in order, the middle item is the   ? .

6. An equation that shows a relationship between quantities that are represented by variables is a(n)   ? .

7. Numbers that describe groups of data items are called   ? .

8. The distance around a figure is the   ? .

Go Online
PHSchool.com

For: Vocabulary quiz
Web Code: adj-0351

Skills and Concepts

3-1 Objectives

▼ To round decimals (p. 129)

▼ To estimate sums and differences (p. 130)

You can estimate the sum of decimals by rounding, front-end estimating, or clustering.

You can estimate the difference of decimals by rounding.

Estimate each sum or difference. State which method you used.

9. $3.14 + 6.952$

10. $10.2538 - 6.095$

11. $14.451 + 9.736$

12. $14.27 - 4.268$

13. $20.681 + 19.39 + 20.56$

14. $12.814 - 6.3791$

15. $9.0426 + 2.7182$

16. $21.9384 - 15.639$

17. $6.257 + 6.129 + 6.34$

18. $19.83 - 14.268$

19. Explain when you would use each estimation method named above to estimate a sum of decimals. Use examples.

🌐 20. **Weather** Last year Lake Jones rose to 672.42 feet during the spring floods. This year Lake Jones rose to 711.36 feet. About how much higher did the lake rise this year?

3-2 Objectives

▼ To estimate products (p. 134)

▼ To estimate quotients (p. 135)

You can estimate a product by rounding. You can estimate a quotient of two decimals by using **compatible numbers.**

Estimate each product or quotient.

21. 8.15(6.04)

22. 19.28 ÷ 5.439

23. 1.9 · 4.92

24. 25.1 ÷ 4.87

25. 12.497 · 0.894

26. 59.3581 ÷ 11.5304

27. 3.59(−2.3291)

28. −17.45 ÷ 3.059

29. (−2.0936)(−5.6892)

3-3 Objectives

▼ To find mean, median, mode, and range of a set of data (p. 139)

▼ To choose the best measure of central tendency (p. 141)

You can use a **measure of central tendency** to describe a collection of data. The **mean** is the sum of the data items divided by the number of data items. The **median** is the middle value or the mean of the two middle values when the data are written in order. The **mode** is the data item that occurs most often. The **range** is the difference between the greatest and least values in a data set. An **outlier** is a data item that is much greater or much less than the rest of the data items.

Find the mean, median, and mode. When an answer is not an integer, round to the nearest tenth. Identify any outliers.

30. 2, 3, 6, 2, 8, 9, 5, 10, 4, 5

31. 16.1, 16.3, 15.9, 16.2, 16.3, 16.3, 15.8

32. 32, 35, 31, 57, 33, 30, 34

33. 0.1, 7.9, 0.2, 0.3, 0.1, 0.2, 0.1, 0.1, 0.3

Which measure of central tendency best describes each situation? Explain.

34. the favorite radio stations of teenagers in your neighborhood

35. the numbers of videos owned by students in your class

36. the prices of 8-oz containers of yogurt at six local grocery stores

3-4 Objectives

▼ To substitute into formulas (p. 145)

▼ To use the formula for the perimeter of a rectangle (p. 146)

A **formula** is an equation that shows a relationship between quantities that are represented by variables. You can use formulas to find such things as **perimeter,** area, and distance.

Evaluate each formula for the values given.

37. distance: $d = rt$
when $r = 35$ mi/h and $t = 2$ h

38. area of a rectangle: $A = \ell w$
when $\ell = 16$ mm and $w = 24$ mm

39. Circumference: $C = 2\pi r$
when $r = 6$ in. Use 3.14 for π.

40. perimeter of a square: $P = 4s$
when $s = 13$ cm

▼ To solve one-step
decimal equations
involving subtraction
(p. 150)

▼ To solve one-step
decimal equations
involving addition
(p. 151)

▼ To solve one-step
decimal equations
involving division
(p. 154)

▼ To solve one-step
decimal equations
involving multiplication
(p. 155)

To solve a one-step equation, use an inverse operation and a property of equality to get the variable alone on one side of the equation.

Solve each equation.

41. $n + 3.8 = 10.9$ **42.** $y - 6.72 = 2.53$ **43.** $h + 0.67 = -1.34$

44. $t - 2.7 = 23.5$ **45.** $12.9 + x = 3.8$ **46.** $5.7 = b - 4.9$

47. $6.3m = 15.75$ **48.** $a \div 4.9 = 8.33$ **49.** $v \cdot 7.1 = 80.23$

50. $c \div 12.5 = 77.5$ **51.** $-5.7z = 110.58$ **52.** $d \div 4.75 = -38.95$

53. Finance On Monday a stock is worth $3.20 per share. By Friday the stock is worth $2.64 per share.
  a. Write an equation to model the change in price.
  b. Solve the equation to find the amount by which the price changed.

The **metric system** of measurement uses a decimal system to relate units to one another. To measure, you must choose an appropriate unit of measure.

Choose an appropriate metric unit of measure. Explain each choice.

54. height of a building   **55.** mass of a bicycle   **56.** amount of milk in a glass

Mental Math Complete each statement.

57. $0.85 \text{ m} = \blacksquare \text{ cm}$ **58.** $160 \text{ mL} = \blacksquare \text{ L}$ **59.** $2.3 \text{ m} = \blacksquare \text{ cm}$

60. $1.6 \text{ kg} = \blacksquare \text{ g}$ **61.** $0.62 \text{ L} = \blacksquare \text{ mL}$ **62.** $80 \text{ g} = \blacksquare \text{ kg}$

63. Explain why centimeters would be an inappropriate unit to measure the height of a mature oak tree.

You can solve some problems by acting them out.

64. School Mike, Don, Tameka, and Rosa sit in the four desks in the last row of desks. Each day they sit in a different order. How many days can they do this before they repeat a seating pattern?

65. Recreation You are hiking with three friends. You pass a group of six hikers going the other way. Each person in one group greets each person in the other group. How many greetings are there? Explain.

Estimate each value.

1. $6.43 - 4.079$

2. $2.06 + 3.91$

3. $5.97 - 1.674$

4. $6.025 + 0.35$

5. $8.54 + 2.3$

6. $6.25 \cdot 9.87$

7. $12.89 \div 3.04$

8. $1.76 \cdot 3.93$

9. $4.96 \div 2.49$

10. $3.2 \cdot 14.69$

Find the mean, median, mode, and range. When an answer is not an integer, round to the nearest tenth. Identify any outliers.

11. $11, 12, 9, 13, 10, 12, 11, 14, 12$

12. $5.3, 5.6, 5.2, 5.0, 5.4, 5.6, 5.1, 5.0$

13. $10.6, 9.8, 11.6, 29.1, 3.4, 11.4, 12.7$

14. $8.7, 8.5, 8.7, 8.5, 8.6, 8.5, 8.7, 8.6$

Evaluate each formula for the given values.

15. area of a rectangle: $A = \ell w$
    when $\ell = 3.8$ in. and $w = 1.5$ in.

16. perimeter of a square: $P = 4s$
    when $s = 4.7$ cm

17. perimeter of a rectangle: $P = 2\ell + 2w$
    when $\ell = 2.9$ m and $w = 6.05$ m

Solve each equation.

18. $x + 7.8 = 12.5$

19. $n - 5.9 = 0.5$

20. $4.1 + c = -1.2$

21. $d - 6.3 = 11$

22. $-9.7 + h = 10.3$

23. $m \div 2.7 = 14.58$

24. $h \cdot 4.7 = 30.55$

25. $b \div (-7.8) = -79.56$

26. $-3.4t = 30.94$

Write an appropriate metric unit of measure for each quantity.

27. the height of a truck

28. the capacity of a standard shampoo bottle

29. the mass of a pineapple

30. the width of a paperback book

Complete.

31. 4.5 m = ■ cm

32. 68 mL = ■ L

33. 90 kg = ■ g

34. $6,700$ cm = ■ m

35. 4 L = ■ mL

36. 50.2 g = ■ kg

For Exercises 37 and 38, write an equation, and then solve.

37. **Shopping** You spend $6.50 on a pair of gloves. You now have $7.00. How much money did you have originally?

38. **Reptiles** The fastest speed recorded for a reptile on land is 9.7 m/s for a spiny-tailed iguana. At this rate, how long would it take this iguana to travel 116.4 m?

39. **Geography** Madrid and Barcelona are cities in Spain. The distance between them is 636,000 m. What is this in kilometers?

40. **Mechanics** A mechanical toy on a circular track goes forward 3 in. and then backward 2 in. How many moves does the toy take to complete one 15-in. revolution of the track?

41. **Data Analysis** Which measure of central tendency best describes the weights of the dogs in one neighborhood?

    15 lb, 20 lb, 18 lb, 27 lb, 15 lb, 70 lb

    A. mean

    B. median

    C. mode

    D. all of the above

42. **Writing in Math** Explain how the outlier in the data set affects the mean.

    $3, 2, 6, 3, 5, 4, 15, 4, 3$

Reading Comprehension Read the passages below. Then answer the questions on the basis of what is stated or implied in each passage.

> **Milk and Calcium** Doctors and dieticians agree that calcium is an important part of good nutrition as calcium helps to build and maintain strong bones. The recommended daily intake of calcium for adults is 1,000 mg. The National Academy of Sciences recommends that people from 9 to 18 years of age get at least 1,300 mg of calcium per day. Milk, perhaps the best-known source for calcium, has 300 mg of calcium per cup.

1. Which is true about *n*, the number of milligrams of calcium recommended daily for an adult?
   - (A) $n > 1{,}000$
   - (B) $n < 1{,}000$
   - (C) $n = 1{,}000$
   - (D) $n = 10{,}000$

2. Which is true about *c*, the number of milligrams of calcium recommended daily for people ages 9 to 18?
   - (E) $c = 1{,}000$
   - (F) $c > 1{,}300$
   - (G) $c < 1{,}300$
   - (H) $c \geq 1{,}300$

3. How many more milligrams of calcium per day does a young person need than an adult?
   - (A) 300 mg
   - (B) 1,000 mg
   - (C) 1,300 mg
   - (D) 10,000 mg

4. How many full cups of milk does 14-year-old Janet have to drink if she is going to get her daily-recommended amount of calcium from milk?

> **Other Sources of Calcium** Although one slice of cheese pizza supplies 220 milligrams of calcium, dairy products are not the only source of calcium. For example, $\frac{3}{4}$ cup of a certain brand of cereal supplies 330 mg of calcium, 1 cup of broccoli supplies 90 mg of calcium, and 3 oz of canned salmon with bones supplies 180 mg of calcium. You can get 300 mg from one cup of calcium-fortified orange juice. However, it is important to know that exercising can do as much to help you build strong bones as calcium in your diet.

5. Which of these foods has the most calcium per portion?
   - (E) cheese pizza
   - (F) cereal
   - (G) broccoli
   - (H) salmon

6. How many cups of broccoli give you 45 mg of calcium?
   - (A) 0.25 cup
   - (B) 0.5 cup
   - (C) 1 cup
   - (D) 2 cups

7. How many cups of orange juice would supply exactly 1,000 mg of calcium?

8. How else can you build strong bones besides getting enough calcium from food?

9. From the items in the passage, plan what you could eat that would give you exactly 1,300 mg of calcium in a day. Make a list to show your one-day diet.

What's $10 Worth?

Applying Decimals If you shop with an older adult, you may have heard the statement, "Ten dollars isn't worth what it used to be!" Of course, $10 is always worth ten $1 bills, or 40 quarters, or 100 dimes. That doesn't change. What does change is the price of items. For example, a stamp for a letter cost $.03 back in 1950. The 2002 cost of a stamp, $.37, is more than twelve times that price. Back in 1950, you could buy 333 first-class stamps with a $10 bill. In 2002, a $10 bill would get you only 27 stamps!

A $10 bill in 1950 looked like this.

A $10 bill in 2000 looked like this.

$10 Bills

Federal Reserve Notes began circulating in 1913. The design remained virtually unchanged until May 2000, and then changed again in 2006.

1975
$.13

Commercial Aviation
USA 13c
1926-1976

2002
$.37

1932
$.03

UNITED STATES
100 YEARS OF PROGRESS
1848 OF WOMEN 1948
3¢

1995
$.32

32
usa

1991
$.29

Percy Lavon Julian
29
Black Heritage USA

MOVI

Averages — Then and Now

Item	1950	2002
New home	$9,422	$169,000
Weekly income	$29	$572
Washing machine	$64.95	$379

Movie Tickets — Then and Now

In 1950, it cost 46¢ to go to a movie in the United States. The average price in 2002 was $5.81—more than 12 times as much.

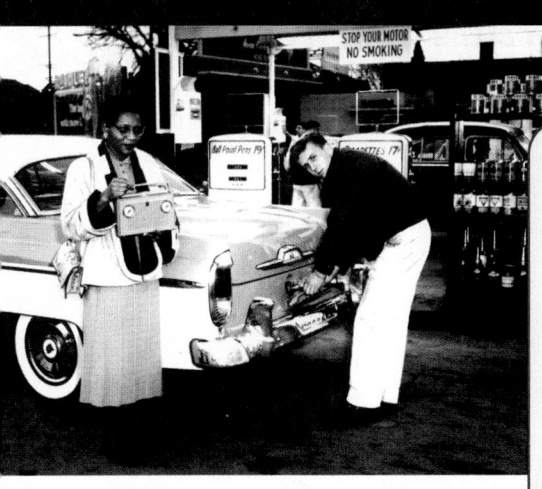

Full Service

In the 1950s, gas-station attendants pumped your gas, checked your oil, and washed your windshield. Mechanics were ready to help if something was wrong with your car.

Activity

Suppose you have a $10 bill.

1. How many pounds of steak could you buy in 1950? In 2002?

2. **a.** How many gallons of gas could you buy in 1950?
   b. How much would that same gas have cost you in 2002?

3. Compare the prices of milk.
   a. What fraction of the 2002 price is the 1950 price?
   b. How many times the 1950 price is the 2002 price?

4. Suppose you earn the average weekly income and you buy the items on the shopping list.
   a. What is your total cost in 1950? In 2002?
   b. What part of your weekly income is this in 1950? In 2002?
   c. **Writing in Math** In which year is the average worker better off, 1950 or 2002? Explain.

Shopping List

2 loaves bread
1 lb coffee
2 gal milk
1 dozen muffins
2 bars soap
1 lb steak
3 cans tuna

Prices of Common Items

Item	Cost in 1950	Cost in 2002
Bread (1 loaf)	$.18	$1.49
Coffee (1 lb)	$.93	$3.29
Cookies (12-oz package)	$.39	$2.59
Gas (1 gal)	$.20	$1.35
Milk (1 gal)	$.92	$3.05
Muffins (6)	$.24	$2.89
Soap (2 bars)	$.29	$1.79
Steak (1 lb)	$.77	$3.89
Tuna (1 large can)	$.25	$1.39

Go Online
PHSchool.com

For: Information about the 1950s
Web Code: ade-0353

What You've Learned

IL Assessment Framework

- **6.8.10:** In Chapter 1, you learned how to add, subtract, multiply, and divide integers.

- **8.8.12:** In Chapter 2, you solved equations by adding, subtracting, multiplying, and dividing.

- **6.8.13:** In Chapter 3, you estimated solutions and solved equations with decimals.

 Check Your Readiness   **for Help** to the Lesson in green.

Multiplying Three or More Factors (Lesson 1-9)

Find each product.

1. $12 \cdot 12 \cdot 12$ **2.** $(-4)(-4)(-4)$ **3.** $9 \cdot 9 \cdot 9 \cdot 9$

4. $5 \cdot 5 \cdot 5 \cdot 5 \cdot 5 \cdot 5$ **5.** $8 \cdot 8 \cdot 8$ **6.** $(-2)(-2)(-2)(-2)(-2)(-2)$

Multiplying Whole Numbers (Skills Handbook, p. 781)

Write two numbers that, when multiplied, result in each product.

7. 12   **8.** 45   **9.** 18   **10.** 63   **11.** 24

12. 50   **13.** 32   **14.** 81   **15.** 54   **16.** 60

17. 28   **18.** 56   **19.** 44   **20.** 36   **21.** 72

Dividing Whole Numbers (Skills Handbook, p. 782)

Find each quotient.

22. $720 \div 8$ **23.** $7,200 \div 8$ **24.** $6\overline{)132}$

25. $3\overline{)147}$ **26.** $\frac{189}{9}$ **27.** $\frac{450}{10}$

28. $424 \div 2$ **29.** $700 \div 5$ **30.** $92 \div 4$

31. $5\overline{)135}$ **32.** $\frac{273}{3}$ **33.** $10\overline{)1,300}$

Factors, Fractions, and Exponents

Chapter
4

 Key Vocabulary

What You'll Learn Next

IL Assessment Framework

In this chapter, you will learn how to

- **6.8.10:** Simplify expressions with exponents.
- **6.8.10:** Simplify fractions.
- **6.8.04:** Write and calculate in scientific notation.
- **6.8.09:** Solve problems by accounting for all possibilities.

 Activity Lab Applying what you learn, on pages 232–233 you will solve problems about cicada emergence cycles.

179

Divisibility and Factors

What You'll Learn

- To use divisibility tests
- To find factors

...And Why

To solve real-world problems involving arrangements

✓ Check Skills You'll Need

Find each quotient.

1. $480 \div 3$ **2.** $365 \div 5$

3. $459 \div 9$ **4.** $288 \div 6$

5. $\frac{354}{2}$ **6.** $\frac{354}{3}$

GO for Help
Skills Handbook, p. 782

🔊 New Vocabulary
- divisible
- factor

1 Using Divisibility Tests

One integer is **divisible** by another if the remainder is 0 when you divide. Because $18 \div 3 = 6$, 18 is divisible by 3. You can test for divisibility using mental math.

Key Concepts — Divisibility Rules for 2, 5, and 10

An integer is divisible by

- 2 if it ends in 0, 2, 4, 6, or 8.
- 5 if it ends in 0 or 5.
- 10 if it ends in 0.

Even numbers end in 0, 2, 4, 6, or 8 and are divisible by 2.
Odd numbers end in 1, 3, 5, 7, or 9 and are not divisible by 2.

1 EXAMPLE — Divisibility by 2, 5, and 10

Is the first number divisible by the second? Explain.

a. 567 by 2   No; 567 does not end in 0, 2, 4, 6, or 8.

b. 1,015 by 5   Yes; 1,015 ends in 5.

c. 111,120 by 10   Yes; 111,120 ends in 0.

✓ Quick Check

1. Is the first number divisible by the second? Explain.

   a. 160 by 5   **b.** 56 by 10   **c.** 53 by 2   **d.** 1,118 by 2

To see a pattern for divisibility by 3 and 9, compare the answers to the questions asked in this table.

Number	Sum of digits	Is the sum divisible by 3?	Is the sum divisible by 9?	Is the number divisible by 3?	Is the number divisible by 9?
282	$2 + 8 + 2 = 12$	Yes	No	Yes	No
468	$4 + 6 + 8 = 18$	Yes	Yes	Yes	Yes
215	$2 + 1 + 5 = 8$	No	No	No	No
1,017	$1 + 0 + 1 + 7 = 9$	Yes	Yes	Yes	Yes

The pattern in the table suggests the following rules for divisibility by 3 and 9.

Vocabulary Tip

The words divisibility, divisor, and dividend are all related to the verb <u>divide</u>.

Key Concepts   Divisibility Rules for 3 and 9

An integer is divisible by
- 3 if the sum of its digits is divisible by 3.
- 9 if the sum of its digits is divisible by 9.

2 EXAMPLE   **Divisibility by 3 and 9**

Is the first number divisible by the second? Explain.

a. 567 by 3   Yes; $5 + 6 + 7 = 18$. 18 is divisible by 3.

b. 1,015 by 9   No; $1 + 0 + 1 + 5 = 7$. 7 is not divisible by 9.

✓ Quick Check

2. Is the first number divisible by the second? Explain.
   a. 64 by 9   **b.** 472 by 3   **c.** 174 by 3   **d.** 43,542 by 9

2   Finding Factors

You can form the three rectangles at the right with 12 squares. Each rectangle has an area of 12 square units. Their dimensions, 1, 2, 3, 4, 6, and 12, are the *factors* of 12. One integer is a **factor** of another nonzero integer if it divides that integer with remainder zero.

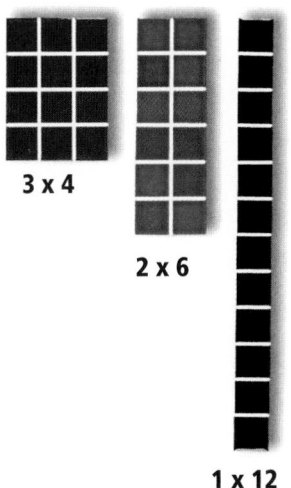

3 x 4

2 x 6

1 x 12

3 EXAMPLE   <u>Real-World</u> 🌐 <u>Problem Solving</u>

Concerts There are 20 students singing at a school concert. Each row of singers must have the same number of students. If there are at least 5 students in each row, what are all the possible arrangements?

   $1 \cdot 20,\ 2 \cdot 10,\ 4 \cdot 5$ **Find the factors of 20.**

There can be 1 row of 20 students, 2 rows of 10 students, or 4 rows of 5 students.

✓ Quick Check

3. List the positive factors of each integer.
   a. 10   **b.** 21   **c.** 24   **d.** 31
   e. What are the possible arrangements for Example 3 if there are 36 students singing at the concert?

EXERCISES

For more exercises, see *Extra Skill and Word Problem Practice*.

Practice and Problem Solving

A Practice by Example

Example 1
(page 180)

GO for Help

Example 2
(page 181)

Is the first number divisible by the second? Explain.

1. 20 by 10   **2.** 37 by 2   **3.** 45 by 5   **4.** 240 by 2

5. 60 by 5   **6.** 123 by 2   **7.** 1,468 by 2   **8.** 2,005 by 10

9. 78 by 9   **10.** 69 by 3   **11.** 108 by 9   **12.** 258 by 3

13. 3,694 by 9   **14.** 5,751 by 9   **15.** 123 by 3   **16.** 456 by 3

Example 3
(page 181)

List the positive factors of each integer.

17. 4   **18.** 8   **19.** 23   **20.** 75

21. Drill Team There are 32 students in the school drill team performance. Each row of team members must have the same number of students. If there are at least 8 students in each row, what are all the possible arrangements?

B Apply Your Skills

State whether each number is divisible by 2, 3, 5, 9, 10, or none. Explain. Some numbers may have more than one divisor.

22. 111   **23.** 131   **24.** 288   **25.** 300

26. 52   **27.** 891   **28.** 4,805   **29.** 437,684

30. a. Which of the following numbers are divisible by both 2 and 3?
     10   66   898   4,710   975
b. Which of the numbers above are divisible by 6?
c. Using your results, write a divisibility rule for 6.

Show all possible ways that each integer can be written as the product of two positive factors.

31. 25   **32.** 28   **33.** 32   **34.** 35

35. 37   **36.** 50   **37.** 53   **38.** 72

Write the missing digit to make each number divisible by 9.

39. 22■,034   **40.** 3■,817   **41.** 2,03■,371   **42.** 1■,111

43. Writing in Math If a number is divisible by 9, is it also divisible by 3? Explain how you reached your conclusion.

44. Reasoning John made oatmeal cookies for a class bake sale. The cookies need to be distributed equally on 2 or more plates. If each plate gets at least 7 cookies, what are the possible combinations for the totals below?
a. 42 cookies   **b.** 56 cookies
c. 60 cookies   **d.** 144 cookies

Challenge 45. **a.** Copy and complete the table.

Number	Last two digits	Are last two digits divisible by 4?	Is the number divisible by 4?
136	36	Yes	Yes
1,268	68	Yes	Yes
314	14	No	No
1,078	▪	▪	▪
696	▪	▪	▪

b. Reasoning Write a divisibility rule for 4.

Open-Ended Write three numbers greater than 20 that match each description.

46. Divisible by 5, but not divisible by 10

47. Divisible by 3, but not divisible by 5, 9, or 10

48. Divisible by 2, 3, 5, and 10, but not divisible by 9

49. **Reasoning** If a is divisible by 2, what can you conclude about $a + 1$? Justify your answer.

ISAT

Multiple Choice 50. Which list shows all the positive factors of 15?
  A. 1, 15   **B.** 1, 3, 15   **C.** 1, 5, 15   **D.** 1, 3, 5, 15

51. Which list shows all the positive factors of 17?
  F. 1, 17   **G.** 1, 7, 17   **H.** 1, 2, 7, 17   **J.** 1, 2, 8, 17

52. Which number is NOT a factor of 438?
  A. 2   **B.** 3   **C.** 5   **D.** 6

Short Response 53. **a.** What three positive numbers less than 100 are divisible by 2, 3, and 5?
  b. Justify your answer.

Mixed Review

Lesson 3-7 **Complete each statement.**

54. 24 ▪ = 24,000 mg

55. 18.2 km = 1,820,000 ▪

Lesson 2-9 56. **Grocery Shopping** You have $5 to spend at the grocery store. You need $2.89 for a gallon of milk. Write and solve an inequality to show how much money m you can spend on a box of cereal.

Lesson 1-3 **Evaluate.**

57. $3y + 3$, for $y = 8$

58. $4(2 + a)$, for $a = 10$

Using Concept Maps to Connect Ideas

For Use With Lesson 4-1

One way to show connections among ideas is to draw a diagam called a concept map. The lines in a concept map connect related ideas.

EXAMPLE

Make a concept map with the terms from Chapter 4 related to factors.

composite number
divisible
factor
greatest common factor
prime factorization
prime number

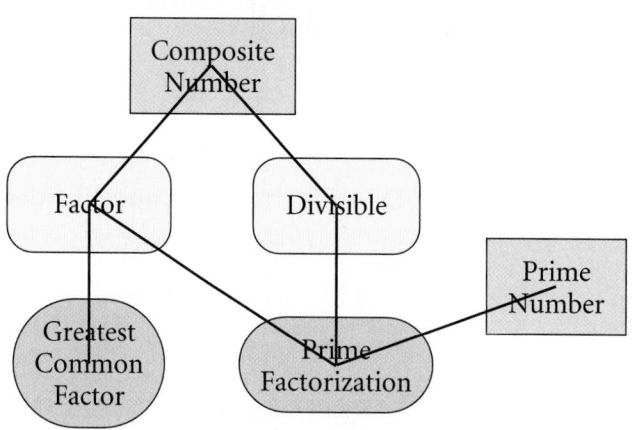

EXERCISES

1. Copy the concept map at the right. Fill in the ovals using the appropriate terms listed below.

axes
coordinate plane
ordered pair
origin
quadrants
x-axis
x-coordinate
y-axis
y-coordinate

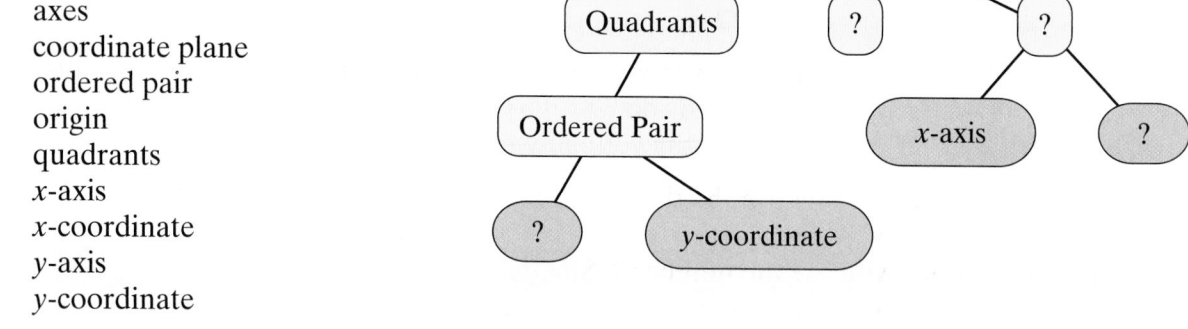

2. Use the list below to make a concept map for exponents.

base
exponent
power
scientific notation

1. Fold a sheet of paper in half as shown below. Count the number of sections made by the fold.

2. Fold it in half again. Count the number of sections made by the two folds.

3. Continue folding the paper. Copy and complete the first two columns of the table below.

Number of Times You Fold the Paper in Half	Number of Sections the Folds Make	Written as Multiplication of 2
1	2	2
2	▪	$2 \cdot 2$
3	▪	▪
4	▪	▪

4. You can rewrite each value in the second column by multiplying 2 several times, as shown in the third column. Copy and complete the third column of the table.

5. Extend your table for 5, 6, and 7 folds.

6. **Reasoning** What do you notice about the number of folds in the first column and the number of times you write the number "2" in the third column?

7. You can write the expressions in the third column using *exponents*. For example, $2 = 2^1$, where the exponent, 1, indicates the number of times you use the number 2. Similarly, $4 = 2 \cdot 2 = 2^2$. Add a fourth column to your table. Write the expression from the third column using exponents.

8. **Predict** Look at the patterns that are developing in your table. What is the digit in the ones' place for the value of 2^{15} expressed without an exponent?

9. a. You can rewrite the equation $\frac{32}{2} = 16$ as $\frac{2^5}{2} = 2^4$. What is the value of $\frac{2^3}{2}$?

   b. **Make a Conjecture** What is the value of 2^0?

4-2 Exponents

 Assessment Framework

6.8.08 Solve problems involving descriptions of numbers, including characteristics and relationships.

6.8.05 Represent repeated factors using exponents.

6.8.10 Identify and apply order of operations to simplify numeric expressions.

 Check Skills You'll Need

Find each product.

1. $3 \cdot 3 \cdot 3 \cdot 3$

2. $-12 \cdot (-12)$

3. $(-4)(-4)(-4)$

4. $10 \cdot 10 \cdot 10 \cdot 10$

 for Help
Lesson 1-9

🔊 **New Vocabulary**

• exponents
• power
• base

GO **Online**

Video Tutor Help
Visit: PHSchool.com
Web Code: ada-0775

1 Using Exponents

You can use **exponents** to show repeated multiplication.

$$\text{base} \rightarrow 2^{\overset{\displaystyle exponent}{\downarrow}}_{\underset{\displaystyle power}{}} = \underbrace{2 \cdot 2 \cdot 2 \cdot 2 \cdot 2 \cdot 2}_{\text{The base 2 is used as a factor 6 times.}} = 64 \leftarrow \begin{array}{l}\text{the value of} \\ \text{the expression}\end{array}$$

A **power** has two parts, a **base** and an exponent. The expression 2^6 is read as "two to the sixth power." Depending on the situation, you may decide to communicate an idea using either a power or the value of the power.

Power	Verbal Expression	Value
12^1	*Twelve to the first power*	12
6^2	*Six to the second power, or six squared*	$6 \cdot 6 = 36$
$(0.2)^3$	*Two tenths to the third power, or two tenths cubed*	$(0.2)(0.2)(0.2) = 0.008$
-7^4	*The opposite of the quantity seven to the fourth power*	$-(7 \cdot 7 \cdot 7 \cdot 7) = -2,401$
$(-8)^5$	*Negative eight to the fifth power*	$(-8)(-8)(-8)(-8)(-8) = -32,768$

1 EXAMPLE Using an Exponent

Write the expression using an exponent.

a. $(-5)(-5)(-5)$

$(-5)^3$ Include the negative sign within parentheses.

b. $-2 \cdot a \cdot b \cdot a \cdot a$

$-2 \cdot a \cdot a \cdot a \cdot b$ Rewrite the expression using the Commutative and Associative Properties.

$-2a^3b$ Write $a \cdot a \cdot a$ using exponents.

✓ **Quick Check**

1. Write using exponents.

     a. $6 \cdot 6 \cdot 6$ **b.** $4 \cdot y \cdot x \cdot y$ **c.** $(-3)(-3)(-3)(-3)$

2 EXAMPLE   Real-World 🌐 Problem Solving

Science A microscope can magnify a specimen 10^3 times. How many times is that?

$10^3 = 10 \cdot 10 \cdot 10$ **The exponent indicates that the base 10 is used as a factor 3 times.**

$\qquad = 1{,}000$ **Multiply.**

The microscope can magnify the specimen 1,000 times.

✓ Quick Check

● **2. a.** Simplify 7^2.   **b.** Evaluate $-a^4$ and $(-a)^4$, for $a = 2$.

B

C

Real-World 🌐 Connection

Human blood cells are shown here magnified (A) 10^2 times, (B) 10^3 times, and (C) 10^4 times.

2 ◢ Using the Order of Operations With Exponents

You can extend the order of operations to include exponents.

Key Concepts | **Order of Operations**

1. Work inside grouping symbols.
2. Simplify any terms with exponents.
3. Multiply and divide in order from left to right.
4. Add and subtract in order from left to right.

---

3 EXAMPLE   Using the Order of Operations

a. Simplify $4(3 + 2)^2$.

$4(3 + 2)^2 = 4(5)^2$ **Work within parentheses first.**

$\qquad\qquad = 4 \cdot 25$ **Simplify 5^2.**

$\qquad\qquad = 100$ **Multiply.**

b. Evaluate $-2x^3 + 4y$, for $x = -2$ and $y = 3$.

$-2x^3 + 4y = -2(-2)^3 + 4(3)$ **Replace x with -2 and y with 3.**

$\qquad\qquad = -2(-8) + 4(3)$ **Simplify $(-2)^3$.**

$\qquad\qquad = 16 + 12$ **Multiply from left to right.**

$\qquad\qquad = 28$ **Add.**

✓ Quick Check

3. a. Simplify $2 \cdot 5^2 + 4 \cdot (-3)^3$.
● **b.** Evaluate $3a^2 + 6$, for $a = -5$.

🌐nline
active math

For: Order of Operations Activity
Use: Interactive Textbook, 4-2

EXERCISES

For more exercises, see *Extra Skill and Word Problem Practice.*

Practice and Problem Solving

A Practice by Example

Example 1
(page 186)

Write using exponents.

1. $8 \cdot 8 \cdot 8$ **2.** $r \cdot r \cdot r \cdot r \cdot s \cdot s$ **3.** $-7 \cdot a \cdot a \cdot b$

4. $5 \cdot 5 \cdot a \cdot a$ **5.** $9 \cdot 9 \cdot 9 \cdot 9 \cdot 9$ **6.** $(-5)(-5)(-5)(-5)$

Example 2
(page 187)

Simplify.

7. 10^4 **8.** 4^3 **9.** 2^6 **10.** $(-4)^3$ **11.** -4^3 **12.** $(-6)^3$

13. Science An electron microscope can magnify a specimen about 10^6 times. How many times is that?

Example 3
(page 187)

Simplify.

14. $3(4 + 2)^2$ **15.** $49 - (4 \cdot 2)^2$ **16.** $-3^2 + 5 \cdot 2^3$

17. $2(9 - 4)^2$ **18.** $25 - (3 \cdot 2)^2$ **19.** $2 \cdot (-2)^4 + 10^1$

Evaluate.

20. $3a^2 - 2$, for $a = 5$ **21.** $c^3 + 4$, for $c = -6$

22. $-4y^2 + y^3$, for $y = 3$ **23.** $2m^2 + n$, for $m = -3$ and $n = 4$

B Apply Your Skills

 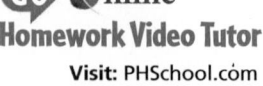

Write using exponents.

24. $-5 \cdot x \cdot x \cdot 3 \cdot y$ **25.** d cubed   **26.** $-2 \cdot a \cdot (-4) \cdot b \cdot b$

Visit: PHSchool.com
Web Code: ade-0402

27. Error Analysis A student gives ab^3 as an answer when asked to write $ab \cdot ab \cdot ab$ using exponents. What is the student's error?

Simplify.

28. -1^8 and $(-1)^8$ **29.** -2^4 and $(-2)^4$ **30.** $15 + (4 + 6)^2 \div 5$

31. $(-4)(-6)^2 (2)$ **32.** $(4 + 8)^2 \div 4^2$ **33.** $(12 - 3)^2 \div (2^2 - 1^2)$

Evaluate each expression.

34. $-6m^2$, for $m = 2$ **35.** $5k^2$, for $k = 1.2$

36. $8 - x^3$, for $x = -2$ **37.** $3(2m + 5)^2$, for $m = 2$

38. $4(2y - 3)^2$, for $y = 5$ **39.** $y^2 + 2y + 5$, for $y = -6$

n	$4n$	4^n	n^4
1	■	■	■
2	■	■	■
3	■	■	■
4	■	■	■

40. a. Copy and complete the table at the left.
    b. For what value(s) of n is each sentence true?
      $4^n = n^4$ $4^n < n^4$ $4^n > n^4$

41. a. Science A certain microscope can magnify a specimen about 10^4 times. How many times is that?
    b. Reasoning Would you use 10^4 or your answer to part (a) to compare the power of the microscope to other microscopes? Explain.

42. Reasoning Does $-a^2 = (-a)^2$ for any values of a? Explain.

43. Mental Math Given that $2^{10} = 1{,}024$, find 2^{11} mentally.

Challenge

Geometry Exercises 44–47 involve cubes made from smaller cubes, like the one at the left. Suppose such a cube has edges of length 5 cm.

44. What is the area of a face?   **45.** What is the volume?

Find the length of an edge of a cube that has each measurement.

46. face area of 64 in.^{2} **47.** a volume of 64 in.^{3}

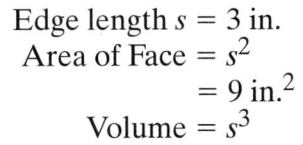

Edge length $s = 3$ in.
Area of Face $= s^2$
          $= 9$ in.^{2}
Volume $= s^3$
          $= 27$ in.^{3}

48. Language Arts Why do you think *squared* and *cubed* are used to indicate the second power and the third power?

49. Reasoning Describe all pairs of values of x and y for which $5x^2y = 5xy^2$. Justify your answer.

50. Writing in Math Evaluate $(-1)^m$ for $m = 2, 4,$ and 6. Then evaluate $(-1)^m$ for $m = 1, 3,$ and 5. Write a conjecture about the sign of an even power of a negative number. Then write a conjecture about the sign of an odd power of a negative number.

ISAT

Test Prep

Multiple Choice

51. What is the value of $(0.5)^2$?
   A. 0.1   **B.** 0.25   **C.** 1.0   **D.** 25

52. What is the value of xy^2 for $x = 3$ and $y = 4$?
   F. 12   **G.** 24   **H.** 36   **J.** 48

53. Which expression equals 1?
   A. -1^2 **B.** $(-1)^3$ **C.** $-(-1)^2$ **D.** $|-1|^3$

Short Response

54. Is $a^3 \geq a$ for all integer values of a? Explain and give an example.

Mixed Review

Lesson 4-1

State whether each number is divisible by 2, 3, 5, 9, 10, or none.

55. 36   **56.** 135   **57.** 171   **58.** 190

59. 253   **60.** 123   **61.** 117   **62.** 30

Lesson 3-3

63. a. Sara's grades are 79, 82, 75, 86, and 93. What is the mean?
   b. What is the median?

Lesson 2-3

Simplify each expression.

64. $3x - 2y + x$ **65.** $w + 8 - 4w - 15$ **66.** $9a + 2(a - 5) + 3$

4-3

Prime Factorization and Greatest Common Factor

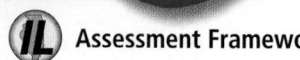
6.8.08 Solve problems involving descriptions of numbers, including characteristics and relationships (e.g., exponents, roots, prime/composite, prime factorization, greatest common factor, least common multiple).

☑ **Check Skills You'll Need**

List the positive factors of each number.

1. 15   **2.** 35   **3.** 7

4. 20   **5.** 100   **6.** 121

GO for Help
Lesson 4-1

🔊 **New Vocabulary**

• **prime number**
• **composite number**
• **prime factorization**
• **greatest common factor (GCF)**

1 | **Finding Prime Factorizations**

Activity

Exploring Prime Numbers

The diagram shows the only rectangle you can make with integer side lengths and an area of 5 square units. Work with a partner. Find the number of rectangles you can make with each number of unit squares: 2, 3, 4, 5, 6, 7, 8, 9, and 10.

1. For which numbers of squares is only one rectangle possible?

2. For which numbers of squares is more than one rectangle possible?

3. List the dimensions of the rectangles you can make with each of the following numbers of unit squares: 13, 15, 17, 19, and 21.

A **prime number** is an integer greater than 1 with exactly two positive factors, 1 and the number itself. The numbers 2, 3, 5, and 7 are prime numbers.

A 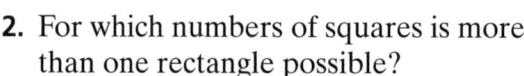 **composite number** is an integer greater than 1 with more than two positive factors. The numbers 4, 6, 8, 9, and 10 are composite numbers. The number 1 is neither prime nor composite.

1 **EXAMPLE** **Prime or Composite?**

State whether each number is *prime* **or** *composite.* **Explain.**

a. 23   Prime; it has only two factors, 1 and 23.

b. 129 Composite; it has more than two factors, 1, 3, 43, and 129.

☑ **Quick Check**

1. Which numbers from 10 to 20 are prime? Which are composite?

Writing a composite number as a product of its prime factors shows the **prime factorization** of the number. You can use a *factor tree* to find prime factorizations. Write the final factors in increasing order from left to right. Use exponents to indicate repeated factors.

2 EXAMPLE   Writing the Prime Factorization

Use a factor tree to write the prime factorization of 825.

Prime → 5 · 165	Start with a prime factor.
Prime → 5 · 33	Continue branching.
Prime → 3 · 11	Stop when all factors are prime.
5 · 5 · 3 · 11	Write the prime factorization.

$825 = 3 \cdot 5^2 \cdot 11$ Use exponents to write the prime factorization.

✓ Quick Check

2. Write the prime factorization of each number.

   a. 72   **b.** 121   **c.** 225   **d.** 236

2 Finding the Greatest Common Factor

Factors that are the same for two or more numbers or expressions are *common factors*. The greatest of these common factors is called the **greatest common factor (GCF).** You can use prime factorization to find the GCF of two or more numbers or expressions. If there are no prime factors and variable factors in common, the GCF is 1.

3 EXAMPLE   Finding the GCF

Find the GCF of each pair of numbers or expressions.

a. 40 and 60

$$40 = 2^3 \cdot 5$$
$$60 = 2^2 \cdot 3 \cdot 5$$

Write the prime factorizations.

Find the common factors. Use the lesser power of the common factors.

$$GCF = 2^2 \cdot 5$$
$$= 20$$

The GCF of 40 and 60 is 20.

b. $6a^3b$ and $4a^2b$

$$6a^3b = 2 \cdot 3 \cdot a^3 \cdot b$$
$$4a^2b = 2 \cdot 2 \cdot a^2 \cdot b$$

$$GCF = 2 \cdot a^2 \cdot b$$
$$= 2a^2b$$

The GCF of $6a^3b$ and $4a^2b$ is $2a^2b$.

Quick Check

3. Use prime factorizations to find each GCF.

   a. $8, 20$ **b.** $12, 87$ **c.** $12r^3, 8r$ **d.** $15m^2n, 45m$

You can find the GCF of two or more numbers or expressions by listing factors or by using prime factorizations.

More Than One Way

A parade organizer wants each of three marching bands to have the same number of band members in each row. The bands have 48, 32, and 56 band members. What is the greatest number of band members possible for each row?

Jasmine's Method

List the factors of each number. Then find the greatest factor the numbers have in common.

48: 1, 2, 3, 4, 6, ⑧ 12, 16, 24, 48

32: 1, 2, 4, ⑧ 16, 32

56: 1, 2, 4, 7, ⑧ 14, 28, 56

The GCF of 48, 32, and 56 is 8. The greatest possible number of band members in each row is 8.

Daryl's Method

Find the prime factorization of each number. Then find the least power of all common prime factors.

48: $2^4 \cdot 3$

32: 2^5

56: $2^3 \cdot 7$

The GCF of 48, 32, and 56 is 2^3, or 8. The greatest possible number of band members in each row is 8.

Choose a Method

1. Which method do you prefer to find the GCF? Explain why.

2. Which method would you use to find the GCF of 4, 8, and 24? Of 54, 27, and 36? Explain why.

EXERCISES

For more exercises, see *Extra Skill and Word Problem Practice.*

Practice and Problem Solving

A Practice by Example

Example 1
(page 190)

State whether each number is prime or composite. Explain.

1. 27   **2.** 19   **3.** 31   **4.** 38

5. 45   **6.** 53   **7.** 87   **8.** 93

GO for Help

Example 2
(page 191)

Write the prime factorization of each number.

9. 8   **10.** 49   **11.** 34   **12.** 42

13. 360   **14.** 115   **15.** 186   **16.** 621

Example 3
(page 191)

Use prime factorization to find each GCF.

17. 10, 45   **18.** 14, 21   **19.** 25, 100   **20.** 57, 84

21. $14c^2, 35c$ **22.** $3y^2, 24y^3$ **23.** $18c^3, 24c^3$ **24.** $6m^3n, 8mn^2$

B Apply Your Skills

Is each number prime, composite, or neither? For each composite number, write the prime factorization.

25. 17   **26.** 1   **27.** 49   **28.** 522

29. Organization A math teacher and a science teacher combine their first-period classes for a group activity. The math class has 24 students and the science class has 16 students. The teachers need to divide the students into groups of the same size. Each group must have the same number of math students. Find the greatest number of groups possible.

Find each GCF.

30. 6, 8, 12   **31.** 42, 65   **32.** 54, 144   **33.** 8, 16, 20

34. 12, 18, 21   **35.** 143, 169   **36.** z, z^2 **37.** $180a^2, 210a$

38. x^2y, xy^2 **39.** a^3b, a^2b^2 **40.** c^3df^2, c^2d^2f **41.** a^2b, b^2c, ac^2

42. Multiple Choice Factors of 6 less than 6 are 1, 2, and 3.
Factors of 8 less than 8 are 1, 2, and 4.
6 is a perfect number: $1 + 2 + 3 = 6$
8 is not a perfect number: $1 + 2 + 4 \neq 8$
Which of the following is a perfect number?
    Ⓐ 24   Ⓑ 26   Ⓒ 28   Ⓓ 30

43. Open-Ended The GCF of 36 and x is 6. What are two possible values for x?

GO **O**nline
Homework Video Tutor
Visit: PHSchool.com
Web Code: ade-0403

44. Seating Arrangements Organizers for a high school graduation have set up chairs in two sections. They put 126 chairs for graduates in the front section and 588 chairs for guests in the back section. If all rows have the same number of chairs, what is the greatest number of chairs possible for a row?

Online *lesson quiz,* **PHSchool.com,** *Web Code:* ada-0403

C Challenge   **Is each number prime, composite, or neither? For each composite number, write the prime factorization.**

45. 253　　　　**46.** 1,575　　　　**47.** 1,003　　　　**48.** 283

Two numbers are *relatively prime* if their GCF is 1. Are the numbers in each pair below relatively prime? Explain.

SAMPLE　　8, 17　Yes, 8 and 17 are relatively prime. The GCF is 1.
　　　　　　7, 35　No, 7 and 35 are not relatively prime. The GCF is 7.

49. 3, 20　　　　**50.** 9, 42　　　　**51.** 13, 52　　　　**52.** 24, 47

53. 52, 65　　　　**54.** 63, 74　　　　**55.** 15, 22　　　　**56.** 42, 72

57. <u>Writing in Math</u>　Explain how to find the prime factorization of 50.

ISAT

Test Prep

Multiple Choice　　In Exercises 58 and 59, what is the GCF of each given pair?

58. $27x^2y^3$ and $46x^2y$
　　A. $3x^2y$　　　　**B.** x^2y^2　　　　**C.** x^2y　　　　**D.** $9x^2y$

59. $25b^2c$ and $42bc$
　　F. bc^2　　　　**G.** bc　　　　**H.** b^2c　　　　**J.** b^2c^2

60. For which pair is the GCF 12?
　　A. 3, 4　　　　**B.** $24x^2$, 36y　　　　**C.** 12xy, 24y　　　　**D.** 3x, 12x

61. Simon is covering a wall with equal-sized tiles that cannot be cut into smaller pieces. The wall is 66 inches high by 72 inches wide. What is the area of the largest square tile that Simon can use?
　　F. 9 in.^{2}　　　　**G.** 16 in.^{2}　　　　**H.** 36 in.^{2}　　　　**J.** 64 in.^{2}

Extended Response　　**62. a.** Is the product of two prime numbers also prime?
　　　　　　　　　　　　b. Justify your answer.　　**c.** Give an example.

Mixed Review

Lesson 4-2　　**Evaluate for $x = 2$ and $y = 5$.**

63. x^2y　　　　**64.** xy^2　　　　**65.** $x^2 + y^2$　　　　**66.** $x^4 - y$

Lesson 3-6　　**Solve each equation.**

67. $3x = 5.4$　　　　　　　　　**68.** $-0.5a = 4.35$

69. $4.32 = 1.6y$　　　　　　　**70.** $-8m = -74.4$

Lesson 2-7　🌐 **71. Bookstore**　A store manager ordered three times as many books as magazines. She ordered a total of 108 books and magazines. How many books did she order?

In a **Venn diagram** you use circles to represent collections of objects. The intersection, or overlap, of two circles indicates what is common to both collections.

1 EXAMPLE

School coaches plan to send notices to all students playing fall or winter sports. How many notices do they need to send?

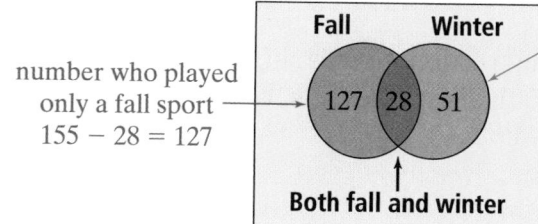

Students in Sports

Season	Students
Fall	155
Winter	79
Both fall and winter	28

number who played only a fall sport
$155 - 28 = 127$

number who played only a winter sport
$79 - 28 = 51$

Add all three numbers to find the number of notices needed.

$127 + 28 + 51 = 206$

Both fall and winter

• The coaches need to send 206 notices.

You can use a Venn diagram to find the GCF of two numbers.

2 EXAMPLE

Find the GCF of 30 and 84.

Include the common prime factors of 30 and 84 in the intersection.

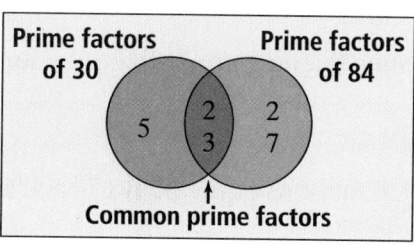

Common prime factors

The GCF is the product of the factors in the intersection.

• The GCF is 2 · 3, or 6.

EXERCISES

1. In a class of 38 students, 32 are wearing jeans, 21 are wearing T-shirts, and 15 are wearing both. How many students are wearing jeans and something other than a T-shirt?

Draw a Venn diagram to find the GCF of each pair of numbers.

2. 24, 56   **3.** 35, 49   **4.** 36, 84   **5.** 72, 108

4-4 Simplifying Fractions

IL Assessment Framework

6.8.10 Identify and apply order of operations to simplify numeric expressions involving integers (including exponents and roots), fractions, and decimals.

✓ **Check Skills You'll Need**

Find each GCF.

1. $14, 21$ **2.** $48, 60$

3. $5mn, 15m^2n$

4. $63r^2, 48s^3$

 for Help
Lesson 4-3

🔊 **New Vocabulary**

• equivalent fractions
• simplest form

Vocabulary Tip

Most fraction names are made by adding *th* or *ths* to the denominator. You read $\frac{1}{4}$ as "one fourth," $\frac{2}{5}$ as "two fifths," and $\frac{8}{10}$ as "eight tenths." Halves and thirds are two exceptions.

 Finding Equivalent Fractions

Each fraction model below represents one whole. The blue model is divided into four equal parts. The orange model is divided into twelve equal parts.

$\frac{3}{4}$ of the model is shaded.

$\frac{9}{12}$ of the model is shaded.

$\frac{3}{4} = \frac{3 \cdot 3}{4 \cdot 3} = \frac{9}{12}$

The fraction models show that $\frac{3}{4} = \frac{9}{12}$. The fractions $\frac{3}{4}$ and $\frac{9}{12}$ are **equivalent fractions** because they describe the same part of a whole.

You can find equivalent fractions by multiplying or dividing the numerator and denominator by the same nonzero factor.

1 EXAMPLE **Finding an Equivalent Fraction**

Find two fractions equivalent to $\frac{4}{12}$.

a. $\frac{4}{12} = \frac{4 \cdot 3}{12 \cdot 3}$

$= \frac{12}{36}$

b. $\frac{4}{12} = \frac{4 \div 4}{12 \div 4}$

$= \frac{1}{3}$

The fractions $\frac{12}{36}$ and $\frac{1}{3}$ are both equivalent to $\frac{4}{12}$.

✓ **Quick Check**

1. Find two fractions equivalent to each fraction.

  a. $\frac{5}{15}$ **b.** $\frac{10}{12}$ **c.** $\frac{14}{20}$

2 Writing Fractions in Simplest Form

A fraction is in **simplest form** when the numerator and the denominator have no common factors other than 1. You can use the GCF to write a fraction in simplest form. In some situations, you may need to choose between simplest form and an equivalent fraction.

Statistics You survey your friends about their favorite sandwich and find that 8 out of 12, or $\frac{8}{12}$, prefer peanut butter. Write this fraction in simplest form. Which fraction best communicates the survey results? Why?

The GCF of 8 and 12 is 4.

$$\frac{8}{12} = \frac{8 \div 4}{12 \div 4} \qquad \text{Divide the numerator and denominator by the GCF, 4.}$$

$$= \frac{2}{3} \qquad \text{Simplify.}$$

The favorite sandwich of $\frac{2}{3}$ of your friends is peanut butter. The fraction $\frac{2}{3}$ best communicates the survey results because most people have a mental picture of $\frac{2}{3}$ but not of $\frac{8}{12}$.

Real-World **Connection**

The average American child will eat 1,500 peanut butter and jelly sandwiches by the time she or he graduates from high school.

✓ Quick Check

2. Write each fraction in simplest form.

 a. $\frac{6}{8}$ **b.** $\frac{9}{12}$ **c.** $\frac{28}{35}$

You can often simplify a fraction that contains a variable. In this book, you may assume that no expression for a denominator equals zero.

3 EXAMPLE **Simplifying a Fraction**

Write in simplest form.

a. $\dfrac{y}{xy}$

$$\frac{y}{xy} = \frac{y^1}{x\not{y}_1} \qquad \text{Divide the numerator and denominator by the common factor, } y.$$

$$= \frac{1}{x} \qquad \text{Simplify.}$$

b. $\dfrac{3ab^2}{12ac}$

$$\frac{3ab^2}{12ac} = \frac{3 \cdot a \cdot b \cdot b}{2 \cdot 2 \cdot 3 \cdot a \cdot c} \qquad \text{Write as a product of prime factors.}$$

$$= \frac{3^1 \cdot a^1 \cdot b \cdot b}{2 \cdot 2 \cdot {}_1 3 \cdot {}_1 a \cdot c} \qquad \text{Divide the numerator and denominator by the common factors.}$$

$$= \frac{b \cdot b}{2 \cdot 2 \cdot c} \qquad \text{Simplify.}$$

$$= \frac{b \cdot b}{4 \cdot c}$$

$$= \frac{b^2}{4c}$$

Test-Taking Tip

You will see the directions *write in lowest terms* on some tests. This is another way of saying "write in simplest form."

✓ Quick Check

3. Write in simplest form. **a.** $\dfrac{b}{abc}$ **b.** $\dfrac{2mn}{6m}$ **c.** $\dfrac{24x^2y}{8xy}$

EXERCISES

For more exercises, see *Extra Skill and Word Problem Practice.*

Practice and Problem Solving

Practice by Example

Example 1
(page 196)

Find two fractions equivalent to each fraction.

1. $\frac{2}{8}$ 2. $\frac{8}{10}$ 3. $\frac{3}{9}$ 4. $\frac{8}{36}$ 5. $\frac{6}{18}$ 6. $\frac{20}{22}$

Example 2
(page 197)

Write each fraction in simplest form.

7. $\frac{3}{9}$ 8. $\frac{4}{10}$ 9. $\frac{12}{48}$ 10. $\frac{2}{10}$ 11. $\frac{4}{12}$ 12. $\frac{6}{15}$

GO for Help

13. **Health** Doctors suggest that most people need about 8 h of sleep each night to stay healthy. What fraction of the day is this? Write your answer in simplest form.

Example 3
(page 197)

Write in simplest form.

14. $\frac{2x}{3x}$ 15. $\frac{4km^2}{12k}$ 16. $\frac{b}{bc}$ 17. $\frac{24x}{16}$

18. $\frac{8pr}{12p}$ 19. $\frac{14a^2}{24a}$ 20. $\frac{4bc}{16b}$ 21. $\frac{40ab^2}{5ab}$

Apply Your Skills

Find two fractions equivalent to each fraction.

22. $\frac{4}{8}$ 23. $\frac{4}{10}$ 24. $\frac{5}{20}$ 25. $\frac{10}{16}$ 26. $\frac{25}{100}$

27. **Error Analysis** A student claims $\frac{65}{91}$ is in simplest form. Do you agree? Explain.

GO for Help

For a guide to reading and solving Exercise 27, see page 200.

Write in simplest form.

28. $\frac{8}{14}$ 29. $\frac{18}{32}$ 30. $\frac{20}{30}$ 31. $\frac{12}{16}$ 32. $\frac{15^3}{15^2}$ 33. $\frac{56pq}{7pq}$

34. $\frac{5c^2d}{15c}$ 35. $\frac{4r^3st}{36st^2}$ 36. $\frac{5t}{10t^2}$ 37. $\frac{x^2y}{3yz}$ 38. $\frac{12gh}{8g^2h^2}$ 39. $\frac{6m^2n^2}{9mn^2}$

40. In a survey, 27 out of 45 students say that chocolate is their favorite flavor of frozen yogurt.
  a. Write the fraction $\frac{27}{45}$ in simplest form.
  b. **Reasoning** When might you want to use the fraction $\frac{27}{45}$?

41. **Open-Ended** Write two fractions whose simplest form is $\frac{3x}{5}$.

42. **Writing in Math** Does $\frac{1}{2}$ of one pizza represent the same amount as $\frac{1}{2}$ of another pizza? Justify your answer.

GO Online

Homework Video Tutor

Visit: PHSchool.com
Web Code: ade-0404

Challenge

PC and On-Line Households in the U.S. (millions)

Households	2000	2001
Total households	105	109
Households with PCs	54	60
Households with Internet access	44	55

Source: U.S. Census Bureau

Data Analysis The table shows the number of personal computers (PCs) and households with Internet access in the United States. For Exercises 43–45, write each fraction in simplest form.

43. In 2000, what fraction of U.S. households had PCs?

44. In 2000, what fraction of U.S. households with PCs had Internet access? (Assume that a household with Internet access had a PC.)

45. a. In 2001, what fraction of U.S. households with PCs had Internet access? (*Hint:* See Exercise 44.)
  b. Was the fraction greater in 2000 or 2001? Explain.

198 Chapter 4 Factors, Fractions, and Exponents

46. Write the numerator and denominator of $\frac{24}{32}$ as products of prime factors. Then use the prime factors to write $\frac{24}{32}$ in simplest form.

Test Prep

Multiple Choice

47. Which fraction is equivalent to $\frac{15}{30}$?

    A. $\frac{2}{4}$ **B.** $\frac{3}{5}$ **C.** $\frac{3}{4}$ **D.** $\frac{5}{6}$

48. What is the simplest form for $\frac{14}{42}$?

    F. $\frac{1}{3}$ **G.** $\frac{7}{21}$ **H.** $\frac{2}{6}$ **J.** $\frac{2}{3}$

49. What is the simplest form for $\frac{6m}{15m}$?

    A. $\frac{2m}{15m}$ **B.** $\frac{3m}{5m}$ **C.** $\frac{3}{5}$ **D.** $\frac{2}{5}$

Short Response

50. **a.** Is $\frac{ab}{5}$ equivalent to $\frac{15a^2b}{75a}$?   **b.** Justify your answer.

Mixed Review

Lesson 4-3

Find the GCF for each pair.

51. $10, 12$ **52.** $28, 60$ **53.** $14a, 21a$ **54.** $24x^2, 40x^3$

Lesson 3-5

Solve each equation.

55. $y + 3.23 = 5.85$ **56.** $b - 2.13 = 9.9$ **57.** $12.8 + z = 6.47$

Lesson 3-2   **58. Oil Spills** A damaged oil tanker spilled 34.7 million gallons of crude oil over 4 days. On the average, about how many gallons did the tanker spill each day?

Checkpoint Quiz 1   **Lessons 4-1 through 4-4**

State whether each number is divisible by 2, 3, 5, 9, 10, or none.

    1. 30   **2.** 54   **3.** 48   **4.** 161   **5.** 2,583

Evaluate each expression.

    6. x^2, for $x = 8$ **7.** a^3, for $a = 5$ **8.** $-2z^2$, for $z = -3$

Write in simplest form.

    9. $\frac{8}{16}$ **10.** $\frac{14}{21}$ **11.** $\frac{16}{28}$ **12.** $\frac{3a}{12a}$ **13.** $\frac{2xy}{x}$

    14. Open-Ended Write two expressions whose GCF is $5a^2$.

Analyzing Errors Read the problem below. Then let Tina's thinking guide you through the solution. Check your understanding with the exercises at the bottom of the page.

A student claims $\frac{65}{91}$ is in simplest form. Do you agree? Explain.

What Tina Thinks and Writes

Do I agree?	The wording of the problem suggests that the student is wrong. I'll write: No. Now I have to "Explain."
What does simplest form mean for a fraction?	The numerator and denominator can have no common factor other than 1.
65 ends in 5, so 65 has 5 as a factor. Is 5 also a factor of 91?	No! 91 does not end in 5. 5 is not a factor of 91.
Are there other possibilities for common factors?	Since 5 is a factor of 65. There has to be another factor. $65 = 5 \cdot 13$
Is 13 a factor of 91?	$91 = 7 \cdot 13$. Aha! I'll finish:

No.
$$\frac{65}{91} = \frac{5 \cdot \cancel{13}^{1}}{7 \cdot \cancel{13}_{1}} = \frac{5}{7}$$
$\frac{5}{7}$ is the simplest form for the fraction.

I'm done!

EXERCISES

Use what you know about factors to decide whether each fraction is in simplest form. If not, simplify.

1. $\frac{17}{51}$ 2. $\frac{39}{91}$ 3. $\frac{51}{57}$ 4. $\frac{57}{76}$ 5. $\frac{57}{87}$

Solve a Simpler Problem

1 Solve a Simpler Problem

Math Strategies in Action Scientists often encounter problems that are very complicated. When they work to develop a new vaccine or develop a new method to fight disease, they usually work on smaller or simpler pieces of the problem first. Sometimes when you solve a problem, it helps to solve other problems that have similar conditions. Here is a problem that shows you how to use this strategy.

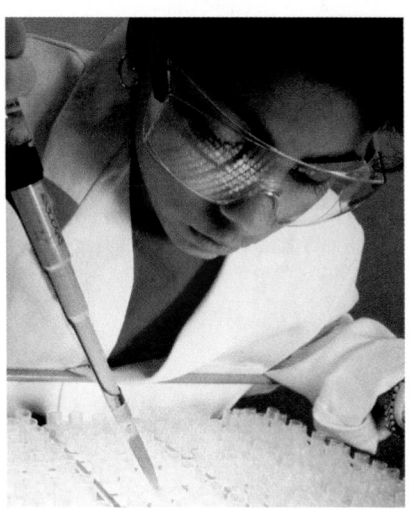

What You'll Learn

• Solve complex problems by first solving simpler cases

. . . And Why

To solve real-world problems involving photography

 Check Skills You'll Need

Compare.
Use < or > to complete each statement.

1. 3 ■ 0

2. −16 ■ −25

3. 0 ■ 1

4. −30 ■ −20

 for Help
Skills Handbook, p. 797

1 EXAMPLE Real-World Problem Solving

Photography Mandy, Jim, Keisha, Darren, Lin, Chris, and Jen are friends. They want to take pictures of themselves with two people in each picture. How many pictures do they need to take?

Understand the Problem

1. What do you need to find?

2. How many people are there in all?

3. How many people will be in each photograph?

Make a Plan

To make sure that you account for every pair of friends, make an organized list.

Solve a simpler problem. Change the problem to a simpler one based on three friends, and then try four friends to see if there is a pattern.

Three Friends (Mandy, Jim, Keisha)
Mandy ⟨ Jim, Keisha
Jim ——— Keisha
(Jim has already been paired with Mandy.)

Four Friends (Mandy, Jim, Keisha, Darren)
Mandy ⟨ Jim, Keisha, Darren
Jim ⟨ Keisha, Darren
Keisha ——— Darren
(Keisha has already been paired with Mandy and with Jim.)

4. What pattern do you see?

5. How many pictures do they need to take?

Check the Answer

You can check to make sure your answer is reasonable by drawing a diagram. Draw line segments to show all possible pairs of friends.

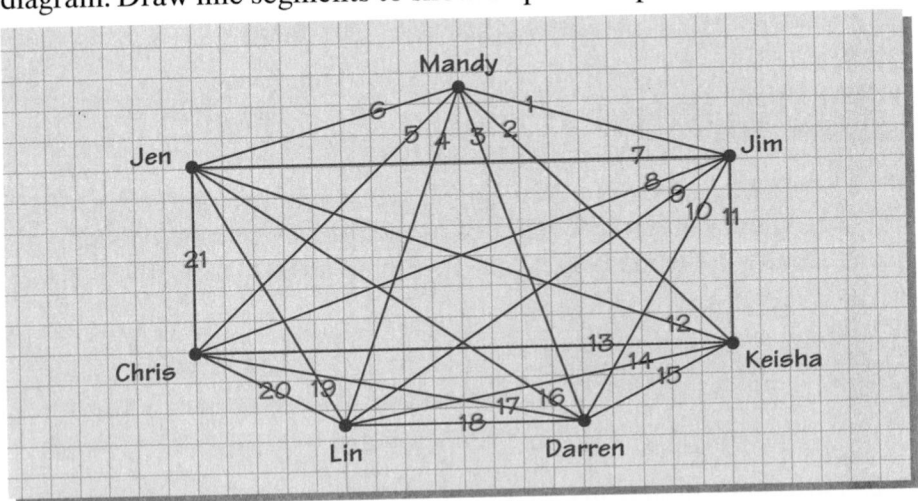

There are 21 line segments. This shows there are 21 pairs of friends.

✓ Quick Check

6. Suppose Mandy and nine friends pair up for pictures. Use the pattern suggested above and find how many pictures there will be.

EXERCISES

Practice and Problem Solving

A Practice by Example

Example 1
(page 201)

for Help

Solve each problem by solving a simpler problem.

1. You decide to number the 58 pages in your journal from 1 to 58. How many digits do you have to write?

2. Geometry What is the total number of triangles in the figure at the right?

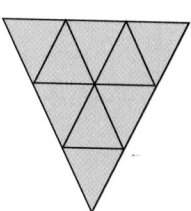

3. You have pepperoni, mushrooms, onions, and green peppers. How many different pizzas can you make by using one, two, three, or four of the toppings?

Solve using any strategy.

B Apply Your Skills

Strategies

- Act It Out
- Draw a Diagram
- Guess, Check, Revise
- Look for a Pattern
- Make a Model
- Make a Table
- Simulate the Problem
- Solve by Graphing
- Use Multiple Strategies
- Work a Simpler Problem
- Work Backward
- Write an Equation
- Write a Proportion

4. Patterns Eight people are at a party. Everyone shakes hands once with everyone else. How many handshakes are there altogether?

5. Geometry You have 24 feet of fence to make a rectangular garden. Each side will measure a whole number of feet. How many different-sized rectangular gardens can you make?

6. You throw three darts at the board shown at the right. If each dart hits the board, what possible point totals can you score?

7. Multiple Choice The bottom row of a stack of blocks contains 11 blocks. The row above it contains 9 blocks. The next higher row contains 7 blocks. The rows continue in this pattern, and the top row contains a single block. How many blocks does the stack contain in all?

A dart landing on the board scores 1, 4, or 10 points.

  Ⓐ 66 blocks   Ⓑ 36 blocks   Ⓒ 28 blocks   Ⓓ 20 blocks

Homework Video Tutor
Visit: PHSchool.com
Web Code: ade-0405

8. A sandwich shop serves turkey, ham, chicken, and egg salad sandwiches. You can have any sandwich on white, wheat, or rye bread. How many different sandwiches could you order?

9. A car manufacturer offers exterior colors of white, blue, red, black, and silver. The manufacturer offers interior colors of black and silver. How many different color combinations are there?

 Challenge

10. You have one penny, one nickel, one dime, and one quarter. How many different amounts of money can you make using one or more of these coins?

Trisha

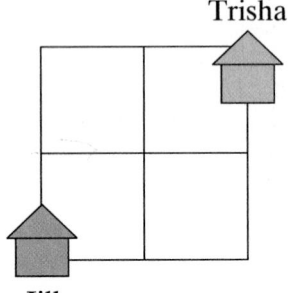

Jill

🌐 **11. Routes** Copy the diagram at the left. Using the paths shown, Jill can walk to Trisha's house in many different ways. Draw each route that is four blocks long. How can you be sure that you have found all possible routes?

🌐 **12. Softball** There are seven softball teams in a league. Each team plays each of the other teams twice. What is the total number of games played?

13. **Geometry** How many different rectangles are there with an area of 36 cm^2 if the side lengths of each, in centimeters, are whole numbers?

ISAT

Test Prep

Multiple Choice

14. Which list shows all the positive factors of 32?
   A. 1, 2, 3, 8, 16, 32   **B.** 1, 2, 4, 8, 16, 32
   C. 1, 2, 3, 4, 8, 16, 32   **D.** 1, 2, 4, 6, 8, 16, 32

15. What is the value of (0.3)^2?
   F. 0.6   **G.** 0.9   **H.** 0.06   **J.** 0.09

16. What is the GCF of 24x^2y^3 and 32x^3y?
   A. 4xy **B.** 4x^2y **C.** 8xy **D.** 8x^2y

17. Which fraction is the simplest form of $\frac{45}{60}$?
   F. $\frac{2}{3}$ **G.** $\frac{3}{4}$ **H.** $\frac{15}{20}$ **J.** $\frac{5}{6}$

Mixed Review

 for Help

Lesson 4-4

Write in simplest form.

18. $\frac{6}{12}$ 19. $\frac{10}{40}$ 20. $\frac{6a^2}{15}$ 21. $\frac{14a^3}{28a^2}$

Lesson 1-7

Write a rule for each pattern.

22. $10, 20, 30, \ldots$ 23. $8, 5, 2, -1, \ldots$ 24. $2, 6, 18, 54, \ldots$

Lesson 1-2

25. Elki has read the first 60 pages of a book. When he has read 35 more pages, he will have read half the book. How many pages are in the book?

Rational Numbers

Assessment Framework

1 Identifying and Graphing Rational Numbers

A **rational number** is any number you can write as a quotient $\frac{a}{b}$ of two integers, where b is not zero. The diagram below shows relationships among rational numbers.

Notice that all integers are rational numbers. This is true because you can write any integer a as $\frac{a}{1}$.

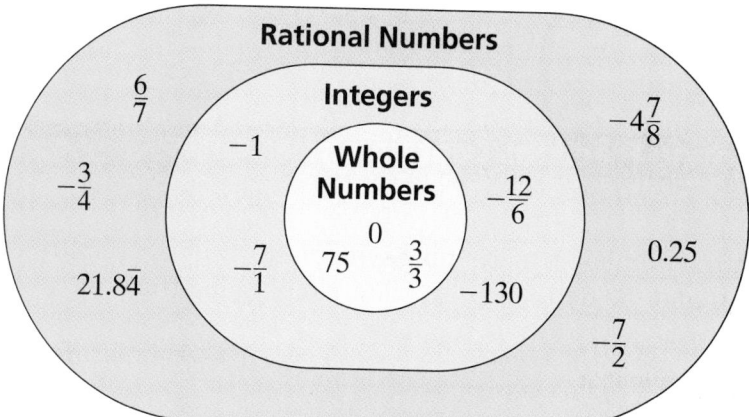

6.8.07 Identify and locate rational and irrational numbers on a number line.

6.8.03 Recognize, translate between, and apply multiple representations of rational numbers (decimals, fractions, mixed numbers, percents, and roots).

✓ Check Skills You'll Need

Write in simplest form.

1. $\frac{2}{10}$ **2.** $\frac{14}{21}$

3. $\frac{28}{35}$ **4.** $\frac{6}{8}$

GO for Help
Lesson 4-4

🔊 New Vocabulary
• rational number

Here are three ways you can write a negative rational number.

$$-\frac{7}{9} = \frac{-7}{9} = \frac{7}{-9}$$

For each rational number, there is an unlimited number of equivalent fractions.

1 EXAMPLE   Writing Equivalent Fractions

Write two lists of fractions equivalent to $\frac{1}{2}$.

$\frac{1}{2} = \frac{2}{4} = \frac{3}{6} = \cdots$ Numerators and denominators are positive.

$\frac{1}{2} = \frac{-1}{-2} = \frac{-2}{-4} = \cdots$ Numerators and denominators are negative.

Problem Solving Hint
The quotient of two integers with the same sign is positive.

✓ Quick Check

1. Write three fractions equivalent to each fraction.
  a. $\frac{1}{3}$ **b.** $-\frac{4}{5}$ **c.** $\frac{5}{8}$ **d.** $-\frac{1}{2}$

You can graph rational numbers on a number line.

2 EXAMPLE **Graphing a Rational Number**

Graph each rational number on a number line.

a. $\frac{1}{2}$ b. $-\frac{8}{10}$ c. 1 d. -0.2

Quick Check

2. Graph each rational number on a number line.

a. $-\frac{1}{2}$ b. $-\frac{4}{10}$ c. -2 d. 0.9

2 Evaluating Fractions Containing Variables

Test-Taking Tip

The top number in a fraction is the <u>numerator</u> and the bottom number is the <u>denominator</u>.

Recall that a fraction bar is a grouping symbol, so you first simplify the numerator and the denominator. Then, simplify the fraction.

Simplify the numerator. ⟶
Simplify the denominator. ⟶ $\dfrac{1 + 9 + 2}{2 - 5} = \dfrac{12}{-3} = -4$ ⟵ simplest form

To simplify a fraction with variables, first substitute for the variables.

3 EXAMPLE **Real-World Problem Solving**

Gridded Response The speed of a car changes from 37 ft/s to 102 ft/s in five seconds. What is its acceleration in feet per second per second (ft/s²)? Use the formula $a = \dfrac{f - i}{t}$ where a is acceleration, f is final speed, i is initial speed, and t is time.

$a = \dfrac{f - i}{t}$ Use the acceleration formula.

$= \dfrac{102 - 37}{5}$ Substitute for the variables.

$= \dfrac{65}{5}$ Subtract.

$= 13$ Write in simplest form.

The car's acceleration is 13 ft/s².

Real-World Connection

The world's fastest car, the *Thrust SSC*, can go from 0 ft/s to 880 ft/s in sixteen seconds.

Quick Check

3. Evaluate for $a = 6$ and $b = -5$. Write in simplest form.

a. $\dfrac{a + b}{-3}$ b. $\dfrac{7 - b}{3a}$ c. $\dfrac{a + 9}{b}$

EXERCISES

For more exercises, see *Extra Skill and Word Problem Practice.*

Practice and Problem Solving

A **Practice by Example**

GO for Help

Example 1
(page 205)

Show the next three fractions equivalent to $\frac{1}{2}$ in each list.

1. $\frac{1}{2}, \frac{2}{4}, \frac{3}{6}, \cdots$

2. $\frac{1}{2}, \frac{-1}{-2}, \frac{-3}{-6}, \cdots$

Write three fractions equivalent to each fraction.

3. $\frac{1}{6}$ **4.** $\frac{3}{5}$ **5.** $-\frac{5}{9}$ **6.** $-\frac{4}{4}$ **7.** $-\frac{2}{3}$ **8.** $\frac{4}{7}$

Example 2
(page 206)

Graph each rational number on a number line.

9. $\frac{1}{10}$ **10.** $-\frac{3}{5}$ **11.** 2 **12.** -0.3 **13.** -0.75 **14.** $\frac{2}{3}$

Example 3
(page 206)

Evaluate for $a = -4$ and $b = -6$. Write in simplest form.

15. $\frac{a}{b}$ **16.** $\frac{a+9}{b}$ **17.** $\frac{b+a}{3a}$ **18.** $\frac{2a+b}{20}$ **19.** $\frac{b+7}{2a}$ **20.** $\frac{b-a}{3b}$

🌐 **21. Boat Races** The speed of a racing boat changes from 0 ft/s to 264 ft/s in six seconds. What is the acceleration of the boat in ft/s^2? Use the acceleration formula given in Example 3.

B **Apply Your Skills**

Write three fractions equivalent to each fraction.

22. $\frac{2}{8}$ **23.** $-\frac{2}{5}$ **24.** $\frac{4}{12}$ **25.** $-\frac{12}{27}$ **26.** $\frac{7}{11}$ **27.** $-\frac{5}{13}$

Write a rational number that is between each pair of numbers.

28. $0, -1$ **29.** $0.9, 1.1$ **30.** $\frac{-1}{5}, \frac{-4}{5}$

Evaluate. Write in simplest form.

31. $\frac{y}{-x}$, for $x = 5$ and $y = -4$ **32.** $\frac{-2y}{x^2}$, for $x = 9$ and $y = 3$

33. $\frac{m}{n}$, for $m = -2$ and $n = 8$ **34.** $\frac{m-n}{-12}$, for $m = -3$ and $n = 6$

35. $\frac{6b-16}{3c}$, for $b = 8$ and $c = 12$ **36.** $\frac{3m-11}{n}$, for $m = 7$ and $n = 14$

37. Multiple Choice The Celsius equivalent of 30.5°F is $-\frac{4}{5}$°C. Which of the following is *not* equivalent to $-\frac{4}{5}$°C?

Ⓐ $\frac{4}{-5}$°C   Ⓑ $\frac{-12}{15}$°C   Ⓒ $-\frac{16}{20}$°C   Ⓓ $\frac{-4}{-5}$°C

38. a. Open-Ended Write two rational numbers between 0 and $\frac{1}{2}$.

  b. How many other rational numbers are between 0 and $\frac{1}{2}$? Explain.

39. Reasoning What are three fractions equivalent to $\frac{a}{b}$? Explain.

🌐 **40. Science** The formula $s = \frac{1,600}{d^2}$ gives the strength s of a radio signal at a distance d miles from the transmitter. What is the strength at 5 mi? Write your answer in simplest form.

41. Writing in Math Explain why a whole number is an integer and an integer is a rational number.

GO Online

Homework Video Tutor

Visit: PHSchool.com
Web Code: ade-0406

C Challenge

Write the opposite and the absolute value of each number.

SAMPLE Find the opposite and the absolute value of $-\frac{3}{5}$.

Opposite:

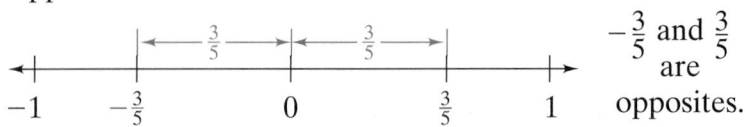

$-\frac{3}{5}$ and $\frac{3}{5}$ are opposites.

Absolute value:

$\left|-\frac{3}{5}\right| = \frac{3}{5}$

42. $\frac{2}{3}$ **43.** $-\frac{5}{6}$ **44.** $\frac{-4}{5}$ **45.** $\frac{2}{-7}$ **46.** $\frac{-3}{-5}$ **47.** $-\frac{a}{b}$

Reasoning Tell whether each statement is true for all positive integers a and b. If the statement is not always true, give a counterexample.

48. $\frac{a^2}{b} > \frac{a}{b}$ **49.** $\frac{3a}{3b} = \frac{a}{b}$ **50.** $\frac{a^2}{b^2} > \frac{a}{b}$

ISAT

Test Prep

Multiple Choice

51. Which three fractions are equivalent to $\frac{3}{4}$?

A. $\frac{6}{8}, \frac{9}{16}, \frac{-6}{-8}$ **B.** $\frac{-3}{4}, \frac{12}{16}, \frac{15}{20}$ **C.** $\frac{6}{8}, \frac{-3}{-4}, \frac{9}{12}$ **D.** $\frac{15}{20}, \frac{12}{16}, \frac{-6}{8}$

52. What is the simplest form of $\frac{y(xy-7)}{10}$ when $x = 6$ and $y = 2$?

F. 3   **G.** $\frac{30}{10}$ **H.** 1   **J.** $\frac{10}{10}$

53. Which pair of numbers is between -3 and -2?

A. $-2\frac{1}{2}, -2\frac{1}{3}$ **B.** $-3\frac{1}{2}, -3\frac{1}{3}$ **C.** $-2, -\pi$ **D.** $-2\frac{1}{2}, -3$

Short Response

54. Is $\frac{a^2}{b^2} > \frac{a}{b}$ true for all negative integers a and b? Explain.

Mixed Review

for Help

Lesson 4-5

55. Patterns Lucia has 4 pairs of slacks, 5 shirts, and 2 sweaters. How many different three-piece outfits can she make?

Lesson 1-9

Multiply or divide.

56. $-7 \cdot 4$ **57.** $19(-5)$ **58.** $-124 \div (-4)$ **59.** $-204 \div 6$

Lesson 1-4

Write the integer represented by each point on the number line.

60. A **61.** B

62. C **63.** D

Exponents and Multiplication

4-7

1L Assessment Framework

6.8.09 Solve problems and number sentences involving addition, subtraction, multiplication, and division using rational numbers, exponents, and roots.

1 Multiplying Powers With the Same Base

In Lesson 4-2, you learned how to use exponents to indicate repeated multiplication. What happens when you multiply two powers with the same base, such as 7^2 and 7^3?

$$7^2 \cdot 7^3 = (7 \cdot 7) \cdot (7 \cdot 7 \cdot 7) = 7^5$$

Notice that $7^2 \cdot 7^3 = 7^5 = 7^{2+3}$. In general, when you multiply powers with the same base, you can add the exponents.

Key Concepts Multiplying Powers With the Same Base

To multiply numbers or variables with the same base, add the exponents.

Arithmetic	Algebra
$2^3 \cdot 2^4 = 2^{3+4} = 2^7$	$a^m \cdot a^n = a^{m+n}$, for positive integers m and n.

You *simplify* an expression by doing as many of the indicated operations as possible.

1 EXAMPLE Multiplying Powers

Simplify each expression.

a. $3 \cdot 3^3$

$3^1 \cdot 3^3 = 3^{1+3}$ **Add the exponents of powers with the same base.**

$= 3^4$

$= 81$ **Simplify.**

b. $a^5 \cdot a \cdot b^2$

$a^5 \cdot a^1 \cdot b^2 = a^{5+1}b^2$ **Add the exponents of powers with the same base.**

$= a^6 b^2$ **Simplify.**

Quick Check

1. Simplify each expression.

a. $2^2 \cdot 2^3$ b. $m^5 \cdot m^7$ c. $x^2 \cdot x^3 \cdot y \cdot y^4$

Check Skills You'll Need

Write using exponents.

1. $k \cdot k \cdot k \cdot k$

2. $m \cdot n \cdot m \cdot n$

3. $2 \cdot 2 \cdot 2 \cdot 2$

4. $5 \cdot 5 \cdot 5$

GO for Help Lesson 4-2

Problem Solving Hint
Recall that $3 = 3^1$ and $a = a^1$ because a base with exponent 1 is equal to the base itself.

2 EXAMPLE Using the Commutative Property

Simplify $-2x^2 \cdot 3x^5$.

$$-2x^2 \cdot 3x^5 = -2 \cdot 3 \cdot x^2 \cdot x^5 \qquad \text{Use the Commutative Property of Multiplication.}$$

$$= -6x^{2+5} \qquad \text{Add the exponents.}$$

$$= -6x^7 \qquad \text{Simplify.}$$

Problem Solving Hint

When in doubt, write it out! If you are unsure about the rules for multiplying powers, write the powers out. For instance, write $x^2 \cdot x^5$ as $(x \cdot x) \cdot (x \cdot x \cdot x \cdot x \cdot x)$. This simplifies to x^7.

✔ Quick Check

2. Simplify each expression.

a. $6a^3 \cdot 3a$ **b.** $-5c^2 \cdot -3c^7$ **c.** $4x^2 \cdot 3x^4$

2 Finding a Power of a Power

You can find the power of a power by using the rule of Multiplying Powers With the Same Base.

$$(7^2)^3 = (7^2) \cdot (7^2) \cdot (7^2) \qquad \text{Use } 7^2 \text{ as a base 3 times.}$$

$$= 7^{2+2+2} \qquad \text{When multiplying powers with the same base, add the exponents.}$$

$$= 7^6 \qquad \text{Simplify.}$$

Notice that $(7^2)^3 = 7^6 = 7^{2 \cdot 3}$. You can raise a power to a power by multiplying the exponents.

Key Concepts **Finding a Power of a Power**

To find a power of a power, multiply the exponents.

Arithmetic	Algebra
$(2^3)^4 = 2^{3 \cdot 4} = 2^{12}$	$(a^m)^n = a^{m \cdot n}$, for positive integers m and n.

○nline
active math

For: Exponent Activity
Use: Interactive Textbook, 4-7

3 EXAMPLE Simplifying Powers of Powers

Simplify each expression.

a. $(3^2)^3$

$$(3^2)^3 = (3)^{2 \cdot 3} \quad \longleftarrow \text{Multiply the exponents.} \longrightarrow$$
$$= (3)^6 \quad \longleftarrow \text{Simplify the exponent.} \longrightarrow$$
$$= 729 \quad \longleftarrow \text{Simplify.}$$

b. $(a^6)^2$

$$(a^6)^2 = a^{6 \cdot 2}$$
$$= a^{12}$$

✔ Quick Check

3. Simplify each expression.

a. $(2^4)^2$ **b.** $(c^5)^4$ **c.** $(m^3)^2$

EXERCISES

Practice and Problem Solving

A Practice by Example

GO for Help

Example 1
(page 209)

Example 2
(page 210)

Example 3
(page 210)

Simplify each expression.

1. $4^2 \cdot 4$
2. $a^2 \cdot a^5$
3. $x^4 \cdot y \cdot x^5 \cdot y$

4. $10^2 \cdot 10^5$
5. $2^2 \cdot 2^5$
6. $x^4 \cdot x^4$

7. $m^{50} \cdot m^2$
8. $(3)^2 \cdot (2)^3 \cdot 2 \cdot 3$
9. $x \cdot y \cdot y \cdot x^5 \cdot y^3$

10. $7b^3 \cdot 4b^4$
11. $-9c^2 \cdot -2c^8$
12. $5x^3 \cdot 2x^6$

13. $4y^7 \cdot 6y^4$
14. $-2a^2 \cdot -2a^2$
15. $9b^2 \cdot -4b^2$

16. $-7x^6 \cdot -5x^8$
17. $-5d^5 \cdot 6d^2$
18. $4b^4 \cdot 12b^7$

19. $(10^3)^2$
20. $(x^3)^4$
21. $(m^6)^4$

22. $(2^2)^3$
23. $(3^2)^4$
24. $(c^2)^8$

25. $(x^5)^7$
26. $(0^5)^8$
27. $(g^8)^{12}$

B Apply Your Skills

GO Online
Homework Video Tutor
Visit: PHSchool.com
Web Code: ade-0407

Complete each equation.

28. $8^2 \cdot 8^{\blacksquare} = 8^9$
29. $c^{\blacksquare} \cdot c^4 = c^{11}$
30. $(9^{\blacksquare})^4 = 9^{16}$

31. $5^6 \cdot 5^{\blacksquare} = 5^{14}$
32. $x^{\blacksquare} \cdot x^{12} = x^{15}$
33. $(a^{\blacksquare})^9 = a^{27}$

Compare. Use >, <, or = to complete each statement.

34. $25^2 \ \blacksquare \ (5^2)^2$
35. $(2^7)^7 \ \blacksquare \ (2^{25})^2$
36. $(4^3 \cdot 4^2)^3 \ \blacksquare \ 4^9$

37. Open-Ended A megabyte is 2^{20} bytes. Use exponents to write 2^{20} in four different ways.

38. Writing in Math Explain why $x^8 \cdot x^2$ has the same value as $x^5 \cdot x^5$.

39. Error Analysis Marcos thinks that $x^4 + x^4$ simplifies to $2x^4$. Doug thinks that $x^4 + x^4$ simplifies to x^8. Which result is correct? Explain.

C Challenge

40. Reasoning Does $-(2^3)^2$ have the same value as $(-2^3)^2$? Justify your answer.

41. Reasoning Which of 2^{30} or 2^{16} is twice the value of 2^{15}? Explain.

Geometry Find the area of each rectangle.

42.

43.

44.

Multiple Choice

45. $(x^2)(y^5)(x) = \underline{\ ?\ }$
  A. x^2y **B.** x^2y^5 **C.** x^3y^5 **D.** x^7y

46. What is the simplest form for $a^{10} \cdot a \cdot a^2$?
  F. $a^{10} \cdot a^3$ **G.** a^{12} **H.** a^{13} **J.** a^{20}

47. $(9^5)^5 = \underline{\ ?\ }$
  A. 9^1 **B.** 9^{10} **C.** 9^{25} **D.** 9^{55}

Short Response

48. a. Find four expressions equivalent to 2^{13}.
  b. Explain why each is equivalent to 2^{13} for part (a).

Mixed Review

GO for Help

Lesson 4-6

Evaluate. Write in simplest form.

49. $\dfrac{mn}{m-6}$, for $m = 4$ and $n = 2$

50. $\dfrac{g + gh}{h - g}$, for $g = -3$ and $h = -5$

Lesson 2-8

Graph the solutions of each inequality on a number line.

51. $x < -3$ **52.** $a > 0$ **53.** $y \le -4$ **54.** $b > -2$

Lesson 1-2 🌐 **55. Party Planning** The Scotts are getting ready for a barbeque. They buy 8 lb of hamburger at \$1.50/lb and 10 lb of chicken at \$1.25/lb. Write and simplify an expression that shows the total cost.

Math at Work

Geophysicist

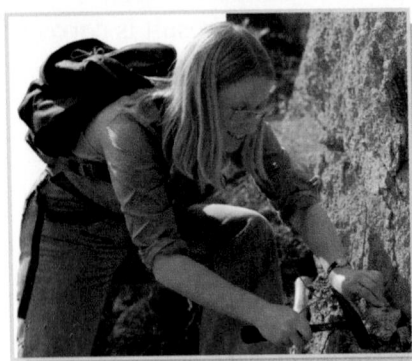

A geophysicist studies Earth's surface, including the history of Earth's crust and rock formations. Geophysicists search for oil, natural gas, minerals, and underground water. They also work to solve environmental problems. They study what makes up Earth's interior, as well as its magnetic, electrical, and gravitational forces. They often study earthquakes and volcanoes.

Geophysicists use physics and mathematics in their studies. Much of their work involves measurement. They use instruments to track sound waves, gravity, energy waves, and magnetic fields. Exponents appear in the data that geophysicists gather because they often work with very large numbers.

Go **Online**
PHSchool.com   **For:** Information about geophysicists
Web Code: adb-2031

Evaluating Expressions With Graphing Calculators

You can use a graphing calculator to evaluate an expression.

1 EXAMPLE

Use a graphing calculator to evaluate $-4x^2 + x - 2$ **for** $x = 6$.

Step 1 First store the value 6 to the variable x.
Press 6 STO▶ x ENTER.

Step 2 Enter $-4x^2 + x - 2$. Press ENTER.

To evaluate the expression in Example 1 for another value of x, start by storing that value to x. Press **ENTRY** *twice* to recall the expression $-4x^2 + x - 2$ from memory. Then press ENTER again. Repeat to evaluate the expression for another value of x.

2 EXAMPLE

Use a graphing calculator to evaluate $3c^3 + 5d - 6$ **for** $c = -2$ **and** $d = 7$.

Press (−) 2 STO▶ . In **TEXT**, press **C** ENTER. Then press **Done**. Press ENTER to store -2 to the variable c. Press 7 STO▶. In **TEXT**, press **D** ENTER. Then press **Done**. Press ENTER to store 7 to the variable d. Enter $3c^3 + 5d - 6$ and then press ENTER to evaluate the expression.

To evaluate the expression for other values of the variables, first store the new values. Press **ENTRY** until the expression appears on the calculator screen. Then press ENTER again to evaluate the expression.

EXERCISES

Use a graphing calculator. Evaluate each expression for the given values of the variable(s). Round to the nearest hundredth where necessary.

1. $x^2 - 3x + 8$
   a. $x = 2$ **b.** $x = -3$ **c.** $x = 4.2$

2. $y^6 + y$
   a. $y = -5$ **b.** $y = 3$ **c.** $y = 1.5$

3. $-4c^2 + 34b - 42$
   a. $c = -12; b = 3$ **b.** $c = 2; b = 4$ **c.** $c = 5.1; b = 4$

4. Evaluate $6x^3 - 2x$ for whole number values of x from 1 to 10.

Exponents and Division

6.8.09 Solve problems and number sentences involving addition, subtraction, multiplication, and division using rational numbers, exponents, and roots.

✓ Check Skills You'll Need
Write in simplest form.

1. $\dfrac{x^2}{x}$ 2. $\dfrac{y}{y^2}$

3. $\dfrac{6xy}{9y}$ 4. $\dfrac{4ab^2}{16b}$

GO for Help
Lesson 4-4

1 Dividing Expressions Containing Exponents

In Lesson 4-7, you learned that you add exponents to multiply powers with the same base. To divide powers with the same base, you subtract exponents. Here's why.

$$\frac{7^8}{7^3} = \frac{7 \cdot 7 \cdot 7 \cdot 7 \cdot 7 \cdot 7 \cdot 7 \cdot 7}{7 \cdot 7 \cdot 7}$$ **Expand the numerator and denominator.**

$$= \frac{7^1 \cdot 7^1 \cdot 7^1 \cdot 7 \cdot 7 \cdot 7 \cdot 7 \cdot 7}{{}_1 7 \cdot {}_1 7 \cdot {}_1 7}$$ **Divide common factors.**

$$= 7^5$$

Notice that $\dfrac{7^8}{7^3} = 7^5 = 7^{8-3}$. This suggests the following rule.

Key Concepts **Dividing Powers With the Same Base**

To divide numbers or variables *with the same nonzero base,* subtract the exponents.

Arithmetic	Algebra
$\dfrac{4^5}{4^2} = 4^{5-2} = 4^3$	$\dfrac{a^m}{a^n} = a^{m-n}$, for $a \neq 0$ and positive integers m and n.

1 EXAMPLE Dividing a Power by a Power

Simplify each expression.

a. $\dfrac{3^8}{3^5}$ b. $\dfrac{a^4}{a^2}$

$\dfrac{3^8}{3^5} = 3^{8-5}$ ⟵ **Subtract the exponents.** ⟶ $\dfrac{a^4}{a^2} = a^{4-2}$

$= 3^3$ ⟵ **Simplify the exponent.** ⟶ $= a^2$

$= 27$ ⟵ **Simplify.**

✓ Quick Check

1. Simplify each expression.

a. $\dfrac{10^7}{10^4}$ b. $\dfrac{x^{25}}{x^{18}}$ c. $\dfrac{12m^5}{3m}$

What happens when you divide powers with the same base and get zero as an exponent? Consider $\frac{3^4}{3^4}$.

$$\frac{3^4}{3^4} = 3^{4-4} = 3^0 \qquad\qquad \frac{3^4}{3^4} = \frac{3^1 \cdot 3^1 \cdot 3^1 \cdot 3^1}{{}_1 3 \cdot {}_1 3 \cdot {}_1 3 \cdot {}_1 3} = \frac{1}{1} = 1$$

Notice that $\frac{3^4}{3^4} = 3^0$ and $\frac{3^4}{3^4} = 1$. This suggests the following rule.

Key Concepts | **Zero as an Exponent**

Arithmetic	**Algebra**
$3^0 = 1$	$a^0 = 1$, for $a \neq 0$.

---

2 EXAMPLE Simplifying When Zero Is an Exponent

Simplify each expression.

a. $\dfrac{(-8)^2}{(-8)^2}$

$\dfrac{(-8)^2}{(-8)^2} = (-8)^{2-2}$ **Subtract the exponents.**

$= (-8)^0$ **Simplify.**

$= 1$

b. $\dfrac{6b^3}{18b^3}$

$\dfrac{6b^3}{18b^3} = \dfrac{1}{3}b^0$ **Subtract the exponents. Simplify $\frac{6}{18}$.**

$= \dfrac{1}{3} \cdot 1$ **Simplify b^0.**

$= \dfrac{1}{3}$ **Multiply.**

✓ **Quick Check**

2. Simplify each expression.

   a. 43^0 **b.** $\dfrac{5^2 x^6}{5x^6}$ **c.** $\dfrac{x^5 y^6}{x^5 y^3}$ **d.** $5x^0$

What happens when you divide powers with the same base and get a negative exponent? Consider $\frac{3^2}{3^4}$.

$$\frac{3^2}{3^4} = 3^{2-4} = 3^{-2} \qquad\qquad \frac{3^2}{3^4} = \frac{3^1 \cdot 3^1}{{}_1 3 \cdot {}_1 3 \cdot 3 \cdot 3} = \frac{1}{3^2}$$

These results suggest the rule at the top of page 216.

Key Concepts — Negative Exponents

Arithmetic	Algebra
$3^{-2} = \dfrac{1}{3^2}$	$a^{-n} = \dfrac{1}{a^n}$, for $a \neq 0$.

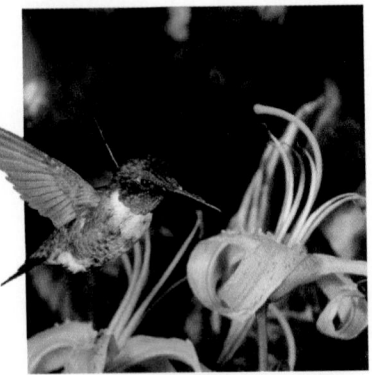

Real-World Connection

Hummingbirds may range from 0.0022 kg to 0.02 kg in mass.

A hummingbird has a mass of about 10^{-2} kg, or $\dfrac{1}{10^2}$ kg. To simplify 10^{-2}, you write $\dfrac{1}{100}$ or 0.01. So the hummingbird has a mass of 0.01 kg. To simplify an expression such as x^{-2}, you write it as $\dfrac{1}{x^2}$, using no negative exponents.

3 EXAMPLE Using Positive Exponents

Simplify each expression.

a. $\dfrac{5^6}{5^8}$ **b.** $\dfrac{m^2}{m^5}$

$\dfrac{5^6}{5^8} = 5^{6-8}$ ← Subtract the exponents. → $\dfrac{m^2}{m^5} = m^{2-5}$

$= 5^{-2}$ $= m^{-3}$

$= \dfrac{1}{5^2}$ ← Write with a positive exponent. → $= \dfrac{1}{m^3}$

$= \dfrac{1}{25}$ ← Simplify.

✓ Quick Check

3. Simplify each expression.

a. $\dfrac{4^5}{4^7}$ **b.** $\dfrac{a^4}{a^6}$ **c.** $\dfrac{3y^8}{9y^{12}}$

You can also write an expression such as $\dfrac{1}{x^2}$ so that there is no fraction bar.

4 EXAMPLE Using Negative Exponents

Online active math

**For: Exponent Activity
Use: Interactive Textbook, 4-8**

Write $\dfrac{x^2 y^3}{x^3 y}$ **without a fraction bar.**

$\dfrac{x^2 y^3}{x^3 y} = x^{2-3} y^{3-1}$ Use the Rule for Dividing Powers With the Same Base.

$= x^{-1} y^2$ Subtract the exponents.

✓ Quick Check

4. Write each expression without a fraction bar.

a. $\dfrac{b^3}{b^9}$ **b.** $\dfrac{m^3 n^2}{m^6 n^8}$ **c.** $\dfrac{x y^5}{x^5 y^3}$

EXERCISES

For more exercises, see *Extra Skill and Word Problem Practice.*

Practice and Problem Solving

A **Practice by Example**

Example 1
(page 214)

GO for Help

Simplify each expression.

1. $\dfrac{2^5}{2^2}$

2. $\dfrac{h^6}{h^2}$

3. $\dfrac{10y^7}{6y^2}$

4. $\dfrac{10b^8}{2b^6}$

5. $\dfrac{6^2}{6^1}$

6. $\dfrac{11^5}{11^3}$

7. $\dfrac{x^7}{x^3}$

8. $\dfrac{a^{27}}{a^{19}}$

Example 2
(page 215)

9. $\dfrac{18x^{20}}{18x^{20}}$

10. $(-4)^0$

11. $\dfrac{w^8z^{15}}{w^8z^8}$

12. 3^0

13. $\dfrac{b^3c^2}{b^3c}$

14. $\dfrac{(-2)^4}{(-2)^4}$

15. $2b^0$

16. $\dfrac{2y^3}{8y^3}$

Example 3
(page 216)

17. $\dfrac{7^3}{7^5}$

18. $\dfrac{m^2}{m^6}$

19. $\dfrac{4a^3}{20a^6}$

20. $\dfrac{100m^{100}}{200m^{200}}$

21. $\dfrac{b^5}{b^8}$

22. $\dfrac{3m}{15m^3}$

23. $\dfrac{6^7}{6^{11}}$

24. $\dfrac{a^2}{a^7}$

Example 4
(page 216)

Write each expression without a fraction bar.

25. $\dfrac{y^4}{y^7}$

26. $\dfrac{a^2b^4}{a^8b^2}$

27. $\dfrac{m^5n^6}{m^7n^8}$

28. $\dfrac{xy^2}{x^4y^9}$

B **Apply Your Skills**

Complete each equation.

29. $\dfrac{x^6}{x^{\blacksquare}} = x^4$

30. $\dfrac{14x^5}{7x^3} = 2x^{\blacksquare}$

31. $\dfrac{10^5}{10^{\blacksquare}} = 1$

32. $\dfrac{1}{a^3} = a^{\blacksquare}$

33. $\dfrac{y^{\blacksquare}}{y^9} = y^{-4}$

34. $\dfrac{1}{-27} = (-3)^{\blacksquare}$

GO Online
Homework Video Tutor
Visit: PHSchool.com
Web Code: ade-0408

35. **Earthquakes** The *magnitude* of an earthquake is a measure of the amount of energy released. An earthquake of magnitude 6 releases about 30 times as much energy as an earthquake of magnitude 5. The magnitude of the 1989 earthquake in Loma Prieta, California, was about 7. The magnitude of the 1933 earthquake in Sanriku, Japan, was about 9. Simplify $\dfrac{30^9}{30^7}$ to find how many times as much energy was released in the Sanriku earthquake.

36. **Error Analysis** A student wrote that $-5^0 = 1$. What was the student's error?

37. **Open-Ended** Write three different quotients that equal 5^{-7}.

38. **Writing in Math** Is -3^{-2} positive or negative? Justify your answer.

Write each expression without a fraction bar.

39. $\dfrac{x^3}{x^5}$

40. $\dfrac{a^9b^3}{a^7b^8}$

41. $\dfrac{m^9n^3}{m^2n^{10}}$

42. $\dfrac{b^{14}c^2}{b^9c^{11}}$

C **Challenge**

Simplify each expression.

43. $\dfrac{5x^2}{10x^{-5}}$

44. $\dfrac{5b^{-7}}{5b^{-2}}$

45. $\dfrac{4^2 + 6^2}{2^2}$

46. $\dfrac{r^{-5}}{s^{-2}}$

Test Prep

Multiple Choice

47. What is a simpler form of $\frac{x^5 y^4}{x^2 y^9}$?

A. $\frac{x^5}{y^3}$ B. $\frac{y^5}{x^3}$ C. $x^3 y^5$ D. $\frac{x^3}{y^5}$

48. What is a simpler form of $\frac{12a^{35}}{36a^{50}}$?

F. $\frac{1^{85}}{3^a}$ G. $\frac{1}{3a^{85}}$ H. $\frac{1}{3a^{15}}$ J. $\frac{1}{3}a^{15}$

49. Which expression is equal to $\frac{42a^6 b^7}{7a^3 b^3}$?

A. $6a^3 b^{-4}$ B. $6a^3 b^4$ C. $6a^{-3} b^4$ D. $6a^{-3} b^{-4}$

Short Response

50. a. Is 5^{-3} a negative number? **b.** Explain your answer.

Mixed Review

 for Help

Lesson 4-7 **Simplify each expression.**

51. $5^2 \cdot 5$ **52.** $x^7 \cdot x^2$ **53.** $2a^9 \cdot 8a^7$

Lesson 3-1 **Estimate using front-end estimation.**

54. $5.68 + 3.24$ **55.** $17.86 + 2.321$ **56.** $20.54 + 5.54$

Lesson 2-7 **57. Number Sense** The sum of three consecutive integers is 264. What are the three integers?

✓ Checkpoint Quiz 2　　　　　　　　　Lessons 4-5 through 4-8

Write three fractions equivalent to each given fraction.

1. $\frac{3}{12}$ **2.** $\frac{12}{36}$ **3.** $\frac{49}{70}$ **4.** $\frac{18}{28}$ **5.** $\frac{4}{5}$

Evaluate for $a = 4$ and $b = -6$. Write in simplest form.

6. $\frac{a}{2b}$ **7.** $\frac{b+a}{a}$ **8.** $\frac{a-b}{15}$ **9.** $\frac{b-a}{a^2}$ **10.** $\frac{3a+b}{24}$

Graph the rational numbers below on the same number line.

11. -0.8 **12.** $\frac{1}{2}$ **13.** 0.6 **14.** $-\frac{2}{10}$ **15.** $\frac{9}{10}$

Simplify each expression.

16. $2^3 \cdot 2^4$ **17.** $(x^5)^{10}$ **18.** $\frac{18a^4}{3a^2}$ **19.** $\frac{x^3}{x^8}$ **20.** $\frac{a^3 b^5}{a^9 b^5}$

21. If 12 of 16 students vote to do a project, what fraction of the students is this? Write the fraction in simplest form.

Scientific Notation

 Assessment Framework

1 Writing and Evaluating Scientific Notation

Activity

Exploring Scientific Notation

1. Copy and complete the chart below.

5×10^4	$= 5 \times 10{,}000$	$= 50{,}000$
5×10^3	$= 5 \times 1{,}000$	$= \blacksquare$
5×10^2	$= 5 \times \blacksquare$	$= \blacksquare$
5×10^1	$= 5 \times \blacksquare$	$= \blacksquare$
5×10^0	$= 5 \times \blacksquare$	$= \blacksquare$
5×10^{-1}	$= 5 \times \frac{1}{10}$	$= 5 \times 0.1 = 0.5$
5×10^{-2}	$= 5 \times \blacksquare \frac{1}{100}$	$= 5 \times 0.01 = 0.05$
5×10^{-3}	$= 5 \times \blacksquare \frac{1}{1{,}000}$	$= 5 \times \blacksquare = 0.005$
5×10^{-4}	$= 5 \times \blacksquare \frac{1}{10{,}000}$	$= 5 \times \blacksquare = \blacksquare$

2. Patterns Describe any related patterns that you see in your chart.

3. a. Based on the patterns you see, simplify 5×10^7.
   b. Simplify 5×10^{-6}.

Scientific notation provides a way to write numbers using powers of 10. You write a number in scientific notation as the product of two factors.

$$7{,}500{,}000{,}000{,}000 = 7.5 \times 10^{12}$$

Second factor is a power of 10.

First factor is greater than or equal to 1, but less than 10.

Scientific notation lets you know the size of a number without having to count digits. For example, if the exponent of 10 is 6, the number is in the millions. If the exponent is 9, the number is in the billions.

6.8.04 Use scientific notation to represent numbers and solve problems.

✔ **Check Skills You'll Need**

Write each expression with a single exponent.

1. $10^3 \cdot 10^5$

2. $10^7 \cdot 10^9$

3. $10^5 \cdot 10^{-3}$

4. $10^{-6} \cdot 10^3$

GO for Help
Lesson 4-7

◄)) **New Vocabulary**

• scientific notation

• standard notation

GO for Help

For a guide to multiplying by powers of ten, see Skills Handbook, page 790.

The total weight of the Statue of Liberty is about 450,000 lb.

1 **EXAMPLE** Real-World Problem Solving

Multiple Choice About 4,200,000 people visit the Statue of Liberty every year. Which of the following represents this number in scientific notation?

Ⓐ 4.2×10^{-6} Ⓑ 4.2×10^6 Ⓒ 42×10^6 Ⓓ 42×10^7

4,200,000	Move the decimal point to get a decimal greater than 1 but less than 10.
6 places	
4.2	Drop the zeros after the 2.
4.2×10^6	You moved the decimal point 6 places. The original number is greater than 10. Use 6 as the exponent of 10.

The answer is B.

✓ Quick Check

● **1.** Write in scientific notation.   **a.** 54,500,000   **b.** 723,000

In scientific notation, you use a negative exponent to write a number between 0 and 1.

2 **EXAMPLE** Writing in Scientific Notation

Write 0.000079 in scientific notation.

0.000079	Move the decimal point to get a decimal greater than 1 but less than 10.
5 places	
7.9	Drop the zeros before the 7.
7.9×10^{-5}	You moved the decimal point 5 places. The original number is less than 1. Use −5 as the exponent of 10.

✓ Quick Check

● **2.** Write in scientific notation.   **a.** 0.00021   **b.** 0.00000005

You can change expressions from scientific notation to **standard notation** by simplifying the product of the two factors.

Test-Taking Tip

When multiplying by a power of 10, move the decimal point to the right. When dividing by a power of 10, move the decimal point to the left.

3 **EXAMPLE** Writing in Standard Notation

Write each number in standard notation.

a. 8.9×10^5 **b.** 2.71×10^{-6}

| 8.90000 | Write zeros while moving the decimal point. | 000002.71 |
| 890,000 | Rewrite in standard notation. | 0.00000271 |

Quick Check

3. Write each number in standard notation.

    a. 3.21×10^7 **b.** 5.9×10^{-8} **c.** 1.006×10^{10}

For a number to be in scientific notation, the digit in front of the decimal must be 1 or between 1 and 10.

4) EXAMPLE   Changing to Scientific Notation

Write each number in scientific notation.

a. 0.37×10^{10}

    $0.37 \times 10^{10} = 3.7 \times 10^{-1} \times 10^{10}$ **Write 0.37 as 3.7×10^{-1}.**

                $= 3.7 \times 10^9$ **Add the exponents.**

b. 453.1×10^8

    $453.1 \times 10^8 = 4.531 \times 10^2 \times 10^8$ **Write 453.1 as 4.531×10^2.**

               $= 4.531 \times 10^{10}$ **Add the exponents.**

Quick Check

4. Write each number in scientific notation.

    a. 16×10^5 **b.** 0.203×10^6 **c.** $7{,}243 \times 10^{12}$

You can compare and order numbers using scientific notation. First compare the powers of 10, and then compare the decimals.

5) EXAMPLE   Comparing and Ordering Numbers

Order 0.064×10^8, 312×10^2, and 0.58×10^7 from least to greatest.

Write each number in scientific notation.

  0.064×10^8 312×10^2 0.58×10^7

      ↓   ↓   ↓

  6.4×10^6 3.12×10^4 5.8×10^6

Order the powers of 10. Arrange the decimals with the same power of 10 in order.

  3.12×10^4 5.8×10^6 6.4×10^6

Write the original numbers in order.

    $312 \times 10^2, 0.58 \times 10^7, 0.064 \times 10^8$

Quick Check

5. Order from least to greatest.

    a. $526 \times 10^7, 18.3 \times 10^6, 0.098 \times 10^9$

    b. $8 \times 10^{-9}, 14.7 \times 10^{-7}, 0.22 \times 10^{-10}$

You can multiply numbers in scientific notation using the rule for Multiplying Powers with the Same Base.

6 **EXAMPLE** **Multiplying With Scientific Notation**

Multiply 3×10^{-7} and 9×10^3. Express the result in scientific notation.

$$(3 \times 10^{-7})(9 \times 10^3) = 3 \times 9 \times 10^{-7} \times 10^3$$ **Use the Commutative Property of Multiplication.**

$$= 27 \times 10^{-7} \times 10^3$$ **Multiply 3 and 9.**

$$= 27 \times 10^{-4}$$ **Add the exponents.**

$$= 2.7 \times 10^1 \times 10^{-4}$$ **Write 27 as 2.7×10^1.**

$$= 2.7 \times 10^{-3}$$ **Add the exponents.**

Quick Check

6. Multiply. Express each result in scientific notation.

    a. $(4 \times 10^4)(6 \times 10^6)$ **b.** $(7.1 \times 10^{-8})(8 \times 10^4)$

7 **EXAMPLE** Real-World Problem Solving

Measurement The Great Pyramid of Giza in Egypt contains about 2.3×10^6 blocks of stone. On the average, each block of stone weighs about 5×10^3 lb. About how many pounds of stone does the Great Pyramid contain?

$$(2.3 \times 10^6)(5 \times 10^3)$$ **Multiply number of blocks by weight of each.**

$$= 2.3 \times 5 \times 10^6 \times 10^3$$ **Use the Commutative Property of Multiplication.**

$$= 11.5 \times 10^6 \times 10^3$$ **Multiply 2.3 and 5.**

$$= 11.5 \times 10^9$$ **Add the exponents.**

$$= 1.15 \times 10^1 \times 10^9$$ **Write 11.5 as 1.15×10^1.**

$$= 1.15 \times 10^{10}$$ **Add the exponents.**

The Great Pyramid contains about 1.15×10^{10} lb of stone.

Real-World Connection

In ancient times, the Great Pyramid of Giza was plundered inside and out. Outside, most of the casing of smooth, white limestone was removed. The height of the pyramid is now about 30 ft less than the original height.

Quick Check

7. **Chemistry** A hydrogen atom has a mass of 1.67×10^{-27} kg. What is the mass of 6×10^3 hydrogen atoms? Express the result in scientific notation.

EXERCISES

For more exercises, see *Extra Skill and Word Problem Practice.*

Practice and Problem Solving

A Practice by Example

Examples 1 and 2
(page 220)

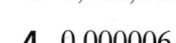
GO for Help

In Exercises 1–7, write each number in scientific notation.

1. 8,900,000,000   **2.** 555,900,000   **3.** 0.000631

4. 0.000006   **5.** 0.209   **6.** 0.00409

7. Solar System Pluto is about 5 billion km from the sun.

Example 3
(page 220)

Write each number in standard notation.

8. 5.94×10^7 **9.** 2.104×10^{-8} **10.** 1.2×10^5

11. 7.2×10^{-4} **12.** 2.75×10^8 **13.** 6.0502×10^{-3}

Example 4
(page 221)

Write each number in scientific notation.

14. 0.09×10^{12} **15.** 0.72×10^{-4}

16. 52.8×10^9 **17.** $3,508 \times 10^{-7}$

Example 5
(page 221)

Order from least to greatest.

18. $16 \times 10^9, 2.3 \times 10^{12}, 0.065 \times 10^{11}$

19. $253 \times 10^{-9}, 3.7 \times 10^{-8}, 12.9 \times 10^{-7}$

20. $65 \times 10^4, 432 \times 10^3, 2.996 \times 10^4$

Example 6
(page 222)

Multiply. Express each result in scientific notation.

21. $(5 \times 10^6)(6 \times 10^2)$ **22.** $(4.3 \times 10^3)(2 \times 10^{-8})$

23. $(9 \times 10^{-3})(7 \times 10^8)$ **24.** $(3 \times 10^2)(2 \times 10^2)$

Example 7
(page 222)

25. Zoology An ant weighs about 2×10^{-5} lb. There are about 10^{15} ants on Earth. How many pounds of ants are on Earth?

B Apply Your Skills

In Exercises 26–29, write each number in standard notation.

26. 9×10^2 **27.** 8.43×10^6 **28.** 6.02×10^{-7}

29. Astronomy One light year is 5.88×10^{12} mi.

30. Multiple Choice The most venomous scorpion gives 9×10^{-6} oz of venom in a bite. How is this expressed in standard notation?
  (A) 0.0000009 oz   (B) 0.000009 oz
  (C) 900,000 oz   (D) 9,000,000 oz

Order from least to greatest.

31. $10^9, 10^{-8}, 10^5, 10^{-6}, 10^0$

32. $55.8 \times 10^{-5}, 782 \times 10^{-8}, 9.1 \times 10^{-5}, 1,009 \times 10^2, 0.8 \times 10^{-4}$

33. Writing in Math Explain how to write each number in scientific notation. **a.** 0.00043   **b.** 523.4×10^5

GO **Online**
Homework Video Tutor
Visit: PHSchool.com
Web Code: ade-0409

Solve. Write each result in scientific notation.

34. Statistics The population density of India is about 8.33×10^2 people per square mile. The area of India is $1.2 \times 10^6 \text{ mi}^2$. What is the approximate population of India?

35. Health Care In the year 2010, the population of the United States is expected to be about 315 million. Health expenditures will be about $8,754 per person. In total, about how much will the United States spend on health care in 2010?

ISAT

Test Prep

Gridded Response

Complete each equation. Grid each answer.

36. In scientific notation, $55,000 = \blacksquare \times 10^{-4}$.

37. In standard notation, $2 \times 10^{-2} = \blacksquare$.

38. Fingernails grow 0.00714 cm per day. In scientific notation, $0.00714 = \blacksquare \times 10^{-3}$.

39. One light year is 5,880,000,000,000 mi. In scientific notation, $5,880,000,000,000 = \blacksquare \times 10^{12}$.

40. The length of a grain of salt is about 4×10^{-3} in. In standard notation, $4 \times 10^{-3} = \blacksquare$

41. The moon is about 380,000 km from Earth. In scientific notation, $380,000 = \blacksquare \times 10^5$.

42. It would take about 760,000,000 half-meter footsteps to walk from Earth to the moon. In scientific notation, $760,000,000 = 7.6 \times 10^{\blacksquare}$.

43. On July 20, 1969, Neil Armstrong became the first person to walk on the moon. Scientists believe his footsteps will remain on the surface of the moon for at least 1×10^8 million years. In standard notation, $1 \times 10^8 = \blacksquare$ million.

Mixed Review

GO for Help

Lesson 4-8

Simplify each expression.

44. $\dfrac{10^7}{10^9}$ **45.** $\dfrac{x^3 y}{xy}$ **46.** $\dfrac{15b^2}{10b^5}$ **47.** $\dfrac{9m^7}{3m^5 n}$

Lesson 3-4

Algebra Use the formula $d = rt$. Find d, r, or t.

48. $r = 46.2$ m/h, $t = 2.75$ h

49. $d = 4.68$ ft, $t = 5.2$ h

50. $d = 988$ cm, $r = 6.5$ cm/s

Lesson 1-8

51. Patterns A clock strikes a chime once at one o'clock, twice at two o'clock, and so on. In a twelve-hour period, what is the total number of chimes the clock strikes?

When you enter a number with more digits than a calculator can display, the calculator translates the number into scientific notation. "E11" in the output below means "$\times 10^{11}$."

112,345,678,999 ENTER $\longrightarrow$ 1.12345679E11 **The display shows the number rounded.**

You can use a calculator to calculate with numbers in scientific notation.

1 EXAMPLE

Use a calculator to find $(9.8 \times 10^5)(4.56 \times 10^4)$.

9.8E5*4.56E4

4.4688E10

Use EE 5 to enter E5 and EE 4 to enter E4.

● The product is 4.4688×10^{10}.

2 EXAMPLE

Use a calculator to find $3.9 \times 10^{-7} + 4.7 \times 10^{-8}$.

3.9E-7+4.7E-8

4.37E-7

Use (−) for negative exponents.

● The sum is 4.37×10^{-7}.

EXERCISES

Use a calculator to simplify. Write each result in scientific notation.

1. $1.5 \times 10^{11} - 2.4 \times 10^8$

2. $6.97 \times 10^5 + 4.8 \times 10^{10}$

3. $(1.02 \times 10^9)(1.98 \times 10^7)$

4. $(5.1 \times 10^3) \div (3.64 \times 10^{10})$

5. $(2.8 \times 10^{13})(3.335 \times 10^{10})$

6. $9.807 \times 10^7 + 7.08 \times 10^{10}$

7. $7.1 \times 10^{-5} - 9.1 \times 10^{-6}$

8. $3.5 \times 10^{-6} + 6.76 \times 10^{-4}$

9. $(2.43 \times 10^{-3})(4.9 \times 10^{-10})$

10. $(1.08 \times 10^4) \div (7.3 \times 10^{-7})$

11. $(5.01 \times 10^{-3})(8.5 \times 10^{-8})$

12. $1.99 \times 10^{-5} - 3.81 \times 10^{-4}$

Test-Taking Strategies

Reading-Comprehension Questions

Reading-comprehension questions require that you read and understand information given to you in print in order to use mathematics to solve the problem.

EXAMPLE

Read the passage below. Then answer the questions based on what is stated or implied in the passage.

> **Solar System Masses** The sun is the largest object in our solar system. It contains approximately 98% of the total solar-system mass. The interior of the sun can hold over 1.3 million Earths. The mass of Earth is 5.98×10^{24} kg. The sun is approximately 330,000 times the mass of Earth.

What is the mass of the sun?

You read, "The sun is approximately 330,000 times the mass of Earth."

$$
\begin{aligned}
\text{Mass of sun} &\approx 330{,}000 \times \text{mass of Earth.} \\
M &\approx 330{,}000 \times 5.98 \times 10^{24} \\
&\approx 3.3 \times 10^{5} \times 5.98 \times 10^{24} \\
&\approx 19.734 \times 10^{29} \\
&\approx 1.97 \times 10^{30}
\end{aligned}
$$

● The mass of the sun is about 1.97×10^{30} kg.

EXERCISES

Read the passage below. Then answer the questions based on what is stated or implied in the passage.

> **Planet Distances** The diameter of Jupiter is 142,800 km. Saturn is almost as big with a diameter of 120,000 km. Earth, by comparison, has a diameter of only 12,756 km. Jupiter's mass is 318 times the mass of Earth. Saturn's mass is only 95 times the mass of Earth.

1. Put the planets named in the above passage in order from smallest to largest, based on their diameters.

2. The mass of Jupiter is about how many times the mass of Saturn?

3. The diameter of Jupiter is about how many times the diameter of Saturn?

4. What could you conclude about Saturn from this passage?

Chapter Review

Vocabulary Review

base (p. 186)
composite number (p. 190)
divisible (p. 180)
equivalent fractions (p. 196)
exponents (p. 186)

factor (p. 181)
greatest common
   factor (GCF) (p. 191)
power (p. 186)
prime factorization (p. 191)

prime number (p. 190)
rational number (p. 205)
scientific notation (p. 219)
simplest form (p. 196)
standard notation (p. 220)

Go Online
PHSchool.com

For: Vocabulary quiz
Web Code: adj-0451

Choose the vocabulary term that correctly completes each sentence.

1. One integer is a __?__ of another integer if it divides that integer with remainder zero.

2. A fraction is in __?__ when the numerator and denominator have no factors in common other than 1.

3. A number that you can write as the quotient $\frac{a}{b}$ of two integers, where b is not zero, is a __?__.

4. You can write numbers using powers of 10 in a shorthand way called __?__.

5. You can show repeated multiplication with __?__.

6. If a positive integer greater than 1 has exactly two factors, 1 and the integer itself, the integer is a __?__.

Skills and Concepts

4-1 Objectives

▼ To use divisibility tests (p. 180)

▼ To find factors (p. 181)

One integer is **divisible** by another if the remainder is zero when you divide. Divisibility tests help you find factors. One integer is a **factor** of another integer if it divides that integer with remainder zero.

List the positive factors of each number.

7. 12   **8.** 30   **9.** 42   **10.** 72   **11.** 111   **12.** 252

4-2 Objectives

▼ To use exponents (p. 186)

▼ To use the order of operations with exponents (p. 187)

To simplify an expression that has an **exponent**, remember that the **base** is the number used as a factor. The exponent shows the number of times the base is used as a factor.

Simplify each expression.

13. 2^3 **14.** $3(10 - 7)^2$

15. $28 + (1 + 5)^2 \cdot 4$ **16.** -5^2

Evaluate each expression.

17. x^2, for $x = 11$

18. $7m^2 - 5$, for $m = 3$

19. $(2a + 1)^2$, for $a = -4$

20. b^2, for $b = -4$

4-3 Objectives

▼ To find the prime factorization of a number (p. 190)

▼ To find the greatest common factor (GCF) of two or more numbers (p. 191)

A **prime number** is an integer greater than 1 with exactly two positive factors, 1 and itself. An integer greater than 1 with more than two factors is a **composite number.** The **prime factorization** of a composite number is the product of its prime factors.

The **greatest common factor (GCF)** of two or more numbers or expressions is the greatest factor that the numbers or expressions have in common. You can list factors or use prime factorization to find the GCF of two or more numbers or expressions.

Is each number *prime, composite,* or *neither?* For each composite number, write the prime factorization. Use exponents where possible.

21. 13   **22.** 20   **23.** 73   **24.** 110   **25.** 87

Find the GCF.

26. $16, 60$

27. $36, 81, 27$

28. $15, 17, 30$

29. $3x^2y, 9x^2$

30. $8a^2b, 14ab^2$

31. $3cd^4, 12c^3d, 6c^2d^2$

32. Reasoning Why is the GCF of two or more positive integers never greater than the least of the numbers?

4-4 Objectives

▼ To find equivalent fractions (p. 196)

▼ To write fractions in simplest form (p. 196)

Equivalent fractions describe the same part of a whole. A fraction is in **simplest form** when the numerator and the denominator have no common factors other than 1. You can use the GCF of the numerator and denominator to write a fraction in simplest form.

Write in simplest form.

33. $\frac{3}{15}$ **34.** $\frac{10}{20}$ **35.** $\frac{16}{52}$ **36.** $\frac{28}{40}$ **37.** $\frac{21}{33}$ **38.** $\frac{9}{54}$

39. $\frac{xy}{y}$ **40.** $\frac{25m}{5m}$ **41.** $\frac{2y}{8y}$ **42.** $\frac{2c}{5c}$ **43.** $\frac{9x^2}{27x}$ **44.** $\frac{36bc}{9c}$

4-5 Objectives

▼ To solve complex problems by first solving simpler cases (p. 201)

When a problem is complicated, you can solve related simpler problems to better understand the problem.

45. Reasoning A school's lockers are numbered 1 to 100. One hundred students enter the school one at a time. The first student opens the lockers. The second student closes the even-numbered lockers. The third student either closes or opens every third locker. The remaining students continue the pattern. After all the students have passed the lockers, which lockers are open?

4-6 Objectives

▼ To identify and graph rational numbers (p. 205)

▼ To evaluate fractions containing variables (p. 206)

A **rational number** is any number you can write as a quotient $\frac{a}{b}$ of two integers, where b is not zero.

Graph the rational numbers below on the same number line.

46. 2   **47.** -0.6 **48.** $-\frac{5}{10}$ **49.** $\frac{2}{10}$

Evaluate each expression for $a = -5$ and $b = -2$. Write in simplest form.

50. $\frac{b}{a}$ **51.** $\frac{a + b}{4b}$ **52.** $\frac{b - a}{a - b}$ **53.** $\frac{b^2}{a}$

4-7 and 4-8 Objectives

▼ To multiply powers with the same base (p. 209)

▼ To find a power of a power (p. 210)

▼ To divide expressions containing exponents (p. 214)

▼ To simplify expressions with integer exponents (p. 215)

To multiply numbers or variables with the same base, add the exponents. To raise a power to a power, multiply the exponents. To divide numbers or variables with the same nonzero base, subtract the exponents.

Simplify each expression.

54. $2^4 \cdot 2^3$ **55.** $7a^4 \cdot 3a^2$ **56.** $b \cdot c^2 \cdot b^6 \cdot c^2$ **57.** $(x^3)^5$

58. $(y^4)^5$ **59.** $\frac{4^8}{4^2}$ **60.** $\frac{b^2}{b^4}$ **61.** $\frac{28xy^7}{32xy^{12}}$

4-9 Objectives

▼ To write and evaluate numbers in scientific notation (p. 219)

▼ To calculate with scientific notation (p. 222)

Scientific notation provides a way to write numbers as the product of two factors, a power of 10 and a decimal greater than or equal to 1, but less than 10. To multiply numbers in scientific notation, multiply the decimals, multiply the powers of ten, and then put the result into scientific notation.

Write each number in scientific notation.

62. 2,000,000   **63.** 458,000,000   **64.** 0.0000007   **65.** 0.0000000059

Write each number in standard notation.

66. 8×10^{11} **67.** 3.2×10^{-6} **68.** 1.119×10^7 **69.** 5×10^{-12}

Order from least to greatest.

70. $3,644 \times 10^9, 12 \times 10^{11}, 4.3 \times 10^{10}$

71. $58 \times 10^{-10}, 8 \times 10^{-10}, 716 \times 10^{-10}$

Multiply. Express each result in scientific notation.

72. $(4 \times 10^9)(6 \times 10^6)$ **73.** $(5 \times 10^7)(3.6 \times 10^3)$

Chapter Test

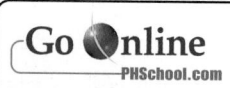
State whether each number is divisible by 2, 3, 5, 9, or 10.

1. 36   **2.** 100   **3.** 270

4. 84   **5.** 555   **6.** 49

List all the factors of each number.

7. 16   **8.** 30   **9.** 41

10. 23   **11.** 55   **12.** 64

Simplify each expression.

13. 5^3 **14.** $2^0 \cdot 2^3$ **15.** $3^2 + 3^3$

16. $4^2 \cdot 1^3$ **17.** $(-9)^2$ **18.** $(7 - 6)^4$

19. $-2(3 + 2)^2$ **20.** $-6^2 + 6$

21. <u>**Writing in Math**</u> A number written in scientific notation is doubled. Must the exponent of the power of 10 change? Explain.

Evaluate for $a = -2$ and $b = 3$.

22. $(a \cdot b)^2$ **23.** a^2b **24.** $b^3 \cdot b^0$

25. $(a + b)^5$ **26.** $b^2 - a$ **27.** $2(a^2 + b^3)$

Is each number *prime* or *composite*? For each composite number, write the prime factorization.

28. 24   **29.** 17   **30.** 42

31. 54   **32.** 72   **33.** 100

Find each GCF.

34. 56, 96   **35.** 36, 60   **36.** 14, 25

37. $15x, 24x^2$ **38.** $14a^2b^3, 21ab^2$

Simplify.

39. $\frac{4}{16}$ **40.** $\frac{44}{52}$ **41.** $\frac{15}{63}$

42. $\frac{a^3}{a^2}$ **43.** $\frac{5b^4}{b}$ **44.** $\frac{8m^4n^2}{40mn}$

Graph the numbers on the same number line.

45. $\frac{1}{10}$ **46.** -0.3 **47.** $-\frac{1}{2}$ **48.** 1

49. You have an 18-ft metal pipe. How many cuts must you make to cut the pipe into 2-ft-long pieces?

Evaluate for $x = 4$ and $y = -3$. Write in simplest form.

50. $\frac{2y}{x^2}$ **51.** $\frac{xy}{5x}$ **52.** $\frac{(x + y)^3}{x}$

53. $\frac{x + 3y}{10}$ **54.** $\frac{y^2 - x}{5}$ **55.** $\frac{x - y}{x + y}$

Simplify each expression.

56. $a^4 \cdot a$ **57.** $(y^3)^6$ **58.** $x^3 \cdot x^6 \cdot y^2$

59. $(a^3)^2$ **60.** $6b^7 \cdot 5b^2$ **61.** $\frac{9^8}{9^2}$

62. $\frac{6a^7}{15a^3}$ **63.** $\frac{b^8}{b^{11}}$ **64.** $\frac{2x^2y^5}{8x^3y^5}$

Write each number in scientific notation.

65. 43,000,000   **66.** 6,000,000,000

67. 0.0000032   **68.** 0.00000000099

Write each number in standard notation.

69. 5×10^5 **70.** 3.812×10^{-7}

71. 9.3×10^8 **72.** 1.02×10^{-9}

Order from least to greatest.

73. $3 \times 10^{10}, 742 \times 10^7, 0.006 \times 10^{12}$

74. $85 \times 10^{-7}, 2 \times 10^{-5}, 0.9 \times 10^{-8}$

Multiply. Express each result in scientific notation.

75. $(3 \times 10^{10})(7 \times 10^8)$

76. $(8.3 \times 10^6)(3 \times 10^5)$

Multiple Choice

Choose the best answer.

1. Which expression is equivalent to $\frac{x^3 y^7}{x^5 y^2}$?
   - (A) $x^{-2} y^5$
   - (B) $x^2 y^5$
   - (C) $x^{-2} y^{-5}$
   - (D) $x^2 y^{-5}$

2. What is the simplest form of $(4c - 5c) + (7 - 2)$?
   - (E) $c + 5$
   - (F) $-c + 5$
   - (G) $9c + 5$
   - (H) $c - 5$

3. Which integer is *not* a solution of $25 + t < 19$?
   - (A) -43
   - (B) -7
   - (C) -8
   - (D) -6

4. Which sentence is true?
   - (E) $16 \geq 2 \cdot 9$
   - (F) $-36 - 10 = 4(5)$
   - (G) $5[-6 - (-2)] = 2 \cdot (-5)2$
   - (H) $32 - (-4 \cdot 6) \leq 54$

5. Which number is divisible by both 3 and 9?
   - (A) 24,000
   - (B) 36,089
   - (C) 45,288
   - (D) 95,500

6. Which expression is equivalent to $-8 \cdot n \cdot n \cdot n \cdot 4 \cdot t$?
   - (E) $-32n^3 t$
   - (F) $-8n^3 + 4t$
   - (G) $-32 \cdot 3n \cdot t$
   - (H) $-32nt^3$

7. Which expression is the GCF of $24x^3$ and $64x$?
   - (A) $1{,}536x^4$
   - (B) $4x^4$
   - (C) $40x^2$
   - (D) $8x$

8. Which expression is equivalent to x^{12}?
   - (E) $x^6 + x^6$
   - (F) $(x^4)^8$
   - (G) $x^2 \cdot x^6$
   - (H) $x^6 \cdot x^6$

9. Which symbol makes $7^2 \cdot 7^5 \ \blacksquare\ (7^5)^2$ true?
   - (A) $>$
   - (B) $<$
   - (C) $=$
   - (D) $\geq$

10. What is the simplest form of $x^5 \cdot y \cdot x^5 \cdot y$?
    - (E) $(x^{25})(2y)$
    - (F) $x^5 y^2$
    - (G) $2x^5 y$
    - (H) $x^{10} y^2$

11. What is the simplest form of $\frac{w^{12} y^{15} z}{w^9 y^7}$?
    - (A) $w^3 y^8 z$
    - (B) $w^{21} y^{22} z$
    - (C) $\frac{w^{21} y^{22} z}{wz}$
    - (D) $\frac{w^3 y^8 z}{wz}$

12. What is the prime factorization of 90?
    - (E) $2 \cdot 3^2 \cdot 5$
    - (F) $2 \cdot 5 \cdot 9$
    - (G) $3 \cdot 3 \cdot 5^2$
    - (H) $2 \cdot 45$

13. Which number is divisible by 2, 3, and 5?
    - (A) 70
    - (B) 105
    - (C) 120
    - (D) 235

Gridded Response

14. Simplify 2^{-3}.

15. Evaluate $\frac{3m - 12}{n}$, for $m = 8$ and $n = 4$.

16. Simplify $2(11 + 7 \cdot 2)$.

17. Evaluate $-a^2 + 4$, for $a = -1$.

18. Simplify $8 + (-8) - (-8)$.

Short Response 19–21.

19. **a.** The product of -6.2 and a number k is -70.68. Write an equation to find k.
    b. Solve for k.

20. What is the GCF of 45 and 54? Explain.

21. **a.** Write a variable expression for the length of the segment.
    b. What is the segment length if $a = 7$?

Extended Response

22. The store sells erasers for $.05, $.10, and $.15. In how many ways can you spend $.20 to buy erasers? Explain your answer using a table.

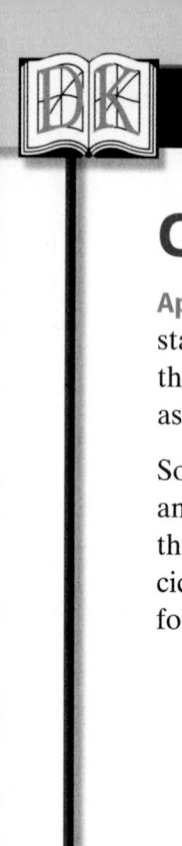
Comparing Life Cycles

Applying Factors and Multiples All living things go through stages of growth and development marked by changes in how they look. Few animals, however, have a life cycle as unusual as the periodic cicadas (sih-CAY-duhs) of North America.

Some of these insects spend 13 or 17 years living underground and feeding on roots. Then, within a matter of days, thousands of them emerge above ground. These large groups of periodic cicadas are called broods. They molt into winged adults but live for only a few more weeks.

Periodic Cicada

An adult cicada perches on a branch to dry its wings.

Cicada Song

A male cicada "sings" using a special membrane on its abdomen called a *tymbal.* Cicada songs continue from dawn until dusk.

Eye

Size: Adult body length 1.2 in. (3 cm)
Habitat: Forests, grasslands, fields, and gardens
Distribution: Eastern North America

Transparent wings

Activity

Use the information in the tables.

1. **a.** When was the last time brood IV emerged?
   b. When will brood IV emerge next?
   c. How many times will brood IV emerge during this century?

2. How many times did brood XXII emerge during the last century?

3. In 1998, a 17-year brood and a 13-year brood both emerged in Missouri.
   a. How many years will pass before they emerge together again?
   b. What year will it be?
   c. **Reasoning** Suppose these two broods are the only cicadas that emerge in Missouri. Before 1998, how many years had passed without adult cicadas in Missouri? Explain.

4. Brood VII and brood XXII recently emerged in the same year. How many years earlier did they also emerge together?

5. Some cicadas are called "dog-day" cicadas. These cicadas have cycles of 2 to 5 years. Suppose broods of 3-year, 4-year, and 5-year cicadas emerged in 2005. In what year would all three broods next emerge together? Explain.

6. Suppose a 17-year cicada emerges, molts, and dies after 4 weeks. What percent of its life has the cicada spent as an adult?

17-Year Cicadas

Brood	Year Seen
III	1997
IV	1998
VII	2001

13-Year Cicadas

Brood	Year Seen
XIX	1998
XXII	2001
XXIII	2002

Gathering Insects

Students taking a class on entomology collect and study insects.

Go Online
PHSchool.com
For: Information about cicadas
Web Code: ade-0453

233

What You've Learned

IL Assessment Framework

- **6.8.10:** In Chapter 1, you learned how to add, subtract, multiply, and divide integers.
- **8.8.12:** In Chapter 2, you solved equations by adding, subtracting, multiplying, and dividing.
- **6.8.08:** In Chapter 4, you investigated exponents.

 Check Your Readiness   **for Help** to the Lesson in green.

Solving Equations (Lessons 3-5 and 3-6)

Solve each equation.

1. $x + 1.8 = 3$ **2.** $n - 41 = 19$ **3.** $a \div (-3) = 15$ **4.** $-19 = p + 21$

5. $6t = 9$ **6.** $40 = z - 34$ **7.** $8d = 64$ **8.** $-0.89 = \frac{x}{2}$

Finding the Greatest Common Factor (Lesson 4-3)

Find the GCF of each group of numbers.

9. $3, 15$ **10.** $16, 20$ **11.** $12, 36$ **12.** $11, 30$ **13.** $30, 40, 210$

14. $45, 80$ **15.** $27, 72$ **16.** $15, 121$ **17.** $30, 500$ **18.** $14, 28, 84$

Reading and Writing Fractions (Lesson 4-4)

Write two equivalent fractions to describe each model.

19.   **20.**   **21.**

Writing Fractions and Decimals (Lesson 4-6)

Write each fraction in simplest form.

22. $\frac{10}{12}$ **23.** $\frac{8}{20}$ **24.** $-\frac{32}{16}$ **25.** $\frac{25}{100}$ **26.** $-\frac{120}{125}$ **27.** $\frac{15}{45}$

28. $\frac{-20}{-75}$ **29.** $\frac{16}{124}$ **30.** $-\frac{18}{81}$ **31.** $-\frac{10}{65}$ **32.** $\frac{14}{84}$ **33.** $\frac{55}{77}$

Divide. Write each quotient as a decimal.

34. $27 \div 5$ **35.** $6 \div 10$ **36.** $10 \div 16$ **37.** $9 \div 12$ **38.** $15 \div 40$

Operations With Fractions

◀)) **Key Vocabulary**

- dimensional analysis (p. 258)
- least common denominator (LCD) (p. 238)
- least common multiple (LCM) (p. 236)
- multiple (p. 236)
- reciprocals (p. 254)
- repeating decimal (p. 242)
- terminating decimal (p. 241)

What You'll Learn Next

(IL) Assessment Framework

In this chapter, you will learn how to

- **6.8.18:** Perform operations with fractions.

- **6.8.09:** Solve equations with fractions.

- **6.8.10:** Find powers of products and quotients.

- Solve problems by working backward.

 Activity Lab Applying what you learn, on pages 288–289 you will solve problems about quiltmaking.

5-1

Comparing and Ordering Rational Numbers

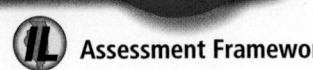 Assessment Framework

6.8.06 Order and compare rational numbers.

 Check Skills You'll Need

Write the prime factorization of each number.

1. 20 **2.** 125 **3.** 45

4. 186 **5.** 621 **6.** 1,575

GO for Help
Lesson 4-3

🔊 **New Vocabulary**

• multiple

• least common multiple (LCM)

• least common denominator (LCD)

1 Finding the Least Common Multiple

A **multiple** of a number is the product of that number and any nonzero whole number.

Multiples of 4: 4, 8, ⑫, 16, 20, ㉔, 28, 32, ㊱, . . .

Multiples of 6: 6, ⑫, 18, ㉔, 30, ㊱, 42, . . .

The numbers 12, 24, and 36 are *common multiples* of 4 and 6. The common multiple 12 is their **least common multiple (LCM).**

1 EXAMPLE Real-World 🌐 Problem Solving

Sports Today, both the school baseball and school soccer teams had games. The baseball team plays every 6 days. The soccer team plays every 5 days. When will both teams have games on the same day again?

6, 12, 18, 24, ㉚, 36, . . . **List the multiples of 6.**

5, 10, 15, 20, 25, ㉚, . . . **List the multiples of 5.**

The LCM is 30. In 30 days both teams will have games again.

✓ Quick Check

1. Find the LCM.

  a. 3, 4   **b.** 4, 5   **c.** 3, 4, 5

You can also use prime factorization to find the LCM.

2 EXAMPLE Using Prime Factorization

Find the LCM of 12 and 40.

$$\left.\begin{array}{l} 12 = 2^2 \cdot ③ \\ 40 = ②^3 \cdot ⑤ \end{array}\right\}$$ **Write the prime factorizations.**

$\text{LCM} = 2^3 \cdot 3 \cdot 5$ **Use the greatest power of each factor.**

$= 120$ **Multiply.**

The LCM of 12 and 40 is 120.

✅ Quick Check

2. Use prime factorization to find the LCM.

a. 6, 16   **b.** 9, 15   **c.** 12, 15, 18

You can find the LCM of a variable expression.

③ EXAMPLE   Finding the LCM of Variable Expressions

Find the LCM of $6a^2$ and $18a^3$.

$$\begin{rcases} 6a^2 = \boxed{2} \cdot 3 \cdot a^2 \\ 18a^3 = 2 \cdot \boxed{3^2} \cdot \boxed{a^3} \end{rcases}$$ Write the prime factorizations.

$\quad$LCM $= 2 \cdot 3^2 \cdot a^3$ $\qquad$ Use the greatest power of each factor.

$\qquad\quad = 18a^3$ $\qquad\qquad$ Multiply.

The LCM of $6a^2$ and $18a^3$ is $18a^3$.

✅ Quick Check

3. Find the LCM.

a. $12x, 15xy$ **b.** $8m^2, 14m^4$ **c.** $25y^2, 15x$

---

2 Comparing Fractions

You can use a number line to compare fractions.

④ EXAMPLE   Using a Number Line

Graph and compare the fractions in each pair.

a. $\dfrac{9}{11}, \dfrac{6}{11}$ **b.** $-\dfrac{1}{2}, -\dfrac{1}{10}$

$\dfrac{9}{11}$ is on the right, so $\dfrac{9}{11} > \dfrac{6}{11}$.

$-\dfrac{1}{2}$ is on the left, so $-\dfrac{1}{2} < -\dfrac{1}{10}$.

⬤nline
active math

For: Fractions Activity
Use: Interactive Textbook, 5-1

✅ Quick Check

4. Use a number line to compare the fractions in each pair.

a. $\dfrac{4}{9}, \dfrac{2}{9}$ **b.** $-\dfrac{4}{9}, -\dfrac{2}{9}$ **c.** $-\dfrac{4}{9}, \dfrac{2}{9}$

Vocabulary Tip

The LCD is sometimes called the <u>lowest common denominator</u>.

When fractions have different denominators, rewrite the fractions with a common denominator. Then compare the numerators. The **least common denominator (LCD)** of two or more fractions is the LCM of the denominators.

5 EXAMPLE — Real-World Problem Solving

Academic Competitions The math team won $\frac{5}{8}$ of its competitions and the debate team won $\frac{7}{10}$ of its competitions. Which team won the greater fraction of competitions?

Step 1 Find the LCM of 8 and 10.

$$8 = 2^3 \text{ and } 10 = 2 \cdot 5$$
$$\text{LCM} = 2^3 \cdot 5 = 40$$

Step 2 Write equivalent fractions with a denominator of 40.

$$\frac{5 \cdot 5}{8 \cdot 5} = \frac{25}{40}$$
$$\frac{7 \cdot 4}{10 \cdot 4} = \frac{28}{40}$$

Step 3 Compare the fractions.

$$\frac{25}{40} < \frac{28}{40}, \text{ so } \frac{5}{8} < \frac{7}{10}.$$

The debate team won the greater fraction of competitions.

Real-World Connection

High school debate teams can have as few as 8 debates and as many as 20 debates in a school year.

✓ Quick Check

5. Compare the fractions in each pair.

   a. $\frac{6}{7}, \frac{4}{5}$ **b.** $\frac{2}{3}, \frac{3}{4}$ **c.** $-\frac{3}{4}, -\frac{7}{10}$

6 EXAMPLE — Ordering Fractions

Order $-\frac{1}{2}, \frac{3}{4}, -1,$ and $\frac{2}{5}$ from least to greatest.

All negative numbers are less than all positive numbers, so $-\frac{1}{2}$ and -1 are both less than $\frac{3}{4}$ and $\frac{2}{5}$. Compare each pair.

$$-1 = \frac{-1}{1}$$
$$\frac{-1}{1} \cdot \frac{2}{2} = \frac{-2}{2}$$

Change -1 into a fraction by using 1 as its denominator. The LCM of 1 and 2 is 2. Use 2 as the common denominator.

$$\frac{3}{4} = \frac{3 \cdot 5}{4 \cdot 5} = \frac{15}{20}$$
$$\frac{2}{5} = \frac{2 \cdot 4}{5 \cdot 4} = \frac{8}{20}$$

The LCM of 2, 4, and 5 is 20. Use 20 as the common denominator.

$$-\frac{2}{2} < -\frac{1}{2} \text{ and } \frac{8}{20} < \frac{15}{20}, \text{ so } -1 < -\frac{1}{2} < \frac{2}{5} < \frac{3}{4}.$$

✓ Quick Check

6. Order from least to greatest.

   a. $\frac{2}{3}, \frac{1}{6}, 1, \frac{5}{12}$ **b.** $\frac{-3}{10}, \frac{1}{5}, -1, \frac{1}{2}, -\frac{7}{12}$

EXERCISES

Practice and Problem Solving

A Practice by Example

Example 1
(page 236)

GO for Help

Find the LCM of each pair by listing multiples.

1. $10, 45$
2. $6, 9$
3. $12, 20$
4. $5, 9$

5. $10, 36$
6. $7, 12$
7. $5, 6$
8. $5, 6, 7$

🌐 **9. Schedules** Both the football and volleyball teams have games today. The football team plays every 7 days. The volleyball team plays every 3 days. When will both teams have games on the same day again?

Examples 2 and 3
(page 236 and 237)

Find the LCM.

10. $20, 36$
11. $15, 27$
12. $8, 14, 20$
13. $5, 12, 15$

14. $12x, 40y$
15. $8x, 25y$
16. $2b^2, 6c^3$
17. $6a^3, 8a$

Example 4
(page 237)

Graph and compare the fractions in each pair.

18. $\frac{4}{5}, \frac{2}{5}$
19. $-\frac{2}{3}, -\frac{1}{3}$
20. $\frac{5}{8}, -\frac{5}{8}$
21. $\frac{11}{12}, \frac{7}{12}$

Example 5
(page 238)

Compare the fractions in each pair.

22. $\frac{5}{6} \blacksquare \frac{3}{4}$
23. $\frac{6}{8} \blacksquare \frac{7}{9}$
24. $\frac{1}{6} \blacksquare \frac{1}{8}$
25. $-\frac{5}{18} \blacksquare -\frac{1}{3}$

🌐 **26. Track and Field** At the track meet, Maria placed first in $\frac{4}{5}$ of her events and Carla placed first in $\frac{2}{3}$ of her events. Who placed first in the greater fraction of events?

Example 6
(page 238)

Order from least to greatest.

27. $\frac{7}{9}, \frac{3}{9}, \frac{5}{9}$
28. $\frac{1}{2}, \frac{1}{3}, \frac{1}{4}$
29. $\frac{2}{5}, \frac{2}{3}, \frac{2}{7}, 2$
30. $\frac{2}{5}, -\frac{3}{8}, -\frac{1}{3}, \frac{2}{4}$

B Apply Your Skills

Mental Math **Compare. Use >, <, or = to complete each statement.**

31. $-\frac{3}{19} \blacksquare \frac{1}{200}$
32. $\frac{-1}{-3} \blacksquare \frac{1}{3}$
33. $\frac{9}{11} \blacksquare \frac{7}{11}$
34. $\frac{-2}{-7} \blacksquare \frac{4}{14}$

35. $\frac{8}{8} \blacksquare \frac{3}{3}$
36. $\frac{2}{10} \blacksquare \frac{2}{100}$
37. $\frac{2}{5} \blacksquare 3\frac{2}{5}$
38. $\frac{-4}{-17} \blacksquare -\frac{5}{2}$

39. Multiple Choice You need $\frac{5}{8}$ yd of fabric for a craft project. You find a piece marked $\frac{2}{3}$ yd. Is the piece long enough? Explain.

Ⓐ No; $\frac{2}{3} > \frac{5}{8}$
Ⓑ No; $\frac{2}{3} < \frac{5}{8}$
Ⓒ Yes; $\frac{2}{3} > \frac{5}{8}$
Ⓓ Yes; $\frac{2}{3} < \frac{5}{8}$

40. The manager of Frank's Snack Shop buys hot dogs in packages of 36. He buys hot dog buns in packages of 20. He cannot buy part of a package. What is the least number of packages of each product he can buy to have an equal number of hot dogs and buns?

Find the LCM.

41. $45, 120, 150$
42. $2, 5, 12, 15$
43. $12x, 40$
44. $7ab, 8a^3b^2, 10a^4$

45. $8x, 18xy$
46. $9b^3, 12bc^2$
47. $4g^2, 10j^4$
48. $2x^3, 5y^2, 15xy^2$

Compare. Use >, <, or = to complete each statement.

49. $\frac{7}{14}$ ■ $\frac{3}{6}$ 50. $-\frac{7}{9}$ ■ $-\frac{2}{3}$ 51. $\frac{8}{5}$ ■ $\frac{3}{2}$ 52. $-\frac{19}{24}$ ■ $-\frac{5}{6}$

53. $-\frac{3}{8}$ ■ $-\frac{6}{16}$ 54. $\frac{10}{11}$ ■ $\frac{4}{5}$ 55. $\frac{1}{2}$ ■ $\frac{2}{4}$ 56. -3 ■ $-\frac{12}{36}$

57. **Writing in Math** Jeremy and Fran want to compare $\frac{5}{8}$ to $\frac{9}{12}$. Jeremy writes equivalent fractions with a denominator of 96. Fran writes equivalent fractions with a denominator of 24. Which method would you prefer? Explain.

C Challenge

58. **Geometry** You have tiles that measure 4 in. by 5 in. What is the smallest square region you can cover without cutting or overlapping the tiles? Explain.

59. **Servings** Suppose you and your brother shared two 12-in. pizzas, a mushroom pizza cut into 8 slices and a cheese pizza cut into 6 slices. If you ate 5 slices of the mushroom pizza, and your brother ate 3 slices of the cheese pizza, who ate more pizza?

ISAT

Test Prep

Multiple Choice

60. What is the LCM of 2, 3, 4, and 5?
    A. 30   **B.** 60   **C.** 90   **D.** 120

61. What is the GCF of $6a^3b$ and $4a^2b$?
    F. a^2b **G.** a^5b^2 **H.** $2a^2b$ **J.** $4a^5b^2$

62. Salt shakers come in boxes of 30 and pepper shakers come in boxes of 24. How many whole boxes of each must you buy to get an equal number of salt and pepper shakers?
    A. 4 salt, 5 pepper   **B.** 5 salt, 4 pepper
    C. 24 salt, 30 pepper   **D.** 30 salt, 24 pepper

Short Response

63. Are the numbers in order from least to greatest: $\frac{5}{8}, \frac{7}{16}, \frac{11}{20}$? Explain.

Mixed Review

GO for Help

Lesson 4-9   **Write in scientific notation.**

64. 5,000,000   65. 0.001394   66. 8,900,000   67. 0.000005

Lesson 4-3   **Find each GCF.**

68. 24, 42   69. 16, 52   70. $25c, 55c^2$ 71. $90xy, 45x^2$

Lesson 2-5   72. **History** The first modern Olympics took place in 1896 in Athens, Greece. One hundred years later, 197 nations took part in the Olympics in Atlanta, Georgia. This was 184 more nations than at the first Olympics. Solve the equation $x + 184 = 197$ to find the number of nations at the first Olympics.

Fractions and Decimals

1 Writing Fractions as Decimals

You can write a fraction as a decimal by dividing the numerator by the denominator. When the division ends with a remainder of zero, the quotient is called a **terminating decimal.**

$$\frac{5}{8} \text{ or } 5 \div 8 \longrightarrow$$

$$
\begin{array}{r}
0.625 \quad \longleftarrow \textbf{quotient} \\
8\overline{)5.000} \\
-4\,8 \\
\hline
20 \\
-16 \\
\hline
40 \\
-40 \\
\hline
0 \quad \longleftarrow \textbf{remainder}
\end{array}
$$

The division process for $5 \div 8$ ends with a remainder of zero. So 0.625 is a terminating decimal.

1 EXAMPLE Real-World 🌐 Problem Solving

Consumer Issues A customer at a delicatessen asks for $\frac{3}{4}$ lb of potato salad. The scale reads 0.75. Is the customer getting the amount of potato salad she requested? Explain.

$$\frac{3}{4} = 3 \div 4 = 0.75$$

Since $\frac{3}{4} = 0.75$, the customer is getting the right amount of potato salad.

✓ Quick Check

1. Write each fraction or mixed number as a decimal.

   a. $\frac{1}{4}$ **b.** $1\frac{7}{8}$

   c. $3\frac{3}{10}$ **d.** $\frac{3}{5}$

6.8.03 Recognize, translate between, and apply multiple representations of rational numbers (decimals, fractions, mixed numbers, percents, and roots).

6.8.06 Order and compare rational numbers.

✓ Check Skills You'll Need
Write the decimals in order from least to greatest.

1. 2.41, 0.241, 24.1, 12.4

2. 1.030, 13.03, 1.300, 1.003

3. 0.1, 0.01, −0.1, −0.01

GO for Help
Skills Handbook, p. 784

🔊 **New Vocabulary**

- **terminating decimal**
- **repeating decimal**

GO Online

Video Tutor Help
Visit: PHSchool.com
Web Code: ada-0775

In a **repeating decimal,** the same block of digits repeats infinitely many times. The block of digits that repeats can be one digit or more than one digit.

2 EXAMPLE **Writing a Repeating Decimal**

Write each fraction as a decimal. State the block of digits that repeats.

a. $\frac{2}{3}$

b. $\frac{15}{11}$

$2 \div 3 = 0.66666\ldots$ ←Divide.→ $15 \div 11 = 1.36363\ldots$

Place a bar over the
$= 0.\overline{6}$ ← block of digits → $= 1.\overline{36}$
that repeats.

$\frac{2}{3} = 0.\overline{6}$; the digit that repeats is 6.

$\frac{15}{11} = 1.\overline{36}$; the block of digits that repeats is 36.

Quick Check

2. Write each fraction as a decimal. State whether the decimal is *terminating* or *repeating*. If the decimal repeats, state the block of digits that repeats.

    a. $\frac{7}{9}$ **b.** $\frac{21}{22}$ **c.** $\frac{11}{8}$ **d.** $\frac{8}{11}$

Calculator Hint
Enter 2 ÷ 3 into your calculator. Then check whether the last digit in the display is 6 or 7 to see how your calculator rounds.

When you compare and order decimals and fractions, it may be helpful to first write the fractions as decimals.

3 EXAMPLE **Ordering Fractions and Decimals**

Write the numbers in order, from least to greatest.

$$\frac{1}{4}, -0.2, -\frac{3}{5}, 1.1$$

$\left.\begin{array}{l} 1 \div 4 = 0.25 \\ -3 \div 5 = -0.6 \end{array}\right\}$ **Change the fractions to decimals.**

$-0.6 < -0.2 < 0.25 < 1.1$ **Compare the decimals.**

From least to greatest, the numbers are $-\frac{3}{5}, -0.2, \frac{1}{4}$, and 1.1.

Quick Check

3. Order from least to greatest.

    a. $0.2, \frac{4}{5}, \frac{7}{10}, 0.5$ **b.** $-\frac{1}{8}, -0.75, -\frac{1}{4}, -0.375$

Reading a decimal correctly provides a way to write a fraction.

Decimal	Read	Fraction
0.43	"forty-three hundredths"	$\frac{43}{100}$

If a decimal is greater than 1, you can write it as a mixed number.

4 EXAMPLE **Writing a Decimal as a Fraction**

Write 1.12 as a mixed number in simplest form.

$1.12 = 1\frac{12}{100}$ **Keep the whole number 1. Write twelve hundredths as a fraction.**

$= 1\frac{12 \div 4}{100 \div 4}$ **Divide the numerator and denominator of the fraction by the GCF, 4.**

$1.12 = 1\frac{3}{25}$ **Simplify.**

✓ Quick Check

4. Write as a fraction or a mixed number in simplest form.

   a. 1.75   **b.** 2.32   **c.** 0.65

You can use algebra to write a repeating decimal as a fraction.

5 EXAMPLE **Writing a Repeating Decimal as a Fraction**

Write the repeating decimal $0.\overline{72}$ as a fraction in simplest form.

$n = 0.\overline{72}$ **Let the variable n equal the decimal.**

$100n = 72.\overline{72}$ **Multiply each side by 10^2, or 100.**

$\begin{array}{r} 100n = 72.\overline{72} \\ -\ n = -0.\overline{72} \\ \hline 99n = 72 \end{array}$ **The Subtraction Property of Equality lets you subtract the same value from each side of the equation.**

$\frac{99n}{99} = \frac{72}{99}$ **Divide each side by 99.**

$n = \frac{72 \div 9}{99 \div 9}$ **Divide the numerator and denominator by the GCF, 9.**

$= \frac{8}{11}$ **Simplify.**

As a fraction in simplest form, $0.\overline{72} = \frac{8}{11}$.

> **Vocabulary Tip**
>
> Properties of Equality allow you to change both sides of an equation in the same way.

✓ Quick Check

5. Write each decimal as a fraction in simplest form.

   a. $0.\overline{7}$ **b.** $0.\overline{54}$ **c.** $0.\overline{213}$

EXERCISES

For more exercises, see *Extra Skill and Word Problem Practice*.

Practice and Problem Solving

A Practice by Example

Example 1
(page 241)

for
Help

Write each fraction or mixed number as a decimal.

1. $\frac{7}{25}$ **2.** $\frac{3}{5}$ **3.** $1\frac{9}{20}$ **4.** $6\frac{1}{4}$

5. Remodeling Randy and Becky measure a carpet. Becky says the carpet's length is $10\frac{5}{16}$ ft. Randy writes "10.3125 ft." Did Randy write the correct measurement? Explain.

Example 2
(page 242)

Write each fraction as a decimal. State whether the decimal is *terminating* **or** *repeating*. **If the decimal repeats, state the block of digits that repeats.**

6. $-\frac{5}{8}$ **7.** $-\frac{1}{6}$ **8.** $\frac{2}{9}$ **9.** $\frac{9}{11}$

Example 3
(page 242)

Order from least to greatest.

10. $1.2, \frac{3}{5}, -0.5, \frac{9}{10}$ **11.** $\frac{1}{2}, \frac{3}{2}, \frac{5}{2}, 0.3$

12. $-\frac{1}{4}, -\frac{1}{8}, -0.75, -0.625$ **13.** $\frac{3}{2}, \frac{2}{5}, \frac{6}{5}, 0.06$

14. $-\frac{7}{10}, -\frac{8}{10}, -0.77, -0.87$ **15.** $2.1, \frac{22}{10}, 2.01, \frac{22}{11}$

Examples 4 and 5
(page 243)

Write each decimal as a fraction or a mixed number in simplest form.

16. 2.25   **17.** 3.4   **18.** 0.08   **19.** 7.15

20. 2.48   **21.** 6.37   **22.** 5.36   **23.** 2.55

24. $0.\overline{5}$ **25.** $0.\overline{126}$ **26.** $0.\overline{27}$ **27.** $-0.\overline{3}$

B Apply Your Skills

Mental Math Compare. Use >, <, or = to complete each statement.

28. $\frac{1}{2}$ ▮ 1.2   **29.** $\frac{7}{8}$ ▮ 0.875   **30.** $\frac{3}{5}$ ▮ 0.25   **31.** $\frac{1}{8}$ ▮ 0.375

32. Number Sense A carpenter has a bolt with diameter $\frac{5}{32}$ in. Will the bolt fit in a hole made by a drill bit with diameter 0.2 in.? Explain.

Write each fraction or mixed number as a decimal.

33. $5\frac{3}{8}$ **34.** $2\frac{5}{16}$ **35.** $\frac{1}{25}$ **36.** $3\frac{4}{5}$ **37.** $-\frac{31}{100}$ **38.** $\frac{7}{11}$

Write as a fraction or a mixed number in simplest form.

39. 0.35   **40.** 6.8   **41.** −3.9   **42.** $10.\overline{105}$

43. Batting averages are usually expressed as decimals. Sarah got 32 hits in 112 times at bat. Lizzie got 26 hits in 86 times at bat.
  a. Data Analysis Find their batting averages to the nearest thousandth.
  b. Probability Based on their batting averages, who is more likely to get a hit? Explain.

GO nline
Homework Video Tutor
Visit: PHSchool.com
Web Code: ade-0502

44. Number Sense Copy and complete this table of some commonly used fractions and decimals. Write the fractions in simplest form.

Fraction	■	■	$\frac{3}{8}$	$\frac{1}{2}$	■	$\frac{3}{4}$	$\frac{7}{8}$
Decimal	0.125	0.25	■	■	0.625	■	■

C) Challenge

Write as a fraction or a mixed number in simplest form.

45. $0.0\overline{6}$ **46.** $0.1\overline{83}$ **47.** 0.272727 **48.** $1.1\overline{9}$

49. Writing in Math Is 3.010010001... a repeating decimal? Explain.

50. Number Sense The number of digits that repeat in a repeating decimal is called the *period* of the decimal. The period of $0.\overline{3}$ is 1.
  a. Write $\frac{5}{7}$, $\frac{4}{13}$, and $\frac{7}{15}$ as decimals.
  b. What is the period of each decimal you wrote in part (a)?

51. Reasoning Seth had just finished a division problem on his calculator when the telephone rang. He got distracted. When he looked back at the calculator, all he could see was the display 0.04040404. What might have been the division problem? Explain.

ISAT

Test Prep

Multiple Choice
52. Which decimal is the closest approximation to $\frac{2}{3}$?
  A. 0.230 **B.** 0.233 **C.** 0.600 **D.** 0.667

53. A clerk puts slices of cheese on a scale until it reads 1.625 lb. What is this amount as a mixed number?
  F. $1\frac{1}{6}$ lb **G.** $1\frac{1}{4}$ lb **H.** $1\frac{5}{8}$ lb **J.** $1\frac{6}{25}$ lb

Short Response
54. Lucia's math teacher asks her to write $\frac{3}{11}$ as a decimal. She enters $3 \div 11$ on her calculator. The calculator displays 0.2727273.   **(a)** Is this the answer Lucia should record?   **(b)** Explain your response.

Mixed Review

Lesson 5-1 **Order the fractions in each group from least to greatest.**
55. $-\frac{1}{3}, \frac{2}{3}, -\frac{5}{6}, \frac{1}{6}$ **56.** $\frac{5}{8}, \frac{3}{8}, \frac{1}{5}, \frac{3}{5}, \frac{1}{8}$ **57.** $-\frac{4}{7}, -\frac{1}{14}, -\frac{3}{14}, -\frac{6}{7}$

Lesson 4-9 **58. Geography** Lake Mead, located between Arizona and Nevada, has a capacity of 34,850,000,000 m^3. Write this number in scientific notation.

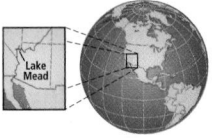

Lessons 3-5 and 3-6 **Solve each equation.**
59. $12.9 + x = 27.3$ **60.** $9.4m = -32.9$

You can round to estimate sums and differences involving fractions and mixed numbers. In one method, you round the fraction or the fraction part of a mixed number to $0, \frac{1}{2},$ or 1.

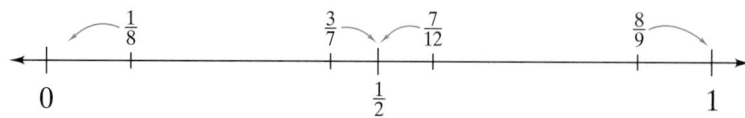

Round to 0 when the numerator is less than half of the denominator.

Round to $\frac{1}{2}$ when the numerator is about half the denominator.

Round to 1 when the numerator and denominator are almost equal.

1 EXAMPLE

Shopping Eva bought $\frac{2}{3}$ lb of Swiss cheese, $\frac{1}{4}$ lb of jack cheese, and $\frac{3}{8}$ lb of cheddar. About how much did she buy altogether?

$\frac{2}{3} \approx 1 \quad \frac{1}{4} \approx 0 \quad \frac{3}{8} \approx \frac{1}{2}$ ⟵ **Round each fraction.**

$1 + 0 + \frac{1}{2} = 1\frac{1}{2}$ ⟵ **Add.**

● Eva bought about $1\frac{1}{2}$ lb of cheese.

You can get reasonable estimates when multiplying by first rounding to the nearest whole number. For division, use compatible numbers.

2 EXAMPLE

a. Estimate $4\frac{1}{8} \cdot 1\frac{9}{10}$.

$4\frac{1}{8} \cdot 1\frac{9}{10}$ **If the fractional part is greater than $\frac{1}{2}$, round up.**

⟱ ⟱

$4 \cdot 2 = 8$ **Multiply.**

b. Estimate $16\frac{1}{5} \div 2\frac{3}{4}$.

$16\frac{1}{5} \div 2\frac{3}{4}$ **$2\frac{3}{4}$ rounds to 3. A number compatible with 3 and close to $16\frac{1}{5}$ is 15.**

⟱ ⟱

$15 \div 3 = 5$ **Divide.**

EXERCISES

Estimate the value of each expression.

1. $\frac{2}{3} + \frac{7}{8}$

2. $5\frac{1}{12} - 2\frac{7}{9}$

3. $\frac{1}{5} + 5\frac{5}{8}$

4. $4\frac{11}{24} - \frac{7}{12}$

5. $\frac{11}{12} \cdot 4$

6. $6\frac{8}{9} \div 1\frac{1}{5}$

7. $10\frac{1}{10} \div 4\frac{7}{8}$

8. $2\frac{4}{5} \cdot 5$

8. Shopping Ira bought $\frac{5}{8}$ lb roast beef and $\frac{3}{4}$ lb of turkey. About how much more turkey did he buy than roast beef?

Adding and Subtracting Fractions

IL Assessment Framework

6.8.18 Solve number sentences and problems involving fractions, decimals, and percents.

6.8.10 Identify and apply order of operations to simplify numeric expressions involving integers, fractions, and decimals.

1 Adding and Subtracting Fractions

Activity

Using Models to Add Fractions

Use the models to answer each question below.

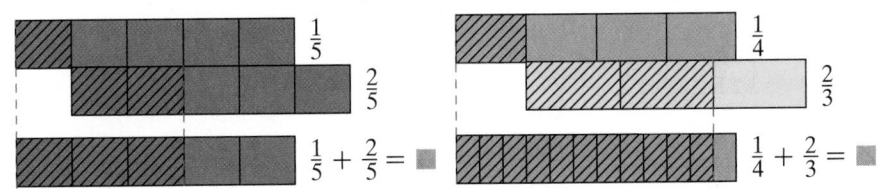

1. a. Refer to the model for $\frac{1}{5} + \frac{2}{5}$. What fraction does $\frac{1}{5} + \frac{2}{5}$ equal?

b. Reasoning The sum of any two fractions can be written as a fraction. Write a conjecture about how to find the numerator and denominator of such a sum.

2. a. Refer to the model for $\frac{1}{4} + \frac{2}{3}$. What fraction does $\frac{1}{4} + \frac{2}{3}$ equal?

b. Can you add the numerators to find the sum? Explain.

c. Can you add the denominators to find the sum? Explain.

✓ **Check Skills You'll Need**

Find the LCM of each group of numbers or expressions.

1. 4, 8   **2.** 9, 18

3. 2n, 5   **4.** 3, 6, 9

5. 8, 5, 4   **6.** 10, n

GO for Help
Lesson 5-1

In the model for $\frac{1}{5} + \frac{2}{5}$ above, you can see that the sum (or difference) of fractions with the same denominator is the sum (or difference) of the numerators. The denominators do not change.

1 EXAMPLE   Simplifying With Like Denominators

Find each sum or difference. Simplify if possible.

a. $\frac{1}{8} + \frac{3}{8}$ **b.** $\frac{9}{x} - \frac{7}{x}$

$\frac{1}{8} + \frac{3}{8} = \frac{1+3}{8}$ **Add or subtract the numerators.** $\frac{9}{x} - \frac{7}{x} = \frac{9-7}{x}$

$= \frac{4}{8} = \frac{1}{2}$ **Simplify.** $= \frac{2}{x}$

✓ Quick Check

1. Find each sum or difference. Simplify if possible.

a. $\frac{3}{7} + \frac{1}{7}$ **b.** $\frac{2}{k} + \frac{3}{k}$ **c.** $\frac{7}{10} - \frac{3}{10}$ **d.** $\frac{11}{y} + \left(-\frac{5}{y}\right)$

Before you can add or subtract fractions with unlike denominators, first write the fractions with a common denominator. The method shown here for addition works with subtraction also.

Arithmetic $\frac{2}{3} + \frac{1}{5}$

$\frac{2}{3} \cdot \frac{5}{5} + \frac{1}{5} \cdot \frac{3}{3}$

$\frac{10}{15} + \frac{3}{15}$

$\frac{13}{15}$

Algebra $\frac{a}{b} + \frac{c}{d}$

$\frac{a}{b} \cdot \frac{d}{d} + \frac{c}{d} \cdot \frac{b}{b}$

$\frac{ad}{bd} + \frac{bc}{bd}$

$\frac{ad + bc}{bd}$

Online active math

For: Fractions Activity
Use: Interactive Textbook, 5-3

2 EXAMPLE Simplifying With Unlike Denominators

Simplify each difference.

a. $\frac{1}{8} - \frac{5}{6}$

$\frac{1}{8} - \frac{5}{6} = \frac{1 \cdot 6 - 8 \cdot 5}{8 \cdot 6}$ Use a common denominator.

$= \frac{6 - 40}{48}$ Use the Order of Operations.

$= \frac{-34}{48} = -\frac{17}{24}$ Simplify.

b. $\frac{1}{8} - \frac{5x}{6}$

$\frac{1}{8} - \frac{5x}{6} = \frac{1 \cdot 6 - 8 \cdot 5x}{8 \cdot 6}$

$= \frac{6 - 40x}{48}$

✓ Quick Check

● **2.** Find each sum or difference.   **a.** $-\frac{7}{8} + \frac{3}{4}$ **b.** $\frac{3}{7} - \frac{2}{m}$

2 Adding and Subtracting Mixed Numbers

Before you add or subtract mixed numbers, write the mixed numbers as improper fractions.

3 EXAMPLE   Real-World 🌐 Problem Solving

Multiple Choice Ali hiked $2\frac{2}{3}$ mi near Mt. Shasta and then another $1\frac{3}{4}$ mi to his campsite. How far did he hike in all?

Ⓐ $\frac{11}{12}$ mi   Ⓑ $1\frac{5}{12}$ mi   Ⓒ $3\frac{11}{12}$ mi   Ⓓ $4\frac{5}{12}$ mi

$2\frac{2}{3} + 1\frac{3}{4} = \frac{8}{3} + \frac{7}{4}$ Write mixed numbers as improper fractions.

$= \frac{8 \cdot 4 + 3 \cdot 7}{3 \cdot 4}$ Rewrite using a common denominator.

$= \frac{32 + 21}{12}$ Use the Order of Operations to simplify.

$= \frac{53}{12} = 4\frac{5}{12}$ Write as a mixed number.

Ali hiked $4\frac{5}{12}$ mi in all. The answer is D.

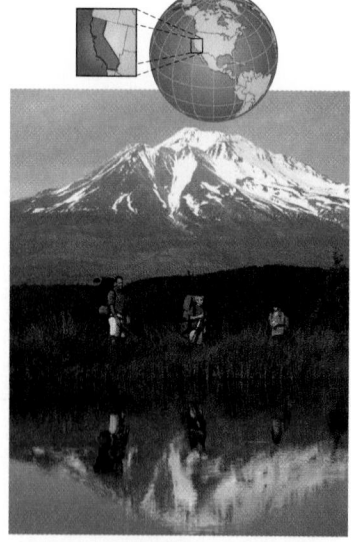

Real-World 🌐 Connection

Mt. Shasta, in northern California, is 14,162 ft high. You can hike the Avalanche Gulch route from Bunny Flat for 6 mi and climb 7,000 ft.

✓ Quick Check

3. Find each sum or difference. Simplify if possible.

   a. $5\frac{3}{4} + \frac{7}{8}$ **b.** $5\frac{2}{3} - 3\frac{1}{6}$ **c.** $2\frac{3}{8} + \frac{7}{8}$

   d. A recipe for punch calls for $1\frac{1}{2}$ qt of orange juice, $1\frac{1}{4}$ qt of ginger ale, and $\frac{3}{4}$ qt of cranberry juice. How many quarts of punch will the recipe make?

You can subtract mixed numbers in more than one way.

More Than One Way

You are making banana bread for a bake sale, using the recipe at the right. You have $1\frac{3}{4}$ c of sugar left in a bag of sugar. How much more sugar do you need?

Banana Bread

5 ripe bananas	3½ cups flour
4 eggs	2 tsp baking soda
1 cup shortening	1 tsp salt
2½ cups sugar	1½ cups chopped walnuts, optional
3 tsp vanilla	

Tina's Method

You write both mixed numbers as improper fractions.

$$2\frac{1}{2} - 1\frac{3}{4} = \frac{5}{2} - \frac{7}{4}$$

$$= \frac{5 \cdot 4 - 2 \cdot 7}{2 \cdot 4}$$

$$= \frac{20 - 14}{8}$$

$$= \frac{\cancel{6}^{3}}{\cancel{8}_{4}} = \frac{3}{4}$$

You need $\frac{3}{4}$ c more sugar.

Kevin's Method

You write $2\frac{1}{2}$ as $2\frac{2}{4}$, and then rewrite it as $1\frac{6}{4}$ before subtracting.

$$2\frac{1}{2} - 1\frac{3}{4} = 2\frac{2}{4} - 1\frac{3}{4}$$

$$= 1\frac{6}{4} - 1\frac{3}{4}$$

$$= \frac{3}{4}$$

You need $\frac{3}{4}$ c more sugar.

Test-Taking Tip

To add or subtract fractions they must have the same denominator. Sometimes you may only have to rename one fraction, but sometimes you may need to rename both.

Choose a Method

1. For the problem above, which method do you prefer? Explain.

2. Which method would you use to find $2\frac{4}{7} - 1\frac{9}{14}$? Which method would you use to find $-1\frac{1}{2} - 1\frac{3}{4}$? Explain your choices.

EXERCISES

For more exercises, see *Extra Skill and Word Problem Practice.*

Practice and Problem Solving

A Practice by Example

Find each sum or difference. Simplify if possible.

Example 1
(page 247)

1. $\frac{3}{16} + \frac{7}{16}$ **2.** $\frac{6}{z} + \left(-\frac{2}{z}\right)$ **3.** $\frac{15}{q} - \frac{8}{q}$ **4.** $\frac{5}{11} + \frac{4}{11}$

5. $\frac{11}{12} - \frac{7}{12}$ **6.** $\frac{7}{8} + \frac{5}{8}$ **7.** $\frac{3}{10} - \frac{7}{10}$ **8.** $\frac{2}{x} + \frac{3}{x}$

Example 2
(page 248)

Simplify each sum or difference.

9. $\frac{3}{4} - \frac{2}{3}$ **10.** $\frac{12}{20} - \frac{1}{4}$ **11.** $-\frac{3}{10} - \frac{5}{100}$ **12.** $\frac{6}{x} - \frac{2}{5}$

Example 3
(page 248)

Find each sum or difference. Simplify if possible.

13. $3\frac{3}{4} + 2\frac{1}{4}$ **14.** $\frac{4}{16} + 1\frac{3}{8}$ **15.** $10\frac{1}{8} + 3\frac{3}{4}$ **16.** $3\frac{5}{8} + 2\frac{7}{12}$

17. $1\frac{5}{9} - 1\frac{2}{9}$ **18.** $5\frac{3}{4} - 2\frac{1}{8}$ **19.** $1\frac{17}{18} - \frac{7}{9}$ **20.** $1\frac{7}{8} - 2\frac{3}{4}$

21. Homework Kim works on Social Studies homework for $2\frac{2}{5}$ h. Then she works on Math homework for $1\frac{1}{4}$ h. How many hours total does Kim spend doing homework?

B Apply Your Skills

Homework Video Tutor
Visit: PHSchool.com
Web Code: ade-0503

Estimation **Estimate each sum or difference.**

22. $2\frac{1}{3} + 7\frac{1}{8}$ **23.** $25\frac{5}{18} - 9\frac{11}{17}$ **24.** $15\frac{3}{4} + 31\frac{1}{2}$ **25.** $-4\frac{7}{8} + 15\frac{1}{10}$

26. <u>Writing in Math</u> Describe why estimating a sum or difference before adding or subtracting is useful.

27. Crafts A doll artist cuts a piece of lace $8\frac{5}{8}$ in. long from a piece $10\frac{1}{2}$ in. long. How many inches of lace are left?

Find each sum or difference.

28. $\frac{12}{15} + \frac{1}{2}$ **29.** $\frac{3}{n} - \frac{3}{10}$ **30.** $\frac{7}{10} + \frac{2d}{3}$ **31.** $\frac{5}{6} + \frac{7}{9}$

Mental Math **Find each sum.**

32. $\frac{3}{4} + \frac{3}{8} + \frac{1}{4}$ **33.** $2\frac{5}{7} + 1\frac{2}{5} + 3\frac{2}{7}$ **34.** $\frac{2}{7} + \frac{x}{2} + \left(-\frac{2}{7}\right)$

35. Weather There were three snowstorms last winter. The storms dropped $3\frac{1}{2}$ in., $6\frac{1}{2}$ in., and $10\frac{3}{4}$ in. of snow. What was the combined snowfall of the three storms?

C Challenge

Use prime factors to find the LCD. Then simplify each expression.

36. $\frac{7}{24} - \frac{15}{90}$ **37.** $\frac{-5}{66} + \frac{-7}{99}$ **38.** $\frac{2}{28} + \frac{1}{49}$

39. Collections Dora and Paul have a collection of x marbles. Dora has $\frac{x}{3}$ marbles. What fraction of the marbles does Paul have?

Multiple Choice

40. Which sum or difference is greater than 0?

A. $-\frac{7}{8} + \frac{3}{4}$ **B.** $-\frac{7}{8} - \frac{3}{4}$ **C.** $-\frac{7}{8} + \left(-\frac{3}{4}\right)$ **D.** $\frac{7}{8} + \left(-\frac{3}{4}\right)$

41. Sue is fishing. She catches a bass weighing $5\frac{1}{4}$ lb. Then she catches three more weighing $3\frac{1}{2}$ lb, $1\frac{3}{4}$ lb, and 2 lb. She releases the smallest fish. What is the total weight of the fish Sue keeps?

F. $8\frac{3}{4}$ lb   **G.** $9\frac{1}{4}$ lb   **H.** $10\frac{3}{4}$ lb   **J.** $12\frac{1}{2}$ lb

42. Which expression is equal to $\frac{1}{3} + \frac{1}{6}$?

A. $\frac{1}{2} + \frac{2}{4}$ **B.** $\frac{1}{4} + \frac{2}{8}$ **C.** $\frac{1}{5} + \frac{2}{10}$ **D.** $\frac{1}{7} + \frac{2}{14}$

Short Response

43. In 2003, first-class postage in the United States costs 37¢ for 1 oz. Your letter weighs $\frac{3}{4}$ oz. **(a)** Do you need extra postage to include a newspaper clipping that weighs $\frac{3}{8}$ oz? **(b)** Explain.

44. José and Letty plan to ride their bicycles at least eight miles. They ride for $5\frac{3}{8}$ miles and stop for a break. Then they ride for another $2\frac{5}{7}$ **(a)**   **(b)**

Mixed Review

Lesson 5-2   **Order from least to greatest.**

45. $\frac{5}{8}, \frac{4}{7}, \frac{3}{6}$ **46.** $\frac{2}{3}, 0.6, 0.66$ **47.** $\frac{10}{9}, \frac{9}{10}, -\frac{9}{10}, -\frac{10}{9}$

Lesson 4-7   **Simplify each expression.**

48. $x \cdot x^2$ **49.** $(x^3)^4$

Lesson 3-3   **50. Data Analysis** Use the data at the right. Find the mean, median, and mode of the annual salaries. Which statistic would you use to encourage someone to take a job at Company A?

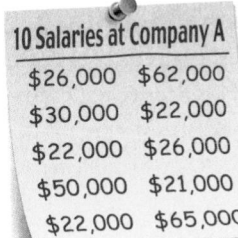

10 Salaries at Company A	
$26,000	$62,000
$30,000	$22,000
$22,000	$26,000
$50,000	$21,000
$22,000	$65,000

✓ Checkpoint Quiz 1   Lessons 5-1 through 5-3

Compare. Use >, <, or = to complete each statement.

1. $\frac{2}{3} \blacksquare \frac{2}{5}$ **2.** $2\frac{2}{3} \blacksquare 2\frac{4}{6}$ **3.** $-\frac{1}{5} \blacksquare -\frac{1}{8}$ **4.** $-1.65 \blacksquare -1\frac{5}{8}$

Write each fraction or mixed number as a decimal and each decimal as a fraction in simplest form.

5. $\frac{51}{100}$ **6.** 0.012 **7.** $1\frac{1}{4}$ **8.** $0.\overline{3}$ **9.** $\frac{5}{6}$ **10.** $0.\overline{51}$

Find each sum or difference. Simplify if possible.

11. $\frac{6}{13} + \frac{5}{13}$ **12.** $\frac{11}{12} - \frac{7}{9}$ **13.** $1\frac{3}{5} + 2\frac{7}{8}$ **14.** $4\frac{1}{7} - 3\frac{10}{21}$

5-4

Multiplying and Dividing Fractions

 Assessment Framework

6.8.18 Solve number sentences and problems involving fractions, decimals, and percents.

6.8.10 Identify and apply order of operations to simplify numeric expressions involving integers, fractions, and decimals.

✓ Check Skills You'll Need

Write each mixed number as an improper fraction.

1. $2\frac{1}{3}$ **2.** $3\frac{3}{10}$ **3.** $1\frac{4}{9}$

4. $4\frac{4}{5}$ **5.** $7\frac{7}{8}$ **6.** $5\frac{1}{7}$

GO for Help
Skills Handbook, p. 794

◀)) New Vocabulary
• reciprocals

1 Multiplying Fractions

ctivity

Modeling Multiplication of Fractions

Use paper folding to find $\frac{2}{3}$ of $\frac{1}{4}$, or $\frac{2}{3} \cdot \frac{1}{4}$.

1. Fold a sheet of paper into fourths as shown. Shade $\frac{1}{4}$ of it.

2. Now unfold the paper and fold it into thirds as shown in the second picture. Shade $\frac{2}{3}$ of it.

3. a. Count the small rectangles.
   b. How many did you shade twice?
   c. What fraction of the small rectangles is this?

4. Use your model to complete:
   $$\frac{2}{3} \cdot \frac{1}{4} = \frac{\blacksquare}{\blacksquare}$$

5. **Modeling** Use paper folding and shading to find $\frac{3}{4} \cdot \frac{1}{2}$.

To multiply fractions, first multiply their numerators and multiply their denominators. Then write the result in simplest form.

1 EXAMPLE Multiplying Fractions

Find $\frac{3}{7} \cdot \frac{4}{5}$. Simplify if possible.

$$\frac{3}{7} \cdot \frac{4}{5} = \frac{3 \cdot 4}{7 \cdot 5} \quad \longleftarrow \text{ Multiply the numerators.}$$
$$\longleftarrow \text{ Multiply the denominators.}$$
$$= \frac{12}{35} \qquad \text{Simplify.}$$

✓ Quick Check

1. Find each product. Simplify if possible.

   a. $\frac{2}{5}\left(\frac{1}{3}\right)$ b. $-\frac{5}{6} \cdot \frac{2}{3}$ c. $\frac{7}{8} \cdot \frac{5}{9}$ d. $-\frac{1}{4}\left(-\frac{3}{8}\right)$

Online
active math

For: Fractions Activity
Use: Interactive Textbook, 5-4

When a numerator and a denominator have common factors, you can simplify before multiplying.

2 EXAMPLE **Simplifying Before Multiplying**

a. Find $\frac{9}{15} \cdot \frac{-5}{9}$.

$$\frac{9}{15} \cdot \frac{-5}{9} = \frac{1\cancel{9}}{3\cancel{15}} \cdot \frac{-1\cancel{-5}}{1\cancel{9}} \quad \text{Divide the common factors.}$$

$$= -\frac{1}{3} \qquad \text{Multiply.}$$

b. Find $\frac{y}{4} \cdot \frac{8}{11}$.

$$\frac{y}{4} \cdot \frac{8}{11} = \frac{y}{1\cancel{4}} \cdot \frac{\cancel{8}^2}{11} \quad \text{Divide the common factors.}$$

$$= \frac{2y}{11} \qquad \text{Multiply.}$$

✓ **Quick Check**

2. Find each product. Simplify if possible.

 a. $\frac{2}{3} \cdot \frac{6}{7}$ b. $-\frac{5}{15} \cdot \frac{21}{25}$ c. $\frac{2x}{9} \cdot \frac{3}{4}$

> **Problem Solving Hint**
> If either the numerator or denominator is negative, or if the negative sign is in front of the fraction, then the entire fraction is negative. $\frac{-17}{24} = -\frac{17}{24}$

To multiply mixed numbers, first write them as improper fractions. Then simplify before multiplying, if possible.

3 EXAMPLE **Real-World Problem Solving**

Geometry Central Park in New York City is a rectangle. It is approximately $2\frac{1}{2}$ mi long and $\frac{1}{2}$ mi wide. What is the area of Central Park?

$$A = 2\frac{1}{2} \cdot \frac{1}{2} \quad \text{Area of a rectangle} = \text{length} \cdot \text{width.}$$

$$= \frac{5}{2} \cdot \frac{1}{2} \quad \text{Write } 2\frac{1}{2} \text{ as an improper fraction, } \frac{5}{2}.$$

$$= \frac{5}{4} \qquad \text{Multiply.}$$

$$= 1\frac{1}{4} \qquad \text{Write as a mixed number.}$$

The area of Central Park is about $1\frac{1}{4}$ mi².

✓ **Quick Check**

3. Find each product. Simplify if possible.

 a. $3\frac{3}{4} \cdot \frac{2}{5}$ b. $\frac{2}{3} \cdot 1\frac{2}{7}$ c. $\left(-2\frac{5}{6}\right) \cdot 1\frac{3}{5}$

Real-World Connection

Central Park is a rectangle. The angle of the photo makes two sides appear to be not parallel.

2 Dividing Fractions

Asking "What is $2 \div \frac{1}{2}$?" is the same as asking "How many halves are in two wholes?" As the oranges show, there are four halves in two wholes.

Numbers like $\frac{1}{2}$ and 2 (or $\frac{2}{1}$) are **reciprocals** because their product is 1. To divide fractions, rewrite the division as a related multiplication in which you multiply by the reciprocal of the divisor.

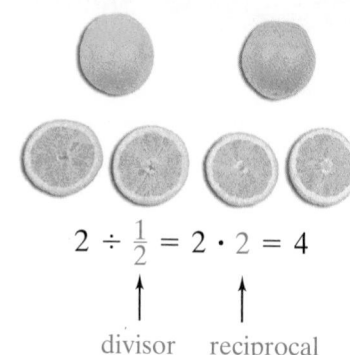

$$2 \div \frac{1}{2} = 2 \cdot 2 = 4$$

divisor   reciprocal

4 EXAMPLE Dividing Fractions

a. Find $\frac{2}{9} \div \frac{2}{5}$.

$$\frac{2}{9} \div \frac{2}{5} = \frac{2}{9} \cdot \frac{5}{2}$$ Multiply by the reciprocal of the divisor.

$$= \frac{\overset{1}{2}}{9} \cdot \frac{5}{\underset{1}{2}}$$ Divide the common factors.

$$= \frac{5}{9}$$ Simplify.

b. Find $\frac{x}{3} \div \frac{x}{4}$.

$$\frac{x}{3} \div \frac{x}{4} = \frac{x}{3} \cdot \frac{4}{x}$$

$$= \frac{\overset{1}{x}}{3} \cdot \frac{4}{1\overset{}{x}}$$

$$= \frac{4}{3} = 1\frac{1}{3}$$

✓ Quick Check

4. Find each quotient. Simplify if possible.

a. $-\frac{1}{4} \div \frac{1}{2}$ b. $\frac{5a}{8} \div \frac{2}{3}$ c. $\frac{3b}{7} \div \frac{6}{7}$

To divide mixed numbers, change the mixed numbers to improper fractions before multiplying by the reciprocal of the divisor.

5 EXAMPLE Dividing Mixed Numbers

Find $1\frac{3}{4} \div \left(-2\frac{5}{8}\right)$.

$$1\frac{3}{4} \div \left(-2\frac{5}{8}\right) = \frac{7}{4} \div \left(-\frac{21}{8}\right)$$ Change to improper fractions.

$$= \frac{7}{4} \cdot \left(-\frac{8}{21}\right)$$ Multiply by $-\frac{8}{21}$, the reciprocal of $-\frac{21}{8}$.

$$= \frac{\overset{1}{7}}{\underset{1}{4}} \cdot -\frac{\overset{2}{8}}{\underset{3}{21}} = -\frac{2}{3}$$ Divide the common factors. Simplify.

✓ Quick Check

5. Find each quotient. Simplify if possible.

a. $1\frac{1}{3} \div \frac{5}{6}$ b. $-1\frac{3}{5} \div 1\frac{1}{5}$ c. $12\frac{1}{2} \div 1\frac{2}{3}$

EXERCISES

For more exercises, see *Extra Skill and Word Problem Practice*.

Practice and Problem Solving

A Practice by Example

Examples 1 and 2
(pages 252 and 253)

 for Help

Example 3
(page 253)

Find each product. Simplify if possible.

1. $\frac{2}{3} \cdot \frac{1}{5}$

2. $-\frac{1}{2}\left(\frac{3}{8}\right)$

3. $-\frac{4}{7} \cdot -\frac{3}{5}$

4. $\left(-\frac{2}{3}\right)\left(\frac{11}{13}\right)$

5. $\left(-\frac{7}{8}\right)\left(-\frac{4}{5}\right)$

6. $\frac{12y}{25} \cdot \frac{5}{6}$

7. $\frac{9}{10} \cdot \frac{15x}{3}$

8. $\frac{5}{9}\left(\frac{9}{10}\right)$

9. $5\frac{7}{8} \cdot \frac{6}{7}$

10. $2\frac{3}{4} \cdot 1\frac{1}{5}$

11. $-1\frac{2}{5} \cdot 2\frac{2}{7}$

12. $-3\frac{2}{5} \cdot -1\frac{2}{3}$

🌐 **13. Homework** Jim spends $\frac{3}{4}$ of an hour on homework. His older sister Gina spends $1\frac{2}{3}$ times as much on her homework as Jim spends on his. How much time does Gina spend doing her homework?

Example 4
(page 254)

Find each quotient. Simplify if possible.

14. $\frac{1}{2} \div \frac{1}{3}$

15. $\frac{5}{8} \div \frac{3}{4}$

16. $-\frac{3}{4} \div \frac{1}{3}$

17. $\frac{11}{12} \div \left(-\frac{7}{8}\right)$

18. $\frac{3}{4} \div \frac{8}{9}$

19. $\frac{3}{4} \div \frac{1}{2}$

20. $\frac{2t}{5} \div \frac{2}{5}$

21. $\frac{1}{x} \div \frac{3}{x}$

Example 5
(page 254)

22. $12\frac{2}{3} \div \frac{3}{4}$

23. $1\frac{3}{8} \div 2\frac{1}{16}$

24. $-1\frac{7}{9} \div \frac{8}{9}$

25. $-3\frac{2}{3} \div \left(-2\frac{4}{9}\right)$

26. $3\frac{1}{2} \div \frac{4}{21}$

27. $7\frac{2}{3} \div 1\frac{5}{6}$

28. $6\frac{3}{4} \div \frac{9}{10}$

29. $1\frac{4}{5} \div \left(-1\frac{1}{2}\right)$

B Apply Your Skills

Find each product. Simplify if possible.

30. $\frac{6x}{7} \cdot \frac{1}{3}$

31. $-\frac{2}{3} \cdot \frac{9}{10}$

32. $\frac{8}{9} \cdot \frac{15}{28}$

33. $-1\frac{1}{4} \cdot 6\frac{2}{3}$

34. $\frac{4}{t} \cdot \frac{3t}{8}$

35. $\frac{4a}{9} \cdot \frac{3}{10}$

36. $1\frac{3}{5} \cdot \left(-2\frac{1}{2}\right)$

37. $\left(-\frac{7}{12}\right)\left(-\frac{5}{6}\right)$

38. Number Sense One granola bar weighs $1\frac{1}{2}$ oz. What is the weight of six granola bars?

Find each quotient. Simplify if possible.

39. $-\frac{1}{2} \div \frac{2}{3}$

40. $\frac{10}{13} \div \frac{15}{26}$

41. $-\frac{5}{6} \div \frac{4}{9}$

42. $\frac{4}{9x} \div \frac{2}{3x}$

43. $\frac{2}{5} \div \frac{15}{16}$

44. $-\frac{6n}{7} \div \frac{n}{3}$

45. $\frac{2}{9} \div \frac{w}{3}$

46. $\frac{3}{8} \div \frac{6}{32}$

Mental Math **Simplify each expression.**

47. $\frac{1}{2} \cdot \frac{2}{5}$

48. $\frac{1}{2} \div \frac{2}{5}$

49. $10 \cdot \frac{1}{4}$

50. $10 \div \frac{1}{4}$

51. $\frac{5}{8} \cdot \frac{3}{5}$

52. $\frac{5}{8} \div \frac{3}{5}$

53. $\frac{3}{7} \cdot \frac{12}{21}$

54. $\frac{3}{7} \div \frac{12}{21}$

🌐 **55. Construction** A cable television crew has to install cable along a road $1\frac{1}{2}$ mi long. The crew takes a day to install each $\frac{1}{4}$ mi of cable. How many days will the installation take?

Ⓐ 6 days   Ⓑ $1\frac{3}{4}$ days   Ⓒ $\frac{3}{4}$ day   Ⓓ $\frac{3}{8}$ day

56. a. Write an expression for the following: The product of $\frac{1}{2}a$ and 3 is decreased by the quotient $a \div (-4)$.

b. Evaluate your expression for $a = 3$.

GO Online
Homework Video Tutor
Visit: PHSchool.com
Web Code: ade-0504

57. A cheetah can run as fast as 64 mi/h. At that speed, how far could a cheetah run in $\frac{1}{16}$ h? $\frac{1}{30}$ h?

58. You are hiking along a trail that is $13\frac{1}{2}$ mi long. You plan to rest every $2\frac{1}{4}$ mi. How many rest stops will you make?

 Challenge

59. <u>Writing in Math</u> Why must you change mixed numbers to improper fractions before multiplying or dividing them?

60. a. Patterns Find each quotient: $\frac{1}{2} \div 2, \frac{1}{2} \div 3, \frac{1}{2} \div 4$, and $\frac{1}{2} \div 5$.
b. Explain what happens to the quotients as the divisor increases in value.

61. Reasoning Write a multiplication equation and a division equation that you could use to show the result of cutting four melons into eight equal slices each.

62. Open-Ended Find two fractions greater than $\frac{1}{2}$ with a product less than $\frac{1}{2}$.

Multiple Choice

63. Which quotient does NOT equal 1?
A. $2\frac{3}{4} \div \frac{11}{4}$ **B.** $\frac{3}{8} \div 0.375$ **C.** $\frac{7}{8} \div \frac{7}{8}$ **D.** $-1\frac{2}{3} \div \left(-\frac{3}{5}\right)$

64. Which expression simplifies to $\frac{x}{3}$?
F. $\frac{5x}{36}\left(\frac{5}{12}\right)$ **G.** $\frac{x}{6}\left(2\frac{2}{5}\right)$ **H.** $\frac{5x}{36}\left(2\frac{2}{5}\right)$ **J.** $\frac{36}{5x}\left(2\frac{2}{5}\right)$

Short Response

65. a. A family wants to travel 300 miles. They drive at an average speed of 65 mi/h for $3\frac{1}{2}$ hours. Have they driven far enough?
b. Explain your answer for part (a).

66. Natasha's bedroom floor is $10\frac{1}{2}$ ft by $14\frac{3}{4}$ ft. She buys 160 ft² of carpet. Does she have enough carpet to cover the floor? Explain.

Mixed Review

 for Help

Lesson 5-3

Add or subtract.

67. $\frac{4}{5} + \frac{6}{7}$ **68.** $\frac{10}{13} - \frac{25}{26}$ **69.** $-\frac{3}{10} + \frac{3}{5}$ **70.** $\frac{16}{21} - \frac{5}{7}$

Lesson 4-4

Simplify each fraction.

71. $\frac{10}{12}$ **72.** $\frac{24}{40}$ **73.** $\frac{45}{10}$ **74.** $\frac{12}{50}$ **75.** $\frac{34}{51}$ **76.** $\frac{105}{135}$

Lesson 2-7

77. Hal's age is three times Ida's age. In 8 years Hal will be twice as old as Ida. How old is Hal?

78. Personal Finance You spent $\frac{1}{4}$ of your money on lunch. After lunch, you gave half of what you had left to a friend, and then you spent \$3 on a book. You have \$4.50 left. How much money did you have before lunch?

Using Customary Units of Measurement

1 | Identifying Appropriate Units of Measure

What You'll Learn

- To identify appropriate customary units
- To convert customary units

. . . And Why

To solve real-world problems involving consumer issues

✓ Check Skills You'll Need

Find each product.

1. $4 \cdot \frac{1}{12}$ **2.** $3\frac{1}{4} \cdot \frac{16}{1}$

3. $1\frac{1}{4} \cdot \frac{8}{1}$ **4.** $4\frac{1}{2} \cdot \frac{1}{3}$

GO for Help
Lesson 5-4

◄)) New Vocabulary

- dimensional analysis

Most people in the United States use the *customary system* of measurement.

Customary Units of Measure

Type	Length	Capacity	Weight
Unit	Inch (in.) Foot (ft) Yard (yd) Mile (mi)	Fluid ounce (fl oz) Cup (c) Pint (pt) Quart (qt) Gallon (gal)	Ounce (oz) Pound (lb) Ton (t)
Equivalents	1 ft = 12 in. 1 yd = 3 ft 1 mi = 5,280 ft = 1,760 yd	1 c = 8 fl oz 1 pt = 2 c 1 qt = 2 pt 1 gal = 4 qt	1 lb = 16 oz 1 t = 2,000 lb

In order to measure an object, you should choose an appropriate unit of measure.

1 EXAMPLE   Choosing a Unit of Measure

Choose an appropriate unit of measure. Explain your choice.

a. weight of a truck   Measure its weight in tons because a truck is very heavy.

b. length of a hallway rug   Measure its length in feet or yards because the length is too great to measure in inches.

✓ Quick Check

1. Choose an appropriate unit of measure. Explain.

   a. length of a swimming pool   **b.** weight of a baby

   c. length of a pencil   **d.** capacity of an eyedropper

You can use *conversion factors* to change from one unit of measure to another in a process called **dimensional analysis**. You use equivalent units to write a conversion factor. For example, $\frac{12 \text{ in.}}{1 \text{ ft}} = 1$, so you can use $\frac{12 \text{ in.}}{1 \text{ ft}}$ to convert from feet to inches.

2 EXAMPLE Using Dimensional Analysis

Gridded Response Use dimensional analysis to convert 10 quarts to gallons.

$$10 \text{ qt} = \frac{10 \text{ qt}}{1} \cdot \frac{1 \text{ gal}}{4 \text{ qt}}$$ Use a conversion factor that changes quarts to gallons.

$$= \frac{{}^5 10 \text{ qt} \cdot 1 \text{ gal}}{{}_2 4 \text{ qt}}$$ Divide the common factors and units.

$$= \frac{5}{2} \text{ gal} = 2\frac{1}{2} \text{ gal}$$ Simplify.

There are $2\frac{1}{2}$ gal in 10 qt. Use $\frac{5}{2}$ for a gridded response.

✓ Quick Check

2. Complete each equation.

   a. 14 oz = ■ lb   **b.** 14 in. = ■ ft   **c.** 14 pt = ■ qt

Converting units can help you make comparisons.

3 EXAMPLE Real-World 🌐 Problem Solving

Consumer Issues At Store A, a $4\frac{1}{4}$-lb bag of cashew nuts costs $15.99. Store B charges the same price for a 76-oz bag of cashews. Which store gives you more for your money?

$$4\frac{1}{4} \text{ lb} = \frac{17}{4} \text{ lb} \cdot \frac{16 \text{ oz}}{1 \text{ lb}}$$ Use a conversion factor that changes pounds to ounces.

$$= \frac{17}{{}_1 4} \text{ lb} \cdot \frac{{}^4 16 \text{ oz}}{1 \text{ lb}}$$ Divide the common factors and units.

$$= 68 \text{ oz}$$ Multiply.

Since 76 oz > 68 oz, Store B gives you more for your money.

✓ Quick Check

3. Complete each equation.

   a. $3\frac{1}{2}$ lb = ■ oz   **b.** $3\frac{1}{2}$ yd = ■ ft   **c.** $3\frac{1}{2}$ pt = ■ c

EXERCISES

Practice and Problem Solving

 Practice by Example

Example 1
(page 257)

 GO for Help

Choose an appropriate unit of measure. Explain your choice.

1. weight of a paper clip

2. capacity of a baby bottle

3. distance to Australia

4. length of a sports field

Example 2
(page 258)

Use dimensional analysis to complete each equation.

5. 3 qt = ■ gal

6. 3 gal = ■ qt

7. 1,000 lb = ■ t

8. 1,000 oz = ■ lb

9. 18 in. = ■ ft

10. 18 ft = ■ in.

Number Sense **Match each measurement from the first group with an equivalent amount from the second group.**

11. 15 mi

12. 15 t

13. 15 in.

14. 15 fl oz

15. 15 c

16. 15 lb

17. 15 pt

A. 30,000 lb

B. $\frac{3}{400}$ t

C. $1\frac{1}{4}$ ft

D. $7\frac{1}{2}$ pt

E. $7\frac{1}{2}$ qt

F. $1\frac{7}{8}$ c

G. 79,200 ft

Example 3
(page 258)

Complete each equation.

18. $\frac{1}{2}$ yd = ■ ft

19. $\frac{1}{2}$ mi = ■ ft

20. $10\frac{1}{2}$ lb = ■ oz

21. $6\frac{1}{2}$ ft = ■ in.

22. $7\frac{1}{2}$ c = ■ fl oz

23. $6\frac{1}{4}$ gal = ■ qt

24. $\frac{3}{4}$ lb = ■ oz

25. $3\frac{1}{2}$ qt = ■ pt

26. $1\frac{1}{3}$ yd = ■ in.

27. $\frac{1}{5}$ t = ■ lb

28. 7 pt = ■ c

29. $5\frac{1}{2}$ mi = ■ ft

🌐 **30. Track and Field** Julia clears $9\frac{1}{2}$ ft in the pole vault. Maya clears 112 in. Which vaulter clears the greater height?

B **Apply Your Skills**

Estimation **Match each indicated measurement with a possible value.**

31. height of a 7-year-old

32. weight of a bag of apples

33. width of your palm

34. amount of water in a vase

35. weight of a peach

36. amount of juice in a child's cup

A. 4 fl oz

B. 4 lb

C. 4 ft

D. 4 c

E. 4 oz

F. 4 in.

37. Hiking You are hiking a 2-mi-long trail. You pass by a sign showing that you have hiked 1,000 ft. How many feet are left?

Is each item likely to be measured by *length*, *weight*, or *capacity*?

38. a hair ribbon

39. a package of meat

40. a bottle of juice

41. a bag of oranges

42. a zipper

43. the contents of an eyedropper

Choose an appropriate unit of measure. Explain your choice.

44. capacity of a cooking pot

45. weight of a medium-sized fish

46. weight of a sheet of paper

47. capacity of a swimming pool

Historical Measures

1 handbreadth = 3 in.
1 span = 9 in.
1 rod = $16\frac{1}{2}$ ft

48. History People once measured lengths in *handbreadths, spans,* and *rods.*

 a. How many are there: handbreadths in 1 span? handbreadths in 1 rod? spans in 1 rod?

 b. Open-Ended Measure the length of an object. Give the length in *handbreadths, spans,* and *rods.*

 c. Writing in Math Consider the measurements you made in part (b). Which unit of measure is the most appropriate for the item you chose? Explain.

49. a. Geography The Mississippi River is about 19,747,200 ft long. What is a better unit of measure? Find the length of the Mississippi using the better unit of measure.

 b. Choose an historical measure from Exercise 48. Find the length of the Mississippi in that unit.

Estimation Is each measurement reasonable? If not, give a reasonable measurement.

50. A textbook weighs 2 oz.

51. The street is 25 ft wide.

52. You drink about 10 gal of liquid per day.

53. A sewing needle is about 2 ft long.

54. A car is 12 yd long.

55. A shoe weighs 1 t.

56. Reasoning A student converted 8 cups to pints. His answer was 16 pints. Use dimensional analysis to determine whether the student's answer is reasonable.

Use estimation, mental math, or paper and pencil to complete each statement.

57. 28 in. = ■ ft

58. 5 c = ■ pt

59. 5 t = ■ lb

60. 2,640 ft = ■ mi

61. 3,000 lb = ■ t

62. 13 pt = ■ qt

63. 70 fl oz = ■ c

64. 1 ft 9 in. = ■ in.

65. 18 qt = ■ gal

66. 3 gal = ■ qt

67. 50 oz = ■ lb

68. 20 c = ■ qt

GO Online
Homework Video Tutor
Visit: PHSchool.com
Web Code: ade-0505

69. Error Analysis Suzanne claims a quarter-pound hamburger is heavier than a 6-oz hamburger. Explain why she is incorrect.

 Challenge **Complete each equation.**

70. $2\frac{1}{4}$ yd $= 6\frac{3}{4}$ ▓

71. 6 qt $= 1\frac{1}{2}$ ▓

72. 100 lb $= \frac{1}{20}$ ▓

73. 6 c $= 48$ ▓

74. $1\frac{1}{2}$ pt $=$ ▓ qt

75. $4\frac{1}{4}$ ft $=$ ▓ in.

ISAT

Gridded Response **Complete each equation.**

76. 9 lb 2 oz $=$ ▓ oz

77. 4 ft $=$ ▓ in.

78. 3 yd 2 ft $=$ ▓ ft

79. 12 pt $=$ ▓ c

80. 8 oz $=$ ▓ lb

81. 7 ft $=$ ▓ yd

82. $4\frac{1}{2}$ c $=$ ▓ pt

83. $1\frac{1}{2}$ gal $=$ ▓ qt

84. $2\frac{1}{2}$ yd $=$ ▓ in.

Mixed Review

Lesson 5-4 **Multiply or divide.**

85. $\frac{9}{11} \div 2\frac{7}{11}$

86. $1\frac{5}{7} \cdot 1\frac{1}{2}$

87. $\frac{9}{10} \div \frac{3}{4}$

88. $2\frac{2}{5} \cdot 3\frac{2}{3}$

Lesson 2-3 **Simplify each expression.**

89. $3x + (-2x) + 3y$

90. $10 - 3t - 4t$

91. $2y - 5y$

Lesson 1-7 **92. Softball** In a single-elimination softball tournament, each team plays until it loses. Eight teams are playing in a single-elimination tournament. How many games must be played?

Math at Work

Technical Artist

Technical artists prepare the drawings used by manufacturing and construction workers. The drawings give visual guidelines and technical details of products, buildings, and structures. Technical artists specify dimensions and materials to be used in the building process, and state procedures and processes to be followed. Many technical artists use computer-aided design (CAD) systems to prepare plans. Since they draw technical plans to scale, fractions and operations with fractions are an important part of their work.

 Go Online
PHSchool.com **For:** Information about technical artists
Web Code: adb-2031

Greatest Possible Error

Measurement is not exact. To the nearest centimeter, each segment at the right measures 3 cm.

When a measurement is rounded to the nearest centimeter, it can vary from the actual length by as much as one half centimeter. The *greatest possible error* of a measurement is half the unit used for measuring.

EXAMPLE

Find the greatest possible error for each measurement.

a. $1\frac{1}{2}$ in.   The measurement is to the nearest $\frac{1}{2}$ in.

Since $\frac{1}{2} \cdot \frac{1}{2} = \frac{1}{4}$, the greatest possible error is $\frac{1}{4}$ in.

b. **15.6 L**   The measurement is to the nearest tenth of a liter.

Since $\frac{1}{2} \cdot 0.1 = 0.05$, the greatest possible error is 0.05 L.

c. **3.004 mm**   The measurement is to the nearest 0.001 mm.

Since $\frac{1}{2} \cdot 0.001 = 0.0005$, the greatest possible error is 0.0005 mm.

EXERCISES

Find the greatest possible error for each measurement.

1. 45.98 mg
2. $12\frac{1}{4}$ in.
3. 54.4 cm
4. $1\frac{3}{4}$ c

5. 3 ft
6. 9 g
7. 12.3 L
8. 15.575 mm

9. $24\frac{1}{2}$ yd
10. 512 m
11. $10\frac{1}{8}$ oz
12. $3\frac{1}{16}$ in.

13. **Geometry** A rectangle measures 12 cm by 10.5 cm. What is the greatest possible error for each measurement?

14. **Carpentry** A carpenter is cutting a table leg that is $2\frac{1}{4}$ ft long.
    a. What is the greatest possible error?
    b. **Writing in Math** Is the greatest possible error acceptable in this situation? Explain.

Work Backward

1   Work Backward

Math Strategies in Action The Longleat hedge maze in England was designed in 1975. The hedges are so high you can't see over them unless you stand on one of the wooden staircases placed throughout the maze. Once you find the center of the maze in its 1.7 miles of pathways, you have to remember the path you followed and work backward to get out.

Visitors to the Longleat hedge maze often take 90 min to reach the center.

Working backward from known information will sometimes help you solve a problem.

1 EXAMPLE   Real-World ● Problem Solving

Time You are planning to go to a baseball game that starts at 1:00 P.M. You want to arrive half an hour early. Your walk to the train station is about 10 minutes long. The train ride to the city takes $\frac{3}{4}$ of an hour. After you arrive in the city, you will need to walk for about 10 more minutes to get to the stadium. What time should you plan to leave?

Understand the Problem

Think about the information you are given.

1. What do you want to find?

2. What is your arrival time?

3. How much time will you spend walking to the train?

4. How much time will you spend on the train?

5. How much time will you spend walking from the train?

What You'll Learn

- To solve problems by working backward

. . . And Why

To solve real-world problems involving time

✓ **Check Skills You'll Need**

Order the fractions from least to greatest.

1. $\frac{1}{2}, \frac{1}{3}, \frac{1}{4}, \frac{1}{5}, \frac{1}{10}$

2. $\frac{7}{3}, \frac{5}{3}, \frac{13}{3}, \frac{3}{3}$

3. $\frac{3}{7}, \frac{3}{5}, \frac{3}{13}, \frac{3}{3}$

4. $-\frac{3}{7}, -\frac{3}{5}, -\frac{3}{13}, -\frac{3}{3}$

GO for Help
Lesson 5-2

You know that the series of events must end at 1:00 P.M. Work backward to find when the events must begin.

Carry Out the Plan

Move the hands of a clock to find your departure time.

6. Write the starting time for each event.

Game starts   Arrive at stadium   Train arrives

30 min

10 min

Train departs   Leave home

45 min

10 min

You should leave home at 11:25 A.M.

Check the Answer

Check whether the departure time is reasonable. Find the total time needed.

10 min + 45 min + 10 min + 30 min = 95 min

Add 95 minutes to your departure time.

11: 25
+ 0: 95
11:120   **120 min = 2 h**

11:120 = 2 hours after 11:00, or 1:00 P.M.

Since the game starts at 1 P.M., your departure time is reasonable.

✓ Quick Check

7. Suppose you must be home by 6:00 P.M. If the return trip takes the same amount of time, how long can the game run in order for you to be at home on time?

EXERCISES

For more exercises, see *Extra Skill and Word Problem Practice.*

Practice and Problem Solving

A Practice by Example

Example 1
(page 263)

GO for Help

Work backward to solve each problem.

1. **Lawn Care** Eduardo wants to finish mowing lawns at 3:00 P.M. on Saturday. It takes $1\frac{1}{2}$ h to mow the first lawn and twice as long to mow the lawn next door. The lawn across the street takes $1\frac{1}{2}$ h to mow. Eduardo plans to take a $\frac{1}{2}$-h break between the second and third lawns. What time should he plan to start mowing?

2. **Travel** Siobhan's family is planning a trip to the Grand Canyon. It will take 5 h of driving along with three $\frac{1}{2}$-h stops. They want to arrive at 3:30 P.M. What time should they plan to leave?

3. **Transportation** Korin is going to a movie. The movie begins at 1:00 P.M. She has a 15-minute walk to the bus from her home and a 5-minute walk from the bus to the movie. The bus ride takes 38 min. What is the latest bus she can take to make the movie?

Strategies

- Act It Out
- Draw a Diagram
- Guess, Check, Revise
- Look for a Pattern
- Make a Model
- Make a Table
- Simulate the Problem
- Solve by Graphing
- Use Multiple Strategies
- Work a Simpler Problem
- Work Backward
- Write an Equation
- Write a Proportion

BUS DEPARTURE TIMES

10:10 A.M.	12:05 P.M.
10:30 A.M.	12:15 P.M.
11:00 A.M.	12:25 P.M.
11:35 A.M.	12:40 P.M.

B Apply Your Skills

Solve using any strategy.

4. Pump A can fill 5 identical tanks in 60 min.
   Pump B can fill 3 tanks that same size in 60 min.
   a. How long does it take pump A to fill one tank?
   b. How long does it take pump B to fill one tank?
   c. How long does it take pumps A and B together to fill one tank?

5. You have two nickels, three dimes, and a quarter. Using at least one of each coin, how many different amounts of money can you make? Explain.

6. **Geometry** Zach's rectangular garden measures 12 ft by 10 ft. He puts a stake in each corner and one every 2 ft along each side. How many stakes are there in all?

nline
Homework Video Tutor
Visit: PHSchool.com
Web Code: ade-0506

7. You spent half of your money at the amusement park and had $15 left. How much money did you have originally?

for Help

For a guide to reading and describing the pattern in Exercise 8, see page 267.

8. Describe the pattern of the numbers below. Then find the next three numbers in the pattern.
   $\frac{2}{3}$, $1\frac{5}{12}$, $2\frac{1}{6}$, $2\frac{11}{12}$, ■, ■, ■, ...

C Challenge

9. **Number Sense** Use the equation at the right. Choose from the numbers 1, 2, 3, 5, and 6, and make four different true equations.

$$\frac{\blacksquare}{\blacksquare} + \frac{\blacksquare}{\blacksquare} = \frac{\blacksquare}{\blacksquare}$$

10. Several freshmen tried out for the school track team.

After Round 1, $\frac{1}{2}$ of the freshmen were eliminated.

After Round 2, $\frac{1}{3}$ of those remaining were eliminated.

After Round 3, $\frac{1}{4}$ of those remaining were eliminated.

After Round 4, $\frac{1}{5}$ of those remaining were eliminated.

After Round 5, $\frac{1}{6}$ of those remaining were eliminated.

The 10 freshmen who remained made it onto the track team. How many freshmen originally tried out?

ISAT

Test Prep

Multiple Choice

11. You spent $\frac{1}{2}$ of your money at the theater and $\frac{1}{4}$ at an arcade. You have $17.50 left. How much money did you have originally?
    A. $70   **B.** $35   **C.** $17.50   **D.** $13.12

12. Angela is twice as old as Brent. Brent is $2\frac{1}{2}$ times as old as Casey. Casey is 5 years old. How old is Angela?
    F. 5 years   **G.** 10 years   **H.** 25 years   **J.** 50 years

13. What is the next number in this pattern?
    $\frac{3}{4}$, $1\frac{1}{2}$, $2\frac{1}{4}$, 3, . . .
    A. $3\frac{1}{4}$ **B.** $3\frac{1}{2}$ **C.** $3\frac{3}{4}$ **D.** 4

Short Response

14. The odometer on Melissa's bike reads 813 miles. When she let Joan borrow the bike last week, it read 799 miles. Joan rode the bike 1 mile to school every day and then back home.   **(a)** Did Joan ride the bike anywhere else?   **(b)** Explain your answer.

Mixed Review

Lessons 5-4 and 1-9

GO for Help

Simplify each expression.

15. $\frac{1}{3} \div \frac{5}{6}$

16. $1\frac{2}{3} \div 1\frac{1}{9}$

17. $\frac{2}{5} \cdot (-20)$

18. $\frac{4}{9} \cdot \frac{5}{12}$

19. $\frac{3}{4} \div 8$

20. $-\frac{1}{6} \cdot (-12)$

21. $-8 \cdot 5$

22. $2 \cdot 3 \cdot (-4) \cdot 5$

23. $-1(-1)$

24. $-56 \div 8$

25. $100 \div (-2)$

26. $-100 \div (-10)$

Lesson 3-2

27. **Estimation** You want to buy three shirts for $15.95 each. Estimate the total cost of the shirts.

Understanding Math Problems Read the problem below. Then let Greg's thinking guide you through the solution. Check your understanding with the exercise at the bottom of the page.

Describe the pattern of the numbers below. Then find the next three numbers in the pattern.

$\frac{2}{3}, 1\frac{5}{12}, 2\frac{1}{6}, 2\frac{11}{12}, \blacksquare, \blacksquare, \blacksquare, \ldots$

What Greg Thinks

I must find what kind of pattern this is so that I can describe it. I'll check the differences between terms.

The differences are the same, $\frac{3}{4}$. I can describe the pattern.

Now I have to find the next three numbers. A fraction calculator would help, but I'll do it longhand.

First I have to find $2\frac{11}{12} + \frac{3}{4}$.

Next, $3\frac{2}{3} + \frac{3}{4}$.

Finally, $4\frac{5}{12} + \frac{3}{4}$.

I'm done!

What Greg Writes

$$1\frac{5}{12} - \frac{2}{3} = \frac{17}{12} - \frac{2}{3} = \frac{17}{12} - \frac{8}{12} = \frac{9}{12}, \text{ or } \frac{3}{4}$$

$$2\frac{1}{6} - 1\frac{5}{12} = \frac{13}{6} - \frac{17}{12} = \frac{26}{12} - \frac{17}{12} = \frac{9}{12}, \text{ or } \frac{3}{4}$$

$$2\frac{11}{12} - 2\frac{1}{6} = 2\frac{11}{12} - 2\frac{2}{12} = \frac{9}{12}, \text{ or } \frac{3}{4}$$

Start with $\frac{2}{3}$ and add $\frac{3}{4}$ repeatedly.

$$2\frac{11}{12} + \frac{3}{4} = 2\frac{11}{12} + \frac{9}{12}$$
$$= 2\frac{20}{12} = 3\frac{8}{12} = 3\frac{2}{3}$$

$$3\frac{2}{3} + \frac{3}{4} = \frac{11}{3} + \frac{3}{4}$$
$$= \frac{44}{12} + \frac{9}{12} = \frac{53}{12} = 4\frac{5}{12}$$

$$4\frac{5}{12} + \frac{3}{4} = 4\frac{5}{12} + \frac{9}{12}$$
$$= 4\frac{14}{12} = 5\frac{2}{12} = 5\frac{1}{6}$$

The next three numbers are $3\frac{2}{3}, 4\frac{5}{12}$, and $5\frac{1}{6}$.

EXERCISE

1. Describe the pattern of the numbers below. Then find the next three numbers in the pattern.
   $1\frac{3}{4}, 3, 4\frac{1}{4}, 5\frac{1}{2}, \blacksquare, \blacksquare, \blacksquare, \ldots$

5-7

Solving Equations by Adding or Subtracting Fractions

 Assessment Framework

8.8.12 Solve linear equations and inequalities in one variable over the rational numbers.

8.8.13 Solve word problems involving unknown quantities.

Check Skills You'll Need

Find each sum or difference.

1. $1\frac{3}{4} - 2\frac{7}{8}$

2. $3\frac{5}{8} + 4\frac{7}{12}$

3. $5\frac{3}{4} - 3\frac{1}{8}$

4. $-4\frac{1}{6} - 3\frac{2}{9}$

 for Help
Lesson 5-3

---

1 Using Subtraction to Solve Equations

You solve equations with fractions the same way you solve equations with integers and decimals, by using inverse operations and the Properties of Equality.

1 EXAMPLE · Real-World · Problem Solving

Recycling In 1999, the average household in the United States recycled about $\frac{1}{4}$ of its solid waste. The Environmental Protection Agency (EPA) has set a goal of recycling about $\frac{1}{3}$ of solid waste. By how much would the average U.S. household need to increase its recycling to meet the EPA goal?

Words	fraction U.S. households recycle	plus	the increase	is	EPA goal

Let n = the increase.

Equation	$\frac{1}{4}$	+	n	=	$\frac{1}{3}$

$\frac{1}{4} + n = \frac{1}{3}$

$\frac{1}{4} - \frac{1}{4} + n = \frac{1}{3} - \frac{1}{4}$ **Subtract $\frac{1}{4}$ from each side.**

$n = \frac{4 \cdot 1 - 3 \cdot 1}{3 \cdot 4}$ **Use 3 · 4 as the common denominator.**

$n = \frac{4 - 3}{12}$ **Use the Order of Operations.**

$n = \frac{1}{12}$ **Simplify.**

To meet the EPA goal, the average U.S. household needs to recycle $\frac{1}{12}$ more of its waste.

Check Is the answer reasonable? The present fraction of solid waste that is recycled plus the increase must equal the goal. Since $\frac{1}{4} + \frac{1}{12} = \frac{3}{12} + \frac{1}{12} = \frac{4}{12} = \frac{1}{3}$, the answer is reasonable.

Quick Check

1. Solve and check each equation.

   a. $y + \frac{8}{9} = \frac{5}{9}$ b. $\frac{2}{3} = u + \frac{3}{5}$ c. $c + \frac{3}{10} = \frac{11}{15}$

You can use addition to solve an equation involving subtraction.

2 EXAMPLE   **Adding a Fraction to Solve an Equation**

Solve $n - \frac{3}{4} = -\frac{5}{8}$.

$$n - \frac{3}{4} = -\frac{5}{8}$$

$$n - \frac{3}{4} + \frac{3}{4} = -\frac{5}{8} + \frac{3}{4}$$ Add $\frac{3}{4}$ to each side.

$$n = \frac{-5 \cdot 4 + 8 \cdot 3}{8 \cdot 4}$$ Use $8 \cdot 4$ as the common denominator.

$$n = \frac{-20 + 24}{32}$$ Use the Order of Operations.

$$n = \frac{4^1}{32_8} = \frac{1}{8}$$ Divide the common factors and simplify.

GO for Help

For a guide to the Order of Operations, see page 187.

☑ **Quick Check**

● **2.** Solve and check the equation $\frac{6}{7} = x - \frac{2}{7}$.

Sometimes you can change denominators easily.

3 EXAMPLE   **Using a Mixed Number to Solve an Equation**

Woodworking Henry cut $1\frac{3}{8}$ yards from a piece of wood. Afterward, the piece of wood was $2\frac{1}{4}$ yards long. The equation $p - 1\frac{3}{8} = 2\frac{1}{4}$ models this situation. How long was the piece of wood before Henry cut it?

Method 1 (mixed numbers)

$$p - 1\frac{3}{8} = 2\frac{1}{4}$$
$$p - 1\frac{3}{8} + 1\frac{3}{8} = 2\frac{1}{4} + 1\frac{3}{8}$$
$$p = 2\frac{2}{8} + 1\frac{3}{8}$$
$$p = 3\frac{5}{8}$$

Method 2 (decimals)

$$p - 1\frac{3}{8} = 2\frac{1}{4}$$
$$p - 1.375 = 2.25$$
$$p - 1.375 + 1.375 = 2.25 + 1.375$$
$$p = 3.625$$

The piece of wood was $3\frac{5}{8}$ yards, or 3.625 yards, long.

☑ **Quick Check**

3. a. Solve $3\frac{7}{18} = z + 1\frac{1}{3}$.
  b. Which method did you use to solve the equation in part (a)? Explain.

EXERCISES

 For more exercises, see *Extra Skill and Word Problem Practice.*

Practice and Problem Solving

A **Practice by Example**

Example 1
(page 268)

Solve and check each equation.

1. $b + \frac{4}{5} = \frac{9}{10}$

2. $g + \frac{9}{10} = \frac{7}{10}$

3. $m + \frac{3}{4} = \frac{1}{4}$

4. $a + \frac{3}{5} = \frac{4}{5}$

5. $\frac{5}{16} = c + \frac{3}{16}$

6. $t + \frac{1}{4} = \frac{5}{9}$

7. Reading Jarrel's goal is to be half finished with the book he is reading by Friday. By Wednesday he has read $\frac{1}{3}$ of the book. How much more does he need to read to meet his goal?

Example 2
(page 269)

Solve and check each equation.

8. $a - \frac{1}{8} = \frac{5}{8}$

9. $t - \frac{2}{3} = \frac{4}{9}$

10. $c - \frac{9}{10} = \frac{1}{3}$

11. $\frac{1}{2} = n - \frac{5}{8}$

12. $a - \frac{5}{8} = \frac{7}{12}$

13. $3 = j - \frac{5}{8}$

Example 3
(page 269)

14. $x + 1\frac{1}{4} = 4\frac{3}{4}$

15. $5\frac{1}{4} = w + 2\frac{1}{2}$

16. $10\frac{1}{2} = x + 1\frac{1}{2}$

17. $z + 7\frac{5}{9} = 7\frac{5}{9}$

18. $c - 2\frac{1}{12} = 3\frac{1}{12}$

19. $y + 4\frac{7}{8} = 2$

B **Apply Your Skills**

Number Sense **Without solving each equation, state whether x is *positive*, *negative*, or *zero*. Justify your response.**

20. $x + 2\frac{9}{11} = 2\frac{9}{11}$

21. $x + \frac{9}{10} = \frac{1}{2}$

22. $x + 4\frac{1}{5} = 5\frac{1}{2}$

23. Growth At the beginning of the school year, Jamie's height was $62\frac{1}{2}$ inches. During the school year she grew $1\frac{3}{4}$ inches, $\frac{1}{8}$ inch more than she grew the previous year.
a. What was Jamie's height at the end of the school year?
b. How tall was Jamie at the start of the previous school year?

Solve and check each equation.

24. $p - 3\frac{2}{3} = 1\frac{1}{3}$

25. $1\frac{3}{8} = b + 2\frac{1}{6}$

26. $y - 4\frac{7}{8} = \frac{3}{4}$

27. $k + 2\frac{1}{9} = 1\frac{1}{3}$

28. $f + 4\frac{5}{12} = 5\frac{3}{8}$

29. $g + 8\frac{4}{9} = 3\frac{1}{6}$

30. $h + 2\frac{1}{2} = 5\frac{7}{10}$

31. $6\frac{1}{4} = a + \frac{5}{8}$

32. $2\frac{1}{16} = d + 5\frac{7}{16}$

33. Seafood A restaurant chef needs $8\frac{1}{2}$ lb of salmon. To get a good price, he buys more than he needs. He ends up with $4\frac{7}{8}$ lb too much. How much salmon did he buy?

34. Carpentry A carpenter used $3\frac{3}{16}$ lb of nails for a job. After the job was over, the remaining nails weighed $1\frac{1}{16}$ lb. How many pounds of nails did the carpenter have at the beginning of the job?

Solve and check each equation.

35. $x + \frac{2}{3} - \frac{1}{3} = 3\frac{1}{3}$

36. $x - \frac{3}{4} + \frac{1}{6} = 1\frac{5}{12}$

37. $x - 2\frac{2}{5} + 3\frac{1}{10} = \frac{3}{5}$

Real-World **Connection**

The average weight of an Alaskan Coho salmon is about $7\frac{9}{10}$ lb.

GO **Online**
Homework Video Tutor

Visit: PHSchool.com
Web Code: ade-0507

C **Challenge**   **38.** <u>Writing in Math</u> Write a problem that you could solve with the equation $x + \frac{1}{2} = 7$. Solve your problem.

39. Environment During a recent wet spell, the water level in Jasper's Pond rose $2\frac{3}{4}$ in. The depth of the pond was then 10 ft 3 in. What was the depth of the water in the pond before the wet spell?

Test Prep   **ISAT**

Multiple Choice   **40.** A tree is $10\frac{1}{2}$ ft tall. Which equation can you use to find the height of the tree before last spring's growth of 8 in.?

A. $t + \frac{8}{12} = 10\frac{1}{2}$ B. $t - \frac{8}{12} = 10\frac{1}{2}$

C. $t + 10\frac{1}{2} = \frac{8}{12}$ D. $t - 10\frac{1}{2} = \frac{8}{12}$

41. What is the value of d in the equation $d + \frac{3}{4} = 4\frac{5}{8}$?

F. $3\frac{1}{2}$ G. $3\frac{7}{8}$ H. $4\frac{1}{4}$ J. $5\frac{3}{8}$

42. What is the value of c in $1\frac{1}{4} - c = \frac{3}{8}$?

A. $-1\frac{5}{8}$ B. $-\frac{7}{8}$ C. $\frac{7}{8}$ D. $1\frac{5}{8}$

Extended Response   **43.** Below is a student's work for solving the equation $x - (-\frac{1}{2}) = 3$.

a. What is the student's error?
b. What likely caused the error?
c. What is the correct value of x?
d. How did the error affect the value of x?

$$x - (-\tfrac{1}{2}) = 3$$
$$x - (-\tfrac{1}{2}) + \tfrac{1}{2} = 3 + \tfrac{1}{2}$$
$$x = 3\tfrac{1}{2}$$

Mixed Review

Lesson 5-5   **Complete each statement.**

44. $2\frac{2}{3}$ ft $= 32$ ■   **45.** $1\frac{1}{2}$ ■ $= 12$ fl oz   **46.** 9 pt $= 4\frac{1}{2}$ ■

47. $\frac{1}{2}$ ■ $= \frac{1}{4}$ qt   **48.** 750 lb $= \frac{3}{8}$ ■   **49.** $1\frac{2}{3}$ ■ $= 5$ ft

Lesson 5-4   **50. a. Jobs** Your job is to paint $\frac{1}{4}$ of the lockers in the school. Your friend agrees to share the job equally with you. What fraction of the lockers will each of you paint?

b. If the job of painting all of the lockers in the school pays $1,100, how much will you earn?

Lesson 3-6   **Solve each equation.**

51. $3.5t = 8.75$ **52.** $\frac{b}{4} = -38$

53. $y \div 7.5 = -3.75$ **54.** $1.7x = 8.5$

5-8

Solving Equations by Multiplying Fractions

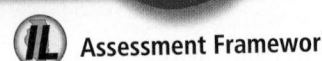 Assessment Framework

8.8.12 Solve linear equations and inequalities in one variable over the rational numbers.

8.8.13 Solve word problems involving unknown quantities.

✓ **Check Skills You'll Need**

Find each product.

1. $\frac{4}{7} \cdot \frac{5}{8}$

2. $\frac{9}{10} \cdot \left(-\frac{5}{3}\right)$

3. $-1\frac{1}{4} \cdot \left(-\frac{5}{1}\right)$

4. $4\frac{1}{2} \cdot \frac{2}{3}$

GO for Help
Lesson 5-4

1 | Using Multiplication to Solve Equations

You know how to undo multiplication by dividing each side of an equation by the same number. You can also multiply each side of an equation by the same fraction to undo multiplication.

1 EXAMPLE | Multiplying by a Reciprocal

Solve $5a = \frac{1}{7}$.

$$5a = \frac{1}{7}$$

$$\frac{1}{5} \cdot (5a) = \frac{1}{5} \cdot \frac{1}{7} \quad \text{Multiply each side by } \frac{1}{5}, \text{ the reciprocal of 5.}$$

$$a = \frac{1}{35} \quad \text{Simplify.}$$

✓ **Quick Check**

1. Solve each equation.

   a. $8x = \frac{5}{7}$ **b.** $2y = \frac{7}{9}$ **c.** $3a = \frac{4}{5}$

When a numerator and a denominator have common factors, you can divide the common factors to help you multiply.

2 EXAMPLE | Simplifying Before Multiplying

Solve $\frac{4}{5}m = \frac{9}{10}$.

$$\frac{4}{5}m = \frac{9}{10}$$

$$\frac{5}{4} \cdot \frac{4}{5}m = \frac{5}{4} \cdot \frac{9}{10} \quad \text{Multiply each side by } \frac{5}{4}, \text{ the reciprocal of } \frac{4}{5}.$$

$$m = \frac{\cancel{5}^{1}}{4} \cdot \frac{9}{\cancel{10}_{2}} \quad \text{Divide common factors.}$$

$$m = \frac{9}{8} \quad \text{Simplify.}$$

$$m = 1\frac{1}{8} \quad \text{Write as a mixed number.}$$

GO for Help

To review reciprocals, see page 254.

✓ **Quick Check**

2. Solve each equation.

   a. $\frac{2}{9}t = \frac{5}{6}$ **b.** $\frac{3}{4}s = \frac{8}{9}$ **c.** $\frac{5}{4} = \frac{5}{4}d$

Solve $-\frac{14}{25}k = \frac{8}{15}$.

$$-\frac{14}{25}k = \frac{8}{15}$$

$$-\frac{25}{14}\left(-\frac{14}{25}k\right) = -\frac{25}{14}\left(\frac{8}{15}\right)$$ Multiply each side by $-\frac{25}{14}$, the reciprocal of $-\frac{14}{25}$.

$$k = -\frac{\overset{5}{25}\cdot\overset{4}{8}}{\underset{7}{14}\cdot\underset{3}{15}} = -\frac{20}{21}$$ Divide common factors and simplify.

Video Tutor Help
Visit: PHSchool.com
Web Code: ada-0775

✓ Quick Check

3. Solve each equation.

a. $-\frac{6}{7}r = \frac{3}{4}$ **b.** $-\frac{10}{13}b = -\frac{2}{3}$ **c.** $-6n = \frac{3}{7}$

---

2 **Solving Equations With Mixed Numbers**

Change mixed numbers to improper fractions before multiplying.

4 **EXAMPLE** **Real-World** **Problem Solving**

Multiple Choice Your teacher needs a shelf to hold a set of textbooks each $1\frac{5}{8}$ in. wide. How many books will fit on a 26-in.-long shelf?

(A) 13 books   (B) 16 books   (C) 40 books   (D) 42 books

Words	width of each book	times	the number of books	is	width of bookshelf

Let n = the number of books.

Equation	$1\frac{5}{8}$	$\cdot$	n	$=$	26

$$1\frac{5}{8}\cdot n = 26$$

$$\frac{13}{8}n = 26$$ Write $1\frac{5}{8}$ as $\frac{13}{8}$.

$$\frac{8}{13}\cdot\frac{13}{8}n = \frac{8}{13}\cdot 26$$ Multiply each side by $\frac{8}{13}$, the reciprocal of $\frac{13}{8}$.

$$n = \frac{8\cdot\overset{2}{26}}{\underset{1}{13}\cdot 1} = 16$$ Divide common factors and simplify.

Your teacher can fit 16 books on the shelf. The answer is B.

Test-Taking Tip

Remember to ask yourself whether your answer is reasonable. If your answer to "How many books?" is $2\frac{1}{2}$, make sure you round down to "2 books."

✓ Quick Check

4. Solve each equation.

a. $3\frac{1}{2}n = 28$ **b.** $-\frac{7}{20} = 1\frac{1}{6}r$ **c.** $-2\frac{3}{4}h = -12\frac{1}{2}$

EXERCISES

For more exercises, see *Extra Skill and Word Problem Practice.*

Practice and Problem Solving

 Practice by Example

Examples 1–3
(pages 272 and 273)

Solve each equation.

1. $6p = \frac{5}{8}$ **2.** $5x = \frac{2}{3}$ **3.** $2k = \frac{5}{6}$ **4.** $7z = \frac{3}{8}$

5. $2y = \frac{1}{3}$ **6.** $3b = \frac{4}{7}$ **7.** $7c = \frac{3}{4}$ **8.** $9y = \frac{5}{7}$

9. $\frac{2}{3}d = \frac{5}{8}$ **10.** $\frac{5}{8} = \frac{5}{8}k$ **11.** $\frac{5}{9} = \frac{1}{8}h$ **12.** $\frac{1}{7}x = \frac{4}{7}$

13. $\frac{3}{4}d = \frac{3}{8}$ **14.** $\frac{10}{27} = \frac{5}{9}t$ **15.** $\frac{2}{7}a = \frac{5}{8}$ **16.** $\frac{1}{9}p = \frac{5}{6}$

17. $-\frac{2}{3}t = -2$ **18.** $-5s = \frac{5}{7}$ **19.** $\frac{8}{9} = -6d$ **20.** $\frac{2}{3}x = -8$

Example 4
(page 273)

21. Construction A sheet of plywood is $\frac{3}{4}$ in. thick. Write and solve an equation to find how many sheets of plywood are in a stack 9 in. high.

Solve each equation.

22. $3 = 1\frac{1}{2}b$ **23.** $2\frac{1}{2}x = \frac{2}{5}$ **24.** $2\frac{1}{3}m = \frac{7}{12}$ **25.** $-1\frac{6}{7}g = -\frac{13}{15}$

26. $\frac{1}{15} = -1\frac{1}{10}t$ **27.** $2\frac{1}{8}k = 7$ **28.** $1\frac{1}{2}n = 3\frac{4}{9}$ **29.** $-9\frac{1}{3} = -1\frac{1}{4}t$

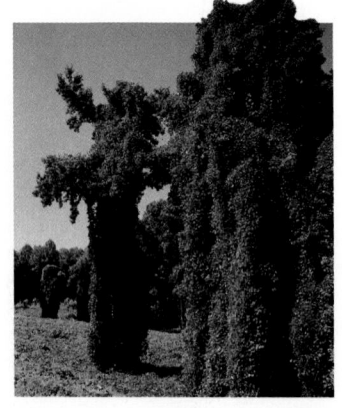 **B** **Apply Your Skills**

Number Sense **Without solving each equation, state whether x is** *positive, negative,* **or** *zero.* **Justify your response.**

30. $17x = -\frac{11}{30}$ **31.** $\frac{1}{57}x = 2$ **32.** $\frac{4}{13}x = 0$ **33.** $-6\frac{1}{2}x = 0$

34. Boat Building Tomás calculates that he will need 86 hours to build a boat. He can work on the boat $8\frac{3}{5}$ hours per week. How many weeks will it take Tomás to build the boat?

35. Biology In ideal conditions, the kudzu plant can grow at least $1\frac{3}{20}$ ft per week. At this rate, how many weeks would it take a kudzu plant to grow 23 ft?

Real-World **Connection**

A native of China and Japan, kudzu was brought to the United States in 1876. Left alone, it grows over trees, telephone poles, and abandoned houses and cars.

Solve each equation.

36. $-\frac{5}{7}x = \frac{9}{10}$ **37.** $\frac{9}{13} = -\frac{6}{11}s$ **38.** $-3b = \frac{2}{3}$

39. $-\frac{12}{13} = -\frac{1}{4}w$ **40.** $3\frac{1}{9}a = \frac{3}{7}$ **41.** $2\frac{3}{4} = -6\frac{3}{5}y$

42. $1\frac{1}{2}m = 1\frac{3}{4}$ **43.** $3\frac{3}{5}p = -4\frac{4}{9}$ **44.** $\frac{1}{8}d = \frac{1}{4}$

45. $\frac{1}{3}y = 2$ **46.** $\frac{3}{7}x = 1$ **47.** $\frac{7}{8}z = 3\frac{1}{2}$

48. Astronomy The Chandra satellite telescope views X-rays in space. It orbits as much as 87,000 miles above Earth. This is about $\frac{1}{3}$ of the distance to the moon. About how far away is the moon?

49. Error Analysis A student solved the equation $-\frac{7}{10}h = 5\frac{3}{5}$ and found the solution 8. Describe and correct the student's error.

50. Writing in Math Describe how you would solve and check the equation $\frac{2}{3}x = 3$.

51. Aviation A small airplane coming in for a landing descends $\frac{5}{66}$ mi/min. About how long does it take to descend 4,000 ft? (*Hint:* 1 mi = 5,280 ft)

 Challenge **Solve each equation.**

52. $-\frac{3}{4}x + \frac{1}{4}x = -6$ **53.** $\frac{5}{8}x - 6\frac{3}{8}x = 1\frac{1}{2}$ **54.** $\frac{-5}{-7}x + \left(-\frac{1}{5}x\right) = -\frac{3}{5}$

55. Reasoning By what would you multiply each side of the equation $ax = 27$ to solve for x? By what would you multiply each side of the equation $\frac{1}{a}x = 27$ to solve for x?

56. Marine Biology A sailfish can swim about $11\frac{1}{3}$ mi in 10 min. About how many miles can a sailfish swim per minute? At that speed, about how many feet does a sailfish swim in one second?

Test Prep

ISAT

Multiple Choice

57. Which equation has a solution greater than 1?

A. $-5x = \frac{5}{8}$ **B.** $-\frac{5}{8}x = 5$ **C.** $\frac{5}{8}x = 5$ **D.** $5x = \frac{5}{8}$

58. What is the value of h in the equation $2\frac{1}{2} + h = -1\frac{3}{8}$?

F. $-3\frac{7}{8}$ **G.** $-1\frac{1}{8}$ **H.** $1\frac{1}{8}$ **J.** $3\frac{7}{8}$

59. The Jones family uses an average of 1 quart of milk each day. At this rate how many days will it take the family to use $5\frac{1}{2}$ gallons of milk?

A. $19\frac{1}{2}$ **B.** 20   **C.** $21\frac{1}{2}$ **D.** 22

60. A single copy of a book is $2\frac{3}{4}$ in. thick. A shipping box will hold a stack of books up to $16\frac{1}{2}$ in. tall. How many copies of the book can you stack in the box?

F. 6   **G.** 8   **H.** 32   **J.** 45

Short Response

Read the passage below before doing Exercises 61 and 62.

Paper Recycling on the Rise During the 1990s, recycling in the United States steadily increased. In 1996, people in the United States recycled about nine twentieths of their paper waste. This amounted to 42.3 million tons of paper, or about 295 lb/person. Only one year earlier, Americans recycled just over two fifths of their paper waste, a total of about 32.7 million tons of paper.

61. How much paper waste did Americans produce in 1995?

62. How much paper waste did Americans produce in 1996?

Lesson 5-7   **Solve each equation.**

63. $j + \frac{3}{4} = \frac{7}{8}$ **64.** $\frac{4}{5} = y - \frac{3}{5}$ **65.** $6\frac{1}{2} = m + 2\frac{7}{8}$

Lesson 5-3 **66. Snacks** One bag of popcorn holds $1\frac{5}{8}$ oz. Another holds $1\frac{3}{4}$ oz.
   a. Which bag holds more popcorn?
   b. How much more?
   c. How much popcorn can the two bags hold in all?

Lessons 4-7 and 4-8   **Simplify each expression.**

67. $3r \cdot r^4$ **68.** $\frac{6x^3}{2x}$ **69.** $10s^2 \cdot 10s^3$

70. $\frac{20a^5}{4a^2}$ **71.** $x^3 \cdot x^{10}$ **72.** $q^5 \cdot 3q$

✓ Checkpoint Quiz 2   Lessons 5-4 through 5-8

Multiply or divide.

1. $\frac{2}{3}(21)$ **2.** $\frac{4}{5} \cdot \frac{5}{8}$ **3.** $-\frac{4}{9}\left(\frac{1}{3}\right)$

4. $\frac{2}{5} \div \frac{3}{10}$ **5.** $-\frac{3}{4} \div \frac{3}{8}$ **6.** $8\frac{1}{2} \div \frac{1}{4}$

Complete each statement.

7. ▦ t = 4,500 lb   **8.** $2\frac{1}{2}$ yd = ▦ in.

9. 24 oz = ▦ lb   **10.** ▦ mi = 1,760 ft

Solve each equation.

11. $y + \frac{2}{5} = \frac{3}{5}$ **12.** $t - \frac{3}{4} = \frac{7}{8}$ **13.** $x - 4\frac{1}{2} = 6\frac{3}{4}$

14. $4t = \frac{24}{35}$ **15.** $\frac{5}{7}y = \frac{1}{3}$ **16.** $5\frac{1}{3} + v = -12$

17. $-\frac{8}{9}g = \frac{3}{5}$ **18.** $\frac{9}{10} = \frac{1}{4}w$ **19.** $1\frac{1}{2}d = \frac{5}{22}$

20. A jetliner is cruising at an altitude of 31,680 ft. What is the altitude in miles?

21. A car is travelling $\frac{11}{12}$ miles per minute. What is the speed of the car in miles per hour?

22. You spend $\frac{1}{3}$ of your money on lunch. Your friend then pays back a loan of $2.50. Later, you spend $4 on a movie ticket and $1.25 for a snack. You have $5.25 left. How much money did you have before lunch?

23. Open-Ended Describe an object you might measure using the customary system of measurement. Choose a unit of measure and estimate the measurement of the object using that unit.

When you solve real-world problems involving fractions or decimals, you can choose to use either fractions or decimals to find the solution. The example below shows two methods to solve the same problem. Consider which method you would use.

EXAMPLE

A football stadium has 110 seating sections. Of these, 0.3 of the sections are lower-level seating close to the field, and $\frac{2}{5}$ are mid-level seating. The rest of the sections are upper-level seating. Find the number of upper-level sections.

Method 1 Using a fraction

Method 2 Using a decimal

Find the portion of seating sections that are lower and mid level.

$0.3 = \frac{3}{10}$	**Write the decimal as a fraction.**	$\frac{2}{5} = 0.4$	**Write the fraction as a decimal.**

$\frac{3}{10} + \frac{2}{5} = \frac{3}{10} + \frac{4}{10}$ **Use a common denominator.** $0.3 + 0.4$

$= \frac{7}{10}$ **Simplify.** 0.7

Find the number of seating sections in the lower and mid levels.

$\frac{7}{10} \cdot 110 = 77$ $0.7 \cdot 110 = 77$

Find the number of seating sections in the upper level.
Since $110 - 77 = 33$, there are 33 upper-level sections.

EXERCISES

1. **Reasoning** Which method would you use in the Example above? Explain.

2. A garden has 200 square feet. You use $\frac{1}{5}$ of the garden for corn, 0.6 of the garden for tomatoes, and the rest for lettuce and herbs. How many square feet do you use for lettuce and herbs?

3. A husband, a wife, and their two children use about 300 gallons of water daily. The husband uses 0.15 of the water and the wife uses $\frac{1}{4}$ of the water. How many gallons do the children use?

5-9

Powers of Products and Quotients

 Assessment Framework

6.8.09 Solve problems and number sentences involving addition, subtraction, multiplication, and division using rational numbers, exponents, and roots.

6.8.10 Identify and apply order of operations to simplify numeric expressions involving integers, fractions, and decimals.

✓ Check Skills You'll Need

Simplify each expression.

1. $(2^2)^3$ **2.** $(3^2)^2$ **3.** $(1^5)^4$

4. $(x^3)^6$ **5.** $(b^2)^5$ **6.** $(a^7)^4$

 for Help
Lesson 4-7

---

1 Finding Powers of Products

You can use the Commutative and Associative Properties of Multiplication to find a pattern in products raised to a power.

$(4 \cdot 2)^3 = (4 \cdot 2) \cdot (4 \cdot 2) \cdot (4 \cdot 2)$	**Write the factors.**
$= 4 \cdot 4 \cdot 4 \cdot 2 \cdot 2 \cdot 2$	**Use the Commutative Property to arrange the factors.**
$= (4 \cdot 4 \cdot 4) \cdot (2 \cdot 2 \cdot 2)$	**Use the Associative Property to group the factors.**
$= 4^3 \cdot 2^3$	**Write the powers.**

This result suggests a rule for simplifying products raised to a power.

Key Concepts **Rule for Raising a Product to a Power**

To raise a product to a power, raise each factor to the power.

Arithmetic

$(5 \cdot 3)^4 = 5^4 \cdot 3^4$

Algebra

$(ab)^m = a^m b^m$,

for any positive integer m

To simplify an expression, you should eliminate as many parentheses as possible.

1 EXAMPLE Simplifying a Power of a Product

Simplify $(4x^2)^3$.

$(4x^2)^3 = 4^3 \cdot (x^2)^3$	**Raise each factor to the third power.**
$= 4^3 \cdot x^{2 \cdot 3}$	**Use the Rule for Raising a Power to a Power.**
$= 4^3 \cdot x^6$	**Multiply exponents.**
$= 64x^6$	**Simplify.**

Vocabulary Tip

Rule for Raising a Power to a Power:
$(a^m)^n = a^{m \cdot n}$

✓ Quick Check

1. Simplify each expression.

a. $(2(3))^3$ **b.** $(2p)^4$ **c.** $(xy^2)^5$ **d.** $(5x^3)^2$

The location of a negative sign affects the value of an expression.

2 EXAMPLE **Working With a Negative Sign**

a. Simplify $(-5x)^2$.
$$(-5x)^2 = (-5)^2(x)^2$$
$$= 25x^2$$

b. Simplify $-(5x)^2$.
$$-(5x)^2 = (-1)(5x)^2$$
$$= (-1)(5)^2(x)^2$$
$$= -25x^2$$

✓ Quick Check

2. Simplify each expression.
- **a.** $(-2y)^4$
- **b.** $-(2y)^4$
- **c.** $(-5a^2b)^3$

2 Finding Powers of Quotients

You can use repeated multiplication to write a power of a quotient.

$$\left(\tfrac{4}{5}\right)^3 = \left(\tfrac{4}{5}\right)\left(\tfrac{4}{5}\right)\left(\tfrac{4}{5}\right) = \frac{4 \cdot 4 \cdot 4}{5 \cdot 5 \cdot 5} = \frac{4^3}{5^3}$$

Key Concepts **Raising a Quotient to a Power**

To raise a quotient to a power, raise both the numerator and denominator to the power.

Arithmetic
$$\left(\tfrac{2}{3}\right)^4 = \frac{2^4}{3^4}$$

Algebra
$$\left(\tfrac{a}{b}\right)^m = \frac{a^m}{b^m}, \text{ for } b \neq 0$$
and any positive integer m

Vocabulary Tip

You read $\left(\tfrac{2}{3}\right)^4$ as "two thirds to the fourth power." You read $\frac{2}{3^4}$ as "two divided by three to the fourth power."

3 EXAMPLE **Real-World** **Problem Solving**

Geometry Find the area of the square tile.

$$A = s^2 \qquad s = \text{length of a side}$$
$$= \left(\tfrac{3}{b}\right)^2$$
$$= \frac{3^2}{b^2} = \frac{9}{b^2}$$

The area of the tile is $\frac{9}{b^2}$ square units.

$$\frac{3}{b}$$

$$\frac{3}{b}$$

✓ Quick Check

3. Simplify each expression.
- **a.** $\left(\tfrac{1}{2}\right)^3$
- **b.** $\left(-\tfrac{2}{3}\right)^4$
- **c.** $\left(\tfrac{2x^2}{3}\right)^3$

EXERCISES

For more exercises, see *Extra Skill and Word Problem Practice.*

Practice and Problem Solving

A Practice by Example

Example 1
(page 278)

GO for Help

Simplify each expression.

1. $(3(2))^2$ **2.** $(3j)^3$ **3.** $(rs^3)^4$ **4.** $(7t^2)^3$

5. $(4a^5)^2$ **6.** $(2c^2)^5$ **7.** $(2x^2)^3$ **8.** $(a^2b^4)^3$

9. $(2a^5)^3$ **10.** $(c^3)^2$ **11.** $(2b)^3$ **12.** $(ac^2)^2$

Example 2
(page 279)

13. $(-10x^3)^4$ **14.** $-(xy)^2$ **15.** $(-5b)^3$ **16.** $-(3x)^2$

17. $(-5c^3)^2$ **18.** $-(x^2y^2)^2$ **19.** $(-3a^4b)^3$ **20.** $-(m^2 \cdot n)^4$

21. The side length of a square tablecloth is $5s^2$ cm.
   a. Find the area of the tablecloth.
   b. Will the tablecloth completely cover a square tabletop with area $20s^4$ cm²? Explain.

Example 3
(page 279)

Simplify each expression.

22. $\left(\frac{2}{5}\right)^2$ **23.** $\left(-\frac{2}{5}\right)^3$ **24.** $\left(\frac{4}{7y}\right)^2$ **25.** $\left(\frac{3x^2}{10}\right)^4$ **26.** $\left(\frac{4}{9}\right)^2$

27. $\left(-\frac{3}{7}\right)^2$ **28.** $\left(-\frac{m}{b^3}\right)^6$ **29.** $\left(\frac{1}{3x^2}\right)^4$ **30.** $\left(-\frac{3}{4}\right)^3$ **31.** $\left(\frac{3t^2}{5}\right)^2$

B Apply Your Skills

Homework Video Tutor
Visit: PHSchool.com
Web Code: ade-0509

Number Sense Complete each equation.

32. $(5 \cdot 2)^{\blacksquare} = 25 \cdot 4$ **33.** $(a^2)^{\blacksquare} = a^2$ **34.** $(4m)^{\blacksquare} = 256m^4$

35. $\left(-\frac{1}{2}\right)^{\blacksquare} = -\frac{1}{8}$ **36.** $\left(\frac{b^{\blacksquare}}{5}\right)^2 = \frac{b^{10}}{25}$ **37.** $\left(\frac{3}{7}\right)^{\blacksquare} = \frac{27}{343}$

Evaluate for $a = -1$, $b = 3$, and $c = \frac{1}{2}$.

38. $(-b^2)^2$ **39.** $\left(\frac{a}{b}\right)^3$ **40.** $(4c^2)^2$ **41.** $(a^2b)^2$

42. Geometry Find the area of a square with side length $4c$ units.

🌐 **43. Furniture** A square table has sides that measure $3x^2$ ft. Write an expression for the area of the tabletop. Simplify your expression.

44. Writing in Math Explain why $(-xy)^2 = (xy)^2$.

Simplify each expression.

45. $(3 \cdot 4)^3$ **46.** $(-2 \cdot 5)^2$ **47.** $(3 \cdot 5)^2$ **48.** $(2ab^3)^2$

49. $\left(-\frac{5}{8}\right)^3$ **50.** $\left(-\frac{2}{x^3}\right)^5$ **51.** $\left(\frac{2c}{7d}\right)^2$ **52.** $\left(-\frac{3a}{b^2}\right)^3$

53. $\left(-\frac{2x}{7y}\right)^2$ **54.** $\left(\frac{2c}{d^2}\right)^4$ **55.** $\left(-\frac{xy}{2xy^4}\right)^5$ **56.** $\left(\frac{x^3}{2y^4}\right)^5$

C Challenge

Number Sense Complete each equation.

57. $(2b^{\blacksquare})^2 = 4b^8$ **58.** $(4 \cdot (-7))^{\blacksquare} = 64 \cdot (-343)$

59. $(gh^2)^{\blacksquare} = g^3h^{\blacksquare}$ **60.** $3(4c^3)^{\blacksquare} = \blacksquare c^{12}$

Geometry Use the formula $V = s^3$, where s is the length of a side, to find the volume of each cube.

61.
$\frac{7}{10}$

62.
$\frac{1}{2}y$

63.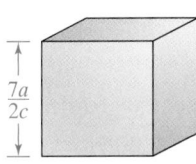
$\frac{7a}{2c}$

Test Prep

Multiple Choice

64. Which expression does NOT simplify to a^{36}?

    A. $(a^2)^{18}$ **B.** $(a^3)^6$ **C.** $(a^6)^6$ **D.** $(a^9)^4$

65. Which equation is FALSE?

    F. $\left|-\frac{1}{7}\right| = \left|\frac{1}{7}\right|$ **G.** $\left(\frac{3}{9}\right)^3 = \frac{3^3}{9^3}$

    H. $\left(-6 \cdot \frac{2}{3}\right)^2 = 6 \cdot \left(\frac{2}{3}\right)^2$ **J.** $\left(\frac{2}{5}\right)^3 = \frac{8}{125}$

66. What is the simplest form of $(2x^3)^4$?

    A. $8x^7$ **B.** $8x^{12}$ **C.** $16x^7$ **D.** $16x^{12}$

Short Response

67. Does $(3y)^7$ equal $3y^7$? Explain.

68. The side length of a square rug is $7b$ ft. **(a)** Will the rug cover a square floor with area $56b^2$ ft²? **(b)** Explain your reasoning.

Mixed Review

Lesson 5-8   Solve each equation.

    69. $\frac{2}{7}h = \frac{7}{8}$ **70.** $7c = 1\frac{5}{9}$ **71.** $\frac{5}{8} = \frac{10}{12}x$ **72.** $10\frac{3}{4} = -5\frac{1}{2}y$

Lesson 3-5 **73. Gardening** Delia bought three shrubs for \$5.99, \$12.99, and \$$x$. She paid a total of \$34.97 for the shrubs. How much did the third shrub cost?

Lesson 1-10   Use the coordinate plane at the right. Write the coordinates of each point named below.

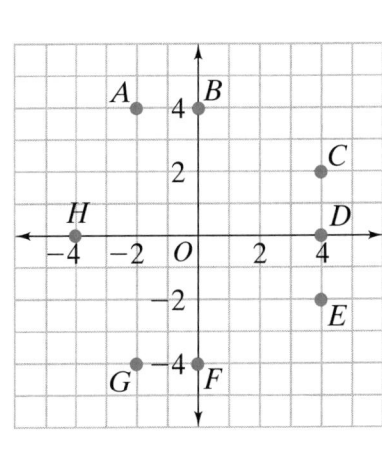

    74. A **75.** C

    76. F **77.** D

    Write the name of each point with the given coordinates.

    78. $(4, -2)$ **79.** $(-4, 0)$

    80. $(0, 4)$ **81.** $(-2, -4)$

On a test item, be sure to answer the question that is asked. Some answer choices are there to "catch" those who read the question carelessly, or those who think carelessly about what they are to find.

1 EXAMPLE

What is the LCM of $4b^2$ and $6b^3$?

A. $2b^2$ **B.** $12b^2$ **C.** $12b^3$ **D.** $24b^3$

You are looking for the LCM, or *least common multiple*.
Choice A is the GCF, or greatest common factor, of $4b^2$ and $6b^3$.
Choice B shows the LCM of 4 and 6, but not of b^2 and b^3.
Choice D shows a common multiple of 4 and 6, but not one that's *least*.
● Choice C is the answer to the question asked.

2 EXAMPLE

Stan needed 6 lb of potatoes for the school picnic. He bought potatoes in 3-lb bags for $1.89 per bag. Zorn bought 10 lb of potatoes to make potato salad for the picnic. He paid $2.59 per 5-lb bag. How much more did Zorn pay for potatoes than Stan?

F. $.70   **G.** $1.40   **H.** $5.18   **J.** $8.96

Choice F is how much more Zorn paid *per bag* of potatoes.
Choice H is how much Zorn paid for 10 lb of potatoes.
Choice J is how much Zorn and Stan paid in all for potatoes.
● Choice G is the answer to the question asked.

EXERCISES

Answer the question asked. Then pick one other answer choice and tell why you might have (incorrectly) selected it as the answer.

1. What is the LCM of $4a$ and $10a^2$?
   A. $2a$ **B.** $4a$ **C.** $20a^2$ **D.** $30a^2$

2. Dante, a landscaper, purchased three trees. The first was $38.99. A second was $54.99. His total bill before tax was $152.98. How much more did he pay for the third tree than for the second one?
   F. $93.98   **G.** $59   **H.** $16   **J.** $4.01

Chapter Review

Vocabulary Review

🔊 **dimensional analysis** (p. 258)
least common denominator (LCD)
   (p. 238)

least common multiple (LCM)
   (p. 236)
multiple (p. 236)

reciprocals (p. 254)
repeating decimal (p. 242)
terminating decimal (p. 241)

Match each word or phrase with its definition.

1. For $\frac{5}{6}$ and $\frac{4}{9}$, this is equal to 18.

2. The pair of fractions $-\frac{13}{45}$ and $-\frac{45}{13}$ are these.

3. For 5, 6, and 12, this is equal to 60.

4. You can convert the fraction $\frac{1}{9}$ to one of these.

5. For 7, one of these is 35.

6. This tells you to multiply 8 ft by $\frac{12\ \text{in.}}{1\ \text{ft}}$ to find the number of inches in 8 ft.

7. You can convert the fraction $\frac{4}{5}$ to one of these.

a. least common multiple (LCM)
b. repeating decimal
c. reciprocals
d. dimensional analysis
e. terminating decimal
f. least common denominator (LCD)
g. multiple

Go **O**nline
──PHSchool.com
For: Vocabulary quiz
Web Code: adj-0551

Skills and Concepts

5-1 Objectives

▼ To find the least common multiple (p. 236)

▼ To compare fractions (p. 237)

A **multiple** of a number is the product of that number and any nonzero whole number.

A *common multiple* of any group of numbers is a number that is a multiple of all the numbers. The common multiple with the least value is the **least common multiple (LCM)** of the numbers.

To compare fractions, use the LCM as the **least common denominator (LCD)** and write equivalent fractions.

Find the LCM of each group of numbers or expressions.

8. 12, 18   **9.** $8m^2, 14m$ **10.** 3, 5, 7   **11.** $6x, 15y$

Compare. Use >, <, or = to complete each statement.

12. $\frac{5}{9}$ ■ $\frac{5}{11}$ **13.** $\frac{2}{3}$ ■ $\frac{3}{4}$ **14.** $-\frac{4}{5}$ ■ $-\frac{7}{8}$ **15.** $\frac{1}{3}$ ■ $\frac{4}{12}$

5-2 Objectives

▼ To write fractions as decimals (p. 241)

▼ To write terminating and repeating decimals as fractions (p. 243)

To write a fraction as a decimal, divide the numerator by the denominator. If the division has a remainder of zero, the decimal is a **terminating decimal.** If the division produces a repeating block of digits, the decimal is a **repeating decimal.** The repeating part of the decimal is written with an overbar.

Reading a decimal correctly provides one way to write it as a fraction. To write a repeating decimal as a fraction, use algebra to eliminate the repeating part.

Write each fraction as a decimal.

16. $\frac{3}{5}$ **17.** $\frac{1}{6}$ **18.** $\frac{5}{8}$ **19.** $\frac{3}{10}$ **20.** $\frac{7}{100}$

Write each decimal as a fraction or mixed number.

21. 0.25 **22.** $0.8\overline{3}$ **23.** 5.6 **24.** $2.\overline{04}$

5-3 Objectives

▼ To add and subtract fractions (p. 247)

▼ To add and subtract mixed numbers (p. 248)

To add or subtract fractions and mixed numbers, write them with a common denominator. Then you can add or subtract the numerators. Change a mixed number to an improper fraction before adding or subtracting.

Add or subtract.

25. $2\frac{1}{3} + \frac{3}{4}$ **26.** $16\frac{4}{5} - 9\frac{2}{3}$ **27.** $\frac{6}{x} + \frac{3}{5}$ **28.** $1\frac{1}{2} - \frac{5}{8}$

29. An upholsterer cuts a piece of cording $1\frac{2}{3}$ ft long from a piece $2\frac{1}{4}$ ft long. How much cording is left?

5-4 Objectives

▼ To multiply fractions (p. 252)

▼ To divide fractions (p. 254)

To multiply fractions, multiply their numerators and their denominators. To divide fractions, multiply the first fraction by the **reciprocal** of the second fraction.

To multiply or divide mixed numbers, write them as improper fractions before multiplying or dividing.

Find each product or quotient.

30. $\frac{1}{4} \cdot \frac{7}{10}$ **31.** $-\frac{2}{3} \div \frac{5}{6}$ **32.** $1\frac{3}{5} \cdot \frac{3}{4}$ **33.** $9\frac{3}{4} \div 2\frac{3}{5}$ **34.** $\frac{3x}{5} \div \frac{6x}{5}$

5-5 Objectives

▼ To identify appropriate customary units (p. 257)

▼ To convert customary units (p. 258)

To convert units of measure in the customary system of measurement, use **dimensional analysis.**

Complete each statement.

35. 30 in. = ■ ft

36. ■ lb = 54 oz

37. 20 yd = ■ ft

38. ■ fl oz = $1\frac{1}{2}$ pt

39. 12 gal = ■ pt

40. $2\frac{3}{4}$ t = ■ lb

5-6 Objectives

▼ To solve problems by working backward (p. 263)

To solve some problems, you have to work backward.

41. Your family is planning a 4-h car trip. Along the way, you are planning to make three $\frac{1}{2}$-h stops. At what time should you leave home to arrive at the destination by 8:00 P.M.?

42. Buses bound for Los Angeles leave the station every hour from 6:00 A.M. to 8:00 P.M. How many buses is that in one day?

43. You sell used CDs at a local flea market. It costs $15 to rent a booth for the day. You spend $8 on lunch, and you make $140 selling CDs. If you have $162.50 at the end of the day, how much money did you have at the start of the day?

5-7 and 5-8 Objectives

▼ To solve equations by subtracting fractions (p. 268)

▼ To solve equations by adding fractions (p. 269)

▼ To solve equations by multiplying fractions (p. 272)

▼ To solve equations by multiplying mixed numbers (p. 273)

To solve equations with fractions, use inverse operations to undo addition or subtraction. You can undo multiplication by multiplying each side of the equation by the same fraction, usually a reciprocal of a fraction in the equation.

Solve each equation.

44. $\frac{1}{8} + x = 2\frac{1}{2}$

45. $x - \frac{1}{3} = \frac{4}{5}$

46. $x + 4\frac{2}{3} = 6$

47. $6x = \frac{1}{9}$

48. $-\frac{3}{4}x = \frac{2}{7}$

49. $2\frac{2}{5}x = \frac{8}{15}$

5-9 Objectives

▼ To find powers of products (p. 278)

▼ To find powers of quotients (p. 279)

To raise a product to a power, raise each factor to the power. To raise a quotient to a power, raise both the numerator and the denominator to the power.

Simplify each expression.

50. $(2d)^4$

51. $(-3(2))^2$

52. $(a^2b)^5$

53. $\left(-\frac{1}{2}\right)^3$

54. $\left(\frac{x}{3}\right)^2$

55. $\left(\frac{2a}{c^2}\right)^4$

Go Online
PHSchool.com
For: Chapter test
Web Code: ada-0552

Find the LCM of each pair.

1. $24, 36$

2. $50, 100$

3. $3x, 2y$

4. $16, 20$

Compare. Use > , < , or = to complete each statement.

5. $\frac{7}{8} \blacksquare \frac{7}{9}$

6. $\frac{2}{3} \blacksquare \frac{10}{15}$

7. $\frac{7}{10} \blacksquare 0.71$

8. $2\frac{3}{5} \blacksquare 2\frac{2}{3}$

9. $-0.87 \blacksquare -\frac{7}{8}$

10. $\frac{3}{4} \blacksquare \frac{14}{20}$

Order from least to greatest.

11. $0.5, \frac{1}{10}, 0, -\frac{1}{4}$

12. $-\frac{3}{5}, -0.\overline{6}, \frac{1}{6}, \frac{2}{3}$

Write each decimal as a fraction.

13. 0.4

14. $0.\overline{7}$

15. $12.\overline{36}$

16. 5.2

17. 0.002

18. $7.\overline{1}$

Write each fraction as a decimal.

19. $\frac{4}{15}$

20. $-\frac{2}{3}$

21. $\frac{3}{8}$

22. $\frac{1}{2}$

23. $\frac{6}{7}$

24. $\frac{5}{9}$

Add or subtract.

25. $\frac{1}{8} + \frac{3}{4}$

26. $\frac{2}{3} - \frac{1}{9}$

27. $-\frac{1}{6x} + \frac{1}{4}$

28. $11\frac{5}{6} - 5\frac{3}{8}$

29. $\frac{2}{3} - \left(-\frac{8y}{9}\right)$

30. $2\frac{1}{5} - \frac{3}{4}$

Multiply or divide.

31. $\frac{3}{5} \cdot \frac{1}{2}$

32. $-\frac{3}{4} \cdot \frac{5}{8}$

33. $\frac{5}{8x} \div \frac{7}{16}$

34. $\frac{4}{m} \div \frac{5m}{9}$

35. $3\frac{3}{4} \cdot 2\frac{4}{5}$

36. $-1\frac{1}{3} \div \left(-\frac{5}{9}\right)$

Complete each equation.

37. $10 \text{ yd} = \blacksquare \text{ ft}$

38. $20 \text{ oz} = \blacksquare \text{ lb}$

39. $\blacksquare \text{ lb} = 1\frac{3}{4} \text{ t}$

40. $6 \text{ pt} = \blacksquare \text{ qt}$

41. $3\frac{1}{2} \text{ qt} = \blacksquare \text{ c}$

42. $\blacksquare \text{ in.} = 1\frac{3}{4} \text{ yd}$

Solve each equation.

43. $m - \frac{2}{3} = \frac{1}{4}$

44. $h + \frac{3}{5} = \frac{9}{10}$

45. $x - \frac{5}{6} = -\frac{5}{6}$

46. $\frac{3}{5}a = 9$

47. $n + \frac{7}{8} = \frac{1}{3}$

48. $2\frac{1}{2}n = 3\frac{3}{4}$

49. $-5b = 3\frac{1}{3}$

50. $\frac{3}{8}y = -15$

Simplify each expression.

51. $(3(4))^2$

52. $(2a)^3$

53. $\left(\frac{3}{4}\right)^3$

54. $(3x^2)^3$

55. $-(2x^2y)^4$

56. $\left(\frac{2y}{5x}\right)^3$

Solve.

57. **Number Sense** Suppose you take a number, subtract 8, multiply by 7, add 10, and divide by 5. The result is 9. What is the original number?

58. You spend $\frac{3}{4}$ of your money on clothes and have $21 left. How much did you have before you bought the clothes?

59. **Writing in Math** Write a word problem for the equation $x - 1\frac{1}{4} = 5$.

60. Two packages each weigh $1\frac{7}{8}$ lb. How much do they weigh altogether?

61. You rode your bicycle a mile and a half to school. Then you rode to a friend's house. Altogether you rode $2\frac{1}{10}$ miles. Write and solve an equation to find how far it is from school to your friend's house.

Reading Comprehension Read each passage below. Then answer the questions on the basis of what is *stated* or *implied* in the passage.

Patterns in the Sky The planet Mercury revolves around the sun about every 87.98 days and turns on its own axis about once every 58.65 (Earth) days. The planet Jupiter revolves around the sun about every 4,329.63 days. It rotates on its axis about once every 0.41 day.

Jupiter has 17 moons, among which four are Ganymede, Io, Callisto, and Europa. These satellites orbit Jupiter about once every 7.16, 1.77, 16.69, and 3.55 days, respectively.

1. How long does it take Callisto to orbit Jupiter?
   - Ⓐ 7.16 days
   - Ⓑ 1.77 days
   - Ⓒ 16.69 days
   - Ⓓ 3.55 days

2. Which of Jupiter's moons travels the fastest?
   - Ⓔ Ganymede
   - Ⓕ Io
   - Ⓖ Callisto
   - Ⓗ Europa

3. How many full rotations on its axis does Jupiter complete in 7 days?

4. Is the rotation of Mercury exactly 58.65 days? Explain.

5. What is a word that means "turns on its own axis"?

Bike Helmets Currently, 19 states and the District of Columbia require bike helmets for people who are under age 16. Even in the states that have no state law requiring helmets, there may be laws in specific counties and cities. Where such laws are in force, a typical fine for each offense is $50. According to the Consumer Product Safety Commission (CPSC), wearing a helmet can reduce the risk of head injury by 85%. The CPSC standard, which all bike helmets must meet, requires a helmet to protect the wearer against an impact on a flat surface at 14 miles per hour and on an irregular surface (such as rocks and curbs) at 11 mph. Recommended youth helmets range in price from $30 to $45.

6. How many states do NOT currently require bike helmets for people under age 16?
   - Ⓐ 50
   - Ⓑ 31
   - Ⓒ 20
   - Ⓓ 19

7. Which inequality best represents the price range p of a recommended youth helmet?
   - Ⓔ $p < \$45$
   - Ⓕ $\$30 < p < \$45$
   - Ⓖ $p > \$30$
   - Ⓗ $\$30 \leq p \leq \$45$

8. About how much more than the price of a helmet is a fine for not wearing a helmet?
   - Ⓐ $10
   - Ⓑ $30
   - Ⓒ $45
   - Ⓓ $50

9. What does *mph* stand for?

10. At what ages do the bike helmet laws of these states no longer apply?

Activity Lab

Quilt Tales

Applying Fractions Quilts are more than simple bed coverings. To historians, quilts are artifacts of the past. Fabrics and dyes provide information about the textile industry. Designs tell stories of life in America. The "Log Cabin" is a traditional quilt block. The red square in the center represents the chimney in the cabin. The strips around the red square symbolize the logs of the cabin. By rotating the blocks, a quilter can make various patterns appear in a quilt.

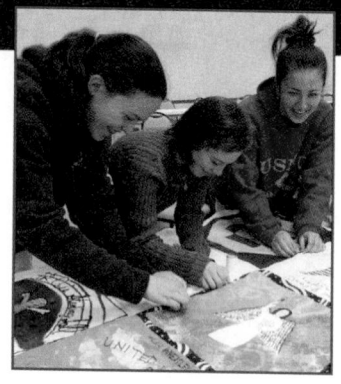

Log Cabin quilt, made around 1865

Activity

Use the pattern and the chart to answer the questions.

1. After you sew them together, the fabric pieces in a Log Cabin quilt are $1\frac{1}{2}$ in. wide. Copy and complete the table for one finished Log Cabin block.

One Log Cabin Block

Piece Number	Finished Dimensions (length × width)
1	$1\frac{1}{2}$ in. × $1\frac{1}{2}$ in.
2	3 in. × $1\frac{1}{2}$ in.
3	■
4	■
5	■
6	■
7	■

Pattern for One Log Cabin Block

2. A seam allowance is the fabric that overlaps when you sew two pieces of fabric together. In quilting, the seam allowance is $\frac{1}{4}$ in., which means that you make a seam $\frac{1}{4}$ in. from the edge of the fabric. Expand your table to include the original dimensions of each of the pieces.

3. a. What are the dimensions of one Log Cabin block?
  b. What are the dimensions of a Log Cabin quilt with four blocks? With nine blocks?

4. Fabric stores sell fabric in multiples of $\frac{1}{8}$ yd. The minimum amount of fabric you can buy is $\frac{1}{8}$ yd, which is a piece of fabric that measures $4\frac{1}{2}$ in. × 44 in. Suppose you decide to make all six blue pieces from the same fabric. How much fabric should you buy for nine blocks?

5. Suppose you have $5\frac{1}{2}$ yards of fabric left over from another quilt. You decide to make all six yellow pieces from this remnant. How much of the remnant will be left after you make a Log Cabin quilt with four blocks?

Go Online
PHSchool.com

For: Information about quilting
Web Code: ade-0553

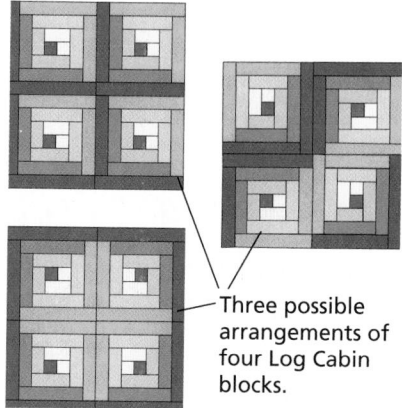

Three possible arrangements of four Log Cabin blocks.

Log Cabin Variations

Some Log Cabin quilts have center squares in colors other than red. When a Log Cabin quilt with black center squares hung on a clothesline, it meant the house was a stop on the Freedom Trail.

Log Cabin quilt, made around 1870

What You've Learned

 Assessment Framework

- **8.8.12:** In Chapter 2, you solved equations by adding, subtracting, multiplying, or dividing.
- **6.8.10:** In Chapter 4, you investigated exponents.
- **6.8.18:** In Chapter 5, you learned how to work with fractions.

 Check Your Readiness

 for Help to the Lesson in green.

Solving Equations by Multiplying or Dividing (Lessons 2-6, 3-6, and 5-8)

Solve each equation.

1. $3x = 48$

2. $94.5 = 7r$

3. $\frac{3}{7}t = \frac{3}{8}$

4. $0.5y = 1.25$

5. $\frac{4}{5}x = 1$

6. $38.5 = 1.4m$

Simplifying Fractions (Lesson 4-4)

Find two fractions equivalent to each fraction.

7. $\frac{1}{4}$

8. $\frac{4}{10}$

9. $\frac{6}{14}$

10. $\frac{2}{9}$

11. $\frac{3}{8}$

12. $\frac{5}{6}$

Write each fraction in simplest form.

13. $\frac{2}{8}$

14. $\frac{6}{24}$

15. $\frac{12}{15}$

16. $\frac{6}{16}$

17. $\frac{18}{42}$

18. $\frac{25}{200}$

19. $\frac{80}{96}$

20. $\frac{40}{1,000}$

Writing Fractions and Decimals (Lesson 5-2)

Write each fraction as a decimal. Write each decimal as a fraction or a mixed number in simplest form.

21. $\frac{7}{20}$

22. 0.06

23. $\frac{30}{8}$

24. 0.35

25. 0.875

26. $3\frac{3}{5}$

27. 1.07

28. $\frac{12}{18}$

29. $11\frac{1}{9}$

30. $0.\overline{3}$

31. $\frac{100}{16}$

32. 3.98

Ratios, Proportions, and Percents

Key Vocabulary

- certain event (p. 310)
- commission (p. 325)
- complement (p. 310)
- cross products (p. 298)
- discount (p. 333)
- event (p. 309)
- impossible event (p. 310)
- indirect measurement (p. 304)
- markup (p. 333)
- odds (p. 311)
- outcomes (p. 309)
- percent (p. 314)
- percent of change (p. 329)
- probability (p. 309)
- proportion (p. 298)
- rate (p. 293)
- ratio (p. 292)
- scale drawing (p. 304)
- similar figures (p. 303)
- unit rate (p. 293)

What You'll Learn Next

 Assessment Framework

In this chapter, you will learn how to

- **6.8.15:** Find and use ratios and unit rates.
- **6.8.16:** Write and solve proportions.
- **6.8.17:** Find and use percents.
- Solve a problem by making a table.

 Activity Lab Applying what you learn, on pages 348–349 you will solve problems about stock trading.

291

6-1

Ratios and Unit Rates

6.8.15 Use ratios to describe problem situations.

1 Writing Ratios

Statistics In the United States, about 10 out of every 15 people eligible to vote are registered to vote. The numbers 10 and 15 form a *ratio*.

✓ **Check Skills You'll Need**

Write in simplest form.

1. $\frac{30}{35}$ 2. $\frac{24}{40}$

3. $\frac{54}{60}$ 4. $\frac{12}{15}$

5. $\frac{14}{42}$ 6. $\frac{40}{24}$

GO for Help
·Lesson 4-4

◀)) **New Vocabulary**

• ratio
• rate
• unit rate

Vocabulary Tip

Regardless of how you write the ratio, you read 10 to 15, 10 : 15 and $\frac{10}{15}$ as "ten to fifteen."

Key Concepts **Ratio**

A **ratio** is a comparison of two quantities by division. You can write a ratio in different ways.

Arithmetic	Algebra
10 to 15 10 : 15 $\frac{10}{15}$	a to b $a : b$ $\frac{a}{b}$, for $b \neq 0$

1 EXAMPLE **Real-World** 🌐 **Problem Solving**

Surveys A survey asked students whether they had after-school jobs. Write each ratio as a fraction in simplest form.

After-School Jobs

Response	Number
Have a Job	40
Don't Have a Job	60
Total	100

a. students with jobs to students without jobs

$$\frac{\text{students with jobs}}{\text{students without jobs}} = \frac{40}{60}$$

$$= \frac{2}{3}$$

b. students without jobs to all students surveyed

$$\frac{\text{students without jobs}}{\text{all students surveyed}} = \frac{60}{100}$$

$$= \frac{3}{5}$$

✓ **Quick Check**

1. Write each ratio as a fraction in simplest form.

   a. students with jobs to all students surveyed

   b. students without jobs to students with jobs

2 Finding Rates and Unit Rates

A **rate** is a ratio that compares quantities in different units.
A **unit rate** is a rate that has a denominator of 1. Examples of
unit rates include unit cost, gas mileage, and speed.

 EXAMPLE Real-World Problem Solving

Multiple Choice The table shows prices for different sizes of the
same dish detergent. Which size has the lowest unit cost?

(A) Trial   (B) Regular   (C) Family   (D) Economy

Trial: $\dfrac{\text{price}}{\text{volume}} \rightarrow \dfrac{\$.78}{6 \text{ fl oz}} = \$.13/\text{fl oz}$

Regular: $\dfrac{\text{price}}{\text{volume}} \rightarrow \dfrac{\$1.20}{12 \text{ fl oz}} = \$.10/\text{fl oz}$ **Find the unit costs.**

Family: $\dfrac{\text{price}}{\text{volume}} \rightarrow \dfrac{\$2.24}{28 \text{ fl oz}} = \$.08/\text{fl oz}$

Economy: $\dfrac{\text{price}}{\text{volume}} \rightarrow \dfrac{\$3.60}{40 \text{ fl oz}} = \$.09/\text{fl oz}$

The family size has the lowest unit cost. The answer is C.

Dish Detergent Prices

Size	Volume (fl oz)	Price
Trial	6	$.78
Regular	12	$1.20
Family	28	$2.24
Economy	40	$3.60

✓ Quick Check

2. Find each unit rate.

   a. Two liters of spring water cost $1.98.
   b. A car goes 425 mi on 12.5 gal of gas.

Test-Taking Tip

When a problem involves two different units, make sure you express your answer in the correct unit.

You can use dimensional analysis to choose conversion factors for
converting rates.

3 EXAMPLE Converting a Rate

Convert 10 mi/h to feet per minute.

$10 \text{ mi/h} = \dfrac{10 \text{ mi}}{1 \text{ h}} \cdot \dfrac{5{,}280 \text{ ft}}{1 \text{ mi}} \cdot \dfrac{1 \text{ h}}{60 \text{ min}}$ **Use conversion factors that convert miles to feet and hours to minutes.**

$= \dfrac{^{1}\cancel{10} \text{ mi}}{1 \text{ h}} \cdot \dfrac{\overset{880}{5{,}280} \text{ ft}}{1 \text{ mi}} \cdot \dfrac{1 \text{ h}}{\underset{6_{1}}{60} \text{ min}}$ **Divide the common factors and units.**

$= \dfrac{880 \text{ ft}}{\text{min}}$ **Simplify.**

10 mi/h equals 880 ft/min.

Online active math

For: Exploring Ratios Activity
Use: Interactive Textbook, 6-1

✓ Quick Check

3. Complete each statement.

   a. 3.5 qt/min = ■ gal/h   **b.** 12 cm/s = ■ m/h

EXERCISES

For more exercises, see *Extra Skill and Word Problem Practice*.

Practice and Problem Solving

A **Practice by Example**

GO for Help

Example 1
(page 292)

Write each ratio as a fraction in simplest form.

1. $9 : 27$ **2.** 12 to 8   **3.** 2 to 18   **4.** $6 : 50$

5. $\dfrac{1,000}{10,000}$ **6.** $3 : 8$ **7.** 7 to 9   **8.** 8 out of 11

9. 3 out of 12 people live in a rural area.

10. 98 homes in 100 have a TV.

11. 70 homes out of 125 have a personal computer.

12. In one class, there are 6 girls for every 10 boys.

Example 2
(page 293)

Find each unit rate.

13. A skydiver falls 144 ft in 3 s.   **14.** A pump moves 42 gal in 7 min.

15. A car travels 676 mi in 13 h.   **16.** 20 c of water evaporate in 5 d.

Example 3
(page 293)

Complete each statement.

17. 720 m/day = ■ m/min   **18.** 1.5 gal/min = ■ qt/h

19. 32 yd/min = ■ in./s   **20.** 0.85 km/s = ■ m/min

21. 80 mi/h = ■ ft/s   **22.** 20 fl oz/min = ■ qt/day

B **Apply Your Skills**

GO **Online**
Homework Video Tutor
Visit: PHSchool.com
Web Code: ade-0601

Write each ratio as a fraction in simplest form.

23. 36 to 48   **24.** 60 to 24   **25.** $16 : 12$ **26.** $15 : 27$

27. Cycling Anna and Julia each take a bicycle trip. Anna rides 20 miles in $1\frac{1}{3}$ hours. Julia rides 246 miles in 16 hours. Which rider has the slower unit rate? By how much?

28. Transportation What is the rate in meters per second of a jetliner that is traveling at a rate of 846 km/h?

29. Error Analysis A student converts 100 ft/min to 500 in./s. Use dimensional analysis to explain why the student's result is not reasonable.

Boys in Two Classes

Class	Number of Boys	Number of Students
A	6	30
B	4	24

Use the table at the left for Exercises 30 and 31.

30. For each class, write the ratio of the number of boys to the total number of students.

31. Which class has the greater ratio of boys to students?

C **Challenge**

32. Writing in Math A student claims that a ratio remains unchanged if 1 is added to both the numerator and the denominator of the fraction. Does $\frac{a}{b}$ equal $\frac{a+1}{b+1}$? Write an explanation, and give an example or a counterexample.

33. Science Density is the ratio of a substance's mass to its volume. A volume of 20 cubic centimeters of gold has a mass of 386 grams. Express the density of gold as a unit rate.

Test Prep

Multiple Choice

34. A 50-lb bag of Glossy Coat Horse Feed costs $23.50. A 25-lb bag costs $15.50. How much money per pound would you save by buying the bag with the lower unit price?

A. $.15   **B.** $.32   **C.** $.47   **D.** $.62

35. Karla and her dad were nailing up plywood. They started at 10:00. Karla drove 30 nails in 10 min, the time it took her dad to drive 50 nails. At that rate for each, when did they finish driving 392 nails in all?

F. 10:30   **G.** 10:39   **H.** 10:45   **J.** 10:49

Short Response

Read the passage below before doing Exercises 36–38.

A Sappy Story

Connecticut has more than 100 farms that produce maple syrup. Sugarers collect sap and boil it down to syrup. In a good year, one small sugarer in Connecticut averages 301 gallons of sap weekly from 200 trees. The sap boils down to just seven gallons of syrup. The syrup sells for $4.50 per half pint or $44 per gallon.

36. Write the ratio of sap to syrup in simplest form.

37. Find the unit prices for syrup sold by the half pint and syrup sold by the gallon. Which has the lower unit price?

38. If the sugarer sells the syrup by the half pint, how much income will there be for 10 weeks of sugaring in a good year?

Mixed Review

for Help

Lesson 5-9

Simplify each expression.

39. $(-3 \cdot 4)^3$ **40.** $(2x^2y)^4$ **41.** $\left(-\dfrac{ab^3}{a^2b}\right)^3$

Lesson 5-2

Compare. Use >, <, or = to complete each statement.

42. $\dfrac{7}{8}$ ■ $\dfrac{14}{24}$ **43.** $\dfrac{4}{12}$ ■ $\dfrac{10}{30}$ **44.** $\dfrac{13}{20}$ ■ 0.6

Lesson 2-7 **45. Vacation** Three friends shared the driving on a long trip. Marla drove 7 mi more than Guido. Guido drove five times as far as Juanita did. Juanita drove 112 mi. How long was the trip?

Suppose you are traveling in a country that uses the metric system. You can use conversion factors (dimensional analysis) to convert a unit of measure from one system to another. For example, since 1 mi ≈ 1.61 km, you can use $\frac{1 \text{ mi}}{1.61 \text{ km}}$ and $\frac{1.61 \text{ km}}{1 \text{ mi}}$ as conversion factors. The table shows some useful conversion factors.

Customary Units and Metric Units	Conversion Factors
1 in. = 2.54 cm	$\frac{1 \text{ in.}}{2.54 \text{ cm}}$ or $\frac{2.54 \text{ cm}}{1 \text{ in.}}$
1 mi ≈ 1.61 km	$\frac{1 \text{ mi}}{1.61 \text{ km}}$ or $\frac{1.61 \text{ km}}{1 \text{ mi}}$
1.06 qt ≈ 1 L	$\frac{1.06 \text{ qt}}{1 \text{ L}}$ or $\frac{1 \text{ L}}{1.06 \text{ qt}}$
1 oz ≈ 28.4 g	$\frac{1 \text{ oz}}{28.4 \text{ g}}$ or $\frac{28.4 \text{ g}}{1 \text{ oz}}$
2.20 lb ≈ 1 kg	$\frac{2.20 \text{ lb}}{1 \text{ kg}}$ or $\frac{1 \text{ kg}}{2.20 \text{ lb}}$

In general, a conversion between systems results in an approximate measurement.

1 ACTIVITY

Suppose you and your family have rented a car in France. You see a sign that says "Paris 60 km." Is it more or less than 60 mi to Paris?

Since 1 mi ≈ 1.61 km, you know that

$$1 \text{ mi} > 1 \text{ km}$$

so 60 mi > 60 km.

● It is less than 60 miles to Paris.

2 ACTIVITY

Use the information from Activity 1. About how many miles is it to Paris?

60 km ≈ 60 km · $\frac{1 \text{ mi}}{1.61 \text{ km}}$ Use a conversion factor that changes kilometers to miles.

= 60 k̶m̶ · $\frac{1 \text{ mi}}{1.61 \text{ k̶m̶}}$ Divide the common units.

= $\frac{60 \text{ mi}}{1.61}$ Multiply.

≈ 37 mi   Divide.

● It is about 37 miles to Paris.

Sometimes you may need to use two or more conversion factors.

3 ACTIVITY

The Eiffel Tower, in Paris, is 324 m tall including its antenna. The Empire State Building, in New York City, is about 1,250 ft tall. Which is taller, the Eiffel Tower or the Empire State Building?

$1{,}250 \text{ ft} = 1{,}250 \text{ ft} \cdot \dfrac{12 \text{ in.}}{1 \text{ ft}} \cdot \dfrac{2.54 \text{ cm}}{1 \text{ in.}}$ **Convert feet to centimeters.**

$= 1{,}250 \text{ ft} \cdot \dfrac{12 \text{ in.}}{1 \text{ ft}} \cdot \dfrac{2.54 \text{ cm}}{1 \text{ in.}}$ **Divide the common units.**

$= 38{,}100 \text{ cm}$ **Multiply.**

$38{,}100 \text{ cm} = 381 \text{ m}$ **Move the decimal point two places to find the number of meters.**

The Empire State Building is about 381 m tall. It is taller than the Eiffel Tower.

EXERCISES

Convert. Where necessary, round to the nearest tenth.

1. 8 in. ≈ ■ cm

2. 16 cm ≈ ■ in.

3. ■ mi ≈ 20 km

4. ■ km ≈ 100 mi

5. ■ L ≈ 50 qt

6. ■ g ≈ 15 oz

7. 15 L ≈ ■ qt

8. ■ lb ≈ 14 kg

9. 44 lb ≈ ■ kg

10. 100 oz ≈ ■ kg

11. ■ L ≈ 212 pt

12. 500 g ≈ ■ lb

13. 1,000 mm ≈ ■ in.

14. ■ gal ≈ 20 L

15. ■ km/h ≈ 10 mi/h

16. Gasoline is sold by the liter in Europe. Suppose your family car has a 20-gal gas tank. How many liters would fill the gas tank? (*Hint:* Change gallons to quarts and quarts to liters.)

17. Travel London, England is about 414 km from Paris, France. Dallas, Texas is about 250 miles from Houston, Texas. Which distance is longer? How much longer?

18. Home Economics A recipe calls for 8 oz of figs. The figs come in packages of 100 g. How many packages should you buy?

19. Writing in Math Explain how you would estimate the number of kilometers in 19 miles.

20. In Exercise 15 above, you may have found that 10 mi/h ≈ 16.1 km/h. Also, 10 mi/h = 880 ft/min (Example 3, p. 293). Convert both 16.1 km/h and 880 ft/min to meters per second and compare.

6-2 Proportions

IL Assessment Framework

6.8.16 Use proportional reasoning to model and solve problems.

 Check Skills You'll Need

Solve each equation.

1. $4x = 52$ **2.** $3y = 18$

3. $5b = 75$ **4.** $7k = 21$

GO for Help
Lesson 2-6

🔊 **New Vocabulary**

• proportion
• cross products

---

1 Solving Proportions

A **proportion** is an equality of two ratios—for example, $\frac{6}{9} = \frac{8}{12}$. You can use the Multiplication Property of Equality to show an important property of all proportions.

If $\frac{a}{b} = \frac{c}{d}$

then $\frac{a}{b} \cdot bd = \frac{c}{d} \cdot bd$ **Multiplication Property of Equality**

$\frac{ab^1 d}{{}_1 b} = \frac{cbd^1}{{}_1 d}$ $\frac{b}{b} = 1$ **and** $\frac{d}{d} = 1$

and $ad = cb$, or $ad = bc$.

The products ad and bc are called the **cross products** of the proportion $\frac{a}{b} = \frac{c}{d}$.

Key Concepts   **Cross Products**

In a proportion, the cross products are equal.

Arithmetic	Algebra
$\frac{6}{9} = \frac{8}{12}$	$\frac{a}{b} = \frac{c}{d}$
$6 \cdot 12 = 9 \cdot 8 = 72$	$ad = bc$

To solve a proportion that contains a variable, you find the value that makes the equation true.

1 EXAMPLE   **Multiplying to Solve a Proportion**

Solve $\frac{x}{9} = \frac{4}{6}$.

Method 1 Multiplication Property of Equality

$$\frac{x}{9} = \frac{4}{6}$$

$$\frac{x}{9} \cdot 9 = \frac{4}{6} \cdot 9$$

$$x = \frac{36}{6}$$

$$x = 6$$

Method 2 Cross products

$$\frac{x}{9} = \frac{4}{6}$$

$$x \cdot 6 = 9 \cdot 4$$

$$6x = 36$$

$$\frac{6x}{6} = \frac{36}{6}$$

$$x = 6$$

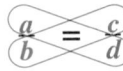

Video Tutor Help
Visit: PHSchool.com
Web Code: ada-0775

GO ⬤**nline**

✓ Quick Check

1. Solve each proportion.

a. $\frac{h}{9} = \frac{2}{3}$ **b.** $\frac{4}{5} = \frac{t}{55}$ **c.** $\frac{22}{d} = \frac{6}{21}$

● Two ratios form a proportion if their cross products are equal.

② EXAMPLE   Testing for a Proportion

Do the ratios $\frac{4}{6}$ and $\frac{10}{14}$ form a proportion? Explain.

$\frac{4}{6} \stackrel{?}{=} \frac{10}{14}$ **Test by writing as a proportion.**

$4 \cdot 14 \stackrel{?}{=} 6 \cdot 10$ **Write the cross products.**

$56 \neq 60$ **Simplify.**

The ratios do not form a proportion. Cross products are not equal.

Test-Taking Tip

In a proportion, the cross products are always equal. If they are not equal, the ratios do not form a proportion.

✓ Quick Check

2. Tell whether the two ratios form a proportion. Explain.

a. $\frac{6}{9}, \frac{4}{6}$ **b.** $\frac{15}{20}, \frac{5}{7}$ **c.** $\frac{7}{12}, \frac{17.5}{30}$

◢2◣ Using Proportions to Solve Problems

You can write and solve proportions for many real-world problems.

③ EXAMPLE   Real-World 🌐 Problem Solving

Multiple Choice One hundred nautical miles equals about 115 standard, or statute, miles. To the nearest mile, how far in statute miles is 156 nautical miles?

Ⓐ 271 statute miles   Ⓑ 180 statute miles

Ⓒ 179 statute miles   Ⓓ 136 statute miles

Let d = distance in statute miles.

distance in nautical miles → $\dfrac{100}{115} = \dfrac{156}{d}$ ← **distance in nautical miles**
distance in statute miles →   ← **distance in statute miles**

$100d = 115(156)$ **Write the cross products.**

$d = \dfrac{115(156)}{100}$ **Divide each side by 100.**

$d \approx 179$ **A calculator may be useful.**

156 nautical miles is about 179 statute miles. The answer is C.

Real-World 🌐 Connection

Sailors and astronauts measure distances in *nautical miles*. This photo of the Great Lakes was taken from the space shuttle at an altitude of 156 nautical miles.

✓ Quick Check

● **3.** To the nearest mile, how far in nautical miles is 100 statute miles?

EXERCISES

For more exercises, see *Extra Skill and Word Problem Practice*.

Practice and Problem Solving

A **Practice by Example**

Example 1
(page 298)

Solve each proportion.

1. $\frac{2}{v} = \frac{1}{8}$ **2.** $\frac{z}{42} = \frac{25}{70}$ **3.** $\frac{4}{h} = \frac{8}{10}$ **4.** $\frac{4}{16} = \frac{s}{8}$

5. $\frac{4}{11} = \frac{x}{22}$ **6.** $\frac{2}{9} = \frac{r}{36}$ **7.** $\frac{12}{n} = \frac{2}{12}$ **8.** $\frac{1}{15} = \frac{3}{p}$

9. $\frac{4}{15} = \frac{a}{75}$ **10.** $\frac{3}{4} = \frac{21}{b}$ **11.** $\frac{13}{c} = \frac{39}{60}$ **12.** $\frac{3}{6} = \frac{7}{d}$

Example 2
(page 299)

Tell whether the two ratios form a proportion. Explain.

13. $\frac{2}{3}$ and $\frac{10}{20}$ **14.** $\frac{25}{80}$ and $\frac{5}{16}$ **15.** $\frac{4}{7}$ and $\frac{20}{25}$ **16.** $\frac{2}{3}$ and $\frac{10}{16}$

17. $\frac{3}{4}$ and $\frac{12}{15}$ **18.** $\frac{3}{8}$ and $\frac{21}{56}$ **19.** $\frac{9}{24}$ and $\frac{15}{40}$ **20.** $\frac{20}{32}$ and $\frac{12}{20}$

Example 3
(page 299)

21. Photocopies At the Copy Shoppe, 18 copies cost $1.08. At that rate, how much will 40 copies cost?

22. Three tea bags are needed to make a gallon of iced tea. How many tea bags are needed to make four gallons?

23. Purchasing Three posters cost $9.60. At that rate, how many posters can you buy for $48?

B **Apply Your Skills**

Tell whether the two ratios form a proportion. Explain.

24. $\frac{3.9}{5.4}$ and $\frac{13}{18}$ **25.** $\frac{54}{60}$ and $\frac{118}{110}$ **26.** $\frac{27}{72}$ and $\frac{48}{128}$ **27.** $\frac{144}{120}$ and $\frac{75}{145}$

Mental Math **Solve by mental math.**

28. $\frac{1}{6} = \frac{a}{72}$ **29.** $\frac{120}{24} = \frac{y}{2}$ **30.** $\frac{10}{v} = \frac{3}{1.5}$ **31.** $\frac{n}{12} = \frac{12}{2}$

32. Exchange Rates On a recent day, the exchange rate for U.S. dollars to European euros was 1.32 dollar per euro. On that day, about how many euros would you get for 25 dollars?

33. Error Analysis Fancy ribbon costs $3 for 15 in. Your friend wants to find the cost of 3 ft of ribbon. He uses the proportion $\frac{3}{15} = \frac{x}{3}$ and gets an answer of $.60. Explain your friend's error.

Solve each proportion. Where necessary, round to the nearest tenth.

34. $\frac{4}{3} = \frac{b}{21}$ **35.** $\frac{6}{25} = \frac{e}{80}$ **36.** $\frac{4}{9} = \frac{f}{15}$ **37.** $\frac{3}{8} = \frac{50}{g}$

38. $\frac{24}{17} = \frac{109}{h}$ **39.** $\frac{7}{9} = \frac{j}{22.5}$ **40.** $\frac{6}{13} = \frac{7.8}{m}$ **41.** $\frac{20}{27} = \frac{1.1}{n}$

Estimation **Estimate the solution of each proportion.**

42. $\frac{11}{a} = \frac{9}{17}$ **43.** $\frac{w}{20} = \frac{6}{23}$ **44.** $\frac{3}{2} = \frac{29}{d}$ **45.** $\frac{20}{3.9} = \frac{s}{6}$

46. $\frac{1.5}{p} = \frac{2.1}{4.1}$ **47.** $\frac{f}{4} = \frac{12}{49}$ **48.** $\frac{60}{g} = \frac{24.1}{8.1}$ **49.** $\frac{9}{4.4} = \frac{x}{19}$

50. At the rate shown in the cartoon, how much would five potatoes cost?

🌐 **51. Quality Control** A microchip inspector found three defective chips in a batch containing 750 chips. At that rate, how many defective chips would there be in 10,000 chips?

52. Reasoning If $\frac{a}{b} = \frac{c}{d}$, will $\frac{a}{c} = \frac{b}{d}$? Assume that $b \neq 0$, $c \neq 0$, and $d \neq 0$. Explain your reasoning.

53. Geometry A rectangle that is 20 cm long and 28 cm wide is the same shape as one that is 9 cm long and z cm wide. Find z.

🌐 **54. Baseball** Your team scores 4 runs in the first three innings of a 9-inning baseball game. If it continues at that rate, how many runs will it score in the game?

  Ⓐ 8 runs Ⓑ 12 runs Ⓒ 13 runs Ⓓ 16 runs

REAL LIFE ADVENTURES by Gary Wise and Lance Aldrich

If the people who own the shops at the airport owned other things.

Write a proportion for each situation. Then solve.

55. 3 oz for $1.65; 5 oz for x dollars

56. 20 lb for $27.50; 12 lb for x dollars

57. 25 yd in $2\frac{1}{2}$ s; 100 yd in x seconds

58. 3 miles in 2.8 minutes; 33.3 miles in x minutes

59. $3\frac{1}{2}$ pounds in 4 cubic inches; x pound in 1 cubic inch

60. **Writing in Math** A truck driver estimates that it will take him 12 h to drive 1,160 km. After 5 h, he has driven 484 km. Is he on schedule? Explain.

Ⓒ Challenge

For Exercises 61–64, use the table.

61. How many times does an adult's heart beat in 270 s?

62. In how many seconds will a newborn's heart beat 35 times?

63. In how many seconds will a 12-year-old's heart beat 17 times?

64. In 45 s, how many more times does a newborn's heart beat than a 6-year-old's heart?

Human Heart Rates

Age (years)	Beats per Minute
newborn	140
1	120
6	100
10	90
12	85
adult	80

Write a proportion for each situation. Then solve.

65. 5 km in 18 min 36 s; 8 km in v minutes

66. 96 oz for $2; y pounds for $10

67. 4 oz for $1.85; 1 lb for t dollars

68. $5.76 for 2 lb 4 oz; c dollars for 1 pound

Test Prep

Multiple Choice

69. Four ounces of orange juice contain 50 calories. About how many calories are in 14 ounces of orange juice?
A. 1 cal   **B.** 14 cal   **C.** 175 cal   **D.** 700 cal

70. A lion's heart beats 12 times in 16 s. How many times does a lion's heart beat in 60 s?
F. 24   **G.** 32   **H.** 45   **J.** 192

71. An artist makes purple paint by mixing red and blue paint in the ratio of 2 parts red to 3 parts blue. What is the ratio of red paint to purple paint?
A. 3:2   **B.** 3:5   **C.** 2:3   **D.** 2:5

Extended Response

72. On Monday, the ratio of Tara's pocket money to her brother Seth's pocket money was . On Tuesday, Tara gave $5 to Seth. Then Tara had twice as much money as Seth. Let $3x$ equal the amount Tara had on Monday and x equal the amount Seth had on Monday.
  a. Write two ratios that each compare the amount of money Tara had on Tuesday to the amount Seth had on Tuesday. Use the ratios to write a proportion.
  b. Solve for x.
  c. Find the amount of money each person had on Monday.

Mixed Review

GO for Help

Lesson 6-1   **Write each ratio as a fraction in simplest form.**

73. ten per thousand   **74.** 30 to 55   **75.** 125:70

Lesson 5-6   **76. Personal Finance** On Saturday afternoon, a student bought two music tapes for $8.95 each and a sweater for $24.95. She received $20 for mowing a lawn. On Saturday night, she had $45.12. How much money did the student have on Saturday morning?

Lessons 1-4 and 5-3   **Tell whether each equation is true or false.**

77. $\left| -2\frac{1}{4} \right| - \left| 2\frac{1}{4} \right| = 0$ **78.** $\left| -2\frac{1}{4} \right| + \left| 2\frac{1}{4} \right| = 0$

79. $-\left| -\frac{9}{4} \right| + \left| 2\frac{1}{4} \right| = 0$ **80.** $\left| -\frac{9}{4} \right| - \left| 2\frac{1}{4} \right| = 0$

Similar Figures and Scale Drawings

1 Using Similar Figures

Similar figures have the same shape, but not necessarily the same size. Similar figures have *corresponding angles* and *corresponding sides*.

The symbol ~ means *is similar to*. At the right, $\triangle ABC \sim \triangle XYZ$.

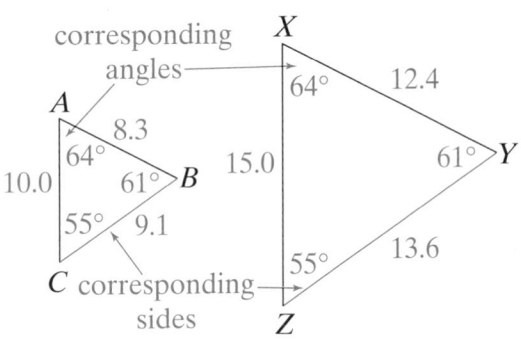

7.8.06 Solve problems involving scale drawings, maps, and indirect measurement.

9.8.11 Solve problems involving congruent and similar figures.

☑ **Check Skills You'll Need**

Solve each proportion. Round to the nearest tenth where necessary.

1. $\frac{2}{3} = \frac{f}{21}$ **2.** $\frac{3}{8} = \frac{50}{p}$

3. $\frac{9}{4} = \frac{15}{p}$ **4.** $\frac{16}{3} = \frac{19}{g}$

GO for Help
Lesson 6-2

🔊 **New Vocabulary**
• similar figures
• indirect measurement
• scale drawing

Key Concepts   Similar Figures

Similar figures have two properties.
- The corresponding angles have equal measures.
- The lengths of corresponding sides are in proportion.

1 EXAMPLE   Using Similar Figures

Parallelogram $ABCD \sim$ parallelogram $EFGH$. Find the value of x.

 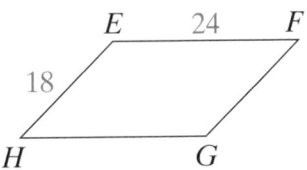

Write a proportion for corresponding sides.

Side *DA* corresponds to side *HE*.	$\frac{x}{18} = \frac{16}{24}$	**Side *AB* corresponds to side *EF*.**
	$x \cdot 24 = 18 \cdot 16$	**Write cross products.**
	$\frac{24x}{24} = \frac{18 \cdot 16}{24}$	**Divide each side by 24.**
	$x = 12$	**Simplify.**

☑ **Quick Check**

1. Parallelogram $KLMN$ is similar to parallelogram $ABCD$ in Example 1. Find the value of y. Round to the nearest tenth.

Online
active math

For: Similar Figures Activity
Use: Interactive Textbook, 6-3

You can use similar figures to compute distances that are difficult to measure directly. Such a process is called **indirect measurement.**

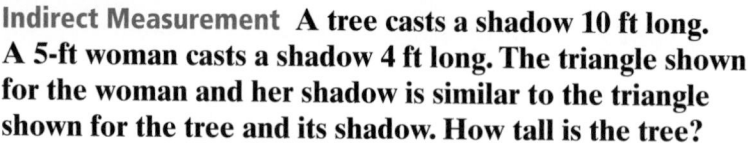

EXAMPLE Real-World Problem Solving

Indirect Measurement A tree casts a shadow 10 ft long. A 5-ft woman casts a shadow 4 ft long. The triangle shown for the woman and her shadow is similar to the triangle shown for the tree and its shadow. How tall is the tree?

$$\frac{4}{10} = \frac{5}{x}$$ Corresponding sides of similar triangles are in proportion.

$$4x = 10 \cdot 5$$ Write cross products.

$$\frac{4x}{4} = \frac{10 \cdot 5}{4}$$ Divide each side by 4.

$$x = 12.5$$ Simplify.

The tree is 12.5 ft tall.

✓ Quick Check

2. **Indirect Measurement** A building 70 ft high casts a 150-ft shadow. A nearby flagpole casts a 60-ft shadow. Draw a diagram. Use similar triangles to find the height of the flagpole.

2 Using Scale Drawings

A **scale drawing** is an enlarged or reduced drawing that is similar to an actual object or place. The ratio of a distance in the drawing to the corresponding actual distance is the *scale* of the drawing.

EXAMPLE Real-World Problem Solving

Maps The scale of the map is 1 in. : 40 mi. About how far from Atlanta is Athens?

Map distance $= 1\frac{1}{2}$ in., or 1.5 in.   Measure the map distance.

$$\frac{\text{map (in.)}}{\text{actual (mi)}} \rightarrow \frac{1}{40} = \frac{1.5}{d} \leftarrow \frac{\text{map (in.)}}{\text{actual (mi)}}$$ Write a proportion.

$$1 \cdot d = 40 \cdot 1.5$$ Write cross products.

$$d = 60$$ Simplify.

Athens is about 60 mi from Atlanta.

✓ Quick Check

3. **Maps** The distance from Atlanta to Macon is about 75 mi. What is the approximate map distance between these two cities?

EXERCISES

For more exercises, see *Extra Skill and Word Problem Practice*.

Practice and Problem Solving

A Practice by Example

Example 1
(page 303)

GO for
Help

Trapezoid *EFGH* ~ trapezoid *MNOP*. Find the indicated value.

1. x

2. y

3. z

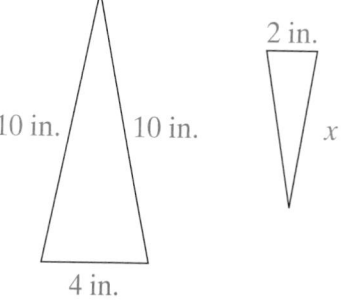

The triangles in each pair are similar. Find the missing length. Round to the nearest tenth where necessary.

4.

5.

6.

7.

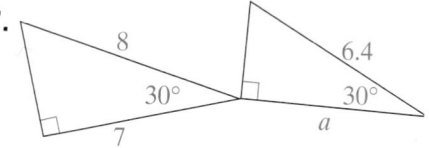

Example 2
(page 304)

8. Indirect Measurement A tree casts a shadow 8 ft long. A 6-ft man casts a shadow 4 ft long. The triangle formed by the tree and its shadow is similar to the triangle formed by the man and his shadow. How tall is the tree?

🌐 **9. Projection** An image on a slide is similar to its projected image. A slide is 35 mm wide and 21 mm high. Its projected image is 85 cm wide. To the nearest centimeter, how high is the image?

Example 3
(page 304)

The scale of a map is 1 cm : 12 km. Find the actual distance for each map distance.

10. 1.5 cm   **11.** 12 cm   **12.** 4.25 cm   **13.** 8.3 cm

🌐 **14. Maps** Duane is drawing a map with a scale of 1 in. : 3 mi. He knows that the distance from Center Point to Comfort is 9 miles. How far apart should Duane locate the two towns on his map?

The scale of a drawing is 1 in. : 25 yd. Find the length on the drawing for each actual length.

15. 100 yd   **16.** 375 yd   **17.** 512.5 yd   **18.** 20 yd

19. Indirect Measurement Jacques has a scale drawing of his bedroom with a scale of 1 cm : 0.4 m. On the drawing, the front window is 3 cm from the door. What is the actual distance in the room?

20. A scale drawing has a scale of 1 in. : 10 ft. What is the distance on the drawing for an actual distance of 20 ft? Of 45 ft?

B Apply Your Skills

The scale of a map is 2 cm : 15 km. Find the actual distance for each map distance.

21. 6 cm   **22.** 2.1 cm   **23.** 10 mm   **24.** 17.4 cm

The length of each piece in a model railroad built on the HO scale is $\frac{1}{87}$ of the actual length. Another popular model is the N scale, for which the scale is $\frac{1}{160}$.

25. The student in the photograph is holding HO and N models of the same locomotive. Which type of model is labeled A? Which type of model is labeled B?

26. Each car on a full-size passenger train is 80 ft long. What is the length in inches of a model passenger car in the HO scale? In the N scale?

27. A diesel locomotive is 60 ft long. What is the length in inches of a model of the locomotive in the N scale?

28. In the O scale, a length is $\frac{1}{48}$ the actual length. An O-scale locomotive is 1.05 ft long. How long is the actual locomotive?

A scale drawing has a scale of $\frac{1}{2}$ in. : 10 ft. Find the length on the drawing for each actual length.

29. 40 ft   **30.** 5 ft   **31.** 35 ft   **32.** $3\frac{1}{2}$ ft

GO **O**nline
Homework Video Tutor
Visit: PHSchool.com
Web Code: ade-0603

33. Open-Ended Give some examples of similar figures you find in everyday life.

The cities of Jackson, Mississippi, and Carson City, Nevada, are 1,750 mi apart.

34. Geography A map of the United States has a scale of 1 in. : 250 mi. How far apart are the cities on the map?

35. On another map, the cities are 5 in. apart. What is the scale?

36. Reasoning A note at the bottom of a map says "not to scale." Explain why that is important information.

A 2-in. length in the scale drawing at the left represents an actual length of 20 ft.

37. Architecture What is the scale of the drawing?

38. What are the actual dimensions of the bath?

39. Find the actual width of the doorways that lead into the bedroom and the bathroom.

40. Find the actual area of the bedroom.

41. Can a bed 6 ft long and 3 ft wide fit into the narrow section of the bedroom? Justify your answer.

C Challenge 🌐 **42. Architecture** The length of a room is 16 ft. The scale of a blueprint is $\frac{1}{2}$ in. : 1 ft. Find the room's length in the blueprint.

43. **Writing in Math** Explain why all squares are similar. For what other shape can you say that all figures are similar? Explain.

44. A boxcar on a freight train is 40 ft long. A model boxcar is 3 in. long. In which scale, HO, N, or O was the model built? (*Hint:* See Exercises 25–28.)

45. You are building a display shelf for your model train. You have 12 cars. Each car is 1.2 ft long. You want 1.2 in. of space between cars. How long must the shelf be?

ISAT

Test Prep

Multiple Choice

46. The scale for a drawing of a garage is 1.5 in. : 12 ft. If one side of the garage is 40 ft, how long would that side be in the drawing?
A. 5 in.   **B.** 0.45 ft   **C.** 5 ft   **D.** 320 in.

47. The scale of a dollhouse is 1 in. : 2 ft. Which is *most likely* to be the measurement of the height of the dollhouse's front door?
F. $3\frac{1}{2}$ in.   **G.** $3\frac{1}{2}$ ft   **H.** 14 in.   **J.** 14 ft

Short Response

48. To plan a rectangular mural 90 ft long and 75 ft wide, you want to make a drawing with a scale of 1 in. : 9 ft. Can you fit the drawing on a piece of paper that is $8\frac{1}{2}$ in. by 11 in.? Explain.

49. Cheryl's goal is to ride 20 miles on a bike. The distance on a map from her house to the park is 4 in. The map scale is 1 in. : 2 mi. **(a)** Will Cheryl meet her goal if she rides from her house to the park and back?   **(b)** Explain in words how you found your answer.

Mixed Review

Lesson 6-2   **Solve each proportion.**
50. $\frac{x}{5} = \frac{32}{80}$ **51.** $\frac{3}{8} = \frac{r}{15}$ **52.** $\frac{40}{w} = \frac{50}{3}$ **53.** $\frac{24}{16} = \frac{204}{c}$

Lesson 6-1 🌐 **54. Gas Mileage** A car travels 264 mi on 12 gal of gas. Find the unit rate in miles per gallon.

Lesson 5-2   **Write each fraction as a decimal.**
55. $\frac{3}{8}$ **56.** $\frac{4}{9}$ **57.** $\frac{7}{16}$ **58.** $\frac{5}{12}$

Lesson 3-3   **Find the mean (to nearest tenth), median, and mode.**
59. 12, 10, 11, 7, 9, 8, 10, 5   **60.** 4.5, 3.2, 6.3, 5.2, 5, 4.8, 6, 3.9

Dilations

Technology

For Use With Lesson 6-3

You can use geometry software to make a scale drawing, or *dilation,* of a figure. First choose the Dilate command. Then choose a center of dilation and a scale, which is also known as a *scale factor.*

ACTIVITY

Draw a triangle. Then draw a dilation with scale factor 3.

Use geometry software. Draw △*ABC*. Draw point *D* on one side of the triangle. Choose *D* as the center of a dilation with scale factor 3.

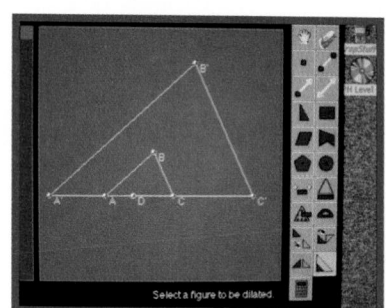

The result is an image like the one at the right. Each side of the dilation is 3 times as long as the corresponding side of △*ABC*.

If you move point *D*, the dilation also will move. If instead you move *A*, *B*, or *C*, the dilation will change as △*ABC* changes.

EXERCISES

Use geometry software to draw △*PQR*.

1. **a.** Draw a point *S outside* △*PQR*. Draw a dilation of △*PQR* with center *S* and scale factor 2.5. Label the dilation △*XYZ*. △*XYZ* is similar to △*PQR*. Angle *X* corresponds to angle *P,* angle *Y* corresponds to angle *Q,* and angle *Z* corresponds to angle *R*.
   b. Compare the location of △*XYZ* to the location of △*PQR*. Does the dilation lie inside the original triangle? Outside the triangle? Do the triangles overlap?
   c. Now move *S* to be *inside* △*PQR*. Once again, compare the locations of the two triangles. How did moving the center of dilation change the relative locations of the triangles?

2. Change the location of point *S* so that △*PQR* and △*XYZ* have the given number of points in common. Print an example of each case.
   a. 0   **b.** 1   **c.** 2   **d.** more than 2

3. With *S* inside △*PQR*, change the scale factor to 0.5. Describe the relative locations of the two triangles.

4. **a.** Keep the scale factor of the dilation at 0.5. Use the Area tool to find the area of △*PQR*. Use the Area tool again to find the area of △*XYZ*. Write a ratio to compare the areas.
   b. Move *P*, *Q*, or *R* to see how the area of △*XYZ* changes as the area of △*PQR* changes. Does the ratio of the areas change?
   c. **Reasoning** What do your results suggest about the areas of similar triangles that have a scale factor of 0.5?

Probability

6-4

1 | **Finding Probability**

ctivity

Exploring Probability

Many board games involve rolling two number cubes and then adding the numbers on the cubes. Are certain sums more likely than others? The table shows the possible rolls and their sums.

Sums of 2 Number Cubes

	1	2	3	4	5	6
1	2	3	4	■	6	7
2	3	4	5	6	■	8
3	4	5	■	7	8	9
4	5	■	7	8	9	10
5	6	7	8	9	10	■
6	■	8	9	10	11	12

1. Copy and complete the table.

2. What is the number of times each sum appears in the table?

3. Which sum appears most frequently?

4. There is a total of 36 sums in the table. Use your answer to Question 3 to write the ratio
$$\frac{\text{number of times the most frequent sum appears}}{\text{total number of sums}}.$$

Outcomes are the possible results of an action. There are six outcomes for rolling a single number cube: 1, 2, 3, 4, 5, and 6.

An **event** is any outcome or group of outcomes. The outcomes are called *favorable outcomes*. In rolling two number cubes, for example, rolling a sum of 4 is an event corresponding to the three favorable outcomes shown here.

Three outcomes result in the event *a sum of 4*.

The outcomes for rolling two number cubes are *random* and therefore *equally likely* to occur. When outcomes are equally likely, you can use a ratio to find the *probability of an event*.

probability of an event $= P(\text{event}) = \dfrac{\text{number of favorable outcomes}}{\text{number of possible outcomes}}$

What You'll Learn
- To find probability
- To find odds

. . . And Why

To solve real-world problems involving the likelihood of events

☑ **Check Skills You'll Need**

Simplify.

1. $1 - \frac{3}{8}$ **2.** $1 - \frac{17}{20}$

3. $1 - \frac{6}{11}$ **4.** $1 - \frac{1}{12}$

GO for Help
Lesson 5-3

◀)) **New Vocabulary**
- outcomes
- event
- probability
- impossible event
- certain event
- complement
- odds

1 EXAMPLE **Finding Probability**

Find P(rolling an even number) with one number cube.

$$\frac{\text{number of favorable outcomes}}{\text{number of possible outcomes}} = \frac{3}{6}$$
←— **3 even-number outcomes**
←— **6 possible outcomes**

$$P(\text{rolling an even number}) = \frac{3}{6}, \text{ or } \frac{1}{2}.$$

✓ Quick Check

1. Find each probability for one roll of a number cube.

    a. P(odd number)   **b.** $P(2)$ **c.** P(5 or 6)

Test-Taking Tip

On a multiple-choice test item, you can eliminate any answer choice showing a probability greater than 1 because a probability cannot be greater than 1.

All probabilities range from 0 to 1.

Probability

←———— less likely   more likely ————→

0   0.5   1

Impossible event   Equally likely   **Certain event**
                      as unlikely

The **complement** of an event is the opposite of that event. The events *no rain* and *rain* are complements of each other. The probability of an event plus the probability of its complement always equals 1.

2 EXAMPLE **Real-World** 🌐 **Problem Solving**

Vital Statistics In the United States, the probability that a child is a twin is 2 in 90, or $\frac{2}{90}$. Find P(not a twin).

$P(\text{twin}) + P(\text{not a twin}) = 1$ **Write an equation.**

$\frac{2}{90} + P(\text{not a twin}) = 1$ **Substitute.**

$\frac{2}{90} - \frac{2}{90} + P(\text{not a twin}) = 1 - \frac{2}{90}$ **Subtract $\frac{2}{90}$ from each side.**

$P(\text{not a twin}) = \frac{88}{90} = \frac{44}{45}$ **Simplify.**

The probability that a child is not a twin is $\frac{44}{45}$.

✓ Quick Check

2. a. When you roll a number cube, what is P(not 2)?
    b. Reasoning What is the complement of an impossible event?

You can think of probability as a ratio of $\frac{part}{whole}$. You can also use a $\frac{part}{part}$ ratio, called **odds,** to describe the likelihood of an event.

$$\text{odds in favor of an event} = \frac{\text{number of } favorable \text{ outcomes}}{\text{number of } unfavorable \text{ outcomes}}$$

$$\text{odds against an event} = \frac{\text{number of } unfavorable \text{ outcomes}}{\text{number of } favorable \text{ outcomes}}$$

3 **EXAMPLE** **Real-World** **Problem Solving**

Coins The reverse sides of five quarters are shown below. If you select one of these quarters at random, what are the odds in favor of it showing at least one human figure on its reverse side?

odds in favor $= \frac{3}{2}$ ← **3 have a human figure.**
                   ← **2 do not.**

The odds are 3 : 2, or 3 to 2, in favor.

> **Vocabulary Tip**
>
> Read odds of 3 : 2 as "three to two."

✅ Quick Check

3. You choose a quarter at random from the five above.
   a. What are the odds in favor of it showing a horse?
   b. What are the odds against it showing a horse?
   c. Consider the event that the quarter shows the outline of a state.
      i. What are the odds in favor of the event?
      ii. What are the odds against the event?

EXERCISES

For more exercises, see *Extra Skill and Word Problem Practice*.

Practice and Problem Solving

A Practice by Example

Examples 1 and 2
(page 310)

for Help

Find each probability for one roll of a number cube.

1. $P(3)$ **2.** $P(3 \text{ or } 4)$ **3.** $P(1, 2, \text{ or } 3)$

4. $P(\text{not } 2, 3, \text{ or } 6)$ **5.** $P(\text{not } 1, 3, 4, \text{ or } 5)$ **6.** $P(\text{less than } 4)$

Find each probability for selecting a letter at random from the word ARKANSAS.

7. $P(A)$ **8.** $P(R)$ **9.** $P(S)$

10. $P(K \text{ or } N)$ **11.** $P(\text{vowel})$ **12.** $P(\text{consonant})$

13. A box of crayons contains one crayon of each of the following colors: red, orange, yellow, green, blue, purple, black, white, pink.
 a. What is the probability of NOT choosing a 6-letter color?
 b. What is the complement of choosing green?

Example 3
(page 311)

14. Suppose you choose a letter at random from the word ARITHMETIC. What are the odds in favor of selecting a vowel? What are the odds against selecting a vowel?

A teacher chooses a student at random from a class of 10 boys and 15 girls. Find the odds in favor of, and the odds against, each event.

15. choosing a girl   **16.** choosing a boy

B Apply Your Skills

Homework Video Tutor
Visit: PHSchool.com
Web Code: ade-0604

Find each probability for one roll of a number cube.

17. $P(7)$ **18.** $P(\text{less than } 3)$ **19.** $P(\text{greater than } 2)$

Find each probability for choosing a letter at random from the word MATHEMATICS.

20. $P(K)$ **21.** $P(M, A, \text{ or } T)$ **22.** $P(\text{vowel})$ **23.** $P(\text{consonant})$

Lola's Socks

Color	Number of Socks
Pink	6
White	4
Green	3
Purple	2

24. Reasoning The table at the left describes the loose socks in Lola's drawer. One morning Lola pulls a sock from the drawer without looking. It is white. She pulls out another sock without looking. Find the probability that it also is white.

You have a set of 36 flash cards numbered from 1 to 36. A card is chosen at random. Find the odds in favor of, and the odds against, each selection.

25. even number   **26.** greater than 20   **27.** multiple of 3

28. prime number   **29.** multiple of 2 *or* 3   **30.** multiple of 2 *and* 3

31. It has only one digit.   **32.** It has more than one digit.

C Challenge

33. Open-Ended Give an example of an event for which the probability equals 1. Justify your answer.

34. Error Analysis Your friend is tossing a coin. He says that heads and tails are equally likely outcomes, so the probability of getting heads is $\frac{50}{50}$. Explain your friend's error.

35. <u>Writing in Math</u> Explain how you can use odds to find probability. Include an example.

Test Prep

Multiple Choice

36. You draw a name at random from a hat holding the names of 6 girls and 8 boys. What are the odds in favor of choosing a boy?
A. 3 to 4   **B.** 4 to 3   **C.** 3 to 7   **D.** 4 to 7

37. Refer to the spinner. What is the probability of the complement of *stopping on either red or yellow*?
F. $\frac{1}{8}$ **G.** $\frac{1}{4}$ **H.** $\frac{3}{8}$ **J.** $\frac{3}{4}$

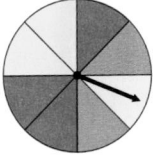

38. Suppose you roll a number cube. Which event has the same probability as (not 1, 2, or 3)?
A. 3 or 4   **B.** less than 5   **C.** not odd   **D.** more than 4

Short Response

39. a. Can a probability be greater than 1?
b. Explain your answer.

Mixed Review

Lesson 6-3

The scale of a map is 3 in. : 20 mi. Find the actual distance for each map distance.

40. 6 in.   **41.** 1 in.   **42.** 4.2 in.   **43.** $10\frac{1}{2}$ in.

Lesson 5-2

Write each decimal as a fraction or mixed number in simplest form.

44. 0.25   **45.** $0.\overline{6}$ **46.** 0.8125   **47.** 5.15

Lesson 2-6 🌐 **48. Ticket Sales** Students paid $855 for tickets to a dance. Each ticket cost $5. Write and solve an equation to find the number of tickets the students purchased.

✓ Checkpoint Quiz 1   Lessons 6-1 through 6-4

Write each phrase as a unit rate.

1. 20 mi in 5 h   **2.** 42 gal in 7 min   **3.** a fall of 144 ft in 3 s

4. Geometry The figures (left) are similar. Find the missing length.

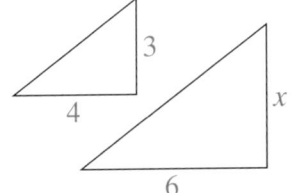

5. A person blinks 112 times in 4 min. At that rate, how many times does the person blink in 1.5 min?

6. Suppose you roll a number cube. What is $P(2 \text{ or } 3)$?

6-5 Fractions, Decimals, and Percents

 Assessment Framework

6.8.03 Recognize, translate between, and apply multiple representations of rational numbers (decimals, fractions, mixed numbers, percents, and roots).

6.8.17 Read, write, recognize, model, and interpret percents, including those less than 1% and greater than 100%.

✓ Check Skills You'll Need

Write each fraction as a decimal.

1. $\frac{5}{8}$ **2.** $\frac{9}{20}$ **3.** $\frac{3}{4}$

4. $\frac{5}{6}$ **5.** $\frac{2}{3}$ **6.** $\frac{8}{11}$

GO for Help
Lesson 5-2

◄)) New Vocabulary
• percent

---

1 Writing Percents as Fractions and Decimals

A **percent** is a ratio that compares a number to 100. Therefore, you can write a percent as a fraction with a denominator of 100.

1 EXAMPLE Writing a Percent as a Fraction

Write each percent as a fraction or a mixed number.

a. 5%

$\frac{5}{100}$ ← Write as a fraction with a denominator of 100. → $\frac{125}{100}$ **b. 125%**

$\frac{1}{20}$ ← Simplify. → $\frac{5}{4}$

Write as a mixed number. → $1\frac{1}{4}$

✓ Quick Check

1. Write each percent as a fraction or mixed number in simplest form.

   a. 58%   **b.** 72%   **c.** 144%

To write a percent as a decimal, write the percent as a fraction with a denominator of 100. Then divide to convert the fraction to a decimal.

2 EXAMPLE Real-World Problem Solving

Households The total number of U.S. households increased by 2.2%. Write 2.2% as a decimal.

$2.2\% = \frac{2.2}{100}$ Write as a fraction with a denominator of 100.

$= 002.2$ Divide by moving the decimal point left two places. You may need to write one or more zeros.

$= 0.022$

✓ Quick Check

2. a. Write 62.5% as a decimal.
   b. Biology About 45% of the people in the United States have type O blood. Write this percent as a decimal and as a fraction in simplest form.

To write a decimal as a percent, rewrite the decimal as a fraction with a denominator of 100. Then write the fraction as a percent.

To write a fraction as a percent, divide to write as a decimal first.

GO for Help

For a guide to writing decimals as fractions, see Lesson 5-2.

3 EXAMPLE **Writing a Number as a Percent**

Write each number as a percent.

a. 0.333

$0.333 = \frac{333}{1,000}$

$= \frac{33.3}{100}$

$= 33.3\%$

b. $\frac{7}{80}$

$\frac{7}{80} = 0.0875$

$= 0.0875$

$= 8.75\%$

✓ Quick Check

3. Write each number as a percent.

  a. 0.4   **b.** $\frac{46}{200}$ **c.** 1.75

2 Ordering Rational Numbers

To compare and order fractions, decimals, and percents, write each fraction or percent as a decimal. Then compare each decimal and order the set of numbers.

4 EXAMPLE **Ordering Rational Numbers**

Four students surveyed their English classes asking, "Do you have a pet in your home?" They reported the results as 0.35, $\frac{2}{5}$, 30%, and 53%. Order the results from least to greatest.

$\frac{2}{5} = 0.40$

$30\% = 0.30$ **Write each fraction or percent as a decimal.**

$53\% = 0.53$

Since $0.30 < 0.35 < 0.40 < 0.53$, the numbers in order from least to greatest are $30\% < 0.35 < \frac{2}{5} < 53\%$.

✓ Quick Check

4. Order each set of numbers from least to greatest.

  a. $\frac{1}{4}, 0.26, 31\%, \frac{2}{7}$ **b.** $88\%, 91\%, \frac{5}{6}, 0.71$ **c.** $1.34, 129\%, 1\frac{1}{5}, 1.41$

Real-World Connection

There are about 55 million dogs and 61 million cats in the United States.

EXERCISES

For more exercises, see *Extra Skill and Word Problem Practice.*

Practice and Problem Solving

A Practice by Example

Example 1
(page 314)

GO for Help

Example 2
(page 314)

Write each percent as a fraction or mixed number in simplest form.

1. 40%　　**2.** 28%　　**3.** 39%　　**4.** 55%　　**5.** 20%

6. 6%　　**7.** 98%　　**8.** 315%　　**9.** 220%　　**10.** 102%

Write each percent as a decimal.

11. 36%　　**12.** 4.4%　　**13.** 1%　　**14.** 6.3%　　**15.** 133%

16. 79.7%　　**17.** 350%　　**18.** 52%　　**19.** 31.4%　　**20.** 0.03%

21. Education In 2000, women made up 40% of freshmen studying computer science at a certain university. Write this percent as a decimal and as a fraction in simplest form.

Example 3
(page 315)

Write each number as a percent.

22. 1.68　　**23.** 0.36　　**24.** 0.70　　**25.** 0.002　　**26.** 2.59

27. $\frac{23}{100}$　　**28.** $\frac{1}{4}$　　**29.** $\frac{7}{20}$　　**30.** $\frac{2}{9}$　　**31.** $\frac{7}{18}$

32. Populations In the United States, about one person in eight lives in California. To the nearest percent, what percent of people in the United States live in California?

Example 4
(page 315)

Order each set of numbers from least to greatest.

33. $\frac{3}{4}, 0.72, 69\%, 0.63$　　**34.** $0.09, 1\%, 11\%, \frac{1}{8}$　　**35.** $3\frac{1}{10}, 3.23, 305\%, 3\frac{2}{15}$

Compare. Use >, <, or = to complete each statement.

36. 0.05% ■ 50%　　**37.** $\frac{7}{12}$ ■ 60%　　**38.** $\frac{140}{130}$ ■ 104%

B Apply Your Skills

Write each fraction as a percent. Round to the nearest tenth of a percent where necessary.

39. $\frac{8}{13}$　　**40.** $\frac{5}{6}$　　**41.** $\frac{111}{100}$　　**42.** $\frac{9}{2}$　　**43.** $\frac{12}{5}$

Estimation About what percent of each flag is red?

44.

Tennessee

45.

North Carolina

GO Online
Homework Video Tutor
Visit: PHSchool.com
Web Code: ade-0605

Probability Find each probability for one roll of a number cube. Write the probability as a percent. Round to the nearest tenth of a percent where necessary.

46. $P(6)$ **47.** $P(\text{even})$ **48.** $P(1 \text{ or } 2)$ **49.** $P(\text{not } 1)$

Copy and complete the table.

	Fraction	Decimal	Percent
50.	$\frac{4}{5}$	■	■
51.	■	0.10	■
52.	■	0.5	■
53.	$\frac{3}{4}$	■	■
54.	■	■	67%
55.	■	■	25%

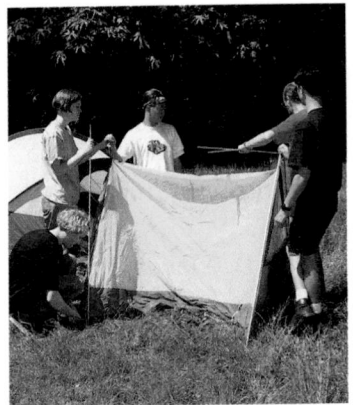

Real-World Connection

Each year, about 51 million Americans go camping.

Reasoning For Exercises 56–59, does each sentence make sense? Explain.

56. About 18% of Americans go camping. That means about 82% do not go camping.

57. A student correctly answered 200% of the items on a test.

58. Today a runner ran 150% of the distance she ran yesterday.

59. On a test, a student missed 12 items and correctly answered 96% of all items.

Order each set of numbers from least to greatest.

60. $0.63, -0.72, 69\%, -\frac{3}{4}, 78\%$ **61.** $11\%, -1\%, \frac{1}{8}, -0.09, 0.093$

62. $3\frac{1}{10}, -3.23, 305\%, -3\frac{2}{15}, 0.399$ **63.** $10.99, -1,015\%, 120\%, 11\frac{5}{8}, -11.15$

64. Maps A map has a scale of 0.01%. Write the scale as a fraction.

65. Jeanette answered 32 questions correctly on a 45-question test. The passing grade was 70%. Did Jeanette pass? Justify your answer.

66. Scale Drawings A scale drawing has a scale of 1 : 12. Write the scale as a percent.

67. Writing in Math Explain how to write a decimal as a percent. Give examples.

68. a. Test Grades On his last math assignment, Kyle answered 5% of the questions incorrectly, or 1 question. How many questions did Kyle answer correctly?

   b. On the same test, Diana answered 16 questions correctly. What percent of the questions did she not answer correctly?

C Challenge

69. Open-Ended Use a percent to describe an everyday event. Then write the percent as a fraction and as a decimal.

70. Reasoning Explain why 0.25 is different from 0.25%.

A crowd filled the 8,000 seats in a stadium. There were 1,400 children and 4,800 men present. Write a ratio and a percent to describe how many seats were filled by each group.

71. men　　　　　　**72.** children　　　　　　**73.** women

ISAT logo on the test prep banner

Test Prep

74. What is 0.2% written as a decimal?
   A. 0.002　　　　**B.** 0.2　　　　**C.** 2　　　　**D.** 20

75. If 12% of an iceberg is above water, what fraction is in the water?
   F. $\frac{3}{25}$　　　**G.** $\frac{12}{88}$　　　**H.** $\frac{22}{25}$　　　**J.** $7\frac{1}{3}$

76. In a basketball free-throw contest, four players take the same number of free throws. Player A makes 33 of 40 free throws. Player B makes $\frac{3}{4}$ of his free throws, Player C makes 85% of her free throws, and Player D makes $\frac{4}{5}$ of his free throws. Which player makes the greatest number of free throws?
   A. Player A　　**B.** Player B　　**C.** Player C　　**D.** Player D

Short Response

77. A baseball player's batting average is the ratio of the number of hits to the number of times at bat.
   a. If Julienne's batting average is .392, what percent of her times at bat are hits?
   b. For part (a), explain your answer.

78. A weather reporter predicts that at least 20% of the 11 counties in her area will get rain this weekend.
   a. If two counties get rain, is the reporter's prediction correct?
   b. Explain your answer.

Mixed Review

GO for Help

Lesson 6-4

Find each probability for choosing a letter at random from the word PROBABLE.

79. $P(\text{B})$　　**80.** $P(\text{vowel})$　　**81.** $P(\text{R})$　　**82.** $P(\text{not L or R})$

Lesson 3-6

Solve each equation.

83. $0.85x = 39.95$　　　　　　**84.** $4.8y = -0.84$

85. $100 = \frac{a}{13.2}$　　　　　　**86.** $\frac{b}{-25} = 1.8$

Lesson 1-9　**87. Test Scores** The average of three test scores is 85. One test score is 90. Another is 72. What is the third?

318 Chapter 6 Ratios, Proportions, and Percents

Proportions and Percents

Assessment Framework

1 Finding Part of a Whole

6.8.18 Solve number sentences and problems involving fractions, decimals, and percents.

You can solve a percent problem by writing and solving a proportion.

A model can help you write a proportion. This model shows that 30 is 75% of 40.

Draw a model. Divide your model into rectangles that are helpful to you.

Write a proportion.

$\frac{75}{100} = \frac{30}{40}$

✓ Check Skills You'll Need

Solve each proportion.

1. $\frac{25}{100} = \frac{x}{28}$

2. $\frac{98.9}{x} = \frac{43}{100}$

3. $\frac{52}{100} = \frac{13}{x}$

4. $\frac{x}{100} = \frac{27}{150}$

GO for Help
to Lesson 6-2

1 EXAMPLE Finding Part of a Whole

Find 65% of 245.

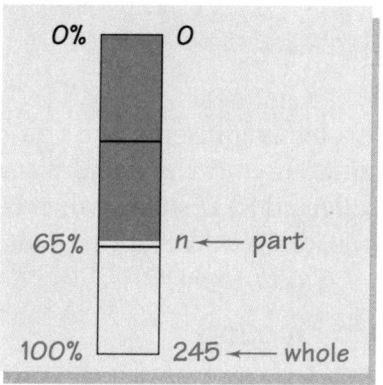

$\frac{65}{100} = \frac{n}{245}$ **Write a proportion.**

$65(245) = 100n$ **Write cross products.**

$\frac{65(245)}{100} = \frac{100n}{100}$ **Divide each side by 100.**

$159.25 = n$ **Simplify.**

65% of 245 is 159.25.

✓ Quick Check

1. Draw a model and write a proportion. Then solve.

a. 25% of 124 is ■. **b.** 43% of 230 is ■. **c.** 12.5% of 80 is ■.

Finding a Percent

What percent of 60 is 52? Round to the nearest tenth of a percent.

$$\frac{n}{100} = \frac{52}{60}$$ Write a proportion.

$$60n = 100(52)$$ Write cross products.

$$\frac{60n}{60} = \frac{100(52)}{60}$$ Divide each side by 60.

$$n = 86.\overline{6}$$ Simplify.

$$\approx 86.7$$ Round.

52 is approximately 86.7% of 60.

✓ Quick Check

2. Round to the nearest tenth.

   a. What percent of 250 is 138?   **b.** 14 is what percent of 15?

---

2 Finding a Whole Amount

Sometimes you know the percent that a part represents, and you want to find the whole amount. For example, your class fundraising committee might announce, "We've collected $207 so far, which is 46% of our goal!" You can use a proportion to calculate the goal.

3 EXAMPLE **Finding the Whole Amount**

207 is 46% of what number?

$$\frac{46}{100} = \frac{207}{n}$$ Write a proportion.

$$46n = 100(207)$$ Write cross products.

$$\frac{46n}{46} = \frac{100(207)}{46}$$ Divide each side by 46.

$$n = 450$$ Simplify.

207 is 46% of 450.

3. Round to the nearest tenth.

  a. 19 is 75% of what number?   **b.** 310 is 99% of what number?

4 EXAMPLE <u>Real-World</u> 🌐 **Problem Solving**

Theaters In 2000, the number of drive-in movie screens in the United States was about 78% of the number in 1990. About how many drive-in screens were there in 1990?

Drive-In Movies

Year	Number of Screens
1990	
1995	847
2000	717

SOURCE: Motion Picture Association of America

$\frac{78}{100} = \frac{717}{n}$ **Write a proportion.**

$78n = 100(717)$ **Write cross products.**

$\frac{78n}{78} = \frac{100(717)}{78}$ **Divide each side by 78.**

$n \approx 919$ **Round to the nearest whole number.**

There were about 919 drive-in screens in 1990.

Check Is the answer reasonable? The original problem says that the number of screens in 2000 was 78% of the number in 1990. Check by estimating:

78% of 919 ≈ 0.8 × 900 = 720, which is close to 717, the number for 2000. So the answer is reasonable.

✓ **Quick Check**

4. Refer to the table in Example 4. In 2000, the number of drive-in movie screens was about 20.1% of the number in 1980. Find the number of drive-in screens in 1980.

Here is a summary of how to use proportions to solve percent problems.

Key Concepts	Percents and Proportions	
Finding the Percent	**Finding the Part**	**Finding the Whole**
What percent of 40 is 6?	What number is 15% of 40?	6 is 15% of what number?
$\frac{n}{100} = \frac{6}{40} \leftarrow \text{part} \atop \leftarrow \text{whole}$	$\frac{15}{100} = \frac{n}{40} \leftarrow \text{part} \atop \leftarrow \text{whole}$	$\frac{15}{100} = \frac{6}{n} \leftarrow \text{part} \atop \leftarrow \text{whole}$

EXERCISES

For more exercises, see *Extra Skill and Word Problem Practice*.

Practice and Problem Solving

A Practice by Example

Example 1
(page 319)

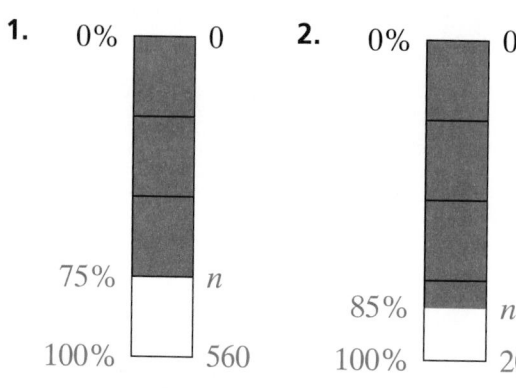

GO for Help

Example 2
(page 320)

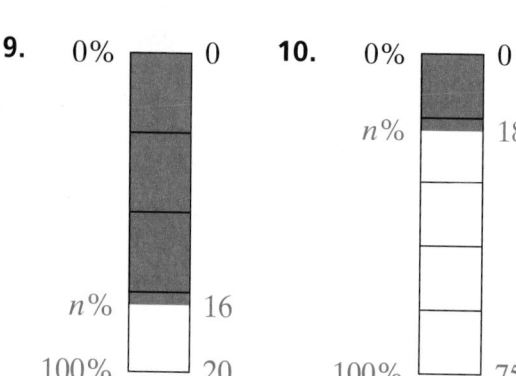

Example 3
(page 320)

Example 4
(page 321)

B Apply Your Skills

GO **Online**
Homework Video Tutor

Visit: PHSchool.com
Web Code: ade-0606

For Exercises 1–22, write and solve a proportion. Where necessary, round to the nearest tenth.

3. 80% of 20 is ■.

4. 40% of 60 is ■.

5. 53% of 70 is ■.

6. 18% of 150 is ■.

7. 16% of 75 is ■.

8. 92% of 625 is ■.

11. ■% of 40 is 30.

12. ■% of 20 is 4.

13. ■% of 25 is 13.

14. 75 is ■% of 250.

15. ■% of 92 is 17.

16. ■% of 80 is 14.

17. 8 is 25% of ■.   **18.** 14 is 35% of ■.   **19.** 31 is 49% of ■.

20. 45 is 93% of ■.   **21.** 1 is 2% of ■.   **22.** 6 is 98% of ■.

23. Population In 1950, the population of Alaska was about 128,535. That was about 20.5% of the population of Alaska in the year 2000. About how many people lived in Alaska in the year 2000?

24. Banking At the beginning of the summer Jeri had $480 in her savings account. That was only 15% of the amount in her savings account at the end of the summer. How much money did Jeri have in her account at the end of the summer?

Write and solve a proportion. Where necessary, round to the nearest whole amount.

25. Find 300% of 50.

26. 250% of ■ is 50.

27. Find 60% of 15.

28. 40,571 is ■% of 76,550.

29. 35% of ■ is 52.5.

30. 121.8 is ■% of 105.

31. Purchasing A bicycle cost $250 last year. The same bike costs $200 this year. What percent of last year's cost is this year's cost?

State	Sales Tax
Georgia	4%
Kansas	5.3%
Pennsylvania	6%
South Carolina	5%
Texas	6.25%

32. Sales Tax The table shows sales tax rates for different states. For each state, find the following amount on a $15,000 car.
   a. the amount of sales tax   **b.** the car's total cost

33. Profit You invested some money and made a profit of $55. Your profit was 11% of your investment. How much did you invest?

34. Nineteen members, or 38%, of the ski club are going on a ski trip. Find the total number of members in the club.

35. Error Analysis Your class has 26 students, which represents 5% of your school's enrollment. Your friend uses the proportion $\frac{5}{100} = \frac{n}{26}$ to find the number of students in your school. Explain your friend's error.

C Challenge   **Write and solve a proportion. Where necessary, round to the nearest tenth.**

36. Find $33\frac{1}{3}\%$ of 54.

37. $12\frac{1}{2}\%$ of ■ is 6.

38. ■% of 36,500 is 912.5.

39. What is $\frac{5}{4}\%$ of 145?

40. Open-Ended Write and solve a word problem involving percents.

41. Writing in Math At Pics, all posters are 30% off. At Pacs, all posters are marked $\frac{1}{3}$ off. Which is the greater discount rate? Explain.

42. Reasoning Do $a\%$ of b and $b\%$ of a represent the same amount? Justify your answer.

ISAT
Test Prep

Gridded Response

43. 42 is 60% of what number?

44. 1.25 is what percent of 25?

45. What number is 30% of 75?

46. A student pole-vaulted 5 ft yesterday. Today she vaulted 20% higher. How many feet higher did she vault today?

Mixed Review

Lesson 6-5   **Write each number as a percent.**

47. 0.08   **48.** 0.523   **49.** $\frac{7}{12}$ **50.** 4.56

Lesson 4-9   **Order from least to greatest.**

51. $10^3, 10^{-2}, 10^{-1}, 10^0$

52. $2.3 \times 10^4, 2.03 \times 10^5, 2.03 \times 10^4, 2.4 \times 10^3$

Lesson 1-1   **53. Family** Peter has four cousins. Paul has c cousins fewer than Peter. Write an expression for the number of Paul's cousins.

6-7 Percents and Equations

IL Assessment Framework

6.8.18 Solve number sentences and problems involving fractions, decimals, and percents.

Check Skills You'll Need

Write each percent as a decimal.

1. 48%   **2.** 5%

3. 23.8%   **4.** 72.25%

5. 136%   **6.** 178.5%

for Help
Lesson 6-5

New Vocabulary
• commission

Video Tutor Help
Visit: PHSchool.com
Web Code: ada-0775

---

1 Writing and Solving Percent Equations

You can solve a percent problem by writing and solving an equation. When you use a percent in an equation, write it as a decimal.

Key Concepts	Percent Equations	
Finding the Percent	**Finding the Part**	**Finding the Whole**
What percent of 40 is 6?	What is 15% of 40?	6 is 15% of what?
$n \cdot 40 = 6$	$n = 0.15 \cdot 40$	$6 = 0.15 \cdot n$

1 EXAMPLE Solving a Percent Equation

What is 85% of 62?

$n = 0.85 \cdot 62$ Write an equation. Write the percent as a decimal.
$n = 52.7$ Simplify.

85% of 62 is 52.7.

Quick Check

1. Write and solve an equation.

   a. 0.96 is what percent of 10?   **b.** 19.2 is 32% of what?

You can also write and solve equations having percents greater than 100%.

2 EXAMPLE Percents Greater Than 100%

What percent of 48 is 54?

$n \cdot 48 = 54$ Write an equation.
$\dfrac{48n}{48} = \dfrac{54}{48}$ Divide each side by 48.
$n = 1.125$ Simplify.
$= 112.5\%$ Change the decimal to a percent.

54 is 112.5% of 48.

Quick Check

2. Write and solve an equation.

   a. What is 145.5% of 20?   **b.** 380 is 125% of what number?

GO Online

2 Using Equations to Solve Percent Problems

Some sales jobs pay an amount based on how much you sell. This amount is called a **commission.**

3 EXAMPLE   Real-World Problem Solving

Gridded Response A real-estate agent makes a 4.5% commission on property she sells. To the nearest dollar, how much commission does she make on the sale of a house for $132,500?

Words   amount of commission   is   4.5%   of $132,500

Let c = amount of commission.

Equation c =   0.045 · 132,500

$$c = 0.045 \cdot 132{,}500$$
$$= 5{,}962.50$$

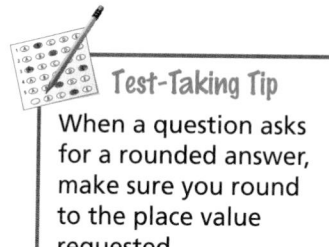

To the nearest dollar, the agent's commission is $5963.

> **Test-Taking Tip**
>
> When a question asks for a rounded answer, make sure you round to the place value requested.

✓ Quick Check

3. **Royalties** A singer receives a 5% royalty on each CD sale. To the nearest cent, find his royalty for a CD that sells for $16.99.

4 EXAMPLE   Real-World Problem Solving

Surveys The graph shows the results of a survey. There were 1,023 people who answered yes. How many people were surveyed?

Words   1,023   is   93%   of   number surveyed

Let n = number surveyed.

Equation   1,023   =   0.93   · n

$$0.93n = 1{,}023$$
$$\frac{0.93n}{0.93} = \frac{1{,}023}{0.93}$$
$$n = 1{,}100$$

1,100 people were surveyed.

Responses to the question "Do you feel good about your life overall?"

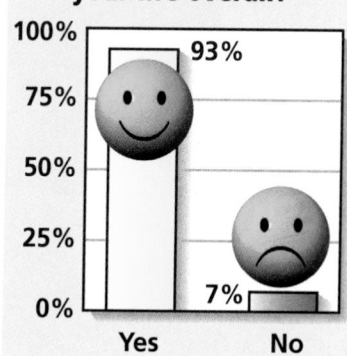

✓ Quick Check

4. In a survey, 952 people, or 68%, preferred smooth peanut butter to chunky. How many people were surveyed?

EXERCISES

For more exercises, see *Extra Skill and Word Problem Practice.*

Practice and Problem Solving

A Practice by Example

Example 1
(page 324)

Example 2
(page 324)

Example 3
(page 325)

Example 4
(page 325)

Write an equation and solve.

1. Find 30% of 30.

2. What percent of 40 is 25?

3. 120 is 15% of what number?

4. What percent of 20 is 11?

5. Find 56% of 75.

6. 85% of z is 106,250. What is z?

7. What percent of 25 is 17?

8. Find 75% of 840.

9. Find 150% of 90.

10. 300% of a is 297. What is a?

11. What percent of 4 is 9?

12. Find 500% of 12.

13. What percent of 150 is 96?

14. 3.5% of d is 0.105. What is d?

15. What percent of 1 is 4.7?

16. Find 15% of 150.

17. Royalties Julius writes novels and receives 12% of the price for each book sold. To the nearest cent, find the royalty Julius receives for a book price of $7.99.

18. Sports An agent makes 16% commission on an athlete's signing bonus. If the bonus is $26,000, what is the agent's commission?

For Exercises 19 and 20, the table gives information about videocassette recorders (VCRs) in the United States.

19. The number of households with VCRs in 1995 was about 93% of the number with VCRs in 1998. About how many households had VCRs in 1998?

20. The number of households with VCRs in 1990 was about 87.5% of the number with VCRs in 1993. About how many households had VCRs in 1993?

Households With VCRs

Year	Households (millions)
1980	1
1985	18
1990	63
1995	77
1998	■

SOURCE: Statistical Abstract of the United States. Go to **www.PHSchool.com** for a data update. Web Code: adg-9041

B Apply Your Skills

Write and solve an equation. Where necessary, round to the nearest tenth or tenth of a percent.

21. Find 225% of 3.6.

22. What percent of 45 is 24?

23. Find 5.5% of 44.

24. 24% of w is 3.6. What is w?

25. What percent of 8 is 20?

26. 9.2% of b is 27.6. What is b?

27. 135% of t is 63. What is t?

28. What is 264% of 12?

29. Commission A salesperson receives 5.4% commission. On one sale, she received $6.48. What was the amount of the sale?

30. Reasoning Describe a situation in which you would use a percent greater than 100%.

Mental Math Use mental math.

31. What percent of 60 is 30?

32. 100% of *t* is 100. What is *t*?

33. Find 5% of 10.

34. What percent of 55 is 11?

35. 50% of *g* is 24. What is *g*?

36. Find 15% of 12.

 Challenge

For Exercises 37 and 38, use the table on page 326. Is each statement true or false? Explain.

37. **Reasoning** The number of households with VCRs in 1985 was less than 10% of the number of households with VCRs in 1990.

38. The number of households with VCRs in 1985 was more than 1,000% of the number in 1980.

39. Polly got a 20% discount on a computer that regularly cost *x* dollars. She paid sales tax of 5%. Later she sold the computer for 70% of what she paid for it. Write an expression for the amount Polly received for the computer.

Writing in Math

Which approach do you prefer to use in solving percent problems—the approach you learned in this lesson, or the one you learned in Lesson 6-6? Explain.

ISAT

Test Prep

Multiple Choice

40. About what percent of 92 is 63?
 A. 63%   **B.** 68%   **C.** 92%   **D.** 146%

41. Seventy students voted for Tim, 25% voted for Li, and the other 40% voted for Mae. How many students voted in the election?
 F. 200   **G.** 135   **H.** 100   **J.** 70

42. What is 158% of 35?
 A. 12.64   **B.** 20.3   **C.** 42.6   **D.** 55.3

Short Response

43. Chan's team won 70% of the 20 games it played. Latisha's team played 15 games and won 80% of them.
 a. Whose team won the greater number of games?
 b. For part (a), explain your answer.

Mixed Review

 for Help

Lesson 6-6

Write a proportion. Then solve.

44. ■% of 360 is 45.   **45.** 35% of 60 is ■.   **46.** 45 is 1.5% of ■.

Lesson 5-8

47. **Creative Writing** Ernest started writing a story on a Friday. He worked on the story for $\frac{1}{2}$ h each day. He took 7 h to finish it. On what day did Ernest finish his story?

Lesson 4-7

Simplify each expression.

48. $10^2 \cdot 10^4$ **49.** $9y^4 \cdot y^5$ **50.** $(x^3)^7$

Estimating With Percents

When you want to estimate the solution to a percent problem, you often want to convert the percents to decimals or fractions. For example, knowing that 78% is a little more than $\frac{3}{4}$ and a little less than 0.8 can help you choose compatible numbers.

ACTIVITY

About 8% of people are left-handed. 8% is almost 10%, or $\frac{1}{10}$, or 0.1, and 8% is also about $\frac{1}{12}$. Which estimate for 8% would you use in each situation?

a. In a group of 72 people, about how many would you expect to be left-handed?

The fraction $\frac{1}{8}$ is compatible with 72, so use 8% $\approx \frac{1}{12}$.

$$\frac{1}{12} \cdot 72 = 6$$

About 6 people in the group would be left-handed.

b. About 55,000 people attended a football game. About how many of them would you expect to be left-handed?

The decimal 0.1 allows you to use mental math, so use 8% $\approx$ 0.1.

$0.1 \cdot 55{,}000 = 5{,}500$ **Move the decimal point one place.**

About 5,500 people at the football game would be left-handed.

c. Twenty people are riding an elevator. About how many of them would you expect to be left-handed?

The fraction $\frac{1}{10}$ is compatible with 20, so use 8% $\approx \frac{1}{10}$.

$$\frac{1}{10} \cdot 20 = 2$$

About 2 people riding the elevator would be left-handed.

EXERCISES

Without solving, choose a compatible number for the percent in each problem. Justify your choice.

1. 23% of 64   **2.** 11% of 350   **3.** 4% of 80   **4.** 67% of 120

Use compatible numbers to solve each problem.

5. 652 students attend Tippitt Middle School. 49% live less than three miles from school. About how many students is this?

6. Mr. Ross's bill for lunch at a restaurant was $22.60. He wants to leave a 15% to 20% tip. Should he leave $2.75, $3.25, or $4? Explain your reasoning.

Percent of Change

 Finding Percent of Increase

6.8.18 Solve number sentences and problems involving fractions, decimals, and percents.

Activity

Exploring Percent of Change

1. Find the change in population from 1980 to 1990 for each state.

2. Which state had the greater change in population?

3. Write the ratio $\frac{\text{change in population}}{\text{1980 population}}$ for each state. Then write each ratio as a percent.

4. Compare the two percents. Which state had the greater population change in terms of percent?

Populations of Two States

State	1980	1990
California	23,668,000	29,786,000
Nevada	800,000	1,202,000

✓ **Check Skills You'll Need**

Write each decimal as a percent.

1. 0.46   **2.** 2.47

3. 0.03   **4.** 5.236

GO for Help
Lesson 6-5

◀)) **New Vocabulary**
• percent of change

The percent a quantity increases or decreases from its original amount is the **percent of change.**

$$\text{percent of change} = \frac{\text{amount of change}}{\text{original amount}}$$

1 EXAMPLE   Finding Percent of Increase

Find the percent of increase from 4 to 7.5.

amount of increase = $7.5 - 4 = 3.5$

percent of increase = $\frac{\text{amount of increase}}{\text{original amount}}$

$= \frac{3.5}{4}$

$= 0.875 = 87.5\%$

The percent of increase from 4 to 7.5 is 87.5%.

✓ Quick Check

1. Find each percent of increase.

a. from 100 to 114   **b.** from 2.0 to 3.2   **c.** from 4,000 to 8,500

2 EXAMPLE   Real-World 🌐 Problem Solving

Waste Management
The annual production of municipal solid waste in the United States has more than doubled since 1960. Find the percent of increase from 1960 to 1990.

Municipal Solid Waste

88 million tons — 1960
121 million tons — 1970
152 million tons — 1980
205 million tons — 1990
232 million tons — 2000

SOURCE: Environmental Protection Agency.
Go to **www.PHSchool.com** for a data update.
Web Code: adg-9041

amount of increase
$= 205 - 88 = 117$

percent of increase
$= \dfrac{\text{amount of increase}}{\text{original amount}}$

$= \dfrac{117}{88}$

$= 1.32\overline{54} \approx 133\%$

The percent of increase from 1960 to 1990 was about 133%.

☑ **Quick Check**

2. **Waste Management** Find the percent of increase in solid-waste production from 1970 to 1980. Round to the nearest percent.

---

2   **Finding Percent of Decrease**

You also can find percent of decrease.

3 EXAMPLE   **Finding Percent of Decrease**

Find the percent of decrease from 1,500 to 1,416.

amount of decrease $= 1{,}500 - 1{,}416 = 84$

percent of decrease $= \dfrac{\text{amount of decrease}}{\text{original amount}}$

$= \dfrac{84}{1{,}500}$

$= 0.056 = 5.6\%$

The percent of decrease is 5.6%.

☑ **Quick Check**

3. Find each percent of decrease. Where necessary, round to the nearest tenth of a percent.

   a. from 9.6 to 4.8   **b.** from 202 to 192   **c.** from 854.5 to 60.6

EXERCISES

For more exercises, see *Extra Skill and Word Problem Practice*.

Practice and Problem Solving

A Practice by Example

Examples 1 and 2
(pages 329, 330)

GO **for Help**

Find each percent of increase.

1. from 30 to 39   **2.** from 50 to 66   **3.** from 4 to 4.5

4. from 48 to 60   **5.** from 32 to 76   **6.** from 5 to 5.5

7. from 55 to 176   **8.** from 38 to 95   **9.** from 2.5 to 3

10. Life Spans In the United States in the 20th century, average life expectancy increased from about 47 years to about 77 years. Find the percent of increase to the nearest percent.

Example 3
(page 330)

Find each percent of decrease. Where necessary, round to the nearest tenth of a percent.

11. from 60 to 48   **12.** from 180 to 54   **13.** from 180 to 108

14. from 280 to 126   **15.** from 240 to 90   **16.** from 42 to 35

17. from 64 to 24   **18.** from 6.5 to 4.8   **19.** from 7.4 to 2.4

20. A computer that cost $1,099 last year costs $999 this year.

21. A racing bicycle that cost $1,500 new costs $845 used.

B Apply Your Skills

GO Online
Homework Video Tutor
Visit: PHSchool.com
Web Code: ade-0608

Find each percent of change. Tell whether the change is an increase or a decrease. Where necessary, round to the nearest tenth of a percent.

22. from 96 to 78   **23.** from 90 to 75   **24.** from 80 to 95

25. from 45 to 105   **26.** from 27 to 72   **27.** from 120 to 95

28. from 87 to 108   **29.** from 59 to 127   **30.** from 77 to 13

31. Error Analysis Eva's first step in finding the percent of change from 7 to 8 was to write $\frac{8-7}{8} = \frac{1}{8}$. Explain Eva's error.

32. Economics The average cost of a gallon of gasoline was $1.29 in 1997 and $1.12 in 1998. Find the percent of decrease.

Mental Math Use mental math to find each percent of change. Tell whether the change is an increase or a decrease.

33. from 25 to 30   **34.** from 40 to 45   **35.** from 50 to 45

36. from 100 to 101.1   **37.** from 40 to 20   **38.** from 15 to 12

C Challenge

39. The population of Growtown increased from 10,000 to 13,000 in one year. In the same year, the population of Slowtown decreased from 30,000 to 24,000.
a. Find each town's percent of increase or decrease in population.
b. If each town maintains the same rate of change, within how many years will the population of Growtown exceed that of Slowtown?

40. **Zoology** Ganesh weighed 213 lb at birth, 300 lb at one month, and 1,061 lb at one year. Find each percent of increase of weight. Round to the nearest percent.
    a. from birth to one month
    b. from one month to one year
    c. from birth to one year
    d. **Writing in Math** Explain why the sum of the percent increase from birth to one month and from one month to one year does not equal the percent increase from birth to one year.

Real-World **Connection**

Ganesh was the first elephant born at the Cincinnati Zoo.

41. a. **Reasoning** 100 is increased by 10%. The result is decreased by 10%. Is the final result 100? Explain.
    b. Compare the final result in part (a) to 100, the original number. Find the percent of change.

Test Prep

Multiple Choice

42. The price of an item is $5.99. With sales tax, you pay $6.35. About what percent of the price of the item is the sales tax?
    A. 3%   **B.** 4%   **C.** 5%   **D.** 6%

43. Kayla was 36 in. tall at age 3. Today, at age 5, she is 42 in. tall. To the nearest percent, what is the percent of change in Kayla's height?
    F. 2%   **G.** 8%   **H.** 14%   **J.** 17%

44. A share of stock sold for $32.13 yesterday. Today, it is selling for $30.08. What is the approximate percent decline in the stock price?
    A. 5%   **B.** 6%   **C.** 7%   **D.** 8%

45. What is the percent of change from 148 to 37?
    F. 3%   **G.** 25%   **H.** 75%   **J.** 111%

Extended Response

46. 200 is decreased by 5%. The result is increased by 5%. What is the final result? Explain why the result is less than 200. Show your work.

Mixed Review

Lesson 6-7

47. **Astronomy** The Space Surveillance Center in Colorado tracks about 8,500 objects in orbit around Earth. All but about 500 objects are junk from past space missions. What percent are junk? Round to the nearest percent.

Lesson 5-3 **Find each sum or difference.**

48. $5\frac{3}{4} - 2\frac{5}{8}$ 49. $-4\frac{1}{3} + 2\frac{1}{2}$ 50. $-6\frac{1}{3} - 6\frac{1}{3}$

Lesson 4-2 **Evaluate each expression.**

51. $3x^2$ for $x = -5$ 52. $[(3 + 12)4]^2$ 53. $(7 + 4y)^2$ for $y = -2$

Markup and Discount

 Assessment Framework

6.8.18 Solve number sentences and problems involving fractions, decimals, and percents.

1 Finding Markups

To make a profit, stores charge more for merchandise than they pay for it. The amount of increase is called the **markup.** The percent of increase is the *percent of markup*.

1 EXAMPLE   Real-World Problem Solving

Music Sales A music store's percent of markup is 67%. A CD costs the store $10.15. Find the markup.

$$\text{markup} = \text{percent of markup} \cdot \text{store's cost}$$
$$= 0.67 \cdot 10.15$$
$$\approx 6.80 \qquad \textbf{Simplify. Round to the nearest cent.}$$

The markup is $6.80.

✓ Quick Check

1. A clothing store pays $56 for a jacket. The store's percent of markup is 75%. Find the markup for the jacket.

The store's cost plus the markup equals the *selling price*.

2 EXAMPLE   Real-World Problem Solving

Retailing A computer store pays $6 for a computer mouse. The percent of markup is 75%. Find the mouse's selling price.

$$0.75 \cdot 6 = 4.50 \qquad \textbf{Multiply to find the markup.}$$
$$6.00 + 4.50 = 10.50 \qquad \textbf{Cost + markup = selling price.}$$

The selling price is $10.50.

✓ Quick Check

2. A $5 cap has a 70% markup. Find the selling price.

2 Finding Discounts

When an item goes on sale, the amount of the price decrease is the **discount.** The percent of decrease is the *percent of discount*.

Sale price = regular price − discount.

✓ Check Skills You'll Need

Write an equation and solve. Round to hundredths as needed.

1. What is 75% of $82?

2. What is 42% of $170?

3. What is 5.5% of $24?

4. What is 80% of $15.99?

GO for Help
Lesson 6-7

◀)) New Vocabulary
- markup
- discount

Vocabulary Tip

20% *off* means a discount of 20%.

3 EXAMPLE **Finding Discount**

Recreation Athletic shoes that regularly sell for **$85.99** are on sale for **20% off.** Find the discount.

$$\text{discount} = \text{percent of discount} \cdot \text{regular price}$$
$$= 0.20 \cdot 85.99$$
$$\approx 17.20 \qquad \textbf{Simplify. Round to the nearest cent.}$$

The discount is $17.20.

✓ Quick Check

3. Pants priced at $21.99 are marked 15% off. Find the discount.

Here are two ways to use percent of discount to find a sale price.

More Than One Way

A video game that regularly sells for $39.95 is on sale for 20% off. What is the sale price?

Eric's Method

Find the discount. Then find the sale price.

$$\text{discount} = \text{percent of discount} \cdot \text{regular price}$$
$$= 0.20 \cdot 39.95$$
$$= 7.99$$
$$\text{sale price} = \text{regular price} - \text{discount}$$
$$= 39.95 - 7.99$$
$$= 31.96$$

The sale price is $31.96.

Michelle's Method

Find the sale price directly. The sale price equals 100% of the regular price minus 20% of the regular price.

$$\text{sale price} = (100\% - 20\%) \cdot \text{regular price}$$
$$= 80\% \cdot \text{regular price}$$
$$= 0.80(39.95)$$
$$= 31.96$$

The sale price is $31.96.

Choose a Method

1. Which method do you prefer? Explain.

2. Find the sale price if the percent of discount is 25%. Round to the nearest cent.

EXERCISES

For more exercises, see *Extra Skill and Word Problem Practice*.

Practice and Problem Solving

 Practice by Example

Example 1
(page 333)

 GO for Help

For Exercises 1–5, find each markup.

1. cost: $1.50
percent of markup: 70%

2. cost: $38
percent of markup: 58%

3. cost: $111.00
percent of markup: 50%

4. cost: $18
percent of markup: 35%

🌐 **5. Beach Gear** A beach store pays $11.40 for each beach umbrella. The store's percent of markup is 75%.

Example 2
(page 333)

For Exercises 6–10, find each selling price.

6. cost: $6
percent of markup: 75%

7. cost: $2.66
percent of markup: 50%

8. cost: $149.99
percent of markup: 100%

9. cost: $67.20
percent of markup: 10%

🌐 **10. Clothing** A clothing store pays $15 for a shirt. The percent of markup is 85%.

Example 3
(page 334)

For Exercises 11–15, find each discount and sale price.

11. regular price: $100
percent of discount: 27%

12. regular price: $24.50
percent of discount: 20%

13. regular price: $700
percent of discount: 30%

14. regular price: $8.49
percent of discount: 5%

🌐 **15. Footwear** Boots, regularly $125, are on sale for 30% off.

B **Apply Your Skills**

Find each selling price. Where necessary, round to the nearest cent.

16. regular price: $180
percent of discount: 40%

17. regular price: $14.99
percent of discount: 15%

18. cost: $9.99
percent of markup: 60%

19. cost: $15
percent of markup: 15%

GO for Help

For a guide to solving
Exercise 20, see
page 337.

🌐 **20. Shopping** An $11 shirt is on sale for 10% off.
a. Describe two different methods of finding the sale price.
b. Use one of the methods to find the sale price.

🌐 **21. Video Sales** Store A is selling a video for 20% off the store's regular price of $25.95. Store B is selling the same video for 30% off the store's regular price of $29.50. Which store's sale price is lower? How much lower is it?

22. Writing in Math Identical sweaters are on sale in two different stores. The sale price in Store A is 30% off the regular price of $25. The sale price in Store B is 40% off the regular price of $30. Which sweater is the better buy? Explain.

GO Online
Homework Video Tutor
Visit: PHSchool.com
Web Code: ade-0609

🌐 **nline** lesson quiz, PHSchool.com, Web Code: ada-0609   **6-9** Markup and Discount **335**

Challenge

23. **Estimation** Suppose you want to buy three books that cost $6.95, $9.95, and $10.95. The bookstore is having a $\frac{1}{4}$-off sale. Your state charges sales tax of 5% of an item's final price. You have $20. Do you have enough money? Justify your answer.

24. **Reasoning** A store buys an item for x and sells it for y. Write expressions for the markup and the percent of markup.

25. Shoes cost a store $56.40. The markup is 17%. Find the selling price by two different methods.

 ISAT

Test Prep

Multiple Choice

26. A $59.50 coat is on sale for $36.50. About how much is the percent of discount?
    A. 37%   **B.** 39%   **C.** 61%   **D.** 63%

27. Michael buys a new lawn mower with a 20% discount coupon. The regular price is $359.99. How much is the discounted price?
    F. $20.00   **G.** $72.00   **H.** $287.99   **J.** $339.99

Short Response

28. Store A advertises a printer at "15% off its regular price of $79.95." Store B next door advertises the same printer at "20% off of $83.95."
    (a) Which printer would you buy?   **(b)** Explain your answer.

Mixed Review

 GO for Help

Lesson 6-8   **Find each percent of decrease. Round to the nearest tenth.**

29. from 90 to 70   30. from 44.4 to 14.8   31. from 1,750 to 1,125

Lesson 5-3 32. **Recipes** A bread recipe calls for $6\frac{1}{2}$ cups of flour. You have $4\frac{3}{4}$ cups. How much more flour do you need?

Lesson 1-10   **Draw a coordinate plane. Graph each point.**

33. $A(1,0)$ 34. $B(-2,3)$ 35. $C(-1,2)$

✓ Checkpoint Quiz 2   Lessons 6-5 through 6-9

Compare. Use >, <, or = to complete each statement.

1. $\frac{14}{25}$ ■ 56%   2. 1.1% ■ 0.11   3. $\frac{3}{11}$ ■ 27%

Write and solve an equation.

4. Find 33% of 120.   5. Find 125% of 42.

6. What percent of 5.6 is 1.4?   7. 15% of q is 9.75. What is q?

8. A car originally priced at $12,000 is sold at a 20% discount. Find the sale price.

Understanding Math Problems Read the problem below. Then let Serena's thinking guide you through the solution. Check your understanding with the exercises at the bottom of the page.

Shopping An $11 shirt is on sale for 10% off.
a. Describe two different methods of finding the sale price.
b. Use one of the methods to find the sale price.

What Serena Thinks

First I need to describe two methods of finding the sale price, then I need to find the sale price.

One way to find the sale price is to find 10% of the price and subtract it.

Another way is to find 90% of the original price.

I need to choose one of the methods. Multiplying by 0.9 is faster than multiplying by 0.1 and subtracting, so that's the method I'll use.

Now I need to write my answers.

What Serena Writes

Two methods:

price − (0.1 × price) = sale price

0.9 × price = sale price

0.9 × 11 = 9.9

a. Method 1: Find the amount of the 10% discount and subtract it from the original price.
Method 2: Find 90% of the original price.
b. The sale price is $9.90.

EXERCISES

Find each sale price.

1. $25 sweater; 15% off

2. $325 stereo; 20% off

3. $85 sneakers; 25% off

4. $15 T-shirt; 10% off

5. $520 TV; 18% off

6. $14 book; 12% off

Make a Table

What You'll Learn

- To solve problems by making a table

... And Why

To solve real-world problems involving population estimates

Check Skills You'll Need

Solve.

1. For two weeks, you double the amount of money you save each day. You save $.01 the first day. How much money will you have at the end of the two weeks?

GO for Help
Lesson 1-8

Math Strategies in Action

Have you ever watched a baseball game at a field that doesn't have a scoreboard? It's hard to keep track of the score!

A scoreboard is a type of table. You can use tables to organize information. Tables are particularly helpful in solving problems that require several steps.

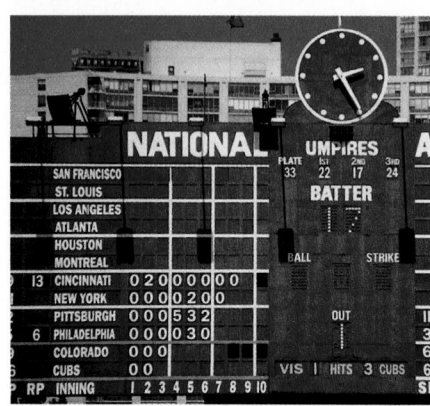

1 EXAMPLE Real-World Problem Solving

Population Growth At the beginning of the year 2000, the population of the United States was about 273.5 million. The rate of population growth was about 0.85% per year. If that rate continues, what will the population be at the beginning of 2010?

Understand the Problem

Read the problem carefully.

1. What information are you asked to find?

2. What information will you need to use to solve the problem?

Make a Plan

Decide on a strategy. You can use the percent of increase to predict the population increase for each year from 2000 to 2010. You can make a table to organize your predictions for each year.

3. How can you find the increase in population from the beginning of 2000 to the end of that year?

4. How can you find the population at the beginning of 2001?

5. The percent of increase is the same each year. Does that mean that the increase in population also will be the same each year? Explain your reasoning.

Carry Out the Plan

Copy and complete the table below.

6. Find the numbers for Column 4 by multiplying the numbers in Columns 2 and 3. Round to the nearest tenth of a million.

7. Find the numbers for Column 5 (and, hence, the next Column 2 entries) by adding the numbers in Columns 2 and 4.

1	2	3	4	5
Year	Population at Beginning of Year (millions)	Rate of Increase (0.85%)	Increase in Population (millions)	Population at End of Year (millions)
2000	273.5	0.0085	2.3	275.8
2001	275.8	0.0085	2.3	278.1
2002	278.1	0.0085	2.4	280.5
2003	280.5	0.0085	2.4	282.9
2004	282.9	0.0085	2.4	285.3
2005	285.3	0.0085	2.4	287.7
2006	287.7	0.0085	2.4	290.1
2007	290.1	0.0085	■	■
2008	■	0.0085	■	■
2009	■	0.0085	■	■
2010	■			

8. Sometimes the number in Column 4 changes from one year to the next, and sometimes it does not change. Explain.

9. What is your prediction for population at the beginning of 2010?

Check the Answer

10. Your friend says that she knows a quicker way to find the answer. Simply multiply 273.5 · 0.0085 · 10 to find the increase for the ten-year period 2000 to 2010. Do you agree with your friend's approach? Explain your reasoning.

✓ Quick Check

11. Suppose the annual percent of increase in population is 0.9%. At that rate, what will the population be at the beginning of 2010?

EXERCISES

For more exercises, see *Extra Skill and Word Problem Practice*.

Practice and Problem Solving

A Practice by Example

GO for Help
Example 1
(page 338)

Make a table to solve each problem.

1. **Population** The population of a town increases at the rate of 1% each year. Today the town's population is 8,500. What will the population be in five years?

2. **Biology** A microbe population increases 100% every 10 min. If you start with 1 microbe, how many will you have at the end of 1 h?

Real-World **Connection**

Microbe cultures grow on agar gel in petri dishes.

3. Cher has forgotten the combination to her locker. She knows it consists of four numbers—3, 5, 7, and 9—but she can't recall the order. She decides to try every possible order until she gets the right one. How many possible orders are there?

4. **Banking** At the beginning of the year 2000, Bob put $100 in a savings account. The bank pays Bob 5% interest on his total savings at the end of each year including all interest added to the account. Assume the interest rate continues and Bob does not deposit any additional money in the account. How much will he have in his savings account, to the nearest cent, after 5 interest payments?

B Apply Your Skills

Use any strategy to solve each problem.

Strategies

- Act It Out
- Draw a Diagram
- Guess, Check, Revise
- Look for a Pattern
- Make a Model
- Make a Table
- Simulate the Problem
- Solve by Graphing
- Use Multiple Strategies
- Work a Simpler Problem
- Work Backward
- Write an Equation
- Write a Proportion

5. Paco has four pairs of jeans and four T-shirts. How many outfits of a T-shirt and a pair of jeans can Paco make?

6. **Geometry** The length of a rectangle is twice the width. The perimeter of the rectangle is 42 cm. Find the length and width.

7. **Number Sense** The difference of two numbers is 18. The sum of the two numbers is 34. What are the two numbers?

8. **Capacity** You fill a container $\frac{3}{4}$ full of water. The amount of water now in the container is 6 quarts. How much can the container hold?

9. **Ticket Sales** A family went to the movies. Tickets cost $4 for each child and $6 for each adult. The total admission charge for the family was $26. List all the possible numbers of adults and children in the family.

10. **Number Sense** A number n is multiplied by $\frac{5}{8}$. The product is subtracted from $\frac{2}{3}$. The result is $\frac{7}{12}$. What is n?

C Challenge

11. **Geometry** The height of a triangle is half the length of its base. The area of the triangle is 12.25 cm^2. Find the height.

GO Online
Homework Video Tutor
Visit: PHSchool.com
Web Code: ade-0610

12. **Water Resources** Water for irrigation is measured in *acre-feet*. One acre-foot is the volume of water that would cover one acre of land to a depth of one foot. How many acre-feet of water would it take to cover 600 acres to a depth of one inch?

Multiple Choice

13. What is the percent of increase from 1.32 to 1.44, rounded to the nearest percent?

  A. 8%   **B.** 9%   **C.** 12%   **D.** 15%

14. A store pays $50.00 for a coat. Its markup is 25%. Later, it puts the coat on sale at 20% off. What is the sale price of the coat?

  F. $40.00   **G.** $50.00   **H.** $52.50   **J.** $62.50

15. The width of a rectangle is half the length. The perimeter of the rectangle is 54 in. What is the length of the rectangle?

  A. 6 in.   **B.** 9 in.   **C.** 18 in.   **D.** 36 in.

Short Response

16. You must give a customer $.40 in change.

  a. In how many ways can you do this without using pennies?

  b. For part (a), make a table.

Mixed Review

Lesson 6-9

GO **for Help**

Find each sale price.

17. regular price: $39
percent of discount: 30%

18. regular price: $159.95
percent of discount: 20%

Lesson 6-4

19. Probability What is the probability that a digit selected at random from the number 364,892 is a multiple of 3?

Lesson 4-4

Write in simplest form.

20. $\frac{16}{36}$ **21.** $\frac{10x}{65x}$ **22.** $\frac{8ab}{2bc}$ **23.** $\frac{12x^2y}{9xy^2}$

Math at Work

Caterer

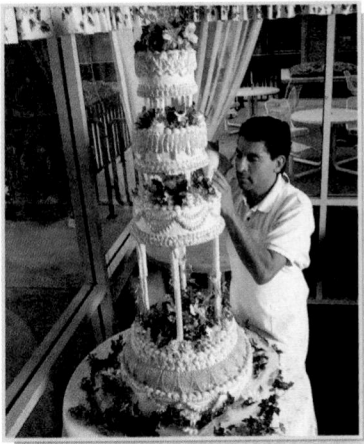

Caterers provide food for parties, weddings, and other events. They plan the menu, buy the ingredients, cook the food, and provide the waitstaff. Some will even arrange for music and seating. For each event, a caterer determines the cost per guest.

The catering business requires a thorough knowledge of ratios, proportions, and percents.

Go Online
PHSchool.com   **For:** Information about caterers
Web Code: adb-2031

Estimation may help you find an answer, check an answer, or eliminate answer choices. If, however, an incorrect choice is very close to the correct choice, you will still have to find the exact answer.

EXAMPLE

A coat regularly priced at $89.95 is on sale at 40% off. What is the sale price of the coat?

A. $35.98   **B.** $49.95   **C.** $53.97   **D.** $54.03

$89.95 \approx \$90$

40% is less than half. The discount will be less than $45, which is half of $90. So, the sale price will be more than $45.

This eliminates choice A.

$40\% \text{ of } 90 = 0.4 \cdot 90$

$$= 36$$

$90 - 36 = 54$, so the sale price is about $54. This eliminates choice B.

Choices C and D are both very close to $54, so you have to compute to find the answer is choice C.

EXERCISES

In Exercises 1–3, which answer choices can you eliminate by using estimation? Explain.

1. A store pays $8.50 for a case of scented candles. The store's percent of markup is 110%. What price will the store charge for the case of candles?

   A. $9.35   **B.** $16.15   **C.** $17.85   **D.** $18.15

2. A store is having a sale. Laverne looks at a $79.80 necklace that is on sale for $59.85. What is the percent of discount?

   F. 20%   **G.** 25%   **H.** $33\frac{1}{3}\%$ **J.** 40%

3. An entomologist noted that in the past five years in the local forest preserve, the population of bees decreased by 35%. In her study, she recorded that the number of active hives five years ago was 35. If the number of active hives decreased at the same rate as the bee population, how many hives are there today?

   A. 17 hives   **B.** 19 hives   **C.** 21 hives   **D.** 23 hives

4. For Exercise 3, explain how you can use estimation in two different ways to help you with the answer choices.

Chapter Review

Vocabulary Review

certain event (p. 310)
commission (p. 325)
complement (p. 310)
cross products (p. 298)
discount (p. 333)
event (p. 309)
impossible event (p. 310)

indirect measurement (p. 304)
markup (p. 333)
odds (p. 311)
outcomes (p. 309)
percent (p. 314)
percent of change (p. 329)
probability (p. 309)

proportion (p. 298)
rate (p. 293)
ratio (p. 292)
scale drawing (p. 304)
similar figures (p. 303)
unit rate (p. 293)

Match the vocabulary terms with their descriptions.

1. a comparison of two quantities by division

2. a ratio that compares a number to 100

3. the amount charged for an item above the cost

4. the amount of a price decrease

5. a ratio that compares quantities in different units

6. a rate that has a denominator of 1

7. two equal ratios

a. markup
b. percent
c. ratio
d. discount
e. unit rate
f. proportion
g. rate

Go Online
PHSchool.com
For: Vocabulary quiz
Web Code: adj-0651

Skills and Concepts

6-1 Objectives

▼ To write and simplify ratios (p. 292)

▼ To find rates and unit rates (p. 293)

A **ratio** is a comparison of two quantities by division. A **rate** is a ratio that compares quantities in different units. A **unit rate** is a rate that has a denominator of 1.

Write each ratio as a fraction in simplest form.

8. $9 : 24$ **9.** $20 : 35$ **10.** $15 : 20$ **11.** $100 : 130$

Write each ratio as a unit rate.

12. 150 mi in 3 h   **13.** \$9.45 for 5 lb   **14.** 270 words in 3 min

6-2 Objectives

▼ To solve proportions (p. 298)

▼ To use proportions to solve problems (p. 299)

A **proportion** is an equality of ratios. To solve a proportion, write the cross products, and then solve.

Solve. Round to the nearest tenth where necessary.

15. $\frac{5}{6} = \frac{n}{42}$ **16.** $\frac{53}{2} = \frac{18}{x}$ **17.** $\frac{15}{a} = \frac{30}{98}$ **18.** $\frac{m}{150} = \frac{21}{25}$

6-3 Objectives

▼ To solve problems that involve similar figures (p. 303)

▼ To solve problems that involve scale drawings (p. 304)

Similar figures have the same shape, but not necessarily the same size. In similar figures, the corresponding angles have equal measures and the corresponding sides are proportional.

A **scale drawing** is an enlarged or reduced drawing of an object.

The figures in each pair are similar. Find _x_.

19.

20.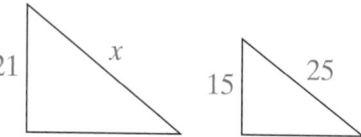

21. A map has a scale of 1 cm : 75 km. What is the distance on the map for an actual distance of 37.5 km?

6-4 Objectives

▼ To find probability (p. 309)

▼ To find odds (p. 311)

Outcomes are the possible results of an action. An **event** is any outcome or group of outcomes. When outcomes are equally likely, you can use formulas to find the **probability** of an event and the **odds** in favor of an event.

$$\text{probability} = \frac{\text{number of favorable outcomes}}{\text{number of possible outcomes}}$$

$$\text{odds} = \frac{\text{number of favorable outcomes}}{\text{number of unfavorable outcomes}}$$

Suppose you select a letter at random from the letters in the word EXPONENT. Find the probability of each event. Then find the odds in favor of the event.

22. selecting P   **23.** selecting N   **24.** selecting a vowel

6-5 Objectives

▼ To write percents as fractions and decimals (p. 314)

▼ To order rational numbers (p. 315)

A **percent** is a ratio that compares a number to 100.

Write each percent as a fraction in simplest form and as a decimal.

25. 24%   **26.** 72%   **27.** 8%   **28.** 0.5%

Write each number as a percent. Round to the nearest tenth of a percent.

29. 0.3   **30.** 0.33   **31.** $\frac{1}{3}$ **32.** 0.35

33. $\frac{16}{18}$ **34.** 0.021   **35.** $\frac{120}{50}$ **36.** 0.0064

6-6 and 6-7 Objectives

▼ To find a part of a whole and a percent (p. 319)

▼ To find a whole amount (p. 320)

▼ To write and solve percent equations (p. 324)

▼ To use equations in solving percent problems (p. 325)

Solve percent problems by using a proportion or an equation.

Write and solve a proportion.

37. Find 15% of 48.

38. 20% of x is 30. What is x?

39. What percent of 300 is 90?

40. 125% of y is 100. What is y?

Write and solve an equation.

41. 35% of a is 70. What is a?

42. Find 68% of 300.

43. What percent of 180 is 9?

44. What percent of 56 is 3.5?

6-8 and 6-9 Objectives

▼ To find percent of increase (p. 329)

▼ To find percent of decrease (p. 330)

▼ To find markups (p. 333)

▼ To find discounts (p. 333)

A **percent of change** is the percent by which a quantity increases or decreases from its original amount.

$$\text{percent of change} = \frac{\text{amount of change}}{\text{original amount}}$$

Markup is a real-world application of percent of increase. **Discount** is a real-world application of percent of decrease.

Find each percent of change. Tell whether the change is an increase or a decrease.

45. 120 to 90

46. 148 to 37

47. 285 to 342

48. 1,000 to 250

49. A cap that cost a retailer $5 was marked up by 75%. Find the selling price.

50. Peaches that are usually priced at $2/lb are on sale for 15% off. Find the sale price.

6-10 Objectives

▼ To solve problems by making a table (p. 338)

Make a table to organize information or to solve problems that have several steps.

51. Alicia bikes 25% of a 100-mi trip on the first day. She bikes $\frac{1}{3}$ of the remaining distance on the second day. On the third day, she bikes 40% of the remaining distance. Make a table to find the number of miles left in Alicia's trip.

52. Describe how you could use a table together with another problem-solving strategy that you have studied. Justify your answer with an example.

Chapter Test

Go Online
PHSchool.com

For: Chapter test
Web Code: ada-0652

Find each unit rate.

1. A car travels 84 mi on 3 gal of gas.

2. A car travels 220 mi in 4 h.

Write = or ≠ to complete each statement.

3. $\frac{7}{8}$ ■ $\frac{40}{42}$ 4. $\frac{3}{5}$ ■ $\frac{45}{75}$

5. $\frac{12}{18}$ ■ $\frac{18}{12}$ 6. $\frac{5}{9}$ ■ $\frac{25}{81}$

Solve each proportion.

7. $\frac{x}{8} = \frac{90}{120}$ 8. $\frac{0.8}{90} = \frac{5.6}{y}$

Write a proportion to describe each situation. Then solve.

9. Three cans of dog food sell for 99¢. Find the cost of 15 cans.

10. A photo that measures 5 in. by 7 in. is enlarged to 7.5 in. by b in.

11. A student reads 45 pages in 2 h and x pages in 3 h.

For Exercises 12–14, use the drawing below. The length of the kitchen in the drawing is $1\frac{1}{4}$ in. The actual length is 20 ft.

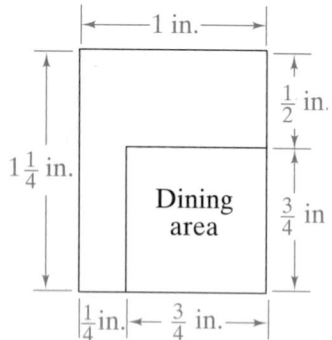

12. What is the scale of the drawing?

13. What is the actual width of the kitchen?

14. What are the actual length and width of the dining area?

Find each probability for one roll of a number cube.

15. $P(1)$ 16. $P(1 \text{ or } 2)$

17. $P(\text{not } 2 \text{ or } 6)$ 18. $P(\text{greater than } 1)$

Write each decimal as a percent.

19. 0.37   20. 0.005   21. 1.02

Write each fraction as a percent.

22. $\frac{5}{8}$ 23. $\frac{7}{16}$ 24. $\frac{5}{4}$

Solve.

25. What percent of 400 is 20?

26. Find 45% of 12.

27. 20% of c is 24. What is c?

28. What percent of 3 is 15?

29. Find 125% of 50.

30. 60% of y is 75. What is y?

Find each percent of change. Tell whether the change is an increase or a decrease. Round to the nearest tenth of a percent.

31. from 60 to 36   32. from 18 to 24

33. from 15 to 25   34. from 85 to 50

35. from 8.8 to 30   36. from 1.2 to 0.2

37. A salesperson made a $128 commission selling merchandise. His commission rate was 5%. Find the dollar amount of his sales.

38. A bicycle that usually sells for $230 is on sale for 15% off. Find the sale price.

39. **Writing in Math** Explain the difference between a markup and a discount.

40. In how many ways can you make $.35 in change without using pennies?

ISAT Test Prep

Multiple Choice

1. What is 56,500,000,000 written in scientific notation?
   - (A) $5.65 \cdot 10^8$
   - (B) $56.5 \cdot 10^{10}$
   - (C) $5.65 \cdot 10^{10}$
   - (D) $565 \cdot 10^9$

2. What is x when $\frac{2}{3}x = 2\frac{2}{9}$?
   - (E) $\frac{3}{10}$
   - (F) $2\frac{5}{8}$
   - (G) $3\frac{1}{3}$
   - (H) $7\frac{2}{3}$

3. What is the correct symbol?
   $$\left|2\frac{4}{5}\right| \blacksquare \left|-\frac{9}{4}\right|$$
   - (A) $>$
   - (B) $<$
   - (C) $=$
   - (D) $\leq$

4. What is the unit rate for a ball moving 252 ft in 4 s?
   - (E) $252 : 4$
   - (F) 63 ft/s
   - (G) 252 ft/s
   - (H) 1,008 ft/s

5. What percent of 63 is 41?
   - (A) about 82%
   - (B) about 65%
   - (C) about 41%
   - (D) about 0.65%

6. Which equation has -4 as a solution?
   - (E) $9z = 36$
   - (F) $-\frac{36}{z} = -9$
   - (G) $z + 9 = 5$
   - (H) $z - 9 = -5$

7. Which has the lowest unit price?
   - (A) 10 oz for $.30
   - (B) $.56 for 20 oz
   - (C) 30 oz for $.87
   - (D) $1.16 for 40 oz

Gridded Response

8. Evaluate $6x - 9$ for $x = 11$.

9. Simplify $(-1)^8 \cdot (-2)^0$.

10. Solve $y + 0.5 = 3$.

11. Find 40% of 40.

Write each fraction as a decimal.

12. $\frac{42}{50}$

13. $\frac{16}{20}$

14. $\frac{33}{55}$

15. $\frac{6}{80}$

16. $\frac{524}{200}$

17. $\frac{45}{1,000}$

Find each probability for one roll of a number cube.

18. $P(5 \text{ or } 6)$

19. $P(\text{less than } 4)$

The scale on a map is 1 in. = 5 mi. Find the actual distance in miles for each map distance.

20. 5.5 in.

21. 12 in.

22. 9.75 in.

Solve each proportion.

23. $\frac{5}{8} = \frac{15}{n}$

24. $\frac{28}{x} = \frac{14}{2.5}$

25. $\frac{n}{9} = \frac{40}{12}$

26. $\frac{6}{21} = \frac{s}{70}$

Write each ratio as a fraction in simplest form.

27. $20 : 45$

28. $8 : 96$

29. $30 : 36$

30. $120 : 80$

Short Response

31. For the similar figures, (a) write a proportion to solve for x. (b) Find x.

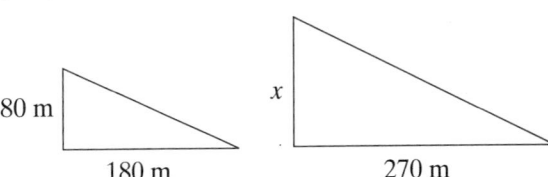

In Exercises 32 and 33, (a) find the sale price. Round to the nearest cent where necessary. (b) Explain your answer.

32. regular price: $58
    percent of discount: 45%

33. regular price: $15.98
    percent of discount: 80%

Extended Response

34. Which is the better buy: (a) Brand A with a regular price of $15.98 and a 30% discount, or Brand B with a regular price of $18.50 and a 40% discount? (b) How much do you save with the better buy? (c) Show your work.

Activity Lab

AWK   SRR   TWP   IKN   S
5s30.6   2s35.58   24s15.06   4s22.76

Calculating Change

Applying Percents When you buy a company's stock, you buy a small piece of the company. The amount you have to pay for a stock varies from day to day or even minute to minute. You can make money by selling the stock for more than you paid for it. You can lose money by selling it for less than you paid for it.

Wall Street

Since 1870, when continuous stock trading began at the New York Stock Exchange, the ringing of a bell signals the beginning (9:30 A.M. EST) and ending (4:00 P.M. EST) of trading each day.

Activity

1. Copy the table. Add another column for the percent of change in price from Monday to Friday. Indicate whether the percent of change is an increase or a decrease.

2. Suppose you and a friend buy stock on Monday and sell it on Friday. You buy 50 shares of Pat's Pastas and 25 shares of Leaping Lizards. Your friend buys 35 shares of Map Makers Plus and 25 shares of Wondermarts. Who made the better investment, you or your friend? Justify your answer.

Seven Stocks

Company	Price per Share on Monday	Price per Share on Friday
All-Star Adventures	$6.25	$5.75
Fun Foods, Inc.	$28.00	$26.60
Leaping Lizards	$19.50	$23.40
Map Makers Plus	$13.00	$14.95
Nature's Nest	$3.80	$4.20
Pat's Pastas	$5.65	$4.45
Wondermarts	$34.00	$32.75

3. Suppose you had $500 to invest on Monday.
  a. Which stock(s) would you buy on Monday, and how many shares of the stock(s) would you buy? Explain.
  b. You sell all your shares on Friday. How much money did you make?

4. a. Research Find the price of a stock in the newspaper or online. Find the price at least one day later.
  b. Writing in Math Would you invest in the company? Explain.

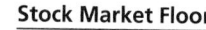

PSFT   APOG   POS   AAPL   FDX   AWK   SRR   TWP
10s4.00   6s14.5   3s19.14   8s50.35   5s22.40   5s30.6   2s35.58   24s15.06

POS is the name
of the stock.

$19.14 is the last traded
price of the stock.

3s means 300 shares sold.

Stock Trader

A stock trader places orders or buys
and sells securities or commodities. A
successful trader is very interested
in numbers and in investing and
understands economic trends.

Stock Certificates

Most securities transactions
today are done without
stock certificates,
although some
people like to have
the actual certificate in
their possession.

Stock Market Floor

Runners at the Chicago Mercantile Exchange
wear yellow jackets for visibility. They take
orders to buy and sell stocks into and out of
the trading areas.

Go Online
PHSchool.com

For: Information about the stock market
Web Code: ade-0653

What You've Learned

 Assessment Framework

- **8.8.12:** In Chapter 2, you learned how to simplify variable expressions and to solve one-step equations and inequalities by adding, subtracting, multiplying, or dividing.

- **8.8.12:** In Chapter 3, you learned how to solve equations by adding, subtracting, multiplying, or dividing decimals.

- **6.8.09:** In Chapter 5, you learned how to solve equations by adding, subtracting, or multiplying fractions.

 Check Your Readiness **GO** **for Help** to the Lesson in green.

Writing Variable Expressions (Lesson 1-1)

Write a variable expression for each situation.

1. three more than p points

2. six fewer than q questions

3. the number of months in y years

4. the value in cents of d dimes

5. twice as many as b baskets

6. eight fewer than n nickels

Simplifying Expressions (Lesson 2-3)

Simplify each expression.

7. $3n + n$

8. $5b + 10 - 8b$

9. $12c + 9 + 7c + 4$

10. $3x + 2y - 7y - 10x$

11. $2(a + 3)$

12. $5(m - 7) + 4m$

Solving Equations (Lessons 2-5, 2-6)

Solve each equation.

13. $a - 3 = 8$

14. $-9 = 12 + x$

15. $\frac{m}{7} = -14$

16. $-10 = -2b$

17. $y \div 2 = 4$

18. $6.8 = c - 2.2$

19. $\frac{x}{-4} = 8$

20. $-40 = 5a$

Solving Inequalities (Lessons 2-9, 2-10)

Solve and graph each inequality.

21. $c + 6 \geq 7$

22. $y - 8 < -6$

23. $5b < 20$

24. $-3x < 0$

25. $12 \leq x + 18$

26. $-\frac{x}{3} \geq -5$

27. $b - 15 \leq 4$

28. $\frac{m}{4} \geq 20$

Solving Equations and Inequalities

 Key Vocabulary

- balance (p. 387)
- compound inequality (p. 381)
- compound interest (p. 387)
- consecutive integers (p. 357)
- interest (p. 386)
- interest rate (p. 386)
- principal (p. 386)
- simple interest (p. 386)

What You'll Learn Next

IL Assessment Framework

In this chapter, you will learn how to

- **8.8.12:** Write and solve multi-step equations.

- **8.8.12:** Write and solve two-step inequalities.

- Find simple interest and compound interest.

- **8.8.11:** Solve problems by writing equations.

 Activity Lab Applying what you learn,
on pages 398–399 you will solve problems about
cellular telephones.

7-1 Solving Two-Step Equations

IL Assessment Framework

8.8.12 Solve linear equations and inequalities in one variable over the rational numbers.

8.8.13 Solve word problems involving unknown quantities.

 Check Skills You'll Need

Solve each equation.

1. $9 + k = 17$

2. $d - 10 = 1$

3. $y - 5 = -4$

4. $x + 16 = 4$

5. $b + 6 = -4$

GO for Help
Lesson 2-5

1 Using Properties to Solve Two-Step Equations

Algebra tiles can help you understand the algebra behind solving the equation $2x + 1 = 5$.

$2x + 1 = 5$

Model the equation.

$2x + 1 - 1 = 5 - 1$
$2x = 4$

Remove 1 tile from each side.

$\dfrac{2x}{2} = \dfrac{4}{2}$

Divide each side into two equal groups.

$x = 2$

Simplify.

To solve a two-step equation, first undo addition or subtraction. Then undo multiplication or division.

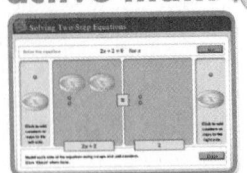

For: Two-Step Equation Activity
Use: Interactive Textbook, 7-1

1 EXAMPLE Undoing an Operation

Solve $3n - 6 = 15$.

$3n - 6 = 15$

$3n - 6 + 6 = 15 + 6$ **Add 6 to each side.**

$3n = 21$ **Simplify.**

$\dfrac{3n}{3} = \dfrac{21}{3}$ **Divide each side by 3.**

$n = 7$ **Simplify.**

Check

$3n - 6 = 15$

$3(7) - 6 \stackrel{?}{=} 15$ **Replace n with 7.**

$21 - 6 \stackrel{?}{=} 15$ **Multiply.**

$15 = 15 \checkmark$ **Simplify.**

✓ Quick Check

1. Solve each equation.

    a. $15x + 3 = 48$ **b.** $\frac{t}{4} - 10 = -6$

    c. $\frac{b}{3} + 13 = 11$ **d.** $9g + 11 = 2$

---

2 **EXAMPLE** **Negative Coefficients**

Solve $5 - x = 17$.

$$5 - x = 17$$
$$-5 + 5 - x = -5 + 17 \quad \text{Add } -5 \text{ to each side.}$$
$$0 - x = 12 \quad \text{Simplify.}$$
$$-x = 12 \quad 0 - x = -x$$
$$-1(-x) = -1(12) \quad \text{Multiply each side by } -1.$$
$$x = -12 \quad \text{Simplify.}$$

> **Vocabulary Tip**
>
> Read "$0 - x = -x$" as "Zero minus x equals the opposite of x."

✓ Quick Check

2. Solve each equation.

    a. $-a + 6 = 8$ **b.** $-9 - \frac{y}{7} = -12$ **c.** $13 - 6f = 31$

---

2 **Solving Problems With Two-Step Equations**

You can use two-step equations to model real-world situations.

3 **EXAMPLE** **Real-World** 🌎 **Problem Solving**

Travel Planning Lynne wants to save $900 to go to Puerto Rico. She saves $45 each week and now has $180. To find how many more weeks w it will take to have $900, solve $180 + 45w = 900$.

$$180 + 45w = 900$$
$$180 + 45w - 180 = 900 - 180 \quad \text{Subtract 180 from each side.}$$
$$45w = 720 \quad \text{Simplify.}$$
$$\frac{45w}{45} = \frac{720}{45} \quad \text{Divide each side by 45.}$$
$$w = 16 \quad \text{Simplify.}$$

It will take Lynne 16 more weeks to have $900.

✓ Quick Check

3. Jacob bought four begonias in 6-in. pots and a $19 fern at a fundraiser. He spent a total of $63. Solve the equation $4p + 19 = 63$ to find the price p of each begonia.

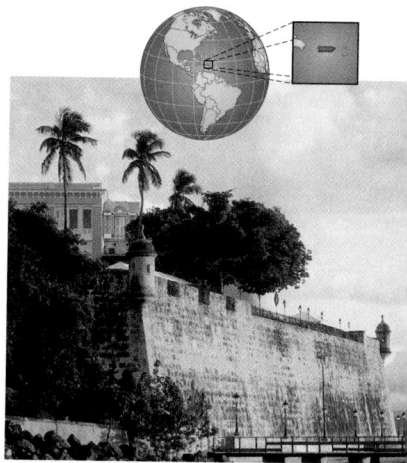

Real-World 🌎 **Connection**

If you fly to San Juan, Puerto Rico, it could cost you $186 to leave from New York, New York, $333 to leave from San Francisco, California, $562 to leave from Reno, Nevada, or $527 to leave from Dallas, Texas.

EXERCISES

For more exercises, see *Extra Skill and Word Problem Practice.*

Practice and Problem Solving

 A Practice by Example

Example 1
(page 352)

 GO for Help

Example 2
(page 353)

Example 3 🌐
(page 353)

State the first step in solving each equation.

1. $2b + 9 = 3$ **2.** $\frac{a}{3} - 4 = 9$ **3.** $4b - 6 = -18$

Solve each equation.

4. $2d - 8 = -10$ **5.** $9x - 15 = 39$ **6.** $\frac{x}{3} + 2 = 0$

7. $12 - 11a = 45$ **8.** $-8c + 1 = -3$ **9.** $5 = -\frac{x}{3} + 10$

10. $18 = -a + 2$ **11.** $4 - \frac{m}{5} = 18$ **12.** $-75 - k = -95$

13. Finance Jose bought a new computer that cost $1,200. He paid $400 down and will pay $50 per week until the balance is paid off. Solve the equation $400 + 50w = 1,200$ to find the number of weeks it will take Jose to pay off the computer.

14. Thomas, Ardell, and Nichole baked muffins, which they shared equally. Nichole ate a muffin on the way home. She then had 14 muffins left. Solve the equation $\frac{m}{3} - 1 = 14$ to find the number of muffins m that Thomas, Ardell, and Nichole baked.

B Apply Your Skills

Solve and check each equation.

15. $15 = -11b + 4$ **16.** $-35 = 4h + 1$ **17.** $10 = 3 + \frac{b}{2}$

18. $12y - 6 = 138$ **19.** $2x + 3 = 15$ **20.** $-6t + (-4) = 14$

21. You bought a CD for $16.95 and eight blank videotapes. The total cost was $52.55 before the sales tax was added. Solve the equation $8t + 16.95 = 52.55$ to find the cost of each blank videotape.

🌐 **22. Savings** You had $235 in your savings account nine weeks ago. You withdrew the same amount each week for eight weeks. Your balance was then $75. Solve the equation $235 - 8m = 75$ to find how much money m you withdrew each week.

Mental Math Solve each equation.

23. $\frac{n}{6} + 2 = -8$ **24.** $4a - 1 = 27$ **25.** $\frac{k}{5} + 3 = 6$

🌐 **26. Construction** A building contractor buys 525 metal bars. Because he is buying more than 500 bars, the wholesaler gives him a discount of $420. The total price is $3,780. Solve the equation $525b - 420 = 3,780$ to find the cost of each metal bar.

27. Carmela wants to buy a digital camera for $249. She has $24 and is saving $15 each week. Solve the equation $15w + 24 = 249$ to find how many weeks w it will take Carmela to save enough to buy the digital camera.

 GO ●nline
Homework Video Tutor
Visit: PHSchool.com
Web Code: ade-0701

354 Chapter 7 Solving Equations and Inequalities

28. Error Analysis A student solved the equation $\frac{x}{4} + 5 = 1$ without showing all the work. The student's solution is incorrect. What error did the student make?

$$\frac{x}{4} + 5 = 1$$
$$\frac{x}{4} = -4$$
$$x = -1$$

29. Writing in Math Explain how the processes of solving $\frac{x}{4} - 2 = 8$ and $\frac{x}{4} = 8$ are different.

Solve and check each equation.

30. $1.5x + 1.2 = 5.7$

31. $-1.7 = 2.2b - 6.1$

32. $3c - 3.2 = 4.6$

33. $\frac{y}{4} + 4.7 = 8.2$

 Challenge ● **34. Nutrition** A soccer player wants to eat no more than 700 calories at a meal that includes a Reuben sandwich and pickles. The sandwich has 464 calories, and the pickles have 7 calories each.
  a. Solve the equation $464 + 7f = 700$ to find the number of pickles the soccer player can eat.
  b. Suppose the soccer player drinks a 200-calorie sports drink with the meal. Solve the equation $664 + 7f = 700$ to find the number of pickles the soccer player can eat now.

ISAT

Test Prep

Multiple Choice
35. What is the solution of $\frac{x}{6} - 8 = 7$?
  A. -6 **B.** 6 **C.** 15 **D.** 90

36. What is the solution of $-11 = 4 - 3$?
  F. -5 **G.** -2 **H.** -1.25 **J.** 1

37. Which is the best estimate for the solution of $29 + 59.2 = 239$?
  A. 4 **B.** 5 **C.** 6 **D.** 7

Short Response
38. At a carnival, Bret buys game tokens for $.25 each. He spends $7.50 for food and $14 in all. How many tokens did he buy?
  a. Write an equation to model this situation.
  b. Solve your equation and answer the question.

Mixed Review

for Help

Lesson 6-9

Find each percent of markup.

39. wholesale price: $34
   selling price: $42.50

40. wholesale price: $45.95
   selling price: $82.71

Lesson 6-4

41. Probability A student is chosen at random from a class of 20 boys and 15 girls. Find the odds that a girl is chosen.

Lesson 2-3

Simplify each expression.

42. $a + 3b + 9a$

43. $2(c + 4) - 5c$

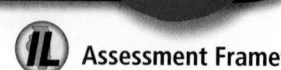

7-2 Solving Multi-Step Equations

IL Assessment Framework

8.8.12 Solve linear equations and inequalities in one variable over the rational numbers.

8.8.13 Solve word problems involving unknown quantities.

 Check Skills You'll Need

Simplify each expression.

1. $2x + 4 + 3x$

2. $5y + y$

3. $8a - 5a$

4. $2 - 4c + 5c$

5. $4x + 3 - 2(5 + x)$

GO for Help
Lesson 2-3

◀))) **New Vocabulary**
• consecutive integers

 Combining Like Terms

Simplifying Equations

The tiles below model the equation $2x + 7 + x = 16$

1. How does this equation differ from others you have seen?

2. a. Group the tiles so that all the x tiles are together. This is the same as combining like terms. Write an equation to represent the tiles once the x tiles are grouped together.
   b. Solve your equation. Check your solution.

Combine like terms to simplify an equation before you solve it.

1 EXAMPLE   **Real-World** 🌐 **Problem Solving**

Model Airplanes Jake and Suki collect model airplanes. Suki has four fewer than twice as many model airplanes as Jake. Together they have 14 models. Solve the equation $m + 2m - 4 = 14$. Find the number of models each person has.

$$m + 2m - 4 = 14$$
$$3m - 4 = 14 \qquad \text{Combine like terms.}$$
$$3m - 4 + 4 = 14 + 4 \qquad \text{Add 4 to each side.}$$
$$3m = 18 \qquad \text{Simplify.}$$
$$\frac{3m}{3} = \frac{18}{3} \qquad \text{Divide each side by 3.}$$
$$m = 6 \qquad \text{Simplify.}$$

Jake has 6 models. Suki has $2(6) - 4 = 8$ models.

Check Is the solution reasonable? Jake and Suki have a total of 14 models. Since $6 + 8 = 14$, the solution is reasonable.

✓ Quick Check

1. **Basketball Scores** One basketball team defeated another by 13 points. The total number of points scored by both teams was 171. Solve the equation $p + p - 13 = 171$ to find the number of points p scored by the winning team.

When you count by 1's from any integer, you are counting **consecutive integers.**

two consecutive integers

120, 121

three consecutive integers

−5, −4, −3

2 **EXAMPLE** Finding Consecutive Integers

Number Sense The sum of three consecutive integers is 96. Find the integers.

Words   sum of three consecutive integers   is   96

Let n = the least integer.

Then $n + 1$ = the second integer,

and $n + 2$ = the third integer.

Equation $n + n + 1 + n + 2$ =   96

$n + (n + 1) + (n + 2) = 96$

$(n + n + n) + (1 + 2) = 96$ Use the Commutative and Associative Properties of Addition to group like terms.

$3n + 3 = 96$ Combine like terms.

$3n + 3 - 3 = 96 - 3$ Subtract 3 from each side.

$3n = 93$ Simplify.

$\dfrac{3n}{3} = \dfrac{93}{3}$ Divide each side by 3.

$n = 31$ Simplify.

If $n = 31$, then $n + 1 = 32$, and $n + 2 = 33$.
The three integers are 31, 32, and 33.

Check Is the solution reasonable? Yes, because $31 + 32 + 33 = 96$.

✓ Quick Check

2. **a. Number Sense** Find four consecutive integers with a sum of 358.
   b. For *consecutive even integers*, the first is n, and the second is $n + 2$. Find two consecutive even integers with a sum of 66.

Test-Taking Tip

Always read problems carefully. It is easy not to see words such as *even* in *consecutive even integers* if you are reading too quickly.

Sometimes you may need to use the Distributive Property when you solve a multi-step equation.

3 EXAMPLE **Using the Distributive Property**

Solve each equation.

a. $2(5x - 3) = 14$

$$2(5x - 3) = 14$$
$$10x - 6 = 14 \qquad \text{Use the Distributive Property.}$$
$$10x - 6 + 6 = 14 + 6 \qquad \text{Add 6 to each side.}$$
$$10x = 20 \qquad \text{Simplify.}$$
$$\frac{10x}{10} = \frac{20}{10} \qquad \text{Divide each side by 10.}$$
$$x = 2 \qquad \text{Simplify.}$$

b. $38 = -3(4y + 2) + y$

$$38 = -3(4y + 2) + y$$
$$38 = -12y - 6 + y \qquad \text{Use the Distributive Property.}$$
$$38 = -12y + y - 6 \qquad \text{Use the Commutative and Associative Properties of Addition to group like terms.}$$
$$38 = -11y - 6 \qquad \text{Combine like terms.}$$
$$38 + 6 = -11y - 6 + 6 \qquad \text{Add 6 to each side.}$$
$$44 = -11y \qquad \text{Simplify.}$$
$$\frac{44}{-11} = \frac{-11y}{-11} \qquad \text{Divide each side by –11.}$$
$$-4 = y \qquad \text{Simplify.}$$

✓ Quick Check

3. Solve each equation.

    a. $-3(m - 6) = 4$ **b.** $3(x + 12) - x = 8$

Key Concepts | **Steps for Solving a Multi-Step Equation**

Step 1 Use the Distributive Property, if necessary.

Step 2 Combine like terms.

Step 3 Undo addition or subtraction.

Step 4 Undo multiplication or division.

EXERCISES

For more exercises, see *Extra Skill and Word Problem Practice.*

Practice and Problem Solving

A Practice by Example

Example 1
(page 356)

Solve each equation.

1. $8a + 4a = 144$ **2.** $9x - 2x = -42$ **3.** $5b + 11 - 2b = 50$

4. $4a + 1 - a = 19$ **5.** $18 = b - 7b$ **6.** $4d + 2d - 3d = 27$

7. Collections Bill and Jasmine together have 94 glass marbles. Bill has 4 more than twice as many marbles as Jasmine. If Jasmine has m marbles, then Bill has $2m + 4$ marbles. Solve the equation $m + 2m + 4 = 94$. Find how many glass marbles each has.

Example 2
(page 357)

Number Sense Find the integers.

8. The sum of two consecutive integers is 131.

9. The sum of three consecutive even integers is 60.

Example 3
(page 358)

Solve each equation.

10. $3(n - 2) = 36$ **11.** $4(y - 1) = 36$

12. $2(8 + n) = 22$ **13.** $-2(a + 3) - a = 0$

14. $3(2x + 1) + x = -39$ **15.** $m + 4(2m - 3) = -3$

B Apply Your Skills

Solve and check each equation.

16. $5x - x = -12$ **17.** $-6 = a + a + 4$

18. $-9 - b + 8b = -23$ **19.** $36 = y - 5y - 12$

20. $-3(2y + 7) = -18$ **21.** $16 = 2(x - 1) - x$

22. $21 = 2(4a + 2)$ **23.** $8 - 3(x - 4) = 4$

Number Sense Find the integers.

24. The sum of four consecutive integers is -22.

25. The sum of five consecutive integers is -65.

26. Error Analysis A student solved the equation $7x - 5 - 5x = 15$ and found $x = 5$. What might be the student's error?

27. Multiple Choice A carpenter is building a fence around a swimming pool. One side of the pool is next to the house and does not need fencing. The carpenter has 120 feet of fencing and plans to use it all. Use the equation $w + 76 + w = 120$. What is the unknown dimension of the enclosed area?
   Ⓐ 22 ft   Ⓑ 44 ft   Ⓒ 76 ft   Ⓓ 120 ft

28. Number Sense Two numbers are w and $3w - 5$. Their sum is 23. Solve the equation $w + 3w - 5 = 23$ to find the numbers.

29. Writing in Math Explain how to solve $3(9 + 4a) - 19 = 32$.

GO Online
Homework Video Tutor
Visit: PHSchool.com
Web Code: ade-0702

30. **Birdhouses** Together, Donal, Yolanda, and Iris made 27 birdhouses for a school fair. Yolanda made n birdhouses. Donal made one more birdhouse than Yolanda, and Iris made one more than Donal. Solve the equation $n + (n + 1) + (n + 1 + 1) = 27$. Find the number of birdhouses each one made.

Geometry For each rectangle, the area is 20 cm². Find the value of x.

31.

4 cm

$(x + 3)$ cm

32.
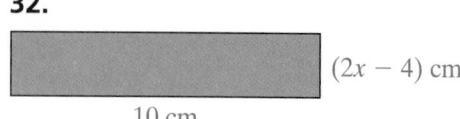
$(2x - 4)$ cm

10 cm

 Challenge

Solve and check each equation.

33. $\frac{1}{3}[2(x - 8) + 1] = 19$

34. $3 = \frac{1}{4}(m - 4) + \frac{1}{4}m$

Number Sense **Find the integers.**

35. The sum of four consecutive odd integers is -72.

36. The sum of five consecutive even integers is 0.

ISAT

Test Prep

Multiple Choice

37. $3(2 + 5) = \underline{\ ?\ }$.
A. $5 + 5$ B. $6 + 5$ C. $6 + 8$ D. $6 + 15$

38. A rectangle has base 5 cm and height $(+ 2)$ cm. Its area is 20 cm². What is the value of x?
F. 2 G. 3.6 H. 4.4 J. 6

39. What is the solution of $-2(- 4) = 12$?
A. -4 B. -2 C. 2 D. 4

Short Response

40. Three consecutive integers have a sum of 63.
a. Write an equation to model this situation. Then solve.
b. Show your work for part (a).

Mixed Review

GO for Help

Lesson 7-1 **Solve each equation.**

41. $10a - 32 = -28$ 42. $5 - 2d = 15$ 43. $\frac{c}{4} - 7 = 5$

Lesson 5-8 44. $\frac{7}{10}a = \frac{3}{5}$ 45. $\frac{2}{7}x = \frac{5}{8}$ 46. $-2\frac{3}{4} = 6\frac{3}{5}b$

Lesson 5-3 47. **Measurement** If you take $\frac{2}{3}$ c of flour from a bowl containing $2\frac{1}{2}$ c of flour, how much flour is left in the bowl?

Multi-Step Equations With Fractions and Decimals

 Assessment Framework

1 Solving Multi-Step Equations With Fractions

Remember, when the coefficient of a variable in an equation is a fraction, you can use the reciprocal to solve the equation.

$$\frac{4}{5}x = 12$$

$$\frac{5}{4} \cdot \frac{4}{5}x = \frac{5}{4} \cdot 12 \qquad \textbf{Multiply each side by } \frac{5}{4}\textbf{, because } \frac{5}{4} \cdot \frac{4}{5} = 1.$$

$$x = 15$$

When you have a multi-step equation and the coefficient of the variable is a fraction, gather the variables on one side of the equation and the constants on the other before multiplying by the reciprocal.

1 EXAMPLE   Using the Reciprocal

Solve $\frac{2}{3}n - 6 = 22$.

$$\frac{2}{3}n - 6 = 22$$

$$\frac{2}{3}n - 6 + 6 = 22 + 6 \qquad \textbf{Add 6 to each side.}$$

$$\frac{2}{3}n = 28 \qquad \textbf{Simplify.}$$

$$\frac{3}{2} \cdot \frac{2}{3}n = \frac{3}{2} \cdot 28 \qquad \textbf{Multiply each side by } \frac{3}{2}\textbf{, the reciprocal of } \frac{2}{3}.$$

$$n = \frac{3 \cdot 28^{14}}{1\,2} \qquad \textbf{Divide common factors.}$$

$$n = 42 \qquad \textbf{Simplify.}$$

Check $\quad \frac{2}{3}n - 6 = 22$

$$\frac{2}{3}(42) - 6 \overset{?}{=} 22 \qquad \textbf{Replace } n \textbf{ with 42.}$$

$$\frac{2 \cdot 42^{14}}{1\,3} - 6 \overset{?}{=} 22 \qquad \textbf{Divide common factors.}$$

$$28 - 6 \overset{?}{=} 22 \qquad \textbf{Multiply.}$$

$$22 = 22 \checkmark$$

✓ Quick Check

1. Solve each equation.

  a. $-\frac{7}{10}k + 14 = -21$ **b.** $\frac{2}{3}(m - 6) = 3$

8.8.12 Solve linear equations and inequalities in one variable over the rational numbers.

8.8.13 Solve word problems involving unknown quantities.

✓ **Check Skills You'll Need**

Solve each equation.

1. $2n + 53 = 47$

2. $4m - 37 = -28$

3. $-26x - 4 = 100$

4. $-3a + 15 = 13$

GO for Help
Lesson 7-1

GO for Help

For a guide to fractions and reciprocals, see pages 254, 272, and Skills Handbook page 796.

GO ● **nline**

Video Tutor Help
Visit: PHSchool.com
Web Code: ada-0775

You can use the Multiplication Property of Equality to simplify the solving of an equation involving fractions. Use the LCM of the denominators to clear the equation of fractions.

GO for Help

For a guide to finding the least common multiple (LCM), see Lesson 5-1.

2 EXAMPLE Using the LCM

Solve $\frac{2}{5}x + 2 = \frac{3}{4}$.

$$\frac{2}{5}x + 2 = \frac{3}{4}$$

$$20\left(\frac{2}{5}x + 2\right) = 20\left(\frac{3}{4}\right)$$ **Multiply each side by 20, the LCM of 5 and 4.**

$$20 \cdot \frac{2}{5}x + 20 \cdot 2 = 20\left(\frac{3}{4}\right)$$ **Use the Distributive Property.**

$$8x + 40 = 15$$ **Simplify.**

$$8x + 40 - 40 = 15 - 40$$ **Subtract 40 from each side.**

$$8x = -25$$ **Simplify.**

$$\frac{8x}{8} = \frac{-25}{8}$$ **Divide each side by 8.**

$$x = -3\frac{1}{8}$$ **Simplify.**

✓ **Quick Check**

2. Solve each equation.

    a. $-\frac{7}{12} + y = \frac{1}{6}$ **b.** $\frac{1}{3}b - 1 = \frac{5}{6}$

2 Solving Multi-Step Equations With Decimals

You can use the properties of equality to solve equations with decimals.

3 EXAMPLE Real-World Problem Solving

Gridded Response Suppose your cell phone plan is $20 per month plus $.15 per minute. Your bill is $37.25. Use the equation $20 + 0.15x = 37.25$. How many minutes are on your bill?

$$20 + 0.15x = 37.25$$

$$20 - 20 + 0.15x = 37.25 - 20$$ **Subtract 20 from each side.**

$$0.15x = 17.25$$ **Simplify.**

$$\frac{0.15x}{0.15} = \frac{17.25}{0.15}$$ **Divide each side by 0.15.**

$$x = 115$$ **Simplify.**

There are 115 minutes on your bill. Grid 115.

✓ **Quick Check**

3. Solve each equation.

    a. $1.5x - 3.6 = 2.4$ **b.** $1.06p - 3 = 0.71$

You can solve multi-step equations containing decimals by calculating with the decimals or by multiplying by a power of 10 to clear the equation of decimals.

Test-Taking Tip

Read the question carefully. Make sure you understand what you are being asked to do before you begin your work.

More Than One Way

Telephone Services For local telephone service, the McNeils pay $9.95/month plus $.035/min for local calls. Last month, they paid $12.75 for local service. To find the minutes m of local calls, solve the equation $0.035m + 9.95 = 12.75$.

Nicole's Method

I can work with decimals as I have before.

$$0.035m + 9.95 = 12.75$$
$$0.035m + 9.95 - 9.95 = 12.75 - 9.95$$
$$0.035m = 2.8$$
$$\frac{0.035m}{0.035} = \frac{2.8}{0.035}$$
$$m = 80$$

The McNeils made 80 min of local calls.

Daryl's Method

Use multiplication to clear the decimals. Use the decimals with the greatest number of decimal places to decide what power of 10 to use.

$$0.035m + 9.95 = 12.75$$
$$1,000(0.035m + 9.95) = 1,000(12.75)$$
$$35m + 9,950 = 12,750$$
$$35m + 9,950 - 9,950 = 12,750 - 9,950$$
$$35m = 2,800$$
$$\frac{35m}{35} = \frac{2,800}{35}$$
$$m = 80$$

The McNeils made 80 min of local calls.

Choose a Method

1. Which method would you use to find the number of minutes? Explain.

2. In Daryl's method, why was each side of the equation multiplied by 1,000?

EXERCISES

For more exercises, see *Extra Skill and Word Problem Practice.*

Practice and Problem Solving

A Practice by Example

Example 1
(page 361)

State the first step in solving each equation. Do not solve.

1. $\frac{1}{4}x + 3 = 2$ **2.** $-\frac{1}{5}y + 2 = -3$ **3.** $\frac{1}{2}(n - 8) = 6$

GO for Help

Solve each equation.

4. $\frac{5}{8}c - 8 = 12$ **5.** $-8 + \frac{3}{5}g = -2$ **6.** $\frac{3}{4}(b + 8) = 15$

Example 2
(page 362)

Mental Math By what number would you multiply each equation to get an equation without denominators? Do not solve.

7. $\frac{1}{2}h - 1 = \frac{3}{8}$ **8.** $\frac{1}{5}y + 3 = \frac{2}{3}$ **9.** $\frac{7}{10}c - 10 = \frac{2}{5}$

Solve each equation.

10. $\frac{1}{4}c + 2 = \frac{3}{4}$ **11.** $8 - \frac{w}{10} = \frac{3}{5}$ **12.** $\frac{2}{3}(a - 3) = \frac{1}{3}$

Example 3
(page 362)

13. $0.7c - 10 = 0.5$ **14.** $1.2n + 3.4 = 10$

15. $-0.8k - 3.1 = -8.3$ **16.** $0.4b + 9.2 = 10$

17. $0.9x + 2.3x = -6.4$ **18.** $-2d + 4.3 = 10.7$

19. Art Dwayne is taking a drawing class. The drawing pencils cost $.97 apiece and a sketchbook costs $5.95. Dwayne spent a total of $11.77. Solve the equation $0.97n + 5.95 = 11.77$ to find the number n of pencils he bought.

B Apply Your Skills

Solve and check each equation.

20. $\frac{5}{8}(p - 4) = 2$ **21.** $p + \frac{1}{3}p = \frac{2}{3}$ **22.** $0.07x + 9.95 = 12.47$

23. $-\frac{3}{4}y + \frac{1}{4} = \frac{1}{2}$ **24.** $\frac{x}{4} - \frac{3x}{2} = -\frac{1}{2}$ **25.** $2.4b + 5.6 = -11.2$

26. $4x + 2 = -28.4$ **27.** $-\frac{1}{3}(x - 9) = -1$ **28.** $\frac{2}{7}k - \frac{1}{14}k = -3$

29. $0.4(a + 2) = 2$ **30.** $\frac{1}{2}(x - 1) = \frac{1}{2}$ **31.** $1.2c + 2.6c = 4.56$

32. White-Water Rafting Six friends hire a raft and guide to go white-water rafting in Colorado. Each person also buys a souvenir photo of the trip for $25.75. The total each person pays is $90.30. To find the cost c of the raft and guide, solve the equation $\frac{c}{6} + 25.75 = 90.30$.

33. Writing in Math At a 15%-off sale, a customer pays $11.01 for a video. Explain how to solve the equation $p - 0.15p = 11.01$ to find the original price p of the video.

Real-World Connection

White-water rafting trips can be as short as two hours or as long as several days.

34. Sales A pair of athletic shoes is on sale for $\frac{1}{4}$ off the original cost. The sale price is $49.95. Solve the equation $c - \frac{1}{4}c = 49.95$ to find the original cost c of the shoes.

35. Geometry Use the rectangle at the right.
  a. Find the value of x if the area is 15 square units.
  b. Find the value of x if the perimeter is 24 units.

5 units
$\leftarrow(\frac{1}{2}x + 1)$ units$\rightarrow$

 Challenge

Solve and check each equation.

36. $12p + 7 = -15 + 6.5p$ **37.** $5(t - 0.4) = -6t$

38. a. A student has grades of 65, 80, 78, and 92 on four tests. Use s to represent the student's grade on the next test. Write an expression for the average of the five tests.
  b. The student wants to have an average of 80 after the fifth test. Use the expression you wrote in part (a) to write an equation.
  c. Solve the equation to find the grade the student must earn on the fifth test to have an average of 80 for the class.

ISAT

Test Prep

Gridded Response

39. What is the solution of $\frac{1}{2}(4 - 16) = 5$?

40. What is the solution of $7.1 = 3.8 + 5.2$?

41. Last season, you scored 48 points in basketball. This is 6 fewer than twice the number of points Gene scored. How many points did Gene score?

42. A cable television company charges $24.95 a month for basic service and $6.95 a month for each premium channel. If your monthly bill is $45.80, how many premium channels are you receiving?

43. A photograph is 4 in. wide and 5 in. long. You want to enlarge it to triple its dimensions. How many times the area of the original will the area of the enlargement be?

Mixed Review

for Help

Lesson 7-2

Solve each equation.

44. $-9 = 3(y + 4)$ **45.** $x + 7 - 3x = 7$ **46.** $5(t - 8) = 10$

Lesson 6-2 **47. Commuting** Mrs. Milton travels 60 mi round-trip to work. She works five days a week. Her car gets about 25 mi/gal of gasoline. About how many gallons of gasoline does Mrs. Milton's car use during her weekly commute?

Lesson 4-2

Write using exponents.

48. $4 \cdot 4 \cdot 4$ **49.** $c \cdot c \cdot c \cdot c \cdot d$ **50.** $9 \cdot a \cdot a \cdot 2$

Write an Equation

IL **Assessment Framework**

8.8.11 Represent and analyze problems with linear equations and inequalities.

✓ **Check Skills You'll Need**

Write an equation to represent each situation.

1. Pierre bought a puppy for $48. This is $21 less than the original price. What was the original price of the puppy?

2. A tent weighs 6 lb. Together, your backpack and the tent weigh 33 lb. How much does your backpack weigh?

3. A veterinarian weighs 140 lb. She steps on a scale while holding a large dog. The scale shows 192 lb. What is the weight of the dog?

 for Help
Lesson 2-4

1 Write an Equation

Math Strategies in Action You probably recognize Albert Einstein's famous formula, $E = mc^2$. Many scientists write and use equations and formulas every day. Banks use equations to calculate interest and loan information. Statisticians use equations to find sports and population statistics. Doctors use equations to calculate correct doses of medicines.

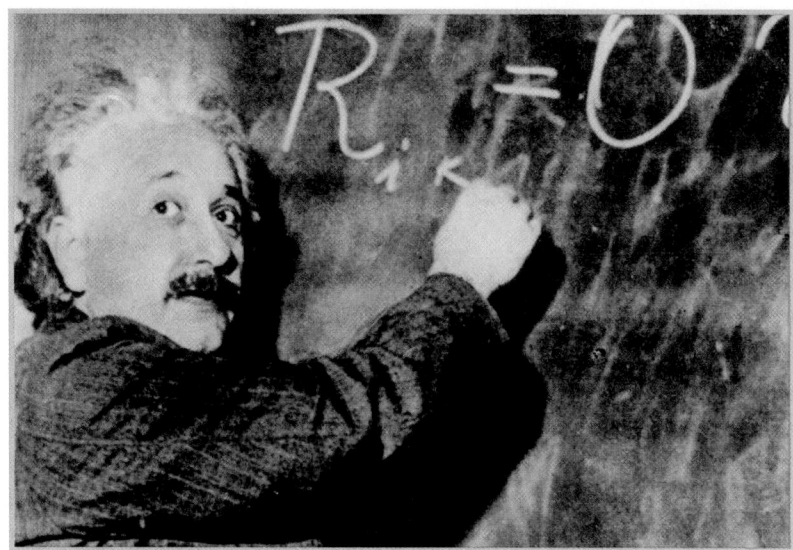

You have written one-step equations for word problems. Now you will extend your skills to more complex situations.

1 EXAMPLE **Real-World** **Problem Solving**

Moving Vans A moving van rents for $29.95 a day plus $.12/mi. Ms. Smith's bill for a two-day rental was $70.46. How many miles did she drive?

Understand the Problem

1. What is the goal of this problem?

2. For how long did Ms. Smith rent the van?

3. What does the van cost without mileage?

4. What is the mileage charge?

Write an equation.

Words	two days	·	price per day	+	cost per mile	·	number of miles	=	$70.46

Let m = the number of miles Ms. Smith drove the van.

Equation	2	·	29.95	+	0.12	·	m	=	70.46

Carry Out the Plan

Solve the equation.

$$2 \cdot 29.95 + 0.12 \cdot m = 70.46$$

$59.9 + 0.12m = 70.46$	**Multiply 2 and 29.95.**
$59.9 - 59.9 + 0.12m = 70.46 - 59.9$	**Subtract 59.9 from each side.**
$0.12m = 10.56$	**Simplify.**
$\dfrac{0.12m}{0.12} = \dfrac{10.56}{0.12}$	**Divide each side by 0.12.**
$m = 88$	**Simplify.**

Ms. Smith drove the van 88 mi.

Check the Answer

You can estimate to check the reasonableness of the answer.

$$\left. \begin{array}{l} 29.95 \approx 30 \\ 0.12 \approx 0.1 \\ 88 \approx 90 \end{array} \right\} \quad \textbf{Round each number.}$$

$2 \cdot 30 + 0.1 \cdot 90 = 60 + 9$	**Multiply.**
$= 69$	**Simplify.**

Since $69 \approx 70.46$, 88 mi is a reasonable answer.

✓ Quick Check

5. a. Suppose that Ms. Smith's bill for the two-day rental was $76.34. How would the equation change? Explain.
   b. Solve the new equation to find how many miles Ms. Smith drove the van.
   c. Estimate to check the reasonableness of your answer to part (b).

6. Mr. Jones rented the same van for three days. His bill was $104.49. How many miles did he drive?

EXERCISES

For more exercises, see *Extra Skill and Word Problem Practice*.

Practice and Problem Solving

A Practice by Example

Example 1
(page 362)

For a guide to reading and solving Exercise 4, see page 370.

Use the *Write an Equation* strategy to solve each problem.

1. The sale price of a sweater is $48. The price is 20% less than the original price. What was the original price?

2. Budgeting Elena has $240 in the bank. She withdraws $15 each week to pay for piano lessons. How many lessons can she afford with her savings?

3. Geometry The perimeter of a rectangle is 64 cm. The length is 4 cm less than twice the width. Find the length and width.

4. Wendy bought a drill at a 10%-off sale. The sale price was $75.60. Find the original price p.

B Apply Your Skills

Solve using any strategy.

5. Lamar's summer job is mowing lawns for a landscaper. His pay is $7.50/h. Lamar also makes $11.25/h for any time over 40 h that he works in one week. He worked 40 h last week plus n overtime hours and made $339.38. How many overtime hours did he work?

6. Number Sense Find two whole numbers with a sum of 15 and a product of 54.

7. Farming A farmer is building a square pen 21 ft on each side. He puts one post at each corner and one post every 3 ft in between. How many posts will he use?

8. It takes 8 painters 6 hours to paint the walls of a gymnasium.
  a. How many person-hours does this job require?
  b. How many hours will 12 painters take to paint the gymnasium?

9. Cathy has a collection of dimes and quarters. The number of dimes equals the number of quarters. She has a total of $2.80. How many of each coin does Cathy have? (*Hint:* Let n = the number of dimes. Since each dime has a value of 10¢, the value of n dimes is $10n$. Since the number of quarters is also n, the value of n quarters is $25n$. Also change the value of $2.80 to its value in cents.)

C Challenge

10. Physics The weight of an object on Venus is about $\frac{9}{10}$ of its weight on Earth. The weight of an object on Jupiter is about $\frac{13}{5}$ times its weight on Earth.
  a. If a rock weighs 23 lb on Venus, how much would it weigh on Earth?
  b. If the same rock were on Jupiter, how much would it weigh?

11. Collections Jackson, Petra, and Tyrone went to the beach and collected seashells over the weekend. Jackson collected s seashells. Petra and Tyrone each collected 13 fewer than twice the number of seashells Jackson collected. At the end of the weekend, they had 94 seashells. How many seashells did each person collect?

Strategies

- Act It Out
- Draw a Diagram
- Guess, Check, Revise
- Look for a Pattern
- Make a Model
- Make a Table
- Simulate the Problem
- Solve by Graphing
- Use Multiple Strategies
- Work a Simpler Problem
- Work Backward
- Write an Equation
- Write a Proportion

GO Online
Homework Video Tutor
Visit: PHSchool.com
Web Code: ade-0704

Test Prep

Multiple Choice

12. What is the solution of $49.95 + 0.6m + 9 = 93.23$ rounded to the nearest whole number?
A. 20   **B.** 57   **C.** 72   **D.** 155

13. What is the solution of $d + 3.95 + 0.25d = 7.70$?
F. 6   **G.** 5   **H.** 4   **J.** 3

14. A car salesman makes a weekly salary of $260 plus 3% of the amount of sales he makes that week. Which equation could be used to find the amount of sales if one week's pay was $1,520?
A. $1,520 = 260 - 0.03x$ **B.** $260 = 1,520 + 0.3x$
C. $1,520 = 260 + 0.03x$ **D.** $260 = 1,520 - 0.3x$

Short Response

15. The perimeter of a rectangle is 15 ft. The height of the rectangle is 3 more than twice its base. **(a)** Write an equation to model this situation. **(b)** Solve the equation and find the height.

Mixed Review

GO for Help

Lesson 7-3

Solve each equation.

16. $\frac{3}{5}k + \frac{1}{5}k = 4$ **17.** $1.4x + 8.8 = 92.8$

Lesson 6-5

Write each percent as a fraction in simplest form and as a decimal.

18. 52%   **19.** 20.5%   **20.** 0.5%   **21.** 205%

Lesson 6-1

22. You can buy 12 pencils for $.80. At this rate, how much will you pay for 27 pencils?

Checkpoint Quiz 1   Lessons 7-1 through 7-4

Solve each equation.

1. $12n + 60 = 300$ **2.** $5y - 9 - 3y = 13$ **3.** $-44 = 3x + 10$

4. $\frac{a}{4} - \frac{3}{4} = \frac{1}{4}$ **5.** $\frac{4}{7}x - 3 = 13$ **6.** $-\frac{x}{6} - 8 = 0$

7. $0.6x + 1.9x = 5$ **8.** $10(5 + m) = 63$ **9.** $2c + 4 + 3c = -26$

10. $\frac{1}{5}(x + 10) = 2$ **11.** $7(2y - 1) = 7$ **12.** $3a + 9 = 27$

Write an equation for each situation. Then solve.

13. Gloria bought a suit at a 25%-off sale. The sale price was $82.50. Find the original price.

14. **Number Sense** Three consecutive integers have a sum of 132. Find the integers.

Understanding Math Problems Read through the problem below.
Then let Elena's thinking guide you through the solution. Check your
understanding with the exercise at the bottom of the page.

Wendy bought a drill at a 10%-off sale. The sale price was $75.60.
Find the original price p.

What Elena Thinks	What Elena Writes
What information is given in the problem? I'll write it down.	A drill was on sale for 10% off. The sale price was $75.60.
What am I trying to find out? I'll write out the question.	What was the original price?
I know that 10% off means that you subtract 10% of the original price from the original price. I'll write this as an equation in words.	Original price minus 10% of the original price is the sale price, $75.60.
I'll use a variable for the original price. And I'll write 10% as the decimal 0.1.	$p - 0.1p = 75.60$
I can write p as $1p$ so that I can subtract like terms. Then I will simplify.	$1p - 0.1p = 75.60$ $0.9p = 75.60$
To finish solving the equation, I divide both sides by 0.9.	$\frac{0.9}{0.9}p = \frac{75.60}{0.9}$ $p = 84$
Is $84.00 a reasonable answer? 10% of 84 is about 8, and $84 - 8$ is 76. This is close to $75.60. Yes, my answer is reasonable.	The original price of the drill was $84.00.

EXERCISE

1. Tanya got a 5% raise at her job at the video store. She now makes
   $6.51 per hour. How much did she make per hour before the raise?

Solving Equations With Variables on Both Sides

1 Solving Equations With Variables on Both Sides

ctivity

Using Models to Solve Equations

Work in pairs.

1. Write an equation for the model at the right.

2. **a.** You must do the same thing to each side of the model. What can you do to get green tiles on only one side?
   b. Show what the model will look like when green tiles are on only one side. Write the new equation.
   c. Solve your new equation.

To solve an equation with a variable on both sides, use addition or subtraction to collect the variable on one side of the equation.

8.8.12 Solve linear equations and inequalities in one variable over the rational numbers.

8.8.13 Solve word problems involving unknown quantities.

✓ Check Skills You'll Need
Solve each equation.

1. $k + 3k = 20$

2. $8x - 3x = 35$

3. $3b + 2 - b = -18$

4. $-8 - y + 7y = 40$

GO for Help
Lesson 7-2

1 EXAMPLE   Collecting the Variable on One Side

Solve $9a + 2 = 4a - 18$.

$$9a + 2 = 4a - 18$$

$9a - 4a + 2 = 4a - 4a - 18$ **Subtract 4a from each side.**

$5a + 2 = -18$ **Combine like terms.**

$5a + 2 - 2 = -18 - 2$ **Subtract 2 from each side.**

$5a = -20$ **Simplify.**

$\dfrac{5a}{5} = \dfrac{-20}{5}$ **Divide each side by 5.**

$a = -4$ **Simplify.**

Check $9a + 2 = 4a - 18$

$9(-4) + 2 \stackrel{?}{=} 4(-4) - 18$ **Substitute −4 for a.**

$-36 + 2 \stackrel{?}{=} -16 - 18$ **Multiply.**

$-34 = -34$ ✓

GO ●nline

Video Tutor Help
Visit: PHSchool.com
Web Code: ada-0775

✓ Quick Check

1. Solve and check each equation.

   a. $4x + 4 = 2x + 36$ **b.** $-15 + 6b = -8b + 13$

2 | Using Equations With Variables on Both Sides

You may need to use the Distributive Property to simplify one or both sides of an equation before you can get the variable alone on one side.

2 EXAMPLE   Real-World Problem Solving

Bicycling Beth leaves home on her bicycle, riding at a steady rate of 8 mi/h. Her brother Ted leaves home on his bicycle half an hour later, following Beth's route. He rides at a steady rate of 12 mi/h. How long after Beth leaves home will Ted catch up?

Real-World Connection

An estimated 87 million people in the United States ride bicycles.

distance Beth travels = distance Ted travels

Words 8 mi/h · Beth's time = 12 mi/h · Ted's time

Let x = Beth's time.

Then $x - \frac{1}{2}$ = Ted's time.

Equation 8 · x = 12 · $\left(x - \frac{1}{2}\right)$

$$8x = 12\left(x - \frac{1}{2}\right)$$

$8x = 12x - 6$	**Use the Distributive Property.**
$8x - 12x = 12x - 12x - 6$	**Subtract 12x from each side.**
$-4x = -6$	**Combine like terms.**
$\frac{-4x}{-4} = \frac{-6}{-4}$	**Divide each side by −4.**
$x = \frac{6}{4}$, or $1\frac{1}{2}$	**Simplify.**

Ted will catch up with Beth $1\frac{1}{2}$ h after she leaves home.

Check Test the result.

At 8 mi/h, Beth will ride 12 mi in $1\frac{1}{2}$ h.

Ted's time is $\frac{1}{2}$ h less than Beth's. He rides for 1 h.

At 12 mi/h, he travels 12 mi in all.

Since Beth and Ted each travel 12 mi, the answer checks.

✓ Quick Check

2. **Travel Time** Car A leaves Eastown traveling at a steady rate of 50 mi/h. Car B leaves Eastown 1 h later following Car A. It travels at a steady rate of 60 mi/h. How long after Car A leaves Eastown will Car B catch up?

EXERCISES

For more exercises, see *Extra Skill and Word Problem Practice*.

Practice and Problem Solving

 Practice by Example

Example 1
(page 371)

 for Help

Copy and complete the steps to each equation.

1.
$$-2a + 7 = a - 8$$
$$-2a + 7 - a = a - 8 - \blacksquare$$
$$\blacksquare + 7 = -8$$
$$\blacksquare + 7 - 7 = -8 - 7$$
$$\blacksquare = -15$$
$$\blacksquare = \frac{-15}{-3}$$
$$a = \blacksquare$$

2.
$$2x + 16 = -x - 5$$
$$2x + 16 + \blacksquare = -x - 5 + \blacksquare$$
$$\blacksquare + 16 = -5$$
$$3x + 16 - \blacksquare = -5 - \blacksquare$$
$$\blacksquare = -21$$
$$\frac{\blacksquare}{3} = \frac{-21}{3}$$
$$x = \blacksquare$$

Solve each equation.

3. $3y - 20 = 8y$
4. $x - 7 = 2x - 6$
5. $5x + 8 = 7x$

6. $3a = a + 22$
7. $2a + 6 = -a - 8$
8. $4w + 8 = 6w - 4$

9. $q + q + q = q + 6$
10. $b + b + 18 = 4b$

Example 2
(page 372)

11. $2(x - 4) = 3x$
12. $7a = 2(a - 10)$

13. $5(n - 3) = 2n - 6$
14. $4(8 - y) = 2y + 16$

15. $2n = 4(n - 8)$
16. $3(y + 7) = 10y$

17. Aviation A jet leaves an airport traveling at a steady rate of 600 km/h. Another jet leaves the same airport $\frac{3}{4}$ h later traveling at 800 km/h in the same direction. How long will it take the second jet to overtake the first?

B **Apply Your Skills**

Solve each equation.

18. $\frac{1}{2}(4d - 2) = d + 5$
19. $20.6 + 2.1x = -8.2x$

20. $-2(y + 6) = y + 3 + 2y$
21. $6(g + 3) = -2(g + 31)$

22. $7a - 4 + 2a = 3a - 2$
23. $3(2y - 0.3) = 19.4 - y$

24. Open-Ended Write a problem that you can represent with an equation with variables on both sides. Write and solve the equation.

Write an equation for each situation. Then solve.

25. Number Sense If a number n is subtracted from 18, the result is four less than n. What is the value of n?

26. Multiple Choice A group of campers and one group leader left a campsite in a canoe traveling at a steady 8 km/h. One hour later, the other group leader left the campsite in a motorboat with the supplies. The motorboat followed the canoe at a steady 20 km/h. How long after the canoe left the campsite did the motorboat overtake it?

    Ⓐ $2\frac{1}{2}$ h   Ⓑ $1\frac{2}{3}$ h   Ⓒ $\frac{3}{4}$ h   Ⓓ $\frac{2}{5}$ h

GO Online
Homework Video Tutor
Visit: PHSchool.com
Web Code: ade-0705

Online lesson quiz, PHSchool.com, Web Code: ada-0705   **7-5 Solving Equations With Variables on Both Sides**   **373**

$$8x + 36 = 4(7 - x)$$
$$8x + 36 = 28 - 4x$$
$$4x + 36 = 28$$
$$4x = -8$$
$$x = -2$$

27. Error Analysis The student who solved the equation at the left made an error. Find the error. State the correct solution.

28. Cell Phones A cellular phone company charges a $27.95 monthly fee and $.12/min for local calls. Another company charges $12.95 a month and $.32/min for local calls. For what number of minutes of local calls are the costs of the plans the same?

29. Writing in Math Describe the steps you would use to solve the equation $5(2a - 3) = 20 + a$.

C Challenge

Solve each equation.

30. $9 - (2k - 3) = k$

31. $2\left(2a + \frac{1}{2}\right) = 3\left(a - \frac{2}{3}\right)$

32. Mental Math Is the solution to $5b = 2b - 42 - 3b$ positive or negative? Explain.

33. Video Rental A video store offers two types of rental cards. Each rental card is good for six months. The gold rental card costs $25 plus $1.75/rental. The silver rental card costs $10 plus $3.25/rental. Explain why someone would prefer one card over the other.

34. Reasoning To solve $\frac{2}{3}b = 10 - b$, you can first (a) multiply each side by $\frac{3}{2}$, (b) multiply each side by 3, or (c) add b to each side. Which first step do you prefer? Why? What is the solution?

ISAT

Test Prep

Short Response   Read the passage below before doing Exercises 35 and 36.

An Algebraic Riddle

Diophantus was a Greek mathematician who lived in the third century. He was one of the first mathematicians to use algebraic symbols.

Most of what is known about Diophantus's life comes from an algebraic riddle from around the early sixth century. The riddle states, "Diophantus's youth lasted one sixth of his life. He grew a beard after one twelfth more. After one seventh more of his life he married. Five years later he and his wife had a son. The son lived exactly one half as long as his father, and Diophantus died four years after his son. All of this adds up to the years Diophantus lived." The riddle, the "facts" of which may or may not be true, results in the following equation:

$$\tfrac{1}{6}a + \tfrac{1}{12}a + \tfrac{1}{7}a + 5 + \tfrac{1}{2}a + 4 = a$$

where a is Diophantus's age at the time of his death.

35. How many years did Diophantus live?

36. How old was Diophantus when he married?

Multiple Choice

37. To which expression does $3(a + 2b) - 3a$ simplify?
  A. $-6a + 6b$ **B.** $3a + 6b$ **C.** $2b$ **D.** $6b$

38. What is the solution of $6(k - 2) = 3k - 6$?
  F. -6 **G.** 2 **H.** $-\frac{4}{3}$ **J.**

39. What is the solution of $2(2x + 3) = -3(x + 5)$?
  A. -7 **B.** $-\frac{21}{5}$ **C.** -3 **D.** $\frac{9}{7}$

40. The Garners rented a moving van for $59.95 plus $.50/mi. Before returning the van, they filled the gas tank, which cost $21.50. The total cost for renting the van, including gas, was $199.45. To the nearest mile, how many miles did the Garners drive the van?
  F. 519 mi   **G.** 279 mi   **H.** 236 mi   **J.** 70 mi

Mixed Review

Lesson 6-9   **Find the price after each discount or markup.**

41. $15; 25% discount   **42.** $88; 32% markup

43. $24; 72% markup   **44.** $110; 75% discount

Lesson 2-10   **Solve and graph each inequality.**

45. $-4x < 32$ **46.** $\frac{a}{-9} \geq -3$ **47.** $-12 < 3y$ **48.** $12 \leq -2y$

Lesson 1-8 **49. Collections** In a collection of dimes and quarters, there are seven more quarters than there are dimes. How many dimes and quarters are there if the collection is worth $3.50?

Math at Work

City Planner

City planners, also called urban planners or regional planners, determine the best use of a community's land and resources for homes, businesses, and recreation. They also work on community problems such as traffic congestion and air pollution. They study the effects of proposed changes in a community, such as the addition of a bus line or a new highway. Planners use mathematical analysis to evaluate different courses of action and to predict the impact of each course on a community.

Go Online
PHSchool.com   **For:** Information about city planners
Web Code: adb-2031

Using Tables to Solve Equations

You can use tables on a graphing calculator to solve one-variable equations.

1 ACTIVITY

Solve $x + 9 = 3x - 7$.

Press Y= and enter

$Y_1 = x + 9$
$Y_2 = 3x - 7$

In **TBLSET**, set TBLStart = 0 and ΔTbl = 1.

In **TABLE**, compare the Y_1 and Y_2 values. $Y_1 = Y_2 = 17$ for X = 8.

X	Y_1	Y_2
3	12	2
4	13	5
5	14	8
6	15	11
7	16	14
8	17	17
9	18	20
X=8		

• The solution of $x + 9 = 3x - 7$ is 8.

2 ACTIVITY

Solve $x + 3 = 3x - 4$.

Enter $Y_1 = x + 3$
$Y_2 = 3x - 4$

In **TABLE**, compare the Y_1 and Y_2 values. Y_1 values are greater than Y_2 values until X changes from 3 to 4. This suggests that $Y_1 = Y_2$ somewhere between 3 and 4.

In **TBLSET**, set TblStart = 3 and ΔTbl = 0.1.

In **TABLE**, compare the Y_1 and Y_2 values. $Y_1 = Y_2 = 6.5$ for X = 3.5.

X	Y_1	Y_2
3	6	5
3.1	6.1	5.3
3.2	6.2	5.6
3.3	6.3	5.9
3.4	6.4	6.2
3.5	6.5	6.5
3.6	6.6	6.8
X=3.5		

• The solution of $x + 3 = 3x - 4$ is 3.5.

EXERCISES

Solve each equation. Round to the nearest tenth where necessary.

1. $p - 5 = 7$

2. $3x = 21$

3. $2y + 5 = 14$

4. $2x + x + 3 = 15$

5. $7m - 3m - 6 = 6$

6. $15 = -3(2q - 1)$

7. $6x - 2 = x + 13$

8. $3y + 12 = 5y - 3$

9. $2n - 5 = 8n + 7$

10. $6a - 9 = -a + 30$

11. $72 - 8c = 32 + 6c$

12. $-2b - 13 = 4b - 10$

13. Use graphing calculator tables to solve the equation $4(x - 2) = -3(x - 6)$. Find the solution to as many places as possible until "table breakdown" occurs. Then solve the equation using pencil and paper. Compare your two results.

Solving Two-Step Inequalities

Assessment Framework

1 | Solving Two-Step Inequalities

You solve two-step inequalities and equations using similar steps.

8.8.12 Solve linear equations and inequalities in one variable over the rational numbers.

8.8.13 Solve word problems involving unknown quantities.

1 EXAMPLE Undoing Operations

Solve and graph $2y - 3 \leq -5$.

$$2y - 3 \leq -5$$

$2y - 3 + 3 \leq -5 + 3$ **Add 3 to each side.**

$\quad\quad 2y \leq -2$ **Simplify.**

$\quad\quad \dfrac{2y}{2} \leq \dfrac{-2}{2}$ **Divide each side by 2.**

$\quad\quad y \leq -1$ **Simplify.**

✓ Quick Check

1. Solve and graph each inequality.

a. $5a - 9 > 11$ **b.** $-10 \geq \frac{1}{2}x - 6$ **c.** $17 + \frac{1}{2}c < 14$

✓ **Check Skills You'll Need**

Solve each inequality. Graph the solutions.

1. $w + 4 \geq -5$

2. $7 < z - 3$

3. $4 > a + 6$

4. $x - 5 \leq -6$

GO for Help
Lesson 2-9

Remember to reverse the direction of the inequality symbol when you multiply or divide by a negative number.

2 EXAMPLE Reversing the Inequality Symbol

Solve $-9 > -\frac{1}{3}x + 6$.

$$-9 > -\tfrac{1}{3}x + 6$$

$-9 - 6 > -\tfrac{1}{3}x + 6 - 6$ **Subtract 6 from each side.**

$\quad\quad -15 > -\tfrac{1}{3}x$ **Simplify.**

$\quad\quad -3(-15) < -3(-\tfrac{1}{3}x)$ **Multiply each side by −3. Reverse the direction of the inequality symbol.**

$\quad\quad 45 < x, \text{ or } x > 45$ **Simplify.**

Problem Solving Hint
If $a > b$ and $c > 0$, then $ac > bc$.
If $a > b$ and $c < 0$, then $ac < bc$.

✓ Quick Check

2. Solve and graph each inequality.

a. $-2m + 4 \leq 34$ **b.** $6 - x > 3$ **c.** $8.3 < -0.5b - 2.7$

Now that you know how to solve two-step inequalities, you can use them to solve real-world problems.

3 EXAMPLE Real-World Problem Solving

Hiking An expedition leader estimates that a group of hikers can carry less than 550 lb of food and equipment. The group must carry 336 lb of equipment as well as 25 lb of food for each climber. What is the greatest possible number of people in the expedition?

Real-World Connection

A pint of water weighs 1 lb. You need about a gallon of water per person per day.

| **Words** | 336 lb of equipment | + | 25 lb of food/ person | times | number of people | is less than | 550 lb |

Let p = the number of people in the expedition.

Inequality   336   +   25   · p <   550

Solve the inequality.

$$336 + 25p < 550$$
$$336 + 25p - 336 < 550 - 336 \quad \textbf{Subtract 336 from each side.}$$
$$25p < 214 \quad \textbf{Simplify.}$$
$$\frac{25p}{25} < \frac{214}{25} \quad \textbf{Divide each side by 25.}$$
$$p < 8.56 \quad \textbf{Simplify.}$$

The greatest possible number of people in the expedition is 8.

Problem Solving Hint
Since $p < 8.56$, the "greatest number of people" must be the greatest whole number less than 8.56.

Check Is the answer reasonable? The original problem states that the total of the equipment plus 25 lb of food per person is less than 550 lb. Since $336 + 25(8) = 536$, the equipment plus the food is less than 550 lb. The answer is reasonable.

✓ Quick Check

3. **Commissions** A stereo salesperson earns a salary of $1,900 per month, plus a commission of 4% of sales. The salesperson wants to maintain a monthly income of at least $2,200. How much must the salesperson sell each month?

EXERCISES

For more exercises, see *Extra Skill and Word Problem Practice*.

Practice and Problem Solving

A Practice by Example

Example 1
(page 377)

 for Help

Tell what you can do to the first inequality in order to get the second. Be sure to list *all* steps.

1. $4x - 2 \le 6; x \le 2$

2. $\frac{1}{2}a - 1 < 3; a < 8$

Solve and graph each inequality.

3. $10 + 4a < -6$

4. $2m + 8 > 0$

5. $6 + 3y > 5$

6. $4x - 9 > -7$

7. $\frac{1}{3}a - 4 \ge -1$

8. $4 + 7a \ge 32$

Example 2
(page 377)

9. $-2x - 1 < 11$

10. $-\frac{b}{7} + 7 \le 6$

11. $2.1 - 0.6y \ge 0.9$

12. $10 \le -8x - 6$

13. $-5y + 3 \ge 28$

14. $-21 - 3m < 0$

Example 3
(page 378)

15. Travel On a trip from Louisiana to Florida, your family wants to travel at least 420 miles in 8 hours of driving. Write and solve an inequality to find what your average speed must be.

16. Number Sense You divide a number x by -3. Then you subtract 1 from the quotient. The result is at most 5. Write and solve an inequality to find all possible solutions.

B Apply Your Skills

Solve each inequality.

17. $-\frac{1}{9}c + 13 \ge 5$

18. $\frac{x}{3} + 11 < 31$

19. $6y - 10 - y > 14$

20. $-\frac{x}{6} - 2 < 4$

21. $\frac{1}{2}c - \frac{1}{4} < -\frac{3}{4}$

22. $-4(2a + 7) \le -12$

Write an inequality for each situation. Then solve.

23. Photography Maureen is ordering photographic reprints and enlargements. She can spend at most $11. She wants to order an 11-in. × 14-in. enlargement and some 3-in. × 5-in. reprints. How many reprints can she order using the price list at the left?

Photo Price List	
Size	Price
3 in. x 5 in.	$.40
4 in. x 6 in.	$.45
5 in. x 7 in.	$1.95
8 in. x 10 in.	$4.95
8 in. x 12 in.	$6.45
11 in. x 14 in.	$7.00
16 in. x 20 in.	$13.95
20 in. x 30 in.	$16.95

24. You want to spend at most $10 for a taxi ride. Before you go anywhere, the taxi driver sets the meter at the initial charge of $2. The meter then adds $1.25 for every mile driven. If you plan on a $1 tip, what is the farthest you can go?

25. Multiple Choice Students in a math class need an average of at least 90 points to earn an A. One student's test scores are 88, 91, and 85. What must the student score on the next test to earn an A?

Ⓐ 88 or above
Ⓑ 90 or above
Ⓒ 96 or above
Ⓓ 98 or above

26. Error Analysis A student solved and graphed the inequality $-12x + 40 > 4$. What error did the student make?

27. Writing in Math A friend was absent from class today. Write a letter to your friend telling how to solve two-step inequalities.

Challenge 🌐 **28. Borrowing** Corey's parents agree to loan Corey $182 to help pay for the school's spring music trip to Florida. Corey agrees to monthly payback amounts of $2, $4, $6, $8, and so on. How long will it take Corey to pay back the $182?

🌐 **29. Sightseeing** You and a friend want to spend at most $20 each on a horse-carriage sightseeing ride. There is an initial charge of $5 and then $2.50 for each quarter-mile driven. You plan on giving a $6 tip. For how many miles can you ride in the carriage?

ISAT

Test Prep

Multiple Choice **30.** Which sign correctly completes
$43(2) - (-3) \blacksquare -58 + (-4)12$?

   A. $\leq$ **B.** $<$ **C.** $=$ **D.** $>$

31. Which graph shows the solution of $-15 < -2x - 7$?

32. Which graph shows the solution of $-15 \geq 7x + 20$?

Extended Response **33.** The perimeter of a triangle is at most 32 cm. One side is 11 cm long. The other two sides are the same length. **(a)** What are the possible lengths of the two congruent sides? **(b)** Draw a diagram and show your work. **(c)** Explain your process.

Mixed Review

Lesson 7-2   **Solve each equation.**

34. $a - 81 = 9a + 7$ **35.** $8x - 15 + 4x = 5x + 6$

Lesson 6-6 🌐 **36. Sales Tax** A stereo costs $262.99. The sales tax rate is 5%. What is the total cost of the stereo?

Lesson 3-4   **Use the distance formula, $d = rt$. Find each missing value.**

37. $r = 45$ mi/h, $t = 3.25$ h   **38.** $d = 351$ mi, $r = 54$ mi/h

39. $d = 12$ cm, $t = 0.25$ h   **40.** $d = 147.825$ mi, $t = 2.25$ h

Activity Lab

Compound Inequalities

For Use With Lesson 7-6

A **compound inequality** is a statement in which two inequalities are joined by the word *and* or the word *or*.

$x > 4$ and $x \le 6$

A solution of a compound inequality joined by *and* is any number that makes both inequalities true.

$x \le -2$ or $x > 3$

A solution of a compound inequality joined by *or* is any number that makes either inequality true.

EXAMPLE

Graph each compound inequality on a number line.

a. $2 \le x$ and $x < 6$

A closed circle shows 2 is a solution.

An open circle shows 6 is not a solution.

$2 \le x$ and $x < 6$

b. $z > 4$ or $z \le 1$

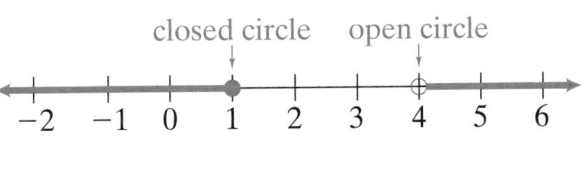

closed circle   open circle

$z > 4$ or $z \le 1$

EXERCISES

Graph each compound inequality.

1. $x \ge 0$ and $x \le 7$

2. $z < -2$ and $z \ge -4$

3. $5 > a$ and $a \ge -6$

4. $b < -1$ or $b > 4$

5. $c < 2$ or $c > 3.5$

6. $y \ge 1$ or $y < -3$

7. $x \le 4$ and $x \ge 3$

8. $n \le -5$ or $n > 0$

9. $3 > m$ and $m > -3$

10. <u>Writing in Math</u> Explain why there are no solutions of the compound inequality $x > 2$ and $x \le 2$.

7-7 Transforming Formulas

✓ **Check Skills You'll Need**

Use each formula for the values given.

1. Use the formula $d = rt$ to find d when $r = 80$ km/h and $t = 4$ h.

2. Use the formula $P = 2\ell + 2w$ to find P when $\ell = 9$ m and $w = 7$ m.

3. Use the formula $A = \frac{1}{2}bh$ to find A when $b = 12$ ft and $h = 8$ ft.

GO for Help
Lesson 3-4

For: Solving Formulas Activity
Use: Interactive Textbook, 7-7

---

1 Solving Formulas for a Given Variable

Remember that a formula shows the relationship between two or more quantities. You can use the properties of equality to transform a formula to represent one quantity in terms of another.

1 EXAMPLE **Transforming in One Step**

Solve the area formula $A = \ell w$ for ℓ.

$A = \ell w$

$\dfrac{A}{w} = \dfrac{\ell w}{w}$ **Divide each side by w.**

$\dfrac{A}{w} = \ell$, or $\ell = \dfrac{A}{w}$ **Simplify.**

✓ **Quick Check**

1. Solve for the variable indicated in red.

     a. $p = s - c$ **b.** $h = \dfrac{k}{j}$ **c.** $I = prt$

Sometimes you need to use more than one step.

2 EXAMPLE **Using More Than One Step**

Solve the perimeter formula $P = 2\ell + 2w$ for ℓ.

$P = 2\ell + 2w$

$P - 2w = 2\ell + 2w - 2w$ **Subtract $2w$ from each side.**

$P - 2w = 2\ell$ **Simplify.**

$\frac{1}{2}(P - 2w) = \frac{1}{2}(2\ell)$ **Multiply each side by $\frac{1}{2}$.**

$\frac{1}{2}P - w = \ell$ **Use the Distributive Property and simplify.**

✓ **Quick Check**

2. Solve for the variable indicated in red.

     a. $5a + 7 = b$ **b.** $P = 2\ell + 2w$ **c.** $y = \frac{x}{3} + 8$

2 Using Formulas to Solve Problems

You can transform formulas to solve real-world problems.

3 EXAMPLE Real-World Problem Solving

Travel You plan a 425-mi trip to Bryce Canyon National Park. You estimate you will average 50 mi/h. To find about how long the trip will take, solve the distance formula $d = rt$ for t. Then substitute to find the time.

$d = rt$

$\dfrac{d}{r} = \dfrac{rt}{r}$ **Divide each side by r.**

$\dfrac{d}{r} = t$, or $t = \dfrac{d}{r}$ **Simplify.**

$t = \dfrac{425}{50} = 8.5$ **Replace d with 425 and r with 50. Simplify.**

It will take you about 8.5 h to complete the trip.

✓ Quick Check

● **3.** Solve the distance formula in Example 3 for r.

4 EXAMPLE Real-World 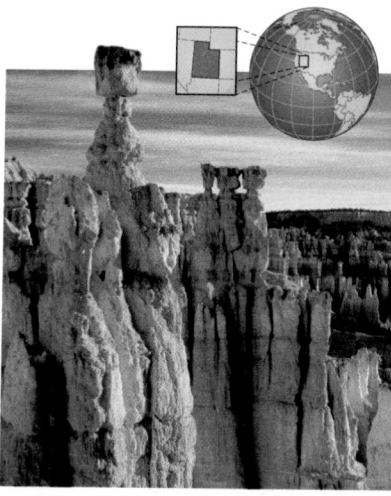 Problem Solving

Multiple Choice An exchange student in your class wants to know the Celsius equivalent of 77°F. Use the formula $F = \frac{9}{5}C + 32$. What is the Celsius equivalent of 77°F?

Ⓐ 81°C   Ⓑ 60.6°C   Ⓒ 45°C   Ⓓ 25°C

$F = \frac{9}{5}C + 32$

$F - 32 = \frac{9}{5}C + 32 - 32$ **Subtract 32 from each side.**

$F - 32 = \frac{9}{5}C$ **Simplify.**

$\frac{5}{9}(F - 32) = \frac{5}{9} \cdot \frac{9}{5}C$ **Multiply each side by $\frac{5}{9}$.**

$\frac{5}{9}(F - 32) = C$, or $C = \frac{5}{9}(F - 32)$ **Simplify and rewrite.**

$C = \frac{5}{9}(77 - 32) = 25$ **Replace F with 77. Simplify.**

77°F is 25°C. The answer is D.

✓ Quick Check

● **4.** Solve the batting average formula, $a = \frac{h}{n}$, for h. Find the number of hits h a batter needs in 40 times at bat n to have an average of 0.275.

Real-World 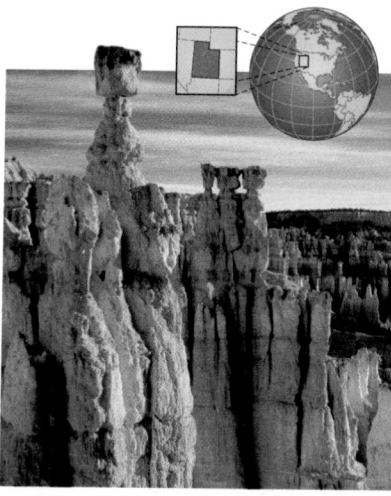 **Connection**

Wind and water, rushing along stone plateaus, erode the stone and create shapes called "fins" and "hoodoos" in Bryce Canyon, Utah. Each year, more than 1.5 million people visit the national park.

 Test-Taking Tip

Formulas can appear in many different forms on a test. Make sure you use the form that will give you the correct answer.

EXERCISES

For more exercises, see *Extra Skill and Word Problem Practice.*

Practice and Problem Solving

 Practice by Example

Examples 1 and 2
(page 382)

 for Help

Complete the steps to solve each equation for the variable indicated in red.

1. $a = 6c + 3$

$a - \blacksquare = 6c + 3 - 3$

$a - \blacksquare = 6c$

$\dfrac{a - 3}{\blacksquare} = \dfrac{6c}{\blacksquare}$

$\dfrac{a - 3}{\blacksquare} = \blacksquare$

2. $g = \dfrac{h}{j}$

$\blacksquare g = j\left(\dfrac{h}{j}\right)$

$jg = \blacksquare$

$\dfrac{jg}{\blacksquare} = \dfrac{h}{g}$

$\blacksquare = \dfrac{h}{g}$

Solve for the variable indicated in red.

3. $V = \ell w h$

4. $P = 4s$

5. $q = \dfrac{p}{d}$

6. $r = 2s - 8$

7. $\dfrac{2}{3}m - 5 = n$

8. $m = \dfrac{a + b}{2}$

Examples 3 and 4
(page 383)

9. Commissions LaTanya sells business suits and gets a 4% commission on her sales. Last week, she received a paycheck that included $196 in commissions. Solve the formula $C = 0.04s$ for s, where C is the amount of commission and s is the amount of sales. Substitute to find LaTanya's sales.

10. Renting You have $12.00 to rent a pair of in-line skates. They rent for $3.00 plus $1.50 per hour. To determine the maximum length of time you can rent the in-line skates, solve the formula $C = 3 + 1.5h$ for h. Then substitute 12 for C.

 Apply Your Skills

Solve for the variable indicated in red.

11. $V = \dfrac{1}{2}\pi r^2 h$

12. $d^2 = \dfrac{3}{2}h$

13. $A = \dfrac{1}{2}(a + b)h$

GO Online
Homework Video Tutor
Visit: PHSchool.com
Web Code: ade-0707

14. a. Construction Bricklayers use the formula $N = 7LH$ to estimate the number N of bricks needed in a wall. L is the length of the wall and H is the height. Solve the formula for H.
  b. If 1,134 bricks are used to build a wall that is 18 ft long, how high is the wall?

15. Writing in Math A formula for the perimeter of a rectangle is $P = 2(b + h)$. Explain how you would find the height of the rectangle if you knew the perimeter and the base.

Challenge **16. a. Economics** Joe uses the formula $p = wh + 1.5wv$ to figure his weekly pay. In the formula, p is the weekly pay, w is the hourly wage, h is the number of regular hours, and v is the number of overtime hours. Solve the formula for v.
  b. Joe's hourly wage is $6.24/h. If he earned $282.36 last week working 40 regular hours plus overtime, how many hours overtime did he work?

Multiple Choice For Exercises 17–19, what is the correct result when you solve for the variable indicated in red?

17. $z = xy$

A. $x = \frac{z}{y}$ **B.** $x = \frac{y}{z}$ **C.** $x = yz$ **D.** $y = xz$

18. $r = 2s - 8$

F. $s = \frac{r+2}{8}$ **G.** $s = r + 4$ **H.** $s = \frac{r+8}{2}$ **J.** $s = 2r + 16$

19. $\frac{2}{3}m - 5 = n$

A. $m = \frac{2}{3}(n + 5)$ **B.** $m = \frac{3}{2}(n + 5)$

C. $m = \frac{3}{2}n + 5$ **D.** $m = \frac{2}{3}n + 5$

20. Use the batting average formula, $a = \frac{h}{n}$. What is the number of hits h for $a = 0.240$ and $n = 25$?

F. 98   **G.** 7   **H.** 6   **J.** 0

Extended Response **21.** Solve $A = \frac{1}{2}(a + b)h$ twice, once for b and once for h. Explain your process for each solution. Then compare the two processes, stating similarities and differences.

Mixed Review

Lesson 7-6 **Solve each inequality.**

22. $3x - 12 > -6$ **23.** $17 \leq -4a + 5$ **24.** $-\frac{b}{2} + 9 < -3$

Lesson 7-1 **25. Budgeting** Audrey wants to buy a dress for $54. She has $6 already and plans to save $8 each week. In how many weeks will she be able to buy the dress?

Lesson 6-7 **Write and solve an equation. Where necessary, round to the nearest tenth or tenth of a percent.**

26. What percent of 20 is 15?   **27.** 80% of what is 25?

Checkpoint Quiz 2   Lessons 7-5 through 7-7

Solve each equation or inequality.

1. $-8a - 6 = 10$ **2.** $9b + 42 = -12$ **3.** $2c + 6 + 7c = 8$

4. $18y = 12y + 24$ **5.** $2x + 5 = 9x - 16$ **6.** $12(m - 4) = 3m - 3$

7. $15 - 10y < 24$ **8.** $23 > -\frac{x}{2} - 5$ **9.** $1.8x - 3.4 > 5.6$

Solve for the variable indicated in red.

10. $s = g + h$ **11.** $3r + 4 = k$ **12.** $I = prt$

Simple and Compound Interest

6.8.18 Solve number sentences and problems involving fractions, decimals, and percents.

✓ Check Skills You'll Need

Find each amount.

1. 6% of $400

2. 55% of $2,000

3. 4.5% of $700

4. $5\frac{1}{2}$% of $325

GO for Help
Lesson 6-7

🔊 New Vocabulary

• principal
• interest
• interest rate
• simple interest
• compound interest
• balance

1 Simple Interest

When you first deposit money in a savings account, your deposit is called **principal.** The bank takes the money and invests it. In return, the bank pays you **interest** based on the **interest rate.** **Simple interest** is interest paid only on the principal.

Key Concepts | **Simple-Interest Formula**

$$I = prt,$$
where I is the interest, p is the principal,
r is the interest rate per year, and t is the time in years.

1 EXAMPLE Real-World 🌐 Problem Solving

Savings Suppose you deposit $500 in a savings account. The interest rate is 4% per year.

a. Find the simple interest earned in six years. Find the total of principal plus interest.

$I = prt$	Use the simple-interest formula.
$I = 500 \cdot 0.04 \cdot 6$	Replace p with 500, r with 0.04, and t with 6.
$I = 120$	Simplify.
total $= 500 + 120 = 620$	Find the total.

The account will earn $120 in six years. The total of principal plus interest will be $620.

b. Find the interest earned in three months. Find the total of principal plus interest.

$t = \frac{3}{12} = \frac{1}{4} = 0.25$	Write the months as part of a year.
$I = prt$	Use the simple-interest formula.
$I = 500 \cdot 0.04 \cdot 0.25$	Replace p with 500, r with 0.04, and t with 0.25.
$I = 5$	Simplify.
total $= 500 + 5 = 505$	Find the total.

The account will earn $5 in three months. The total of principal plus interest will be $505.

Quick Check

1. Find the simple interest.

   a. principal = $250
      interest rate = 4%
      time = 3 years

   b. principal = $250
      interest rate = 3.5%
      time = 6 months

2 Compound Interest

When a bank pays interest on the principal and on the interest an account has earned, the bank is paying **compound interest.** The principal plus the interest is the **balance,** which becomes the principal on which the bank figures the next interest payment.

Test-Taking Tip

To write a percent as a decimal, move the decimal point two places to the right.

2 EXAMPLE Real-World Problem Solving

Multiple Choice You deposit $400 in an account that earns 5% interest compounded annually (once per year). What is the balance in your account after 4 years? In your last calculation, round to the nearest cent.

Ⓐ $510.51   Ⓑ $486.20   Ⓒ $480.00   Ⓓ $463.05

Principal at Beginning of Year	Interest	Balance
Year 1: $400.00	$400.00 \cdot 0.05 = 20.00$	$400 + 20 = 420.00$
Year 2: $420.00	$420.00 \cdot 0.05 = 21.00$	$420 + 21 = 441.00$
Year 3: $441.00	$441.00 \cdot 0.05 = 22.05$	$441 + 22.05 = 463.05$
Year 4: $463.05	$463.05 \cdot 0.05 = 23.1525$	$463.05 + 23.1525 \approx 486.20$

After four years, the balance is $486.20. The answer is B.

Quick Check

2. Make a table and find the balance. The interest is compounded annually.

   a. principal = $500
      interest rate = 3%
      time = 2 years

   b. principal = $625
      interest rate = 2%
      time = 4 years

Vocabulary Tip

Interest periods:
Annual—1 per year
Semiannual—2 per year
Quarterly—4 per year
Monthly—12 per year
Daily—360 per year
      (not 365)

You can find a balance using compound interest in one step with the compound interest formula and a calculator. An *interest period* is the length of time over which interest is calculated. The interest period can be a year or less than a year.

Key Concepts — Compound-Interest Formula

$$B = p(1 + r)^n,$$

where B is the final balance, p is the principal,
r is the interest rate for each interest period, and
n is the number of interest periods.

Calculator Hint

Remember to use the parentheses on your calculator when evaluating the compound-interest formula.

You can use this formula to solve Example 2.

$B = p(1 + r)^n$

$B = 400(1 + 0.05)^4$ **Replace p with 400, r with 0.05, and n with 4.**

$B \approx 486.20$ **Use a calculator. Round to the nearest cent.**

The balance is $486.20. Using the formula means there are fewer calculations and fewer chances for mistakes.

When interest is compounded semiannually (twice per year), you must *divide* the interest rate by the number of interest periods, which is 2.

$$\frac{6\% \text{ annual}}{\text{interest rate}} \div \frac{2 \text{ interest}}{\text{periods}} = \frac{3\% \text{ semiannual}}{\text{interest rate}}$$

To find the number of payment periods, *multiply* the number of years by the number of interest periods per year.

3 EXAMPLE   <u>Real-World</u> Problem Solving

Online active math

For: Calculating Interest Activity
Use: Interactive Textbook, 7-8

Investing Find the balance on a deposit of $1,000 that earns 4% interest compounded semiannually for 5 years.

The interest rate r for compounding semiannually is $0.04 \div 2$, or 0.02. The number of payment periods n is 5 years $\times$ 2 interest periods per year, or 10.

$B = p(1 + r)^n$ **Use the compound-interest formula.**

$B = 1,000(1 + 0.02)^{10}$ **Replace p with 1,000, r with 0.02, and n with 10.**

$B \approx 1,218.99$ **Use a calculator. Round to the nearest cent.**

The balance is $1,218.99.

✓ Quick Check

3. Find the balance for each account.
   Amount deposited: $900, annual interest: 2%, time: 3 years

   a. compounding annually   b. compounding semiannually

EXERCISES

For more exercises, see *Extra Skill and Word Problem Practice*.

Practice and Problem Solving

A Practice by Example

Example 1
(page 386)

GO for Help

Find the simple interest. Then find the total of principal plus interest.

1. principal = $200
interest rate = 4%
time = 2 years

2. principal = $870
interest rate = 3%
time = 9 months

Example 2
(page 387)

Complete each table. Compound the interest annually. In your last calculation, round to the nearest cent.

3. $3,000 at 4% for 3 years

Principal at Start of Year	Interest	Balance
Year 1: $3,000	▓	▓
Year 2: ▓	▓	▓
Year 3: ▓	▓	▓

4. $10,000 at 6% for 3 years

Principal at Start of Year	Interest	Balance
Year 1: $10,000	▓	▓
Year 2: ▓	▓	▓
Year 3: ▓	▓	▓

Example 3
(page 388)

Find each balance.

5. $495 at 4% compounded annually for 2 years

6. $1,280 at 3% compounded annually for 3 years

7. $2,000 at 2% compounded semiannually for 2 years

8. $15,600 at 3% compounded semiannually for 3 years

B Apply Your Skills

9. Savings You deposit $600 in a savings account for 3 years. The account pays 8% annual interest compounded quarterly.
a. What is the quarterly interest rate?
b. What is the number of payment periods?
c. Find the final balance in the account.

Find each balance.

10. $3,000 at 2% compounded annually for 4 years

11. $500 at a simple-interest rate of 3% for 4 years

12. $35 at a simple-interest rate of 2.5% for 1 year

13. $8,900 at 4.5% compounded semiannually for 5 years

14. $54,500 at 3% compounded semiannually for 9 years

15. $900 at a simple-interest rate of 3.25% for 3 months

16. Multiple Choice Calculate the amount of simple interest on $9,000 deposited at an interest rate of 5% for 2 years.
Ⓐ $900   Ⓑ $922.50   Ⓒ $9,900   Ⓓ $9,922.50

17. Open-Ended Choose an amount of money to be invested and an interest rate. Find the value of the investment after 5 years if the interest is simple interest; if the interest is compounded annually.

18. Writing in Math Explain the difference between simple interest and compound interest.

GO Online
Homework Video Tutor
Visit: PHSchool.com
Web Code: ade-0708

C Challenge   **19. Borrowing** Leroy borrows $800 at 5.3% annual interest compounded semiannually. He makes no payments.
  a. How much will he owe after four years?
  b. How much interest will he owe in four years?

 20. Investing Ling invests $1,000 in an account paying 8% interest.
  a. Compare the account balances after 5 years of simple interest and after 5 years of interest compounded annually.
  b. After how many years of compounded interest will the account balance be about twice Ling's initial investment?
  c. Reasoning What would the simple interest rate have to be for the investment to double in the same amount of time?

Writing in Math

Many banks compound interest on a daily basis. Explain what it means to compound interest daily.

ISAT

Test Prep

Multiple Choice

21. Matthew invests $5,000 at 4% simple interest. About how much interest will he earn in eight months?
  A. $133   **B.** $200   **C.** $5,133   **D.** $5,200

22. Which formula could be used to find the balance on a deposit of $520, earning 7% interest compounded semiannually for 3 years?
  F. $B = 520(1 + 0.035)^3$ **G.** $B = 520(0.07)^3$
  H. $B = 520(1 + 0.035)^6$ **J.** $B = 520(0.07)^6$

23. What is the balance after 8 years on a deposit of $500, earning 7% interest compounded semiannually?
  A. $657.97   **B.** $658.40   **C.** $856.91   **D.** $866.99

Short Response

24. A savings account pays 4% simple interest.
  a. How much interest does an $800 deposit earn in 4 years?
  b. How much more would the $800 earn in 4 years at 5%?

25. Greg deposits $800 into a savings account that earns 3% interest compounded annually.
  a. What is Greg's balance after four years?
  b. Make a table to explain your answer.

Mixed Review

Lesson 7-7   **Solve for the variable indicated in red.**

  26. $f = \dfrac{15m}{a}$ **27.** $y = 4x - 9$ **28.** $d = \dfrac{5}{8}k + 1$

Lesson 6-3 **29. Architecture** A floor plan has a scale of $\frac{1}{4}$ in. : 5 ft. Find the length on the drawing for an actual length of 60 ft.

Lesson 1-10   **Graph each point on a coordinate plane.**

  30. $A(-2, 0)$ **31.** $C(-4, -5)$ **32.** $D(1, -3)$

Credit-Card Interest

When you use a credit card, you are charged interest each month on the balance in your account. You can use a spreadsheet to investigate the interest charged on a credit-card account.

You use a credit card to buy a $450 airline ticket. You are charged 1.8% monthly interest on your account balance, and you make a $40 payment each month. Using a spreadsheet program, create a spreadsheet with the formulas shown in red.

	A	B	C	D	E	F
			Planned Monthly		New	Total
1	Month	Balance	Payment	Interest	Balance	Interest
2	1	450	40	=B2*0.018	=B2+D2−C2	=D2
3	=A2+1	=E2				=F2+D3
4						
	. . .	. . .	. . .	. . .	. . .	. . .

The arrows indicate you should use the Fill Down feature of your spreadsheet program. This will calculate successive months for you.

EXERCISES

Use your spreadsheet. Round any totals to the nearest cent.

1. **a.** In which month is the balance less than the monthly payment?
   b. Your last payment is the balance plus the interest in the month you found in part (a). What is the amount of the last payment?
   c. What is the total interest paid on this account?

2. **a.** Change the monthly payment to $60 a month. In which month is the balance less than the monthly payment?
   b. What is the total interest paid on this account?

3. **a.** Create a new spreadsheet using a beginning balance of $1,200, 2.1% monthly interest, and a monthly payment of $100. What is the total interest paid on this account in 5 months?
   b. Change the monthly payment to $200. What is the total interest paid on this account in 5 months?
   c. **Reasoning** What can you conclude about the relationship between the size of monthly payments and the amount of interest charges?

Before you do all the work involved in solving a multiple-choice problem, you usually can eliminate some answer choices. This can save you time in finding the correct answer. Also, it improves your chances of making a correct guess.

1 EXAMPLE

What is the solution to $\frac{3}{4}(x - 2) = \frac{3}{2}$?

A. -2 **B.** 2   **C.** 3   **D.** 4

The product on the left must equal the positive number on the right. Thus, since $\frac{3}{4}$ is positive, the value of $(x - 2)$ must also be positive.

The choices -2 and 2 do not give positive values for $(x - 2)$. You can eliminate choices A and B. Then substitute 4 for x and use mental math to find that D is the correct choice.

2 EXAMPLE

What is the solution to $x + 0.05x = 420$?

F. 400   **G.** 410   **H.** 420   **J.** 450

On the left, a fraction of x is added to x and the result is 420. Thus the value of x must be less than 420. You can eliminate choices H and J. Then check 400 in the equation to find that F is the correct choice.

EXERCISES

Show how you can eliminate one or two of the answer choices for each multiple-choice question.

1. What is the solution to $\frac{x - 2}{-3} = -4$?

    A. -13 **B.** -10 **C.** 11   **D.** 14

2. What is the solution to $x - 0.15x = 680$?

    F. 620   **G.** 675   **H.** 760   **J.** 800

3. On a field trip to the zoo, 21 students voted to have sandwiches for lunch. This represents $\frac{7}{8}$ of the class. How many students are in the class?

    A. 24   **B.** 25   **C.** 38   **D.** 40

4. The area of a rectangle is 64 in.^{2}. If the area is increased by 25%, which of the following could be the dimensions of the new rectangle?

    F. 6 in. by 8 in.   **G.** 10 in. by 8 in.   **H.** 10 in. by 10 in.   **J.** 8 in. by 8 in.

Chapter Review

Vocabulary Review

balance (p. 387)
compound inequality (p. 381)
compound interest (p. 387)

consecutive integers (p. 357)
interest (p. 386)
interest rate (p. 386)

principal (p. 386)
simple interest (p. 386)

Choose the vocabulary term that correctly completes the sentence.

1. A bank pays __?__ when it pays interest on the principal and on the interest an account has earned.

2. The amount of money first deposited into a savings account is called the __?__.

3. The principal plus the interest is the __?__ of the account.

4. When you count by 1s from any integer, you are counting __?__.

5. A bank pays interest based on its advertised __?__.

6. __?__ is paid only on the principal of an account.

7. A bank pays you __?__ for the use of your money.

.Go Online
PHSchool.com
For: Vocabulary quiz
Web Code: adj-0751

Skills and Concepts

7-1 Objectives

▼ To solve two-step equations (p. 352)

▼ To use two-step equations to solve problems (p. 353)

To solve two-step equations, undo addition and subtraction, then undo multiplication and division.

Solve each equation.

8. $2a - 7 = -15$
9. $3 = -6x + 15$
10. $\frac{c}{4} + 10 = 22$

11. $1.5y + 3.4 = 7.9$
12. $\frac{2}{3}y - 9 = 5$
13. $8 = 9x - 7$

7-2 and 7-3 Objectives

▼ To combine like terms to simplify an equation (p. 356)

▼ To use the Distributive Property to simplify an equation (p. 358)

▼ To solve multi-step equations with fractions (p. 361)

▼ To solve multi-step equations with decimals (p. 362)

To solve multi-step equations, remove grouping symbols and combine like terms first. Then follow the steps for solving two-step equations.

Solve each equation.

14. $8m - 3m = 4$
15. $6 - 2y - y = 12$

16. $\frac{2}{3}q + 5 = \frac{3}{4}$
17. $\frac{1}{4}(b - 7) = 8$

18. $1.06x - 3 = 0.71$
19. $-2(5 + 6c) + 16 = -90$

20. **Number Sense** Find four consecutive integers with a sum of -66.

7-4 Objectives

▼ To write an equation to solve a problem (p. 366)

One strategy for solving problems is to write an equation and then solve the equation.

Write an equation. Then solve.

21. A pair of jeans is on sale for 15% off the original price. The sale price of the jeans is $29.74. What was the original price?

22. A bank teller is counting his money and notices that he has an equal number of tens and twenties. He also has $147 in other bills. If the total value of the bills he has is $1,167, how many tens and twenties does he have?

🌐 23. **Finance** Jalisha invested some money and made an 8% profit. The current value of her investment is $1,296. How much did she invest initially?

7-5 Objectives

▼ To solve equations with variables on both sides (p. 371)

▼ To use equations with variables on both sides (p. 372)

To solve equations with variables on both sides, first simplify both sides of the equation. Then use properties of equality to get the variable alone on one side of the equation.

Solve each equation.

24. $7x = 33 - 4x$

25. $2a - 24 - 3a = 5a$

26. $5x + 7 = -5x + 19$

27. $4x - 26 = 5(2 - x)$

28. $8(b + 3) = 4b - 4$

29. $2x - (9 - 3x) = 8x - 11$

🌐 30. **Travel Time** A refrigerated truck leaves a rest stop traveling at a steady rate of 56 mi/h. A car leaves the same rest stop $\frac{1}{4}$ h later following the truck at a steady rate of 64 mi/h. How long after the truck leaves the rest stop will the car overtake the truck?

7-6 Objectives

▼ To solve two-step inequalities (p. 377)

▼ To use two-step inequalities to solve problems (p. 378)

Solving two-step inequalities involves the same steps as solving two-step equations. Reverse the direction of the inequality symbol when you multiply or divide by a negative number.

Solve and graph each inequality.

31. $2a - 3 > 11$

32. $9y + 13 \le -14$

33. $-6c + 12 \ge 8$

34. $23 < 7 - 4x$

35. $\frac{8}{9}x + 5 < -3$

36. $-\frac{b}{2} + 14 > 13$

37. $-17 > \frac{x}{3} - 19$

38. $x + 4x + 9 \ge 6$

🌐 **39. Computers** Last year's computer model is on sale for $799. You can add more memory to the computer. Each chip of 8 megabytes of memory costs $25. How many megabytes of memory can you add if you have at most $1,000 to spend? Write and solve an inequality.

7-7 Objectives

▼ To solve a formula for a given variable (p. 382)

▼ To use formulas to solve problems (p. 383)

Use the properties of equality to transform a formula.

Solve for the variable indicated in red.

40. $r = 6km$ **41.** $8x = 6y$

42. $Q = gp$ **43.** $a = b - 2c$

44. $w = 3a + 5n$ **45.** $e = \frac{h}{6} + 11$

7-8 Objectives

▼ To solve simple-interest problems (p. 386)

▼ To solve compound-interest problems (p. 387)

You can calculate **simple interest** using the formula $I = prt$, where I is the interest, p is the **principal** (original amount deposited), r is the **interest rate** per year, and t is the time in years.

Compound interest is interest paid on both the principal and interest. It is found using the formula $B = p(1 + r)^n$, where B is the final **balance,** p is the principal, r is the interest rate for each interest period, and n is the number of interest periods.

Find the simple interest.

46. $150 deposited at an interest rate of 4.5% for 2 years

47. $2,525 deposited at an interest rate of 2.5% for 4 years

48. $6,000 deposited at an interest rate of 3% for 6 months

Find each balance.

49. $8,000 at 2% compounded annually for 3 years

50. $17,500 at 4.25% compounded annually for 6 years

51. $22,000 at 3% compounded semiannually for 8 years

52. $33,800 at 3.5% compounded semiannually for 5 years

53. The more interest periods there are, the more interest you make on an investment. Do you agree with this statement? Explain.

Go Online
PHSchool.com

For: Chapter test
Web Code: ada-0752

Solve each equation.

1. $3x + 4 = 19$

2. $5 + \frac{c}{9} = -31$

3. $2y - 15 = 11$

4. $8a + 3 = -12.2$

5. $\frac{3}{5}b - 8 = 4$

6. $\frac{m}{2} - 5 = 7$

7. $-83 = 9x - 2$

8. $18 - \frac{a}{4} = -5$

9. $\frac{3}{5}y + \frac{2}{5} = \frac{4}{5}$

10. $-23 - c = -19$

11. $3x + 4x = 21$

12. $\frac{1}{2}(10y + 4) = 17$

13. $2(7b - 6) - 4 = 12$

14. $2m - 6 = m$

15. $\frac{2}{3}a - 5 + \frac{8}{9}a = -19$

16. $0.015x + 3.45 = 4.65$

17. $12y + 3 = 9y - 15$

18. $3(2b + 6) = 4b - 8$

Write an equation. Then solve.

19. **Number Sense** Find three consecutive integers with a sum of 267.

20. A rental car company charges $35 a day plus $.15/mi for a mid-size car. A customer owes $117.15 for a three-day rental. How many miles did the customer drive?

21. **Travel Time** A moving truck leaves a house and travels at a steady rate of 40 mi/h. The family leaves the house 1 h later following the same route in a car. They travel at a steady rate of 60 mi/h. How long after the moving truck leaves the house will the car catch up with the truck?

22. **Coin Collections** The Jaspers collect nickels, dimes, and quarters in a jar. When they count the change in the jar, there are twice as many nickels as there are quarters. If there is $15.30 in dimes and $74.80 in all, how many quarters are there?

Solve and graph each inequality.

23. $7m - 8 > 6$

24. $2x - 6 \geq -9$

25. $-9a - 1 \leq 26$

26. $22 < 6c + 4$

27. $\frac{b}{3} + 12 > -3$

28. $-\frac{2}{3}x + 8 \leq 2$

29. $11 > -3y + 2$

30. $16 - 4a > 8$

31. **Commissions** An insurance salesperson earns a salary of $4,200 per month plus a commission of 3% of sales. How much must the salesperson sell to have a monthly income of at least $4,500?

32. **Writing in Math** How is solving a two-step inequality different from solving a two-step equation?

Solve for the variable indicated in red.

33. $H = 3w + 2$

34. $g = cst$

35. $R = 6n + 4p$

36. $y = \frac{x}{5} - 4$

Find the simple interest.

37. $800 deposited at an interest rate of 1.5% for 3 years

38. $1,050 deposited at an interest rate of 2% for 9 months

39. $2,500 deposited at an interest rate of 4.25% for 5 years

Find each balance.

40. $12,000 at 4% compounded annually for 4 years

41. $1,950 at 5% compounded annually for 2 years

42. $18,500 at 4.5% compounded semiannually for 5 years

43. $75,000 at 3% compounded semiannually for 8 years

Reading Comprehension Read the passage below. Then answer the questions on the basis of what is *stated* or *implied* in the passage.

Income Tax The United States Tax Relief Act of 2001 lowered the percentage of tax that individuals must pay on their taxable income. The table below compares the tax rate for 2001 with the new, lower tax rate for 2002 for unmarried individuals.

Taxable Income	2001 Tax	2002 Tax
Up to $27,050	15% of taxable income	15% of taxable income
$27,051 to $65,550	$4,057.50 + 28% of excess over $27,050	$4,057.50 + 27.5% of excess over $27,050
$65,551 to $136,750	$14,837.50 + 31% of excess over $65,550	$14,465 + 30.5% of excess over $65,550
$136,751 to $297,350	$36,909.50 + 36% of excess over $136,750	$36,361 + 35.5% of excess over $136,750
Over $297,350	$94,725.50 + 39.6% of excess over $297,350	$93,374 + 39.1% of excess over $297,350

1. Why was the United States Tax Relief Act called a "Tax Relief" act?

2. Which expression shows the amount of tax owed by an unmarried person with taxable income of $40,000 for 2002?
   - Ⓐ 0.275(40,000)
   - Ⓑ 4,057.50 + 0.275(12,950)
   - Ⓒ 4,057.50 + 0.275
   - Ⓓ 4,057.50 + 0.275(40,000)

3. Which expression shows the amount of tax owed by an unmarried person with taxable income of $72,000 for 2002?
   - Ⓔ 14,465 + 0.305(72,000)
   - Ⓕ 0.305(65,500)
   - Ⓖ 14,465 + 0.305(72,000 − 65,550)
   - Ⓗ 0.305(72,000)

4. About how much tax did an unmarried person with taxable income of $27,500 owe for 2002?
   - Ⓐ $0   Ⓑ $4,000   Ⓒ $7,500   Ⓓ $27,000

5. About how much tax did an unmarried person with taxable income of $300,000 owe for 2002?
   - Ⓔ $90,000   Ⓕ $95,000
   - Ⓖ $117,000   Ⓗ $210,000

6. About how much less tax would an unmarried person whose taxable income is $50,000 owe for 2002 than for 2001?
   - Ⓐ $0   Ⓑ $10   Ⓒ $100   Ⓓ $1,000

7. In 2002, his first year out of high school, Joacquim expected to have a taxable income of $25,000. How much tax relief did Joacquim gain for 2002 compared to what he would have had to pay for 2001?

Wireless Style

Applying Equations Cell-phone use has increased dramatically since the mid-1990s. Millions of people worldwide own cell phones. If you are one of them, you probably purchased a calling plan from a service provider. These providers charge different fees for a variety of services.

Throw It Away!

A credit-card-sized disposable cell phone offers approximately one hour of talk time.

SND   END

1 2 3
4 5 6
7 8 9
* 0 #

The circuits are printed metallic ink instead of tiny wires.

Activity

1. Suppose you are shopping for a calling plan. You expect to use 10 long-distance minutes per month.
   a. Use the table below and the total-cost equation to find out how much you will pay for the first month of each calling plan.
   b. **Writing in Math** Which plan would you choose? Explain.

2. Suppose a friend is also shopping for a calling plan. Your friend expects to use 60 long-distance minutes each month.
   a. Use the table below and the total-cost equation to find out how much your friend will pay for the first month of each calling plan.
   b. Which plan do you think your friend would choose? Explain.

3. **Number Sense** Without calculating, which plan would be the least expensive to use in the second month? Explain.

Total-Cost Equation
$$c = m + d\ell + a$$

c = total cost
m = monthly fee
ℓ = long-distance rate
d = long-distance minutes
a = activation fee

Monthly Fee The amount a customer pays each month for basic service

Long-Distance Rate The amount a customer pays for each minute of a call made outside the local calling area

Activation Fee A one-time fee paid to start phone service

Calling Plan	A	B	C	D
Monthly Fee	$19.99	$34.99	$19.99	$29.99
Long-Distance Rate	$.15	$.15	$.00	$.20
Activation Fee	$36.00	$24.00	$30.00	$35.00

Antenna

Antenna

Where's the Cell-Phone Tower?
Cell phone companies often camouflage their towers to make them blend in with the surrounding landscape.

Go Online
PHSchool.com

For: Information about cell phones
Web Code: ade-0753

What You've Learned

 Assessment Framework

- **9.8.05:** In Chapter 1, you used inductive reasoning to write rules for patterns. You also graphed points in a coordinate plane.

- **6.8.10:** In Chapter 4, you simplified fractions by finding the GCF of the numerator and denominator.

- **8.8.12:** In Chapter 7, you solved two-step and multi-step equations and inequalities using inverse operations.

Check Your Readiness **for Help** to the Lesson in green.

Describing Number Patterns (Lesson 1-7)

Write the next two numbers in each pattern.

1. $8, 5, 2, -1, \ldots$ **2.** $43, 37, 31, 25, \ldots$ **3.** $4.5, 6, 7.5, 9, \ldots$ **4.** $-3, -5, -7, -9, \ldots$

Graphing Points (Lesson 1-10)

Write the coordinates of each point.

5. A **6.** B **7.** C

8. D **9.** E **10.** F

Draw a coordinate plane. Graph each point.

11. $M(0, -2)$ **12.** $H(-2, 4)$ **13.** $J(6, 1)$

14. $K(5, -3)$ **15.** $L(-4, -3)$ **16.** $G(3, 0)$

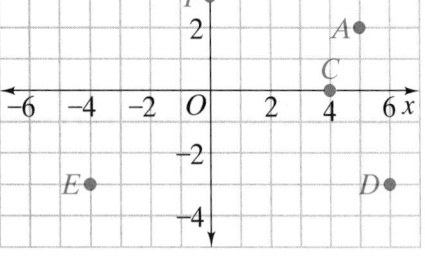

Simplifying Fractions (Lesson 4-4)

Write each fraction in simplest form.

17. $\dfrac{-5 - (-4)}{12 - (-6)}$ **18.** $\dfrac{15 - (-12)}{17 - 8}$ **19.** $\dfrac{-4 - 1}{-7 - (-2)}$ **20.** $\dfrac{4.3 - 3.5}{7.1 - 4.7}$

Transforming Equations (Lesson 7-7)

Solve each equation for y.

21. $4x + y = 3$ **22.** $y - 4 = -2x$ **23.** $2x - y = 6$ **24.** $8 + y + 6x = 0$

25. $12 - y = x$ **26.** $2y + x = 5$ **27.** $5y - 20 = x$ **28.** $3x + 4y = 12$

Linear Functions and Graphing

◀)) **Key Vocabulary**

- domain (p. 404)
- function (p. 404)
- function notation (p. 422)
- function rule (p. 422)
- linear equation (p. 410)
- linear inequality (p. 445)
- negative correlation (p. 429)
- no correlation (p. 429)
- positive correlation (p. 429)
- range (p. 404)
- relation (p. 404)
- scatter plot (p. 427)
- slope (p. 415)
- slope-intercept form (p. 417)
- solution (p. 409)
- system of linear equations (p. 439)
- system of linear inequalities (p. 447)
- trend line (p. 434)
- vertical-line test (p. 405)
- *y*-intercept (p. 417)

What You'll Learn Next

 Assessment Framework

In this chapter, you will learn how to

- Determine whether a relation is a function.

- **8.8.01:** Solve linear equations.

- **8.8.10:** Solve systems of linear equations and inequalities.

- **8.8.10:** Solve a problem by graphing.

 Activity Lab Applying what you learn, on pages 458–459 you will solve problems about electronic devices.

You can use graphs to show real-world relationships visually.
Labels can help explain the parts of a graph.

1 EXAMPLE

Transportation The graph at the
right shows one trip from home
to school and back. The trip
combines walking and getting a
ride from a neighbor. Tell what the
graph shows by labeling each part.

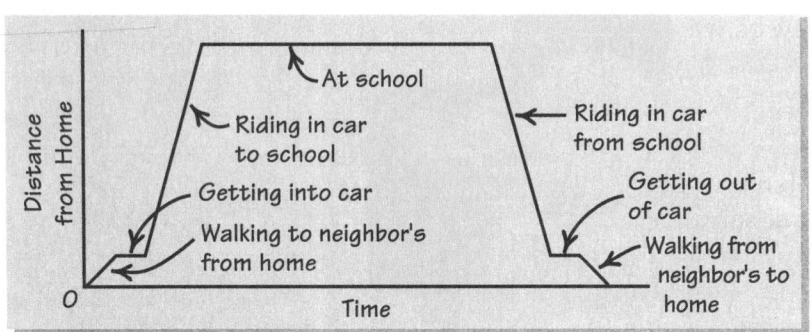

Label the parts of each graph.

1.

2.

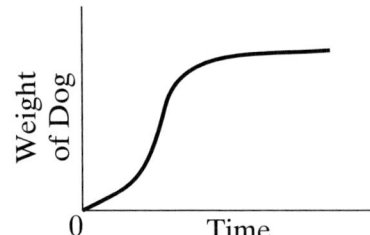

3. The graph at the right is a *step graph*. It shows the prices
at a parking garage.
   a. How much does parking cost for an hour or less?
   b. How much does parking cost for 4 hours and
   20 minutes?
   c. A receipt from the parking garage is for $7. What
   is the greatest length of time the car could have been
   in the garage?

4. Reasoning Use the graph at the right. Jolene and Tamika were sprinting. Which girl ran faster? Explain.

When you draw a graph without actual data, you are making a sketch. A sketch can help you visualize relationships.

2 EXAMPLE

You go to an amusement park and ride a moving horse on a carousel. Sketch a graph to show your height above the ground. Identify your axes and include labels for each part.

Sketch a graph for each situation. Identify your axes and include labels for each part.

5. the temperature outside during one 24-hour period

6. your speed as you take a trip on a train

7. the total distance you travel as you go to a concert and return home

8. the distance above ground of a pole vaulter's feet at a track meet

9. You pour water at a constant rate into the container shown at the right. Sketch a graph of the water level as you fill the container.

8-1

Relations and Functions

IL Assessment Framework

8.8.01 Analyze, extend, and create sequences or linear functions, and determine algebraic expressions to describe the nth term of a sequence.

 Check Skills You'll Need

Graph each point.

1. $A(3, 4)$ **2.** $B(-3, 1)$

3. $F(2, 0)$ **4.** $D(2, -2)$

5. $C(-4, -3)$

6. $E(0, -4)$

GO for Help
Lesson 1-10

🔊 **New Vocabulary**

- relation
- domain
- range
- function
- vertical-line test

1 | Identifying Relations and Functions

The table shows the results of a canned-food drive.

You can write the data in the table as a **relation,** a set of ordered pairs. The first coordinate of each ordered pair is the number of students in a homeroom. The second coordinate is the number of cans the students in that homeroom collected.

Food for Life Canned-Food Drive

Homeroom	Number of Students	Number of Cans
101	25	133
102	22	216
103	24	148
104	22	195
105	20	74
106	21	150

Here is the relation represented by the table:

$\{(25, 133), (22, 216), (24, 148), (22, 195), (20, 74), (21, 150)\}$

The braces, { }, indicate that these are all the ordered pairs in this relation. The first coordinates are the **domain** of the relation. The second coordinates are the **range** of the relation.

Some relations are functions. In a **function,** each member of the domain is paired with exactly one member of the range.

You can draw a *mapping diagram* to see whether a relation is a function.

1 EXAMPLE | Identifying a Function

Is each relation a function? Explain.

a. {(0, 1), (1, 2), (1, 3), (2, 4)}

List the domain values and the range values in order.

Draw arrows from the domain values to their range values.

There are two range values for the domain value 1. This relation is *not* a function.

Vocabulary Tip

This is the second use of the word <u>range</u>. The first appears in Lesson 3-3. You must read and use "range" in context, that is, according to the meanings of the words that appear with it.

b. {(0, 1), (1, 2), (2, 2), (3, 4)} **c.** {(0, 1), (1, 3), (2, 2), (3, 4)}

There is one range value
for each domain value.
This relation is a function.

There is one range value
for each domain value.
This relation is a function.

✓ Quick Check

1. Is each relation a function? Explain.

   a. {(−2, 3), (2, 2), (2, −2)}   **b.** {(−5, −4), (0, −4), (5, −4)}

Functions can model many everyday situations when one quantity
depends on another. One quantity *is a function of* the other.

2 EXAMPLE   Real-World 🌐 Problem Solving

**Cooking Is the time needed to cook a turkey a function of the
weight of the turkey? Explain.**

The time the turkey cooks (range value) is determined by the
weight of the turkey (domain value). This relation is a function.

✓ Quick Check

2. a. For the United States Postal Service, is package weight
     a function of the postage paid to mail the package?
     Explain.
   b. Is the cost of postage a function of package weight?
     Explain.

Real-World 🌐 Connection

You can estimate the
cooking time of a turkey:
20 minutes per pound
unstuffed, or 30 minutes
per pound stuffed.

2 Graphing Relations and Functions

Graphing a relation on a coordinate plane gives you a visual way to
tell whether the relation is a function. If the relation is a function, then
any vertical line passes through at most one point on the graph. If you
can find a vertical line that passes through two points on the graph,
then the relation is *not* a function. This is the **vertical-line test.**

3 EXAMPLE Using the Vertical-Line Test

Vocabulary Tip

The first value in an ordered pair, the *x-coordinate*, shows horizontal position.

The second value in an ordered pair, the *y-coordinate*, shows vertical position.

a. Graph the relation shown in the table.

Graph the ordered pairs (−4, −3), (2, 0), (2, 3), (4, 3), and (5, −4).

x-coordinates   *y*-coordinates

Domain Value	Range Value
−4	−3
2	0
2	3
4	3
5	−4

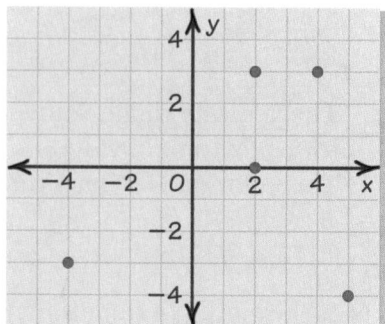

b. Use the vertical-line test. Is the relation a function? Explain.

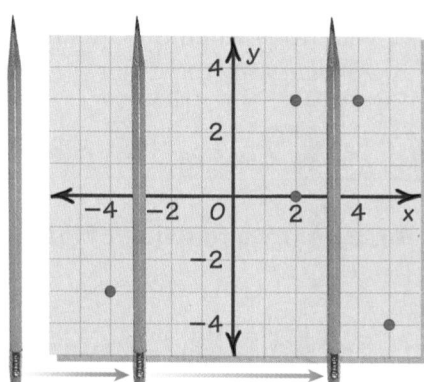

Pass a pencil across the graph as shown. Keep the pencil vertical (parallel to the *y*-axis) to represent a vertical line.

The pencil held vertically would pass through both $(2, 0)$ and $(2, 3)$, so the relation is *not* a function.

✓ Quick Check

3. **Algebra** Graph the relation shown in each table. Use the vertical-line test. Is the relation a function? Explain.

a.

x	y
−6	−5
−3	−2
0	−2
1	0
4	3
5	7

b.

x	y
−7	4
−2	6
−1	−1
−1	3
0	5
1	5

c.

x	y
−5	4
−4	4
−3	4
0	0
1	4
2	4

For more exercises, see *Extra Skill and Word Problem Practice.*

Practice and Problem Solving

 A Practice by Example

Example 1
(page 404)

 GO for Help

Is each relation a function? Explain.

1. Domain   Range
−5
−2 ⟶ −2
2 ⟶ 3
5

2. Domain   Range
−5
−4 ⟶ −1
−3 ⟶ 2
6

3. Domain   Range
3 ⟶ −5
6 ⟶ −2
0
7 ⟶ 1

4. $\{(3, -1), (3, 0), (-3, 4), (3, 8)\}$ **5.** $\{(-3, -2), (-1, 0), (1, 0), (5, -2)\}$

Example 2
(page 405)

6. Walking Is the time you take to go to the library a function of the distance to the library? Explain.

7. Is the price of a one-year subscription to your favorite magazine a function of the age of the subscriber? Explain.

8. Sewing Is the price of a piece of cloth a function of the length of the cloth? Explain.

9. Is the number of students on a field trip a function of the number of buses used? Explain.

10. Is the number of buses used for a field trip a function of the number of students on the field trip? Explain.

Example 3
(page 406)

Graph the relation shown in each table. Use the vertical-line test. Is the relation a function? Explain.

11.
x	y
−5	2
−1	4
2	−5
4	−1

12.
x	y
−5	−5
−3	−3
1	1
2	2

13.
x	y
−1	3
−1	2
0	−4
4	2

14.
x	y
3	−1
2	−1
−4	0
2	4

B Apply Your Skills

Graph each relation. Is the relation a function? Explain.

15. $\{(0, 1), (3, 5), (2, 2), \left(-\frac{1}{2}, -\frac{4}{5}\right)\}$ **16.** $\{(-1, 9), (0, -1), (-1, 4), (4, 9)\}$

17. $\{(-1, 1), (-2, 1), (-2, 2), (0, 2)\}$

18. $\{(4, -8), (4, -6), (1, 2), (1, 5), (1, -6)\}$

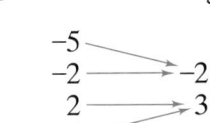 GO Online
Homework Video Tutor
Visit: PHSchool.com
Web Code: ade-0801

19.
x	y
−5	6
−2	3
3	2
6	4

20.
x	y
3	−7
1	−5
−1	−5
−3	−7

21.
x	y
−7	3
−5	1
−5	−1
−7	−3

22.
x	y
6	−2
1	−1
0	−2
−1	−3

23. Writing in Math Is every relation a function? Is every function a relation? Explain.

24. Geometry Explain why the area of a square is a function of the length of a side of the square.

25. Error Analysis Your friend says that a relation is not a function when two ordered pairs have the same *y*-coordinate. Explain your friend's error.

C Challenge

Patterns In each function below, there is a pattern to how the range values relate to the domain values. Describe the pattern.

26. $\{(-2, 0), (0, 2), (3, 5), (8, 10)\}$ **27.** $\{(-5, 5), (-1, 1), (0, 0), (3, -3)\}$

28. $\{(-1, -0.5), (2, 1), (7, 3.5)\}$ **29.** $\{(1, 1), (2, 4), (3, 9), (4, 16)\}$

30. a. Open-Ended Write two different relations for which the domain is $\{-1, 0, 1\}$ and the range is $\{1, 2\}$.
  b. Graph your relations. Use the vertical-line test to tell whether each relation is a function.

ISAT

 Test Prep

Multiple Choice

For Exercises 31 and 32, which choice best explains why the relation IS or IS NOT a function?

31. $\{(-5, 7), (-2, -1), (0, 3), (4, 7)\}$
  A. A function; only one range value exists for each domain value.
  B. A function; two domain values exist for range value 7.
  C. Not a function; the relation passes the vertical line test.
  D. Not a function; two domain values exist for range value 7.

32. $\{(-8, -4), (-2, 0), (1, 3), (-2, 6)\}$
  F. A function; only one range value exists for each domain value.
  G. A function; two range values exist for domain value -2.
  H. Not a function; the relation passes the vertical line test.
  J. Not a function; two range values exist for domain value -2.

Short Response

33. Answer and explain.   **(a)** Is the number of people expected to attend a picnic a function of the number of sandwiches made for the picnic?   **(b)** Is the number of sandwiches made for a picnic a function of the number of people expected to attend?

Mixed Review

Lesson 7-8 **34. Banking** You invest $1,200 in an account that earns 3.5% interest compounded annually. Find the account balance after four years.

 GO for Help

Lessons 7-1 and 7-3

Solve each equation.

35. $-42 + 3c = -6$ **36.** $\frac{3}{2}t - 4 = \frac{1}{2}$ **37.** $2m - 4.9 = -3.6$

Equations With Two Variables

 Assessment Framework

8.8.07 Represent linear equations and quantitative relationships on a rectangular coordinate system, and interpret the meaning of a specific part of a graph.

1 Finding Solutions of Two-Variable Equations

In previous chapters, you solved equations with one variable, such as $2x + 5 = 7x$. In this chapter, you will find solutions of equations with two variables, such as $y = 3x + 4$. An ordered pair that makes such an equation a true statement is a **solution** of the equation.

1 EXAMPLE Finding a Solution

Find the solution of $y = 3x + 4$ for $x = -1$.

$y = 3x + 4$

$y = 3(-1) + 4$ **Replace x with -1.**

$y = -3 + 4$ **Multiply.**

$y = 1$ **Add.**

A solution of the equation is $(-1, 1)$.

✓ Quick Check

1. Find the solution of each equation for $x = -3$.

   a. $y = 2x + 1$ **b.** $y = -4x + 3$ **c.** $y = 0x - 4$

✓ **Check Skills You'll Need**

Evaluate each expression for $x = 2$.

1. $2 + x$ **2.** $x - 12$

3. $8x - 13$ **4.** $24 \div 2x$

GO for Help
Lesson 1-3

◀)) **New Vocabulary**

- solution
- linear equation

You can use two-variable equations to model real-world situations.

2 EXAMPLE   Real-World 🌐 Problem Solving

Gridded Response The equation $t = 21 - 0.01n$ models the normal low July temperature in degrees Celsius at Mount Rushmore, South Dakota. In the equation, t is the temperature at n meters above the base of the mountain. Find the normal low July temperature at 300 m above the base.

$t = 21 - 0.01n$

$t = 21 - 0.01(300)$ **Replace n with 300.**

$t = 21 - 3$ **Multiply.**

$t = 18$ **Subtract.**

A solution of the equation is $(300, 18)$. The normal low July temperature at 300 m above the base of the mountain is $18°C$.

Mt. Rushmore is 1,745 m tall.

✓ Quick Check

2. Find the normal low July temperature at 700 m above the base of Mount Rushmore.

---

2 **Graphing Equations With Two Variables**

An equation with two variables can have many solutions. One way to show these solutions is to graph them, which also gives a graph of the equation. A **linear equation** is any equation whose graph is a line. All the equations in this lesson are linear equations.

3 EXAMPLE   **Graphing a Linear Equation**

Graph $y = -\frac{1}{2}x + 3$.

Make a table of values to show ordered-pair solutions.

x	$-\frac{1}{2}x + 3$	(x, y)
-2	$-\frac{1}{2}(-2) + 3 = 1 + 3 = 4$	$(-2, 4)$
0	$-\frac{1}{2}(0) + 3 = 0 + 3 = 3$	$(0, 3)$
4	$-\frac{1}{2}(4) + 3 = -2 + 3 = 1$	$(4, 1)$

Graph the ordered pairs. Draw a line through the points.

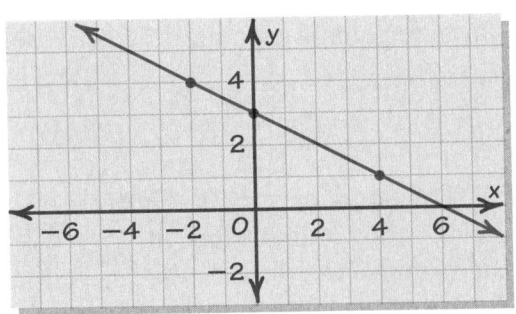

Vocabulary Tip

The expression $-\frac{1}{2}x$ means "the opposite of $\frac{1}{2}x$." So when the value of x is -2, the expression $-\frac{1}{2}x$ represents the opposite of one half of -2, which is 1.

✓ Quick Check

3. Graph each linear equation.

   a. $y = 2x + 1$ **b.** $y = 3x - 2$ **c.** $y = -\frac{1}{2}x + 4$

If you use the vertical-line test on the graph in Example 3, you see that every x-value has exactly one y-value. This means that the relation $y = -\frac{1}{2}x + 3$ is a function. A linear equation is a function *unless* its graph is a vertical line.

GO Online

Video Tutor Help
Visit: PHSchool.com
Web Code: ada-0775

Graphing $y = a$ and $x = b$

Graph each equation. Is the equation a function?

a. $y = 2$

For every value of x, $y = 2$.

This is a horizontal line. The equation $y = 2$ is a function.

b. $x = 2$

For every value of y, $x = 2$.

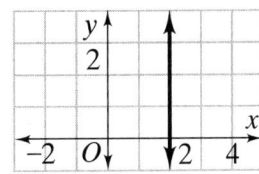

This is a vertical line. The equation $x = 2$ is *not* a function.

✓ Quick Check

4. Graph each equation. Is the equation a function?

   a. $x = 1$ **b.** $y = -4$ **c.** $x = 0$

You may find it helpful to solve an equation for y before you find solutions and graph the equation.

Graphing by Solving for y

Solve $3x + y = -5$ for y. Then graph the equation.

Solve the equation for y.

$$3x + y = -5$$
$$3x + y - 3x = -5 - 3x \quad \textbf{Subtract 3x from each side.}$$
$$y = -3x - 5 \quad \textbf{Simplify.}$$

Make a table of values.

x	$-3x - 5$	(x, y)
-2	$-3(-2) - 5 = 1$	$(-2, 1)$
-1	$-3(-1) - 5 = -2$	$(-1, -2)$
0	$-3(0) - 5 = -5$	$(0, -5)$

Graph.

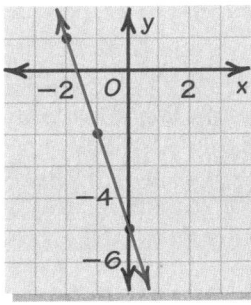

✓ Quick Check

5. Solve each equation for y. Then graph the equation.

   a. $2x + y = 3$ **b.** $y - x = 5$ **c.** $-3x + 2y = 6$

EXERCISES

For more exercises, see *Extra Skill and Word Problem Practice*.

Practice and Problem Solving

A Practice by Example

Example 1
(page 409)

GO for Help

Find the solution of each equation for $x = -5$.

1. $y = 4x + 2$ **2.** $y = -3x - 1$ **3.** $y = 8x$

Find the solution of $y = -x - 3$ for the given value of x.

4. -2 **5.** -1 **6.** 0 **7.** 1 **8.** 2 **9.** 3

Example 2
(page 409)

The equation $k = 1.6d$ gives an approximate relationship between d miles and k kilometers. Express each distance in kilometers.

10. the 430 miles between Boise, Idaho, and Reno, Nevada

11. the 665 miles between Columbus, Ohio, and Des Moines, Iowa

Examples 3 and 4
(pages 410 and 411)

Graph each linear equation. Is the equation a function?

12. $y = x - 3$ **13.** $y = -x - 2$ **14.** $y = \frac{2}{3}x - 2$

15. $y = x + 3$ **16.** $y = x - 10$ **17.** $y = 2x - 1$

18. $x = 7$ **19.** $y = 0$ **20.** $x = -2$

Example 5
(page 411)

Solve each equation for y. Then graph the equation.

21. $-4x + y = 16$ **22.** $-3y = 3x - 9$ **23.** $2x - 4y = 12$

24. $y - 6 = 0.5x$ **25.** $-3x = 2y$ **26.** $2y - 3x = 10$

B Apply Your Skills

27. Writing in Math Explain how you can determine from a linear equation whether the solutions of the equation form a function.

GO Online
Homework Video Tutor
Visit: PHSchool.com
Web Code: ade-0802

Is each ordered pair a solution of $4x - 3y = 6$? Explain.

28. $(3, 2)$ **29.** $(-3, -2)$ **30.** $(0, 2)$ **31.** $(2, 0)$

Find the solutions of each equation for $x = -2, 1,$ and 4.

32. $y = 7 - 3x$ **33.** $y = \frac{1}{4}x + 6$ **34.** $y = \frac{3}{5}x - 6$

$$3x + 4y = 12$$
$$4y = 12 - 3x$$
$$y = 3 - 3x$$

35. Error Analysis A student solved $3x + 4y = 12$ for y. Her work is at the left. What error did the student make?

36. José is driving on a highway. The equation $d = 55t$ relates the number of miles d and the amount of time in hours t. About how many hours does José spend driving 100 mi?

37. If you swim the backstroke, you burn 9 cal/min (calories per minute). If you swim the butterfly stroke, you burn 12 cal/min. The equation $9x + 12y = 360$ models how you can burn 360 cal by swimming the backstroke for x min and the butterfly for y min.
   a. Find the solutions of the equation for $x = 0$ and $y = 0$. Explain what your solutions mean.

412 Chapter 8   Linear Functions and Graphing

b. Graph the solutions you found in part (a). Draw a line through the two points.

🌐 **c. Language Arts** The solutions you found in part (a) are the *y-intercept* and the *x-intercept* of the line. Explain why these names are appropriate.

d. Use your graph from part (b). If you swim the butterfly stroke for 10 min, how long should you swim the backstroke to burn a total of 360 calories?

ISAT

Test Prep

Multiple Choice

For Exercises 38 and 39, which ordered pair is a solution for the given equation?

38. $y = 2x + 7$

A. (13, 3)   **B.** (3, 13)   **C.** (2, 8)   **D.** (8, 2)

39. $y = -3x - 4$

F. (1, −1)   **G.** (1, 1)   **H.** (−7, 1)   **J.** (1, −7)

Short Response

Read the passage below before doing Exercises 40 and 41.

Mountains Under the Sea

There is a mountain range in the Pacific Ocean far beneath the surface. Jacques Piccard and Donald Walsh descended to 35,814 ft to make a record dive in these mountains in a submersible.

There is tremendous pressure at these depths. The pressure of the air at sea level is 14.7 lb/in.^{2}, and the pressure increases about 0.44 lb/in.^{2} for every foot an object descends below sea level.

40. What is the pressure at 10 ft below sea level?

41. The equation $y = 14.7 + 0.44x$ gives the pressure y in pounds per square inch at a depth of x feet below sea level.

a. Find the pressure at the depth of the record dive.

b. Find the pressure at half the depth of the record dive.

Mixed Review

Lesson 8-1

Is each relation a function? Explain.

42. {(2, 4), (3, 6), (−3, 6), (1, 2)}   **43.** {(0, 3), (2, 1), (−7, 2), (1, 1)}

44. {(3, 4), (2.3, 6), (3, −7)}   **45.** {(0, −1), (0, 0), (−1, 0), (−2, −1)}

Lessons 4-9 and 5-5 🌐 **46. Astronomy** The sun orbits the Milky Way galaxy at about 135 mi/s. How far does the sun travel in an hour? In a week? Write your answers in scientific notation.

Patterns A landscaper has designed a pattern for tile pathways that lead to a sundial. The figures below show the first three designs in his pattern.

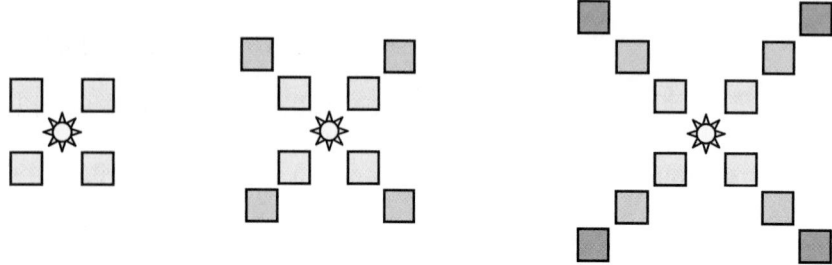

ACTIVITY

1. Use color tiles to build the first five designs that follow the landscaper's pattern. Record your results in a table like the one below.

Design Number	1	2	3	4	5
Number of Tiles	■	■	■	■	■

2. **Writing in Math** Without building the design, find the number of tiles needed to build the seventh design. Explain your reasoning.

3. A **proportional relationship** is a relationship in which two pairs of numbers form a proportion. For example, the coordinate pairs $(1, 2)$ and $(2, 4)$ have a proportional relationship because $\frac{1}{2} = \frac{2}{4}$. Do the pairs in the table from Question 1 have a proportional relationship? Explain.

4. Graph the data from the table on a coordinate plane. Use the graph to predict the number of tiles needed for the 50th design. For the hundredth design.

5. **Reasoning** How many tiles would you need for the nth design? Explain.

6. **Multiple Choice** Which equation could you use to find the number of tiles t needed for any design number x?
   - Ⓐ $t = 4x$
   - Ⓑ $t = x + 4$
   - Ⓒ $t = 2x$
   - Ⓓ $t = 2x + 2$

7. Suppose the landscaper replaced the sundial with a tile. How would the pattern change? How would the equation change? Explain.

Slope and *y*-intercept

 Assessment Framework

1 Finding the Slope of a Line

Understanding Slope

1. **a.** Graph $y = x$, $y = 2x$, and $y = 3x$ on one coordinate plane.
   b. How does the graph of $y = kx$ change as k, the coefficient of x, increases?

2. **a.** Graph $y = x$ and $y = -x$ on the same coordinate plane.
   b. How are the graphs of $y = x$ and $y = -x$ alike? Different?

The ratio that describes the tilt of a line is its slope. If a line slants upward from left to right, it has positive slope. If it slants downward, it has negative slope. To calculate slope, you use this ratio.

$$\textbf{slope} = \frac{\text{vertical change}}{\text{horizontal change}} = \frac{\text{rise}}{\text{run}}$$

8.8.09 Interpret the meaning of slope and intercepts in linear situations.

8.8.07 Represent linear equations and quantitative relationships on a rectangular coordinate system, and interpret the meaning of a specific part of a graph.

✓ **Check Skills You'll Need**

Find each difference.

1. $-4 - 5$ **2.** $3 - (-2)$

3. $6 - 9$ **4.** $-1 - (-1)$

GO **for Help**
Lesson 1-6

◀)) **New Vocabulary**
- slope
- *y*-intercept
- slope-intercept form

1 EXAMPLE Using Rise and Run to Find Slope

Find the slope of each line.

a.
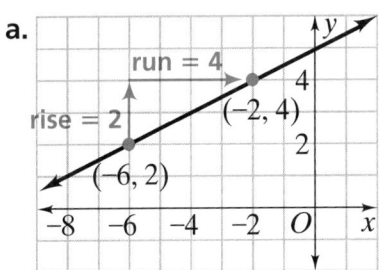

$$\text{slope} = \frac{\text{rise}}{\text{run}} = \frac{2}{4} = \frac{1}{2}$$

b.
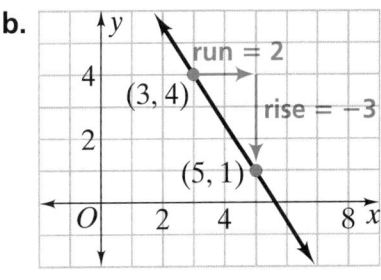

$$\text{slope} = \frac{\text{rise}}{\text{run}} = \frac{-3}{2} = -\frac{3}{2}$$

✓ **Quick Check**

1. What is the slope of the ski trail at the right?

If you know two points of a line, you can find the slope of the line using the following formula.

$$\text{slope} = \frac{\text{difference in } y\text{-coordinates}}{\text{difference in } x\text{-coordinates}}$$

The y-coordinate you use first in the numerator must correspond to the x-coordinate you use first in the denominator.

2 EXAMPLE   **Using Coordinates to Find Slope**

Find the slope of the line through $C(-2, 6)$ and $D(4, 3)$.

$$\text{slope} = \frac{\text{difference in } y\text{-coordinates}}{\text{difference in } x\text{-coordinates}} = \frac{3 - 6}{4 - (-2)} = \frac{-3}{6} = \frac{-1}{2} = -\frac{1}{2}$$

✓ Quick Check

2. Find the slope of the line through each pair of points.

a. $V(8, -1), Q(0, -7)$ **b.** $S(-4, 3), R(-10, 9)$

Horizontal and vertical lines are special cases for slope.

3 EXAMPLE   **Finding Slope for Special Cases**

Find the slope of each line.

a.

$$\text{slope} = \frac{2 - 2}{1 - (-3)} = \frac{0}{4} = 0$$

Slope is 0 for a horizontal line.

b.
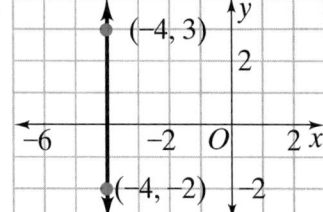

$$\text{slope} \frac{-2 - 3}{-4 - (-4)} = \frac{-5}{0}$$

Division by zero is undefined. Slope is *undefined* for a vertical line.

Test-Taking Tip
You may say that a vertical line has *no slope*. But be sure that you do not confuse *no slope* with *slope 0*.

✓ Quick Check

3. Find the slope of each line.

a.

b.

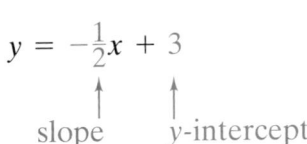

2 Using Slope to Graph Linear Equations

Here is the graph of $y = -\frac{1}{2}x + 3$.

The slope of the line is $\frac{-2}{4}$, or $-\frac{1}{2}$.

The **y-intercept** of the line is the point where the line crosses the y-axis. The constant in the equation is the y-intercept.

$$y = -\frac{1}{2}x + 3$$
$$\uparrow \qquad \uparrow$$
$$\text{slope} \quad \text{y-intercept}$$

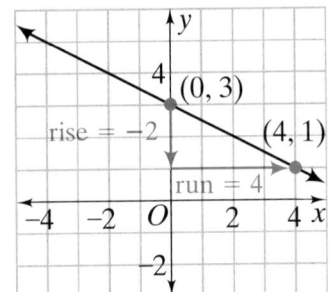

Vocabulary Tip

The word <u>intercept</u> sounds like <u>intersect</u>, which means "to cross." Think of the y-intercept as where the line crosses the y-axis.

Key Concepts — Slope-Intercept Form

The equation $y = mx + b$ is the **slope-intercept form.** In this form, m is the slope of the line, and b is the y-intercept.

You can use slope-intercept form to help you graph an equation.

4 EXAMPLE — Real-World Problem Solving

Engineering A ramp slopes from a warehouse door down to a street. The function $y = -\frac{1}{3}x + 2$ models the ramp, where x is the horizontal distance in feet from the bottom of the door and y is the height in feet above the street. Graph the equation.

Step 1 Since the y-intercept is 2, graph $(0, 2)$.

Step 2 Since the slope is $-\frac{1}{3}$ or $\frac{-1}{3}$, move 1 unit down from $(0, 2)$. Then move 3 units right to graph a second point.

Step 3 Draw a line through the points.

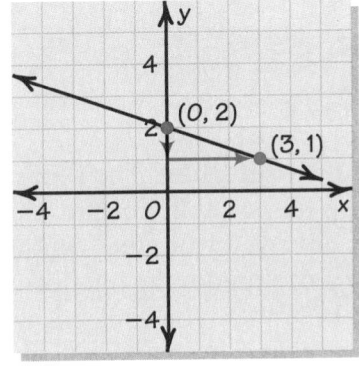

Online
active math

For: Writing Equations Activity
Use: Interactive Textbook, 8-3

✓ Quick Check

4. Graph each equation.

   a. $y = 2x - 3$

   b. $y = -x + 4$

EXERCISES

For more exercises, see *Extra Skill and Word Problem Practice*.

Practice and Problem Solving

A Practice by Example

Example 1
(page 415)

GO for Help

Find the slope of each line.

1.

2.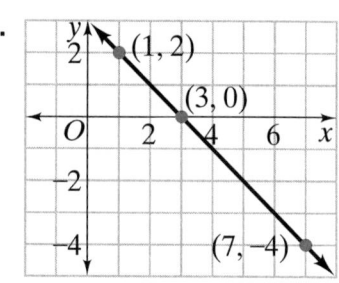

Example 2
(page 416)

Find the slope of the line through each pair of points.

3. $A(2, 6), B(8, 1)$

4. $E(1, -2), F(4, -8)$

5. $N(-5, 2), Q(1, -4)$

6. $G(3, 4), H(6, 10)$

7. $P(-3, 0), Q(4, -5)$

8. $A(2, 4), B(-1, -2)$

Example 3
(page 416)

Find the slope of each line.

9.

10.

Example 4
(page 417)

Identify the slope and *y*-intercept of the graph of each equation. Then graph the equation.

11. $y = 7x + 3$

12. $y = -x$

13. $y = \frac{1}{2}x - 8$

14. $y = 2x + 1$

15. $y = -3x - 1$

16. $y = x - 4$

17. $y = 4$

18. $y = -3x + 3$

19. $y = -\frac{3}{2}x + 6$

20. **Architecture** The roof of an A-frame cabin slopes from the peak of the cabin down to the ground. It suggests the letter A when viewed from the front or the back. The equation $y = -3x + 15$ can model the line formed by one side of the roof. For a point (x, y) on the roof, x is the horizontal distance in feet from the center of the base of the house, and y is the height of the roof in feet. Graph the equation.

B Apply Your Skills

21. **Error Analysis** A student said that the slope of the line through $(8, 4)$ and $(2, 2)$ is 3. What error could this student have made?

22. **Open-Ended** Write equations for five different lines that intersect at $(0, 3)$.

Find the slope of each line.

23.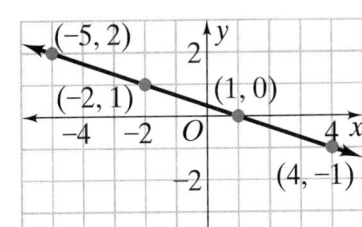

24.

25. Construction The slope of a roof is its *pitch*. You indicate the pitch of a roof by a ratio $a : b$, where a is the number of feet of rise for every b feet of run. In the photos at the left, which house has a roof with steeper pitch? Explain.

26. Multiple Choice Find the slope of the line through $(0, -4)$ and $(3, -3)$.

     Ⓐ $\frac{3}{4}$ Ⓑ $\frac{2}{3}$ Ⓒ $\frac{1}{3}$ Ⓓ -1

Find the slope of the line through each pair of points.

27. $C\left(\frac{1}{2}, \frac{3}{4}\right), D\left(\frac{1}{4}, \frac{3}{4}\right)$ **28.** $L(7, -6.3), M(5, -1.3)$

29. $J(2.1, 3), K(2.1, 4.2)$ **30.** $A\left(\frac{2}{3}, 2\frac{2}{3}\right), B\left(2\frac{2}{3}, \frac{2}{3}\right)$

Solve each equation for y. Then graph the equation.

31. $y - 2x = 4$ **32.** $y + 3 = 5x$ **33.** $2y + 2x = 2$

34. $3y + 2x = 3$ **35.** $y - \frac{1}{2}x = 0$ **36.** $y + 3 = 0$

37. $2y = x - 8$ **38.** $-4y = x + 48$ **39.** $3y - 2x = 15$

40. Does the point $(-3, 4)$ lie on the graph of $y = -2x + 1$? Explain.

41. Does the point $(-2, -4)$ lie on the graph of $2y - 6x = 4$? Explain.

Ⓒ Challenge   **42.** Graph the line with no slope that passes through $(4, -2)$.

43. a. Graph the groups of equations on three coordinate planes.

Group 1	Group 2	Group 3
$y = 2x - 5$	$y = -3x - 1$	$y = -6$
$y = 2x$	$y = -3x$	$y = 1$
$y = 2x + 3$	$y = -3x + 4$	$y = 4.5$

   b. Writing in Math How are the lines in each group related to each other? Explain.

   c. Reasoning What is the coefficient of x in the equation of a graph that has slope 0?

44. Construction The slope of a road is its *grade*. What do you think it means for the grade of a road to be 4%?

45. Find the slope of the line at the left using two points. Then find the slope using two other points. Are the slopes the same? Explain.

Test Prep

Gridded Response   For Exercises 46–48, what is the slope of the line through the points of each pair?

46. $T(0, 5)$, $U(-3, -2)$ **47.** $Q(9, 5)$, $R(4, -5)$ **48.** $C(1, 7)$, $D(-8, 7)$

For Exercises 49–51, what is the y-intercept of the graph of each equation?

49. $y = -4x + 7$ **50.** $y = -2x$ **51.** $y = 1.9$

Mixed Review

GO for Help

Lesson 7-6   **Solve and graph each inequality.**

52. $4x + 5 < 17$ **53.** $18 \le 5 - 2x$ **54.** $-x + 6 > 31$

Lesson 6-8   **Find each percent of change. Tell whether the change is an increase or a decrease.**

55. from 10 to 9   **56.** from 20 to 30   **57.** from 52 to 39

Lesson 6-7   **58. Ticket Sales** During the 2004 season, New York theater goers bought 11.3 million tickets for a total of $749.0 million. Theater goers spent a total of 3.2% more than the year before. What was the total amount spent during 2003?

Math at Work

Movie-Camera Operator

Lights . . . camera . . . action! These are familiar words for movie-camera operators. When the action begins, movie-camera operators are responsible for capturing the action on film. One scene in a movie can cost hundreds of thousands of dollars, so a scene has to be filmed correctly in as few tries as possible. Camera operators are trained in the effective use of lighting, lens filters, and camera angles. The operators determine the precise movements of the camera and its platform and the camera angles in advance of the actual shooting. It takes a good understanding of algebra and coordinate geometry to do that!

Go Online
PHSchool.com   **For:** Information about movie-camera operators
Web Code: adb-2031

You can use a graphing calculator to graph equations in slope-intercept form and find solutions.

ACTIVITY

Graph $y = 3x - 2$.

Step 1 Press the **Y=** key. Enter $3x - 2$.

Step 2 Press **ZOOM** **6** to graph your equation with the standard viewing window.

Step 3 Press **TABLE** to see solutions.

Step 4 Sketch the graph using values from the table of solutions.

EXERCISES

Graph each equation.

1. $y = 2x + 1$

2. $y = x - 4$

3. $y = 3x + 2$

4. $y = -x$

5. $y = -x + 4$

6. $y = 4x - 3$

7. $y = -3x - 2$

8. $y = \frac{1}{2}x - 5$

9. $y = -\frac{1}{2}x + 2$

10. Graph $y = \frac{2}{3}x - 2$, $y = \frac{2}{3}x + 2$, and $y = \frac{2}{3}x + 6$, in the standard viewing window. Tell what you observe, and explain.

8-4

Writing Rules for Linear Functions

What You'll Learn

- To write a function rule for a word relationship
- To write a function rule by analyzing a table or graph

...And Why

To solve real-world problems involving measurements

✓ Check Skills You'll Need

Find the slope of the line through each pair of points.

1. $A(3, 1)$, $B(2, 1)$

2. $S(3, 4)$, $T(1, 2)$

3. $P(0, -2)$, $Q(0, 2)$

4. $C(-5, 2)$, $D(4, -1)$

 for Help

Lesson 8-3

🔊 New Vocabulary

- function notation
- function rule

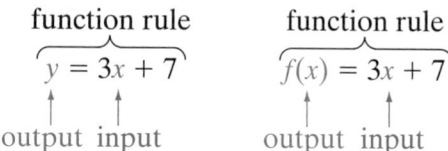

1 Writing Rules From Words

You can write a function using **function notation,** in which you use $f(x)$ instead of y. You read $f(x)$ as "f of x." You can think of a domain value as an *input* and the resulting range value as the *output*. A **function rule** is an equation that describes a function.

$$\overbrace{y = 3x + 7}^{\text{function rule}} \qquad \overbrace{f(x) = 3x + 7}^{\text{function rule}}$$
output input   output input

1 EXAMPLE   Real-World 🌐 Problem Solving

Multiple Choice Paulo works at a local store. Each week he earns a $300 salary plus a 3% commission on his sales. What are Paulo's earnings for one week if his sales are $2,500?

Ⓐ $375   Ⓑ $1,000   Ⓒ $1,503   Ⓓ $1,545

Step 1 Write a function rule.

| Words | total earnings | are | $300 | plus | 3% | of | sales |

Let s = the amount of his sales.

Let $t(s)$ = total earnings, a function of his sales.

Rule $t(s)$ =   300   +   0.03 · s

A rule for the function is $t(s) = 300 + 0.03s$.

Step 2 Evaluate the function for $s = 2,500$.

$t(s) = 300 + 0.03s$

$t(2,500) = 300 + 0.03(2,500)$ **Replace s with 2,500.**

$t(2,500) = 300 + 75$ **Multiply.**

$t(2,500) = 375$ **Add.**

Paulo earns $375 if his sales are $2,500. The answer is A.

✓ Quick Check

1. Scrumptious Snack Mix is sold by mail order. It costs $3/lb, plus $4 for shipping and handling. Write a function rule for the total cost $c(p)$ based on the number of pounds p bought. Use your function to find the total cost of 5 lb of snack mix.

2 Writing Rules From Tables or Graphs

To write a function rule from a table, look for a pattern. The slope m is $\dfrac{\text{difference in } f(x) \text{ values}}{\text{difference in } x \text{ values}}$, and b is the value of $f(x)$ when $x = 0$.

Test-Taking Tip

To find a pattern, you may need to add, subtract, multiply, divide, or use a power. You could also need to use a combination of these operations.

2 EXAMPLE **Writing a Function Rule From a Table**

Write a rule for the linear function in the table below.

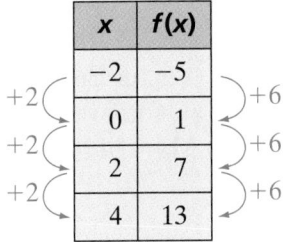

x	f(x)
−2	−5
0	1
2	7
4	13

As the *x* values increase by 2, the *f(x)* values increase by 6.
So $m = \dfrac{6}{2} = 3$.

When $x = 0$, $f(x) = 1$. So $b = 1$.

A rule for the function is $f(x) = 3x + 1$.

✓ Quick Check

2. Write a rule for each linear function.

a.
x	f(x)
−1	−2
0	0
1	2
2	4

b.
x	f(x)
−3	6
0	0
3	−6
6	−12

c.
x	y
−6	−11
−4	−7
−2	−3
0	1

You can use slope-intercept form, $f(x) = mx + b$ or $y = mx + b$, when you write a rule for a linear function.

Problem Solving Hint

y and $f(x)$ may be used interchangeably in a function rule.

3 EXAMPLE **Writing a Function Rule From a Graph**

Write a rule for the linear function graphed below.

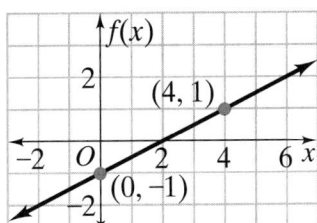

slope $= \dfrac{1 - (-1)}{4 - 0} = \dfrac{2}{4} = \dfrac{1}{2}$

y-intercept $= -1$

A rule for the function is $f(x) = \dfrac{1}{2}x - 1$.

✓ Quick Check

3. Write a rule for the function graphed at the right.

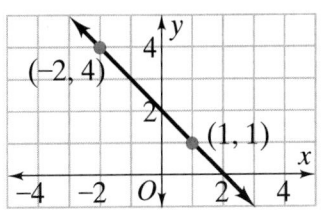

EXERCISES

For more exercises, see *Extra Skill and Word Problem Practice.*

Practice and Problem Solving

A Practice by Example

Example 1
(page 422)

GO for Help

Write a function rule for each situation. Then use your function as indicated.

1. **Money** You give a salesperson $20 for a purchase and receive change. Use your function to find the amount of change from a $4.50 purchase.

2. **Science** The temperature *t* in *Kelvin* is 273.15 more than the temperature *c* in degrees *Celsius*. Use your function to find the equivalent temperature in Kelvin for 100°C.

3. **Physics** The force of gravity is less on Mars than it is on Earth. As a result, the weight of an object on Mars *m* is 40% of its weight on Earth *w*. Use your function to find the weight on Mars of a space probe that weighs 15 lb on Earth.

Example 2
(page 423)

In Exercises 4–8, write a rule for each linear function.

4.

x	f(x)
−9	−18
0	−9
9	0
18	9

5.

x	f(x)
−4	4
−2	2
0	0
2	−2

6.

x	y
0	−2.4
2	−4.8
4	−7.2
6	−9.6

Example 3
(page 423)

7.

8.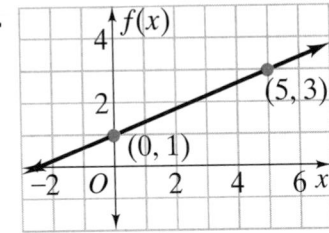

9. a. **Writing in Math** Describe the advantages you see in using a rule for a function rather than listing function values in a table.
   b. Describe the disadvantages.

B Apply Your Skills

10. **Measurement** Write a rule that expresses the number of quarts *q* of a liquid as a function of each of the following.
    a. the number of pints *p*   b. the number of fluid ounces *f*

11. a. **Measurement** Express the number of inches $n(d)$ as a function of the number of yards *d*.
    b. Use your function to find the number of inches in 4 yards.

Problem Solving Hint

8 fluid ounces = 1 cup
2 cups = 1 pint
2 pints = 1 quart
4 quarts = 1 gallon

12. a. **Geometry** Write a rule that expresses the perimeter $p(s)$ of a square as a function of the length *s* of one side.
    b. Use your function to find the perimeter of a square with side length 7 cm.

Examples 2 and 3 suggest that you can write a rule for a linear function if you know any of the following about its graph.
(a) the slope m and y-intercept b;
(b) the slope m and any point (p, q) of the graph;
(c) any two points (r, s) and (u, v) of the graph.

Sample A line through points $(-2, 6)$ and $(4, 3)$ has slope
$$\frac{3 - 6}{4 - (-2)} = -\frac{1}{2}.$$

Using $-\frac{1}{2}$ for the slope, an equation of the line is $\qquad y = -\frac{1}{2}x + b.$

Using $(4, 3)$, substitute 4 for x and 3 for y: $\qquad 3 = -\frac{1}{2}(4) + b$

So, $3 = -2 + b$, and the y-intercept b is 5. The rule is $\quad y = -\frac{1}{2}x + 5.$

Write a rule for the linear function with slope m and y-intercept b.

13. $m = 2, b = -4$ **14.** $m = -\frac{1}{3}, b = -2$ **15.** $m = 0, b = 2$

Write a rule for the linear function whose graph has slope m and contains the given point.

16. $m = -\frac{1}{4}; (4, 0)$ **17.** $m = 3; (-2, -2)$ **18.** $m = \frac{3}{4}; (6, 4)$

19. Multiple Choice Write a rule for the linear function whose graph contains the points $(1, -1)$ and $(4, -1)$.
   Ⓐ $y = x - 1$ Ⓑ $y = -x + 1$ Ⓒ $y = -x$ Ⓓ $y = -1$

Write a rule for the linear function whose graph contains the two given points.

20. $(1, 1), (2, 5)$ **21.** $(3, 0), (8, 2)$ **22.** $(-3, 2), (4, -1.5)$

Ⓒ Challenge

23. a. Choose two points from the table and write a rule for the linear function.
   b. Choose two other points from the table and write a rule for the linear function.
   c. **Writing in Math** Compare the rules from parts (a) and (b). Justify your observations.

x	y
-6	-15
1	-1
7	11
11	19

Data Analysis For Exercises 24 and 25, use the data below.

24. Write a function rule for the total monthly cost for electric space heating.

25. a. Write a function rule for the total monthly bill of a home customer.
   b. Suppose a home customer receives a bill for $22.52 one month. How many kilowatt-hours did the customer use that month?

Electricity Rates

Type of Account	Charge per Kilowatt-hour (¢/kWh)	Monthly Charge ($)
Home	4.968	6.87
Space Heating	5.691	7.77

Multiple Choice

26. Which rule gives the same relationship between x and y as $x + y = 6$?

  A. $y = x + 6$ **B.** $y = x - 6$ **C.** $y = 6 - x$ **D.** $y = -6 - x$

27. Which function rule describes the number of centimeters y as a function of a number of millimeters x?

  F. $y = 100x$ **G.** $y = 10x$ **H.** $y = 0.1x$ **J.** $y = 0.01x$

28. Which rule shows the relationship of pounds, p, to ounces, z?

  A. $z = 16p$ **B.** $z = 32p$ **C.** $p = 16z$ **D.** $p = 32z$

Short Response

29. a. One gallon equals 4 quarts. Write a rule that expresses the number of quarts q as a function of the number of gallons g.

  b. Use your function from part (a) to find the number of quarts in 17 gallons.

Mixed Review

GO for Help

Lesson 8-3

Find the slope of the line through each pair of points.

30. $C(0, -2), D(2, 1)$ **31.** $J(3, -1), K(6, 1)$ **32.** $G(12, 8), H(6, 2)$

Lesson 6-4

Probability **Find each probability for choosing a letter at random from the letters in the word FUNCTION.**

33. $P(\text{N or C})$ **34.** $P(\text{consonant})$ **35.** $P(\text{not T})$

Lesson 3-5 **36. Sports** In 1999, Hicham El Guerrouj of Morocco ran the mile in world-record time. Had he taken 1.26 seconds longer, his time would have matched the previous record of 3 min, 44.39 s. Write and solve an equation to find the 1999 record time.

Checkpoint Quiz 1

Lessons 8-1 through 8-4

1. Find three solutions of $9x - 2y = 18$.

2. Graph $3x - y = 5$ on a coordinate plane.

3. Is $\{(-2, 0), (-1, 3), (0, -2), (3, -1)\}$ a function? Explain.

4. **Writing in Math** Explain how to use the vertical-line test to determine whether a relation is a function.

Find the slope of the line through the given points.

5. $A(1, 5), B(3, 15)$ **6.** $D(-2, -4), F(0, -6)$ **7.** $G(-3, 4), H(-3, -6)$

8. What are the slope and the y-intercept of $y = -2x + 5$?

9. Measurement Write a rule to describe the number of pounds $p(n)$ as a function of a number of tons n.

Scatter Plots

IL Assessment Framework

1 Interpreting and Drawing Scatter Plots

ctivity

Making Scatter Plots

1. **Data Collection** For each person in your group, measure the height and *hand span*, the greatest distance possible between the tips of the thumb and little finger on one hand.

2. Graph the lengths as ordered pairs (height, hand span).

3. **a.** Share your data with the class. Make a graph of the class data.
   b. Reasoning Compare the two graphs you made. Does one graph show a relationship between heights and hand spans more clearly than the other? Explain.

A **scatter plot** is a graph that shows the relationship between two sets of data. To make a scatter plot, graph the data as ordered pairs.

1 EXAMPLE   Real-World 🌐 Problem Solving

Multiple Choice The scatter plot shows education and income data. How many years of education does the person who earns $100,000 have?

- Ⓐ 12 years
- Ⓑ 14 years
- Ⓒ 15 years
- Ⓓ 16 years

The point (16, 100) has income coordinate 100. The person earning $100,000 in a year has 16 years of education. The answer is D.

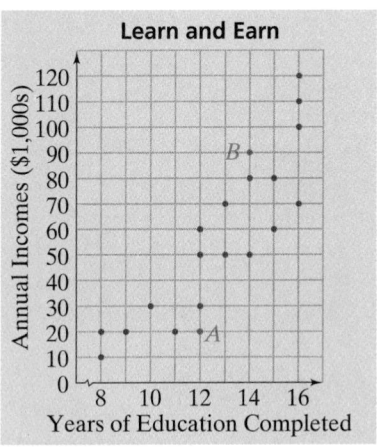

Learn and Earn

✓ Quick Check

1. **a.** Describe the person represented by point *A* in the example.
   b. Describe the person represented by point *B*.
   c. How many people have exactly 12 years of education?

10.8.01 Read, interpret, and make predictions from data represented in a bar graph, line plot, Venn diagram, chart/table, line graph, scatterplot, circle graph, stem–and–leaf plot, or histogram.

✓ Check Skills You'll Need
Write the coordinates of each point.

1. *A*
2. *B*
3. *C*
4. *D*

GO for Help
Lesson 1-10

🔊 New Vocabulary
- scatter plot
- positive correlation
- negative correlation
- no correlation

Climate Use the table to make a scatter plot of the latitude and temperature data.

Climate Data

City	Location (degrees north latitude)	Daily Mean Temperature (°F)	Mean Annual Precipitation (inches)
Atlanta, GA	34	61	51
Boston, MA	42	51	42
Chicago, IL	42	49	36
Duluth, MN	47	39	30
Honolulu, HI	21	77	22
Houston, TX	30	68	46
Juneau, AK	58	41	54
Miami, FL	26	76	56
Phoenix, AZ	33	73	8
Portland, ME	44	45	44
San Diego, CA	33	64	10
Wichita, KS	38	56	29

SOURCES: *The World Almanac* and *The Statistical Abstract of the United States*. Go to **www.PHSchool.com** for a data update. Web Code: adg-9041

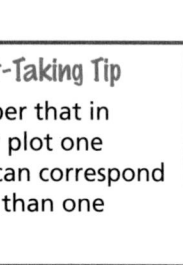

Test-Taking Tip

Remember that in a scatter plot one *y*-value can correspond to more than one *x*-value.

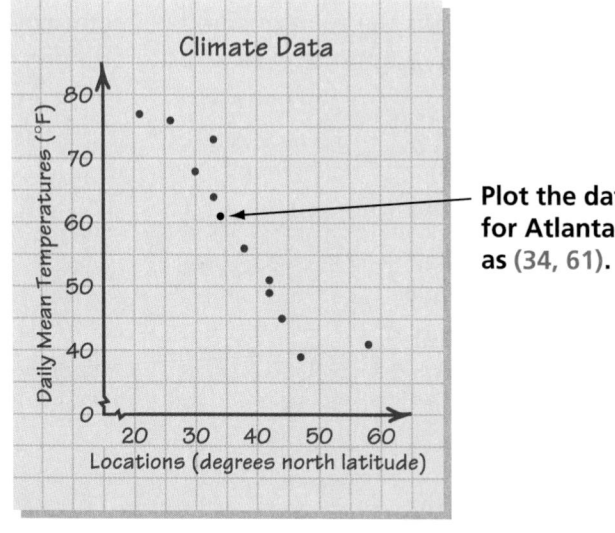

Plot the data for Atlanta as (34, 61).

✓ **Quick Check**

2. Use the table in Example 2.

   a. Make a scatter plot of the latitude and precipitation data.

   b. Make a scatter plot of the temperature and precipitation data. Plot temperatures along the horizontal axis of the graph.

2 Using Scatter Plots to Find Trends

You can use scatter plots to look for trends. The next three scatter plots show the types of relationships two sets of data may have.

Vocabulary Tip

"Positive slope" in a scatter plot suggests a positive correlation. "Negative slope" suggests a negative correlation.

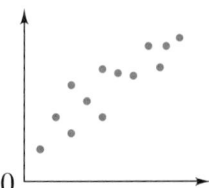

Positive correlation
As one set of values increases, the other set tends to increase.

Negative correlation
As one set of values increases, the other set tends to decrease.

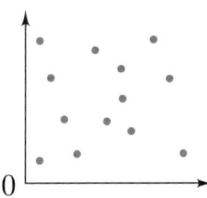

No correlation
The values show no relationship.

3 EXAMPLE   Real-World 🌐 Problem Solving

Sports Use the scatter plot below. Is there a *positive correlation*, a *negative correlation*, or *no correlation* between the years and the winning times? Explain.

Olympic Games: Men's 110-Meter Hurdles

Since 1952, the winning times have generally decreased. There is a negative correlation.

✓ Quick Check

3. **Sports** Use the scatter plot at the right. Is there a *positive correlation*, a *negative correlation*, or *no correlation* between the years and the winning distances? Explain.

Olympic Games: Women's Long Jump

EXERCISES

For more exercises, see *Extra Skill and Word Problem Practice.*

Practice and Problem Solving

A Practice by Example
Example 1
(page 427)

GO for Help

For a guide to reading
and solving Exercises
1–3, see page 433.

Statistics The scatter plot shows
the average times that 15 students
spent watching television and on
physical activities in a day.

1. Describe the student represented
   by point *A*.

2. How many students averaged 1 hour
   of physical activity?

3. How many students averaged
   5 hours of watching television?

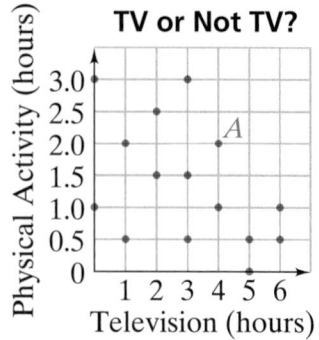

Example 2
(page 428)

Nutrition For Exercises 4–6, use the table below. Make a scatter plot
for the data indicated. Graph calories on the horizontal axis.

Nutritional Values for 100 Grams of Food

Food	Fat (grams)	Protein (grams)	Carbohydrate (grams)	Energy (calories)
Bread	4	8	50	267
Cheese	33	25	1	403
Chicken	4	31	0	165
Eggs	11	13	1	155
Ground beef	19	27	0	292
Milk	3	3	5	61
Peanuts	49	26	16	567
Pizza	5	12	33	223
Tuna	1	26	0	116

SOURCE: U. S. Department of Agriculture Nutrient Database
for Standard Reference

4. calories and grams of protein

5. calories and grams of fat

6. calories and grams of carbohydrates

Example 3
(page 429)

Is there a *positive correlation,* a *negative correlation,* or *no
correlation* between the sets of data in each scatter plot? Explain.

7.   8.   9.

10.   11.   12.

Apply Your Skills **Data Analysis** **The scatter plot below shows the relationship between the distances from school and the times it takes to get to school for the students in one class.**

13. How long does it take the student who lives 0.5 mi from school to get to school?

14. How many students live closer than 1 mi from school?

15. Multiple Choice How many students take longer than 35 min to get to school?
- Ⓐ 3 students
- Ⓑ 4 students
- Ⓒ 14 students
- Ⓓ 17 students

Graph: Time (min) on vertical axis (10, 20, 30, 40); Distance (mi) on horizontal axis (0, 1, 2, 3, 4, 5).

GO nline
Homework Video Tutor
Visit: PHSchool.com
Web Code: ade-0805

Would you expect a *positive correlation,* a *negative correlation,* or *no correlation* between each pair of data sets? Explain.

16. the age of pets in a home and the number of pets in that home

17. the temperature outside and the number of layers of clothing

18. your grade on a test and the amount of time you studied

19. the shoe sizes and the shirt sizes for men

20. the times candles take to burn and their original heights

21. the number of students in a school and the number of stores nearby

22. latitude and precipitation (see p. 428 Quick Check 2a)

23. temperature and precipitation (see p. 428 Quick Check 2b)

 Challenge

24. Writing in Math Describe a pair of data sets, different from any in this lesson, for which you would expect to see a scatter plot with a negative correlation. Explain.

25. Ticket Prices The table at the right shows the average prices of movie tickets and the numbers of movie admissions.
 a. Make a scatter plot of the data in the table. Graph prices on the horizontal axis.
 b. **Data Analysis** Is there a *positive correlation,* a *negative correlation,* or *no correlation* between the numbers of admissions and the prices of tickets?
 c. **Reasoning** Would your answer to part (b) be the same if you graphed ticket prices on the vertical axis instead? Explain.

Year	Number of Admissions (millions)	Average Ticket Price
1990	1,189	$4.23
1992	1,173	$4.15
1994	1,292	$4.18
1996	1,339	$4.42
1998	1,481	$4.69

SOURCE: Motion Picture Association of America

Multiple Choice

26. Which scatter plot shows that as the numbers of pages in magazines increase, the weights of the magazines increase?

A.

B.

C.

D.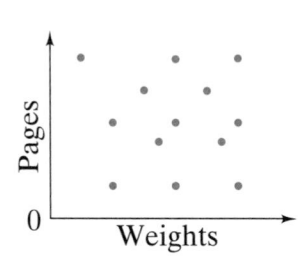

27. Which pair of data sets would most likely have no correlation?
- **F.** the distances cars can travel on full tanks of gasoline and the amounts of gasoline their tanks can hold
- **G.** the ages of children under 12 years old and their heights
- **H.** people's ring sizes and the numbers of rings they own
- **J.** the numbers of students and the numbers of teachers in each school in your state

Short Response

In Exercises 28–30, **(a)** describe a graph with each given type of correlation. **(b)** Sketch a graph showing each type of correlation.

28. positive   **29.** negative   **30.** no correlation

Mixed Review

GO for Help

Lesson 8-4

Write a rule for each function.

31.

x	y
−4	−10
−2	−5
0	0
2	5

32.

x	y
−6	5
−3	3
0	1
3	−1

33.

x	f(x)
−2	9
1	6
4	3
7	0

Lesson 7-7

Solve each formula for the variable indicated in red.

34. $V = \frac{1}{3}Bh$ **35.** $A = \frac{1}{2}(b + c)h$ **36.** $S = \frac{a}{1 - r}$

Lesson 6-7 🌐 **37. Personal Finance** Ms. Jimenez earns $27,000 per year. She is paid weekly. She puts 8% of her salary in a retirement fund. How much money goes into this fund each week?

Analyzing Data Read the problems below. Then let Will's thinking guide you through the solutions. Check your understanding with the exercises at the bottom of the page.

Statistics The scatter plot shows the average times that 15 students spent watching television and the average times they spent on physical activity in a day.

1. Describe the student represented by point A.

2. How many students averaged 1 hour of physical activity?

3. How many students averaged 5 hours of watching television?

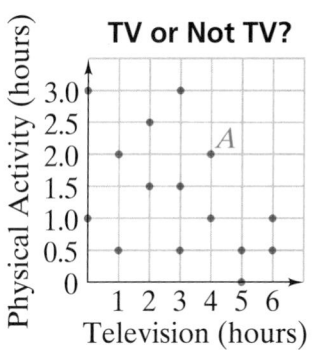

What Will Thinks

Before I begin, I need to read and understand the graph.

The first question wants me to describe the student represented by point A. I need to find the coordinates of the point and state what the coordinates mean in this situation.

The second question wants me to find the number of students who averaged 1 hour of physical activity. I need to find the points whose y-coordinate is 1. Three points represent three students.

The last question wants me to find the number of students who averaged 5 hours of watching TV. I need to find the points whose x-coordinate is 5. Two points represent two students.

What Will Writes

Horizontal axis = hours of TV
Vertical axis = hours of physical activity
Each point is (TV hours, activity hours).

Point A has coordinates (4, 2).
(4, 2) means (4 TV hours, 2 activity hours).

The student averaged 4 hours of TV viewing and 2 hours of physical activity each day.

Points with y-coordinate 1:
(0, 1)   (4, 1)   (6, 1)
Three students averaged 1 hour of physical activity.

Points with x-coordinate 5:
(5, 0)   (5, 0.5)
Two students averaged 5 hours of TV.

EXERCISES

1. Would you expect there to be a positive correlation, a negative correlation, or no correlation between hours of physical activity and hours of watching television? Justify your choice.

2. Does the scatter plot suggest a positive correlation, a negative correlation, or no correlation? Explain.

IL Assessment Framework

10.8.04 Identify or draw a reasonable approximation of the line of best fit from a set of data or a scatter plot, and use the line to make predictions.

✓ Check Skills You'll Need

Write a rule for each linear function.

1.

2.

for Help
Lesson 8–4

🔊 New Vocabulary
• trend line

Online active math

For: Writing Equations Activity
Use: Interactive Textbook, 8-6

1 Solve by Graphing

Math Strategies in Action
Businesses and government agencies use scatter plots to look for trends and make predictions.

For example, the park service at Isle Royale, Michigan, surveys the moose and wolf populations each spring. They use a scatter plot to show the relationship between them.

On the scatter plot they draw a **trend line** that closely fits the data points in the scatter plot. Using the trend line, they can predict the size of one population from the size of the other.

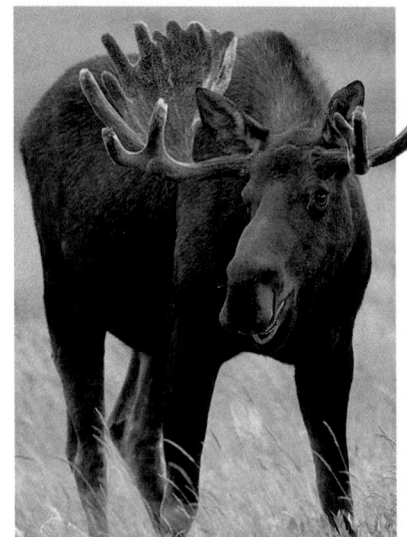

Real-World 🌐 Connection

Moose, like the one shown above, have wolves as a principal predator.

1 EXAMPLE   Real-World 🌐 Problem Solving

Wildlife Use the data in the table below. Suppose there were 18 wolves one year. About how many moose would you expect to be on the island that year?

Isle Royale Populations

Year	Wolf	Moose	Year	Wolf	Moose	Year	Wolf	Moose
1982	14	700	1988	12	1,653	1994	15	1,800
1983	23	900	1989	11	1,397	1995	16	2,400
1984	24	811	1990	15	1,216	1996	22	1,200
1985	22	1,062	1991	12	1,313	1997	24	500
1986	20	1,025	1992	12	1,600	1998	14	700
1987	16	1,380	1993	13	1,880	1999	25	750

SOURCE: Isle Royale National Park Service

1. What are the two variables?

2. What are you trying to predict?

You can graph the data in a scatter plot. If the points show a correlation, you can draw a trend line. You can then use the line to predict other data values.

Step 1 Make a scatter plot by graphing the (wolf, moose) ordered pairs. Use the x-axis for wolves and the y-axis for moose.

Step 2 Sketch a trend line. The line should be as close as possible to each data point. There should be about as many points above the trend line as below it.

Isle Royale Populations

Step 3 To predict the number of moose when there are 18 wolves, find 18 along the horizontal axis.
Look up to find the point on the trend line that corresponds to 18 wolves. Then look across to the value on the vertical axis, which is about 1,200.

There will be about 1,200 moose when there are 18 wolves.

You can write an equation for a trend line. You can use the equation to make predictions.

✓ Quick Check

3. **a.** What is the y-intercept of the trend line above?
   b. Locate one other point on the trend line. Then find the slope of the trend line.
   c. Write an equation for the trend line in slope-intercept form.
   d. Use the equation you wrote in part (c). Find the solution of the equation when $x = 18$.

EXERCISES

For more exercises, see *Extra Skill and Word Problem Practice*.

Practice and Problem Solving

A Practice by Example

Example 1
(page 434)

GO for Help

Solve each problem by graphing.

Statistics For Exercises 1 and 2, use the data below. The table shows the populations of some states and the numbers of cars registered in those states.

State Populations and Cars

State	Population (millions)	Registered Cars (millions)	State	Population (millions)	Registered Cars (millions)
FL	14.4	7.2	NY	18.1	7.9
GA	7.3	3.8	OH	11.2	6.6
IL	11.8	6.2	PA	12.0	5.9
KS	2.6	1.2	SC	3.7	1.8
ME	1.2	0.6	TN	5.3	3.0
MS	2.7	1.3	TX	19.1	7.4
NV	1.6	0.6	WA	5.5	2.6

SOURCE: *Statistical Abstract of the United States.* Go to **www.PHSchool.com** for a data update. Web Code: adg-2041

1. a. Use the data to make a scatter plot of the data. Use the population data for the horizontal axis.
 b. Draw a trend line.
 c. Predict how many cars are registered by the 32.2 million people in California.
 d. Write an equation for your trend line. Predict the number of cars registered by the 7.3 million people in North Carolina.

2. Writing in Math Is there a correlation between the two data sets? Explain.

3. Data Analysis Use the data in the table below. Predict the number of gallons bought for $15.

Gasoline Purchases

Dollars Spent	12	14	11	12	10	6	10	8
Gallons Bought	7.3	8.0	5.9	6.5	5.7	3.5	5.1	4.4

B Apply Your Skills

Solve using any strategy.

🌐 **4. Clothing** You are choosing from four t-shirts and three pairs of jeans. How many different outfits can you make from these clothes?

🌐 **5. Business** A supermarket charges $1.17 for a 12-oz jar of salsa and $1.89 for a 20-oz jar. Now the producer is introducing a 16-oz jar of the same salsa. What do you think would be a fair price for this new size? Justify your answer to the manager of the store.

Strategies

- Act It Out
- Draw a Diagram
- Guess, Check, Revise
- Look for a Pattern
- Make a Model
- Make a Table
- Simulate the Problem
- Solve by Graphing
- Use Multiple Strategies
- Work a Simpler Problem
- Work Backward
- Write an Equation
- Write a Proportion

GO Online
Homework Video Tutor
Visit: PHSchool.com
Web Code: ade-0806

6. (Algebra) A plumber charges $45 for a service call, plus $70/h for her time.
   a. Find the cost of a two-hour service call.
   b. How long was a service call that cost $150?

7. **Engineering** To provide wheelchair access, a ramp with a slope of $\frac{1}{15}$ is being built to a door of a building. Suppose that the bottom of the door is 3 ft above street level. How far will the ramp extend from the building?

Challenge 8. **Physics** As the weight held by a spring increases, the length of the spring increases proportionally. Suppose a 2-lb weight stretches a spring to 15 in., and a 12-lb weight stretches the same spring to 20 in. What is the length of the spring with no weight attached?

9. The data table on page 434 shows 18 data pairs. Its scatter plot (page 435) shows 17 plotted points. Make a conjecture as to why this is so. Study the table to verify or disprove your conjecture.

ISAT

Test Prep

Multiple Choice

10. Which ordered pair is a solution for $4x - 3y = 6$?
    A. $(-3, 2)$ B. $(3, 2)$ C. $(3, -2)$ D. $(-3, -2)$

11. What is the slope of the line through $A(2, 6)$ and $B(8, -1)$?
    F. $-\frac{6}{7}$ G. $-\frac{4}{9}$ H. $\frac{5}{6}$ J. $-\frac{7}{6}$

12. What is the slope of the graph of $3x - 2y = 6$?
    A. $-\frac{3}{2}$ B. $-\frac{2}{3}$ C. $\frac{2}{3}$ D. $\frac{3}{2}$

13. What is the y-intercept of the graph of $3x - 2y = 6$?
    F. -3 G. 2 H. 3 J. 6

Short Response

14. One gallon equals 4 quarts. **(a)** Write a rule that expresses the number of gallons g of a liquid as a function of the number of quarts q. **(b)** Use the rule to find the number of gallons in 30 quarts.

Mixed Review

GO for Help

Lesson 8-2

Lessons 7-2 and 7-5

Lesson 6-6

Find the solutions of each equation for $x = -3, 0,$ and 2.

15. $y = -3x$ 16. $y = \frac{1}{3}x + 4$ 17. $y = 0.5x - 2$

Solve each equation.

18. $3x + 7 = 4x - 12$ 19. $7t + 3 - 4t = -6$

20. $8(2 - c) - 12 = -3c$ 21. $-2x + 3(5 - x) = 5$

22. **Food** About 150 million of the 20 billion hot dogs consumed in the United States each year are eaten during the Fourth of July weekend. What percent of the hot dogs are eaten at this time?

Measuring Bounce Height

When you drop a tennis ball, how high will it bounce on the first bounce? Does the height you drop it from affect how high it bounces? Scientists collect data and use scatter plots to determine answers to questions like these.

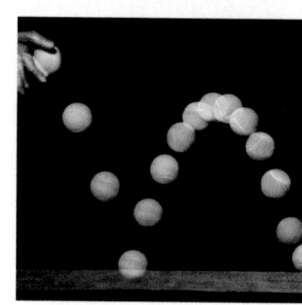

ACTIVITY

You will need a meter stick and a tennis ball. Drop the ball from various heights and record the height of the first bounce in a table like the one below. (*Hint:* You will get more accurate measurements if you tape the meter stick to the wall and drop the ball close to it.)

Drop height (cm)	100	90	80	70	60	50	40
Bounce height (cm)	■	■	■	■	■	■	■
Bounce height (cm)	■	■	■	■	■	■	■
Bounce height (cm)	■	■	■	■	■	■	■
Average bounce height (cm)	■	■	■	■	■	■	■

1. **a.** Drop the tennis ball three times from each height. Record your results.
   b. Take an average of the three bounce heights. Record the average bounce height for each drop height.

2. Use the data in your table to make a scatter plot. Graph drop height along the *x*-axis and average bounce height along the *y*-axis.

3. **a.** Draw a trend line on your scatter plot. You should have about the same number of data points above and below your trend line.
   b. Write an equation for your trend line.

4. **Predict** Use your trend line to predict the bounce height of a tennis ball dropped from a height of 200 cm and from 250 cm.

5. The first bounce of a tennis ball reaches a height of 125 cm. Use your trend line. Estimate the drop height.

Solving Systems of Linear Equations

IL Assessment Framework

8.8.07 Represent linear equations and quantitative relationships on a rectangular coordinate system, and interpret the meaning of a specific part of a graph.

1 Graphing Systems of Linear Equations

Two or more linear equations form a **system of linear equations.** A *solution of the system* is any ordered pair that is a solution of each equation in the system.

You can solve some systems of equations by graphing the equations on a coordinate plane and identifying the point(s) of intersection.

1 EXAMPLE Solving a System by Graphing

Solve the system $y = -x + 1$ and $y = 2x + 4$ by graphing.

Step 1 Graph each line.

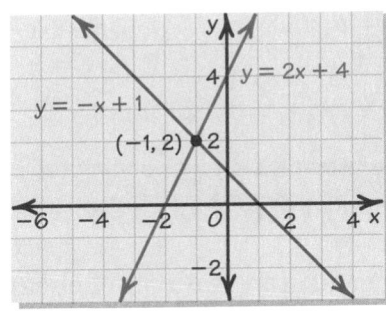

Step 2 Find the point of intersection.

The lines intersect at one point, $(-1, 2)$. The solution is $(-1, 2)$.

Check See whether $(-1, 2)$ makes both equations true.

$y = -x + 1$

$2 \overset{?}{=} -(-1) + 1$ ⟵ **Replace x with -1 and y with 2.** ⟶ $2 \overset{?}{=} 2(-1) + 4$

$2 = 2$ ✔ **The solution checks.** $2 = 2$ ✔

$y = 2x + 4$

✓ Quick Check

1. Solve each system of equations by graphing. Check each solution.

   a. $y = x - 6$
   $\quad\;\; y = -2x$

   b. $y = 3x - 3$
   $\quad\;\; x + y = 1$

When the graphs of two equations are parallel, there is no point of intersection. The system has *no solution*.

When the graphs of two equations are the same line, all the points on the line are solutions. The system has *infinitely many solutions*.

✓ Check Skills You'll Need

Graph each equation.

1. $y = -x - 4$

2. $y = 2x - 1$

3. $-4x = 6y$

4. $3x - 2y = 5$

 for Help
Lesson 8-2

◀)) **New Vocabulary**

• **system of linear equations**

 nline

Video Tutor Help
Visit: PHSchool.com
Web Code: ada-0775

2 EXAMPLE   Solving Special Systems

Solve each system of equations by graphing.

a. $x + y = 1; y = -x + 3$

b. $x - 2y = 4; 2x - 4y = 8$

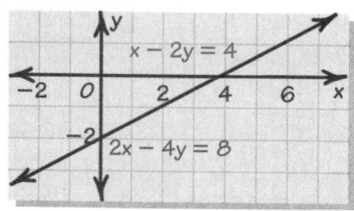

The lines are parallel. They do not intersect. There is no solution.

The graphs are the same line. There are infinitely many solutions.

✓ Quick Check

2. Solve each system by graphing.

a. $y = x - 6;$
$\quad x - y = 6$

b. $y = x + 4;$
$\quad y = x$

---

2   Using Systems of Linear Equations

You can write and graph systems of equations to solve problems.

3 EXAMPLE   Using a System of Equations

Find two numbers with a sum of 6 and a difference of 4.

Step 1 Write equations.

Let x = the greater number.
Let y = the lesser number.

Equation 1 Sum   is   6.
$\qquad\qquad x + y = 6$

Equation 2 Difference   is   4.
$\qquad\qquad x - y = 4$

Step 2 Graph the equations.

The lines intersect at $(5, 1)$.
The numbers are 5 and 1.

Check Since the sum of 5 and 1 is 6 and the difference of 5 and 1 is 4, the answer is correct.

✓ Quick Check

3. Find two numbers with a difference of 2 and a sum of -8.

Graphing Calculator Hint

You can use a graphing calculator to check your solution of a system. Write the equations in slope-intercept form, press **Y=**, and enter them as Y_1 and Y_2.

In the **TABLE** screen, find the x-value that gives the same value for Y1 and Y2.

You can solve some problems involving two variables by writing
and graphing a system of equations, or you may be able to use one
variable to write and solve an equation.

More Than One Way

Carpentry A carpenter cuts an 8-ft board into two pieces. One
piece is three times as long as the other. What is the length of
each piece?

Roberto's Method

Write and graph a system of equations.

Let x = length of longer piece; y = length of shorter piece.

Equation 1   Longer piece is three times shorter piece.

$$x = 3 \cdot y$$

Equation 2   Sum of lengths is eight.

$$x + y = 8$$

Graph the equations.

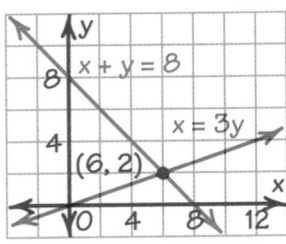

The lines intersect at (6, 2). The lengths are 6 ft and 2 ft.

Michelle's Method

Write a one-variable equation.

Let x = length of shorter piece; 3x = length of longer piece.

Equation   Shorter piece plus longer piece is 8 feet.

$$x + 3x = 8$$
$$4x = 8$$
$$x = 2$$

The shorter piece is 2 ft, and the longer piece is 3(2) = 6 ft.

Choose a Method

1. Which method would you use to find
   the lengths? Explain.

2. In Roberto's Method, suppose *x* = length
   of shorter piece. What difference would this make
   in the equations and the graph?

EXERCISES

For more exercises, see *Extra Skill and Word Problem Practice.*

Practice and Problem Solving

Practice by Example

Example 1
(page 439)

GO for Help

Check whether $(-1, 5)$ is a solution of each system of equations. Show your work.

1. $x + y = 4$
$x - y = 6$

2. $y = -2x + 3$
$y = x - 4$

3. $2x = y - 7$
$2y = -x + 9$

Solve each system of equations by graphing. Check each solution.

4. $y = x + 1$
$y = 3x - 7$

5. $y = 2x + 5$
$x + y = 8$

6. $y = x + 1$
$y = -x - 3$

7. $y = x + 5$
$y = -2x + 8$

8. $y = x - 4$
$y = 3x$

9. $y = 2x - 2$
$y = 6$

Example 2
(page 440)

10. $-3x + y = 5$
$y = 3x - 7$

11. $y = -x - 3$
$y = -x + 2$

12. $y = -6 - 2x$
$2x + y = -6$

13. $y = -2x + 1$
$2x + y = -1$

14. $y = 3x$
$-y = -3x$

15. $y = x + 2$
$x - y = -2$

Example 3
(page 440)

16. Find two numbers with a sum of -8 and a difference of 4. Let x be the greater number and y be the lesser number.

Apply Your Skills

Is each ordered pair a solution of the given system of equations? Show your work.

17. $2x + 5y = 3$
$y = 7.5x; (1.5, 0.2)$

18. $6x - 6y = 2$
$3x + 9y = -7; \left(-\frac{1}{3}, -\frac{2}{3}\right)$

19. Kites A four-foot-long wooden rod is cut into two pieces to make a kite. One piece is three times as long as the other.
  a. Let $x =$ the length of the longer piece.
  Let $y =$ the length of the shorter piece.
  Write a system of equations to find the length of each piece.
  b. Solve the system by graphing. State the length of each piece.

Solve each system of equations by graphing. Check each solution.

20. $x + y = 3$
$2x = 10 - 2y$

21. $y = 2x - 4$
$2x - y = 4$

22. $x - y = -4$
$x + y = 6$

23. $2x - 4y = 4$
$y = 0.5x - 1$

24. $y = x - 2$
$x + 3y = 6$

25. $3y - 2x = 3$
$6y = 4x + 6$

26. Geometry The perimeter of a rectangle is 24 ft. Its length is five times its width. Let x be the length and y be the width. What is the area of the rectangle?

27. The difference of two numbers is 5. The result when the greater number is decreased by twice the lesser is 9. Let x be the greater number and y be the lesser number. Find the numbers.

28. There are 11 animals in a barnyard. Some are chickens and some are cows. There are 38 legs in all. Let x be the number of chickens and y be the number of cows. How many of each animal are in the barnyard?

29. One sales position pays \$200/wk plus 10% commission. Another sales position pays \$150/wk plus 20% commission.
   a. For each job, write an equation that relates the amount of sales x for one week to the money earned y.
   b. Solve the system from part (a) to find the amount of sales in a week that will earn the same amount from each job. Show your work.
   c. If weekly sales at each job are about \$600, at which job can you earn more money? Explain.

30. a. Graph each system of equations on a separate coordinate plane.
   $y = 3x + 1; y = 3x - 2$ $y = -2x - 1; y = -2x + 4$
   b. **Writing in Math** Based on part (a), write a conjecture about solutions to systems of equations that have the same slope.

C Challenge   **Open-Ended Write a system of equations with the given solutions.**

31. no solution   **32.** one solution   **33.** infinitely many

34. Geometry The graphs of $y = 3$, $y = 7$, $x = 2$, and $x = 5$ contain the sides of a rectangle. Find the area of the rectangle.

35. Solve the system $y = x + 2$, $y = 4x + 11$, and $y = -2x - 7$.

ISAT

Test Prep

Multiple Choice **36.** What is the solution of the system below?
   $y = x + 4; y = 4x + 1$
   A. (0, 1)   **B.** (0, 4)   **C.** (1, 4)   **D.** (1, 5)

37. How many solutions does the system below have?
   $2x + 4y = 10; x + 2y = 10$
   F. 0   **G.** 1   **H.** 2   **J.** infinitely many

38. Use the system $x + y = -6$; $x - y = 2$. How are the x-coordinate and the y-coordinate of the solution related?
   A. $y = -2x$ **B.** $y = 2x$ **C.** $x = -2y$ **D.** $x = 2y$

Extended Response **39.** There are 16 questions on a test. Each question is worth either 5 points or 10 points. The total is 100 points.
   a. Let x = the number of 5-point questions.
      Let y = the number of 10-point questions.
      Write a system of equations to find the number of each type of question.
   b. Solve the system by graphing.
   c. How many questions of each type are on the test?

Lesson 8-5

40. Use the scatter plot at the right.
  a. How much time did the person who saw four movies spend?
  b. How many people saw more than three movies?
  c. How many people spent less than three hours watching movies?

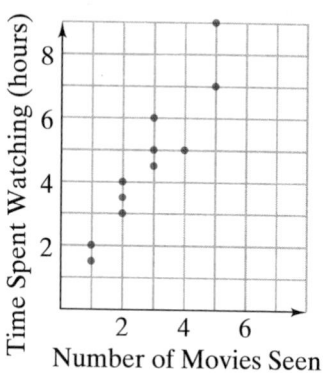

Lesson 7-6

Solve each inequality.

41. $1 - x < 5$

42. $3t - 1 \leq 17$

43. $-2c + 5 \geq 3$

44. $m + 4 > -10$

Lesson 6-4

Probability **Find each probability for one roll of a number cube.**

45. $P(2)$ **46.** $P(6 \text{ or } 5)$ **47.** $P(-1)$ **48.** $P(4, 2, \text{ or } 5)$

✓ **Checkpoint Quiz 2**   **Lessons 8-5 through 8-7**

1. a. Statistics Use the table at the right. Make a scatter plot relating daily newspaper circulation and television sets.
  b. Is there is a *positive correlation*, a *negative correlation*, or *no correlation* between daily newspaper circulation and the number of television sets in homes? Explain.
  c. Data Analysis Draw a trend line on your scatter plot. Use it to predict the number of television sets when newspaper circulation is 55 million.

Media in the United States

Year	Daily Newspaper Circulation (millions)	Television Sets in Homes (millions)
1980	62	128
1985	63	155
1990	62	193
1991	61	193
1992	60	192
1993	60	201
1994	59	211
1995	57	217
1996	57	223

SOURCE: *Statistical Abstract of the United States.*
Go to **www.PHSchool.com** for a data update.
Web Code: adg-9041

Solve each system by graphing.

2. $y = -4x$
     $y = -x + 6$

3. $x - y = 1$
     $x + y = -7$

4. $6x + 2y = 12$
     $y = 3x$

5. Measurement One gallon of liquid occupies 231 cubic inches. Write a rule that expresses the number of gallons $g(c)$ as a function of the number of cubic inches c.

6. Find two numbers with a sum of -4 and a difference of 10.

Graphing Linear Inequalities

8-8

IL Assessment Framework

8.8.10 Identify, graph, and interpret up to two inequalities with a single variable on a number line.

8.8.11 Represent and analyze problems with linear equations and inequalities.

1 Graphing Linear Inequalities

If you replace the equal sign in a linear equation with $>$, $<$, $\geq$, or $\leq$, the result is a **linear inequality.** The graph of a linear inequality is a region of the coordinate plane bounded by a line. Every point in the region is a solution of the inequality.

1 EXAMPLE Graphing a Linear Inequality

Graph each inequality on a coordinate plane.

a. $y \leq x + 2$ **b.** $y < -2x$

Step 1 Graph the boundary line.

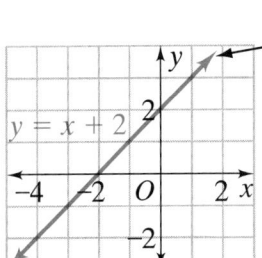

Points on the boundary line make $y \leq x + 2$ true. Use a solid line.

Points on the boundary line do *not* make $y < -2x$ true. Use a dashed line.

Step 2 Test a point not on the boundary line.

Test $(0, 0)$ in the inequality.

$y \leq x + 2$

$0 \overset{?}{\leq} 0 + 2$ **Substitute.**

$0 \leq 2$ ✔ **true**

Test $(1, 1)$ in the inequality.

$y < -2x$

$1 \overset{?}{<} -2(1)$ **Substitute.**

$1 < -2$ ✘ **false**

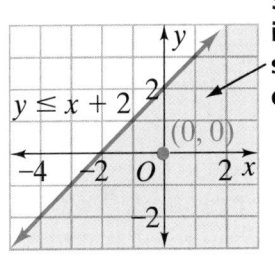

Since the inequality is true for (0, 0), shade the region containing (0, 0).

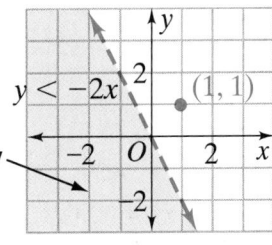

Since the inequality is false for (1, 1), shade the region that does *not* contain (1, 1).

✓ Check Skills You'll Need

Is the given value of x a solution of the inequality? Explain.

1. $x + 3 \geq -2; x = -5$

2. $5 - x < 4; x = 1$

3. $-2 - 2x \leq 6; x = -4$

4. $4x + 1 > -7; x = -2$

GO **for Help**
Lesson 7-6

🔊 New Vocabulary

- linear inequality
- system of linear inequalities

Online
active math

For: Inequalities Activity
Use: Interactive Textbook, 8-8

✓ Quick Check

1. Graph each inequality on its own coordinate plane.

    a. $y \geq 3x - 1$ **b.** $y > -x + 3$ **c.** $y < 2x - 4$

---

2 EXAMPLE   **Real-World** **Problem Solving**

Grocery Shopping **Apricots cost \$3/lb. Tomatoes cost \$1/lb. You plan to spend no more than \$10. How many pounds of each can you buy?**

Step 1 Write an inequality.

Words		cost of apricots	plus	cost of tomatoes	is at most	ten dollars

Let x = number of pounds of apricots.

Let y = number of pounds of tomatoes.

Inequality	$3x$	+	y	≤	10

Real-World **Connection**

There are over 3,700 farmers markets in the United States.

Step 2 Write the equation of the boundary line in slope-intercept form.

$$3x + y \leq 10$$
$$y \leq -3x + 10$$
$$y = -3x + 10$$

Step 3 Graph $y = -3x + 10$ in Quadrant I since weight is not negative.

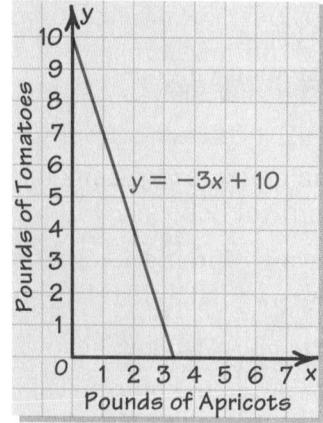

Step 4 Test $(1, 1)$.

$$y \leq -3x + 10$$
$$1 \overset{?}{\leq} -3(1) + 10$$
$$1 \leq 7 \ ✔$$

The inequality is true. $(1, 1)$ is a solution.

Step 5 Shade the region containing $(1, 1)$.

The graph shows the possible solutions. For example, you could buy 1 pound of apricots and 5 pounds of tomatoes.

✅ Quick Check

2. Adult tickets to the school play cost $4. Children's tickets cost $2. Your goal is to sell tickets worth at least $30. Let x be the number of children's tickets and y be the number of adult tickets. Graph a linear inequality to show how many of each type of ticket you must sell to reach your goal.

---

2 | Graphing Systems of Linear Inequalities

Two or more linear inequalities form a **system of linear inequalities.** A *solution of a system of linear inequalities* is any ordered pair that makes each inequality in the system true. To solve a system, graph the inequalities on one coordinate plane.

3 EXAMPLE | Solving a System of Linear Inequalities

Solve the system $y > x$ and $y \le -x + 2$ by graphing.

Step 1 Graph $y > x$ on a coordinate plane.

Step 2 Graph $y \le -x + 2$ on the same coordinate plane.

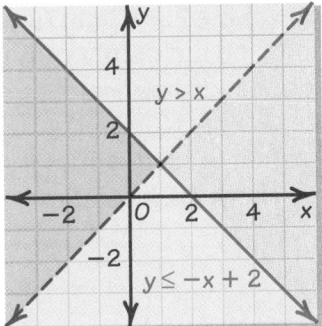

The solutions are the coordinates of all the points in the region that is shaded in both colors.

Check The point $(-1, 0)$ is in the solution region. Check whether $(-1, 0)$ makes both of the inequalities true.

$y > x$
$0 \overset{?}{>} -1$ **Replace x with -1 and y with 0.**
$0 > -1$ ✔   **The solution checks.**

$y \le -x + 2$
$0 \overset{?}{\le} -(-1) + 2$
$0 \le 3$ ✔

✅ Quick Check

3. Solve each system by graphing.

   a. $y \le -2x - 5$
       $y < \frac{1}{2}x$

   b. $y > x - 1$
       $y < 3x + 4$

8-8 Graphing Linear Inequalities   **447**

EXERCISES

For more exercises, see *Extra Skill and Word Problem Practice.*

Practice and Problem Solving

 Practice by Example

Example 1
(page 445)

 GO for Help

The graph of each inequality is bounded by a line. State whether the boundary line is solid or dashed.

1. $y > x$ **2.** $y \leq -x + 1$ **3.** $y \geq x - 1$

Graph each inequality on its own coordinate plane.

4. $y > x - 6$ **5.** $y \leq -x + 8$ **6.** $y > x + 2$

7. $y \geq 2x - 1$ **8.** $y < -\frac{1}{3}x + 1$ **9.** $y \leq 2x + 1$

Example 2
(page 446)

Solve each inequality for y.

10. $4x + y < -3$ **11.** $-y \leq 2x$ **12.** $2x + 3y \leq 7$

For Exercises 13–15, show all the solutions by writing and graphing a linear inequality.

13. Find two nonnegative numbers with a sum greater than three.

14. A number is greater than or equal to three times another number. What are the numbers?

15. Collections Melissa has a collection of dimes and nickels with a total face value of less than one dollar. Let x be the number of dimes and y be the number of nickels. How many of each type of coin does she have?

Example 3
(page 447)

Solve each system of inequalities by graphing. Use a point on the x- or y-axis to check each solution.

16. $y > -x$
  $y < x + 6$

17. $y \leq x$
  $y \geq -x - 4$

18. $y > -x$
  $y > 2x + 3$

19. $y \leq -x + 1$
  $y > x - 5$

B **Apply Your Skills**

Choose a linear inequality to match each graph.

20.

21.

A. $-y \geq x$ **B.** $-y \leq x$
C. $-y \geq -x$ **D.** $-y \leq -x$

F. $x < -4$ **G.** $x > -4$
H. $-x < -4$ **J.** $-x > -4$

22. Writing in Math Describe the difference between the graph of $y < -x$ and the graph of $-y < x$.

Graph each inequality on its own coordinate plane.

23. $x - y > 10$ **24.** $y \le 5$ **25.** $y \ge -\frac{2}{3}x$

26. $9x + 3y < 3$ **27.** $x - 2y \ge -12$ **28.** $-6x - 4y > 8$

29. a. Income You can earn $6/h mowing lawns and $3/h baby-sitting. You want to earn at least $45. Let x = number of hours mowing lawns and y = number of hours baby-sitting. Write a linear inequality to model this situation.
   b. Graph the linear inequality.
   c. If you baby-sit for 6 hours, what is the number of hours you will need to mow lawns to earn $45?

Write the equation of each boundary line in slope-intercept form. State whether the boundary line is solid or dashed.

30. $x + y < -3$ **31.** $x - y \ge 7$ **32.** $-y > 4x$

33. $-y \le -\frac{1}{2}x$ **34.** $5x + 3y \le 9$ **35.** $4x - 2y > 10$

36. Multiple Choice Medium drinks cost $2 and large drinks cost $3. Let x be the number of medium drinks sold and y be the number of large drinks sold. How many drinks must the vendor sell to have at least $60 in sales?
   Ⓐ $2x + 3y < 60$ Ⓑ $2x + 3y \le 60$
   Ⓒ $2x + 3y > 60$ Ⓓ $2x + 3y \ge 60$

Solve each system of inequalities by graphing.

37. $2x + y \le 4$ **38.** $x + y > -3$ **39.** $x < 6$
   $y + 1 \ge -2x$ $x - y < 5$ $y \le 2x$

40. $y < 4$ **41.** $-2x + y > 1$ **42.** $3x + y > 5$
   $x > -5$ $x + 2y < 2$ $y \ge -2$

43. Writing in Math How is graphing an inequality on a coordinate plane similar to graphing an inequality on a number line? How is it different?

Ⓒ Challenge

Open-Ended Write a system of inequalities with the solutions indicated. If such a system is not possible, tell why.

44. no solutions   **45.** all real numbers   **46.** the points of a line

Reasoning Write a system of inequalities to describe each graph.

47.   **48.**

Multiple Choice

49. Which inequality has the same solutions as $y \geq -2x + 1$?
 A. $2x + y \leq 1$ **B.** $2x + y \geq 1$
 C. $2x - y \leq 1$ **D.** $2x - y \geq 1$

50. Which describes the graph of $y \leq -x + 2$?
 F. shading above a solid boundary line
 G. shading below a solid boundary line
 H. shading above a dashed boundary line
 J. shading below a dashed boundary line

51. You want to spend less than $20 on asparagus and green beans. Asparagus costs $3.00 per pound and green beans cost $.50 per pound. Let a represent the asparagus and g represent the green beans. Which inequality models what you can spend?
 A. $3a + 0.5g > 20$ **B.** $3a + 0.5g \geq 20$
 C. $3a + 0.5g < 20$ **D.** $3a + 0.5g \leq 20$

52. Which inequality has a graph with shading below a dashed boundary line?
 F. $2x + y > -3$ **G.** $2x + y \geq -3$
 H. $2x + y \leq -3$ **J.** $2x + y < -3$

53. Which point is a solution of the system $y \geq 0; x \leq 0$?
 A. $(1, 1)$ **B.** $(-1, 1)$ **C.** $(1, -1)$ **D.** $(-1, -1)$

Short Response

54. Explain how to graph $y \geq 2x + 3$. Then graph the inequality.

Mixed Review

for Help

Lesson 8-7

Solve each system of equations by graphing. Check each solution.

55. $x + y = 8$ **56.** $y = 2x - 1$ **57.** $3y = -2x - 3$
     $x - y = -2$ $2x - y = 3$ $3y = x - 12$

Lesson 6-6 🌐 **58. Endangered Animals** In 2005, there were 242 California condors. Of these birds, 132 were in captivity, 61 were living free in California, and 49 were living free in Arizona.
 a. What percent of the condors were living free in Arizona? Round your answer to the nearest tenth of a percent.
 b. What percent of the condors were living free in all? Round your answer to the nearest tenth of a percent.

Lessons 5-7 and 5-8

Solve each equation.

59. $m - \frac{2}{3} = \frac{1}{6}$ **60.** $\frac{5}{4}c = \frac{3}{2}$ **61.** $\frac{3}{4} + w = \frac{9}{10}$

Lesson 4-6

Evaluate each expression for $c = 4$ and $m = -3$.

62. $\frac{c + m}{5}$ **63.** $\frac{m - c}{2}$ **64.** $\frac{2c - m}{-4}$ **65.** $\frac{4m}{2 - c}$

Graphing Inequalities

Graphing an inequality on a calculator is similar to graphing an equation. If your calculator does not graph dashed lines, you have to remember the type of boundary line you need for the inequality.

EXAMPLE

Graph $y > -x + 4$.

Step 1 Press the Y= key.
Enter $-x + 4$.

```
Plot1  Plot2  Plot3
\Y1■ -X+4 ■
\Y2=
\Y3=
\Y4=
```

Step 2 Press ◄ to move to the left of Y1.
Press ENTER twice when
y is greater than the right side of the equation.
Press ENTER three times when
y is less than the right side of the equation.

Step 3 Press ZOOM 6 to graph the inequality with the standard viewing window. Then sketch the inequality.

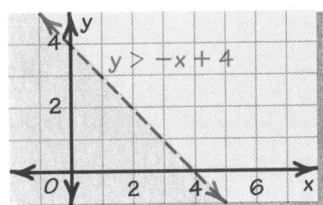

EXERCISES

Graph each inequality. Be sure your boundary line is correct.

1. $y > 3x + 1$ **2.** $y \le 2x$ **3.** $y < -x - 5$ **4.** $y \ge 4x + 6$

5. $y \le -2x - 4$ **6.** $y < x + 7$ **7.** $y > -3x + 4$ **8.** $y \ge -\frac{2}{5}x + 1$

Graph each system of inequalities. Sketch the solutions.

9. $y > -x$
$y < x + 6$

10. $y \le x$
$y \ge -x - 4$

11. $y > -x$
$y > 2x + 3$

12. $y \le -x + 1$
$y > x - 5$

13. Find and graph a system of inequalities that has no solution.

14. Find and graph a system of inequalities whose solutions are the points of a line.

A multiple-correct-answer test item presents you with a question and several possible answers labeled with Roman numerals. You have to decide which of the answers are correct. Then you pick your list of correct answers from the lettered choices given.

A good strategy to follow is to test each answer and mark it if correct.

EXAMPLE

For which equation(s) is $(4, 6)$ a solution?

I. $x - y = -2$ **II.** $-x - y = -10$ **III.** $x - y = 2$ **IV.** $y - x = 2$

A. I and II only   **B.** I, II, and III only   **C.** I, II, and IV only   **D.** III only

Test each answer.

Substitute 4 for x and 6 for y.

I. $x - y = -2$ **II.** $-x - y = -10$ **III.** $x - y = 2$ **IV.** $y - x = 2$

$4 - 6 = -2$ $-4 - 6 = -10$ $4 - 6 = 2$ $6 - 4 = 2$

true   true   not true   true

● Statements I, II, and IV (only) are correct; choice C.

EXERCISES

1. The slope of a line is -2. Through which pairs of points could the line pass?

I. $(0, 3)$ and $(-2, 7)$ **II.** $(0, -1)$ and $(2, -5)$ **III.** $(0, 0)$ and $(3, 6)$ **IV.** $(2, -3)$ and $(-1, 3)$

A. I and II only   **B.** I, II, and III only   **C.** I, II, and IV only   **D.** III only

2. For which system(s) of equations is $(2, 3)$ the solution?

I. $y = x + 1$ and $y = -x + 5$ **II.** $y = 2x - 1$ and $y = \frac{1}{2}x + 2$

III. $y = 3x - 3$ and $y = -2x + 7$ **IV.** $y = \frac{1}{4}x + \frac{5}{2}$ and $y = -3x + 3$

F. I and III only   **G.** I, II, and III only   **H.** I, II, and IV only   **J.** III and IV only

3. Which system(s) of equations has no solution?

I. $y = 3x - 1$ and $y = -3x + 1$ **II.** $y = 1.5x - 2$ and $y = \frac{3}{2}x + 2$

III. $x + y = 1$ and $y = -x + 3$ **IV.** $2x + y = 4$ and $2y = 4x + 2$

A. III only   **B.** II and III only   **C.** I, II, and III only   **D.** I, II, III, and IV

Chapter Review

Vocabulary Review

domain (p. 404)
function (p. 404)
function notation (p. 422)
function rule (p. 422)
linear equation (p. 410)
linear inequality (p. 445)
negative correlation (p. 429)
no correlation (p. 429)

positive correlation (p. 429)
range (p. 404)
relation (p. 404)
scatter plot (p. 427)
slope (p. 415)
slope-intercept form (p. 417)
solution (p. 409)

system of linear
    equations (p. 439)
system of linear
    inequalities (p. 447)
trend line (p. 434)
vertical-line test (p. 405)
y-intercept (p. 417)

Choose the vocabulary term that correctly completes the sentence.

1. The tilt or slant of a line is its __?__ .

2. To determine whether the graph shows a function, use the __?__ .

3. On a scatter plot, when one set of values increases while the other decreases, the data is said to have a __?__ .

4. When each member of a relation's domain is paired with exactly one member of the range, the relation is a __?__ .

5. Any equation whose graph is a line is a __?__ .

6. The first coordinates in a set of ordered pairs is the __?__ of the relation.

7. The second coordinates in a set of ordered pairs is the __?__ of the relation.

8. An ordered pair that makes an equation a true statement is a __?__ of the equation.

Go Online
PHSchool.com
For: Vocabulary quiz
Web Code: adj-0851

Skills and Concepts

8-1 Objectives

▼ To determine whether a relation is a function (p. 404)

▼ To graph relations and functions (p. 405)

Any set of ordered pairs is a **relation.** The **domain** of a relation is the set of first coordinates of the ordered pairs. The **range** is the set of second coordinates. A **function** is a relation in which no two ordered pairs have the same first coordinate.

Is each relation a function? Explain.

9. $\{(2, 3), (4, 3), (0, 1), (-2, 3)\}$

10.

x	−3	4	−1	−4
y	0	2	0	1

11. Domain   Range

2 ——→ −1
3 ——→ 0
4 ——→ 3

12. Is the amount of a long-distance telephone bill a function of time spent talking on the telephone? Explain.

8-2 Objectives

▼ To find solutions of equations with two variables (p. 409)

▼ To graph linear equations with two variables (p. 410)

A solution of an equation with two variables is any ordered pair that makes the equation true. The graph of a **linear equation** is a line.

Find the solutions of each equation for $x = -3, 0,$ and 2.

13. $y = x + 5$ **14.** $y = -4x$ **15.** $y = \frac{1}{2}x + 3$ **16.** $y = 6 - 2x$

8-3 Objectives

▼ To find the slope of a line (p. 415)

▼ To use slope-intercept form in graphing a linear equation (p. 417)

Slope is a measure describing the tilt of a line, which you can calculate using the ratio $\frac{\text{vertical change}}{\text{horizontal change}}$, or $\frac{\text{difference in } y\text{-coordinates}}{\text{difference in } x\text{-coordinates}}$.

One form of a linear equation is the slope-intercept form, $y = mx + b$, where m is the slope and b is the y-intercept.

Identify the slope and y-intercept of each equation. Then graph each equation.

17. $x + y = 7$

18. $x - y = -2$

19. $2x + 5y = 10$

20. $3x - 2y = 12$

Find the slope of each line.

21.

22.

23.

8-4 Objectives

▼ To write a function rule for a word relationship (p. 422)

▼ To write a function rule by analyzing a table or graph (p. 423)

You can write a **function rule** from a verbal description, from a table of values, or from a graph.

Write a rule for each function.

24.

x	f(x)
-2	2
-1	1
0	0
1	-1

25.

x	y
-3	-5
-2	-3
-1	-1
0	1

26.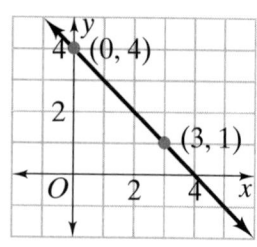

27. Tickets to a play cost $14 each by mail, plus a $2 processing fee for each order of one or more tickets. Write a rule to describe total cost $c(t)$ as a function of the number of tickets t.

A **scatter plot** is a graph that shows the relationship between two sets of data. A scatter plot can help you find trends between sets of data.

Use the scatter plot at the right.

28. How long did the person who used 240 calories ride a bicycle?

29. How many calories did the person who bicycled 50 minutes use?

30. Data Analysis Is there a positive correlation, a negative correlation, or no correlation between the time spent bicycling and the calories used? Explain.

Calories Used While Bicycling

31. Data Analysis Carefully place a straightedge (preferably transparent) on the scatter plot to serve as a trend line. Use the trend line to predict the number of calories a person uses on a 70-min bicycle ride.

Two or more linear equations with the same variables form a **system of linear equations.** A solution of a system of equations is any ordered pair that makes each equation true.

Two or more linear inequalities with the same variables form a **system of linear inequalities.** A solution of a system of inequalities is any ordered pair that makes both inequalities true. You can solve a system by graphing.

Graph each inequality.

32. $y > 2x + 5$

33. $y \leq -x + 1$

34. $y \geq \frac{1}{2}x - 3$

35. $y < 3x - 2$

Solve each system by graphing.

36. $y = \frac{1}{2}x - 3$
$y = -\frac{1}{2}x + 1$

37. $3x + 2y = 6$
$x + 4y = -8$

38. $y = x - 5$
$y = -2x + 1$

39. $y < 3x + 2$
$y > 3x - 1$

40. Explain why it is possible for a system of linear equations to have no solutions.

Chapter Test

Go Online
PHSchool.com

For: Chapter test
Web Code: ada-0852

Is each relation a function? Explain.

1. $\{(-2, -12), (-2, 0), (-2, 4), (-2, 11)\}$

2. $\{(8, 1), (4, 1), (0, 1), (-15, 1)\}$

3. $\{(-4, -6), (-3, -2), (1, -2), (1, 0), (1, 3)\}$

4. $\{(0, 1), (0, 2), (1, 2), (1, 3), (3, 1), (4, 2)\}$

Graph each equation.

5. $y = 2x$

6. $y = -x - 2$

7. $2x - y = 4$

8. $3y = x - 6$

Find the slope of the line through each pair of points.

9. $C(0, 1)$ and $D(-5, 1)$

10. $M(-4, 1)$ and $N(6, 3)$

11. $J(-1, -2)$ and $K(2, 7)$

12. $P(4, 9)$ and $Q(-6, 12)$

Write a rule for each function.

13.

x	$f(x)$
-2	-3
-1	-5
0	-7
1	-9

14.

x	$f(x)$
-3	4
0	1
3	-2
6	-5

Is there a *positive correlation*, a *negative correlation*, or *no correlation* between the sets of data in each scatter plot? Explain.

15.

16.

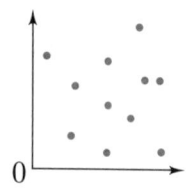

Graph each inequality.

17. $y \geq 3x - 1$

18. $y < -x + 5$

Solve each system by graphing.

19. $y = x - 1$
$x = 2y$

20. $x + y = 4$
$2x + 2y = 8$

21. $x + y = 3$
$y = x - 5$

22. $y \leq 3x - 2$
$y > x + 4$

23. **Writing in Math** Is the amount of sales tax paid a function of the labeled price of a taxable item? Explain.

24. **Writing in Math** Is a person's age a function of his or her height? Explain.

25. Use the data in the table below.

New York Thruway Tolls

Distance (miles)	Toll (dollars)	Distance (miles)	Toll (dollars)
112	3.50	125	3.90
137	3.75	100	3.10
112	3.40	22	0.70
69	1.65	58	1.80
69	2.15	137	4.25
169	5.70	43	1.80
90	2.80	84	3.05
188	5.85	164	5.10

a. Make a (distance, toll) scatter plot.
b. Draw a trend line. Predict the toll if a car travels 200 mi on the toll road.
c. Use your trend line to predict how far a car traveled on the toll road if there was a $4.50 toll.
d. Write an equation of your trend line.

26. **Open-Ended** The slope of a line through the origin is $-\frac{2}{3}$. Find the coordinates of two points on the line.

ISAT Test Prep

Multiple Choice

1. An empty pot weighs 1 lb 11 oz. With oatmeal in it, the pot weighs 3 lb 7 oz. How much does the oatmeal weigh?
   - (A) 5 lb 2 oz
   - (B) 2 lb 3 oz
   - (C) 1 lb 12 oz
   - (D) 1 lb 4 oz

2. Which equation has a solution of 8?
   - (E) $8x + 8 = 64$
   - (F) $\frac{b}{2} + 7 = 10$
   - (G) $2z + 5 = 11$
   - (H) $5n - 13 = 27$

3. Four friends split the cost of renting a car for a snorkeling trip. Each person also rents a snorkel for $2. Each person pays a total of $15. Which equation will help find the cost c of renting the car?
   - (A) $+ 2 = 15$
   - (B) $15 - 2^4 = c$
   - (C) $15 - 4c = 2$
   - (D) $\frac{c}{2} + 4 = 15$

4. Sara and Juan collect soccer cards. Sara has 6 fewer than three times the number of cards Juan has. Together they have 42 cards. Solve $c + (3c - 6) = 42$ to answer: How many cards does each have?
   - (E) Sara has 9 cards; Juan has 33 cards.
   - (F) Sara has 33 cards; Juan has 9 cards.
   - (G) Sara has 12 cards; Juan has 30 cards.
   - (H) Sara has 30 cards; Juan has 12 cards.

5. Which ordered pair is *not* a solution of $4x + 2y = 16$?
   - (A) $(-2, 12)$
   - (B) $(5, -2)$
   - (C) $(2, 5)$
   - (D) $(1, 6)$

6. Which function represents the number of kilograms $k(n)$ as a function of the number of grams n?
   - (E) $k(n) = 100n$
   - (F) $k(n) = 0.01n$
   - (G) $k(n) = 1{,}000n$
   - (H) $k(n) = 0.001n$

7. Which point is a solution of the system?
   $y = x + 2; y = 2x - 2$
   - (A) $(6, 4)$
   - (B) $(1, 3)$
   - (C) $(4, 6)$
   - (D) no solution

8. What is the solution of $-2(x - 1) \le -6$?
   - (E) $x \le 4$
   - (F) $x \le -4$
   - (G) $x \ge 4$
   - (H) $x \ge -4$

Gridded Response

9. The probability that a couple will give birth to a pair of twins is 1 in 90. About how many pairs of twins would you expect to find in 250,000 births?

10. Find the slope of the line through $(3, 2)$ and $(1, -2)$.

11. In the scatter plot below, each point represents an athlete who ran in the 100-m race. Greg won the race in the least amount of time. What is Greg's age in years?

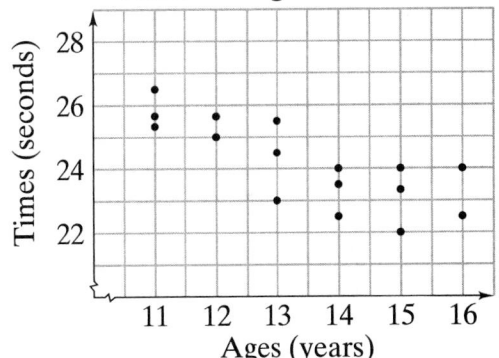

Athletes' Ages and Times

Short Response

Find the solutions of each equation for the given values of x. Show your work.

12. $y = x + 12; x = -3, 0,$ and 2

13. $4x - 4y = 8; x = 0, 2,$ and 4

Extended Response

14. **a.** Write the equation $x + \frac{1}{2}y = 4$ in slope-intercept form.
    b. Find the slope and the y-intercept of the line in part (a).
    c. Graph the equation in part (a).

Activity Lab

Virtual Progress

Applying Graphs Technology changes every day. When your grandparents were kids, they watched black-and-white TVs, listened to records, and used typewriters. Today, people watch color TVs, listen to compact discs, and use computers. Tired of walking your dog? Robotic pets hit the market in 2000. Interested in becoming an astronaut? Pilots and astronauts train with virtual reality gear.

Vision sensors

Individual motors control the joints.

New and Different Pets

Robotic pets use computers and artificial intelligence to interact with their environments.

Activity

Use the information on these two pages to answer the questions.

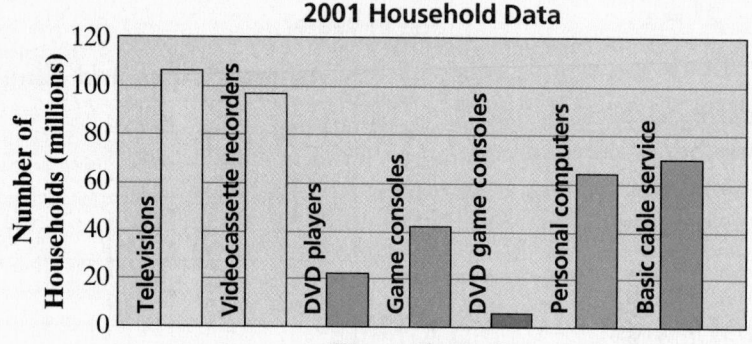

2001 Household Data

Number of Households (millions) / Electronic Device

(Televisions, Videocassette recorders, DVD players, Game consoles, DVD game consoles, Personal computers, Basic cable service)

1. How many households have a television and not a VCR?

2. How many households with televisions do not have basic cable?

3. The number of households with personal computers is how many times the number with DVD game consoles?

4. How many times as many households have a television as have a DVD player?

5. How many households will get their first DVD player between 2001 and 2006?

6. **a.** About 70% of DVD households rent at least one DVD movie per month. How many households is this?

   b. Suppose this percent stays constant. About how many households will rent at least one DVD movie per month in 2006?

7. **Reasoning** What do you think is likely to happen to the number of households with VCRs by 2006? Explain.

Intelligent Modeling
3-D glasses help this researcher "touch" carbon atoms from a microscopic world in a virtual reality room.

At Home Viewing
In 1997, most people watched movies at home on VCRs. Then DVDs hit the market. About 70 million households had DVD players by the year 2006.

Go Online
PHSchool.com

For: Information about DVDs
Web Code: ade-0853

What You've Learned

IL Assessment Framework

- **8.8.12:** In Chapter 3, you learned how to solve equations by multiplying or dividing decimals, and how to use formulas.

- **6.8.09:** In Chapter 5, you learned how to solve equations by multiplying fractions.

- **8.8.12:** In Chapter 7, you learned how to solve multi-step equations by using inverse operations.

INSTANT CHECK SYSTEM ✓ **Check Your Readiness**   **GO** **for Help** to the Lesson in green.

Finding Perimeters (Lesson 3-4)

Find the perimeter of each figure.

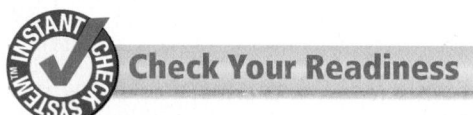

1. 1.2 cm, 3.6 cm, 1.2 cm, 6.5 cm, 6.5 cm, 1.2 cm, 3.6 cm, 1.2 cm

2. 2.4 in., 2.4 in., 3.2 in., 3.2 in., 3.2 in.

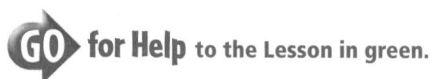

3. 10.8 m, 10.8 m, 28.8 m, 28.8 m, 10.8 m, 10.8 m

4. 1.5 ft, 2.4 ft, 1 ft, 1.5 ft

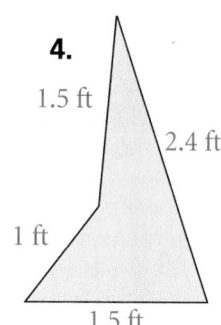

Dividing Decimals by Whole Numbers (Skills Handbook, p. 789)

Find the radius of each circle.

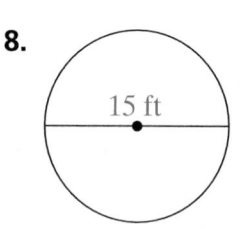

5. 12 cm   **6.** 1 in.   **7.** 5.6 cm   **8.** 15 ft

Graphing on the Coordinate Plane (Lesson 1-10)

Graph each point on the same coordinate plane.

9. $A(0, 7)$ **10.** $B(-2, 5)$ **11.** $E(4, 0)$ **12.** $D(2, -4)$ **13.** $C(-3, -1)$

14. $F\left(1\frac{1}{2}, -3\right)$ **15.** $G(0, 0)$ **16.** $J(0, -1)$ **17.** $I(-4, -5)$ **18.** $H(-5, -5)$

Spatial Thinking

🔊 Key Vocabulary

- adjacent angles (p. 469)
- alternate interior angles (p. 470)
- angle bisector (p. 497)
- complementary (p. 469)
- congruent angles (p. 469)
- congruent figures (p. 484)
- corresponding angles (p. 470)
- parallel (p. 463)
- perpendicular bisector (p. 496)
- perpendicular lines (p. 496)
- polygon (p. 474)
- reflection (p. 508)
- regular polygon (p. 476)
- rotation (p. 511)
- segment (p. 462)
- segment bisector (p. 496)
- supplementary (p. 469)
- symmetry (pp. 507, 512)
- translation (p. 501)
- vertical angles (p. 469)

What You'll Learn Next

 Assessment Framework

In this chapter, you will learn how to

- **7.8.02:** Use properties of figures to solve problems.
- **9.8.06:** Classify geometric figures.
- Construct figures.
- **9.8.06:** Solve a problem by drawing a diagram.

 Activity Lab Applying what you learn, on pages 522–523 you will solve problems about Ferris wheels.

461

9-1 Introduction to Geometry: Points, Lines, and Planes

What You'll Learn

To name basic geometric figures

To recognize intersecting lines, parallel lines, and skew lines

. . . And Why

To build a basic vocabulary in geometry and to solve problems in architecture

 Check Skills You'll Need

Describe the number-line graph of each inequality.

1. $a \geq 3$ **2.** $a \leq 0$

3. $a \leq 5$ **4.** $a \geq -2$

 for Help
Lesson 2-8

🔊 New Vocabulary
• point   • line
• plane   • segment
• ray   • parallel
• skew

1   Points, Lines, and Planes

Geometric shapes are evident in many human-made and natural structures. Notice the hexagonal shape of each cell of the honeycomb in the photo below. Two other examples of geometry in nature are the spiral structure of a snail's shell and the shape of a snowflake.

Basic Geometric Figures

Name	Sample	Symbolic Name	Description
Point	• A	Point A	A **point** is a location in space. It has no size.
Line	A B n	$\overleftrightarrow{AB}$, $\overleftrightarrow{BA}$, or n	A **line** is a series of points that extends in opposite directions without end. A lowercase letter can name a line.
Plane	A B M D C	$ABCD$ or M	A **plane** is a flat surface with no thickness. It contains many lines and extends without end in the directions of all its lines.
Line segment or segment	Q P	$\overline{PQ}$, or $\overline{QP}$	A **segment** is a part of a line. It has two endpoints. PQ represents the length of $\overline{PQ}$.
Ray	C R	$\overrightarrow{CR}$	A **ray** is a part of a line. It has exactly one endpoint. Name its endpoint first.

You can combine the basic geometric figures to create many other geometric figures.

1 EXAMPLE **Naming Geometric Figures**

Name each figure in the diagram.

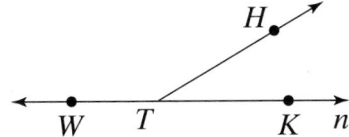

a. Name four points.
   $H, K, T,$ and W Name a point with a capital letter.

b. Name four different segments.
   $\overline{HT}, \overline{WT}, \overline{TK},$ and $\overline{WK}$ Name a segment by its endpoints.

c. Write five other names for $\overleftrightarrow{WT}$.
   $\overleftrightarrow{WK}, \overleftrightarrow{TK}, \overleftrightarrow{KT}, \overleftrightarrow{KW},$ or $\overleftrightarrow{TW}$ There is one line pictured. It has several names.

d. Name five different rays.
   $\overrightarrow{TH}, \overrightarrow{TW}, \overrightarrow{TK}, \overrightarrow{WK},$ or $\overrightarrow{KW}$ The first letter names the endpoint of the ray.

✓ Quick Check

1. Name each figure in the diagram.

   a. three points
   b. two segments
   c. two rays

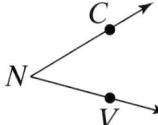

2 Intersecting, Parallel, and Skew Lines

Two lines *intersect* if they have exactly one point in common. Two lines that lie in the same plane and do not intersect are **parallel.** You use the symbol ∥ to indicate "is parallel to." Segments and rays are parallel if they lie in parallel lines.

Vocabulary Tip

The symbol ∥ used for "parallel" looks like two parallel lines.

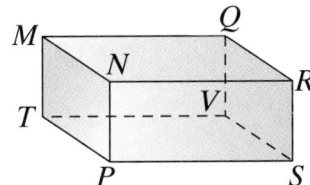

$\overline{MN}$ intersects $\overline{NP}$.
$\overline{MN} \parallel \overline{QR}$

Skew lines are lines that do not lie in the same plane. They are not parallel and they do not intersect. Skew segments must be parts of skew lines. In the diagram above, $\overline{MN}$ and $\overline{RS}$ are skew.

2 EXAMPLE   Real-World 🌐 Problem Solving

Problem Solving Hint
One way to find skew segments in this figure is to look for a vertical segment and a horizontal segment that do not intersect.

Architecture **This structure is the frame of a room. Name the figures described below.**

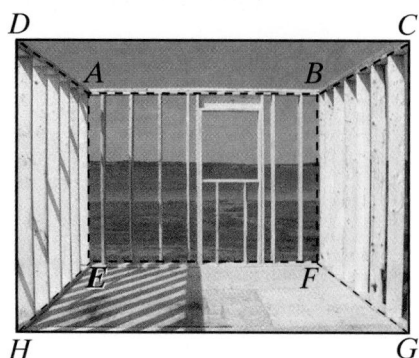

a. four segments that intersect $\overline{DH}$ $\overline{AD}, \overline{CD}, \overline{EH}, \overline{GH}$

b. three segments parallel to $\overline{DH}$ $\overline{AE}, \overline{BF}, \overline{CG}$

c. four segments skew to $\overline{DH}$ $\overline{AB}, \overline{BC}, \overline{EF}, \overline{FG}$

✓ Quick Check

2. Use the diagram above. Name each of the following.

  a. four segments that intersect $\overline{EF}$
  b. three segments parallel to $\overline{EF}$
  c. four segments skew to $\overline{EF}$

3 EXAMPLE   **Drawing Lines**

Online active math

For: Lines and Planes Activity
Use: Interactive Textbook, 9-1

Draw two parallel lines. Then draw a segment that intersects the parallel lines.

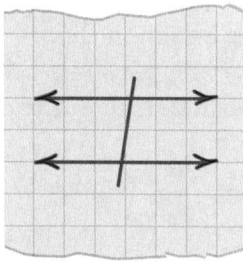

Use the lines on a piece of notebook paper or graph paper to help you draw parallel lines. Then draw a segment that intersects the two lines.

✓ Quick Check

3. Use notebook paper or graph paper. Draw the figures indicated.

  a. three parallel segments
  b. a ray that intersects the parallel segments of part (a)
  c. a segment, $\overline{AB}$ **d.** a ray, $\overrightarrow{QR}$ **e.** a line, $\overleftrightarrow{LM}$

EXERCISES

Practice and Problem Solving

A Practice by Example

Example 1
(page 463)

GO for Help

Name the indicated figures in each diagram.

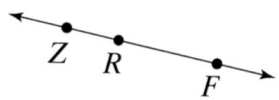

1. three points
2. three different segments
3. four different rays

4. all points
5. all segments
6. all lines

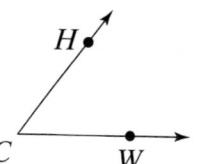

7. all segments
8. all lines
9. all rays

10. all rays
11. all points

Example 2
(page 464)

Name all indicated segments.

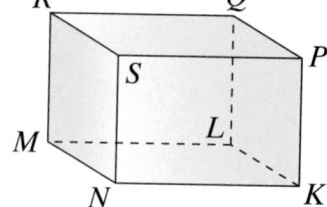

12. that intersect $\overline{DE}$
13. that are parallel to $\overline{DE}$
14. that are skew to $\overline{DE}$

15. that intersect $\overline{MN}$
16. that are parallel to $\overline{MN}$
17. that are skew to $\overline{MN}$

🌐 **Packaging** For the cereal box (left), name each of the following.

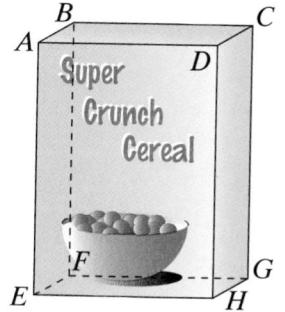

18. four segments that intersect $\overline{AE}$
19. three segments parallel to $\overline{AE}$
20. four segments skew to $\overline{AE}$

Example 3
(page 464)

21. Use notebook paper or graph paper. Draw three segments that are parallel to each other. Draw a line that intersects the parallel segments.

22. Draw two parallel rays.   23. Draw $\overrightarrow{VB}$.

24. Draw $\overleftrightarrow{CD}$ so that it intersects two segments, $\overline{FG}$ and $\overline{HJ}$.

B Apply Your Skills

Modeling Draw each of the following. If not possible, explain.

25. $\overleftrightarrow{PQ} \parallel \overleftrightarrow{RS}$ 26. $\overrightarrow{AB} \parallel \overline{BC}$ 27. $\overline{JK}$ skew to $\overleftrightarrow{LM}$

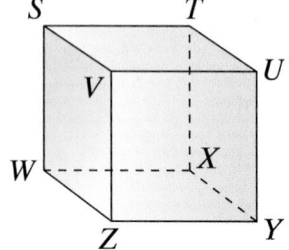

Algebra Write an equation. Then find the length of each segment.

28.

$2x$	3

|←———— $8x$ ————→|

29.

6	$5x$	$4x + 1$

|←———— $12x + 1$ ————→|

Use the figure at the left. Name a segment to make each statement true.

30. ■ ∥ $\overline{XY}$ 31. ■ ∥ $\overline{YZ}$ 32. ■ ∥ $\overline{WX}$ 33. ■ ∥ $\overline{SV}$

Complete with *always*, *sometimes*, or *never* to make a true statement.

34. $\overrightarrow{AB}$ and $\overrightarrow{BC}$ are __?__ on the same line.

35. $\overrightarrow{AB}$ and $\overrightarrow{AC}$ are __?__ the same ray.

36. $\overline{AX}$ and $\overline{XA}$ are __?__ the same segment.

37. $\overleftrightarrow{TQ}$ and $\overleftrightarrow{QT}$ are __?__ the same line.

38. Skew lines are __?__ in the same plane.

39. Two lines in the same plane are __?__ parallel.

40. **Writing in Math** Explain what the symbols $\overline{AB}$ and AB represent. Use examples.

41. **Error Analysis** A student says that $\overrightarrow{AB}$ is the same ray as $\overrightarrow{BA}$. Explain the student's error.

🌐 42. **City Planning**
Use the map. Tell whether the streets in each pair appear to be parallel or intersecting.
a. N.W. Highway and Fifth Avenue
b. N.W. Highway and B Street
c. A and C Streets   d. B and C Streets   e. C and Main Streets

C Challenge

43. a. Suppose a town installs a mailbox at a point *P*. How many straight roads can the town plan that lead to *P*?
b. Suppose a town installs mailboxes at points *P* and *R*. How many straight roads might the town plan to build that pass by both mailboxes?

44. a. On a coordinate plane, draw a line through $\left(-\frac{1}{2}, -1\right)$ and $\left(1, 1\frac{1}{2}\right)$. Then draw a line through $(-1, 1)$ and $\left(\frac{1}{2}, 3\frac{1}{2}\right)$.
b. What appears to be true of the two lines that you drew in part (a)?
c. Find the slope of each line.
d. **Inductive Reasoning** Make a conjecture based on your answer to parts (b) and (c).

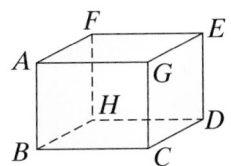

Test Prep

Multiple Choice

Use the figure at the left for Exercises 45–48.

45. Which segment is skew to $\overline{AB}$?
   A. $\overline{BC}$ **B.** $\overline{CD}$ **C.** $\overline{DE}$ **D.** $\overline{GC}$

46. Which segment is parallel to $\overline{ED}$?
   F. $\overline{BH}$ **G.** $\overline{AF}$ **H.** $\overline{AB}$ **J.** $\overline{GE}$

47. Which segment does NOT intersect $\overline{AG}$?
   A. $\overline{AB}$ **B.** $\overline{GC}$ **C.** $\overline{AF}$ **D.** $\overline{BC}$

48. Which describes *BHDC*?
   F. point   **G.** line   **H.** plane   **J.** ray

Short Response

49. Draw a line and label three of its points as *A*, *B* and *C*.
   a. Explain why both $\overleftrightarrow{AB}$ and $\overleftrightarrow{BA}$ are names for your line.
   b. State another name for your line.

Mixed Review

Lesson 8-8

Graph each inequality in its own coordinate plane.

50. $y \geq -2x + 6$ **51.** $y > x + 1$ **52.** $x \leq -4$

Lessons 5-3 and 5-4

Simplify each expression.

53. $\frac{3}{8} + \frac{7}{12}$ **54.** $2\frac{3}{4} - 1\frac{5}{6}$ **55.** $1\frac{1}{3} + 2\frac{1}{6}$ **56.** $2\frac{1}{2} - 3\frac{2}{3}$

57. $\frac{5}{8} \cdot \frac{3}{4}$ **58.** $2\frac{2}{3} \div \frac{3}{8}$ **59.** $1\frac{1}{4} \cdot 3$ **60.** $4\frac{3}{8} \div 4$

Math at Work

Choreographer

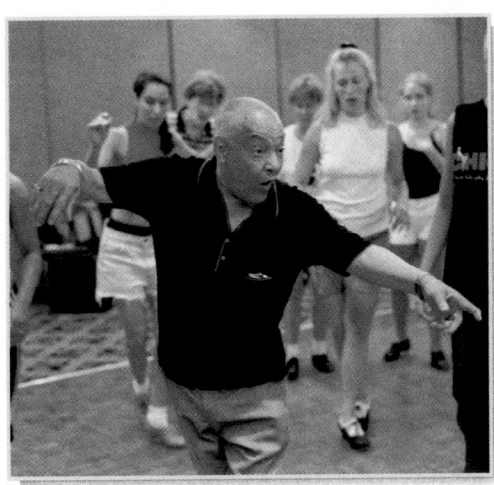

Choreographers are usually experienced dancers whose hard work and dedication have earned them the opportunity to create original dances. Choreographers have an excellent sense of timing and spatial positioning.

Many choreographed dance numbers reflect geometric shapes such as triangles and quadrilaterals. Next time you see a dance group perform, be on the lookout for geometry—it will help you think like a choreographer!

Go Online
PHSchool.com   **For:** Information about choreographers
Web Code: adb-2031

An *angle* is formed by two rays with a common endpoint. The rays are the *sides* of the angle. The common endpoint is the *vertex*. You can name the angle at the right ∠*ABC*, ∠*CBA*, ∠*B*, or ∠1.

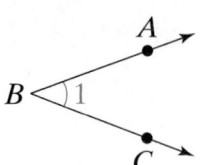

You can classify angles using their measures.

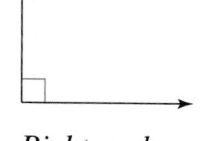

Acute angle
less than 90°

Right angle
90°

Obtuse angle
greater than 90°
and less than 180°

Straight angle
equal to 180°

You can use a protractor to draw and to measure angles.

ACTIVITY

Draw a 120° angle.

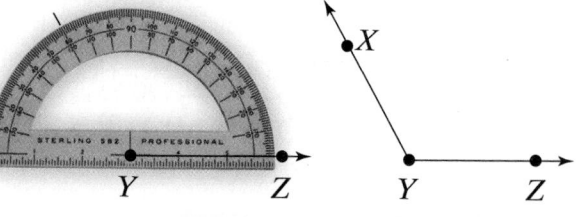

Step 1 Draw $\overrightarrow{YZ}$.

Step 2 Place the center of the protractor over *Y*. Make sure $\overrightarrow{YZ}$ passes through zero on the protractor scale.

Step 3 Place a mark on your paper at 120° such that ∠*XYZ* will be obtuse.

Step 4 Draw $\overrightarrow{YX}$. The measure of ∠*XYZ* is 120°.

EXERCISES

Draw an angle with the given measure.

1. 45°   **2.** 110°   **3.** 80°   **4.** 60°   **5.** 30°   **6.** 150°

Measure each angle. Then classify it as *acute, right,* **or** *obtuse.*

7.   **8.**   **9.**   **10.**

Angle Relationships and Parallel Lines

IL Assessment Framework

1 Adjacent and Vertical Angles

In this lesson you will learn to identify special pairs of angles.

Adjacent angles share a vertex and a side but no points in their interiors.

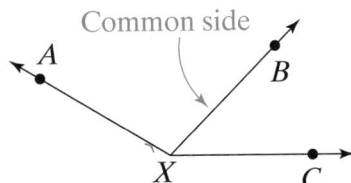

Common side

$\angle AXB$ and $\angle BXC$ are adjacent angles.

$\angle AXC$ and $\angle BXC$ are not adjacent angles.

Vertical angles are formed by two intersecting lines and are opposite each other. Vertical angles have the same measure.

$\angle 1$ and $\angle 3$ are vertical angles.
$\angle 2$ and $\angle 4$ are vertical angles.

Angles that have the same measure are **congruent angles.** In the diagram above, $\angle 1$ is congruent to $\angle 3$. You can write this as $\angle 1 \cong \angle 3$. You can write *the measure of* $\angle 1$ as $m\angle 1$. Since $\angle 1 \cong \angle 3$, $m\angle 1 = m\angle 3$.

If the sum of the measures of two angles is 180°, the angles are **supplementary.**

If the sum of the measures of two angles is 90°, the angles are **complementary.**

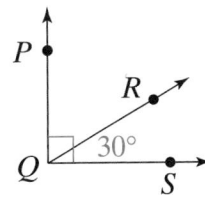

$\angle ABC$ and $\angle CBD$ are supplementary.

$\angle ABC$ and $\angle X$ are supplementary.
$\angle X$ and $\angle RQS$ are complementary.

$\angle PQR$ and $\angle RQS$ are complementary.

9.8.08 Identify or analyze relationships of angles formed by intersecting lines and angles formed by radii of a circle.

✓ Check Skills You'll Need

Solve.

1. $n + 45 = 180$

2. $75 + x = 90$

3. $3y = 2y + 90$

4. $2a + 15 = a + 45$

 for Help
Lesson 7-5

🔊 **New Vocabulary**

• adjacent angles
• vertical angles
• congruent angles
• supplementary
• complementary
• transversal
• corresponding angles
• alternate interior angles

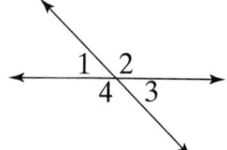

1 EXAMPLE   Finding the Measure of an Angle

In the diagram at the left, find the measure of ∠1 if $m\angle 4 = 135°$.

$m\angle 1 + m\angle 4 = 180°$	∠1 and ∠4 are supplementary.
$m\angle 1 + 135° = 180°$	Replace $m\angle 4$ with 135°.
$m\angle 1 + 135° - 135° = 180° - 135°$	Solve for $m\angle 1$.
$m\angle 1 = 45°$	

✓ Quick Check

1. If $m\angle 8 = 20°$, find the measures of ∠5, ∠6, and ∠7.

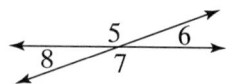

2   Relating Angles and Parallel Lines

A line that intersects two other lines in different points is a
transversal. Some pairs of angles formed by transversals
and two lines have special names.

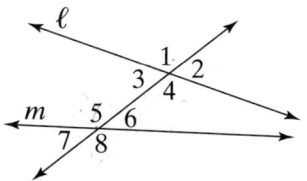

Corresponding angles lie on
the same side of the transversal
and in corresponding positions.
∠1 and ∠5, ∠3 and ∠7,
∠2 and ∠6, and ∠4 and ∠8
are corresponding angles.

Alternate interior angles
are in the interior of a pair of
lines and on opposite sides of
the transversal.
∠3 and ∠6, and ∠4 and ∠5
are alternate interior angles.

When a transversal intersects two parallel lines, corresponding
angles are congruent. Alternate interior angles are also congruent.

GO ●nline

Video Tutor Help
Visit: PHSchool.com
Web Code: ada-0775

2 EXAMPLE   Identifying Congruent Angles

In the diagram, $\ell \parallel m$. Identify each of the following.

a. congruent corresponding angles

∠1 ≅ ∠3, ∠2 ≅ ∠4, ∠8 ≅ ∠6,
∠7 ≅ ∠5

b. congruent alternate interior angles

∠3 ≅ ∠7, ∠2 ≅ ∠6

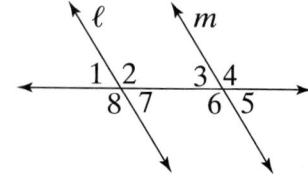

✓ Quick Check

2. In the diagram, $a \parallel b$. Name four pairs of congruent corresponding angles and two pairs of congruent alternate interior angles.

When solving a problem that involves parallel lines, you can often choose whether to use corresponding angles or alternate interior angles.

More Than One Way

The windowpanes at the right are held in place by parallel strips of lead. Lines r and s are parallel and line q is a transversal. If $m\angle 1 = 65°$, what is $m\angle 4$?

Nicole's Method

Use corresponding angles.

$\angle 1 \cong \angle 3$ because they are corresponding angles, so $m\angle 3 = 65°$. $\angle 3$ and $\angle 4$ are supplementary, so $m\angle 3 + m\angle 4 = 180°$.

$$m\angle 3 + m\angle 4 = 180°$$
$$65° + m\angle 4 = 180°$$
$$65° + m\angle 4 - 65° = 180° - 65°$$
$$m\angle 4 = 115°$$

Eric's Method

Use alternate interior angles.

$\angle 1$ and $\angle 2$ are supplementary.

$$m\angle 1 + m\angle 2 = 180°$$
$$65° + m\angle 2 = 180°$$
$$65° + m\angle 2 - 65° = 180° - 65°.$$
$$m\angle 2 = 115°$$

$\angle 2$ and $\angle 4$ are alternate interior angles, so they are congruent. If $m\angle 2 = 115°$, then $m\angle 4 = 115°$.

Choose a Method

1. Which method do you prefer? Explain why.
2. What is another way to solve the problem?

EXERCISES

For more exercises, see *Extra Skill and Word Problem Practice.*

Practice and Problem Solving

A **Practice by Example**

Example 1
(page 470)

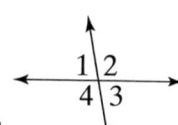

GO for **Help**

For Exercises 1 and 2, copy and complete the sentence.

1. ∠1 and ∠2 are __?__ angles.

2. ∠1 and ∠3 are __?__ angles.

3. Find the measures of ∠1, ∠2, and ∠3 if $m\angle 4 = 100°$.

For Exercises 4 and 5, name the angle vertical to ∠1. Name an angle adjacent to ∠1. Then find $m\angle 1$.

4.

5.

Example 2
(page 470)

For Exercises 6–8, use the figure at the right.

6. Name four pairs of corresponding angles.

7. Name the alternate interior angles.

8. Suppose $\overleftrightarrow{AB} \parallel \overleftrightarrow{MN}$. Name all angles congruent to ∠8.

9. a. In the figure at the right, $x \parallel y$. List all angles that are congruent to ∠1.

   b. If $m\angle 5 = 45°$, what are the measures of the other angles?

B **Apply Your Skills**

10. In the figure at the right, find the sum of the measures of ∠1, ∠2, and ∠3.

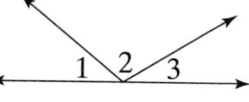

11. Fill in the blank. The sum of the measures of two angles is 90°. The angles are __?__ angles.

12. In the figure at the left, name the angle vertical to ∠1. Name an angle adjacent to ∠1. Then find $m\angle 1$.

13. **Writing in Math** Describe how you will keep from confusing the definitions of supplementary angles and complementary angles.

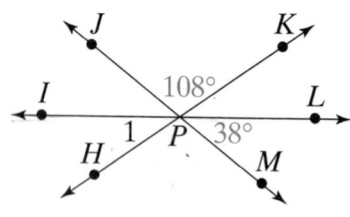

14. **Reasoning** Angles on the "outside" of two lines and on opposite sides of a transversal are called *alternate exterior angles*. The transversal q intersects two parallel lines m and n. If $m\angle 1 = 84°$, what is the measure of ∠5? Explain your reasoning.

GO **Online**
Homework Video Tutor
Visit: PHSchool.com
Web Code: ade-0902

15. **Algebra** Use the figure for Exercise 14. If $m\angle 8 = 2x + 5$ and $m\angle 4 = x + 10$, what is the value of x?

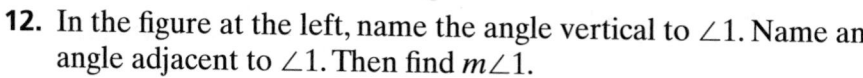

472 Chapter 9 Spatial Thinking

16. (Algebra) Given $a \parallel b$ at the right, find the measures of $\angle 1$ and $\angle 2$.

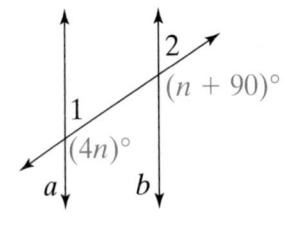

C Challenge **17. a.** (Algebra) Write an equation and find the value of x.

b. Find $m\angle KQB$.

c. Find $m\angle KQR$.

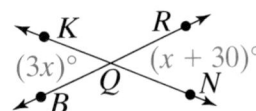

ISAT

Multiple Choice

18. What is $m\angle 3$?

A. 22° **B.** 68°

C. 158° **D.** 202°

19. If $\ell \parallel m$, what is $m\angle 6$?

F. 22 **G.** 68

H. 158 **J.** 202

Short Response

Read the passage below before doing Exercises 20 and 21.

New Road Approved

The Middleton City Board approved the proposal for a new road parallel to Highway 10. This new road, to be called Leeway Road, will help ease traffic flow in downtown Middleton during rush hour. Leeway Road will intersect both Sand Avenue and Piper Street.

20. When Leeway Road is built, what will $m\angle 1$ be? Explain.

21. If $m\angle$ is 130° when Leeway Road is built, what criterion is Leeway Road NOT meeting?

Lesson 9-1

Draw each figure.

22. $\overline{AB}$ **23.** $\overrightarrow{CD}$ **24.** $\overrightarrow{DC}$ **25.** $\overleftrightarrow{EF}$ **26.** $\angle GHI$

Lesson 6-9

Find the sale price.

27. $25 at 10% discount **28.** $324 at 20% discount

Lesson 4-5

29. In a single-elimination tournament, a team plays until it loses a game or wins the tournament. Eight teams play in a tournament. How many games must be played to decide a tournament winner?

Classifying Polygons

1 Classifying Triangles

A **polygon** is a *closed* plane figure with at least three *sides*. The sides meet only at their endpoints.

A triangle is a polygon with three sides. You can classify triangles by angle measures. In the Activity Lab on page 468 you reviewed how to classify angles. You can also classify triangles by side lengths. Tick marks are used to indicate congruent sides of a figure.

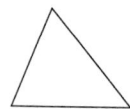
Acute triangle
three acute angles

Right triangle
one right angle

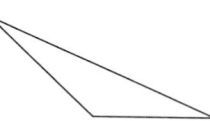
Obtuse triangle
one obtuse angle

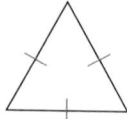
Equilateral triangle
three congruent sides

Isosceles triangle
at least two congruent sides

Scalene triangle
no congruent sides

1 EXAMPLE Classifying a Triangle

Classify the triangle by its sides and angles.

The triangle has two congruent sides and one right angle.

The triangle is an isosceles right triangle.

8 in.

8 in.

✓ Quick Check

1. Judging by appearance, classify each triangle by its sides and angles.

a.

b.

c.

You can also classify quadrilaterals by their sides and angles.

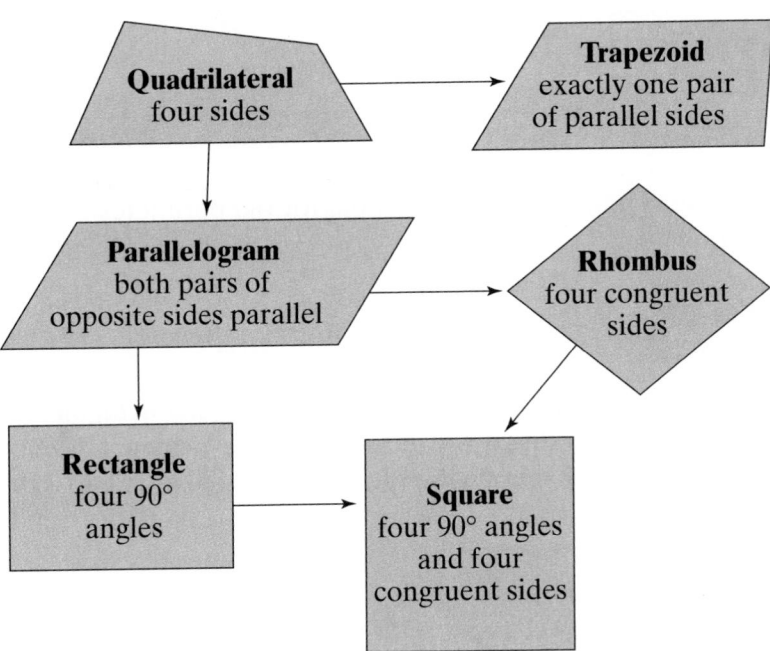

- **Quadrilateral** four sides
- **Trapezoid** exactly one pair of parallel sides
- **Parallelogram** both pairs of opposite sides parallel
- **Rhombus** four congruent sides
- **Rectangle** four 90° angles
- **Square** four 90° angles and four congruent sides

2 EXAMPLE **Classifying Quadrilaterals**

Name the types of quadrilaterals that have both pairs of opposite sides parallel.

All parallelograms have opposite sides parallel. Parallelograms include rectangles, rhombuses, and squares.

✓ Quick Check

2. Name the types of quadrilaterals that have four right angles.

In later math courses, you will prove that a parallelogram has opposite sides congruent and opposite angles congruent.

Polygons are named using their vertices. Start at one vertex and list them in consecutive order.

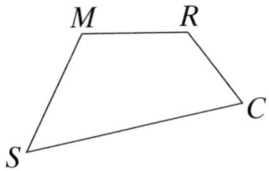

Starting from *M*, the name of this figure is quadrilateral *MRCS* or quadrilateral *MSCR.*

> **Vocabulary Tip**
>
> The plural of <u>vertex</u> is <u>vertices</u>.

A **regular polygon** has all sides congruent and all angles congruent. Some regular polygons are shown below.

Triangle

Square

Pentagon

Hexagon

You can use algebra to write a formula for the perimeter of a regular polygon.

3 EXAMPLE **Real-World Problem Solving**

Gridded Response A contractor is framing a regular octagonal gazebo. Write a formula for the perimeter of the gazebo in terms of the length of a side. Evaluate the formula for a side length of 7 ft.

To write a formula, let x = the length of each side. The perimeter of the regular octagon is

$$x + x + x + x + x + x + x + x.$$

The formula for the perimeter is $P = 8x$.

$P = 8x$ **Write the formula.**

$= 8(7)$ **Substitute 7 for x.**

$= 56$ **Simplify.**

For a side length of 7 ft, the perimeter is 56 ft.

Real-World Connection

Most gazebos are regular hexagons or regular octagons.

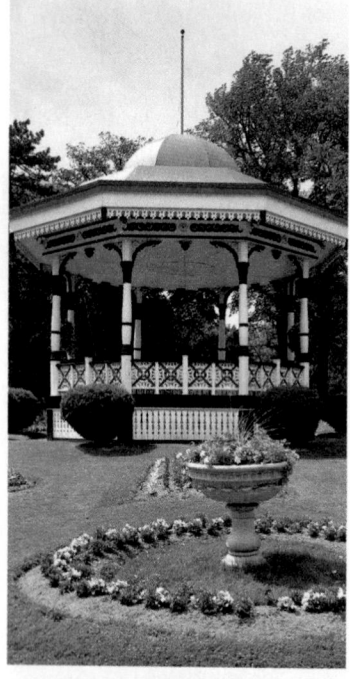

✓ **Quick Check**

3. a. **Algebra** Write a formula to find the perimeter of a regular hexagon.
   b. Use the formula to find the perimeter if one side is 16 cm.

EXERCISES

For more exercises, see *Extra Skill and Word Problem Practice.*

Practice and Problem Solving

A Practice by Example

Example 1
(page 474)

GO for Help

Judging by appearance, classify each triangle by its sides and angles.

1.

2.

3.

Example 2
(page 475)

Name the types of quadrilaterals that have the given property.

4. four congruent sides

5. exactly one pair of parallel sides

6. two pairs of parallel sides

7. opposite sides congruent

8. four congruent angles

9. opposite angles congruent

Example 3
(page 476)

(Algebra) **Write and use a formula for the perimeter of each figure. Use the formula to find the perimeter.**

10. an equilateral triangle with one side 3.5 cm

11. a square with one side 12.5 in.

12. a regular hexagon with one side $\frac{5}{8}$ in.

13. Architecture The Pentagon is a pentagonal-shaped building near Washington, D.C., that is home to the United States Department of Defense. Write a formula for the perimeter of a regular pentagon in terms of the length of a side. Evaluate the formula to find the perimeter of the Pentagon, which has a side length of 921 ft.

B Apply Your Skills

Open-Ended Sketch each figure.

14. an isosceles right triangle

15. a scalene obtuse triangle

16. an isosceles obtuse triangle

17. an isosceles acute triangle

18. a scalene right triangle

19. an equilateral triangle

20. Judging by appearance at the left, classify the triangle suggested by the edges of the piano, the piano lid, and the prop.

21. Draw a parallelogram without a right angle but with four congruent sides. What is another name for this figure?

22. Multiple Choice What is the perimeter of an isosceles triangle with congruent sides of 16.2 cm and a third side half that length?
  Ⓐ 8.1 cm   Ⓑ 16.2 cm   Ⓒ 32.4 cm   Ⓓ 40.5 cm

23. Find the perimeter of a scalene triangle with two side lengths of 8 in. and 5 in., and a third side length that is the average of the other two side lengths.

GO ●nline
Homework Video Tutor
Visit: PHSchool.com
Web Code: ade-0903

Name the types of quadrilaterals that do *not* have the given property.

24. four congruent sides

25. four 90° angles

Name three different figures in each flag. For each triangle, state the type of triangle.

26.

Flag of Philippines

27.

Flag of Antigua

Writing in Math

Are all equilateral triangles isosceles? Are all isosceles triangles equilateral? Explain.

The lengths of two sides of an isosceles triangle are given. What is the perimeter? Explain.

28. 10 cm, 12 cm   29. 5 cm, 12 cm   30. 12 cm, 12 cm

31. a. [Algebra] A decagon is a polygon with 10 sides. Write a formula for the perimeter of a regular decagon.
    b. Find the perimeter of a regular decagon with sides of 14.5 m.
    c. Find the length of a side of a regular decagon that has a perimeter of 22 ft.

ISAT

Test Prep

Multiple Choice

32. What is the perimeter of a regular pentagon with a side length of 4.9 cm?
    A. 4.9 cm   B. 14.7 cm   C. 24.5 cm   D. 29.4 cm

33. What is the perimeter of a square that has a side length of $\frac{3}{4}$ ft?
    F. $\frac{3}{16}$ ft   G. $\frac{3}{4}$ ft   H. 3 ft   J. 4 ft

Short Response

34. Is a square a rhombus? Explain your answer.

35. Is a square a rectangle? Explain your answer.

Mixed Review

GO for Help

Lesson 9-2   36. A transversal intersects two parallel lines, forming eight angles. One angle measures 60°. Sketch a diagram showing the measures of all eight angles.

Lesson 8-7   37. **Parades** A town parade included modern and antique cycles. The modern cycles had two wheels and the antique cycles had three wheels. Altogether there were 64 wheels on the 28 cycles. How many of the cycles had three wheels?

Lessons 7-2 and 7-5   **Solve each equation.**

38. $x + 20 + 2x = 41$ 39. $53 - 6x = 13 - 2x$

Extension

Angles of a Polygon

For Use With Lesson 9-3

In previous courses, you learned that the sum of the measures of the angles of a triangle is 180°. Now you have the tools to prove that this is true with deductive reasoning.

In the figure, $\overleftrightarrow{AC} \parallel \overleftrightarrow{DE}$. If two parallel lines are cut by a transversal, then alternate interior angles are congruent. Therefore, $\angle 1 \cong \angle 4$, or $m\angle 1 = m\angle 4$. Similarly, $m\angle 3 = m\angle 5$. $\angle ABC$ is a straight angle, so $m\angle 1 + m\angle 2 + m\angle 3 = 180°$. Substitute $m\angle 4$ for $m\angle 1$ and $m\angle 5$ for $m\angle 3$ and you get $m\angle 4 + m\angle 2 + m\angle 5 = 180°$. These are the angles of $\triangle DBE$.

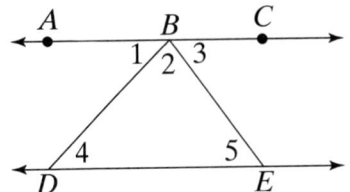

You can use triangles to find the sum of the measures of the angles of any polygon.

EXAMPLE

Find the sum of the measures of the angles of a hexagon.

The hexagon has   **6** vertices.
From vertex A, there are **5** segments to the other vertices.
The segments determine **4** triangles.

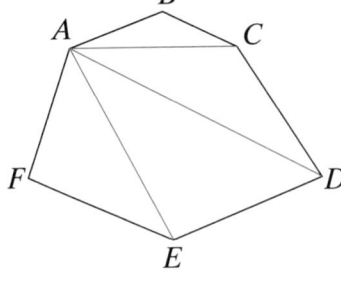

number of triangles	·	number of degrees in angles of triangle	=	sum of measures of angles of hexagon
4	·	180°	=	720°

EXERCISES

Find the sum of the measures of the angles of each polygon.

1. a quadrilateral

2. a decagon (10 sides)

3. an octagon

4. a dodecagon (12 sides)

5. Reasoning Write a formula for the sum of the measures of the angles of an n-gon (n sides).

6. Find the value of x in the figure at the right.

7. Writing in Math The sum of the measures of the angles of a polygon is 1,260°. Explain how you can find the number of sides.

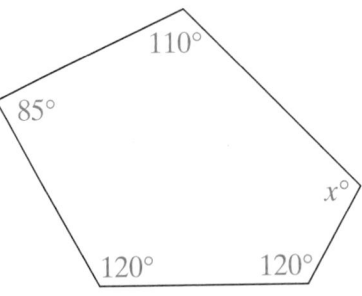

Find the number of sides in the polygon whose angle measures have the given sum.

8. 540°

9. 900°

10. 1,620°

11. 18,000°

Draw a Diagram

What You'll Learn

• To draw a diagram to solve a problem

. . . And Why

To find the number of diagonals in an octagon

☑ **Check Skills You'll Need**

Sketch each figure.

1. equilateral triangle

2. rectangle

3. pentagon

4. hexagon

5. octagon

GO for Help
Lesson 9-3

1 | **Draw a Diagram**

Math Strategies in Action
Car designers rely on computer-design programs to create, test, and modify their plans. The process of drawing a diagram helps them discover any problems they may have and see possible solutions.

Drawing a diagram is an important problem-solving tool.

1 EXAMPLE **Real-World** **Problem Solving**

How many diagonals does an octagon have?

Understand the Problem

In reading the problem, make sure you understand the meanings of all of the terms.

1. What is an octagon?

2. What is a diagonal?

Make a Plan

One strategy for solving this problem is to draw a diagram and count the diagonals. An octagon has eight sides. You can draw five diagonals from one vertex of an octagon.

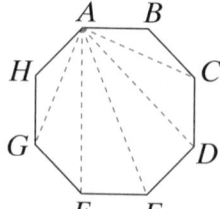

$\overline{AG}, \overline{AF}, \overline{AE}, \overline{AD}$, and $\overline{AC}$ are some of the diagonals.

3. There are 5 diagonals drawn from vertex A. Copy the diagram. Now find the number of diagonals you can draw from vertex B.

4. How many new diagonals can you draw from vertex C?

Carry Out the Plan

It may be helpful to organize your results as you count the diagonals.

Make a table similar to the one below and fill in the number of diagonals from each vertex. Do not count a diagonal twice. (The segment from *A* to *C* is the same segment as the one from *C* to *A*.)

Then add to find the total number of diagonals.

Vertex	Number of Diagonals
A	5
B	5
C	4
D	■
E	■
F	■
G	■
H	■
Total	■

Check the Answer

Counting the diagonals after they have all been drawn is not an easy task. To check your results, you may want to try a different approach.

Start with figures with fewer sides and see whether there is a pattern to the total numbers of diagonals as you increase the number of sides.

   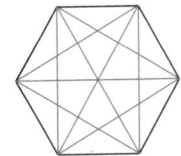

Figure	Number of Sides	Number of Diagonals
Triangle	3	0
Quadrilateral	4	2
Pentagon	5	5
Hexagon	6	9

Notice that the total number of diagonals increases as you increase the number of sides of the polygon. First the number increases by 2, then by 3, and then by 4. Continue this pattern to check your results.

✓ Quick Check

5. How many diagonals does a decagon have?

EXERCISES

For more exercises, see *Extra Skill and Word Problem Practice.*

Practice and Problem Solving

A Practice by Example

GO for Help

Example 1
(page 480)

Solve by drawing a diagram.

1. **Retail Delivery** A furniture delivery truck leaves the store at 8 A.M. It travels 6 miles east, then 4 miles south, then 2 miles west, and then 4 miles north. At the end of this route, how far is the truck from the store?

2. Bill is older than Jim and younger than Jose. Jose is older than Chris and younger than Tandala. Chris is older than Jim. Bill is younger than Tandala. Chris is older than Bill. Who is youngest?

3. **Geometry** How many triangles can you form in a hexagon if you draw all of the diagonals from only one vertex?

4. **Game Schedules** Eight soccer teams are to play each other two times in a season. How many games will be played?

5. There are 25 students in a math class. Ten students are in the math club. Twelve students are in the band. Five students are in both. How many students in the math class are members of neither club?

B Apply Your Skills

Solve using any strategy.

6. **Geometry** Snoozles are always born as twins, and each snoozle always moves in the opposite direction from its twin. Twin snoozles are at the origin of a coordinate plane. One follows the path $(0, 0)$ to $(1, 3)$ to $(2, 2)$ to $(4, 7)$. What path will its twin travel?

7. **Measurement** Maureen cut a 20-cm ribbon into exactly three pieces. The first piece is 3 cm shorter than the second piece. The third piece is 4 cm shorter than the second piece. Find the length of the shortest piece.

8. **Car Rental** A rental car costs $34.95 for the first 150 miles and $.35 for each additional mile. How much will the rental car cost for driving 275 miles?

9. A student was standing in the middle of a line. Twenty-three students were ahead of her. How many students were in the line?

10. **Writing in Math** Suppose you want to find the thickness of one sheet of paper. Describe the problem solving method you would use.

11. Shana has three pets, a dog, a cat, and a bird. One of them is named Sammy. Noodles is younger than both the bird and the dog. Fluffy is green. Which pet has the name Sammy?

12. **Geometry** You can draw one segment to connect two points and three distinct segments to connect three named points. How many segments can you draw to connect five points if no three of the points lie on the same line?

Strategies

- Act It Out
- Draw a Diagram
- Guess, Check, Revise
- Look for a Pattern
- Make a Model
- Make a Table
- Simulate the Problem
- Solve by Graphing
- Use Multiple Strategies
- Work a Simpler Problem
- Work Backward
- Write an Equation
- Write a Proportion

GO Online
Homework Video Tutor
Visit: PHSchool.com
Web Code: ade-0904

13. Two friends rented a canoe for 10 days. One friend used the canoe for 6 days. The other friend used the canoe for 4 days. How much of the $150 rental fee should each friend pay?

 Challenge

14. Container A has twice the capacity of container B. Container A is full of sand and container B is empty. Suppose $\frac{1}{8}$ of the sand in container A is poured into container B. What fractional part of container B will contain sand?

15. Points $P, Q, R,$ and S appear in that order on a line. The ratio $PQ : QR$ is 3 : 4, and the ratio $QR : RS$ is 2 : 5. The length PQ is 6 in. Find the length PS.

ISAT

Test Prep

Multiple Choice

16. How many diagonals does a hexagon have?
  A. 6   **B.** 9   **C.** 12   **D.** 18

17. Some taxicabs begin each trip by setting the meter to $1.50. The meter then adds $.40 for each $\frac{1}{4}$ mi traveled. If a trip costs $7.90, how far did the cab travel?
  F. 160 mi   **G.** 16 mi   **H.** 8 mi   **J.** 4 mi

18. What is the perimeter of a regular hexagon with side length of 6.3 cm?
  A. 25.2 cm   **B.** 31.5 cm   **C.** 37.8 cm   **D.** 50.4 cm

Short Response

19. A coin collector has 53 rare coins. This is 12 fewer than 5 times the number there were a year ago.   **(a)** Write an equation you could use to find out how many coins the collector had a year ago. **(b)** Solve the equation and show your work.

Mixed Review

 for Help

Lesson 9-3

Classify each triangle by its sides and angles.

20. no congruent sides and one right angle

21. three congruent sides

22. one obtuse angle and no congruent sides

23. a 90° angle and two congruent sides

Lesson 8-8 **24. Ticket Sales** Adult tickets for the school musical sell for $8 and student tickets sell for $5 each. Let x be the number of adult tickets sold and y be the number of student tickets sold. The school hopes to make at least $1,000. Write an inequality to model the situation. Show all solutions by graphing the inequality.

Write each decimal as a fraction in simplest form and as a percent.

Lesson 6-5
25. 0.14   **26.** 4.5   **27.** 0.11   **28.** 0.02   **29.** 0.125   **30.** 1

Congruence

 Assessment Framework

9.8.11 Solve problems involving congruent and similar figures.

 Check Skills You'll Need

$\triangle ABC \sim \triangle XYZ$. For the given part of $\triangle ABC$, find the corresponding part of $\triangle XYZ$.

1. $\angle A$ 2. $\angle C$

3. $\overline{AB}$ 4. $\overline{CA}$

 for Help

Lesson 6-3

🔊 **New Vocabulary**

• congruent figures

Test-Taking Tip

When two triangles are congruent, you can sketch the shapes side by side to help identify congruent parts.

 Identifying Corresponding Parts

Activity

Exploring Congruence

1. Have each member of your group cut plastic straws 3 cm, 6 cm, and 7 cm long. String an 18-cm string through the three straws. Tie the string just tight enough to form a strong triangle without bending any straws.

2. Hold the triangles up to one another to compare. Are they the same size and shape? Describe how the angle measures compare.

Congruent figures have the same size and shape, and their corresponding parts have equal measures.

The triangles at the right are congruent. You use tick marks to indicate congruent segments, and arcs to mark congruent angles. You write a congruence statement by listing the corresponding angles in the same order.

You can use corresponding parts of congruent triangles to find distance.

$\triangle ABC \cong \triangle EDF$

$\angle A \cong \angle E$	$\overline{AB} \cong \overline{ED}$
$\angle B \cong \angle D$	$\overline{BC} \cong \overline{DF}$
$\angle C \cong \angle F$	$\overline{AC} \cong \overline{EF}$

1 EXAMPLE **Real-World** 🌐 **Problem Solving**

Measurement $\triangle AMN \cong \triangle ABC$. **Name the corresponding parts.**

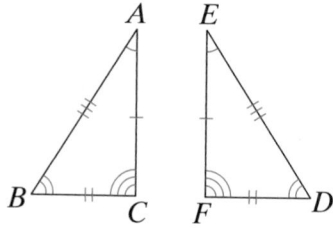

a. congruent angles

$\angle M \cong \angle B, \angle N \cong \angle C,$
$\angle MAN \cong \angle BAC$

b. congruent sides

$\overline{MN} \cong \overline{BC}, \overline{NA} \cong \overline{CA}, \overline{MA} \cong \overline{BA}$

c. Find the distance from M to N.

Since $\overline{MN} \cong \overline{BC}$ and $BC = 100$ yd, $MN = 100$ yd.

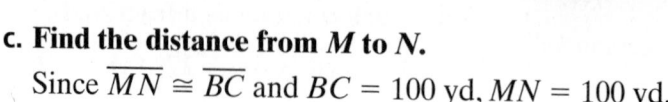

✅ Quick Check

1. $\triangle ABC \cong \triangle DEC$. List all pairs of congruent corresponding sides and angles. Then find AC.

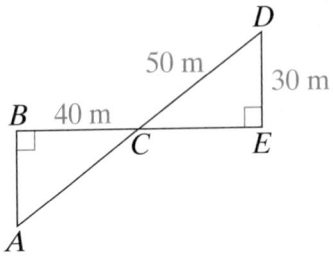

2 | Identifying Congruent Triangles

You use corresponding parts of triangles to identify congruent triangles. Below are three of the ways to show that two triangles are congruent.

Side–Side–Side
(SSS)

Side–Angle–Side
(SAS)

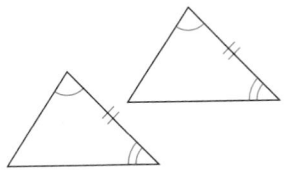

Angle–Side–Angle
(ASA)

2 EXAMPLE   Identifying Congruent Triangles

List the congruent corresponding parts of each pair of triangles. Write a congruence statement for the triangles.

a.

b.

$\overline{MO} \cong \overline{RQ}$	**Side**
$\angle M \cong \angle R$	**Angle**
$\overline{MN} \cong \overline{RP}$	**Side**

$\triangle MNO \cong \triangle RPQ$ by SAS.

$\angle WAB \cong \angle XAB$	**Angle**
$\overline{AB} \cong \overline{AB}$	**Side**
$\angle ABW \cong \angle ABX$	**Angle**

$\triangle WAB \cong \triangle XAB$ by ASA.

GO Online

Video Tutor Help

Visit: PHSchool.com
Web Code: ada-0775

✅ Quick Check

2. For the two highlighted triangles, list the congruent corresponding parts. Write a congruence statement (and reason) for the triangles.

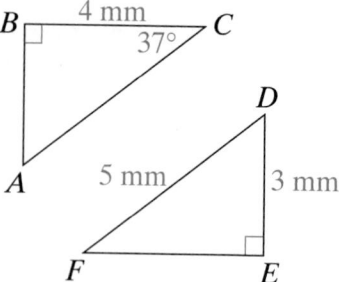

A Practice by Example

Example 1
(page 484)

GO for Help

$\triangle ABC \cong \triangle DEF.$
Complete each statement.

1. $\angle A \cong \blacksquare$ **2.** $\angle B \cong \blacksquare$

3. $m\angle C = \blacksquare$ **4.** $m\angle B = \blacksquare$

5. $m\angle A = \blacksquare$ **6.** $\overline{AC} \cong \blacksquare$

7. $\overline{EF} \cong \blacksquare$ **8.** $\overline{BA} \cong \blacksquare$

9. $AC = \blacksquare$ **10.** $FE = \blacksquare$

11. $\triangle CBA \cong \blacksquare$ **12.** $\triangle BAC \cong \blacksquare$ **13.** $\triangle ACB \cong \blacksquare$

🌐 **Quilt Patterns** Use the quilt design for Exercises 14–16.

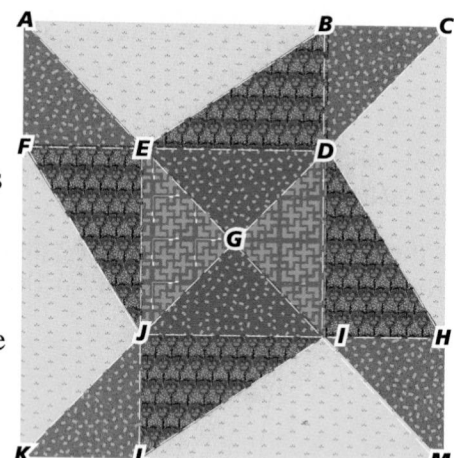

14. The yellow triangles are congruent. Name the corresponding congruent angles.

15. The red-and-blue triangles are congruent. Name the corresponding congruent sides.

16. The dark blue triangles are isosceles and congruent, and $GD = 10$ in. Find the distance from G to I.

Example 2
(page 485)

For each pair of triangles, list the congruent corresponding parts. Write a congruence statement (and reason) for the triangles.

17.   **18.**   **19.**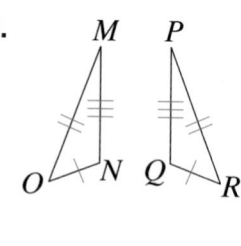

B Apply Your Skills

Assume that $\triangle ABC \cong \triangle XYZ.$ Answer the following.

20. Name the corresponding congruent angles.

21. Name the corresponding congruent sides.

GO ●nline
Homework Video Tutor
Visit: PHSchool.com
Web Code: ade-0905

22. Multiple Choice If $AB = 12$ cm and $BC = 15$ cm, what is the length of $\overline{YZ}$?
Ⓐ 3 cm   Ⓑ 12 cm   Ⓒ 15 cm   Ⓓ 27 cm

GO for Help

For a guide to reading
the diagram in
Exercise 23, see
page 489.

**For each pair of triangles, list the congruent corresponding parts.
Write a congruence statement (and reason) for the triangles.**

23.

24.

25.

26.

Error Analysis The two figures in the diagram (left) are congruent.
State whether each congruence statement is correct and explain.

27. $RAVK \cong NLUC$

28. $RKVA \cong ULNC$

29. $ARKV \cong CULN$

30. $\overline{NL} \cong \overline{KV}$

31. $\angle V \cong \angle C$

32. $\angle VAR \cong \angle LUC$

C Challenge

**Explain why the triangles in each pair are congruent. Then find the
missing measures in each diagram.**

33.

34.

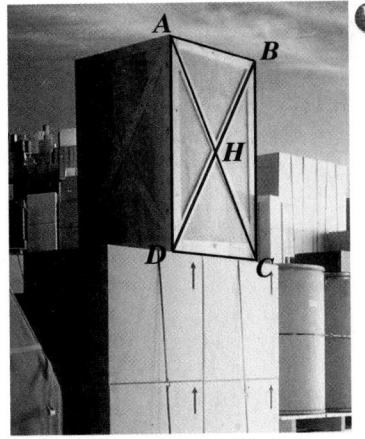

🌐 **35. Containers** The end of the shipping container at the left is a
rectangle. The diagonals are congruent and intersect at point H.
$\overline{HB} \cong \overline{HD}$ and $\overline{AH} \cong \overline{CH}$. Which triangle is congruent to the
given triangle? Explain.
   a. $\triangle ABH$ **b.** $\triangle ADC$

36. Reasoning $\triangle KWR$ is *equiangular* (all angles are congruent).
$\triangle ABJ$ is also equiangular. Can you use **Angle-Angle-Angle**
(**AAA**) to show that two triangles are congruent? Use diagrams
to justify your conclusion.

37. Writing in Math $\triangle ABC \cong \triangle XYZ$. What can you conclude about
the perimeters of the triangles? Explain.

Multiple Choice

38. If $\triangle AND \cong \triangle PCK$, which statement must be true?
A. $\overline{AN} \cong \overline{PK}$ **B.** $\angle N \cong \angle C$ **C.** $\overline{ND} \cong \overline{PC}$ **D.** $\angle AND \cong \angle PKC$

39. Which is the correct congruence statement?
F. $\triangle BCD \cong \triangle FED$ by ASA
G. $\triangle BCD \cong \triangle FED$ by SSS
H. $\triangle CDB \cong \triangle DEF$ by ASA
J. $\triangle BDC \cong \triangle FED$ by SAS

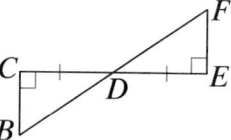

40. Quadrilateral $JKLM \cong$ quadrilateral $PQRS$. Which is a correct congruence statement?
A. $\overline{JK} \cong \overline{RS}$ **B.** $\overline{LM} \cong \overline{QR}$ **C.** $\angle K \cong \angle Q$ **D.** $\angle M \cong \angle P$

Mixed Review

GO for Help

Lesson 9-4

41. Students are evenly spaced as they sit around a round table. The fourth student is directly across from the eleventh student. How many students are seated at the table?

Lesson 6-7

Algebra **Write and solve an equation.**

42. What percent of 50 is 20?

43. 15% of what number is 12?

44. Find 125% of 200.

Lesson 5-1

Order from least to greatest.

45. $\frac{1}{2}, \frac{5}{6}, \frac{3}{8}, \frac{2}{3}$

46. $\frac{3}{8}, \frac{2}{3}, \frac{3}{4}, \frac{4}{5}$

47. $\frac{1}{6}, \frac{1}{5}, \frac{1}{7}, \frac{1}{4}$

Checkpoint Quiz 1

Lessons 9-1 through 9-5

Name the figure that has the properties described.

1. a part of a line with one endpoint

2. a series of points that extends in two directions without end

3. a segment congruent to $\overline{PR}$ when $\triangle LMN \cong \triangle PQR$

4. two rays with a common endpoint

5. **Algebra** In the diagram at the right, $a \parallel b$.
  a. Write an equation to find x.
  b. Find $m\angle TAV$.
  c. Find $m\angle TAN$.
  d. Find $m\angle DNK$.

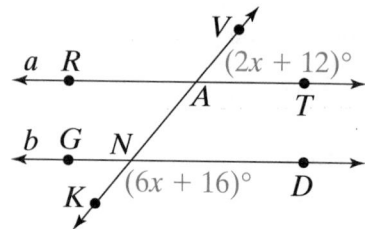

6. Open-Ended Draw a triangle that is scalene and has a right angle.

Guided Problem Solving

Understanding Math Problems Read the problem below. Then let Shelley's thinking guide you through reading the diagram. Check your understanding with the exercises at the bottom of the page.

List the congruent corresponding parts of the triangles. Write a congruence statement (and reason) for the triangles.

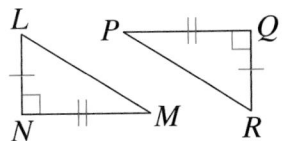

What Shelley Asks	**What Shelley Thinks and Writes**
What does the diagram show?	Two triangles The little squares show right angles. The tick marks show congruent sides.
What are the corresponding points?	Points L, N, M correspond to R, Q, and P.
What congruent parts do I know?	The single ticks show $\overline{LN} \cong \overline{RQ}$. The double ticks show $\overline{NM} \cong \overline{QP}$. I also know right angles are congruent. I'll write: $\overline{LN} \cong \overline{RQ}$ $\overline{NM} \cong \overline{QP}$ $\angle N \cong \angle Q$
Can I write a congruence statement?	I can write a congruence statement if I have SSS, SAS, or ASA.
Do I have SSS, SAS, or ASA?	I have congruence for two sides and an angle. SAS is the only possibility.
Do I have SAS?	The angles have to be between the sides. They are! I have SAS.
I must write the congruence statement (and reason).	I'll write: $\triangle LNM \cong \triangle RQP$ by SAS

EXERCISES

Write a congruence statement (and reason) for the triangles.

1.

2.

3.

9-6 Circles

☑ **Check Skills You'll Need**

Solve each proportion. Round to the nearest whole number where necessary.

1. $\frac{10}{100} = \frac{x}{360}$

2. $\frac{75}{100} = \frac{x}{360}$

3. $\frac{0.8}{5.3} = \frac{x}{360}$

4. $\frac{1.6}{5.3} = \frac{x}{360}$

 for Help
Lesson 6-2

🔊 **New Vocabulary**

- circle
- central angle

 Finding Circumference

(A)ctivity

Exploring Pi

1. Work in groups. Each member of your group should have a ruler, string, and several circular objects, such as jar lids. Make a chart similar to the chart below. Record your results.

Object	Diameter	Circumference	Ratio $\frac{\text{Circumference}}{\text{Diameter}}$
▦	▦	▦	▦
▦	▦	▦	▦

2. Measure the diameter of each circle to the nearest millimeter.

3. Find the circumference of each circle by wrapping a string around the outside of the circle. Then straighten the string and measure its length to the nearest millimeter.

4. Calculate the ratio $\frac{\text{circumference}}{\text{diameter}}$ to the nearest tenth.

5. Make a conjecture about the relationship between the circumference of a circle and its diameter.

A **circle** is the set of all points in a plane that are the same distance from a given point, called the *center* of the circle.

Radius is a segment that has one endpoint at the center and the other point on the circle.

Circumference is the distance around the circle.

Diameter is a chord that passes through the center of a circle.

Chord is a segment whose endpoints are on the circle.

The ratio of every circle's circumference C to its diameter d is the same. It has a special symbol, π, which is pronounced "pie." Both 3.14 and $\frac{22}{7}$ are good approximations for this ratio. Use $\frac{22}{7}$ for π when calculations involve fractions, and use 3.14 when they do not.

If you multiply both sides of the equation $\frac{C}{d} = \pi$ by d, you get $C = \pi d$, which is a formula for the circumference of a circle.

Key Concepts **Circumference of a Circle**

The circumference of a circle is π times the diameter.

$$C = \pi d \qquad C = 2\pi r$$

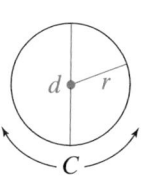

1 EXAMPLE Finding Circumference

Find the circumference of the circle at the right.

$C = \pi d$ **Write the formula.**

$C \approx (3.14)6$ **Replace π with 3.14 and d with 6.**

   $= 18.84$ **Simplify.**

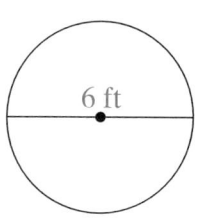

6 ft

The circumference of the circle is about 18.84 ft.

✓ Quick Check

1. Find the circumference of each circle.

   a. diameter = $2\frac{4}{5}$ in.   **b.** radius = 30 mm   **c.** diameter = 200 mi

2 Making Circle Graphs

To make a circle graph, you find the measure of each *central angle*. A **central angle** is an angle whose vertex is the center of a circle. There are 360° in a circle.

2 EXAMPLE Real-World 🌐 Problem Solving

Budget Make a circle graph for Juan's weekly budget shown at the right.

Use proportions to find the measures of the central angles.

$\dfrac{20}{100} = \dfrac{r}{360}$ $\dfrac{25}{100} = \dfrac{\ell}{360}$ $\dfrac{15}{100} = \dfrac{c}{360}$ $\dfrac{40}{100} = \dfrac{s}{360}$

   $r = 72°$ $\ell = 90°$ $c = 54°$ $s = 144°$

- Use a compass to draw a circle.
- Draw the central angles with a protractor.
- Label each section.
- Add a title and necessary information.

Juan's Weekly Budget

Recreation (r)	20%
Lunch (ℓ)	25%
Clothes (c)	15%
Savings (s)	40%

✅ Quick Check

2. Make a circle graph for the data. Round the measure of each central angle to the nearest degree.

Blood Types of Population

Type A	Type B	Type AB	Type O
40%	12%	5%	43%

---

3 EXAMPLE   Real-World 🌐 Problem Solving

Multiple Choice Which circle graph best represents the data below?

Test-Taking Tip

When you use data to make a circle graph, your proportions will involve the total of the data, not 100.
0.3 + 0.4 + 1.3 + 1.8 = 3.8, so your proportions will compare 3.8 million visits to 360°.

Visits to Kentucky's National Recreation Areas

Site	Visits (millions)
Abraham Lincoln's Birthplace	0.3
Big South Fork	0.4
Cumberland Gap	1.3
Mammoth Caves	1.8

Ⓐ   Ⓑ   Ⓒ   Ⓓ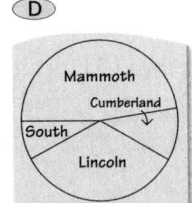

Mammoth Caves have the most visits, so that section of the graph should be the largest. You can eliminate choices A and C. Abraham Lincoln's birthplace receives the fewest visits, so that section of the graph should be the smallest. You can eliminate choice D. The answer is B.

✅ Quick Check

3. Students at Western High School work in the following places: restaurants, 140; library, 15; auto shop, 60; retail stores, 75; and other places, 30. Draw a circle graph to show where students at Western High School work. Round the measures of the central angles to the nearest degree.

EXERCISES

For more exercises, see *Extra Skill and Word Problem Practice.*

Practice and Problem Solving

 Practice by Example

Example 1
(page 491)

 for Help

Find the circumference of each circle.

1. 100 in.

2. 2 mi

3. 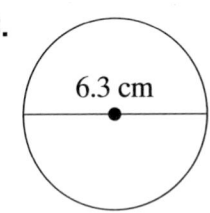 6.3 cm

Find the circumference of each circle with the given radius or diameter.

4. radius = 3.5 cm   **5.** radius = $4\frac{2}{3}$ ft   **6.** diameter = 0.1 m

7. radius = 18 in.   **8.** radius = 90 ft   **9.** diameter = $\frac{1}{2}$ yd

Examples 2 and 3
(pages 491 and 492)

Find the measures of the central angles that you would draw to represent each percent in a circle graph. Round to the nearest degree.

10. 35%   **11.** 50%   **12.** 30%   **13.** 1%   **14.** 25%   **15.** 75%

16. Income Make a circle graph for the data.

What College Students Earn

Monthly Income from Jobs	No job	Less than $200	$200 to $399	$400 or over
Percent of Total Number of Students	33%	14%	25%	28%

 Apply Your Skills

Find the circumference of each circle with the given radius or diameter.

17. radius = 0.6 in   **18.** radius = 10.25 mi   **19.** diameter = 4.6 yd

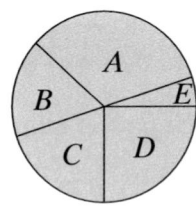

20. Multiple Choice Nancy spends a third of her salary on rent, a fifth on utilities, a fourth on food, 5% on transportation, and she saves a sixth. Which section of the graph (at left) represents Nancy's rent?
   Ⓐ Section *A*   Ⓑ Section *B*   Ⓒ Section *C*   Ⓓ Section *D*

21. The data below show how a group of students travel to school each day. Make a circle graph for the data.

How Students Travel to School

Transportation	Walk	Bicycle	Bus	Car	Other
Number of Students	55	80	110	40	15

🌐 **22. Finance** In a recent survey, families were asked how they spend extra income. Twenty-two families said they went to the movies, 34 said they eat out, 83 went on vacations, and the remaining 75 put it into savings. Make a circle graph for the data.

GO **Online**
Homework Video Tutor
Visit: PHSchool.com
Web Code: ade-0906

23. Writing in Math Write a paragraph to a student who was not in class describing how to make a circle graph.

Challenge 24. A *tangent* to a circle is a line, segment, or ray in the same plane as the circle and which intersects the circle in exactly one point. A *secant* is a line, segment, or ray that intersects a circle in two points. Use the diagram to identify the following.

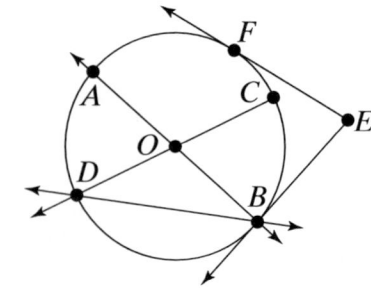

a. one diameter   b. four radii
c. two secants   d. three chords
e. two tangents

Diameter	Circumference
1 in.	3.14 in.
5 in.	15.7 in.
8 in.	25.1 in.
10 in.	31.4 in.

25. The data at the left represent the circumference and the diameter of four circles of different sizes.
   a. Graph the points on a coordinate plane. Use the diameter as the *x*-coordinate and the circumference as the *y*-coordinate.
   b. Connect the points with a line.
   c. Find the slope of the line.
   d. **Reasoning** Explain the meaning of slope in this situation.

ISAT

 Test Prep

Gridded Response 26. To the nearest degree, what is the measure of the central angle that represents 46% in a circle graph?

27. To the nearest tenth of a centimeter, what is the circumference of a circle with a radius of 2.5 cm? Use 3.14 for π.

28. To the nearest tenth of an inch, what is the circumference of a circle with a diameter of 8 in.? Use 3.14 for π.

Mixed Review

 GO for Help

Lesson 9-5 **List the congruent corresponding parts of each pair of triangles. Write a congruence statement for the triangles.**

29.

30.

Lesson 8-1 **Is each relation a function? Explain.**

31. $\left\{\left(4,\frac{1}{2}\right),\left(6,\frac{1}{2}\right),\left(-2,\frac{1}{2}\right)\right\}$ 32. $\left\{(1,0),(1,5),\left(1,3\frac{1}{4}\right)\right\}$

Lesson 6-2 🌐 33. **Physical Fitness** While exercising, your heart beats 32 times in 15 s. At this rate, how many times will it beat in 2 min?

Constructions

1 Congruent Segments and Angles

In constructions, you use only a *compass* and *straightedge* (an unmarked ruler) to accurately copy a segment or an angle, or draw an accurate bisector. A compass is a tool used to draw circles or parts of circles. An *arc* is part of a circle.

1 EXAMPLE Constructing a Congruent Segment

Construct a segment congruent to $\overline{AB}$.

Step 1 Draw a ray with endpoint C.

Step 2 Open the compass to the length of $\overline{AB}$.

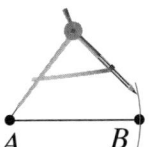

Step 3 With the *same* compass setting, put the compass tip on C. Draw an arc that intersects the ray. Label the intersection D.

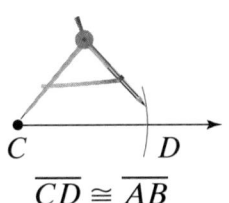

$$\overline{CD} \cong \overline{AB}$$

✓ Quick Check

1. Draw a segment. Construct a segment twice the length of the segment you drew.

What You'll Learn

- To construct a segment or an angle congruent to a given segment or angle
- To construct segment bisectors and angle bisectors

...And Why

To construct precise drawings such as those that architects use

✓ Check Skills You'll Need

State the meaning of each symbol.

1. B 2. $\overline{AB}$

3. $\overrightarrow{AB}$ 4. $\overleftrightarrow{AB}$

GO for Help
Lesson 9-1

🔊 New Vocabulary

- **perpendicular lines**
- **segment bisector**
- **perpendicular bisector**
- **angle bisector**

Real-World 🌐 Connection

To work with a compass easily, here is one way to hold it.

② EXAMPLE **Constructing a Congruent Angle**

Construct an angle congruent to ∠E.

Step 1 Draw a ray with endpoint Q.

Step 2 With the compass point at E, draw an arc that intersects the sides of ∠E. Label the intersection points F and G.

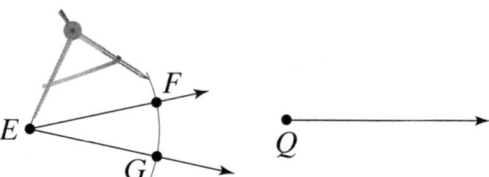

Step 3 With the *same* compass setting, put the compass tip on Q. Draw an arc intersecting the ray at point P.

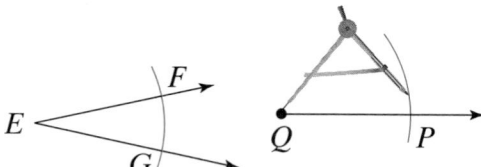

Step 4 Open the compass to the length of $\overline{FG}$. Using this setting, put the compass tip at P. Draw an arc to determine the point R. Draw $\overrightarrow{QR}$.

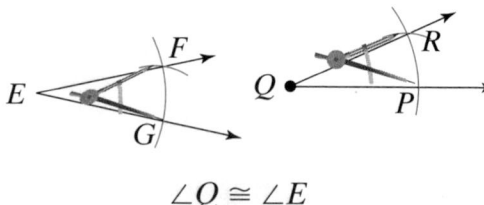

$$\angle Q \cong \angle E$$

✓ Quick Check

2. Draw an obtuse angle. Construct an angle congruent to the angle you drew.

② Constructing Bisectors

The figures below show some special relationships intersecting lines may have.

Vocabulary Tip

To bisect means to divide into two equal parts. Therefore, a bisector divides a segment or angle into two congruent parts.

Perpendicular lines, segments, or rays intersect to form right angles.

A segment bisector is a line, segment, or ray that divides a segment into two congruent segments.

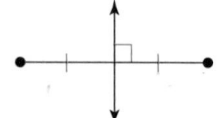

A perpendicular bisector is a line, segment, or ray that is perpendicular to the segment it bisects.

3 EXAMPLE   Constructing a Perpendicular Bisector

Construct the perpendicular bisector of $\overline{PQ}$.

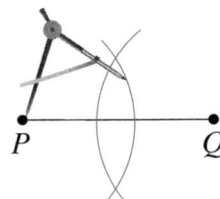

Step 1 Open the compass to more than half the length of $\overline{PQ}$. Put the compass tip at P. Draw an arc intersecting $\overline{PQ}$. With the same compass setting, repeat from point Q.

Step 2 Label the points of intersection of the two arcs as S and T. Draw $\overleftrightarrow{ST}$. Label the intersection of $\overleftrightarrow{ST}$ and $\overline{PQ}$ as point M.

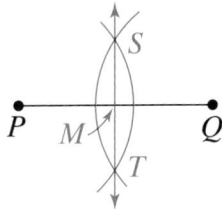

$\overleftrightarrow{ST}$ is perpendicular to $\overline{PQ}$ and $\overleftrightarrow{ST}$ bisects $\overline{PQ}$.

✓ Quick Check

● **3.** Draw a segment. Construct its perpendicular bisector.

An **angle bisector** is a ray that divides an angle into two congruent angles.

4 EXAMPLE   Constructing an Angle Bisector

Construct the bisector of $\angle A$.

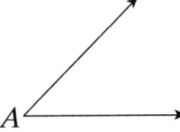

Step 1 Put the compass tip at A. Draw an arc that intersects the sides of $\angle A$. Label the points of intersection B and C.

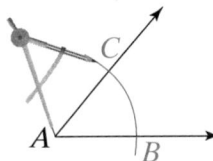

Step 2 Put the compass tip at B. Draw an arc. With the same compass setting, repeat with the compass tip at C. Make sure the arcs intersect. Label the intersection of the arcs D. Draw $\overrightarrow{AD}$.

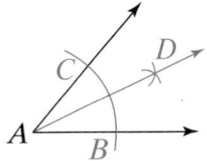

$\overrightarrow{AD}$ bisects $\angle BAC$.

✓ Quick Check

● **4.** Draw an obtuse angle. Construct its angle bisector.

EXERCISES

For more exercises, see *Extra Skill and Word Problem Practice*.

Practice and Problem Solving

A Practice by Example

Example 1
(page 495)

Example 2
(page 496)

For Exercises 1–4, draw a diagram similar to one that is given. Then construct each figure.

1. $\overline{EF}$ congruent to $\overline{XY}$

2. $\overline{GH}$ twice the length of $\overline{XY}$

3. $\angle D$ congruent to $\angle A$

4. $\angle Y$ congruent to $\angle X$

5. Draw an acute angle. Construct an angle congruent to the angle you drew.

Example 3
(page 497)

For Exercises 6 and 7, first draw diagrams similar to ones shown.

6. Construct the perpendicular bisector of $\overline{MN}$.

7. Construct the perpendicular bisector of $\overline{CD}$.

8. Draw $\overline{DE}$ at least 4 in. long. Then construct its perpendicular bisector.

Example 4
(page 497)

For Exercises 9 and 10, first draw diagrams similar to ones shown.

9. Construct the bisector of $\angle J$.

10. Construct the bisector of $\angle K$.

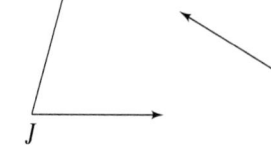

11. Use a protractor to draw a right angle. Construct its angle bisector.

B Apply Your Skills

For Exercises 12–14, draw a figure similar to the one that is given. Then construct each figure.

12. $\overline{MN}$ three times the length of $\overline{CD}$

13. $\overline{PQ}$ 1.5 times the length of $\overline{CD}$

14. $\triangle ABF$ with two angles congruent to $\angle X$

15. Draw an angle and label it $\angle A$. Then construct $\angle I$ so that $m\angle I = 2m\angle A$.

16. Construct a 90° angle.

17. **Writing in Math** How are constructing a segment bisector and constructing an angle bisector alike?

GO ●nline
Homework Video Tutor
Visit: PHSchool.com
Web Code: ade-0907

498 Chapter 9 Spatial Thinking

18. Open-Ended Use your compass to make a design. Decorate your design.

19. The bisector of $\angle XYZ$ is $\overrightarrow{YN}$. If the measure of $\angle XYN$ is 55°, what is the measure of $\angle XYZ$?

C Challenge

20. a. Draw a point and a line. Construct the perpendicular segment from the point to the line. (*Hint:* Place your compass tip at the point. Open your compass far enough to draw an arc that intersects the line in two points. Construct the perpendicular bisector of the segment between the two points.)

b. An *altitude* of a triangle is a perpendicular segment from a vertex to a line containing the side opposite the vertex. Draw a large acute triangle. Construct its three altitudes.

21. Draw $\triangle PQR$. To construct $\triangle ABC$ congruent to $\triangle PQR$, first construct $\overline{AB}$ congruent to $\overline{PQ}$. Use a compass setting the length of $\overline{PR}$. Draw an arc with the compass tip at A. Then use a compass setting the length of $\overline{QR}$. With the compass tip at B draw an arc that intersects the first arc. Label the intersection C. Draw $\overline{AC}$ and $\overline{BC}$.

Test Prep

Multiple Choice

22. The bisector of $\angle ABC$ is $\overrightarrow{BD}$. If the measure of $\angle$ ___ is 50°, what is the measure of $\angle$ ___ ?
  A. 25°   **B.** 50°   **C.** 100°   **D.** 130°

23. $\overrightarrow{DB}$ is the bisector of $\angle CDE$. Which statement must be true?
  F. $\angle CDE \cong \angle BDE$ **G.** $\angle CDB \cong \angle EDC$
  H. $\angle CDB \cong \angle BDE$ **J.** $\angle EDC \cong \angle EBC$

Extended Response

24. Explain how to construct each figure.
  a. a 45° angle   **b.** a $22\frac{1}{2}$° angle   **c.** a $67\frac{1}{2}$° angle
  d. Do one of the constructions (a)–(c).

Mixed Review

for Help

Lesson 9-6

Find the measure of the central angle that would represent each percent in a circle graph. Round your answer to the nearest degree.

25. 12%   **26.** 45%   **27.** 5%   **28.** 25%

Lesson 8-7

29. Number Sense Find two numbers with a sum of 25 and a difference of 15.

Lesson 7-8

Find the simple interest.

30. $1,000 deposited at an interest rate of 2% for 3 years

31. $150 deposited at an interest rate of 4% for 6 months

Prefixes and Common Meanings

Earlier in this book, you made index cards to learn new words and symbols. Here are two more strategies for learning new vocabulary.

Strategy 1 Break words apart into prefixes and roots. Then combine the meaning of the two parts.

Sample: *bisector* has the prefix *bi* and the root *sector*.

Bi means "two" and sector means "section." So bisector means "two sections."

Here are some common prefixes and roots that you have used in this chapter.

deca (ten)	*dia* (through)	*equi* (equal)
gon (angle)	*hexa* (six)	*octa* (eight)
para (beside)	*penta* (five)	*poly* (many)
quadri (four)	*tri* (three)	

Strategy 2 Think about common meanings of words.

Sample: an acute pain is a sharp pain, and an acute angle makes a sharp point.

Connecting the word *acute* with the word *sharp* will help you remember that an acute angle measures less than 90°.

EXERCISES

Use a dictionary. Break each word into a prefix and a root. Then combine the meanings. Does the meaning you wrote make sense given the definition of the word? Explain.

1. hexagon   **2.** parallel   **3.** decagon

4. polygon   **5.** triangle   **6.** diagonal

Tell how the common word can help you remember the mathematical term.

7. interior (of your school); interior angles

8. (stand up) straight; straight angle

Tell how the words are related.

9. diagonal; diameter   **10.** vertex; vertical

Translations

1 Graphing Translations

You can move pattern blocks by sliding them, flipping them, or turning them. Each of these moves is a type of transformation. A **transformation** is a change of position or size of a figure.

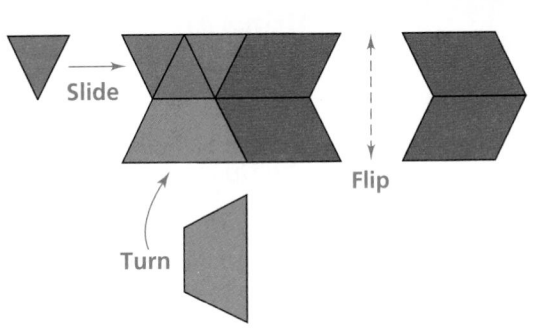

Slide

Flip

Turn

9.8.06 Represent and identify geometric figures using coordinate geometry, including those resulting from transformations.

A **translation** is a transformation that moves points the same distance and in the same direction. A figure and its translated image are congruent. You can see examples of translations or slides in wallpaper, fabric, and wrapping paper.

The figure you get after a transformation is called the **image.** To name the image of a point, you use *prime* notation. The figure at the right shows the translation of A to its image A'.

Image of A

✓ **Check Skills You'll Need**
Graph each point.

1. $A(-4, 3)$ **2.** $B(0, 2)$

3. $C(1, 4)$ **4.** $D(4, -2)$

5. $E(-2, -3)$

GO **for Help**
Lesson 1-10

🔊 **New Vocabulary**
• **transformation**
• **translation**
• **image**

1 EXAMPLE Translating a Figure

Graph the image of △KRT after a translation 5 units to the right and 3 units down.

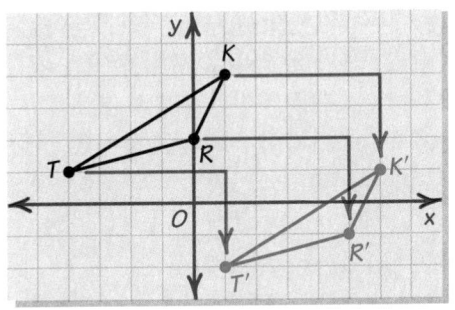

✓ Quick Check

1. On a coordinate plane, draw △KRT. Graph the image of △KRT after each translation.
   a. 4 units to the left   **b.** 5 units down
   c. 4 units to the left and 5 units down

You can describe a transformation using arrow ($\rightarrow$) notation, which describes the *mapping* of a figure onto its image.

2 EXAMPLE **Using Arrow Notation**

The movement of point *P* is both horizontal and vertical. Use arrow notation to describe this translation.

The point moves from $P(-2, 2)$ to $P'(1, -1)$, so the translation is $P(-2, 2) \rightarrow P'(1, -1)$.

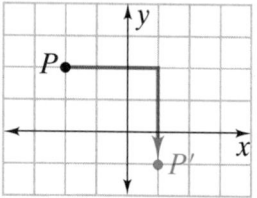

✓ **Quick Check**

2. Use arrow notation to describe a translation of $B(-1, 5)$ to $B'(3, 1)$.

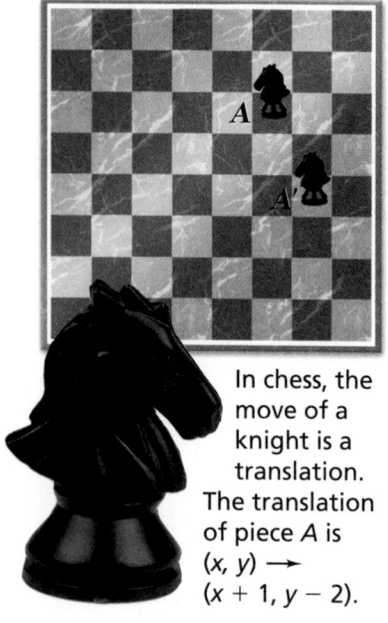

In chess, the move of a knight is a translation. The translation of piece *A* is $(x, y) \rightarrow (x + 1, y - 2)$.

You can also use arrow notation to write a general rule that describes a transformation. To write a rule for a translation, choose corresponding points on a figure and its image. Subtract the coordinates of the figure from the coordinates of its image.

3 EXAMPLE **Writing a Rule**

Write a rule to describe the translation of $\triangle PQR$ to $\triangle P'Q'R'$.

Use $P(3, 2)$ and its image $P'(-2, 5)$ to find the horizontal and vertical translations.

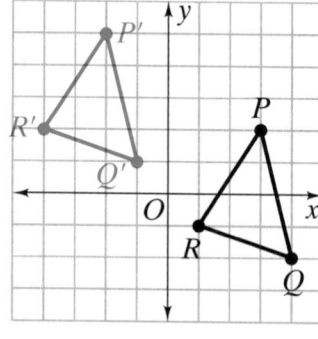

Horizontal translation: $-2 - 3 = -5$
Vertical translation: $5 - 2 = 3$

The rule is $(x, y) \rightarrow (x - 5, y + 3)$

✓ **Quick Check**

3. Write a rule to describe the translation of quadrilateral *ABCD* to quadrilateral *A'B'C'D'*.

EXERCISES

For more exercises, see *Extra Skill and Word Problem Practice.*

Practice and Problem Solving

A Practice by Example

Example 1
(page 501)

Graph the image of △QRS for the given translation.

1. 2 units to the right

2. 5 units down

3. 3 units to the right and 5 units down

4. 1 unit to the left and 3 units down

5. 2 units to the right and 1 unit up

6. 3 units to the left and 2 units up

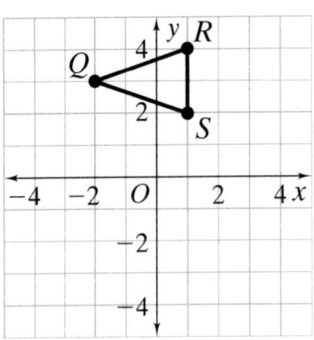

△HIJ has the coordinates given. Graph the triangle and its translation 3 units to the right and 2 units down.

7. $H(-1, 1), I(1, 4), J(1, 3)$ **8.** $H(0, 0), I(-3, -1), J(-1, -2)$

9. $H(-1, -2), I(0, 1), J(1, -2)$ **10.** $H(-4, 3), I(-2, 0), J(-4, 1)$

Use arrow notation to describe the translation.

Example 2
(page 502)

11. $A(1, 5)$ to $A'(2, 7)$ **12.** $W(-2, -6)$ to $W'(4, 9)$

13. $S(3, 3)$ to $S'(11, 1)$ **14.** $D(-9, -4)$ to $D'(0, 1)$

Example 3
(page 502)

Write a rule to describe each translation.

15.

16.

17.

18.

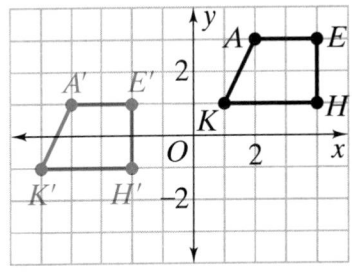

Write a description of each rule.

19. $(x, y) \rightarrow (x - 11, y + 4)$ **20.** $(x, y) \rightarrow (x + 5, y - 2)$

21. $(x, y) \rightarrow (x - 6, y - 3)$ **22.** $(x, y) \rightarrow (x + 3, y + 9)$

9-8 Translations   **503**

Complete with *horizontal* or *vertical* to make a true statement.

23. In a __?__ translation, the *y*-coordinate changes and the *x*-coordinate stays the same.

24. In a __?__ translation, the *x*-coordinate changes and the *y*-coordinate stays the same.

The endpoints of a segment are given. Graph each segment and its image for the given translation.

25. $A(0,0), B(0,5)$; 2 units left

26. $C(0,0), D(0,1)$; 1 unit up

27. $E(0,0), F(2,0)$; 4 units down

28. $G(0,0), H(-4,0)$; 4 units up

29. $J(0,0), K(5,5)$; 1 unit right

30. $L(-1,3), M(2,1)$; 5 units left

GO Online
Homework Video Tutor
Visit: PHSchool.com
Web Code: ade-0908

Write a rule to describe each translation.

31.

32.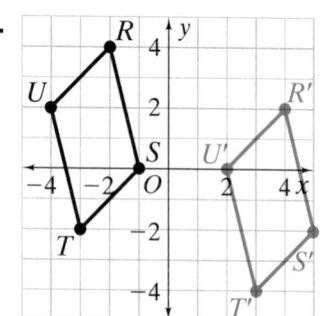

The endpoints of a segment are given. Graph each segment and its image for the given translation.

33. $N(3,3), P(-3,4)$;
3 units left, 2 units down

34. $Q(2,-1), R(-2,1)$;
2 units right, 3 units up

35. $S(4,3), T(1,-5)$;
4 units left, 1 unit up

36. $U(-4,-5), V(2,1)$;
3 units right, 2 units down

37. Translate point $T(2,5)$ 2 units to the right and 6 units up. Translate its image, point T', 4 units to the left and 1 unit down. What are the coordinates of the image of point T'?

C Challenge

38. **Writing in Math** Describe and explain the result of moving a figure *a* units horizontally and then $-a$ units horizontally.

39. **Art** You can use translations to draw three-dimensional figures. First draw a figure on graph paper. Translate the figure. Connect each vertex with its image. Use dashes for sides that are not visible. Try this, first with a rectangle; then with a triangle.

40. A rule like $(x, y) \rightarrow (2x, 2y)$ describes a dilation (see p. 308) of the coordinate plane. This dilation has center $(0,0)$ and scale factor 2.
   a. $\overline{AB}$ has endpoints $A(4,0)$ and $B(0,3)$. Describe its image, $\overline{A'B'}$, for the dilation above. How do lengths AB and $A'B'$ compare?
   b. Describe a coordinate-plane dilation that has center $(0,0)$ and scale factor $\frac{1}{2}$. Describe its effect on $\overline{AB}$ from part (a).

Multiple Choice

41. Which coordinates represent a translation of $B(-4, 1)$ 3 units to the right and 2 units down?
A. $B'(-7, 3)$　　**B.** $B'(-6, 4)$　　**C.** $B'(-1, -1)$　　**D.** $B'(-2, -4)$

42. Which points show the translation $(x, y) \rightarrow (x - 1, y + 4)$?
F. $A(4, 2), A'(5, -2)$　　　　**G.** $A(4, 2), A'(3, 6)$
H. $A(4, 2), A'(8, 1)$　　　　**J.** $A(4, 2), A'(0, 3)$

43. Quadrilateral $WXYZ$ has vertices $W(0, 0)$, $X(-4, 2)$, $Y(-4, 6)$, and $Z(0, 4)$. Quadrilateral $W'X'Y'Z'$ has vertices $W'(2, -3)$, $X'(-2, -1)$, $Y'(-2, 3)$, and $Z'(2, 1)$. Which rule describes the translation?
A. $(x, y) \rightarrow (x - 3, y + 2)$　　**B.** $(x, y) \rightarrow (x + 2, y - 3)$
C. $(x, y) \rightarrow (x - 2, y + 3)$　　**D.** $(x, y) \rightarrow (x + 3, y - 2)$

Short Response

44. You translate the graph of $y = 2x + 4$ by 3 units down and 4 units right.
　a. Write a rule to describe the translation.
　b. What is the slope of the graph of the image?

Mixed Review

Lesson 9-6

45. Make a circle graph of the data in the table.

Lesson 5-4　**Simplify each product.**

46. $\frac{3}{7} \cdot \frac{7}{9}$

47. $\frac{1}{2} \cdot \frac{8}{11}$

48. $\frac{1}{2} \cdot \frac{1}{8}$

Preferred Pizza Topping

Topping	Number of Votes
Cheese	12
Pepperoni	8
Sausage	4
Mushroom	5

✓ Checkpoint Quiz 2　　　　　　　Lessons 9-6 through 9-8

Use the circle graph.

1. Eighty people attended a catered meal. Twenty-eight people ordered fish, half ordered chicken, and twelve ordered the vegetarian meal. Which section represents each of the meals?

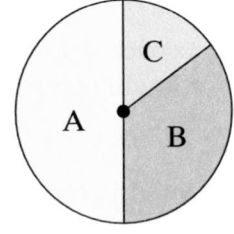

2. Determine the measure of the central angle of each section in the circle graph.

3. **Open-Ended** Draw a segment about $\frac{3}{4}$ in. long. Construct an equilateral triangle with sides of this length.

4. Graph $\overline{NR}$ with endpoints $N(2, 7)$ and $R(-4, 0)$. Then graph its image after a translation 4 units right and 3 units down.

In Chapter 6, you used geometric software to create dilations of geometric figures. You can also dilate geometric figures in a coordinate plane.

ACTIVITY

Geometry $\triangle ABC$ has vertices $A(0, 0)$, $B(-1, 2)$, and $C(3, 3)$. **Draw the triangle and its image under a dilation of scale factor 2 on the same coordinate plane.**

Step 1 The scale factor is 2. Multiply the coordinates of each vertex by 2.

$A(0, 0)$, so A' has coordinates $(0 \cdot 2, 0 \cdot 2)$, or $(0, 0)$.

$B(-1, 2)$, so B' has coordinates $(-1 \cdot 2, 2 \cdot 2)$, or $(-2, 4)$.

$C(3, 3)$, so C' has coordinates $(3 \cdot 2, 3 \cdot 2)$, or $(6, 6)$.

Step 2 Draw $\triangle ABC$ on a coordinate plane. **Step 3** Draw $\triangle A'B'C'$ with vertices $(0, 0)$, $(-2, 4)$, and $(6, 6)$.

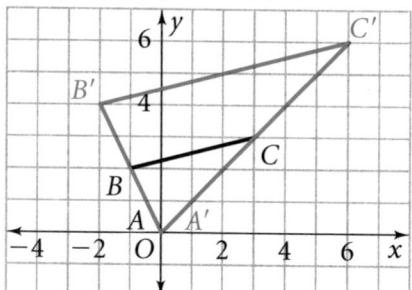

EXERCISES

Draw each figure and its image under the given dilation on the same coordinate plane.

1. $\triangle TRI$, vertices $T(-5, -5)$, $R(0, 0)$, and $I(-1, -3)$; scale factor 2

2. quadrilateral $MNPQ$, vertices $M(0, 0)$, $N(1, 4)$, $P(4, 5)$, and $Q(7, 0)$; scale factor 0.5

3. square $RECT$, vertices $R(0, 0)$, $E(2, -5)$, $C(5, 2)$, and $T(7, -3)$; scale factor 2

4. $\triangle NGL$, vertices $N(4, 4)$, $G(7, 4)$, and $L(5, 0)$; scale factor 3

Symmetry and Reflections

IL Assessment Framework

9.8.06 Represent and identify geometric figures using coordinate geometry, including those resulting from transformations.

1 Identifying Lines of Symmetry

A figure has **reflectional symmetry** when one half is a mirror image of the other half. A **line of symmetry** divides a figure with reflectional symmetry into two congruent halves.

A pattern for the back of a shirt is shown below. To make a shirt, you place the pattern on a folded piece of material, with the dashed lines of the pattern on the fold. After cutting the material, the back of the shirt will look like this.

The fold is the line of symmetry.

The shirt has one line of symmetry.

It is possible for a figure to have more than one line of symmetry.

✓ Check Skills You'll Need

Graph each line.

1. $x = 0$ **2.** $y = 0$

3. $x = 3$ **4.** $y = 2$

5. $x = -1$ **6.** $x = y$

GO for Help
Lesson 8-3

◀)) New Vocabulary

• reflectional symmetry
• line of symmetry
• reflection
• line of reflection

1 EXAMPLE Finding Lines of Symmetry

Draw the lines of symmetry. Tell how many there are.

a.

one line of symmetry

b.

six lines of symmetry

✓ Quick Check

1. Copy each figure. Draw all lines of symmetry.

a.

b.

2 | Graphing Reflections

A **reflection** is a transformation that flips a figure over a **line of reflection.** The reflected figure, or image, is congruent to the original figure. Together, an image and its reflection have line symmetry, the line of reflection being the line of symmetry.

2 EXAMPLE   Reflecting Over an Axis

Graph the image of △ABC after a reflection over the y-axis.

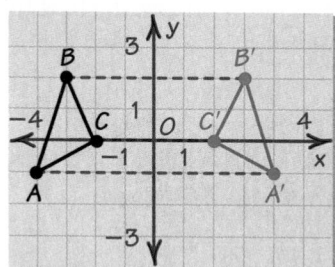

Since *A* is 4 units to the left of the *y*-axis, *A′* is 4 units to the right of the *y*-axis. Reflect the other vertices. Draw △*A′B′C′*.

✅ Quick Check

● **2.** Graph the image of △ABC after a reflection over the x-axis.

You can reflect images over lines other than the axes.

3 EXAMPLE   Reflecting Over a Line

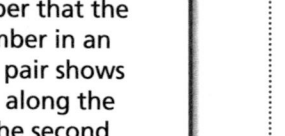

Test-Taking Tip

Remember that the first number in an ordered pair shows position along the x-axis. The second number shows position along the y-axis.

△*PQR* has vertices *P*(−1, 3), *Q*(1, 6), and *R*(4, 5). After a reflection over *y* = 2, what are the coordinates of *Q*?

  Ⓐ (−1, 1)   Ⓑ (1, −2)   Ⓒ (1, −6)   Ⓓ (4, −1)

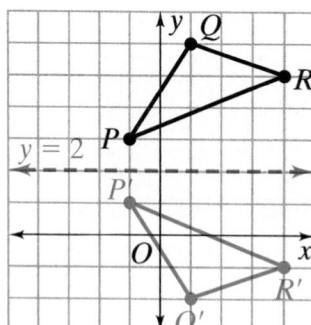

Graph *y* = 2. Since *P* is 1 unit above the red line, *P′* is 1 unit below the red line.

Reflect the other vertices. Draw △*P′Q′R′*.

Point *Q′* has coordinates (1, −2). The answer is B.

✅ Quick Check

3. Graph the image △*ABC* with vertices *A*(3, 0), *B*(2, 3), and *C*(5, −1) after a reflection over each line.

  ● **a.** *x* = 2   **b.** *y* = −1

EXERCISES

For more exercises, see *Extra Skill and Word Problem Practice.*

Practice and Problem Solving

A Practice by Example

Example 1
(page 507)

Copy each figure. Draw all lines of symmetry.

1. 2. 3.

Example 2
(page 508)

In Exercises 4–8, graph each figure and its image after a reflection over the given line.

4.

the *x*-axis

5.

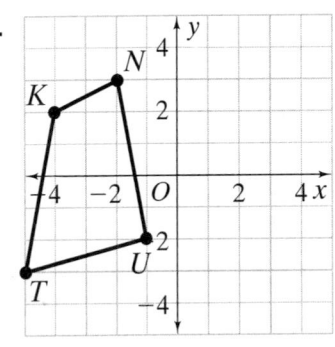

the *y*-axis

Example 3
(page 508)

6. $\triangle ABC$ with $A(2, 0)$, $B(6, 0)$, $C(2, -6)$; line $x = 1$

7. $\triangle KLM$ with $K(-1, 1)$, $L(3, 2)$, $M(0, 3)$; line $y = -1$

8. $\triangle WXY$ with $W(-1, -1)$, $X(0, 0)$, $Y(-5, 0)$; line $y = 2$

B Apply Your Skills

Draw each figure. Draw all the lines of symmetry.

9. rhombus   10. square   11. isosceles triangle

12. **Writing in Math** Can a reflection image of an angle have a measure that is different from the original angle? Explain.

Graph each point and its image after a reflection over the given line. Name the coordinates of the image.

13. $H(-8, 3)$; $y = 4$ 14. $J(-8, 3)$; $y = 2$ 15. $V(5, 0)$; $x = -2$

16. $A(2, 5)$; $y = x$ 17. $B(0, 3)$; $y = 0$ 18. $C(4, 0)$; $x = 0$

19. **Multiple Choice** What are the coordinates of the image of point $R(3, -4)$ after a reflection over the line $x = 5$?
    Ⓐ $R'(-4, 6)$ Ⓑ $R'(-4, 3)$ Ⓒ $R'(6, -4)$ Ⓓ $R'(7, -4)$

Reasoning Decide whether each statement is *always* true, *sometimes* true, or *never* true.

20. When corresponding points of an original figure and its reflection are connected, the resulting segments are all perpendicular to the line of reflection.

21. When a point is reflected over a horizontal line, the *y*-coordinate of the point stays the same.

GO Online
Homework Video Tutor
Visit: PHSchool.com
Web Code: ade-0909

The given point is reflected over line 1. Then the image is reflected over line 2. Name the coordinates of the second image.

22. $A(3, -2)$
line 1: y-axis
line 2: x-axis

23. $B(-1, 5)$
line 1: x-axis
line 2: $y = 3$

24. $C(-5, -1)$
line 1: $x = 2$
line 2: y-axis

25. a. On a coordinate plane, graph the line $y = x$ and $\triangle ABC$ with vertices $A(5, 3), B(6, -1)$, and $C(2, -1)$.
   b. To graph the image of $\triangle ABC$ over the line $y = x$, trace the axes and $\triangle ABC$ on tracing paper. Fold the paper along $y = x$. Trace over the triangle so that it makes an impression on your original graph. Label A', B', and C' appropriately and draw $\triangle A'B'C'$.
   c. Connect A to A', B to B', and C to C'. What do you notice about the line $y = x$ and these segments?
   d. Complete: The line of reflection is the __?__ of the segment that connects a point to its image.

ISAT

Test Prep

Multiple Choice

26. Which type of figure has at least two lines of symmetry?
   A. parallelogram
   C. isosceles triangle
   B. trapezoid
   D. rhombus

27. How many lines of symmetry does a rectangle have?
   F. 0   **G.** 1   **H.** 2   **J.** 4

Short Response

In Exercises 28 and 29, **(a)** state whether each statement is *always* true, *sometimes* true, or *never* true.   **(b)** Explain your reasoning.

28. When a point is reflected over a horizontal line, the x–coordinate stays the same.

29. When a point is reflected over a horizontal line and is NOT on the line, the y–coordinate stays the same.

Mixed Review

GO for Help

Lesson 9-8

The endpoints of a segment are given. Graph the segment and its image for the given translation.

30. $A(4, 3), B(5, 7)$;
3 units left, 2 units down

31. $X(0, -1), Y(2, 7)$;
2 units right, 3 units up

Lesson 8-2

Graph each equation.

32. $x + 3 = y$ **33.** $y - 8 = x$ **34.** $2y = x + 10$

Lesson 1-8

35. If six people meet, and each person shakes every other person's hand, how many handshakes are there in all?

Rotations

IL Assessment Framework

1 Graphing Rotations

A **rotation** is a transformation that turns a figure about a fixed point called the **center of rotation.** The angle measure of the rotation is the **angle of rotation.**

In the diagram, $\triangle QPR$ is rotated 90° about the center of rotation, point P. Notice that $m\angle QPQ' = 90°$ and $m\angle RPR' = 90°$. A figure and its rotation image are congruent.

In the diagram, the direction of the rotation is *counterclockwise*. All rotations in this book will be counterclockwise.

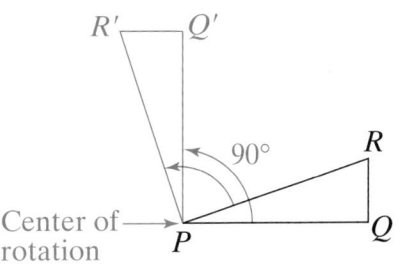

You can graph a rotation on a coordinate plane.

1 EXAMPLE   Finding a Rotation Image

Find the vertices of the image of $\triangle ABC$ after a rotation of 180° about the origin.

    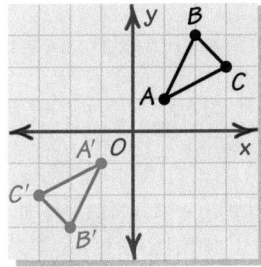

Step 1 Draw $\triangle ABC$. Place a piece of tracing paper over the graph. Trace the vertices of the triangle, the x-axis, and the y-axis. Then place your pencil at the origin to rotate the paper.

Step 2 Rotate the paper 180°. Make sure the axes line up. Mark the position of each vertex by pressing through the paper. Connect the vertices of the rotated triangle.

The vertices of the image are $A'(-1, -1)$, $B'(-2, -3)$, and $C'(-3, -2)$.

9.8.06 Represent and identify geometric figures using coordinate geometry, including those resulting from transformations.

☑ **Check Skills You'll Need**

Graph each triangle.

1. $A(1, 3), B(4, 1),$ $C(3, -2)$

2. $J(-2, 1), K(1, -3),$ $L(1, 4)$

3. $X(4, 0), Y(0, 2)$ $Z(-2, -3)$

GO **for Help**
Lesson 1-10

🔊 **New Vocabulary**

- rotation
- center of rotation
- angle of rotation
- rotational symmetry

✓ Quick Check

1. Copy the graph of △ABC in Example 1. Draw its image after a rotation of 90° about the origin. Name the coordinates of the vertices of the image.

2 | Identifying Rotational Symmetry

A figure has **rotational symmetry** if you can rotate it 180°, or less, so that its image matches the original figure. The angle (or its measure) through which the figure rotates is the angle of rotation.

The wheel at the right has rotational symmetry. You can turn the wheel from its original position to four other positions (five positions in all) and its picture will be as you see here. The smallest such turn moves A to A'. The angle of rotation is 360° ÷ 5, or 72°.

2 EXAMPLE   Real-World 🌐 Problem Solving

Botany **Judging from appearance, state whether the flower has rotational symmetry. If so, what is the angle of rotation?**

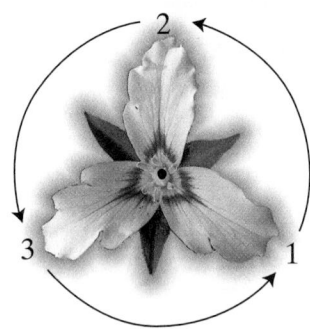

> The flower can match itself in 3 positions.
>
> The pattern repeats in 3 equal intervals. 360° ÷ 3 = 120°

The figure has rotational symmetry. The angle of rotation is 120°.

✓ Quick Check

2. Judging from appearance, tell whether each figure has rotational symmetry. If so, what is the angle of rotation?

a.   b.   c.

A Practice by Example

Example 1
(page 511)

GO for Help

In Exercises 1–8, graph each figure and its image after a rotation of
(a) 180° and (b) 90° about the origin.

1.

2.
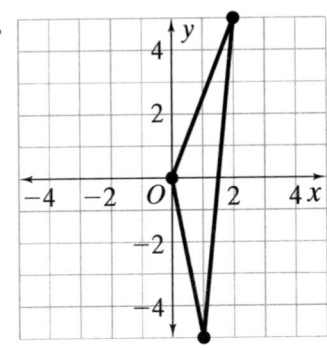

3. point $D(-1, -3)$

4. point $E(3, 2)$

5. $\triangle KLM$ with $K(3, 0)$,
$L(2, 4)$, $M(2, 2)$

6. $\triangle STU$ with $S(0, -4)$,
$T(-4, -4)$, $U(-4, -3)$

7. $\triangle CDE$ with $C(-2, 0)$,
$D(-3, 5)$, $E(-1, 2)$

8. $\triangle GHI$ with $G(-4, -1)$,
$H(-2, -5)$, $I(-2, -1)$

Example 2
(page 512)

🌐 Natural Science Judging from appearance, tell whether each figure
has rotational symmetry. If so, what is the angle of rotation?

9.

10.

11.

12.

B Apply Your Skills

13. The vertices of a triangle are $V(0, 0)$, $W(2, 5)$, and $X(1, 5)$. On
separate coordinate planes, graph the triangle and its images after
rotations of (a) 90° and (b) 180° about $(1, 1)$.

14. Writing in Math Describe something in your classroom that has
rotational symmetry. What is the angle of rotation?

In Exercises 15–18, does the figure have rotational symmetry? If so, what is the angle of rotation?

15. equilateral triangle

16. rectangle

17. regular pentagon

18. trapezoid

19. For Exercises 15–18, tell (a) whether each figure has line symmetry and (b) the number of lines of symmetry.

Each figure below is an image formed by rotating the figure at the left. What is each angle of rotation?

20. **21.** **22.**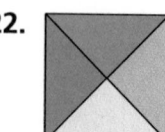

C Challenge

23. △*JKL* has vertices *J*(4, 4), *K*(3, 2) and *L*(5, 1).
  a. Graph its image, △*J'K'L'*, after a rotation of 90° about the origin. Name the coordinates of the vertices of the image.
  b. Graph the image of △*J'K'L'* after a reflection over the *y*-axis.

24. Reasoning Is a rotation of 180° the same as a reflection over the *y*-axis? Justify your answer.

ISAT

Test Prep

Multiple Choice

25. Which letter has rotational symmetry?
  A. H **B.** J **C.** K **D.** L

26. Which number has rotational symmetry?
  F. 2 **G.** 4 **H.** 6 **J.** 8

27. Which object does NOT have rotational symmetry?
  A. daisy **B.** ceiling fan **C.** glove **D.** picture frame

Short Response

28. Which types of triangles have rotational symmetry? Explain.

Mixed Review

Lesson 9-9

The vertices of △*ABC* are *A*(5, 6), *B*(0, 3), and *C*(3, 2). Graph △*ABC* and its image after a reflection over the given line.

29. *x* = −2 **30.** *y* = −2 **31.** *x*-axis

Lesson 8-3

Find the slope of the line through each pair of points.

32. *A*(5, 9), *B*(5, 14) **33.** *E*(2, 1), *F*(8, 4) **34.** *C*(−2, 4), *D*(−7, 14)

Lesson 4-5

35. Number Sense How many three-digit numbers greater than 500 can you form using the digits 2, 6, and 8 exactly once each?

A tessellation is a repeating pattern of figures that completely covers a plane without gaps or overlaps. You can see tessellations in art, architecture, and nature.

You can use translations, rotations, and reflections to make a tessellation.

EXAMPLE

Show how the figure at the right forms a tessellation.

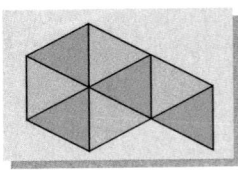

Rotate and translate the figure to cover the plane.

EXERCISES

Make multiple copies of each figure on graph paper. Determine whether each figure can form a tessellation. If it can, show the tessellation.

1.

2.

3.

4.

5. **Open-Ended** The diagram below shows how to make a shape to use as a repeating figure for a tessellation. Follow the diagram and make your own tessellation.

6. **Reasoning** Draw regular polygons with 3, 4, 5, 6, 7, and 8 sides. Which ones can you use to make a tessellation?

Sometimes for a problem, you may find it helpful to draw a diagram to keep track of the facts and actually see how the given information is related. Then you can use the diagram to help you solve the problem.

1 EXAMPLE

Shayna has nearly completed the annual Walk for Hunger. She began at the Start/Finish line and walked south for $\frac{1}{2}$ mile. Then she walked $1\frac{1}{2}$ miles east. She walked 1 mile north and then walked $\frac{1}{4}$ mile west. She turned right and walked $\frac{1}{4}$ mile. Then she turned left and walked $1\frac{1}{4}$ miles. Then she walked $\frac{1}{2}$ mile south. How far is it directly back to the Start/Finish line?

A. $\frac{1}{4}$ mile **B.** $\frac{1}{2}$ mile **C.** $1\frac{1}{4}$ miles **D.** $1\frac{1}{2}$ miles

Draw a diagram on grid paper if possible. Label each segment with its distance. If you draw the diagram carefully, it will show that Shayna is $\frac{1}{4}$ mile from the Start/Finish line. The correct choice is A.

2 EXAMPLE

The endpoints of the diameter of a circle are at $(-4, 5)$ and $(4, 5)$ in a coordinate plane. At what points does the circle intersect the y-axis?

F. $(0, 0), (0, 8)$ **G.** $(0, 1), (0, 8)$ **H.** $(0, 0), (0, 9)$ **J.** $(0, 1), (0, 9)$

On grid paper locate the given points $(-4, 5)$ and $(4, 5)$. Sketch the diameter. Locate its midpoint, $(0, 5)$, the center of the circle. The radius is 4. Sketch the circle. The circle must intersect the y-axis 4 units above and below $(0, 5)$. The points of intersection are $(0, 1)$ and $(0, 9)$, choice J.

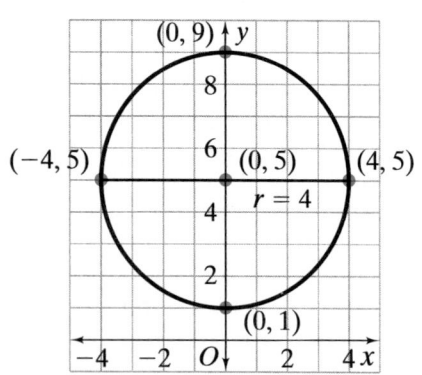

EXERCISES

1. In Example 1, how far has Shayna walked?
   A. $4\frac{1}{4}$ miles **B.** $4\frac{1}{2}$ miles **C.** $5\frac{1}{4}$ miles **D.** $5\frac{1}{2}$ miles

2. A triangle has vertices $(-2, 1), (5, 1),$ and $(0, 6)$. What is its area?
   F. $17\frac{1}{2}$ units^2 **G.** 21 units^2 **H.** 35 units^2 **J.** 42 units^2

Chapter Review

Vocabulary Review

adjacent angles (p. 469)
alternate interior angles (p. 470)
angle bisector (p. 497)
angle of rotation (p. 511)
center of rotation (p. 511)
central angle (p. 491)
circle (p. 490)
complementary (p. 469)
congruent angles (p. 469)
congruent figures (p. 484)
corresponding angles (p. 470)
image (p. 501)

line (p. 462)
line of reflection (p. 508)
line of symmetry (p. 507)
parallel (p. 463)
perpendicular bisector (p. 496)
perpendicular lines (p. 496)
plane (p. 462)
point (p. 462)
polygon (p. 474)
ray (p. 462)
reflection (p. 508)
reflectional symmetry (p. 507)

regular polygon (p. 476)
rotation (p. 511)
rotational symmetry (p. 512)
segment (p. 462)
segment bisector (p. 496)
skew (p. 463)
supplementary (p. 469)
transformation (p. 501)
translation (p. 501)
transversal (p. 470)
vertical angles (p. 469)

Match the vocabulary terms on the right with their descriptions on the left.

1. Angles that have the same measure, are opposite each other, and are formed by two intersecting lines

2. A flip of a figure over a line of reflection

3. A __?__ divides a figure with reflectional symmetry in half.

4. An angle whose vertex is the center of a circle

5. A change of position or size of a figure

6. A location in space

7. In a plane, all points the same distance from a given point

8. A line that intersects two other lines at different points

a. central angle
b. line of symmetry
c. reflection
d. transformation
e. vertical angles
f. transversal
g. point
h. circle

For: Vocabulary quiz
Web Code: adj-0951

Skills and Concepts

9-1 Objectives

▼ To name basic geometric figures (p. 462)

▼ To recognize intersecting lines, parallel lines, and skew lines (p. 463)

A **point** is a position in space. All geometric figures are made up of points. A **line** is a series of points that extend in two directions without end. A **segment** is a part of a line and has two endpoints. A **ray** is a part of a line with exactly one endpoint. An angle is two rays that intersect at their endpoints.

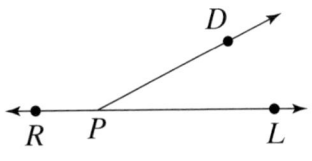

Name the following in the figure above.

9. 3 angles   10. 3 rays   11. a line   12. 4 points   13. 4 segments

9-2 Objectives

▼ To identify adjacent and vertical angles (p. 469)

▼ To relate angles formed by parallel lines and a transversal (p. 470)

Adjacent angles share a vertex and a side but no points in their interiors. **Vertical angles** are formed by intersecting lines and are **congruent.** If parallel lines are crossed by a **transversal** their **corresponding angles** are congruent. **Alternate interior angles** formed by a transversal and parallel lines are also congruent.

In the diagram at the right, m ∥ n.

14. Name all angles congruent to ∠1.

15. Name two pairs of supplementary angles.

16. Name all pairs of corresponding angles.

17. Name all pairs of alternate interior angles.

18. If $m \angle 2 = 75°$, find the measures of all the other angles.

9-3 and 9-5 Objectives

▼ To classify triangles (p. 474)

▼ To classify quadrilaterals (p. 475)

▼ To identify corresponding parts of congruent triangles (p. 484)

▼ To determine whether triangles are congruent (p. 485)

A **polygon** is a closed figure with at least three sides. Polygons with the same size and shape are **congruent.** A triangle can be classified by its angles and its sides. You can show two triangles are congruent using **Side-Side-Side, Side-Angle-Side,** and **Angle-Side-Angle.** You can classify some quadrilaterals as parallelograms, rectangles, squares, rhombuses, or trapezoids.

Use the most precise name for each figure described.

19. a triangle with all sides congruent

20. a parallelogram with all sides congruent and four 90° angles

21. a triangle with all acute angles and exactly two congruent sides

22. a quadrilateral with exactly one pair of parallel sides

List the congruent corresponding parts of each of the triangles below. Write a congruence statement (and reason) for the triangles.

23.

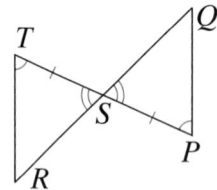

24.

Drawing a diagram can help you visualize a problem.

25. A house is to be built on a lot 70 ft wide by 100 ft deep. The shorter side of the lot faces the street. The house must be set back from the street at least 25 ft. It must be 20 ft from the back lot line and 10 ft from each side lot line. What are the maximum length and width of the house?

You can use these formulas to find the circumference of a circle:
$$C = \pi d \text{ and } C = 2\pi r.$$
There are 360° in a circle. An angle whose vertex is the center of a circle is a **central angle.**

26. Find the circumference of a circle with a diameter of 14 cm.

27. Television Programming Suppose a survey indicates that at 8 P.M. 40% of viewers watched channel X, 25% watched channel Y, and 35% watched channel Z. Make a circle graph of the data.

You can use a compass and straightedge to construct congruent segments, congruent angles, **segment bisectors,** and **angle bisectors.**

Draw △CDE with an obtuse ∠D.

28. Construct the bisector of ∠D.

29. Construct the perpendicular bisector of $\overline{DE}$.

9-8, 9-9, and 9-10 Objectives

▼ To graph translations (p. 501)

▼ To describe translations (p. 502)

▼ To identify a line of symmetry (p. 507)

▼ To graph a reflection of a geometric figure (p. 508)

▼ To graph rotations (p. 511)

▼ To identify rotational symmetry (p. 512)

A **transformation** is a change of position or size of a figure. The figure after the transformation is called the **image.** You can transform figures in a plane by a **translation,** a **reflection,** or a **rotation.**

What is the image of point $A(7, -2)$ after each transformation?

30. 4 units right, 3 units up   **31.** reflection over the y-axis

32. rotation of 90° about $(0, 0)$ **33.** reflection over the line $y = -1$

34. How do translations, reflections, and rotations affect the size and shape of an image? Explain.

Chapter Test

Go Online
PHSchool.com
For: Chapter test
Web Code: ada-0952

Use the diagram to name the following.

1. all segments containing point G

2. all pairs of vertical angles

3. all rays containing point M

4. a line containing point T

Use the diagram to name the following.

5. four segments that intersect $\overline{AB}$

6. three segments parallel to $\overline{AB}$

For Exercises 7 and 8, name all possible polygons for each description.

7. quadrilateral with at least one pair of parallel sides and at least two right angles

8. quadrilateral with one diagonal that divides it into two congruent equilateral triangles

9. Find the perimeter of an equilateral triangle that has a side measure of 60 cm.

10. Find the perimeter of a square that has a side measure of 60 cm.

11. The perimeter of a rectangle is 58 cm. One side is 18 cm. Find the lengths of the other three sides.

A segment has endpoints $A(-3, -6)$ and $M(-3, -4)$. Find the coordinates of the endpoints after each transformation.

12. a translation of 4 units right and 3 units up

13. a reflection over the y-axis

14. a rotation of 90° about the origin

15. Draw a segment. Construct its perpendicular bisector.

16. Draw an obtuse angle. Construct its angle bisector.

Use the diagram for Exercises 17 and 18.

17. If $m\angle 2 = 130°$, find $m\angle 4$.

18. **Writing in Math** Describe how you can find $m\angle 1$ if you know $m\angle 2$.

19. **Statistics** Forty two-year-old children were asked to name their favorite color. Five chose yellow, seven chose blue, and fourteen chose red. The rest chose other colors.
    a. To make a circle graph, what should be the measure of the central angle representing blue, red, and yellow? Round to the nearest degree.
    b. Create a circle graph for the information.

20. If $\overline{AB} \cong \overline{CD}$, $\angle A \cong \angle D$, and $\angle B \cong \angle C$, what method can you use to show that $\triangle ABE \cong \triangle DCF$?

21. **Open-Ended** Draw and describe a figure that has rotational symmetry.

22. a. The measures of two angles of a triangle are 50° and 35°. What is the measure of the third angle?
    b. Classify the triangle by its angles.

23. $\triangle CAB \cong \triangle DEB$. Find as many angle measures and side lengths as you can.

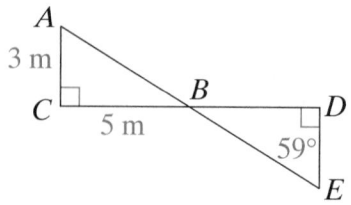

ISAT Test Prep

READING COMPREHENSION

Reading Comprehension Read each passage below. Then answer the questions on the basis of what is *stated* or *implied* in the passage.

> **A Day in a Life** A market research firm studied the activities of a large group of people during a 24-hour day. The firm then found their average numbers of hours for certain activities. It found people spent 8 hours sleeping, 6 hours working, 3 hours on leisure activities, 1 hour eating, and the rest of the day on other activities.

1. On the average, how many hours did people spend daily doing other activities?
   - (A) 3 h
   - (B) 4 h
   - (C) 5 h
   - (D) 6 h

2. On the average, how many hours did people spend sleeping each week?
   - (E) 7 h
   - (F) 8 h
   - (G) 48 h
   - (H) 56 h

3. A circle graph for the daily activities would show how many regions?
   - (A) 4
   - (B) 5
   - (C) 6
   - (D) 8

4. In a circle graph for the daily activities, what would be the measure of the central angle for time spent working?
   - (E) 6°
   - (F) 45°
   - (G) 90°
   - (H) 120°

5. In a circle graph for the daily activities, what region would be half the size of another region?
   - (A) Working
   - (B) Leisure activities
   - (C) Eating
   - (D) Other activities

> **In Line With New Friends** Anna had doubts about her first day at the new school, but they faded quickly when she found herself next to Biff and Carly at lunch. They quickly discovered that Anna was the new girl who had moved into the house that sits between theirs on Poplar Road. Anna watched Biff scratch a line on a napkin. "Look, Anna. My house is here, at *B*. Carly's is here at *C*. Carly's is five times as far from my house as your house is. She's 100 yards away from you. Guess that means you're going to have to be my next best friend!"

Let *A*, *B*, and *C* represent the homes of Anna, Biff, and Carly, respectively.

6. Which statements are true?
   - I. *A*, *B*, and *C* are all on Poplar Road.
   - II. *B* is between *A* and *C*.
   - III. *A* is closer to *B* than to *C*.

   - (E) I only
   - (F) I and III only
   - (G) II and III only
   - (H) I, II, and III

7. How far apart are *A* and *C*?
   - (A) 25 yd
   - (B) 50 yd
   - (C) 100 yd
   - (D) 125 yd

8. How far apart are *B* and *C*? Show your work.

9. About how long did it take for Anna's doubts about her first day at the new school to fade?
   - (E) 1 h
   - (F) 4 h
   - (G) 8 h
   - (H) 1 day

Circle Riding

Applying Circles Have you ever ridden on a Ferris wheel? Since its introduction in 1893, millions of people worldwide have enjoyed riding Ferris wheels. The basic structure of Ferris wheels remains quite similar to the one George W. Ferris created.

The First Ferris Wheel

George W. Ferris built his ride for the 1893 World's Fair in Chicago. It was an instant success.

Each car held 60 people.

Ticket Sales

The ride sold more than $725,000 worth of tickets during the exposition.

Activity

Use the information on these two pages to answer these questions.

1. How far does a rider travel in one turn of each Ferris wheel?

2. For each wheel, estimate the number of turns needed for a rider to travel one mile.

3. Tickets for a ride on George W. Ferris's wheel cost $.50.
   a. At least how many tickets were sold?
   b. Suppose every ticket-holder rode for two turns of the wheel. At least how many turns did the wheel have to make?

4. Cosmo Clock 21 makes one rotation in 15 min. Find your car's location and the angle of rotation after the given time.
   a. 3 min   b. 5 min   c. 9 min   d. 12 min

5. **Writing in Math** Explain why 28 · 60 more people could ride at one time on the first Ferris wheel than on Cosmo Clock 21.

Ferris Wheel Statistics

Measure	First Ferris Wheel	Cosmo Clock 21
Diameter (ft)	250	328
Height, including base (ft)	264	369
Number of Passenger Cars	36	60
Number of People per Car	60	8

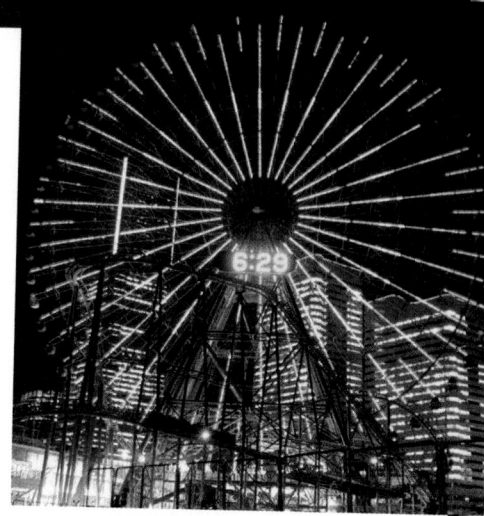

The Biggest Ride

With a maximum capacity of 480 riders, Cosmo Clock 21, in Yokohama, Japan, holds more riders than any other operating Ferris wheel. Even so, waiting time for this attraction is often more than one hour.

Go Online
PHSchool.com

For: Information about Ferris wheels
Web Code: ade-0953

What You've Learned

 Assessment Framework

- **8.8.12:** In Chapter 7, you learned to solve multi-step equations and inequalities using inverse operations.

- **8.8.10:** In Chapter 8, you graphed and solved linear equations and inequalities.

- **9.8.11:** In Chapter 9, you learned how to classify polygons and identify corresponding parts of congruent triangles.

Check Your Readiness **GO for Help** to the Lesson in green.

Finding the Areas of Rectangles and Squares (Geometric Formulas, p. 802)

Find the area of each figure.

1.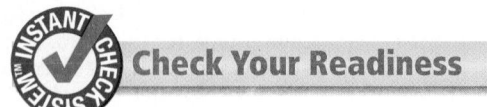
6 m
6 m

2.
2.5 in.
8 in.

3.
5 cm
9 cm

Simplifying Expressions With Exponents (Lesson 4-7)

Simplify each product.

4. $5 \cdot 3^2$ **5.** $3.14 \cdot 5^2$ **6.** $6 \cdot 12^2$ **7.** $4^2 \cdot 3$ **8.** $10^2 \cdot 3$ **9.** $3.14 \cdot 12^2$

Multiplying by a Fraction (Lesson 5-4)

Find each product.

10. $\frac{1}{2} \cdot 12$

11. $\frac{1}{2} \cdot 13 \cdot 3$

12. $\frac{1}{2}(10 + 8)$

13. $\frac{1}{2} \cdot 20x$

14. $\frac{1}{2} \cdot 5x \cdot 2x$

15. $\frac{1}{2}(10)(6 + 5)$

16. $\frac{1}{2}(62)(30 + 14)$

17. $\frac{1}{3}(20)(35 + 40)$

18. $\frac{1}{3}(3)(5 + 3)$

Finding the Circumferences of Circles (Lesson 9-6)

Find the circumference of each circle. Use 3.14 for π.

19. $d = 50$ yd

20. $r = 100$ m

21. $d = 5.5$ in.

Area and Volume

Chapter 10

LESSONS

 Key Vocabulary

- altitude (p. 527)
- altitude of a triangle (p. 533)
- area (p. 526)
- cone (p. 545)
- cubic unit (p. 563)
- cylinder (p. 545)
- lateral area (p. 552)
- net (p. 546)
- prism (p. 545)
- pyramid (p. 545)
- slant height (p. 558)
- space figure (p. 545)
- sphere (p. 545)
- surface area (p. 551)
- volume (p. 563)

What You'll Learn Next

(IL) Assessment Framework

In this chapter, you will learn how to

- **7.8.02:** Find the areas of figures.
- **7.8.04:** Find the surface areas of space figures.
- **7.8.04:** Find the volumes of space figures.
- **7.8.02:** Solve a problem by making a model.

 Activity Lab Applying what you learn, on pages 584–585 you will solve problems about playing fields.

Area: Parallelograms

IL Assessment Framework

7.8.02 Solve problems involving perimeter/circumference and area of polygons, circles, and composite figures using diagrams, models, and grids or by measuring or using given formulas.

✓ Check Skills You'll Need

Use $A = \ell w$ and find the third value.

1. $A = 54$ in.^{2}, $w = 6$ in.

2. $\ell = 35$ m, $w = 7$ m

3. $A = 25$ cm^2, $\ell = 2.5$ cm

4. $\ell = 7.2$ ft, $w = 7.2$ ft

 for Help
Lesson 3-4

🔊 **New Vocabulary**

• area

• altitude

 Finding Areas of Rectangles

Activity

Discovering an Area Formula

1. Use a 3 in.-by-5 in. index card. Find the area of the card.

2. Draw a line from one vertex to a point on another side to create a triangle. Cut along that line.

3. Use the pieces to form a parallelogram that is not a rectangle.

4. What is the area of your parallelogram? Explain.

The **area** of a figure is the number of square units it encloses. The rectangle outlined in red encloses 8 square units, each with area 1 cm^2 (1 square centimeter). So, the area of the rectangle is 8 cm^2.

You can use the formula $A = bh$ to find the area of a rectangle, where b is the length of one side and h is the length of the other. For the rectangle above, $A = 4 \cdot 2 = 8$. So, the area is 8 cm^2.

When you find area, the dimensions must be in the same unit.

---

1 EXAMPLE Real-World 🌎 Problem Solving

Parades Find the area of the marching band's rectangular banner.

Step 1 Change the units so that they are the same.

  1 yd = 3 ft   **Change 1 yard to feet.**

Step 2 Find the area.

  $A = bh$ **Use the formula for the area of a rectangle.**

  $= (7)(3)$ **Replace b and h with the dimensions 7 and 3.**

  $= 21$ **Simplify.**

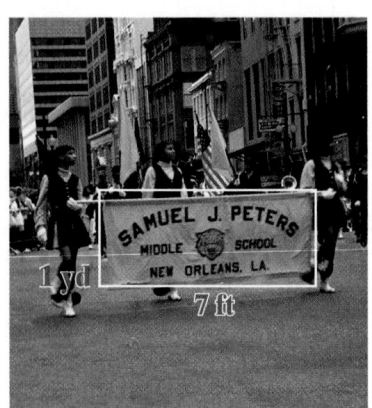

The area of the banner is 21 ft^2.

✓ Quick Check

1. Find the area of each rectangle.

a.

1 m

10 cm

b.

2 yd

2 ft

  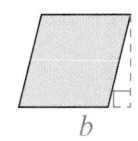

---

2 | Finding Areas of Parallelograms

A rectangle is a special kind of parallelogram. The formula for the area of a parallelogram follows from the formula for the area of a rectangle. The height h of a parallelogram is the length of an *altitude*.

An **altitude** is a line segment perpendicular to the line containing a base of the figure and drawn from the side opposite that base.

Key Concepts | Area of a Parallelogram

The area of a parallelogram is the product of any base length b and the corresponding height h.

b

h

h

b

h

b

$$A = bh$$

Vocabulary Tip

For any base in a figure, the corresponding height is the length of an altitude to that base.

---

2 EXAMPLE | Finding Area of a Parallelogram

Find the area of each parallelogram.

8 in.

3.5 in.

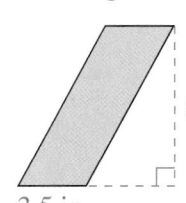

8 in.

3.5 in.

$A = bh$ **area formula**

$= (3.5)(8)$ **Substitute.**

$= 28$ **Simplify.**

The area of each is 28 in.²

Online
active math

For: Area Activity
Use: Interactive Textbook, 10-1

✓ Quick Check

2. Find the area of each parallelogram.

a.

3 m

2 m

b.

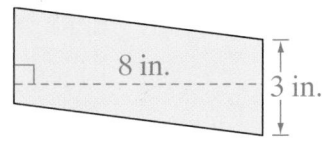

8 in.

3 in.

c. How do the areas of two parallelograms compare when the dimensions of one are twice the dimensions of the other?

EXERCISES

For more exercises, see *Extra Skill and Word Problem Practice.*

Practice and Problem Solving

A Practice by Example

Example 1
(page 526)

GO for Help

Example 2
(page 527)

Find the area of each parallelogram.

1.
3 yd
15 ft

2.
100 cm
1 m

3.
4 ft
1 yd

4.
23 ft
17 ft / 16 ft

5.
2 m
1.5 m

6.
0.5 m
20 cm

7.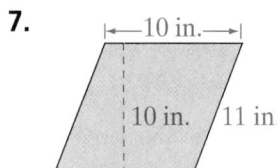
10 in.
10 in. / 11 in.

8.
5.5 ft
8 ft
5 ft

9.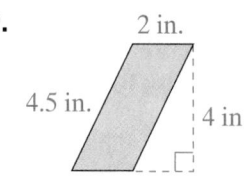
2 in.
4.5 in.
4 in.

10. Find the area of a parallelogram with the given dimensions.
 a. base 3 cm, height 5 cm **b.** base 9 cm, height 15 cm
 c. How do the areas of two parallelograms compare when the dimensions of one are three times the dimensions of the other?

B Apply Your Skills **11.** **Sports** A football field is 300 ft long, from goal line to goal line, and 160 ft wide, from sideline to sideline. What is the area of a football field?

Find the area of each parallelogram.

12.
10,560 ft
2 mi

13.
7 cm
20 mm

14.
5 m
200 cm

15.
22 in.
30 in.
77 in.

Coordinate Geometry The vertices of a parallelogram are given. Draw each parallelogram. Find its area.

GO Online
Homework Video Tutor
Visit: PHSchool.com
Web Code: ade-1001

16. $A(0,0), B(3,0), C(4,3), D(1,3)$

17. $W(-2,0), X(-3,3), Y(2,0), Z(1,3)$

18. Find the area of the figure at the right. Assume that all angles are right angles.

2 m 2 m 2 m
3 m 4 m
7 m

19. Writing in Math The two parallelograms below have the same perimeter. Are the areas the same? Explain.

3 m

2 m

3 m

2 m 1.5 m

C Challenge

Reasoning In Exercises 20 and 21, find the ratio of the areas of the parallelograms (smaller to larger). Justify each answer.

20. The bases are the same length. The height of one parallelogram is twice the height of the other.

21. The height and the length of a base of one parallelogram are both twice those of the other parallelogram.

22. Open-Ended You want to make a 400-ft^2 vegetable garden. You plan to build a fence to keep the rabbits out. To spend the least amount of money, you want to use as little fencing as possible.
a. Draw and list three possible dimensions for your garden.
b. Which of the three will need the least amount of fencing?

Find the area of each shaded region. Assume that all angles that appear to be right angles are right angles.

23.

8 ft

4 ft | 2 ft | 2 ft | 2 ft | 2 ft

24.

7 m

2.8 m 2.8 m

2.8 m 2.8 m

4 m

100 ft
42 ft
30 ft
30 ft
70 ft | 60 ft
10 ft
20 ft

25. a. Landscaping Find the area of the yard at the left. Assume that all angles that appear to be right angles are right angles.
b. How many square yards of sod do you need to cover the yard?
c. One bag of fertilizer covers approximately 2,000 ft^2. How many bags should you buy to cover the yard?

ISAT

Test Prep

Multiple Choice

26. Square *ABCD* has perimeter *x* units. What is its area in terms of *x*?
A. $\frac{x^2}{16}$ units^2 **B.** $4x^2$ units^2 **C.** units^2 **D.** units^2

27. A parallelogram has base 18 cm and height 9 cm. What is its area?
F. 27 cm^2 **G.** 81 cm^2 **H.** 162 cm^2 **J.** 324 cm^2

28. What is the side length of a square with area 16 cm^2?
A. 256 cm^2 **B.** 32 cm^2 **C.** 8 cm **D.** 4 cm

29. A rectangle has base *r* and height *s*. Which formula gives its area?
F. $= {}^2$ **G.** $= {}^2$ **H.** = **J.** $= 2 + 2$

Political Sign Regulations Set

The City Council issued the following regulations for political signs in the upcoming election:
1. Only one sign may be posted on a single lot of land.

2. Sign areas may not exceed 32 ft².
3. Signs cannot be more than 6 ft in height.
4. All signs must be removed no later than 7 days after the election.

Mixed Review

Lesson 9-10   **The endpoints of a segment are given. Graph each segment and its image after a rotation of 90° about the origin.**

32. $A(5, 8), B(2, 4)$ **33.** $C(0, 3), D(3, -5)$ **34.** $E(-2, -3), F(-2, 4)$

Lesson 9-2   **35.** Find the measures of two supplementary angles if the difference of their measures is $56°$.

Lesson 5-4   **Simplify each expression.**

36. $\frac{2}{5} \cdot 2\frac{1}{2}$ **37.** $\frac{2}{5} \div 2\frac{1}{2}$ **38.** $3\frac{2}{3} \cdot \frac{3}{4}$ **39.** $3\frac{2}{3} \div \frac{3}{4}$

Math at Work

Pharmacist

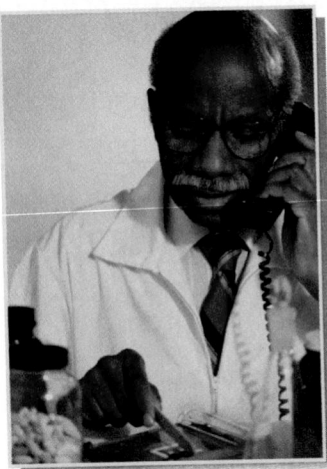

Pharmacists dispense medications. They also talk to their customers about the possible side effects of medications. To do this, they must thoroughly understand how prescription drugs are made.

Sometimes a doctor prescribes a special medication that a pharmacist must mix. The pharmacist must measure the ingredients in the exact proportions that the patient needs. In a situation such as this, mathematics is essential.

Go Online   **For:** Information about pharmacists
PHSchool.com **Web Code:** adb-2031

Activity Lab

Perimeter and Area of Similar Figures

Hands-On   For Use With Lesson 10-1

When you know the perimeter of one of two similar figures, you can find the perimeter of the other figure.

1 ACTIVITY

- **On a piece of grid paper, draw a 3 unit-by-4 unit rectangle.**
- **Draw three different rectangles, each larger than but similar to the original rectangle. Label them I, II, and III.**

1. Use your rectangles to complete a table like the one below.

Rectangle	Perimeter	Area
Original	$2(3 + 4) = 14$	$3 \cdot 4 = 12$
I	■	■
II	■	■
III	■	■

2. Use the information in the table from Question 1 to complete a table like the one below.

Rectangles	Ratio of Corresponding Sides (in simplest form)	Ratio of Perimeters (in simplest form)	Ratio of Areas (in simplest form)
I: Original	■ : ■	■ : ■	■ : ■
II: Original	■ : ■	■ : ■	■ : ■
III: Original	■ : ■	■ : ■	■ : ■

3. Use the table from Question 2.
   a. **Reasoning** How is the ratio of perimeters related to the ratio of corresponding sides? Explain.
   b. How is the ratio of areas related to the ratio of corresponding sides? Explain.
   c. Without using grid paper, find the perimeter of a rectangle similar to the original rectangle you drew but with sides half as long.
   d. Find the area of the rectangle.

When you know the area of one of two similar figures, you can use a proportion to find the area of the other figure.

Parallelogram *GRAM* is similar to parallelogram *PQNO*. Parallelogram *GRAM* has an area of 54 in.² Find the area of parallelogram *PQNO*.

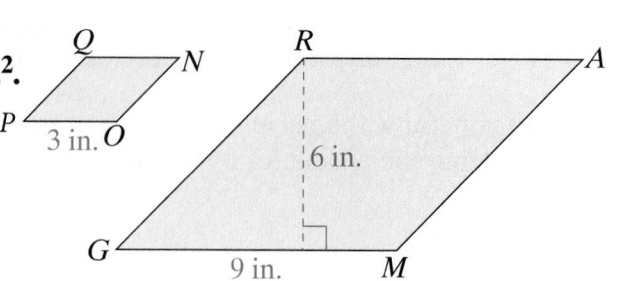

The ratio of corresponding sides is $\frac{3}{9}$, or $\frac{1}{3}$. The ratio of the areas is $\frac{1^2}{3^2}$, or $\frac{1}{9}$.

$\frac{1}{9} = \frac{A}{54}$ **Write a proportion.**

$9A = 54$ **Use cross-products.**

$A = 54 \div 9$ **Solve for A.**

$= 6$

● The area of parallelogram *PQNO* is 6 in.²

EXERCISES

Each pair of parallelograms is similar. Find the perimeter of each parallelogram.

1.

2.
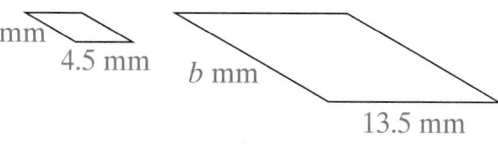

Each pair of parallelograms is similar. Find the ratio of perimeters and the ratio of areas for each pair.

3.

4.
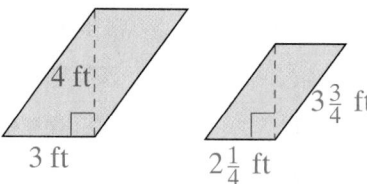

Each pair of parallelograms is similar. Find the area of the larger parallelogram.

5.

6.
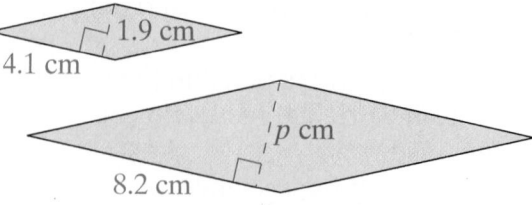

Area: Triangles and Trapezoids

IL Assessment Framework

1 Finding Areas of Triangles

A diagonal divides a parallelogram into two congruent triangles.

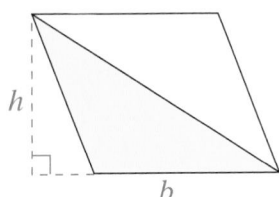

You can see that the area of a triangle is half the area of a parallelogram. An **altitude of a triangle** is the perpendicular segment from a vertex of a triangle to the line containing the opposite side. The height is the length of the altitude.

> **7.8.02** Solve problems involving perimeter/ circumference and area of polygons, circles, and composite figures using diagrams, models, and grids or by measuring or using given formulas.

✔ **Check Skills You'll Need**

Find each product.

1. $\frac{1}{2} \cdot 16$ **2.** $\frac{1}{2} \cdot 14 \cdot 6$

3. $\frac{1}{2} \cdot 5 \cdot 15$

4. $\frac{1}{2} \cdot 2\frac{1}{2} \cdot 8$

GO **for Help**
Lesson 5-4

◀)) **New Vocabulary**
• altitude of a triangle

Key Concepts   **Area of a Triangle**

The area of a triangle equals half the product of any base length b and the corresponding height h.

$$A = \frac{1}{2}bh$$

---

1 EXAMPLE   Finding Area of a Triangle

Find the area of the triangle.

$A = \frac{1}{2}bh$ **Use the formula for the area of a triangle.**

$= \frac{1}{2} \cdot 8 \cdot 3$ **Replace b with 8 and h with 3.**

$= 12$ **Simplify.**

The area is 12 cm^2.

✔ **Quick Check**

1. Find the area of each triangle.

a.

b.

2 **EXAMPLE** <u>Real-World</u> **Problem Solving**

Gridded Response **How much siding does a builder need to cover the side of the house shown at the left?**

Area of triangle	Area of rectangle
$A = \frac{1}{2}bh$	$A = bh$
$= \frac{1}{2} \cdot 16 \cdot 9$	$= 16 \cdot 10$
$= 72$	$= 160$

Add to find the total: $72 + 160 = 232$.

The builder needs 232 ft^2 of siding.

✓ Quick Check

2. Find the area of the shaded figure.

---

2 **Finding Areas of Trapezoids**

 not in this position

A diagonal divides a trapezoid into two triangles. Notice that the triangles have the same height but different bases.

You can add the areas of the triangles to find the area of the trapezoid.

Area of $\triangle ABC$	Area of $\triangle ADC$
$A = \frac{1}{2}bh$	$A = \frac{1}{2}bh$
$= \frac{1}{2} \cdot 9 \cdot 4$	$= \frac{1}{2} \cdot 6 \cdot 4$
$= 18$	$= 12$

The areas of the two triangles are 18 cm^2 and 12 cm^2. The area of the trapezoid is the sum of the areas of the two triangles, 30 cm^2.

You can use this information to find a formula for the area of a trapezoid.

Test-Taking Tip

To find the area of an irregular figure, you may need to use more than one area formula. Make sure you know the area formulas for triangles, parallelograms, and trapezoids.

In a trapezoid, the parallel sides are its bases. For the figure at the right the bases are b_1 and b_2. The height is h.

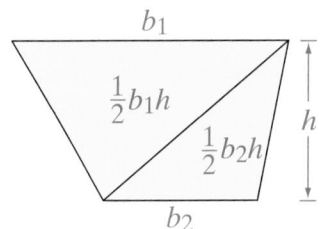

The area of the trapezoid is $\frac{1}{2}b_1h + \frac{1}{2}b_2h$.

By using the Distributive Property, you can see that

$\frac{1}{2}b_1h + \frac{1}{2}b_2h$ is $\frac{1}{2}h(b_1 + b_2)$.

So, the area of the trapezoid is $\frac{1}{2}h(b_1 + b_2)$.

Key Concepts   **Area of a Trapezoid**

The area of a trapezoid is half the product of the height and the sum of the lengths of the bases.

$$A = \tfrac{1}{2}h(b_1 + b_2)$$

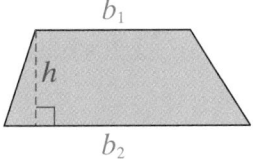

---

3 EXAMPLE   **Real-World 🌐 Problem Solving**

Erie Canal **The Erie Canal opened in 1825 and was hailed as an engineering marvel. Below is a cross section of the Erie Canal. Find the area of the trapezoidal cross section.**

$A = \frac{1}{2}h(b_1 + b_2)$ **Use the formula for the area of a trapezoid.**

$A = \frac{1}{2} \cdot 4(28 + 40)$ **Replace h with 4, b_1 with 28, and b_2 with 40.**

$\quad = \frac{1}{2} \cdot 4(68)$ **Simplify.**

$\quad = 2 \cdot 68$

$\quad = 136$

The area of the cross section is 136 ft^2.

Real-World 🌐 Connection

The Erie Canal is 363 miles in length.

✓ Quick Check

3. Find the area of each trapezoid.

a.

b.

EXERCISES

For more exercises, see *Extra Skill and Word Problem Practice*.

Practice and Problem Solving

A Practice by Example

Example 1
(page 533)

GO for Help

Find the area of each triangle.

1.

2.

3.

Example 2
(page 534)

Find the area of each shaded figure.

4.

5.

6. Interior Design A designer wants to cover the wall shown at the left below with wallpaper. How much wallpaper does she need?

(figure: wall)

Example 3
(page 535)

7. Shipping One end of an air cargo container has the shape shown at the right above. Find the area of the trapezoid.

Find the area of each trapezoid.

8.

9.

10.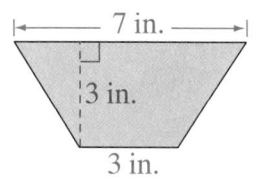

B Apply Your Skills

11. Reasoning A triangle and a parallelogram both have areas of 20 cm² and bases of 5 cm. How do their heights compare?

12. Writing in Math Are $\left(\frac{1}{2} \cdot 3\right) \cdot 8$ and $3 \cdot \left(\frac{1}{2} \cdot 8\right)$ equal? Explain how this can help in finding the area of a triangle.

13. A trapezoid has area 50 in.² The two bases are 5 in. and 15 in. What is the height of the trapezoid?

14. Open-Ended Sketch and label two different triangles so that both have areas of 180 in.²

GO Online
Homework Video Tutor
Visit: PHSchool.com
Web Code: ade-1002

Find the area of each shaded region.

15.

16.

C Challenge

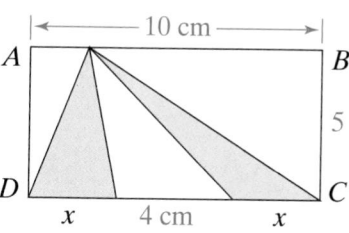

Reasoning In Exercises 17 and 18, find the ratios of the areas of the trapezoids (larger to smaller). Justify each answer.

17. The height and the lengths of the bases of one trapezoid are all twice those of the other trapezoid.

18. The trapezoids have the same height. One trapezoid has base lengths b and $2b$. The other has base lengths b and $4b$.

19. *ABCD* (left) is a rectangle. What is the area of the shaded region?

ISAT
Test Prep

Multiple Choice

20. What are possible dimensions for a triangle with area 32 cm²?
  A. $b = 4$ cm   **B.** $b = 2$ cm   **C.** $b = 8$ cm   **D.** $b = 6$ cm
  $h = 8$ cm $h = 16$ cm $h = 8$ cm $h = 8$ cm

21. A trapezoid has an area of 56 in². One base is 6 in. and the height is 8 in. What is the length of the other base?
  F. 6 in.   **G.** 8 in.   **H.** 10 in.   **J.** 14 in.

Short Response   What is the number of square units in each figure? Show your work.

22.

23.

Mixed Review

GO for Help

Lesson 10-1   **Find the area of each parallelogram.**

24.

25.

Lessons 7-1 and 7-3   **Solve each equation.**

26. $16 + 2y = 9$ **27.** $5.5a + 2 = 10.5$ **28.** $\frac{1}{2}b - 10 = 24$

Lesson 6-9   **29.** Suppose you bought two books for $15. The original prices of the two books were the same, but you were able to buy one for half price. What was the full price of each book?

10-3 Area: Circles

IL Assessment Framework

7.8.02 Solve problems involving perimeter/circumference and area of polygons, circles, and composite figures using diagrams, models, and grids or by measuring or using given formulas.

 Check Skills You'll Need

Simplify each expression.

1. $3.14 \cdot 4^2$

2. $3.14 \cdot 5^2$

3. $3.14 \cdot 9^2$

4. $3.14 \cdot 0.5^2$

GO for Help
Lesson 4-2

1 Finding Areas of Circles

ctivity

Finding the Formula for Area of a Circle

1. Use a compass to draw a circle. Cut out the circle.

2. Fold the circle in half, and then in half again. Fold it in half a third and fourth time.

3. Cut out the 16 wedges that you have formed with the folds.

4. Arrange the wedges in a row as shown below.

5. Notice that the new shape resembles a parallelogram. How does the base of the parallelogram (the side shown in red) relate to the circumference of the circle? How does the height of the parallelogram relate to the radius of the circle?

6. Use the formula for the area of a parallelogram to estimate the area of your circle.

The diagram above shows the relationship between the area of a circle and a figure that is like a parallelogram. The height h of the parallelogram is about the same as the radius r of the circle. The base b is about half the circumference C of the circle.

You can use the formula for the area of a parallelogram to suggest the formula for the area of a circle.

$A = bh$ **Use the formula for the area of a parallelogram.**

$A = \left(\tfrac{1}{2}C\right)(r)$ **Substitute $\tfrac{1}{2}C$ for b and r for h.**

$A = \tfrac{1}{2}(2\pi r) \cdot r$ **Substitute $2\pi r$ for C.**

$A = \pi r^2$ **Simplify.**

Key Concepts   Area of a Circle

The area of a circle equals the product of π and the square of the radius r.

$$A = \pi r^2$$

GO Online

Video Tutor Help
Visit: PHSchool.com
Web Code: ada-0775

You can express the *exact area* of a circle by using π.

1 EXAMPLE   Finding Area of a Circle

Find the exact area of a circle with diameter 12 cm.

$A = \pi r^2$

$\quad = \pi(6)^2$ $r = \frac{1}{2}d; r = 6$

$\quad = 36\pi$ **Simplify.**

The area is 36π cm^2.

✓ Quick Check

● **1.** Find the exact area of a circle with radius 50 in.

For real-world situations, you usually want an approximate value for the area of a circle. If you are finding an approximate area, use 3.14 or the value provided by a calculator for π.

2 EXAMPLE   Real-World 🌐 Problem Solving

Biology The size of a jaguar's territory depends on how much food is available. In a situation where there is plenty of food, the circular territory of the jaguar may be as small as 3 mi in diameter. Find the area of such a region to the nearest square mile.

$A = \pi r^2$

$\quad = \pi(1.5)^2$ $r = \frac{1}{2}d; r = 1.5$

$\quad = 2.25\pi$ **exact area**

$\quad \approx (2.25)(3.14)$ **Use 3.14 for π.**

$\quad = 7.065$ **approximate area**

The area of the region is about 7 mi^2.

✓ Quick Check

● **2.** Find the approximate area of a circle with radius 6 mi.

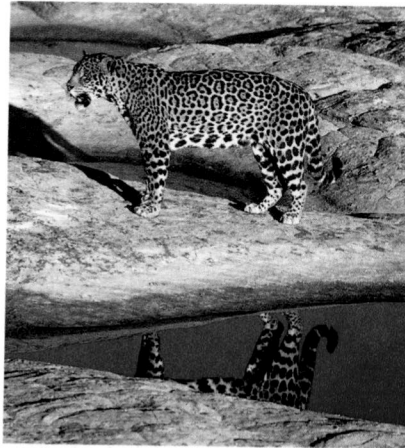

Real-World 🌐 Connection

During a drought a jaguar may need to search for food in a territory as large as 6 mi in diameter.

2 Finding Areas of Irregular Figures

To find the area of an irregular figure, you can sometimes separate it into figures with areas you know how to find.

3 EXAMPLE — Real-World Problem Solving

Multiple Choice A pound of grass seed covers approximately 675 ft². Grass seed comes in 3-lb bags. Find the area of the lawn at the right below. How many bags of grass seed do you need to buy to cover the lawn?

- Ⓐ 4 bags
- Ⓑ 3 bags
- Ⓒ 2 bags
- Ⓓ 1 bag

Test-Taking Tip
Remember to follow the order of operations when finding the area of a circle or half a circle. Square the radius first, and then multiply by an approximation of π.

Area of region that is one half of a circle

area of circle $= \pi r^2$

area of half circle $= \frac{1}{2}\pi r^2$

$A \approx \frac{1}{2}(3.14)(15)^2$ **Replace π with 3.14 and r with 15.**

$A = 353.25$

Area of region that is a rectangle

area of rectangle $= bh$

$A = 45 \cdot 25$ **Replace b with 45 and h with 25.**

$A = 1{,}125$

The area of the lawn is about 353 ft² + 1,125 ft² = 1,478 ft².

$1{,}478 \div 675 \approx 2.19$ **Divide to find the amount of seed.**

You need to buy one 3-lb bag of grass seed. The answer is D.

✓ Quick Check

3. Find the area of the shaded region to the nearest tenth.

EXERCISES

For more exercises, see *Extra Skill and Word Problem Practice.*

Practice and Problem Solving

A Practice by Example

Examples 1 and 2
(page 539)

 for Help

Find the area of each circle. Give the exact area, and an approximate area to the nearest square unit.

1.
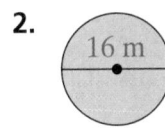
12 ft

2.
16 m

3.
60 cm

🌐 **4. Recreation** A standard dartboard has a diameter of 18 in. What is its area to the nearest square inch?

🌐 **5. Culinary Arts** A culinary student decorates an 8-in.-diameter round cake. What is the approximate area of the top of the cake?

Example 3
(page 540)

Find the area of each figure to the nearest square unit.

6.

|← 10 in. →|
7 in.   3.5 in.

7.
|← 40 yd →|
40 yd

Find the area of each shaded region to the nearest square unit.

8.
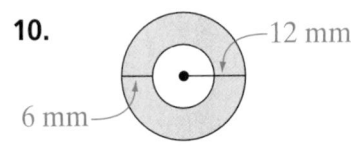
3 in.

9.
10 mi
20 mi

10.
12 mm
6 mm

🌐 **11. Lawn Care** A groundskeeper wants to use sod to cover the lawn shown in green in the diagram. Each piece of sod covers 3 ft². About how many pieces of sod are needed?

40 ft
20 ft
12 ft

B Apply Your Skills

Number Sense **Match each object with its most likely area.**

12. dinner plate   **A.** 0.8 in.²

13. quarter   **B.** 110 in.²

14. 12-in. circular pizza   **C.** 7 in.²

15. jar lid   **D.** 16,000 in.²

16. the center circle on a basketball court   **E.** 80 in.²

Pool
10 ft
15 ft
Border

🌐 **17. Pool Design** Covering for the pool border is sold by the square yard (whole-number amounts only). It costs $20/yd².
    a. What is the area of the border in square feet?
    b. About how much will the covering cost?

10-3 Area: Circles   **541**

Find the area of each circle. Give the exact area, and an approximate area to the nearest tenth.

18. $r = 12$ mi   **19.** $r = 0.3$ m **20.** $d = 1.5$ in.   **21.** $d = 8.4$ mm

22. Open-Ended Describe a real-life situation, not used in this lesson, where you might use the formula for the area of a circle.

23. Which has a greater area, four circles, each with radius 1 m, or one circle with radius 4 m? Explain.

24. How many circles with radius 2 cm will have the same total area as a circle with radius 4 cm?

Find the area of each shaded region to the nearest square unit.

25.   **26.**   **27.**

28. Writing in Math What is the area of the largest circle that will fit in a square with area 64 cm²? Explain.

C Challenge **29. Can Lids** A manufacturer cuts lids for eight cans from one rectangular sheet of aluminum as shown at the left.
a. What is the radius of each lid?
b. How many square inches of aluminum do the lids require?
c. How many square inches of aluminum are wasted?

30. Consumer Issues You can buy a 10-in. diameter pizza for $6.50, a 12-in. pizza for $8.50, or a 14-in. pizza for $10.50.
a. What is the area of each pizza to the nearest square inch?
b. What is the price per square inch of each pizza?
c. Reasoning Is the largest pizza the best buy? Explain.

ISAT

Test Prep

Multiple Choice For Exercises 31–33, what is the exact area of each circle having radius *r* or diameter *d*?

31. $r = 11$ mi
   A. 5.5π mi²   **B.** 11π mi²   **C.** 22π mi²   **D.** 121π mi²

32. $r = \frac{1}{2}$ m
   F. $\frac{1}{4}\pi$ m²   **G.** $\frac{1}{2}\pi$ m²   **H.** π m²   **J.** 2π m²

33. $d = 1.2$ in.
   A. 2.4π in.²   **B.** 1.44π in.²   **C.** 0.36π in.²   **D.** 0.18π in.²

Short Response **34.** Which has a greater area, **(a)** a circle with radius 2 m or a square with side length 2 m?   **(b)** Explain your answer.

Mixed Review

Lesson 10-2

Find the area of each figure.

35.

5 mi
3 mi
$6\frac{1}{2}$ mi

36.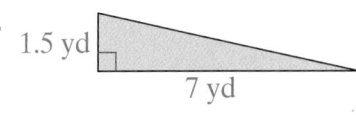

1.5 yd
7 yd

Lesson 9-4

37. Square $ABCD$ has side length 8 in. $\triangle BXY$ is isosceles. Its congruent sides have length 2 in. How many triangles congruent to $\triangle BXY$ can you cut from square $ABCD$?

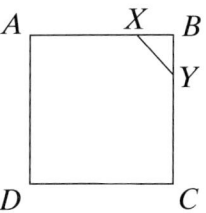

Lesson 5-3

Find each sum or difference.

38. $4\frac{3}{5} + 5\frac{2}{3}$ **39.** $5\frac{2}{3} - 4\frac{3}{5}$ **40.** $\frac{7}{8} + \frac{5}{6}$ **41.** $\frac{7}{8} - \frac{5}{6}$

✓ Checkpoint Quiz 1   Lessons 10-1 through 10-3

Find the area of each figure.

1.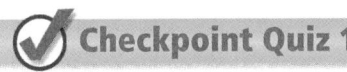

10 in.
10 in.

2.

10 in.
10 in.

3.

20 in.
15 in.

4.

20 yd
12 yd   13 yd
30 yd

5.

35 cm
30 cm
70 cm

6.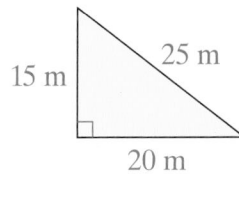

25 m
15 m
20 m

Find the area of each figure. Give the exact area, and an approximate area to the nearest square unit.

7.

10 yd

8.

16 ft

9.

40 cm
20 cm

Activity Lab

Three Views of an Object

Hands-On

For Use With Lesson 10-4

A solid is a three-dimensional figure.

You can draw a solid *in perspective* (p. 548) to show that it is three-dimensional.

Isometric Dot Paper

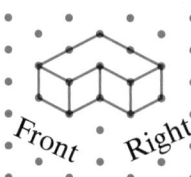

You can use isometric dot paper to draw a three-dimensional view.

Rectangular Graph Paper

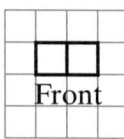

You can use rectangular graph paper to draw top, front, and side views.

EXAMPLE

Draw the top, front, and right-side views of the solid.

Isometric

Top

Front

Right Side

EXERCISES

Draw the top, front, and right-side views of each solid.

1.
2.
3.
4.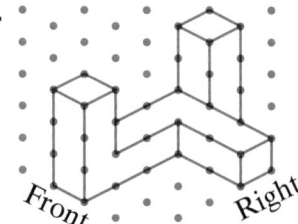

5. The top, front, and right-side views are given.
   Draw an isometric view on isometric dot paper.

Top

Front

Right Side

Space Figures

1 Naming Space Figures

The figures below are common three-dimensional figures, also called **space figures** or solids. The space figures you will study in this book are prisms, pyramids, cylinders, cones, and spheres.

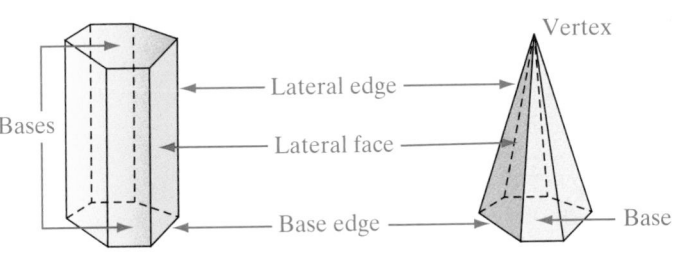

Prism

A **prism** has two parallel bases that are congruent polygons, and lateral faces that are parallelograms.

Pyramid

A **pyramid** has a base that is a polygon. The lateral faces are triangles.

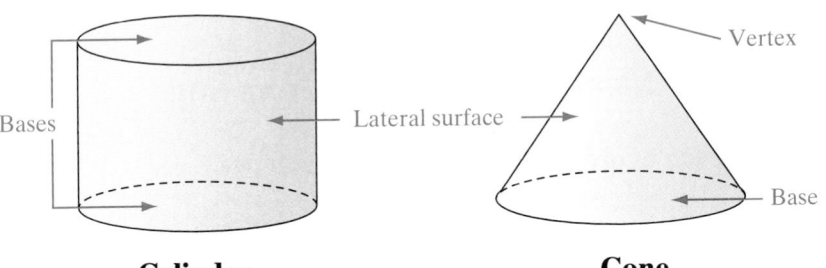

Cylinder

A **cylinder** has two parallel bases that are congruent circles.

Cone

A **cone** has one circular base and one vertex.

Sphere

A **sphere** is the set of all points in space that are a given distance from a given point called the center.

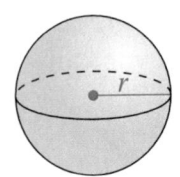

What You'll Learn

- To identify common space figures
- To identify space figures from nets

. . . And Why

To identify the space figures often used in constructing buildings

✓ Check Skills You'll Need

Judging by appearance, classify each polygon.

1.

2.

3.

4.
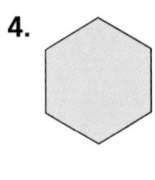

GO for Help
Lesson 9-3

◀)) New Vocabulary

- space figures
- prism
- pyramid
- cylinder
- cone
- sphere
- net

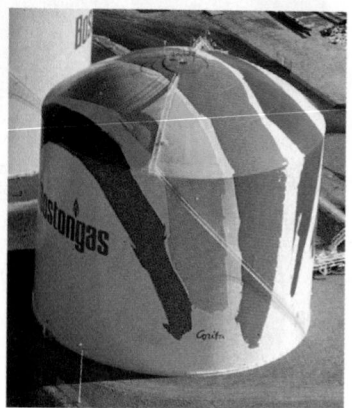

Real-World 🌐 Connection

This space figure displays the 73,000-ft² "Rainbow" by Corita Kent.

You can use the shape of a base to help you name a space figure.

1 EXAMPLE **Naming Space Figures**

For each figure, describe the bases and name the figure.

a.

The bases are triangles. The figure is a triangular prism.

b.
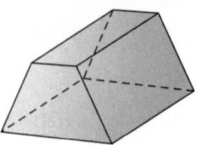

The bases of the prism are trapezoids. The figure is a trapezoidal prism.

✓ **Quick Check**

1. Name each figure.

a.

b.

2 Identifying Space Figures From Nets

A **net** is a pattern you can form into a space figure.

2 EXAMPLE **Naming Space Figures From Nets**

Name the space figure you can form from each net.

a.
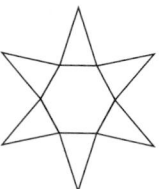

With a hexagonal base and triangular sides, you can form a hexagonal pyramid.

b.
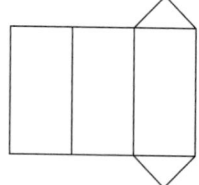

With two triangular bases and rectangular sides, you can form a triangular prism.

✓ **Quick Check**

2. Name the space figure you can form from each net.

a.

b.

Vocabulary Tip

Recall that a <u>cube</u> is a rectangular prism with six congruent square faces.

EXERCISES

For more exercises, see *Extra Skill and Word Problem Practice*.

Practice and Problem Solving

A Practice by Example

Example 1
(page 546)

GO for Help

For each figure, describe the base(s), if any, and name the figure.

1.

2.

3.

4.

5.

6.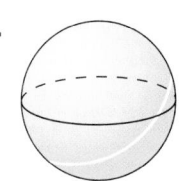

Example 2
(page 546)

Name the space figure you can form from each net.

7.

8.

9.

10.

11.

12.

B Apply Your Skills

For Exercises 13–15, write the most precise name for each space figure that has the given properties.

13. four lateral faces that are triangles

14. three lateral faces that are rectangles

15. a lateral surface and one circular base

Vocabulary Tip

<u>Lateral</u> means "on the side." The lateral faces of a prism or pyramid are the surfaces that connect with a base. See page 545.

16. What type of space figure does each object suggest?
  a. a shoe box   **b.** a teepee   **c.** a basketball

Open Ended Draw a net for each space figure.

17. pentagonal pyramid   **18.** an object in your classroom

19. Multiple Choice Which net can be folded to make a cube?

A

B

C

D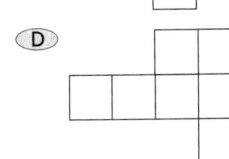

10-4 Space Figures **547**

20. A net is made of 4 congruent rectangles and 2 congruent squares whose sides are the same length as the shorter sides of the rectangles. Name a space figure you can form from this net.

Match each container with the correct net.

21. **22.** **23.**

A. **B.** **C.**

24. <u>Writing in Math</u> Suppose you see a net for a rectangular prism and a net for a rectangular pyramid. Explain how you can match each net with its name.

25. Draw a net to represent a rectangular box that is 10 cm long, 8 cm wide, and 4 cm high. Label dimensions on the net.

C **Challenge**

26. A cube is easy to draw in *one-point perspective*. Draw a cube in one-point perspective by following the steps below.

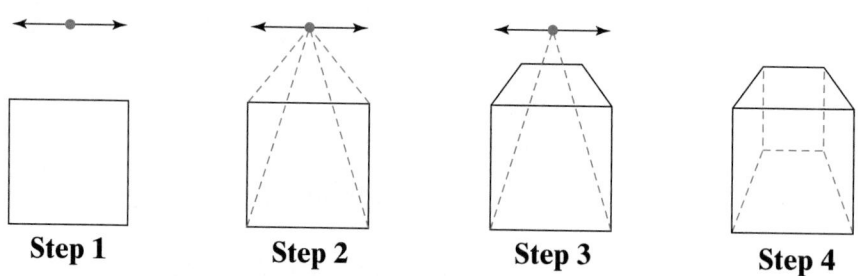

Step 1   Step 2   Step 3   Step 4

Step 1 Begin by drawing a square for the front. Draw a *horizon line* parallel to one horizontal edge of your square. Select a *vanishing point* on the horizon line.

Step 2 Draw lines, called *vanishing lines,* from the vertices of the square to the vanishing point.

Step 3 Draw a line segment parallel to the horizon line. Use this segment to determine the top and back edges.

Step 4 Draw dashed lines for the hidden back vertical and horizontal edges. Erase the horizon line and unnecessary parts of the vanishing lines.

27. Using steps like those suggested in Exercise 26, make a one-point perspective drawing of each figure.
   a. triangular prism   **b.** cylinder

Multiple Choice

28. Which of the following is a net for a cylinder?

A.

B.

C.

D.

29. Which space figure can you form from the net?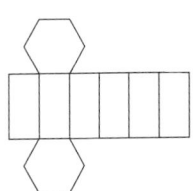

F. hexagonal pyramid
G. triangular pyramid
H. triangular prism
J. hexagonal prism

30. Which space figure has three lateral faces that are triangles?
A. triangular pyramid
B. pentagonal prism
C. square prism
D. triangular prism

31. Which space figure has 6 faces that are all regular quadrilaterals?
F. triangular pyramid
G. pentagonal prism
H. square prism
J. triangular prism

32. A rectangular prism has how many faces?
A. 2
B. 4
C. 6
D. 8

Short Response

33. a. Draw a net for a cylinder that has diameter 4 in. and height 6 in.
b. Label your drawing.

Mixed Review

Lesson 10-3

For each circle, find the exact area and an approximate area.

34.

2.5 m

35.

0.1 m

36.

20 m

Lessons 9-4 **37. Mowing Lawns** A rectangular yard is 20 ft by 40 ft. Your lawn mower will mow a 2-ft-wide path. What is the least number of turns you must make to mow the lawn?

Lesson 8-3 Write each equation in slope-intercept form.

38. $3x - y = 6$ **39.** $2x - 2y = 10$ **40.** $-8y - 16 = 24x$

If you cut a label from a can, you will see that the label is a rectangle. The area of the can covered by the label is the *lateral area* of the can.

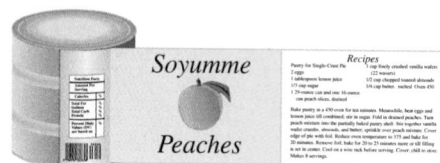

ACTIVITY

- **Cover the sides of several cans with paper.**

- **For each can, make sure your paper covers it from top to bottom. Match the edges of the paper carefully, making sure they don't overlap.**

- **Take the paper off the can. Measure the length and width of the paper. Find the area of the paper.**

1. Copy and complete the table below. Extend it as needed.

Length of Paper	Width of Paper	Lateral Area of Can
■	■	■
■	■	■

2. Add a column to your table. Measure the diameter of the top of each can. Record the diameters in your table.

3. Add another column to your table.
   a. Calculate the circumference of each can. Record the circumferences in your table.
   b. **Reasoning** How is the circumference of the can related to the length of the rectangle of paper? Explain.

4. **Multiple Choice** Suppose you are using the paint roller at the right to paint a wall. Which is closest to the area that the roller will cover in one complete roll?

   Ⓐ 28 in.^{2} Ⓑ 81 in.^{2}
   Ⓒ 84 in.^{2} Ⓓ 85 in.^{2}

Surface Area: Prisms and Cylinders

IL Assessment Framework

1 Finding Surface Areas of Prisms

Prisms and cylinders can be *right* or *oblique*.

Right prism   Oblique prism   Right cylinder   Oblique cylinder

In this text, you may assume that prisms and cylinders are right unless otherwise stated.

Surface area (S.A.) is the sum of the areas of the base(s) and the lateral faces of a space figure. One way to find the surface area of a space figure is to find the area of its net. You measure surface area in square units.

1 EXAMPLE Finding Surface Area Using a Net

Find the surface area of the rectangular prism using a net.

8 in.
5 in.
20 in.

40 in.² ← 20 in. → 40 in.²

8 in. | 160 in.²
5 in. | 100 in.²
8 in. | 160 in.²
5 in. | 100 in.²

Draw and label a net.

Find the area of each rectangle in the net.

$40 + 40 + 160 + 100 + 160 + 100 = 600$ **Add the areas.**

The surface area is 600 in.²

Quick Check

1. **a.** Find the surface area of the triangular prism.
   b. A similar triangular prism has dimensions twice those shown here. Find its surface area.
   c. How do surface areas of similar prisms compare when dimensions are doubled?

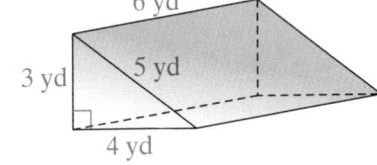

6 yd
3 yd   5 yd
4 yd

Check Skills You'll Need

Find the circumference of each circle with the given radius or diameter.

1. $r = 5$ in.

2. $r = 4.2$ cm

3. $d = 8$ ft

4. $d = 6.8$ in.

GO for Help
Lesson 9-6

New Vocabulary
- surface area
- lateral area

7.8.04 Solve problems involving the volume or surface area of a right rectangular prism, right circular cylinder, or composite shape using an appropriate formula or strategy.

Test-Taking Tip

Some tests may use the same letters in the formulas for surface area and lateral area. Check your work.

Another way to find the surface area of a prism is to use the *lateral area* and the base areas. **Lateral area (L.A.)** of a prism is the sum of the areas of the lateral faces.

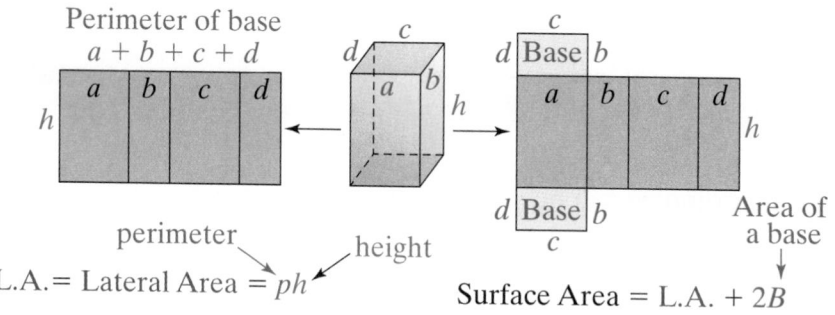

L.A. = Lateral Area = ph

Surface Area = L.A. + $2B$

To find surface area, it is a good idea to find lateral area first.

GO for Help

B represents the area of a base. For a list of area formulas, see the table on page 802.

> **Key Concepts**   **Surface Area of a Prism**
>
> The lateral area of a prism is the product of the perimeter of the base and the height.
>
> $$\text{L.A.} = ph$$
>
> The surface area of a prism is the sum of the lateral area and the areas of the two bases.
>
> $$\text{S.A.} = \text{L.A.} + 2B$$
>
>
>
>
>
> P Perimeter of base
>
> h
>
> B Area of base

2 EXAMPLE   **Finding Surface Area Using Formulas**

GO for Help

For a guide to reading a formula, see page 557.

Find the surface area of the triangular prism at the right.

Step 1 Find the lateral area.

$$\begin{aligned} \text{L.A.} &= ph && \text{Use the formula for lateral area.}\\ &= (5 + 5 + 6)12 && p = 5 + 5 + 6 \text{ and } h = 12.\\ &= 192 \end{aligned}$$

Step 2 Find the surface area.

$$\begin{aligned} \text{S.A.} &= \text{L.A.} + 2B && \text{Use the formula for surface area.}\\ &= 192 + 2\left(\tfrac{1}{2} \cdot 6 \cdot 4\right) && \text{L.A.} = 192 \text{ and } B = \tfrac{1}{2} \cdot 6 \cdot 4.\\ &= 192 + 24\\ &= 216 \end{aligned}$$

The surface area of the triangular prism is 216 cm^2.

✓ **Quick Check**

● **2.** Find the surface area of the prism at the right.

3 m   6 m   4 m

2 Finding Surface Areas of Cylinders

If you cut a label from a soup can, you will see that the label is a rectangle. The height of the rectangle is the height of the can. The base length of the rectangle is the circumference of the can.

For: Surface Area Activity
Use: Interactive Textbook, 10-5

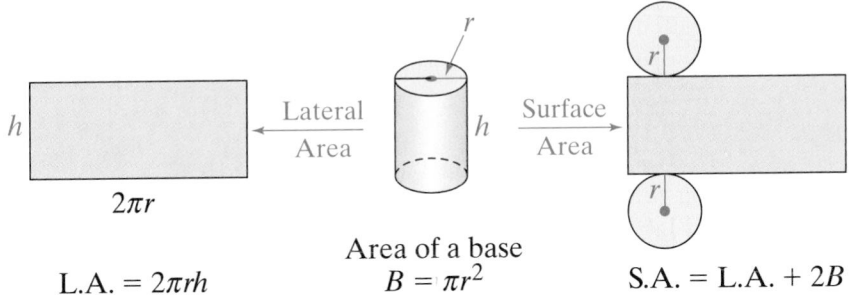

L.A. $= 2\pi rh$ Area of a base $B = \pi r^2$ S.A. $=$ L.A. $+ 2B$

Key Concepts   **Surface Area of a Cylinder**

The lateral area of a cylinder is the product of the circumference of the base and the height of the cylinder.

$$\text{L.A.} = 2\pi rh$$

The surface area of a cylinder is the sum of the lateral area and the areas of the two bases.

$$\text{S.A.} = \text{L.A.} + 2B$$

B is the area of a base.

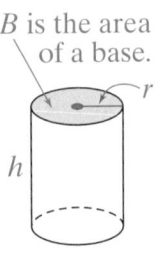

---

3 EXAMPLE   Finding Surface Area of a Cylinder

Packaging Find the surface area of the can at the right.

Step 1 Find the lateral area.

L.A. $= 2\pi rh$ Use the formula for lateral area.
$\approx 2(3.14)(3.5)(11.5)$ $r = 3.5$ and $h = 11.5$.
≈ 253

Step 2 Find the surface area.

S.A. $=$ L.A. $+ 2B$ Use the formula for surface area.
$\approx 253 + 2(3.14)(3.5)^2$ L.A. ≈ 253 and $B = \pi(3.5)^2$.
$\approx 253 + 77$
$= 330$

The surface area of the can is about 330 cm^2.

3.5 cm

11.5 cm

✓ Quick Check

● **3.** Find the surface area of a can with radius 5 cm and height 20 cm.

EXERCISES

For more exercises, see *Extra Skill and Word Problem Practice*.

Practice and Problem Solving

 Practice by Example

Example 1
(page 551)

for Help

Find, to the nearest square unit, the surface area of the space figure represented by each net.

1.

2.

3. The base of a rectangular prism is 3 in. by 5 in. The height is 11 in.
 a. Draw and label a net for the prism.
 b. Find the surface area of the prism.
 c. A similar rectangular prism has dimensions three times the dimensions of the given prism. Find its surface area.
 d. How do surface areas of similar prisms compare when dimensions are tripled?

Example 2
(page 552)

Find the surface area of each prism.

4.

5.

6.

7.

8.

9.

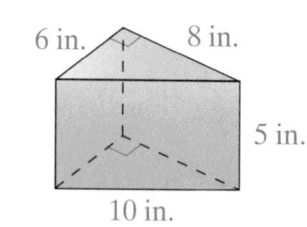

Example 3
(page 553)

Find the surface area of the cylinder shown or represented. Round to the nearest tenth.

10.

11.

12.

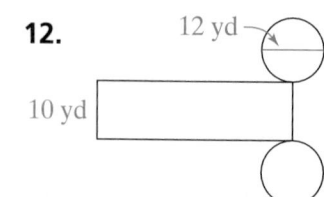

13. **Gift Wrapping** Juliet is trying to wrap a can of mixed nuts that is a birthday gift for her brother. The can has a radius of 8 cm and a height of 10 cm. Approximately how many square centimeters of wrapping paper will cover the gift?

B Apply Your Skills

14. A cylinder has radius 8 ft and height 12 ft. Draw and label a net for the cylinder. Find its surface area.

15. Find the surface area of a square prism with base edge 7 m and height 15 m.

16. Find the area of the top and lateral surface of a cylindrical water tank with radius 20 ft and height 30 ft.

17. **Multiple Choice** A tent is approximately the shape of a triangular prism. Which is closest to the surface area of the tent?
    Ⓐ 10,800 in.²   Ⓑ 7,632 in.²
    Ⓒ 6,840 in.²   Ⓓ 1,020 in.²

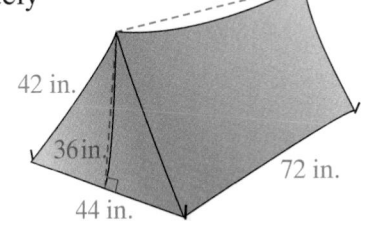

18. Find the surface area of a cylinder with radius 10 cm and height 8 cm.

GO **O**nline
Homework Video Tutor
Visit: PHSchool.com
Web Code: ade-1005

19. **Painting** The neighborhood swimming pool needs to be painted. The pool is 40 ft by 60 ft. The depth of the pool is 6 ft throughout.
    a. How many sides need to be painted?
    b. What is the total number of square feet to be painted?
    c. The materials for painting the pool cost $1.50 per square yard. What is the cost of the materials for painting the pool?

20. **Error Analysis** A student explains that the two cylinders at the right have the same surface area. Explain the student's error.

21. **Open-Ended** Describe a real-world situation in which you need to know the surface area of a space figure.

22. <u>**Writing in Math**</u> In a triangular prism, what is the difference between the height of a base and the height of the prism?

23. **Packaging** You have made two boxes with lids. Which box required more cardboard, a box 8 in. by 6.25 in. by 10.5 in., or a box 9 in. by 5.5 in. by 11.75 in.? Explain.

C Challenge

24. **Reasoning** Use the cubes with side lengths of 1, 2, and 3 units.
    a. Find the surface area of each cube.
    b. If the length of each side of a cube is doubled, how does that affect the surface area?
    c. If the length of each side of a cube is tripled, how does that affect the surface area?

4 ft

7 ft

|← 15 ft →|

🌐 **25. Construction** The concrete figure at the left has a hole in it. The surface will be painted except for the inside of the hole. Find the total surface area to be painted to the nearest square foot.

26. Reasoning Which has the greater effect on the surface area of a cylinder: doubling the base radius or doubling the height? Justify your answer.

ISAT
Test Prep

Multiple Choice

8 cm

5 cm

5 cm

10 cm

5 cm

27. Which figure would cost more to paint?
  A. the square prism
  B. the cylinder
  C. They would cost the same.
  D. cannot be determined

28. What is the approximate surface area of the space figure represented by the net?
  F. 8,777 cm²
  G. 8,333 cm²
  H. 8,202 cm²
  J. 4,387 cm²

27 cm

84.8 cm

27 cm

90 cm

29. Each edge of cube is 40 cm long. What is the surface area of the cube? Use 2.5 cm ≈ 1 in.
  A. 256 in.²   **B.** 1,536 in.²   **C.** 3,840 in.²   **D.** 9,600 in.²

30. A cylinder has height 10 in. and base radius 2.5 in. What is its lateral area, to the nearest whole unit?
  F. 235 in.²   **G.** 215 in.²   **H.** 196 in.²   **J.** 157 in.²

Mixed Review

GO for Help

Lesson 10-4 **Name each space figure.**

31.   **32.**   **33.**

Lesson 9-9 **Graph each point and its image after a reflection over the given line.**

34. $A(0, 9)$; x-axis   **35.** $B(-3, 5)$; y-axis   **36.** $C(3, -1)$; $x = 2$

Lesson 6-2 🌐 **37. Recipes** A recipe that serves 6 people calls for $\frac{1}{2}$ teaspoon of salt. In preparing this recipe for 25 people, about how many teaspoons of salt should you use?

Understanding Math Problems For the problem below, let Diana's thinking guide you through using the formulas. Check your understanding with the exercises at the bottom of the page.

10 ft

10 ft

4 ft

4 ft

Error Analysis A student explains that the two cylinders at the right have the same surface area. Explain the student's error.

What Diana Thinks	**What Diana Writes**

First I need to use the formula for the surface area of a cylinder. → S.A. = L.A. + 2B

For L.A., use the formula $2\pi rh$ and for B, use πr^2. r indicates the radius of each base and h indicates the height of each cylinder. → S.A. = $22\pi rh + 2(\pi r^2)$

For the cylinder on the left, r is 5 and h is 4. Now I will substitute these values and simplify. →
<u>Cylinder on Left</u>
S.A. = $2(3.14)(5)(4) + 2(3.14)(5)^2$
     = 282.6

For the cylinder on the right, r is 2 and h is 10. I will substitute these values again and simplify. →
<u>Cylinder on Right</u>
S.A. = $2(3.14)(2)(10) + 2(3.14)(2)^2$
     = 150.72

Compare the surface areas. Then answer the question. →
The surface areas are not equal. The student incorrectly assumed that you can interchange diameter and height and have the same surface areas.

EXERCISES

Write the formula you use to find the surface area of each figure. Give the meaning and value of each letter or letters in the formula.

1.
3 in.
5 in.   20 in.

2.
3 cm   5 cm
4 cm   10.5 cm

3.
1 m
2 m

4. Error Analysis For Exercise 3, Hans says that the surface area of the cylinder is 12.56 m². What is his error?

10-6

Surface Area:
Pyramids, Cones, and Spheres

(IL) Assessment Framework

7.8.02 Solve problems involving perimeter/ circumference and area of polygons, circles, and composite figures using diagrams, models, and grids or by measuring or using given formulas.

✓ Check Skills You'll Need

Use the Order of Operations to simplify each expression.

1. $\frac{2}{3}(9\pi) + \frac{1}{2}(8\pi)$

2. $\frac{3}{4}(12\pi) + \frac{2}{5}(15\pi)$

3. $\frac{1}{6}(24\pi) + \frac{1}{3}(3\pi)$

4. $\frac{5}{8}(32\pi) + \frac{1}{7}(14\pi)$

 for Help
Lesson 5-4

🔊 **New Vocabulary**
• slant height

---

1 Finding Surface Areas of Pyramids

In this text, all pyramids are *regular* pyramids. They have regular polygons for bases and congruent isosceles triangles for lateral faces.

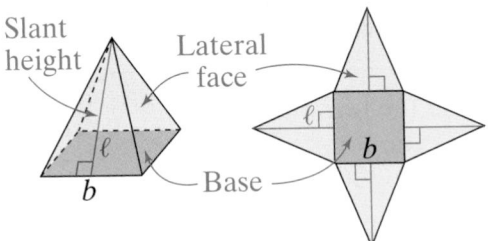

You can use the **slant height** ℓ, the height of a face, to find the area of the lateral faces. If n is the number of lateral triangular faces,

$$\text{L.A. is } n\left(\tfrac{1}{2}b\ell\right) \text{ or } \tfrac{1}{2}p\ell.$$

Key Concepts   **Surface Area of a Pyramid**

The lateral area of a pyramid is one half the product of the perimeter of the base and the slant height.

The surface area of a pyramid is the sum of the lateral area and the area of the base.

$$\text{L.A.} = \tfrac{1}{2}p\ell \qquad \text{S.A.} = \text{L.A.} + B$$

---

1 EXAMPLE   Finding Surface Area of a Pyramid

Find the surface area of the square pyramid.

Step 1 Find the lateral area.

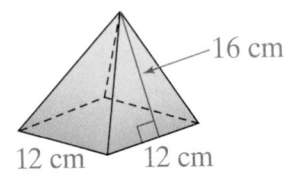

$\text{L.A.} = \tfrac{1}{2}p\ell$ **Use the formula for lateral area.**

$\quad = \tfrac{1}{2} \cdot 48 \cdot 16$ **$p = 4(12)$ and $\ell = 16$.**

$\quad = 384$

Step 2 Find the surface area.

$\text{S.A.} = \text{L.A.} + B$ **Use the formula for surface area.**

$\quad = 384 + 12^2$ **L.A. $= 384$ and $B = 12^2$.**

$\quad = 384 + 144$

$\quad = 528$

The surface area of the pyramid is 528 cm^2.

✅ Quick Check

1. A pyramid has a square base with edge 20 ft. The slant height is 8 ft. Find the surface area.

---

2 **Finding Surface Areas of Cones and Spheres**

Online
active math

For: Surface Area Activity
Use: Interactive Textbook, 10–6

In this text, every cone is a right circular cone with the vertex of the cone directly over the center of the circular base.

L.A. is $\frac{1}{2}(2\pi r)\ell$ or L.A. $= \pi r\ell$.

> **Key Concepts** **Surface Area of a Cone**
>
> The surface area (S.A.) of a cone is the sum of the lateral area and base area.
>
> L.A. $= \pi r\ell$ S.A. $=$ L.A. $+ B$

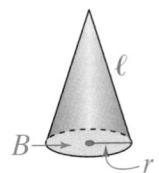

---

2 EXAMPLE   **Finding Surface Area of a Cone**

Find the surface area of the cone at the right.

L.A. $= \pi r\ell$ **Use the formula for lateral area.**
     $\approx 3.14(4)(10)$ $r = 4$ **and** $\ell = 10$.
     $= 125.6$

10 cm

4 cm

S.A. $=$ L.A. $+ B$ **Use the formula for surface area.**
     $\approx 125.6 + 3.14(4)^2$ **L.A.** $\approx$ **125.6 and** $B = \pi(4)^2$.
     $= 125.6 + 50.24$
     $= 175.84$

The surface area of the cone is about 176 cm^2.

✅ Quick Check

2. A cone has slant height 39 ft and radius 7 ft. Find its surface area.

A sphere has the same area as four circles with the same radius.

GO **Online**

> **Key Concepts**   **Surface Area of a Sphere**
>
> The surface area of a sphere of radius r is
>   S.A. $= 4\pi r^2$.

Video Tutor Help
Visit: PHSchool.com
Web Code: ada-0775

| 10 in. |

3 EXAMPLE   <u>Real-World</u> 🌐 Problem Solving

Basketball Calculate the surface area of a basketball.

$$\text{S.A.} = 4\pi r^2 \qquad \text{Use the formula for surface area.}$$

$$\approx 4(3.14)(5)^2 \qquad r = 5$$

$$= 314$$

The surface area of the basketball is about 314 in.^{2}.

✓ Quick Check

- **3.** A sphere has a radius of 6 cm. Find its surface area.

You can find the surface area of a space figure that combines two or more figures you have studied.

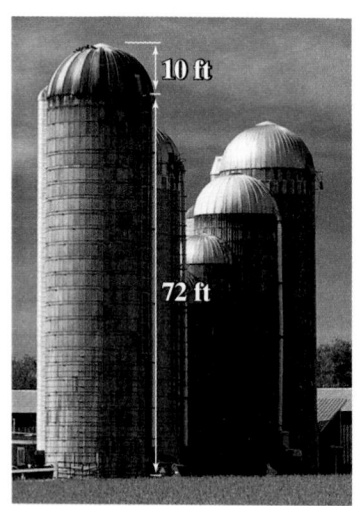

10 ft

72 ft

More Than One Way

Find the surface area of the silo formed by a half sphere and a cylinder. The diameter of the silo is 20 ft.

Roberto's Method

Find the area of each space figure. Then find their sum.

One half sphere   Cylinder

$$\text{S.A.} = \tfrac{1}{2}(4\pi r^2) \qquad\qquad \text{L.A.} = 2\pi rh$$

$$\approx \tfrac{1}{2}(4)(3.14)(10^2) \qquad \approx 2(3.14)(10)(72)$$

$$= 628 \qquad\qquad\qquad\quad = 4{,}521.6$$

Surface area of silo is about $628 + 4{,}521.6$, or $5{,}149.6 \text{ ft}^2$.

Jasmine's Method

Combine formulas before substituting values.

$$\begin{aligned}
\text{Surface area} &= \tfrac{1}{2}\text{S.A.} \quad + \text{L.A.}\\
\text{of silo} &\quad\ \text{of sphere} \quad \text{of cylinder}\\
&= \tfrac{1}{2}(4\pi r^2) + 2\pi rh\\
&= 2\pi r^2 + 2\pi rh\\
&= 2\pi r(r + h)\\
&\approx 2(3.14)(10)(10 + 72)\\
&= 5{,}149.6
\end{aligned}$$

Surface area of silo is about $5{,}149.6 \text{ ft}^2$.

Choose a Method

1. Which method do you prefer? Explain.

EXERCISES

For more exercises, see *Extra Skill and Word Problem Practice.*

Practice and Problem Solving

A Practice by Example

Examples 1–3
(pages 558 and 560)

GO for Help

Find the surface area of each space figure, to the nearest square unit.

1.
22 cm
10 cm   10 cm

2.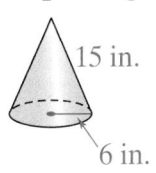
15 in.
6 in.

3.
18 cm

4.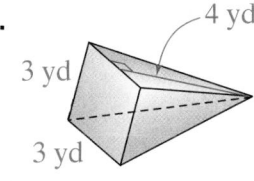
4 yd
3 yd
3 yd

5.
20 cm
30 cm

6.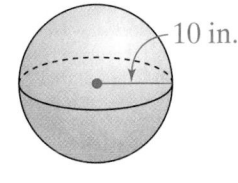
10 in.

7. The length of the base of a square pyramid is 7 cm. Its slant height is 4 cm. Find the surface area of the square pyramid.

8. The base of a cone has radius 3 ft. Its slant height is 8 ft. Find the surface area of the cone.

9. Engineering A spherical ball bearing has a radius of 8 mm. Find the surface area of the ball bearing.

B Apply Your Skills

Find the surface area of each space figure, to the nearest square unit.

10.
6.7 cm
4.5 cm
4.5 cm

11.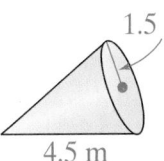
1.5 m
4.5 m

12.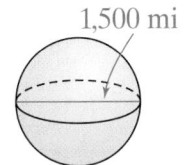
1,500 mi

13. Multiple Choice A globe has a diameter of 18 inches. What is the surface area of the globe to the nearest square inch?
Ⓐ 226 in.^{2} Ⓑ 254 in.^{2} Ⓒ 1,017 in.^{2} Ⓓ 4,072 in.^{2}

14. Error Analysis A friend tells you that the surface area of a square prism with base length 4 m and height 5 m is the same as the surface area of a square pyramid with base length 4 m and height 5 m. Explain your friend's error.

Find the surface area of each figure to the nearest square unit.

15.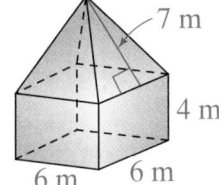
7 m
4 m
6 m   6 m

16.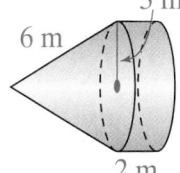
3 m
6 m
2 m

17.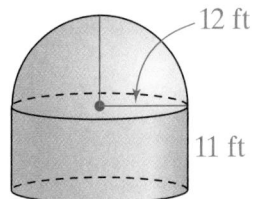
12 ft
11 ft

18. Writing in Math Write a paragraph explaining how to find the surface area of a cone with slant height 10 in. and base radius 8 in.

C Challenge **19. Geography** Approximately 70% of Earth's surface is covered by water. If the diameter of Earth is approximately 13,000 km, find the approximate surface area *not* covered by water.

20. Architecture The spherical planetarium (left) at the American Museum of Natural History in New York City is 87 ft in diameter.
   a. What is the surface area of the sphere?
   b. The sphere is covered by 2,474 panels to absorb sound. What is the average area of each panel, to the nearest tenth of a square foot?

21. Reasoning Which has the greater surface area, a cylinder with height 2 in. and radius of base 2 in., or a sphere with radius 2 in.? Justify your answer.

ISAT

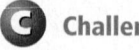

Test Prep

Multiple Choice

22. What is the surface area of the figure at the right?
   A. 2,150 in.²   **B.** 2,600 in.²
   C. 3,000 in.²   **D.** 3,200 in.²

15 in. — 20 in. — 20 in. — 20 in.

23. What is the ratio of the surface area of a sphere with radius 2 ft to the surface area of a sphere with radius 5 ft?
   F. 2 to 5   **G.** 4 to 25   **H.** 16 to 125   **J.** 18 to 20

Extended Response

24. A water storage tank with a roof that is in the shape of a cone has a diameter of 10 ft. The height of the cylindrical part of the tank is 15 ft. The slant height of the roof is 8 ft. **(a)** What is the radius of the tank? **(b)** What is the lateral area of the cylindrical part of the tank? **(c)** What is the surface area of the entire tank?

Mixed Review

Lesson 10-5

Find the surface area to the nearest square unit.

25.
24 in. — 12 in.

26.
22 cm — 10 cm — 14 cm

Lesson 8-7

27. Under rate plan A a new computer costs $200 down and $20 a month. Under rate plan B the computer costs $175 down and $25 a month. After how many months will the amount paid be the same for both plans?

Lesson 4-1

List all the factors of each number.

28. 21   **29.** 100   **30.** 25   **31.** 32

Volume: Prisms and Cylinders

IL Assessment Framework

7.8.04 Solve problems involving the volume or surface area of a right rectangular prism, right circular cylinder, or composite shape using an appropriate formula or strategy.

1 | Finding the Volumes of Prisms

The **volume** of a three-dimensional figure is the number of cubic units needed to fill it. A **cubic unit** is the space occupied by a cube with edges one unit long.

Consider filling the rectangular prism at the right with centimeter cubes.

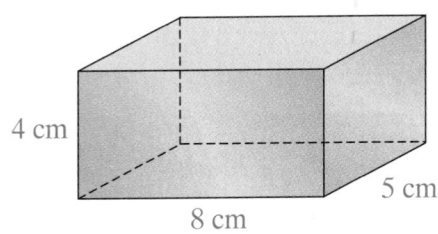

The bottom layer of the prism contains $8 \cdot 5 = 40$ centimeter cubes, or a volume of 40 cm³ (cubic centimeters).

The prism has four layers of cubes, so it contains $4 \cdot 40$, or 160, centimeter cubes in all.

The volume of the prism is 160 cm³.

The volume found for the rectangular prism above suggests the following formula.

Check Skills You'll Need

Find the area of each circle.

1. radius = 8 cm

2. radius = 12 cm

3. diameter = 20 cm

 for Help
Lesson 10-3

🔊 **New Vocabulary**

• volume
• cubic unit

Key Concepts | **Volume of a Prism**

The volume V of a prism is the product of the base area B and the height h.

$$V = Bh$$

6 cm

10 cm

21 cm

1 **EXAMPLE**   Finding Volume of a Prism

Find the volume of the triangular prism at the left.

$V = Bh$ **Use the formula for volume.**

$= 30 \cdot 21$ $B = \frac{1}{2} \cdot 10 \cdot 6 = 30$

$= 630$ **Simplify.**

The volume is 630 cm^3.

✓ **Quick Check**

● **1.** Find the volume of the triangular prism.

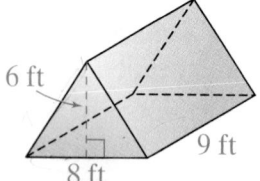

6 ft

9 ft

8 ft

2   **Finding the Volumes of Cylinders**

You can calculate the volume of a cylinder in much the same way that you calculate the volume of a prism.

Key Concepts   **Volume of a Cylinder**

The volume V of a cylinder is the base area B times the height h.

$$V = Bh$$

r

h

B

2 **EXAMPLE**   <u>Real-World</u> 🌎 <u>Problem Solving</u>

Multiple Choice **What is the volume of the juice can to the nearest cubic centimeter?**

Ⓐ 128 cm^3 Ⓑ 139 cm^3

Ⓒ 256 cm^3 Ⓓ 436 cm^3

3.4 cm

$V = Bh$ **Use the formula for volume.**

$V = \pi r^2 h$ $B = \pi r^2$

$\approx 3.14 \cdot 3.4^2 \cdot 12$ **Replace r with 3.4 and h with 12.**

$= 435.5808$ **Simplify.**

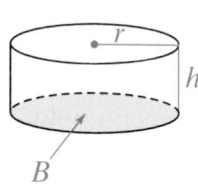

12 cm

The volume is about 436 cm^3. The answer is D.

✓ **Quick Check**

2. **a.** Find the volume of the cylinder to the nearest cubic foot.
     b. How does the volume of this cylinder compare with one having twice its dimensions?

11 ft

5 ft

A Practice by Example

Example 1
(page 564)

Find the volume of each prism.

1.
3 cm 4 cm 9 cm

2.
10 cm 8 cm 18 cm

3.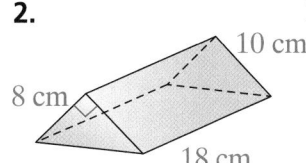
2 m 3 m 4 m

Example 2
(page 564)

For Exercises 4–7, find the volume of each cylinder to the nearest cubic unit.

4.
9 in. 21 in.

5.
8 m 30 m

6.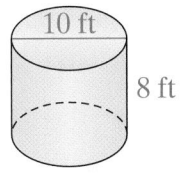
10 ft 8 ft

7. a. a mailing tube 25 in. long with a diameter of 4 in.
  b. a mailing tube with double the dimensions in part (a)
  c. How do the volumes of the two mailing tubes compare?

B Apply Your Skills

8. Multiple Choice Wood for a fireplace is often sold by the cord. A cord is 8 ft × 4 ft × 4 ft. How many cubic feet are in a cord of wood?
  Ⓐ 144 ft³   Ⓑ 128 ft³   Ⓒ 32 ft³   Ⓓ 16 ft³

9. Storage A storage box measures 24 in. by 12 in. by 3 in. Find its volume to the nearest cubic centimeter (1 in. = 2.54 cm).

Find each missing dimension. Use $\pi \approx 3.14$.

10.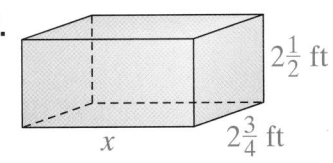
$2\frac{1}{2}$ ft $2\frac{3}{4}$ ft x
$V = 38.5$ ft³
Length = ▇

11.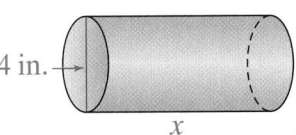
4 in. x
$V = 125.6$ in.³
Height ≈ ▇

12.
x 9 cm 3.5 cm
$V = 50.4$ cm³
Height of triangle = ▇

13.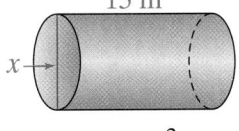
13 m x
$V = 1,256$ m³
Diameter ≈ ▇

GO **O**nline
Homework Video Tutor
Visit: PHSchool.com
Web Code: ade-1007

Writing in Math Describe one real object with the given shape. Explain why you might want to find the volume of the object.

14. triangular prism   **15.** cylinder   **16.** rectangular prism

Challenge **17. Construction** Concrete is sold by the yard, which means by the cubic yard. It costs $70 per yard. How many cubic feet are in a cubic yard? How much would it cost to pour a slab that is 14 ft by 16 ft by 6 in. for a patio?

18. Reasoning The two stacks of paper in the photo at the left contain the same number of sheets. The first stack forms an oblique prism; the second forms a right prism. The stacks have the same height, base, and volume. Use this information to find the volume of the oblique prism shown below the stacks.

3 in.

4 in.   3 in.

3 in.

19. Error Analysis A student explains that a cylinder with radius 1 in. and height 3 in. has half the volume of one with radius 2 in. and height 3 in. Explain the student's error.

ISAT

 Test Prep

Multiple Choice

20. One side of a triangle is 5 cm and its corresponding height is 15 cm. The triangle is the base of a triangular prism with height 5 cm. What is the volume of the prism?
A. 12.5 cm³   **B.** 37.5 cm³   **C.** 187.5 cm³   **D.** 375.0 cm³

21. What is the height of a rectangular prism with length 5 ft, width 2 ft, and volume 120 ft³?
F. 12 ft   **G.** 10 ft   **H.** 6 ft   **J.** 2 ft

Extended Response

22. A manufacturer is deciding whether to package table salt in a cylinder or in a rectangular prism made of cardboard. The cylinder has radius 4 cm and height 13.5 cm. The prism is 7 cm by 7 cm by 13.5 cm.
a. What volume of salt will each package hold?
b. Each package will use how many square centimeters of cardboard?
c. Which seems to be the better type of package? Explain.

Mixed Review

Lessons 10-5 and 10-6
GO for Help

Find the surface area of each figure, to the nearest square unit.

23.
5 cm
13 cm

24.
7 cm
6 cm
6 cm

25.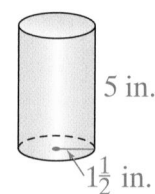
5 in.
$1\frac{1}{2}$ in.

Lesson 9-2

26. If $a \parallel b$ in the figure at the right, find the measures of angles 2–8 in terms of x.

Lesson 5-6 **27. Money** Juan has $3.80 in coins. He has 6 quarters and 12 dimes. The rest are nickels. How many nickels does he have?

A calculator can help you avoid a *rounding error*. However, you have to know how to work with exact values in unsimplified form.

EXAMPLE

Find the volume of a cylinder with height 6 and circumference 15. Round to the nearest tenth.

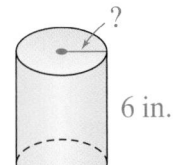

6 in.

Method 1		**Method 2**
$C = 2\pi r$	formula for circumference	$C = 2\pi r$
$15 = 2\pi r$	C = 15	$15 = 2\pi r$
$\frac{15}{2\pi} = r$	Divide by 2π.	$\frac{15}{2\pi} = r$
$2.4 \approx r$	Simplify (at left).	
$V = Bh$	formula for volume	$V = Bh$
$= \pi r^2 h$	$B = \pi r^2$	$= \pi r^2 h$
$\approx \pi(2.4)^2(6)$	Replace r and h.	$= \pi\left(\frac{15}{2\pi}\right)^2(6)$
≈ 108.6	Use a calculator.	≈ 107.4

In Method 1, the intermediate value $r \approx 2.4$ gives a final result that has a greater *rounding error*. In Method 2, note that the formula for volume uses the exact value of the radius, $\frac{15}{2\pi}$.

EXERCISES

What intermediate value must you find to solve the problem? Give its exact value and its approximate value to the nearest tenth.

1. Find the area of a circle with circumference 12.

2. Find the volume of a cylinder with radius 3 and lateral area 10.

Solve each problem to the nearest tenth by two methods. In one method, use an approximate intermediate value. In the other method, use the exact intermediate value.

3. Find the surface area of a cone with slant height 5 and lateral area 9.

4. Find the surface area of a sphere with circumference 13.

5. Find the surface area and volume of a cylinder with lateral area 10 and height 8.

6. Writing in Math In the Example, which method do you think makes better use of the calculator? Explain.

Make a Model

What You'll Learn

• To make a model

. . . And Why

To build the largest box possible from a given rectangle

 Check Skills You'll Need

Draw each figure described below.

1. a rectangle with small squares drawn in each corner

2. a rectangle divided into eight congruent rectangles

3. two parallelograms that have different shapes but the same perimeter

GO for Help
Lesson 9-3

Math Strategies in Action When architects and product designers plan projects, they build models. They use many different prototypes to compare sizes and layouts.

1 EXAMPLE Real-World 🌐 Problem Solving

Packaging A box company makes boxes to hold popcorn. Each box is made by cutting the square corners out of a rectangular sheet of cardboard. The rectangle is $8\frac{1}{2}$ in. by 11 in. What are the dimensions of the box that will hold the most popcorn if the square corners have side lengths 1 in., 2 in., 3 in., and 4 in.?

Understand the Problem

1. What is the goal of the problem?

2. What information do you have to help you build a model?

Make a Plan

To find the size that will hold the greatest amount of popcorn, you must find the dimensions that will give you the greatest volume.

Build four boxes using sheets of $8\frac{1}{2}$ in.-by-11 in. paper. Test four whole-number lengths of cuts.

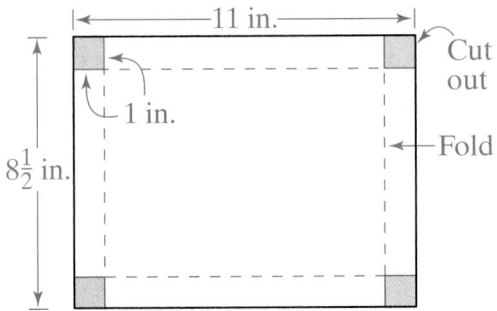

3. **a.** What are the dimensions of the box with corners 1 in. by 1 in.?
   b. What is the volume of this box?

4. When you cut a 2 in.-by-2 in. square from each corner, what effect does that have on the length, width, and height of the box?

Carry Out the Plan

Measure to find the dimensions of each of your boxes. Then find the volume of each box.

5. Which box has the greatest volume?

6. Is it possible to create a box with 5 in.-by-5 in. corners? Explain.

Check the Answer

A table is another way to organize your information and solve the problem.

7. List the size of the cut, and then find the length, width, and height of the box. Find each volume.

Size of Cut	Length	Width	Height	Volume
1 in.	9 in.	6.5 in.	1 in.	58.5 in.³
2 in.	■ in.	■ in.	■ in.	■ in.³
3 in.	■ in.	■ in.	■ in.	■ in.³
4 in.	■ in.	■ in.	■ in.	■ in.³

✓ Quick Check

8. **a.** Use a table to find the volume of a box folded from an $8\frac{1}{2}$ in.-by-11 in. sheet of paper if the square corners are $1\frac{1}{2}$ in.; $2\frac{1}{2}$ in.; $3\frac{1}{2}$ in.
   b. Did you find dimensions of a box that holds a greater volume than you did in Question 7? Which dimensions are they?

EXERCISES

For more exercises, see *Extra Skill and Word Problem Practice*.

Practice and Problem Solving

A Practice by Example

Example 1
(page 568)

GO for Help

Solve by making a model.

1. You cut square corners off a piece of cardboard with dimensions 16 in. by 20 in. You then fold the cardboard to create a box with no lid. To the nearest inch, what dimensions will give you the greatest volume?

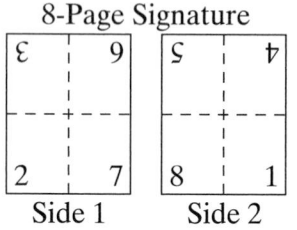

8-Page Signature

Side 1   Side 2

2. **Publishing** Newspapers, books, and magazines often are printed in groups of 8, 16, or 32 pages, called *signatures*. The diagram at the left shows how pages should be positioned for an 8-page signature. The pages are positioned to print on both sides of the paper that is fed through the printing press. When the paper is folded, the pages are in order. Make a model to show one way to position the pages in a 16-page book.

B Apply Your Skills

Solve using any strategy.

3. The length of a rectangle is twice its width. The perimeter of the rectangle is 90 cm. What are the length and width?

Strategies

- Act It Out
- Draw a Diagram
- Guess, Check, Revise
- Look for a Pattern
- Make a Model
- Make a Table
- Simulate the Problem
- Solve by Graphing
- Use Multiple Strategies
- Work a Simpler Problem
- Work Backward
- Write an Equation
- Write a Proportion

4. **Packaging** A company packages snack mix in cylindrical tubes. Each tube is made from a rectangle of cardboard. The bases of the cylinder are plastic. The cardboard comes in $8\frac{1}{2}$ in.-by-11 in. sheets. To hold the greatest amount of mix, should the longer side or shorter side be the height? Justify your answer.

5. **Pets** A dog owner wants to use 200 ft of fencing to enclose the greatest possible area for his dog. He wants the fenced area to be rectangular. What dimensions should he use?

6. **Writing in Math** You want to find how the length of a pendulum affects the time the pendulum takes to swing back and forth. Explain how you would model the situation.

7. An alphabet book will have one letter on each page. Eight pages will be printed on a single piece of paper. You fold the paper in half. Then you fold it in half again and trim the edges. The eight pages appear in order. Draw the layout for two sides of the large sheet for the letters A–H. Explain why two layouts are possible.

C Challenge

8. **Reasoning** In the parts (a)–(c), how many of the indicated cubes are there in this 3-by-3-by-3 cube?
    a. 1-by-1-by-1 cubes
    b. 2-by-2-by-2-cubes
    c. 3-by-3-by-3 cubes
    d. How many 3-by-3-by-3 cubes would be in a 5-by-5-by-5 cube?

GO Online
Homework Video Tutor
Visit: PHSchool.com
Web Code: ade-1008

9. One base of a trapezoid is twice as long as the other base. The height is the same as the shorter base. If the area is 24 cm^2, what is the height of the trapezoid?

Multiple Choice

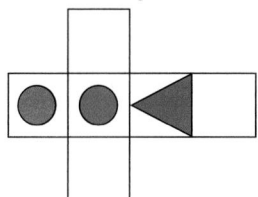

Which space figure below can you fold from the net at the left?

A rectangle has a perimeter of 24. The length and width are integers. For the least possible area, what are its dimensions?

    1 by 11   1 by 24   2 by 4   6 by 6

If you double the height and width of a rectangular prism, how many times greater is the volume?

    $\frac{1}{4}$ $\frac{1}{2}$ 2   4

Mixed Review

Lesson 10-7

 for Help

Find the volume of each figure, to the nearest tenth.

13.   **14.**   **15.**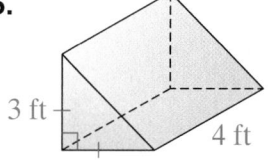

Lesson 8-2

Find the solutions of each equation when x is 0, 1, and -1.

16. $2x - y = 10$ **17.** $5x + y = 15$ **18.** $2x + 3y = 6$

Checkpoint Quiz 2   Lessons 10-4 through 10-8

Name each space figure. Find its surface area, to the nearest square unit.

1.   **2.**   **3.**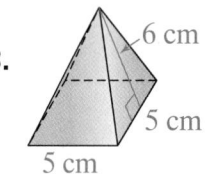

Find the volume of each figure to the nearest tenth.

4.   **5.**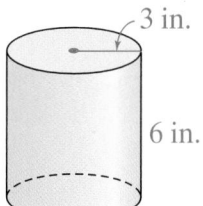

6. Open-Ended Choose a space figure. Draw its net.

10-9

Volume: Pyramids, Cones, and Spheres

What You'll Learn

- To find volumes of pyramids and cones
- To find volumes of spheres

. . . And Why

To find out how much water is displaced by a space figure

 Check Skills You'll Need

Multiply.

1. $\frac{1}{3}(3.14)(2)^2(5)$

2. $\frac{1}{3}(4)^2(6)$

3. $\frac{4}{3}(3.14)(2)^3$

4. $\frac{4}{3}(3.14)(0.5)^3$

GO for Help
Lesson 5-4

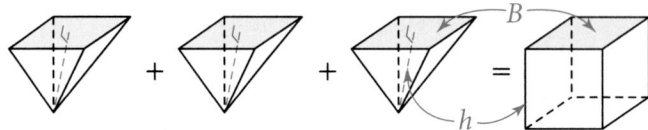

1 Finding Volumes of Cones and Pyramids

You can fill three pyramids with sand and pour the contents into a prism with the same height and base. You will fill the prism evenly to the top.

The volume of the pyramid is one third the volume of the prism.

The same relationship is true of a cone and a cylinder with the same radius and height.

Key Concepts | Volume of a Cone and of a Pyramid

The volume V of a cone or a pyramid is $\frac{1}{3}$ the product of the base area B and the height h.

$$V = \frac{1}{3}Bh$$

1 EXAMPLE Finding Volume of a Cone

Find the volume of the cone.

$V = \frac{1}{3}Bh$ **Use the formula for volume.**

$V = \frac{1}{3}\pi r^2 h$ $B = \pi r^2$

$\approx \frac{1}{3}(3.14)(3)^2(10)$ **Replace r with 3 and h with 10. Simplify.**

$= 94.2$

The volume of the cone is about 94 ft^3.

 Quick Check

1. Find the volume, to the nearest cubic unit, of a cone with height 5 cm and radius of base 2 cm.

GO Online

Video Tutor Help
Visit: PHSchool.com
Web Code: ada-0775

Finding Volume of a Pyramid

Find the volume of the square pyramid.

$V = \frac{1}{3}Bh$ **Use the formula for volume.**

$V = \frac{1}{3}s^2h$ $B = s^2$

$= \frac{1}{3}(6)^2(10)$ **Replace s with 6 and h with 10.**

$= 120$ **Simplify.**

10 ft

6 ft

The volume of the pyramid is 120 ft³.

✓ Quick Check

2. Find the volume of a square pyramid that has a side of 5 ft and a height of 20 ft.

2 Finding Volumes of Spheres

Below is the formula for the volume of a sphere.

Key Concepts   **Volume of a Sphere**

The volume V of a sphere with radius r is $\frac{4}{3}\pi$ times the cube of the radius.

$$V = \frac{4}{3}\pi r^3$$

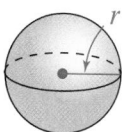

r

---

3 EXAMPLE   **Real-World ⚙ Problem Solving**

Snow Spheres You build a snow statue with snow spheres. What is the volume of the snow in the bottom sphere?

$V = \frac{4}{3}\pi r^3$ **Use the volume formula.**

$\approx \frac{4}{3}(3.14)(1.5)^3$ **Replace r with 1.5.**

$= 14.13$ **Simplify.**

The volume of the bottom snow sphere is about 14 ft³.

✓ Quick Check

3. Find the volume of each sphere to the nearest whole number.

   a. radius = 15 m   **b.** diameter = 7 mi

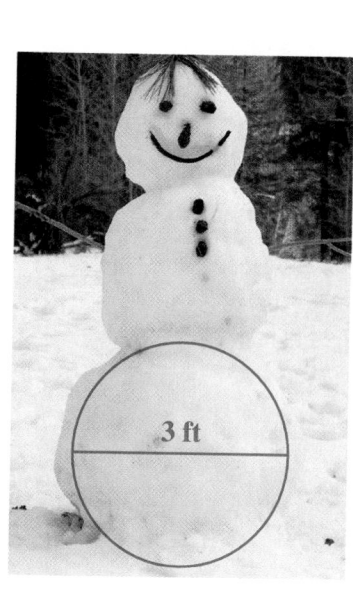

3 ft

EXERCISES

For more exercises, see *Extra Skill and Word Problem Practice*.

Practice and Problem Solving

A **Practice by Example**

Example 1
(page 572)

In Exercises 1–4, find the volume of each cone to the nearest cubic unit.

1.
6 yd
2 yd

2.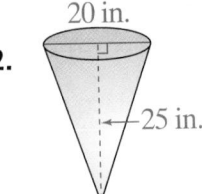
20 in.
25 in.

3. height 12 cm, radius 21 cm

4. height 7 in., radius 7 in.

Example 2
(page 573)

In Exercises 5–8, find the volume of each square pyramid.

5.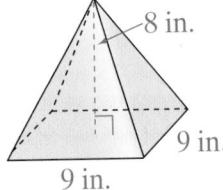
8 in.
9 in.
9 in.

6.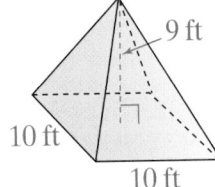
9 ft
10 ft
10 ft

7. edge 3.2 cm, height 6 cm

8. edge 90 mm, height 300 mm

Example 3
(page 573)

Find the volume of each sphere to the nearest whole number.

9.
10 in.

10.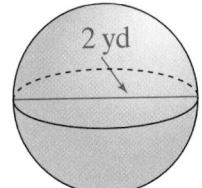
2 yd

11. $r = 12$ cm   12. $r = 3.5$ in.   13. $d = 60$ yd   14. $d = 30$ m

B **Apply Your Skills**

15. **Plants** A cone-shaped paper cup is 7 cm high with a diameter of 6 cm. If the ivy plant on Julia's desk needs 240 mL of water, about how many paper cups of water will she use to water it? (1 mL = 1 cm^3)

16. **Snacks** How much frozen yogurt can you pack inside a cone that is 5 in. high with a radius of 1.25 in.?

17. **Packaging** Tennis balls with a diameter of 2.5 in. are sold in cans of three (left). The can is a cylinder. What is the volume of the space in the can not occupied by tennis balls? Assume the balls touch the can on the sides, top, and bottom.

18. **Writing in Math** Explain how you remember formulas for finding volumes of prisms and pyramids, cylinders and cones, and spheres.

19. **Physics** You place a steel ball with diameter 4 cm in a water-filled cylinder that is 5 cm in diameter and 10 cm high. What volume of water will spill out of the cylinder?

574 Chapter 10   Area and Volume

Find the missing dimension. Round to the nearest unit.

20.

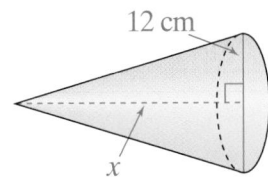

12 cm

x

$V = 819 \text{ cm}^3$
Height ≈ ■

21.

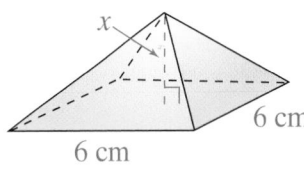

x

6 cm

6 cm

$V = 38 \text{ cm}^3$
Height = ■

22. Sphere: volume $= 36\pi \text{ yd}^3$, diameter $= $ ■

23. Cone: volume $= 424 \text{ m}^3$, diameter $= 18 \text{ m}$, height ≈ ■

C Challenge

24. You want to fill the top part of an hourglass $\frac{2}{3}$ full of salt. The height of the hourglass is 20 cm, and the radius of the base is 8 cm. Find the volume of salt needed.

25. Error Analysis A student tells a class that if you double the radius of a sphere, the volume will be multiplied by 6. Explain the student's error.

ISAT

Test Prep

Gridded Response

26. The eight segments from the center of a cube to the eight corners of the cube form the edges of six pyramids. If one edge of the cube is 4 in., what is the volume of each pyramid, to the nearest cubic inch?

27. What is the volume of a square pyramid with height 3.25 yd and base edge 5.5 yd, to the nearest tenth of a cubic yard?

28. What is the volume of a sphere with diameter 5.5 m, to the nearest cubic meter?

29. What is the volume of a cone with radius 4.8 cm and height 1.2 cm, to the nearest tenth of a cubic centimeter? Use 3.14 for π.

30. How many cones of radius 1 m and height 1 m have total volume equal to the volume of a sphere with radius 1 m?

Mixed Review

GO **for Help**

Lesson 7-5

Solve each equation.

31. $\frac{5}{6}x = \frac{1}{6}x + 12$ **32.** $5y + 2 = 3y - 10$ **33.** $3a + 10 = 12 - 2a$

Lesson 5-9

Simplify each expression.

34. $(3ab^2)^3$ **35.** $-(4x)^2$ **36.** $(-2p^2)^4$ **37.** $\left(-\frac{3}{8}\right)^2$ **38.** $\left(\frac{2x}{y^3}\right)^2$

Scaling and Volume

For Use With Lesson 10-9

Similar solids have the same shape, and all their corresponding dimensions are proportional. The ratio of corresponding edge lengths of two similar solids is the *similarity ratio*.

1 ACTIVITY

The rectangular prisms at the right are similar.
  a. Find the similarity ratio.
  b. Find the ratio of the surface areas.
  c. Find the ratio of the volumes.

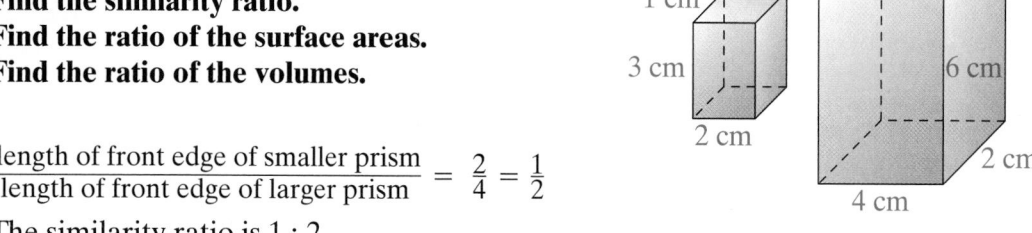

1 cm
3 cm
2 cm
4 cm
6 cm
2 cm

a. $\dfrac{\text{length of front edge of smaller prism}}{\text{length of front edge of larger prism}} = \dfrac{2}{4} = \dfrac{1}{2}$

The similarity ratio is 1 : 2.

b. The ratio of the surface areas is the square of the similarity ratio.

$\left(\dfrac{1}{2}\right)^2 = \dfrac{1^2}{2^2} = \dfrac{1}{4}$

The ratio of the surface areas is 1 : 4.

GO for Help

For a guide to area ratios, see pages 531–532.

c. Calculate the volume of each prism. Then find the ratio.

volume of smaller prism = $1 \times 2 \times 3 = 6$
volume of larger prism = $2 \times 4 \times 6 = 48$

$\dfrac{\text{volume of smaller prism}}{\text{volume of larger prism}} = \dfrac{6}{48} = \dfrac{1}{8}$

The ratio of the volumes is 1 : 8.

You can use what you know about exponents to compare the similarity ratio and the ratio of volumes.

2 ACTIVITY

Use exponents to relate the similarity ratio to the ratio of the volumes that you found in Activity 1.

Since $8 = 2 \cdot 2 \cdot 2 = 2^3$, raise the similarity ratio to the third power.

$\left(\dfrac{1}{2}\right)^3 = \dfrac{1^3}{2^3} = \dfrac{1}{8}$

The ratio of volumes is the similarity ratio raised to the third power.

You can use a proportion to find the volumes of similar solids.

3 **ACTIVITY**

The cubes at the right are similar. Find the volume V of the larger cube.

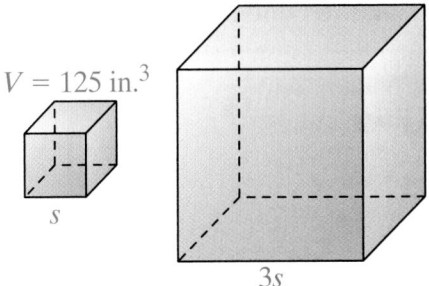

$V = 125$ in.^{3}

The ratio of the volumes is $\left(\frac{1}{3}\right)^3$, or $\frac{1}{27}$.

$\frac{1}{27} = \frac{125}{V}$ **Write a proportion.**

$V = 27 \cdot 125$ **Use cross-products.**

$\quad = 3{,}375$ **Multiply.**

● The volume of the larger cube is 3,375 in.^{3}.

EXERCISES

Each pair of prisms is similar. Find the similarity ratio and ratio of volumes of each.

1.

3 mm   2 mm   6 mm   4 mm
3 mm   6 mm

2.

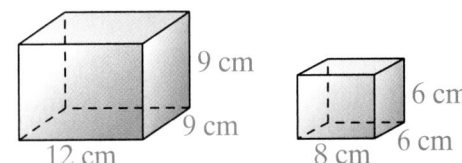

9 cm   6 cm
9 cm   6 cm
12 cm   8 cm

3.

4 m   6 m
4 m   6 m
4 m   6 m
6 m

4.

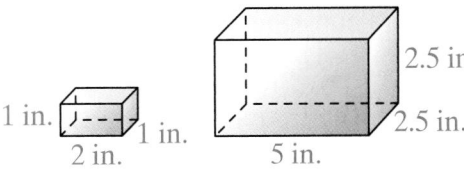

2.5 in.
1 in.   2.5 in.
1 in.
2 in.   5 in.

Each pair of prisms is similar. Find the volume of the larger prism.

5.

$V = 64$ ft^3

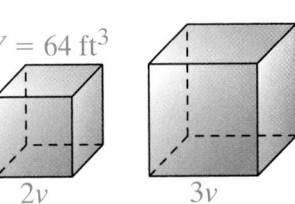

2v   3v

6.

$V = 192$ m^3

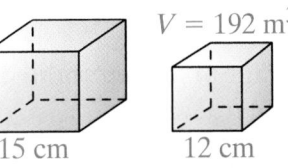

15 cm   12 cm

7.

$V = 3.375$ yd^3

1.5b yd   2.25b yd

8.

$V = 6$ in.^{3}

r   2r

Some multiple-choice questions cannot be answered because there is insufficient information or there is more than one possible answer. If so, then one of the answer choices will be "cannot be determined."

1 EXAMPLE

What is the surface area of the figure at the right?

A. 2,600 in.^{2} **B.** 3,200 in.^{2} **C.** 8,600 in.^{2} **D.** cannot be determined

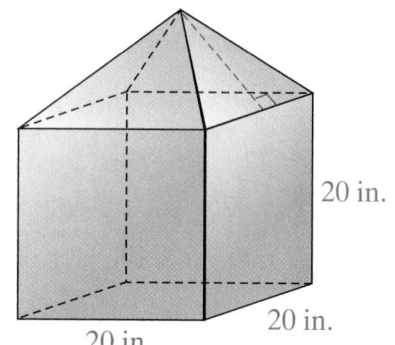

20 in.

20 in.

20 in.

The bottom part is a cube. You know its length, width, and height, so you can find its base area and its lateral area. The top part is a pyramid. You know the perimeter of the base, but you need to know the slant height of its faces to find its lateral area.

● There is insufficient information. The correct choice is D.

2 EXAMPLE

A rectangular prism with height 5 cm has volume 60 cm^3. What is the perimeter of the base?

F. 14 cm   **G.** 16 cm   **H.** 26 cm   **J.** cannot be determined

You know $V = Bh$.

$$60 = B(5) \qquad \textbf{Replace } \textbf{\textit{V}} \textbf{ with 60 and } \textbf{\textit{h}} \textbf{ with 5.}$$

$$12 = B \qquad \textbf{Solve for } \textbf{\textit{B}}.$$

For $B = 12$ cm^2, the rectangular base can be 1 cm by 12 cm, 2 cm by 6 cm, or 3 cm by 4 cm. The perimeter can be 26 cm (choice H), 16 cm (choice G), or 14 cm (choice A).

● There is more than one possible answer. The correct choice is J.

EXERCISES

If the answer to an exercise cannot be determined, choose "cannot be determined" and explain your reasoning.

1. The base of a square prism has sides of 14 in. What is the surface area of the prism?

   A. 56 in.^{2} **B.** 196 in.^{2} **C.** 784 in.^{2} **D.** cannot be determined

2. A trapezoid has height 8 and area 28. What are the lengths of its bases?

   F. 6 and 1   **G.** 5 and 2   **H.** 4 and 3   **J.** cannot be determined

Chapter Review

Vocabulary Review

altitude (p. 527)
altitude of a triangle (p. 533)
area (p. 526)
cone (p. 545)
cubic unit (p. 563)

cylinder (p. 545)
lateral area (p. 552)
net (p. 546)
prism (p. 545)
pyramid (p. 545)

slant height (p. 558)
space figure (p. 545)
sphere (p. 545)
surface area (p. 551)
volume (p. 563)

Choose the vocabulary term that correctly completes the sentence.

1. The sum of the areas of the lateral faces of a prism is the __?__ of a prism.

2. A __?__ is a space figure with one circular base and one vertex.

3. The __?__ of a parallelogram is a line segment drawn from the side opposite the base to the base, that is perpendicular to the base.

4. The __?__ of a three-dimensional figure is the number of cubic units needed to fill it.

5. The set of all points in space that are a given distance from a given point called the center is a __?__ .

6. A __?__ has two parallel bases that are congruent circles.

7. The __?__ of a figure is the number of square units it encloses.

Go Online
PHSchool.com
For: Vocabulary quiz
Web Code: adj-1051

Skills and Concepts

10-1 and 10-2 Objectives

▼ To find areas of rectangles (p. 526)

▼ To find areas of parallelograms (p. 527)

▼ To find areas of triangles (p. 533)

▼ To find areas of trapezoids (p. 534)

The **area** of a polygon is the number of square units enclosed by the polygon. To find the areas of parallelograms, triangles, or trapezoids, use the appropriate formulas.

parallelogram

$A = bh$

triangle

$A = \frac{1}{2}bh$

trapezoid

$A = \frac{1}{2}h(b_1 + b_2)$

Find the area of the shaded region in each figure.

8. Parallelogram

9. Trapezoid

2 cm
4 cm
5 cm

10.

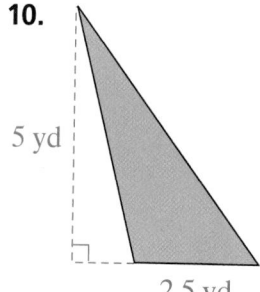

5 yd

2.5 yd

21 m

9 m

To find the area of a circle, use the formula $A = \pi r^2$. Use 3.14 for π.

Find the area of each figure to the nearest square unit.

11.
10 m

12.
8 mm

13.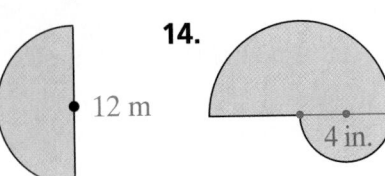
12 m

14.
4 in.

Name **pyramids** and **prisms** by the shapes of their bases. A **cylinder** is a space figure with two circular bases. **Cones** have one circular base and one vertex. **Nets** are flat patterns for space figures.

Name the space figure represented by each net.

15.

16.

17.

The **lateral area** of a prism is the sum of the areas of the lateral faces. The lateral area of a cylinder is the area of the curved surface. The **surface area** of a prism or a cylinder is the sum of the lateral area and the areas of the two bases.

To find surface area, use the appropriate formula.

prism	cylinder
L.A. = ph	L.A. = $2\pi rh$
S.A. = L.A. + $2B$	S.A. = L.A. + $2B$

Find the surface area to the nearest square unit. Use 3.14 for π.

18.
3 cm
4 cm
10 cm

19.
85 m
300 m

20.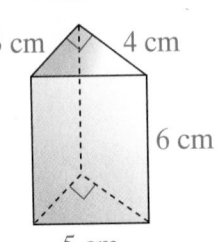
3 cm   4 cm
6 cm
5 cm

21.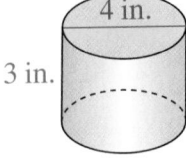
4 in.
3 in.

10-6 Objectives

▼ To find surface areas of pyramids (p. 558)

▼ To find surface areas of cones and spheres (p. 559)

For pyramids and cones, use **slant height** ℓ to find the lateral area. For a regular pyramid, if n is the number of lateral faces, you can find the area of one face and then multiply by n. The lateral area of a cone is the area of the curved surface. The surface area of a pyramid or a cone is the sum of the lateral area and the base area.

To find surface area, use the appropriate formula.

pyramid	cone	sphere
$\text{L.A.} = n\left(\frac{1}{2}b\ell\right)$	$\text{L.A.} = \pi r\ell$	
$\text{S.A.} = \text{L.A.} + B$	$\text{S.A.} = \text{L.A.} + B$	$\text{S.A.} = 4\pi r^2$

Find the surface area of each figure, to the nearest square unit.

22.

4 cm, 6 cm, 6 cm

23.

6 cm, 3 cm

24.
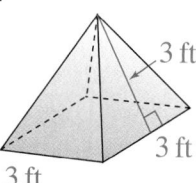
5 ft

25.
3 ft, 3 ft, 3 ft

10-8 Objective

▼ To make a model (p. 568)

To solve some problems, make a model.

26. A gift box measures 6 in. along each edge. You cut a rectangular sheet of wrapping paper to get a single piece with which you can cover the box without overlapping. What are the smallest possible dimensions of the original sheet of wrapping paper?

27. A 12 m-by-15 m rectangular garden has a walk 1 m wide around it. Describe how you would find the area of the walk.

10-7 and 10-9 Objectives

▼ To find volumes of prisms (p. 563)

▼ To find volumes of cylinders (p. 564)

▼ To find volumes of cones and pyramids (p. 572)

▼ To find volumes of spheres (p. 573)

Volume is the measure of how much a space figure can hold.

To find volume, use the appropriate formula.

prisms and cylinders	pyramids and cones	spheres
$V = Bh$	$V = \frac{1}{3}Bh$	$V = \frac{4}{3}\pi r^3$

Find each volume to the nearest cubic unit.

28.

8, 12

29.

3, 2 ft, 3 ft

30.

6, 11

31.

8

Chapter Test

Go Online
PHSchool.com
For: Chapter test
Web Code: ada-1052

Use 3.14 for π as needed on this page.

Find the area of each figure.

1.

2.

3.

4.

5.

6.

Find the missing measures.

7. circle
$d = 4$ cm
$A = \blacksquare$ cm^2

8. triangle
$b = 7$ m
$h = 4$ m
$A = \blacksquare$ m^2

Name the space figure for each net.

9.

10.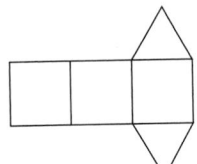

Find the surface area of each figure.

11.

12.

13.

14.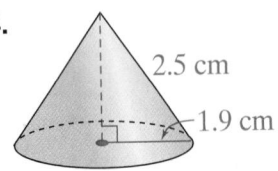

Find the volume of each figure to the nearest cubic unit.

15.

16.

17.

18.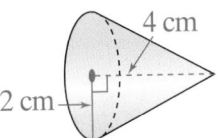

19. The height of a rectangle is doubled while the base is unchanged. How does this affect the area? Explain.

20. In cubic feet, how much greater is the volume of a cone with height 10 ft and radius 6 ft than the volume of a square pyramid with height 10 ft and base edge length 6 ft?

21. The diameter of Mars is about 4,000 mi.
   a. Find the approximate surface area.
   b. Find the approximate volume.

22. A box is 25.5 cm by 17 cm by 5 cm.
   a. How much dry dishwashing detergent can it hold?
   b. Without overlap, how much cardboard is needed to make the box?

23. **Writing in Math** How is the formula for volume of a prism like the formula for volume of a pyramid? How are the formulas different?

24. A rectangular piece of sheet metal measures 26 in. by 20 in. A square measuring 2 in. by 2 in. is cut out of each corner, and the sides are folded to form a box. What is the volume of the box?

25. **Open-Ended** Draw a net for a rectangular prism.

582 Chapter 10 Chapter Test

ISAT Test Prep

Multiple Choice

Choose the best answer.

1. The average nose has about 6,000,000 cells that detect odors. What is this number in scientific notation?
   - Ⓐ $6 \cdot 10^5$
   - Ⓑ $6 \cdot 10^6$
   - Ⓒ $6 \cdot 10^7$
   - Ⓓ $6 \cdot 10^8$

2. Which equation represents the statement *The sum of twice a number and five times another number is 40?*
   - Ⓔ $40 = 2x + 5y$
   - Ⓕ $5y = \frac{40}{2x}$
   - Ⓖ $2x \cdot 5y = 40$
   - Ⓗ $5y = \frac{1}{2}x + 40$

3. In which situation are two angles supplementary?
   - Ⓐ The sum of their measures is 180°.
   - Ⓑ They share a vertex.
   - Ⓒ The sum of their measures is 90°.
   - Ⓓ They have the same measure.

4. What space figure can you form from the net?
   - Ⓔ square pyramid
   - Ⓕ triangular pyramid
   - Ⓖ triangular prism
   - Ⓗ hexagonal prism

5. Figure A is a rectangle 10 in. long and 7.5 in. wide. Figure B is a parallelogram with height 12 in. and base length 7.5 in. Which statement is true?
   - Ⓐ area of A > area of B
   - Ⓑ area of A < area of B
   - Ⓒ area of A = area of B
   - Ⓓ cannot be determined

Gridded Response

Find each area.

6.

7.
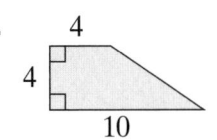

Find each area to the nearest square unit.

8.

9.
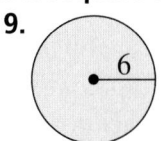

Find the surface area of each figure to the nearest square unit.

10.

11.

12.

13.

14.

15.
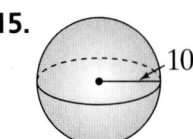

Short Response

Find the volume of each figure, to the nearest cubic unit. Show your work.

16.

17.

18.

19.

20.

21.
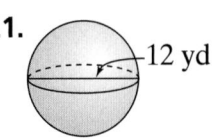

Extended Response

22. A cylinder has diameter 3 cm and height 6 cm. **(a)** Draw and label a net. **(b)** Find the surface area of the cylinder to the nearest square centimeter. **(c)** Find the volume.

Playing Fields

Applying Area Have you ever played a team sport such as soccer, basketball, or ice hockey? If so, you had to follow the rules of the game. You probably found that these include rules about your appearance and the equipment you use, as well as other game equipment such as goals, backboards, or hockey pucks. There are even rules for the space in which you play. One purpose of these rules is to provide all players with an equal chance of success.

Football Gridiron

Parallel lines run 5 yd apart from goal line to goal line along the playing area of a football field. The playing area, or gridiron, is 300 ft long.

For: Information about sports
Web Code: ade-1053

Hockey Rink

A hockey rink uses quarter circles with 28-ft radii to keep the puck from getting caught in the corners.

Basketball Court

A basketball court can be up to 4 yd shorter than regulation size and up to 2 yd narrower. Its dimensions must remain in proportion.

Soccer Field

Each soccer team plays both ends of the field during a game, switching goals after the first 45-min half.

Activity

1. Copy the table. Find the area of each field.

For Exercises 2 and 3, how many times the area of the smaller field is the area of the larger field?

2. a soccer field and a football field

3. a professional basketball court and a junior high basketball court

4. <u>Writing in Math</u> Why do you think the basketball courts are different sizes?

Playing Fields

Sport		Length	Width	Area
Basketball				
Professional and college		94 ft	50 ft	■
High school		82 ft	46 ft	■
Junior high school		74 ft	42 ft	■
Football (with end zones)		120 yd	$53\frac{1}{3}$ yd	■
Ice hockey		200 ft	85 ft	■
Soccer (maximum)		130 yd	100 yd	■

For Exercises 5–7, on each field, how much playing area is outside the indicated part? Round to the nearest whole number where necessary.

5. a professional basketball court, outside the two rectangular free-throw lanes, each 19 ft by 14 ft

6. a. a soccer field, outside two penalty areas, each 44 yd wide and 18 yd deep, in front of each goal

b. the same field, outside the two penalty areas and the 10-yd-radius center circle

7. a hockey rink, outside its five face-off circles, each with a radius of 15 ft

8. In the New York Giants' football stadium, the grass surface is 433 ft long and 269 ft wide. What is the area of the grass surface outside the playing field?

What You've Learned

IL Assessment Framework

- **8.8.12:** In Chapter 7, you learned to solve two-step equations and inequalities, multi-step equations, equations with variables on both sides, and to transform formulas.

- **9.8.06:** In Chapter 9, you learned about points, lines, and planes; congruence, constructions, translations, symmetry, and reflections.

- **7.8.04:** In Chapter 10, you learned to calculate areas, surface areas, and volumes.

Check Your Readiness

for Help to the Lesson in green.

Understanding Coordinates (Lesson 1-10)

Name the point with the given coordinates.

1. $(0, 3)$ **2.** $(1, -4)$ **3.** $(-2, 2)$

4. $(-5, -1)$ **5.** $(3, 5)$ **6.** $(6, -4)$

Write the coordinates of each point.

7. A **8.** E **9.** M

10. J **11.** L **12.** P

Simplifying Numbers With Exponents (Lesson 4-2)

Simplify each expression.

13. 10^2 **14.** 6^2 **15.** 2^2 **16.** 9^2 **17.** 11^2

18. 0.2^2 **19.** 7^2 **20.** 2.3^2 **21.** 4^2 **22.** 5^2

Solving Proportions (Lesson 6-2)

Solve each proportion.

23. $\frac{1}{3} = \frac{a}{12}$ **24.** $\frac{h}{5} = \frac{20}{25}$ **25.** $\frac{24}{6} = \frac{4}{x}$ **26.** $\frac{2}{7} = \frac{c}{35}$

27. $\frac{e}{5} = \frac{32}{80}$ **28.** $\frac{18}{g} = \frac{3}{10}$ **29.** $\frac{4}{11} = \frac{28}{m}$ **30.** $\frac{21}{13} = \frac{42}{a}$

31. $\frac{2}{15} = \frac{c}{75}$ **32.** $\frac{1}{4} = \frac{8}{x}$ **33.** $\frac{13}{p} = \frac{39}{51}$ **34.** $\frac{x}{20} = \frac{40}{100}$

Right Triangles in Algebra

🔊 **Key Vocabulary**

- angle of depression (p. 622)
- angle of elevation (p. 620)
- cosine (p. 614)
- distance (p. 598)
- hypotenuse (p. 592)
- irrational number (p. 589)
- legs (p. 592)
- midpoint (p. 600)
- perfect square (p. 588)
- sine (p. 614)
- square root (p. 588)
- tangent (p. 614)
- trigonometric ratio (p. 614)
- trigonometry (p. 614)

What You'll Learn Next

 Assessment Framework

In this chapter, you will learn how to

- **6.8.14:** Find the square roots of numbers.

- **9.8.03:** Find the missing measures of right triangles.

- Use the Distance and Midpoint Formulas.

- Solve a problem by writing a proportion.

 Activity Lab Applying what you learn, on pages 632–633 you will apply ratios to solve problems about proportions in rectangles.

11-1

Square Roots and Irrational Numbers

IL Assessment Framework

6.8.14 Estimate the square or cube root of a number less than 1,000 between two whole numbers.

✓ Check Skills You'll Need

Write the numbers in each list without using exponents.

1. $1^2, 2^2, 3^2, \ldots, 12^2$

2. $10^2, 20^2, 30^2, \ldots, 120^2$

GO for Help
Lesson 4-2

🔊 New Vocabulary

- perfect square
- square root
- irrational number

Vocabulary Tip

The symbol $\sqrt{100}$ is the positive square root of 100, so you may read $-\sqrt{100}$ as "the negative square root of 100."

---

1 Finding Square Roots

Consider the three squares shown below.

Each square has sides with integer length. The area of a square is the *square* of the length of a side. The square of an integer is a **perfect square.**

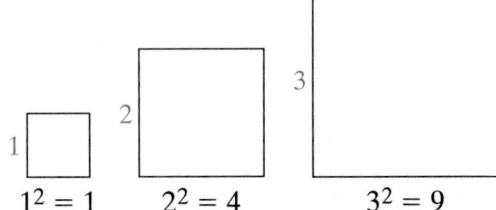

$1^2 = 1$ $2^2 = 4$ $3^2 = 9$

The inverse of squaring a number is finding a **square root.** The square-root radical, $\sqrt{}$, indicates the nonnegative square root of a number. In this book, you may assume that an expression under a square-root radical is greater than or equal to zero.

1 EXAMPLE Simplifying Square Roots

Simplify each square root.

a. $\sqrt{64}$
$\sqrt{64} = 8$

b. $-\sqrt{121}$
$-\sqrt{121} = -11$

✓ Quick Check

1. Simplify each square root.
  a. $\sqrt{100}$ **b.** $-\sqrt{100}$ **c.** $\sqrt{16}$ **d.** $-\sqrt{16}$

The first thirteen perfect squares are

  $0, 1, 4, 9, 16, 25, 36, 49, 64, 81, 100, 121,$ and $144.$

Memorizing these will help you solve problems efficiently.

For an integer that is not a perfect square, you can estimate a square root. For example, 8 is between the perfect squares 4 and 9.

$$\sqrt{4} \qquad \qquad \sqrt{8}\ \sqrt{9}$$
$$\xleftarrow{\qquad} \underset{2}{|}\ |\ |\ |\ |\ |\ |\ |\ |\ |\ \underset{3}{|} \xrightarrow{\qquad} \quad \sqrt{8} \text{ is between } \sqrt{4} \text{ and } \sqrt{9}.$$

Since 8 is closer to 9 than to 4, $\sqrt{8}$ is closer to 3 than to 2. So, $\sqrt{8} \approx 3.$

EXAMPLE <u>Real-World</u> 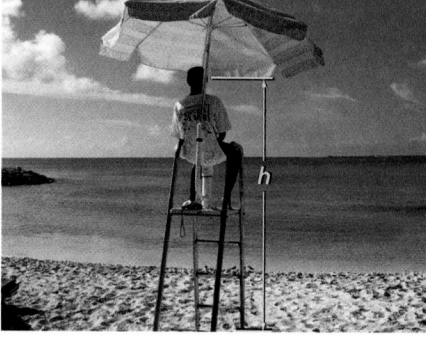Problem Solving

Lifeguarding You can use the formula $d = \sqrt{1.5h}$ to estimate the distance d, in miles, to a horizon line when your eyes are h feet above the ground. Estimate the distance to the horizon seen by a lifeguard whose eyes are 10 feet above the ground.

$d = \sqrt{1.5h}$	Use the formula.
$d = \sqrt{15}$	Replace h with 10 and multiply.
$\sqrt{9} < \sqrt{15} < \sqrt{16}$	Find perfect squares close to 15.
$\sqrt{16} = 4$	Find the square root of the closest perfect square.

The lifeguard can see about 4 miles to the horizon.

Real-World Connection

This lifeguard can see nearly 1 mile farther than he can standing on the beach.

✓ **Quick Check**

2. Estimate to the nearest integer.

a. $\sqrt{27}$ b. $-\sqrt{72}$ c. $\sqrt{50}$ d. $-\sqrt{22}$

---

2 **Classifying Real Numbers**

You can express a rational number as the ratio of two integers $\frac{a}{b}$, with $b \neq 0$. In decimal form, a rational number either terminates or repeats. An **irrational number** has decimal form that neither terminates nor repeats, and it cannot be written as the ratio of two integers. Together, rationals and irrationals form the real numbers.

If an integer is not a perfect square, its square root is irrational.

GO for Help

For a guide to rational numbers, see Lesson 4-6.

3 **EXAMPLE** **Identifying Irrational Numbers**

Use a calculator. Identify each number as rational or irrational.

a. $\sqrt{18}$ irrational, because 18 is not a perfect square

b. $\sqrt{121}$ rational, because 121 is a perfect square

c. 432.8   rational, because it is a terminating decimal

d. 0.1212 . . .   rational, because it is a repeating decimal

e. 0.120120012 . . .   irrational; it neither terminates nor repeats

f. π irrational; it cannot be represented as $\frac{a}{b}$, where a and b are integers

Online active math

For: Square Root Activity
Use: Interactive Textbook, 11-1

✓ **Quick Check**

3. Identify each number as rational or irrational. Explain.

a. $\sqrt{2}$ b. $-\sqrt{81}$ c. 0.53   d. $\sqrt{42}$

EXERCISES

For more exercises, see *Extra Skill and Word Problem Practice*.

Practice and Problem Solving

 Practice by Example

Example 1
(page 588)

Simplify each square root.

1. $\sqrt{4}$ **2.** $-\sqrt{36}$ **3.** $\sqrt{1}$ **4.** $\sqrt{25}$

5. $-\sqrt{49}$ **6.** $\sqrt{81}$ **7.** $-\sqrt{9}$ **8.** $-\sqrt{169}$

Example 2
(page 589)

Estimate to the nearest integer.

9. $\sqrt{10}$ **10.** $\sqrt{17}$ **11.** $-\sqrt{39}$ **12.** $-\sqrt{55}$

13. Viewing Distance The observation windows at the top of the Washington Monument in Washington, D.C., are 500 ft high. Using the formula $d = \sqrt{1.5h}$ of Example 2, estimate the distance you can see to the horizon from the observation windows.

Example 3
(page 589)

Use a calculator. Identify each number as rational or irrational. Explain.

14. 4.1010010001 . . . **15.** $\sqrt{87}$

16. $-\sqrt{16}$ **17.** $-0.\overline{3}$

18. $\sqrt{5}$ **19.** 2,222,222

20. $\sqrt{144}$ **21.** 0.31311 . . .

B **Apply Your Skills**

Simplify each square root.

22. $\sqrt{196}$ **23.** $\sqrt{\frac{4}{9}}$ **24.** $\sqrt{\frac{25}{49}}$ **25.** $\sqrt{\frac{36}{64}}$

Estimate to the nearest integer.

26. $\sqrt{7}$ **27.** $\sqrt{2}$ **28.** $\sqrt{40}$ **29.** $-\sqrt{80}$

30. $\sqrt{58}$ **31.** $-\sqrt{98}$ **32.** $\sqrt{14}$ **33.** $\sqrt{105}$

Identify each number as rational or irrational. Explain.

34. $\sqrt{0}$ **35.** 1.001001001 . . . **36.** 2.3010010001 . . .

37. Reasoning What do you get when you square $\sqrt{x}$?

38. Writing in Math A classmate was absent for today's lesson. Explain to him or her how to estimate $\sqrt{30}$.

39. a. Patterns You can create irrational numbers. For example, the number 1.010010001 . . . shows a pattern, yet it is irrational. What pattern do you see?

b. Open-Ended Name three irrational numbers between 9 and 10.

GO **Online**
Homework Video Tutor
Visit: PHSchool.com
Web Code: ade-1101

590 **Chapter 11** Right Triangles in Algebra

Algebra Find two integers that make each equation true.

40. $a^2 = 9$　　**41.** $b^2 = 25$　　**42.** $y^2 = 100$　　**43.** $m^2 = \frac{100}{25}$

44. Geometry Find the length of a side of a square with area 81 cm².

C Challenge **45. Geometry** The area of a circle is 12 in.². Estimate its radius to the nearest inch.

If a number is the product of three identical factors, each factor is the *cube root* of the number. Since $2^3 = 8$, 2 is the cube root of 8. In Exercises 46–49, find the number *n* that makes each equation true.

46. $n^3 = -8$　　**47.** $n^3 = 27$　　**48.** $n^3 = -27$　　**49.** $n^3 = 343$

On your graphing calculator, press MATH 4 to show the cube-root radical $\sqrt[3]{}$. Use it to find each cube root.

50. $\sqrt[3]{-8}$　　**51.** $\sqrt[3]{125}$　　**52.** $\sqrt[3]{-1{,}331}$　　**53.** $\sqrt[3]{15{,}625}$

Test Prep

ISAT

Multiple Choice　Joe is hiking in national park wilderness. His radio transmits signals as far as the horizon. Use the formula $d = \sqrt{1.5h}$, where d is the line-of-sight distance to the horizon in miles and h is height in feet, to answer the following questions.

54. Joe has the transmitter at a height of 6 ft. About how far is it from the transmitter to the horizon?
　A. 3 mi　　**B.** 5 mi　　**C.** 7 mi　　**D.** 9 mi

55. Joe sets his receiver on the ground. What is the farthest away that a transmitter 4 ft above the ground can be in order to reach Joe?
　F. 0 mi　　**G.** 1.2 mi　　**H.** 2.4 mi　　**J.** 6 mi

Short Response **56.** Joe wants to talk with his base camp that he knows is 6 mi away.
　(a) Explain how Joe could find the height at which he should have the transmitter. **(b)** Find that height.

Mixed Review

GO for Help

Lesson 10-9　**Find the volume of each figure in cubic centimeters.**

57. sphere with $r = 0.03$ m　　**58.** cone with $r = 4$ cm, $h = 10$ cm

Lesson 6-5 **59.** Shannon scored 17 correct on a 25-item test. The passing grade was 65%. Did Shannon pass? Explain.

Lesson 4-1 **List the positive factors of each number.**

60. 18　　**61.** 22　　**62.** 33　　**63.** 45　　**64.** 50　　**65.** 90

11-2 The Pythagorean Theorem

IL Assessment Framework

9.8.03 Find the length of any side of a right triangle using the Pythagorean theorem.

1 Using the Pythagorean Theorem

Activity

Exploring Right Triangles

1. On graph paper, create right triangles with legs a and b. Measure the length of the third side c with another piece of graph paper.

   Copy and complete the table below.

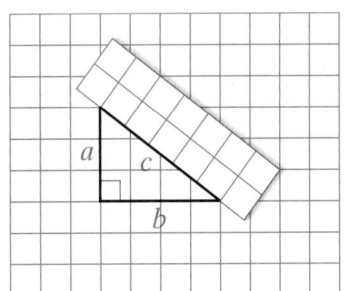

a	b	c	a^2	b^2	c^2
3	4	■	9	16	■
5	12	■	25	144	■
9	12	■	81	144	■

2. Based on your table, use $>$, $<$, or $=$ to complete the following statement.

$$a^2 + b^2 \;■\; c^2$$

Check Skills You'll Need

Simplify.

1. $4^2 + 6^2$ **2.** $5^2 + 8^2$

3. $7^2 + 9^2$ **4.** $9^2 + 3^2$

GO for Help
Lesson 4-2

🔊 **New Vocabulary**

- legs
- hypotenuse

Vocabulary Tip

A <u>right</u> <u>triangle</u> is a triangle with a 90° angle.

In a right triangle, the two shortest sides are **legs.** The longest side, which is opposite the right angle, is the **hypotenuse.** The Pythagorean Theorem shows how the legs and hypotenuse of a right triangle are related.

Key Concepts | Pythagorean Theorem

In any right triangle, the sum of the squares of the lengths of the legs is equal to the square of the length of the hypotenuse.

$$a^2 + b^2 = c^2$$

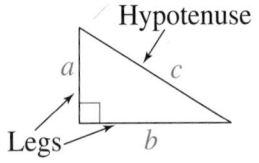

You will prove the Pythagorean Theorem in a future math class. For now, you will use the theorem to find the length of a leg or the length of a hypotenuse.

1 EXAMPLE Using the Pythagorean Theorem

Find c, the length of the hypotenuse, in the triangle at the right.

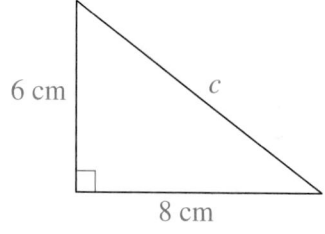

$c^2 = a^2 + b^2$ **Use the Pythagorean Theorem.**

$c^2 = 6^2 + 8^2$ **Replace a with 6 and b with 8.**

$c^2 = 100$ **Simplify.**

$c = \sqrt{100} = 10$ **Find the positive square root of each side.**

The length of the hypotenuse is 10 cm.

✓ Quick Check

1. The lengths of two sides of a right triangle are given. Find the length of the third side.

     a. legs: 3 ft and 4 ft   **b.** leg: 12 m; hypotenuse: 15 m

You can use a calculator or a table of square roots to find approximate values for square roots.

2 EXAMPLE Finding an Approximate Length

Find the value of x in the triangle at the right. Round to the nearest tenth.

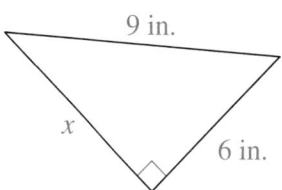

$a^2 + b^2 = c^2$ **Use the Pythagorean Theorem.**

$6^2 + x^2 = 9^2$ **Replace a with 6, b with x, and c with 9.**

$36 + x^2 = 81$ **Simplify.**

$x^2 = 45$ **Subtract 36 from each side.**

$x = \sqrt{45}$ **Find the positive square root of each side.**

Then use one of the two methods below to approximate $\sqrt{45}$.

Method 1 Use a calculator.
A calculator value for $\sqrt{45}$ is 6.7082039.

    $x \approx 6.7$ **Round to the nearest tenth.**

Method 2 Use a table of square roots.
Use the table on page 800. Find 45 in the N column. Then find the corresponding value in the $\sqrt{N}$ column. It is 6.708.

    $x \approx 6.7$ **Round to the nearest tenth.**

The value of x is about 6.7 in.

✓ Quick Check

2. In a right triangle, the length of the hypotenuse is 15 m and the length of a leg is 8 m. What is the length of the other leg, to the nearest tenth of a meter?

3 EXAMPLE **Real-World** **Problem Solving**

Multiple Choice The carpentry terms *span, rise,* and *rafter length* are illustrated in the diagram at the left. A carpenter wants to make a roof that has a span of 24 ft and a rise of 8.5 ft. What should the rafter length be?

 14.7 ft   Ⓑ 15.5 ft   Ⓒ 20.5 ft   Ⓓ 32.5 ft

$c^2 = a^2 + b^2$	Use the Pythagorean Theorem.
$c^2 = 12^2 + 8.5^2$	Use half the span, 12 ft. Replace *a* with 12 and *b* with 8.5.
$c^2 = 144 + 72.25$	Square 12 and 8.5.
$c^2 = 216.25$	Add.
$c = \sqrt{216.25}$	Find the positive square root.
$c \approx 14.7$	Round to the nearest tenth.

The rafter length should be about 14.7 ft. The answer is A.

Quick Check

3. **Carpentry** What is the rise of a roof if the span is 22 feet and the rafter length is 14 feet? Round to the nearest tenth of a foot.

2 **Identifying Right Triangles**

The *Converse of the Pythagorean Theorem* allows you to substitute the lengths of the sides of a triangle into the equation $a^2 + b^2 = c^2$ to check whether a triangle is a right triangle. If the equation is true, the triangle is a right triangle.

4 EXAMPLE **Finding a Right Triangle**

Is a triangle with sides 12 m, 15 m, and 20 m a right triangle?

$a^2 + b^2 = c^2$	Write the equation for the Pythagorean Theorem.
$12^2 + 15^2 \stackrel{?}{=} 20^2$	Replace *a* and *b* with the shorter lengths and *c* with the longest length.
$144 + 225 \stackrel{?}{=} 400$	Simplify.
$369 \neq 400$	

The triangle is not a right triangle.

Quick Check

4. Can you form a right triangle with the three lengths given? Explain.

   a. 7 in., 8 in., $\sqrt{113}$ in.   **b.** 5 mm, 6 mm, 10 mm

For more exercises, see *Extra Skill and Word Problem Practice.*

Practice and Problem Solving

 Practice by Example

Examples 1 and 2
(page 593)

 for Help

In each right triangle, find each missing length to the nearest tenth.

1.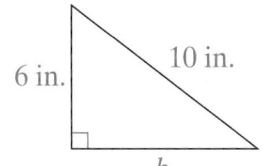
5 cm
c
12 cm

2.
8 m
8 m
k

3.
6 in.
10 in.
b

4.
6 mm
h
3 mm

The lengths of two sides of a right triangle are given. Find the length of the third side. Round to the nearest tenth where necessary.

5. legs: 12 in. and 16 in.

6. legs: 21 ft and 28 ft

7. leg: 48 ft; hypotenuse: 50 ft

8. leg: 33 ft; hypotenuse: 55 ft

Example 3
(page 594)

Use the Pythagorean Theorem to solve each problem.

9. Carpentry Use the diagram in Example 3 on page 594. A carpenter wants to make a roof that has a rise of 5 ft and a rafter length of 16 ft. What is the half span? The span?

10. House Painting A painter places an 11-ft ladder against a house. The base of the ladder is 3 ft from the house. How high on the house does the ladder reach?

11. Hiking Darla hikes due north for 6 km. She then turns due east and hikes 3 km. What is the direct distance between her starting point and stopping point, rounded to the nearest tenth of a kilometer?

Example 4
(page 594)

Can you form a right triangle with the three lengths given? Explain.

12. 4 m, 6 m, 7 m   **13.** 4 mi, 5 mi, 6 mi   **14.** 7 in., 24 in., 25 in.

15. $6, 7, \sqrt{85}$ **16.** 8 in., 10 in., 12 in.   **17.** 5 cm, 12 cm, 13 cm

 Apply Your Skills

Use the triangle at the right. Find the missing length to the nearest tenth of a unit.

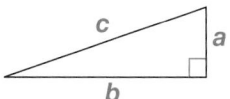
c
a
b

18. $a = 2$ in., $b = 4$ in., $c = $ ▨

19. $a = 1.4$ m, $b = 2.8$ m, $c = $ ▨

20. $a = 3$ ft, $c = 5$ ft, $b = $ ▨

21. $b = 2.7$ km, $c = 3.4$ km, $a = $ ▨

22. Reasoning Is a triangle with side lengths of $\sqrt{12}$ cm, $\sqrt{7}$ cm, and $\sqrt{5}$ cm a right triangle? Explain.

Any three positive integers that make $a^2 + b^2 = c^2$ true form a *Pythagorean triple*. Does each group of three integers below form a Pythagorean triple? Show your work.

23. $3, 4, 5$ **24.** $7, 24, 25$ **25.** $10, 24, 25$ **26.** $5, 12, 13$

27. For each group in Exercises 23–26 that forms a Pythagorean triple, multiply the integers by 2. Do the three new numbers form a Pythagorean triple? Show your work.

28. Landscaping Jim works for a landscaping company. He must plant and stake a tree. The stakes are 2 ft from the base of the tree. They are connected to wires that attach to the trunk at a height of 5 ft. If there is 6 in. of extra length at both ends of each wire, how long must each wire be, to the nearest tenth of a foot?

5 ft

2 ft

Can you form a right triangle having the three given lengths? Explain.

29. $\sqrt{5}$ yd, $\sqrt{3}$ yd, $\sqrt{2}$ yd   **30.** 1 m, 0.54 m, 0.56 m

31. Quilting The diagonals for a quilting frame must be the same length to ensure the frame is rectangular. What should the lengths of the diagonals be for a quilting frame 86 in. by 100 in.? Draw a sketch and then solve.

32. Writing in Math Can you form a right triangle having side lengths of $3p$ ft, $4p$ ft, and $5p$ ft? Explain.

C Challenge

d_2

4 in.

d_1

8 in.

6 in.

33. Geometry In the rectangular prism at the left, d_1 is the diagonal of the base of the prism, and d_2 is the *diagonal of the prism*.
  a. Find d_1.
  b. The triangle formed by d_1, d_2, and the side that is 4 in. is a right triangle. Use your answer to part (a) to find d_2.
  c. Find the diagonal of a rectangular prism with dimensions 9 in., 12 in., and 5 in.

Find the value of n in each diagram. Give your answer as a square root.

34.

35.

36.

37.

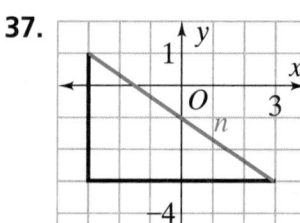

Multiple Choice

For Exercises 38 and 39, the lengths of two sides of a right triangle are given. What is the length of the third side?

38. legs: 36 m and 48 m

   A. 5 m   **B.** 12 m   **C.** 50 m   **D.** 60 m

39. leg: 6 m; hypotenuse: $\sqrt{85}$ m

   F. 7 m   **G.** 8 m   **H.** 9 m   **J.** 10 m

Extended Response

40. a. Can segments with lengths 3 ft, 4 ft, and 5 ft form a right triangle? Explain.

   b. Ancient builders are said to have used ropes with 12 equally-spaced knots to make sure that square corners were indeed right angles. How could you use such a rope to determine whether a corner in your room forms a right angle?

   c. Explain your answer in part (b).

Mixed Review

Lesson 11-1

Identify each number as rational or irrational.

41. $\sqrt{36}$ **42.** $0.\overline{6}$ **43.** $-\sqrt{12}$ **44.** -33.3 **45.** $0.\overline{654}$

Lesson 5-9

Simplify each expression.

46. $(bc)^5$ **47.** $(2x^2)^4$ **48.** $(-3b)^3$ **49.** $(a^5b^2)^4$ **50.** $\left(\frac{3m}{5}\right)^2$

Lesson 4-9 **51. Geography** Greenland is the world's largest island and has an area of 2,175,600 km². Express this area in scientific notation.

Math at Work

Air-Traffic Controller

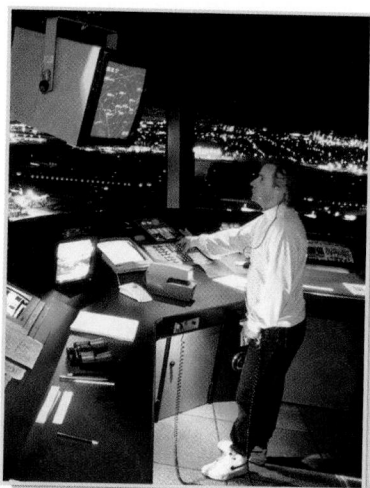

When we think of airline safety, many of us think of pilots. But there is also a network of people, the air-traffic controllers, who work hard to ensure the safe operation of aircraft. Using radar and visual observation, they closely monitor the location of each plane. They coordinate the movement of air traffic to make certain that aircraft stay a safe distance apart. They also coordinate landings and takeoffs to keep delays at a minimum.

In their jobs, air-traffic controllers use angle measurements in some of the same ways you do when you solve problems in algebra and geometry.

Go Online
PHSchool.com

For: Information about air-traffic controllers
Web Code: adb-2031

11-3 Distance and Midpoint Formulas

What You'll Learn

- To find the distance between two points using the Distance Formula
- To find the midpoint of a segment using the Midpoint Formula

. . . And Why

To find the perimeters of figures on the coordinate plane

✓ Check Skills You'll Need

Write the coordinates of each point.

1. A **2.** D **3.** G **4.** J

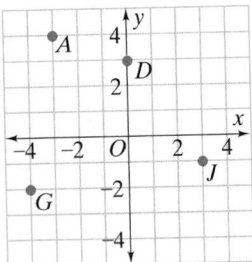

GO for Help
Lesson 1-10

◄)) New Vocabulary

- distance
- midpoint

1 Finding Distance

In the graph at the right, you can locate point $C(7, 1)$ to form a right triangle with points $A(2, 1)$ and $B(7, 3)$. Using the Pythagorean Theorem, you can find AB.

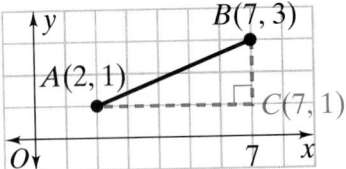

$$(AB)^2 = (AC)^2 + (BC)^2$$

$$(AB)^2 = (7 - 2)^2 + (3 - 1)^2$$
AC equals the difference in x values.
BC equals the difference in y values.

$$(AB)^2 = 5^2 + 2^2$$ **Simplify.**

$$AB = \sqrt{25 + 4} = \sqrt{29} \approx 5.4$$ **Find the square root.**

You can use the Pythagorean Theorem to find the length of a segment on a coordinate plane, or you can use the *Distance Formula*. The Distance Formula is based on the Pythagorean Theorem.

Key Concepts | **Distance Formula**

You can find the **distance** d between any two points (x_1, y_1) and (x_2, y_2):

$$d = \sqrt{(x_2 - x_1)^2 + (y_2 - y_1)^2}$$

---

1 EXAMPLE | Using the Distance Formula

Find the distance between $A(6, 3)$ and $B(1, 9)$.

$$d = \sqrt{(x_2 - x_1)^2 + (y_2 - y_1)^2}$$ **Use the Distance Formula.**

$$d = \sqrt{(1 - 6)^2 + (9 - 3)^2}$$ **Replace (x_2, y_2) with (1, 9) and (x_1, y_1) with (6, 3).**

$$d = \sqrt{(-5)^2 + 6^2}$$ **Simplify.**

$$d = \sqrt{61}$$ **Find the exact distance.**

$$d \approx 7.8$$ **Round to the nearest tenth.**

The distance between A and B is about 7.8 units.

✓ Quick Check

1. Find the distance between the two points in each pair. Round to the nearest tenth.

   a. $(3, 8), (2, 4)$ **b.** $(10, -3), (1, 0)$

You can also use the Distance Formula to solve geometry problems. Wait until the last step to round your answer.

② EXAMPLE   Finding Perimeter

Find the perimeter of $ABCD$.

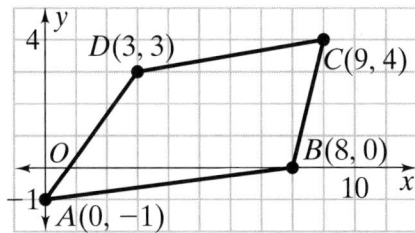

Use the Distance Formula to find the side lengths.

$AB = \sqrt{(8 - 0)^2 + (0 - (-1))^2}$ **Replace (x_2, y_2) with (8, 0) and (x_1, y_1) with (0, −1).**

$\quad = \sqrt{64 + 1} = \sqrt{65}$ **Simplify.**

$BC = \sqrt{(9 - 8)^2 + (4 - 0)^2}$ **Replace (x_2, y_2) with (9, 4) and (x_1, y_1) with (8, 0).**

$\quad = \sqrt{1 + 16} = \sqrt{17}$ **Simplify.**

$CD = \sqrt{(3 - 9)^2 + (3 - 4)^2}$ **Replace (x_2, y_2) with (3, 3) and (x_1, y_1) with (9, 4).**

$\quad = \sqrt{36 + 1} = \sqrt{37}$ **Simplify.**

$DA = \sqrt{(0 - 3)^2 + ((-1) - 3)^2}$ **Replace (x_2, y_2) with (0, −1) and (x_1, y_1) with (3, 3).**

$\quad = \sqrt{9 + 16} = \sqrt{25} = 5$ **Simplify.**

$\text{perimeter} = \sqrt{65} + \sqrt{17} + \sqrt{37} + 5 \approx 23.268126$

The perimeter is about 23.3 units.

✓ Quick Check

2. Find the perimeter of $\triangle DEF$ at the right. Round to the nearest tenth.

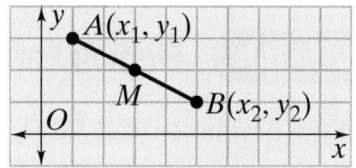

2 / Finding the Midpoint

The **midpoint** of a segment $\overline{AB}$ is the point M on $\overline{AB}$ halfway between the endpoints A and B where $AM = MB$.

Key Concepts   Midpoint Formula

You can find the midpoint of a line segment with endpoints $A(x_1, y_1)$ and $B(x_2, y_2)$:

$$M\left(\frac{x_1 + x_2}{2}, \frac{y_1 + y_2}{2}\right)$$

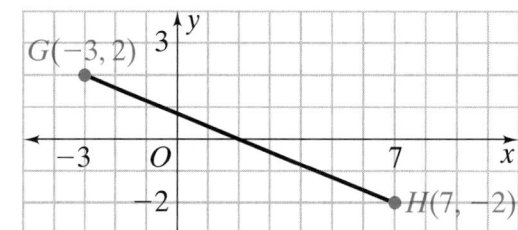

3 EXAMPLE   Finding the Midpoint of a Segment

Multiple Choice **What are the coordinates of the midpoint of $\overline{GH}$?**

Ⓐ $(-3, 2)$ Ⓑ $(0, 2)$ Ⓒ $(2, 0)$ Ⓓ $(7, 2)$

$\left(\dfrac{x_1 + x_2}{2}, \dfrac{y_1 + y_2}{2}\right)$ **Use the Midpoint Formula.**

$= \left(\dfrac{-3 + 7}{2}, \dfrac{2 + (-2)}{2}\right)$ **Replace (x_1, y_1) with $(-3, 2)$ and (x_2, y_2) with $(7, -2)$.**

$= \left(\dfrac{4}{2}, \dfrac{0}{2}\right)$ **Simplify the numerators.**

$= (2, 0)$ **Write the fractions in simplest form.**

The coordinates are $(2, 0)$. The answer is C.

Test-Taking Tip

The x-coordinate of the midpoint is the mean of the x-coordinates of the endpoints. The same is true for the y-coordinate.

✓ Quick Check

3. Find the midpoint of each segment.

a.

b.
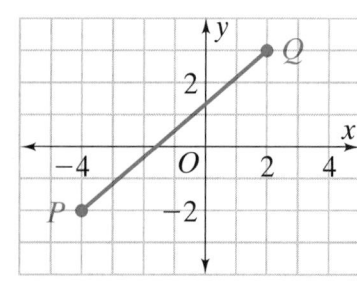

EXERCISES

For more exercises, see *Extra Skill and Word Problem Practice*.

Practice and Problem Solving

A Practice by Example

Example 1
(page 598)

GO for Help

Find the distance between the two points of each pair. Round to the nearest tenth.

1. $(1, 5), (5, 2)$ **2.** $(6, 0), (-6, 5)$ **3.** $(-5, 10), (11, -7)$

4. $(-6, 12), (-3, -7)$ **5.** $(8, -1), (-5, 11)$ **6.** $(12, 3), (-12, 4)$

Example 2
(page 599)

Geometry Find the perimeter of each figure.

7.

8.
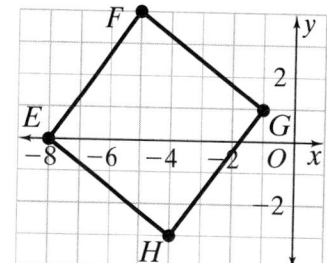

Example 3
(page 600)

Find the midpoint of each segment.

9.

10.

B Apply Your Skills

For Exercises 11 and 12, find both the length and the midpoint of the segment joining the two given points. Round to the nearest tenth.

11. $S(9, 12)$ and $U(-9, -12)$ **12.** $K(23, 4)$ and $W(-2, 16)$

13. A segment has endpoints $A(-3, 5)$ and $B(2, 1)$.
   a. Find the midpoint M of the segment.
   b. Use the Distance Formula to verify that $AM = MB$.

GO for Help

For a guide to solving
Exercise 13, see
page 603.

14. Error Analysis A student's calculation of the
midpoint of the segment with endpoints
$A(-4, 2)$ and $B(6, 6)$ is shown at the right.
What mistake did the student make?

$$\left(\frac{(6-(-4)}{2}, \frac{(6-2)}{2} \right)$$
$$= \left(\frac{10}{2}, \frac{4}{2} \right)$$
$$= (5, 2)$$

15. Reasoning The midpoint of $\overline{AB}$ is
$(3, 5)$. The coordinates of A are $(-6, 1)$.
What are the coordinates of B?

GO Online
Homework Video Tutor
Visit: PHSchool.com
Web Code: ade-1103

When you use the indicated formula, does it matter which point you choose as (x_1, y_1)? Explain.

16. the Midpoint Formula   **17.** the Distance Formula

Online lesson quiz, PHSchool.com, Web Code: ada-1103   **11-3** Distance and Midpoint Formulas   **601**

C Challenge 18. **Geometry** The three vertices of a triangle have coordinates $P(-3, 1)$, $Q(2, -5)$, and $R(4, 6)$. Determine whether the triangle is scalene, isosceles, or equilateral. Show your work.

19. **Writing in Math** Explain how using the Midpoint Formula involves finding averages.

ISAT

Gridded Response

Use the diagram for Exercises 20 and 21.

20. What is the number of square units in the square?

21. What is the perimeter of the square, to the nearest tenth?

22. What is the length, to the nearest tenth, of the segment whose endpoints are $A(3, 7)$ and $B(8, 21)$?

Mixed Review

Lesson 11-2 **Can you form a right triangle with the lengths given?**

23. 8 m, 15 m, 17 m   24. 5 in., 8 in., 5 in.   25. 20 yd, 12 yd, 16 yd

Lesson 10-4 26. **Geometry** Draw a net to represent a rectangular prism that is 4 in. long, 3 in. wide, and 2 in. high. Label dimensions on the net.

Lesson 6-2 **Solve each proportion.**

27. $\frac{3}{8} = \frac{a}{24}$ 28. $\frac{11}{c} = \frac{66}{72}$ 29. $\frac{5}{6} = \frac{n}{15}$ 30. $\frac{b}{1.9} = \frac{7}{9.5}$

Checkpoint Quiz 1   **Lessons 11-1 through 11-3**

Estimate to the nearest integer.

1. $-\sqrt{3}$ 2. $\sqrt{14}$ 3. $\sqrt{27}$ 4. $\sqrt{90}$ 5. $-\sqrt{45}$ 6. $\sqrt{105}$

The lengths of two legs of a right triangle are given. Find the length of the hypotenuse. Round to the nearest tenth.

7. 6 ft, 8 ft   8. 8 m, 14 m   9. 7 yd, 24 yd   10. 5 cm, 5 cm

Find the length of $\overline{AB}$ and the midpoint of $\overline{AB}$. Round the length of $\overline{AB}$ to the nearest tenth.

11. $A(0, -2)$ and $B(-6, -9)$ 12. $A(8, 11)$ and $B(-5, 2)$

13. **Open-Ended** Name three irrational numbers between 10 and 20.

Understanding Math Problems Read the problem below.
Then let Leo's thinking guide you through the solution. Check your
understanding with the exercises at the bottom of the page.

A segment has endpoints $A(-3, 5)$ and $B(2, 1)$.
a. Find the midpoint M of the segment.
b. Use the Distance Formula to verify that $AM = MB$.

What Leo Thinks | ## What Leo Writes

First I need to find the midpoint of $\overline{AB}$.
I'll use the Midpoint Formula.
Substitute.

$$\left(\frac{x_1 + x_2}{2}, \frac{y_1 + y_2}{2}\right) = \left(\frac{-3 + 2}{2}, \frac{5 + 1}{2}\right)$$

Simplify.

$$= \left(-\frac{1}{2}, 3\right) \text{ or } (-0.5, 3)$$

Next I need to verify that this is the
midpoint M by showing that $AM = MB$.
Since *verify* means "prove," I need to
show a reason for each step.

Step   Reason

First I'll find AM.

$AM = \sqrt{(-0.5 - (-3))^2 + (3 - 5)^2}$
    Distance Formula

$AM = \sqrt{10.25}$ Simplify.

Next I'll find MB.

$MB = \sqrt{(2 - (-0.5))^2 + (1 - 3)^2}$
    Distance Formula

$MB = \sqrt{10.25}$ Simplify.

I need to summarize my findings.

$AM = MB = \sqrt{10.25}$, so $(-0.5, 3)$ is the
midpoint of $\overline{AB}$.

EXERCISES

Solve each problem. Justify your steps to verify your answer.

1. Find the perimeter of the triangle with vertices located at $(5, 9)$,
$(7, 4)$, and $(-3, 7)$.

2. The vertices of a triangle are located at $(-1, 5), (2, 5),$ and $(2, 1)$.
Show that this is a right triangle. (*Hint:* Use the Distance Formula
and the Converse of the Pythagorean Theorem.)

Write a Proportion

What You'll Learn

• To write a proportion from similar triangles

. . . And Why

To solve problems of unknown distance

 Check Skills You'll Need

Solve each proportion.

1. $\frac{1}{3} = \frac{a}{12}$ 2. $\frac{h}{5} = \frac{20}{25}$

3. $\frac{1}{4} = \frac{8}{x}$ 4. $\frac{2}{7} = \frac{c}{35}$

GO for Help
Lesson 6-2

Math Strategies in Action You can't measure distance across the Grand Canyon with a tape measure. Yet, distances across it have been measured. How were they measured?

Surveyors sometimes find such distances indirectly using similar triangles and proportions. You learned about these in Lessons 6-2 and 6-3. Now let's see how you can use similar right triangles and proportions to find measurements indirectly.

1 EXAMPLE   Real-World Problem Solving

Surveying To find the distance from Q to P across a canyon, a surveyor picks points R and S such that $\overline{RS}$ is perpendicular to $\overline{RP}$. He locates point T on $\overline{SP}$ such that $\overline{QT}$ is perpendicular to $\overline{RP}$. The two triangles, $\triangle PRS$ and $\triangle PQT$, are similar. He then measures $\overline{RS}$, $\overline{RQ}$, and $\overline{QT}$. What is the distance QP across the canyon?

Problem Solving Hint
If problems involving distance do not include diagrams, draw your own to help you solve the problem.

Not drawn to scale

Understand the Problem

1. What information is given?

2. What are you asked to find?

Since $\triangle PQT \sim \triangle PRS$ and you know three lengths, writing and solving a proportion is a good strategy to use. It is helpful to draw the triangles as separate figures.

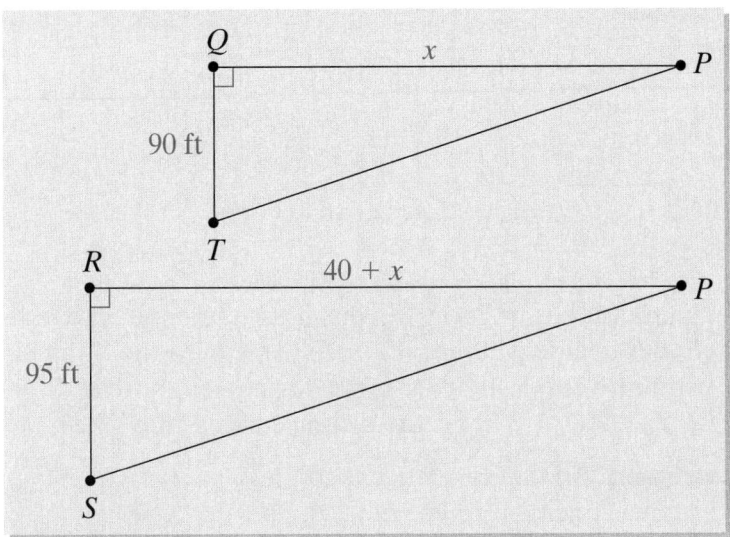

Write a proportion using the legs of the similar right triangles.

$\dfrac{x}{40 + x} = \dfrac{90}{95}$	**Write a proportion.**
$95x = 90(40 + x)$	**Write cross products.**
$95x = 3{,}600 + 90x$	**Use the Distributive Property.**
$5x = 3{,}600$	**Subtract 90x from each side.**
$x = 720$	**Divide each side by 5.**

The distance QP across the canyon is 720 ft.

Solving problems that involve indirect measurement often makes use of figures that *overlap*. Use the diagram on page 604 to answer the following questions.

✓ Quick Check

3. Which segments overlap?

4. A common error students make is to use part of a side in a proportion. For example, some students might think $\frac{40}{95}$ is equal to $\frac{x}{90}$. How does drawing the triangles as separate figures help you avoid this error?

Practice and Problem Solving

 A Practice by Example

Example 1
(page 604)

 GO for Help

In Exercises 1–2, write a proportion and find the value of each *x*.

1. $\triangle ABE \sim \triangle ACD$

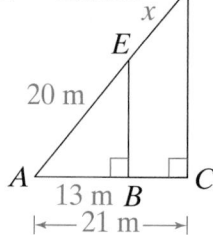

20 m
E
D
x
A
13 m *B*
C
|← 21 m →|

2. $\triangle GHI \sim \triangle KJI$

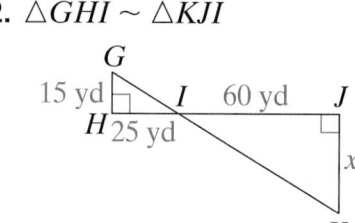

15 yd
G
H 25 yd
I 60 yd *J*
x
K

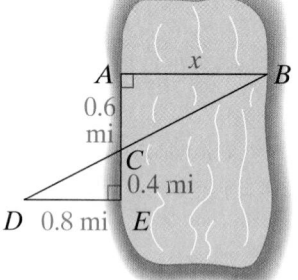

A *x* *B*
0.6 mi
C
0.4 mi
D 0.8 mi *E*

3. A swimmer needs to know the distance *x* across a lake (at left) to help her decide whether it is safe to swim to the other side. She estimates the distance using the triangles shown. $\triangle ABC \sim \triangle EDC$. What is the distance across the lake?

 4. Landscaping A landscaper needs to find the distance *x* across a piece of land. She estimates the distance using the similar triangles at the right. What is the distance?

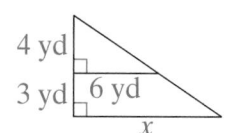

4 yd
3 yd 6 yd
x

B Apply Your Skills **5. Indirect Measurement** To estimate the height of a tree, Milton positions a mirror on the ground so he can see the top of the tree reflected in it. His height, his distance from the mirror, and his line of sight to the mirror determine a triangle. The tree's height, its distance from the mirror, and the distance from the top of the tree to the mirror form a similar triangle. Use the measurements shown to determine the height of the tree.

5 ft
2 ft   11.2 ft
x

Strategies

- Act It Out
- Draw a Diagram
- Guess, Check, Revise
- Look for a Pattern
- Make a Model
- Make a Table
- Simulate the Problem
- Solve by Graphing
- Use Multiple Strategies
- Work a Simpler Problem
- Work Backward
- Write an Equation
- Write a Proportion

Solve using any strategy.

6. There are 30 students in a math class. Twelve belong to the computer club, and eight belong to the photography club. Three belong to both clubs. How many belong to neither club?

7. Jake spent $\frac{3}{8}$ of his money on a book and $\frac{1}{2}$ of what was left on a magazine. He now has $6.25. How much money did he start with?

8. Hai takes 12 minutes to walk to school. He wants to get there 15 minutes early to meet with his lab partner. What time should he leave his house if school starts at 8:10 A.M.?

9. Number Sense Christa thought of a number. She added 4, multiplied the sum by -5, and subtracted 12. She then doubled the result and got -34. What number did Christa start with?

 GO **Online**
Homework Video Tutor
Visit: PHSchool.com
Web Code: ade-1104

C Challenge

10. The height of the Eiffel Tower is 984 ft. A souvenir model of the tower is 6 in. tall. At 5 P.M. in Paris, the shadow of the souvenir model is 8 in. long. The Eiffel Tower and its shadow determine two legs of a right triangle that are similar to the two legs of a right triangle determined by the souvenir model and its shadow. About how long is the shadow of the Eiffel Tower?

11. Architecture Madison Square Garden in New York City is built in the shape of a circle. Its diameter is 404 ft and it accommodates 20,234 spectators. To the nearest tenth of a square foot, how much area is there for each spectator?

12. **Algebra** You serve a tennis ball from one end of a tennis court, 39 ft from the net. You hit the ball at 9 feet above the ground. It travels in a straight path down the middle of the court, and just clears the top of the 3-ft net. This is illustrated in the diagram. $\triangle PQR \sim \triangle MQS$. How far from the net does the ball land?

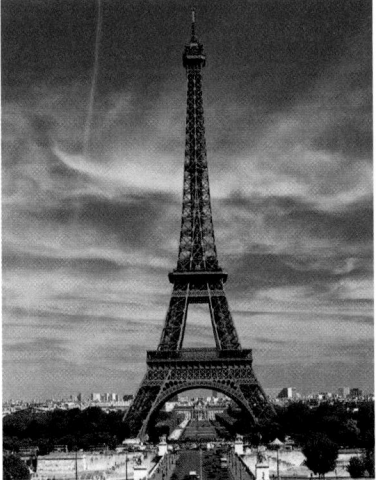

Real-World **Connection**

The Eiffel Tower was named for its designer, Gustave Eiffel, who also designed the Statue of Liberty framework.

ISAT

Test Prep

Multiple Choice

13. In the diagram at the right, what is ?
A. 43.75   B. 28
C. 26.25   D. 17

14. What is the value of x in this proportion, $\frac{65}{50} = \frac{x + 36}{x}$?

F. 15   G. 60   H. 120   J. 156

Short Response

15. Suppose a friend says to you " is to +
a. Write a proportion to solve for .
b. Solve your proportion.

Mixed Review

GO for Help

Lesson 11-3

Find the midpoint of each segment with given endpoints.

16. $A(2, 3)$ and $B(4, 7)$ **17.** $L(-1, 2)$ and $M(2, 6)$

Lessons 9-3

Sketch each figure.

18. isosceles right triangle   **19.** scalene obtuse triangle

Lesson 7-4 **20. Fundraising** Keith collected twice as much money as Lucy for a walkathon. Together they collected $120. How much money did each person collect?

11-5

Special Right Triangles

What You'll Learn

- To use the relationships in 45°-45°-90° triangles
- To use the relationships in 30°-60°-90° triangles

. . . And Why

To find distances in real-world situations, such as in sports

  Check Skills You'll Need

Find the missing side of each right triangle.

1. legs: 6 m and 8 m

2. leg: 9 m; hypotenuse: 15 m

3. legs: 27 m and 36 m

4. leg: 48 m; hypotenuse: 60 m

 for Help
Lesson 11-2

 **Using 45°-45°-90° Triangles**

The Pythagorean Theorem requires that you understand square roots. The rule for Multiplying Square Roots will help you work with square roots more efficiently.

Key Concepts   **Multiplying Square Roots**

For nonnegative numbers, the square root of a product equals the product of the square roots.

Arithmetic	Algebra
$\sqrt{9 \cdot 2} = \sqrt{9} \cdot \sqrt{2}$	If $a \geq 0$ and $b \geq 0$, then $\sqrt{ab} = \sqrt{a} \cdot \sqrt{b}$.

The rule for Multiplying Square Roots is especially useful with an isosceles right triangle, which is also known by its angle measures as a 45°-45°-90° triangle. You can use the rule to relate the lengths of the sides and the hypotenuse in such a triangle.

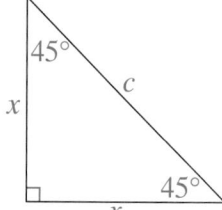

$c^2 = a^2 + b^2$	**Use the Pythagorean Theorem.**
$c^2 = x^2 + x^2$	**Replace a and b with x.**
$c^2 = 2x^2$	**Simplify.**
$c = \sqrt{2x^2}$	**Find the square root.**
$c = \sqrt{2} \cdot \sqrt{x^2}$	**Use the rule for Multiplying Square Roots.**
$c = \sqrt{2} \cdot x$, or $x\sqrt{2}$	**Simplify.**

This shows the following special relationship.

Key Concepts   **45°-45°-90° Triangles**

In a 45°-45°-90° triangle, the legs are congruent and the length of the hypotenuse is the length of a leg times $\sqrt{2}$.

$$\text{hypotenuse} = \text{leg} \cdot \sqrt{2}$$

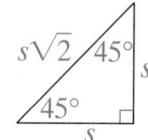

1 EXAMPLE   Finding Length of the Hypotenuse

Find the length of the hypotenuse in the triangle at the right.

$$\text{hypotenuse} = \text{leg} \cdot \sqrt{2}$$ **Use the 45°-45°-90° relationship.**

$$x = 6 \cdot \sqrt{2}$$ **The length of the leg is 6.**

$$\approx 8.5$$ **Use a calculator.**

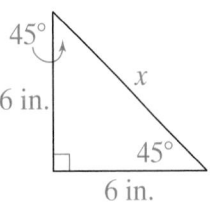

The length of the hypotenuse is about 8.5 in.

✓ Quick Check

1. The length of each leg of an isosceles right triangle is 4.2 cm. Find the length of the hypotenuse. Round to the nearest tenth.

You can use 45°-45°-90° triangles in real-world situations.

2 EXAMPLE   Real-World 🌐 Problem Solving

Gridded Response A baseball diamond is a square. The distance from any base to the next is 90 ft. How far is it from home plate to second base?

$$\text{hypotenuse} = \text{leg} \cdot \sqrt{2}$$ **Use the 45°-45°-90° relationship.**

$$= 90 \cdot \sqrt{2}$$ **The length of the leg is 90.**

$$\approx 127.28$$ **Use a calculator.**

The distance from home plate to second base is about 127 ft.

✓ Quick Check

2. Gymnasts use mats that are 12 m by 12 m for floor exercises. A gymnast does cartwheels across the diagonal of a mat. What is the length of the diagonal to the nearest meter?

> **Test-Taking Tip**
> If you can't remember the formulas for special triangles, use the Pythagorean Theorem.

2 Using 30°-60°-90° Triangles

Another special right triangle is the 30°-60°-90° triangle. You can form two congruent 30°-60°-90° triangles by bisecting an angle of an equilateral triangle. This is shown in the diagram.

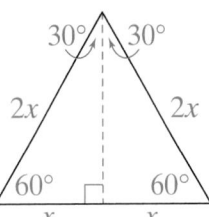

In the diagram, the length of the hypotenuse of each 30°-60°-90° triangle is twice the length of the shorter leg. You can use the Pythagorean Theorem to find the length of the longer leg.

For the figure at the right, find the length of the longer leg.

$(2x)^2 = x^2 + b^2$ **Use the Pythagorean Theorem.**

$4x^2 = x^2 + b^2$ **Simplify.**

$3x^2 = b^2$ **Subtract x^2 from each side.**

$\sqrt{3x^2} = b$ **Find the square root.**

$\sqrt{3} \cdot \sqrt{x^2} = b$ **Rule for Multiplying Square Roots**

$b = \sqrt{3} \cdot x$, or $x\sqrt{3}$ **Simplify.**

This shows the special relationship of the hypotenuse and the legs in a 30°-60°-90° triangle.

Key Concepts **30°-60°-90° Triangle**

In a 30°-60°-90° triangle, the length of the hypotenuse is 2 times the length of the shorter leg. The length of the longer leg is the length of the shorter leg times $\sqrt{3}$.

hypotenuse = 2 · shorter leg

longer leg = shorter leg · $\sqrt{3}$

---

3 EXAMPLE   **Finding Lengths in a 30°-60°-90° Triangle**

Find the missing lengths in the triangle.

hypotenuse = 2 · shorter leg

$x = 2 \cdot 5$ **The length of the shorter leg is 5.**

$x = 10$ **Simplify.**

longer leg = shorter leg · $\sqrt{3}$

$y = 5 \cdot \sqrt{3}$ **The length of the shorter leg is 5.**

$y \approx 8.7$ **Use a calculator.**

The length of the hypotenuse is 10 ft, and the length of the longer leg is about 8.7 ft.

✓ Quick Check

3. Find the missing lengths in each 30°-60°-90° triangle.

a.

b.

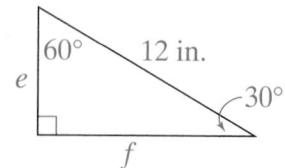

EXERCISES

For more exercises, see *Extra Skill and Word Problem Practice*.

Practice and Problem Solving

A Practice by Example

Example 1
(page 609)

GO for Help

The lengths of the legs of an isosceles right triangle are given. Find the length of each hypotenuse to the nearest tenth.

1.

2.

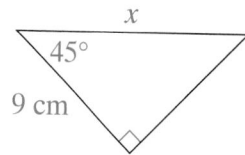

3. legs: 5.4 in.   **4.** legs: 17 ft   **5.** legs: 21 m

Example 2
(page 609)

6. Ballet A ballet teacher wants to divide his square classroom in half diagonally with masking tape. How much tape will he need if the side length of the classroom is 40 ft?

7. Flooring A square piece of tile with sides 12 in. is cut along a diagonal. What is the length of the diagonal rounded to the nearest inch?

Example 3
(page 610)

Find the missing lengths. Round to the nearest tenth.

8.

9.

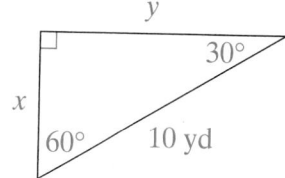

B Apply Your Skills

10.

11.

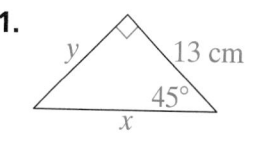

GO Online
Homework Video Tutor
Visit: PHSchool.com
Web Code: ade-1105

12. Error Analysis A student says that a right triangle with a hypotenuse of length $2\sqrt{2}$ in. has to be an isosceles right triangle. What mistake might the student have made?

13. Writing in Math Explain how to find the lengths of the longer leg and hypotenuse of a 30°-60°-90° triangle if the shorter leg is 10 ft.

14. Mrs. Fernandez wants to string a rope diagonally across her square classroom for her students to hang their completed art projects. If one side of the room measures 20 ft, what is the minimum length of rope she can use?

Simplify. Use the rule for Multiplying Square Roots.

15. $\sqrt{3} \cdot \sqrt{27}$ **16.** $\sqrt{50} \cdot \sqrt{2}$ **17.** $\sqrt{36} \cdot \sqrt{4}$

C Challenge

18. Reasoning The smaller angles of a 30°-60°-90° triangle are in the ratio 1 : 2. Are the shorter sides also in the ratio 1 : 2? Explain.

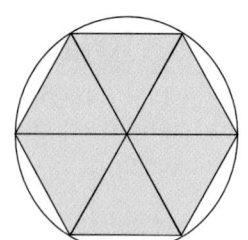

19. Geometry A polygon is inscribed in a circle if all of its vertices lie on the circle. To find the area of the hexagon inscribed in a circle with a diameter of 8 in., answer each of the following.

   a. The segments shown form 6 congruent equilateral triangles. What is the length of each side of each triangle?

   b. What is the height of one triangle?

   c. What is the area of one triangle?

   d. What is the area of the hexagon?

Writing in Math

Sketch a 45°-45°-90° triangle. Use *x* for the length of one leg. Explain how to find the lengths of the other sides of the triangle.

---

20. Geometry You can inscribe a regular hexagon in a circle using a compass and straightedge.

   a. Use your compass to construct a circle. Keep the compass at the same setting. Place the tip of the compass on the circle. Mark an arc on the circle. Place the tip of the compass where the arc intersects the circle and mark another arc. Continue around the circle until you have six arcs on the circle. Join consecutive arcs with segments.

   b. Measure the diameter of the circle. Use this measure and Exercise 19 to find the area of your hexagon.

ISAT

Test Prep

Multiple Choice

21. In the triangle at the right, what is *x*, to the nearest tenth?

   A. 8.7   **B.** 8   **C.** 5.7   **D.** 2

22. In a 30°-60°-90° triangle, the length of the longer leg is 10. What is the length of the hypotenuse, to the nearest tenth?

   F. 5.0   **G.** 5.8   **H.** 11.5   **J.** 17.3

Short Response

In Exercises 23–25, **(a)** tell whether a triangle with sides of the given lengths could be 45°-45°-90° or 30°-60°-90°. **(b)** Explain your answers.

23. 6, 8, 10   **24.** 5, 5, $5\sqrt{2}$ **25.** 15, $7.5\sqrt{3}$, 7.5

Mixed Review

Lesson 11-4

26. Surveying A surveyor needs to find the distance across a lake. He estimates the distance using the similar triangles at the right. What is the distance?

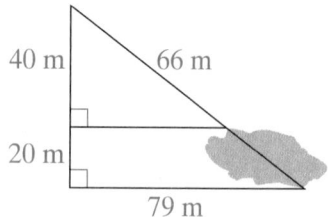

Lesson 9-6

Find the circumference of each circle with the given radius or diameter.

27. radius = 4 in.   **28.** diameter = 6 m   **29.** radius = 2.5 ft

Lesson 8-1

Is each relation a function? Explain.

30. $\{(-1, 3), (0, 4), (1, 5)\}$ **31.** $\{(2, 3), (3, 4), (4, 5), (5, 6)\}$

You can simplify square roots of expressions that contain variables. Assume that the value of each variable is not negative.

1 EXAMPLE

Write each square root without a radical sign.

a. $\sqrt{25x^2}$

$\sqrt{25x^2} = \sqrt{(5x)^2}$ Write $25x^2$ as the square of $5x$.

$\qquad = 5x$ Simplify.

b. $\sqrt{p^6}$

$\sqrt{p^6} = \sqrt{(p^3)^2}$ Use the rule for the Power of a Power.

$\qquad = p^3$ Simplify.

You can also simplify expressions that have nonsquare factors by using the rule for Multiplying Square Roots.

2 EXAMPLE

Simplify each square root.

a. $\sqrt{x^9}$

$\sqrt{x^9} = \sqrt{x^8 \cdot x}$ Use the rule for Multiplying Powers with the Same Base.

$\qquad = \sqrt{x^8} \cdot \sqrt{x}$ Use the rule for Multiplying Square Roots.

$\qquad = x^4 \sqrt{x}$ Simplify.

b. $\sqrt{48x}$

$\sqrt{48x} = \sqrt{16 \cdot 3x}$ Find a perfect square factor.

$\qquad = \sqrt{16} \cdot \sqrt{3x}$ Use the rule for Multiplying Square Roots.

$\qquad = 4\sqrt{3x}$ Simplify.

EXERCISES

Write each square root without the radical sign.

1. $\sqrt{49y^2}$ **2.** $\sqrt{100m^{12}}$ **3.** $-\sqrt{25x^6}$ **4.** $\sqrt{a^2b^{10}}$ **5.** $-\sqrt{169w^{26}}$

Simplify each square root.

6. $\sqrt{a^{12}}$ **7.** $\sqrt{36x^4}$ **8.** $\sqrt{81b^8}$ **9.** $-\sqrt{64a^{16}}$ **10.** $-\sqrt{x^4y^{12}}$

11. $\sqrt{c^7}$ **12.** $\sqrt{x^{23}}$ **13.** $-\sqrt{20m}$ **14.** $\sqrt{27b^{11}}$ **15.** $-\sqrt{72a^{19}}$

Sine, Cosine, and Tangent Ratios

What You'll Learn

• To find trigonometric ratios in right triangles

• To use trigonometric ratios to solve problems

. . . And Why

To find lengths that cannot be measured directly

Check Skills You'll Need

Solve each problem.

1. A 6-ft man casts an 8-ft shadow while a nearby flagpole casts a 20-ft shadow. How tall is the flagpole?

2. When a 12-ft tall building casts a 22-ft shadow, how long is the shadow of a nearby 14-ft tree?

for Help

Lesson 6-3

◀)) New Vocabulary

• **trigonometry**
• **trigonometric ratio**
• **sine**
• **cosine**
• **tangent**

Video Tutor Help

Visit: PHSchool.com
Web Code: ada-0775

1 **Finding Ratios in Right Triangles**

Activity

Exploring Ratios in Similar Right Triangles

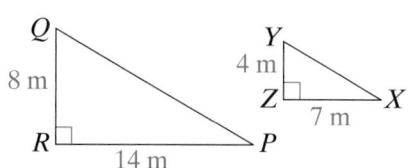

1. In the diagram at the right, $\triangle PQR \sim \triangle XYZ$. Find the length of the hypotenuse of each triangle. Round to the nearest whole number.

2. In the triangles above, $\angle P$ is the smallest angle of $\triangle PQR$ and $\angle X$ is the smallest angle of $\triangle XYZ$. For each figure, write the following ratios in simplest form.

   a. $\dfrac{\text{length of leg opposite smallest angle}}{\text{length of hypotenuse}}$

   b. $\dfrac{\text{length of leg adjacent to smallest angle}}{\text{length of hypotenuse}}$

   c. $\dfrac{\text{length of leg opposite smallest angle}}{\text{length of leg adjacent to smallest angle}}$

3. What do you notice about the two ratios you wrote for each part of Question 2?

The word **trigonometry** means triangle measure. The ratio of the lengths of two sides of a right triangle is a **trigonometric ratio.** To write trigonometric ratios, you must identify sides that are opposite and adjacent to the acute angles of a triangle.

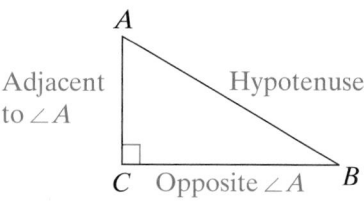

Trigonometric Ratios

$$\textbf{sine } \angle A = \frac{\text{length of leg opposite } \angle A}{\text{length of hypotenuse}} = \frac{CB}{AB}$$

$$\textbf{cosine } \angle A = \frac{\text{length of leg adjacent to } \angle A}{\text{length of hypotenuse}} = \frac{AC}{AB}$$

$$\textbf{tangent } \angle A = \frac{\text{length of leg opposite } \angle A}{\text{length of leg adjacent to } \angle A} = \frac{CB}{AC}$$

You can use these abbreviations when you find trigonometric ratios for a given acute $\angle N$.

$$\sin N = \frac{\text{opposite}}{\text{hypotenuse}} \qquad \cos N = \frac{\text{adjacent}}{\text{hypotenuse}} \qquad \tan N = \frac{\text{opposite}}{\text{adjacent}}$$

Vocabulary Tip

The abbreviations for sine, cosine, and tangent are sin, cos, and tan, respectively.

1 EXAMPLE Writing Trigonometric Ratios

For $\triangle XYZ$, find the sine, cosine, and tangent of $\angle X$.

$$\sin X = \frac{\text{opposite}}{\text{hypotenuse}} = \frac{5}{13}$$

$$\cos X = \frac{\text{adjacent}}{\text{hypotenuse}} = \frac{12}{13}$$

$$\tan X = \frac{\text{opposite}}{\text{adjacent}} = \frac{5}{12}$$

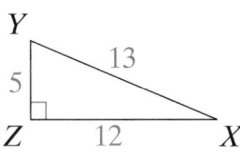

Quick Check

● **1.** For $\triangle XYZ$ above, find the sine, cosine, and tangent of $\angle Y$.

Online
active math

For: Trig Ratio Activity
Use: Interactive Textbook 11-6

Trigonometric ratios are usually expressed in decimal form as approximations. If you know the measure of an acute angle of a right triangle, you can use a calculator or a table of trigonometric ratios to find approximate values for the sine, cosine, and tangent of the angle.

2 EXAMPLE Using a Calculator

Find the trigonometric ratios of 42° using a calculator or the table on page 801. Round to four decimal places.

$\sin 42° \approx 0.6691$ **Scientific calculator: Enter 42 and press the key labeled SIN, COS, or TAN.**

$\cos 42° \approx 0.7431$

$\tan 42° \approx 0.9004$ **Table: Find 42° in the first column. Look across to find the appropriate ratio.**

Graphing Calculator Hint

If you use a graphing calculator, enter the trigonometric ratio name before you enter the angle measure. Be sure the calculator is in degree mode.

Quick Check

2. Find each value. Round to four decimal places.

   a. $\sin 10°$ **b.** $\cos 75°$ **c.** $\tan 53°$ **d.** $\cos 22°$

2 Using Trigonometric Ratios to Solve Problems

You can use trigonometric ratios to find measures in right triangles indirectly. The advantage to using trigonometric ratios is that you need only an acute angle measure and the length of one side to find the lengths of the other two sides.

4° x 1 ft
A
Not drawn to scale

Ramps **What is the length of the wheelchair ramp at the left?**

You know the angle and the side opposite the angle. You want to find x, the length of the hypotenuse.

$$\sin A = \frac{\text{opposite}}{\text{hypotenuse}}$$ **Use the sine ratio.**

$$\sin 4° = \frac{1}{x}$$ **Substitute 4° for the angle and 1 for the side opposite.**

$$x(\sin 4°) = 1$$ **Multiply each side by x.**

$$x = \frac{1}{\sin 4°}$$ **Divide each side by sin 4°.**

$$x \approx 14.3$$ **Use a calculator.**

The ramp is about 14.3 ft long.

✓ Quick Check

3. How long is the longer leg under the ramp in Example 3?

More Than One Way

Ladders **Find the height, x, that the ladder reaches.**

8 ft x

68°

3 ft

Kevin's Method

Use the Pythagorean theorem.
$$3^2 + x^2 = 8^2$$
$$9 + x^2 = 64$$
$$x^2 = 55$$
$$x = \sqrt{55} \approx 7.4$$

The ladder reaches about 7.4 ft.

Tina's Method

Use a trigonometric ratio.
$$\sin 68° = \frac{x}{8}$$
$$8(\sin 68°) = x$$
$$7.4 \approx x$$

The ladder reaches about 7.4 ft.

Choose a Method

1. Which method do you prefer to use? Explain.

2. What information is needed for each method?

Practice and Problem Solving

A Practice by Example

Example 1
(page 615)

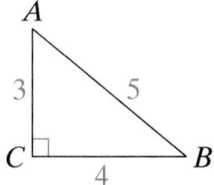

For Exercises 1–3, find the length of the indicated side.

1. the leg opposite ∠A

2. the leg adjacent to ∠A

3. the hypotenuse of △ABC

4. Find the sine, cosine, and tangent of ∠A.

Use △QRS for Exercises 5 and 6.

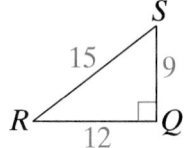

5. Find the sine, cosine, and tangent of ∠R.

6. Find the sine, cosine, and tangent of ∠S.

Example 2
(page 615)

Find each value. Round to four decimal places.

7. tan 89°   8. sin 30°   9. cos 14°   10. sin 67°

11. tan 28°   12. cos 89°   13. tan 11°   14. sin 83°

Example 3
(page 616)

15. **Waterskiing** The angle that a waterskiing ramp forms with the surface of the water is 15°, and the ramp rises 5 ft. Approximately how long is the ramp?

16. **Loading Ramps** The ramp on the back of a mover's truck is 12 ft long. If the angle of the ramp with the ground is 22°, about how high is the floor of the truck above the ground?

B Apply Your Skills

Use right triangles to find the ratios. Show your diagrams.

17. tan 45°   18. cos 60°   19. sin 30°   20. cos 30°

21. <u>Writing in Math</u> Tom says the missing length in the triangle at the right can be found using the tangent ratio. Jed says it can be found using the sine ratio. Who is correct? Explain.

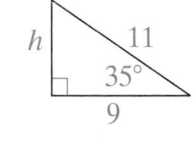

22. **Hot-Air Balloons** A hot-air balloon climbs continuously along a 30° angle to a height of 5,000 feet. To the nearest tenth of a foot, how far has the balloon traveled to reach 5,000 feet? Draw a sketch, and then solve.

C Challenge

23. **Reasoning** Find the sine of an angle and the cosine of its complement. Do this for several angles. Make a conjecture.

Homework Video Tutor
Visit: PHSchool.com
Web Code: ade-1106

24. A wire from a radio tower is supported by a 23-ft brace.
    a. How tall is the radio tower?
    b. What is the measure of the angle formed by the wire and the ground?

Multiple Choice   In Exercises 25 and 26, how high on a wall does a 12-ft ladder reach?

25. The base of the ladder is 3 ft from the wall.
    A. 4.0 ft   **B.** 10.0 ft   **C.** 11.6 ft   **D.** 12 ft

26. The ladder forms a 60° angle with the ground.
    F. 10.4 ft   **G.** 8.0 ft   **H.** 6.9 ft   **J.** 6.0 ft

Short Response   Read the passage below before doing Exercises 27 and 28.

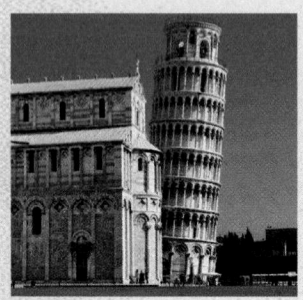

The Tilting Tower

Building began on the bell tower at Pisa, Italy, in 1173. Shortly after that, the 55.9-m tower began to lean and has continued to lean even more over the centuries. In 1993, the tower had a tilt that was 5.5° from the vertical. In the spring of 1999, engineering experts began work at the base to correct some of the lean. They completed the work in 2001 after decreasing the lean by 0.5°. The engineers hope their work will stabilize the tower for the next 300 years.

27. In 2001, what was the tilt of the tower in degrees?

28. In 2001, about how many meters from the vertical was the top of the tower?

Mixed Review

Lesson 11-5

Find the missing lengths.

29.
$45°$
a
4 m   4 m

30.
y
$30°$

31.
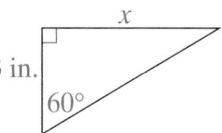
x
13 in.   7 ft
$60°$

Lesson 9-7   **32. Geometry** $\overleftrightarrow{GT}$ is the perpendicular bisector of $\overline{RA}$ at point E. Name two congruent segments.

Lesson 8-2   **Find the solutions of each equation for $x = -1, 0,$ and 3.**

33. $y = -3x + 2$ **34.** $x + y = 20$ **35.** $6x - 2y = 12$

Checkpoint Quiz 2   **Lessons 11-4 through 11-6**

Tell whether a triangle with sides of the given lengths is 45°-45°-90°, 30°-60°-90°, or neither.

1. $8, 8, 8\sqrt{2}$ **2.** $1, 2, \sqrt{3}$ **3.** $12\sqrt{3}, 12, 24$

Find each value. Round to four decimal places.

4. $\cos 61°$ **5.** $\tan 30°$ **6.** $\sin 32°$ **7.** $\sin 87°$

You can use a calculator or a trigonometric-ratio table to find the degree measure of an acute angle of a right triangle if two sides of the triangle are known. If you are using a graphing calculator, be sure you are in degree mode.

EXAMPLE

You have a map charting a ship's course. The ship is traveling from the port along the course shown. What is the angle from due north of the ship's course?

The angle formed by due north, the port, and the ship is the angle at which the ship is traveling. This is angle X.

$$\cos X = \frac{191}{325}$$

To find $m\angle X$ with a calculator:

Press **TRIG cos^{-1}** 191 ÷ 325 ENTER.

$m\angle X \approx 54°$

To find $m\angle X$ using the table of trigonometric ratios on page 801:

$\cos X = \frac{191}{325} \approx 0.5877$ **Divide.**

$m\angle X \approx 54°$

In the cosine column, find the decimal closest to 0.5877, which is 0.5878. Read the angle measure across from 0.5878.

● The ship is traveling at a 54° angle from due north.

EXERCISES

Find the measure of each acute angle. Round to the nearest degree.

1.

2.

3.
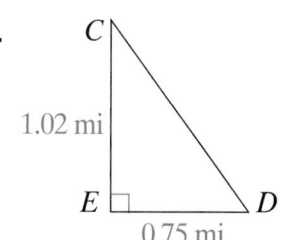

In △PQR, ∠Q is a right angle. Find the measures of ∠P and ∠R to the nearest tenth.

4. $PQ = 3$, $PR = 5$

5. $RQ = 12$, $PR = 13$

6. $PQ = 20$, $RQ = 21$

11-7

Angles of Elevation and Depression

What You'll Learn

• To use trigonometry to find angles of elevation

• To use trigonometry to find angles of depression

. . . And Why

To solve real-world problems in subjects such as surveying and navigation

 Check Skills You'll Need

Find each trigonometric ratio.

1. sin 45°   **2.** cos 32°

3. tan 18°   **4.** sin 68°

5. cos 88°   **6.** tan 84°

GO for Help
Lesson 11-6

🔊 **New Vocabulary**

• angle of elevation

• angle of depression

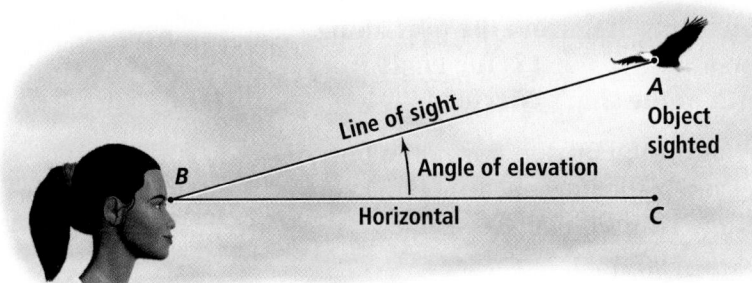

1 Angles of Elevation

Civil engineers and navigators use the terms *angle of elevation* and *angle of depression* to describe the angles at which they observe things. An **angle of elevation** is formed by a horizontal line and a line of sight above it. It is used when you must look up at an object.

$\angle ABC$ is an angle of elevation.

1 EXAMPLE **Real-World 🌐 Problem Solving**

Kite Flying Marcus is flying a kite. He lets out 40 yd of string and anchors it to the ground. He determines that the angle of elevation of the kite is 52°. What is the height x of the kite from the ground?

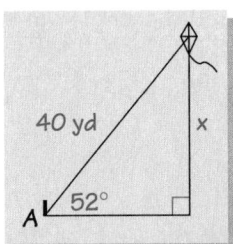

Draw a picture.

$\sin A = \dfrac{\text{opposite}}{\text{hypotenuse}}$ **Choose an appropriate trigonometric ratio.**

$\sin 52° = \dfrac{x}{40}$ **Substitute 52° for the angle measure and 40 for the hypotenuse.**

$40(\sin 52°) = x$ **Multiply each side by 40.**

$32 \approx x$ **Simplify.**

The kite is about 32 yd from the ground.

1. The angle of elevation from a ship to the top of a lighthouse is 12°. The lighthouse is known to be 30 m tall. How far is the ship from the base of the lighthouse?

In real life, a person's line of sight is parallel to the ground at eye height. In some problems you must account for this.

2 EXAMPLE   Real-World 🌐 Problem Solving

Indirect Measurement Felicia wants to determine the height of a tree. From her position 20 ft from the base of the tree, she sees the top of the tree at an angle of elevation of 73°. Felicia's eyes are 5 ft from the ground. How tall is the tree, to the nearest foot?

Draw a picture.

$$\tan = \frac{\text{opposite}}{\text{adjacent}}$$ Choose an appropriate trigonometric ratio.

$$\tan 73° = \frac{x}{20}$$ Substitute 73 for the angle measure and 20 for the adjacent side.

$$20(\tan 73°) = x$$ Multiply each side by 20.

$$65 \approx x$$ Use a calculator or a table.

$$65 + 5 = 70$$ Add 5 to account for the height of Felicia's eyes from the ground.

The tree is about 70 ft tall.

✅ **Quick Check**

2. A rock climber looks at the top of a vertical rock wall at an angle of elevation of 74°. He is standing 4.2 m from the base of the wall and his eyes are 1.5 m from the ground. How high is the wall, to the nearest tenth of a meter?

Vocabulary Tip

With an <u>angle</u> of <u>elevation</u>, the object sighted is elevated, or above the horizontal line. With an <u>angle</u> of <u>depression</u>, the object is depressed, or below the horizontal line.

An **angle of depression** is formed by a horizontal line and a line of sight below it. It is used when you must look down at an object.

$\angle XYZ$ is an angle of depression.

3 EXAMPLE **Real-World** **Problem Solving**

Navigation An airplane is flying 0.5 mi above the ground. If the pilot must begin a 3° descent to an airport runway at that altitude, how far is the airplane from the beginning of the runway (in ground distance)?

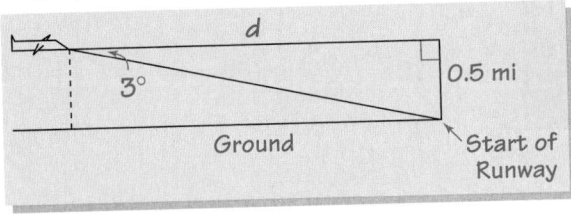

Not drawn to scale

Draw a picture.

$\tan 3° = \dfrac{0.5}{d}$ **Choose an appropriate trigonometric ratio.**

$d \tan 3° = 0.5$ **Multiply each side by d.**

$\dfrac{d \tan 3°}{\tan 3°} = \dfrac{0.5}{\tan 3°}$ **Divide each side by tan 3°.**

$d = \dfrac{0.5}{\tan 3°}$ **Simplify.**

$d \approx 9.5$ **Use a calculator.**

The airplane is about 9.5 mi from the airport.

✓ Quick Check

3. A group of people in a hang-gliding class are standing on top of a cliff 70 m high. They spot a hang glider landing on the beach below them. The angle of depression from the top of the cliff to the hang glider is 72°. How far is the hang glider from the base of the cliff?

GO Online

Video Tutor Help
Visit: PHSchool.com
Web Code: ada-0775

EXERCISES

For more exercises, see *Extra Skill and Word Problem Practice.*

Practice and Problem Solving

A Practice by Example

Examples 1 and 2
(pages 620 and 621)

 for Help

1. In Example 1, Marcus's kite drops so that the angle of elevation is 48°. Find the height of the kite above the ground.

2. In Example 2, Felicia spots a nest in the tree at an angle of elevation of 65°. How high above the ground is the nest?

Find *x* to the nearest tenth.

3.

4.

Example 3
(page 622)

For Exercises 5 and 6, draw a sketch and solve.

5. An airplane descends at an angle of 2°. Its altitude decreases by 2.5 miles. What is the ground distance covered by the airplane?

6. An airplane descends at an angle of 22.5° over a ground distance of 0.5 mi. By how many miles, to the nearest tenth, does its altitude decrease?

B Apply Your Skills

Name the angles of elevation and depression in each figure.

7.

8.

 for Help

For a guide to reading and solving Exercise 9, see page 625.

9. Bird Watching A rare bird is spotted in a tree by a bird-watching group. The group is 9.5 yd from the base of the tree. The angle of elevation to the bird is 57°. How far is the bird from the group along the line of sight? Draw a sketch, and then solve.

10. Navigation The angle of elevation from a ship to the top of a lighthouse is 4°. If the top of the lighthouse is known to be 50 m above sea level, how far is the ship from the lighthouse?

11. Writing in Math How do you decide which trigonometric ratio to use to solve a problem?

12. Find the distance *x* of the car from the office building at the left.

13. Meteorology A meteorologist measures the angle of elevation of a weather balloon as 53°. A radio signal from the balloon indicates that it is 1,620 m (line-of-sight) from the meteorologist's location. How high above ground is the weather balloon?

14. Error Analysis A student made the drawing at the right to solve an angle-of-depression problem. What mistake has the student made?

🌐 **15. Aeronautics** The pilot of a helicopter at an altitude of 6,000 ft sees a second helicopter at an angle of depression of 43°. The altitude of the second helicopter is 4,000 ft. What is the distance from the first helicopter to the second along the line of sight?

C Challenge 🌐 **16. Astronomy** The diagram suggests a method for finding depths of moon craters from Earth. Astronomers calculate that the distance from R to H is 3 km when the angle of depression of the sun's rays is 12°.

a. How high is the rim of the crater from the floor of the crater?
b. When the angle increases to 14°, how much shorter is the crater's shadow on the crater floor?

🌐 **17. Surveying** Surveyors find that a canyon is 4 km wide. From one canyon rim, the angle of depression to the base of the canyon wall below the other rim is 7°. The angle of depression to a river is 8°. How far is the river from the far canyon wall?

ISAT

Test Prep

Multiple Choice

18. A ramp has an angle of elevation of 19° and a length of 35 ft. What is the height in inches of the ramp at its high end?
A. 11 in. **B.** 12 in. **C.** 137 in. **D.** 145 in.

19. A radio transmitting tower casts a shadow that extends 344 feet from the base of the tower. A line connecting the sun, the top of the tower, and the end of the shadow forms an angle of depression of 16°. Approximately how high is the tower?
F. 344 ft **G.** 99 ft **H.** 1,200 ft **J.** 1,248 ft

Mixed Review

for Help

Lesson 11-6

Find each value. Round to four decimal places.

20. $\tan 29°$ **21.** $\sin 80°$ **22.** $\cos 34°$ **23.** $\sin 76°$ **24.** $\cos 45°$

Lesson 10-3

Find the area of each circle. Give an exact area using π and an approximate area to the nearest tenth.

25. $r = 8$ in. **26.** $r = 1.9$ cm **27.** $r = 10$ mm **28.** $r = 4.5$ in.

Lesson 6-2
🌐 **29. Baking** A recipe that serves four people calls for $1\frac{1}{2}$ c of flour. How many cups of flour are needed to serve ten people?

Guided Problem Solving

Understanding Word Problems Read the problem below. Then let Cheryl's thinking guide you through the solution. Check your understanding with the exercise at the bottom of the page.

Bird Watching A rare bird is spotted in a tree by a bird-watching group. The group is 9.5 yd from the base of the tree. The angle of elevation to the bird is 57°. How far is the bird from the group along the line of sight? Draw a sketch, and then solve.

What Cheryl Thinks

I'll draw a sketch. In it, I'll show:
angle of elevation = 57°,
distance from tree = 9.5 yd,
right angle near base of tree.

I must find the line-of-sight distance to the bird. That's along the hypotenuse of the right triangle. I'll name it x.

I know an angle and the adjacent leg. I want to find the hypotenuse. I'll use the cosine ratio.

I can solve this equation.

I'll use a calculator and round.

Now I can write the answer.

What Cheryl Writes

57°
9.5 yd

x

57°
9.5 yd

$$\cos 57° = \frac{\text{adjacent}}{\text{hypotenuse}}$$

$$= \frac{9.5}{x}$$

$$x(\cos 57°) = 9.5$$

$$\frac{x(\cos 57°)}{\cos 57°} = \frac{9.5}{\cos 57°}$$

$$x = \frac{9.5}{\cos 57°}$$

$$x \approx 17.4$$

The bird is about 17.4 yd from the group along the line of sight.

EXERCISE

1. A hot-air balloon is 150 feet high. The angle of depression from the pilot to her assistant on the ground is 25°. What is the line-of-sight distance from the pilot to her assistant, to the nearest foot?

Test-Taking Strategies

Using a Variable

You can solve many problems by letting a variable be an unknown quantity you want to find. Use the variable in an equation. Then solve the equation to help solve the problem.

1 EXAMPLE

When José visited France he saw a large model of the Statue of Liberty. He wondered how tall the model was, so he measured its shadow. The shadow was 100 feet. He measured the height and shadow of a vertical pole. The pole measured 4 feet and its shadow was 5 feet. How tall was the model of the Statue of Liberty?

The unknown quantity is the height of the model. Sketch similar triangles (not to scale). Let x be the height. Then write a proportion using x.

$\dfrac{5}{100} = \dfrac{4}{x}$ **Write a proportion.**

$5x = 100(4)$ **Write cross products.**

$5x = 400$ **Simplify.**

$x = 80$ **Divide each side by 5.**

4 ft   5 ft   x   100 ft

● The model was 80 ft tall.

2 EXAMPLE

City code requires that wheelchair ramps rise no more than 1 in. for every horizontal foot. To meet the code, you build a ramp the entire length of your house, 36 ft. What is the ramp's angle of elevation?

The unknown quantity is the measure of the angle that the ramp forms with the ground. Let x be that measure. You know the side opposite and the side adjacent the angle.

3 ft   36 ft   ?

$\tan x = \dfrac{3}{36}$ **Use the tangent ratio.**

≈ 0.0833 **Write as a decimal.**

$x \approx 5$ **Use a calculator (see page 619).**

● The angle of elevation of the ramp is about 5°.

EXERCISE

1. You are flying a kite at the end of 200 ft of string. The angle of elevation is 30°. You are holding the end of the string at eye level, 5 ft above the ground. How high is the kite from the ground? Draw a diagram. Show how to use a variable. Then find how high the kite is.

Chapter Review

Vocabulary Review

🔊)) angle of depression (p. 622)
angle of elevation (p. 620)
cosine (p. 614)
distance (p. 598)
hypotenuse (p. 592)

irrational number (p. 589)
legs (p. 592)
midpoint (p. 600)
perfect square (p. 588)
sine (p. 614)

square root (p. 588)
tangent (p. 614)
trigonometric ratio (p. 614)
trigonometry (p. 614)

Match the vocabulary terms on the right with their descriptions on the left.

1. the two shortest sides of a right triangle

2. an angle formed by a horizontal line and a line of sight above it

3. the ratio of the lengths of two sides of a right triangle

4. the longest side of a right triangle, opposite the right angle

5. a number that cannot be expressed as a ratio of two integers

6. The inverse of squaring a number is finding this.

   a. irrational number
   b. square root
   c. legs
   d. trigonometric ratio
   e. hypotenuse
   f. angle of elevation

Go Online
PHSchool.com
For: Vocabulary quiz
Web Code: adj-1151

Skills and Concepts

11-1 Objectives

▼ To find square roots of numbers (p. 588)

▼ To classify real numbers (p. 589)

The square of an integer is a **perfect square.** The inverse of squaring a number is finding a **square root.** The symbol $\sqrt{}$ indicates the positive square root of a number. A number that cannot be expressed as the ratio of two integers $\frac{a}{b}$, where b is not zero, is **irrational.** If a positive integer is not a perfect square, its square root is irrational.

Simplify each square root.

7. $\sqrt{1}$ 8. $-\sqrt{16}$ 9. $\sqrt{49}$ 10. $\sqrt{64}$ 11. $-\sqrt{36}$

Estimate to the nearest integer.

12. $\sqrt{5}$ 13. $\sqrt{11}$ 14. $\sqrt{33}$ 15. $\sqrt{62}$ 16. $\sqrt{91}$

Identify each number as rational or irrational. Explain.

17. 0.55 18. $\sqrt{64}$ 19. $0.\overline{45}$ 20. $\sqrt{15}$ 21. $0.123123\ldots$

22. Explain why $0.12122122212222\ldots$ is an irrational number.

11-2 Objectives

▼ To use the Pythagorean Theorem (p. 592)

▼ To identify right triangles (p. 594)

In a right triangle, the two shortest sides are the **legs.** The longest side, which is opposite the right angle, is the **hypotenuse.** The Pythagorean Theorem states that in any right triangle the sum of the squares of the lengths of the legs is equal to the square of the length of the hypotenuse ($a^2 + b^2 = c^2$).

Can you form a right triangle with the three lengths given? Show your work.

23. 1 mi, 3 mi, 3 mi

24. 8 yd, 15 yd, 17 yd

25. $\sqrt{6}$ ft, $\sqrt{10}$ ft, 4 ft

26. 30 m, 40 m, 50 m

11-3 Objectives

▼ To find the distance between two points using the Distance Formula (p. 598)

▼ To find the midpoint of a segment using the Midpoint Formula (p. 600)

The Distance Formula states that the **distance** d between any two points (x_1, y_1) and (x_2, y_2) is $d = \sqrt{(x_2 - x_1)^2 + (y_2 - y_1)^2}$. The Midpoint Formula states that the **midpoint** of a line segment with endpoints $A(x_1, y_1)$ and $B(x_2, y_2)$ is $\left(\dfrac{x_1 + x_2}{2}, \dfrac{y_1 + y_2}{2}\right)$.

Find the distance between each pair of points. Round to the nearest tenth.

27. $(3, 0), (0, 2)$

28. $(-1, 7), (3, 10)$

29. $(4, -5), (-8, -1)$

30. $(-10, -12), (-8, -11)$

31. $(2, -14), (9, -20)$

32. $(10, 4), (-2, -2)$

Find the midpoint of each segment with the given endpoints.

33. $H(0, 1)$ and $J(4, 7)$

34. $K(2, 6)$ and $L(4, 2)$

35. $M(-7, 8)$ and $P(3, -4)$

36. $A(4, 9)$ and $B(5, 11)$

37. $X(-15, -12)$ and $Y(-9, -4)$

38. $D(20, 18)$ and $E(-15, -19)$

11-4 Objectives

▼ To write a proportion from similar triangles (p. 604)

You can write a proportion to solve indirect measurement problems using similar triangles.

39. Engineering An engineer needs to know what length to plan for a bridge across a river. She estimates the distance using the similar triangles $\triangle ABC$ and $\triangle DEC$ in the figure at the right. What is the distance a across the river?

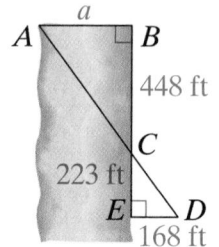

11-5 Objectives

▼ To use the relationships in 45°-45°-90° triangles (p. 608)

▼ To use the relationships in 30°-60°-90° triangles (p. 609)

In a 45°-45°-90° triangle, the length of the hypotenuse is the length of a leg times $\sqrt{2}$.

In a 30°-60°-90° triangle, the length of the hypotenuse is 2 times the length of the shorter leg, and the length of the longer leg is the length of the shorter leg times $\sqrt{3}$.

Find the values of the variables, rounded to the nearest tenth, if necessary.

40.

41.

42.

43.
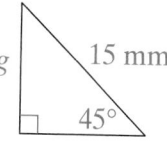

11-6 and 11-7 Objectives

▼ To find trigonometric ratios in right triangles (p. 614)

▼ To use trigonometric ratios to solve problems (p. 615)

▼ To use trigonometry to find angles of elevation (p. 620)

▼ To use trigonometry to find angles of depression (p. 622)

The ratios of the lengths of two sides of a right triangle are **trigonometric ratios.** Three trigonometric ratios are **sine, cosine,** and **tangent.** You can use these abbreviations when you find trigonometric ratios for a given acute $\angle N$.

$$\sin N = \frac{\text{opposite}}{\text{hypotenuse}} \qquad \cos N = \frac{\text{adjacent}}{\text{hypotenuse}} \qquad \tan N = \frac{\text{opposite}}{\text{adjacent}}$$

An **angle of elevation** is formed by a horizontal line and a line of sight above it. An **angle of depression** is formed by a horizontal line and a line of sight below it.

Find each value. Round to four decimal places.

44. $\sin 16°$ **45.** $\tan 82°$ **46.** $\cos 25°$ **47.** $\tan 3°$ **48.** $\sin 87°$

49. $\cos 73°$ **50.** $\cos 46°$ **51.** $\tan 45°$ **52.** $\sin 79°$ **53.** $\tan 13°$

Solve each problem. Round to the nearest unit.

54. A loading ramp forms a 28° angle with the ground. If the base of the ramp is 15 ft long, how high does the ramp reach?

55. Melanie is flying a kite and lets out 100 ft of string. Rosa determines that from Melanie's hands the angle of elevation of the kite is 71°. Melanie's hands are 4.3 ft from the ground. What is the height of the kite?

Chapter Test

Go Online
PHSchool.com
For: Chapter test
Web Code: ada-1152

Simplify each square root.

1. $\sqrt{25}$ **2.** $-\sqrt{81}$ **3.** $\sqrt{100}$

4. $-\sqrt{4}$ **5.** $\sqrt{16}$ **6.** $\sqrt{49}$

Estimate to the nearest integer.

7. $\sqrt{6}$ **8.** $\sqrt{12}$ **9.** $\sqrt{45}$

10. $\sqrt{78}$ **11.** $\sqrt{85}$ **12.** $\sqrt{118}$

Identify each number as rational or irrational.

13. $0.999\ldots$ **14.** $\sqrt{24}$

15. $\sqrt{100}$ **16.** $420,420$

Find each missing length to the nearest tenth of a unit.

17.

18.

19.

20.
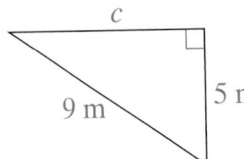

Find the distance between the points of each pair. Round to the nearest tenth.

21. $(0,0), (4,6)$ **22.** $(5,-3), (-6,2)$

23. $(-8,-9), (1,2)$ **24.** $(-1,-3), (-4,-7)$

Find the midpoint of each segment with the given endpoints.

25. $C(5,0)$ and $D(3,6)$

26. $M(9,-4)$ and $P(2,8)$

27. To estimate the height of a tree, Joan positions a mirror on the ground so she can see the top of the tree reflected in it. Joan's height, her distance from the mirror, and her line of sight to the mirror determine a triangle. The tree's height, its distance from the mirror, and the distance from the top of the tree to the mirror determine a similar triangle. Use the measurements below to find the height of the tree.

Find the missing lengths.

28.

29.
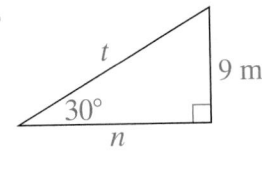

Find each value. Round to four decimal places.

30. $\sin 47°$ **31.** $\tan 75°$ **32.** $\cos 86°$

33. $\tan 29°$ **34.** $\cos 60°$ **35.** $\sin 67°$

36. Writing in Math Explain how a trigonometric ratio can be used to find a measurement indirectly.

37. Navigation The captain of a ship sights the top of a lighthouse at an angle of elevation of 12°. The captain knows that the top of the lighthouse is 24 m above sea level. What is the distance from the ship to the lighthouse?

Reading Comprehension **Read the passage below. Then answer the questions on the basis of what is *stated* or *implied* in the passage.**

Early Geometry The early Babylonians and Egyptians used practical geometry in their buildings, but it was a Greek named Thales who first wrote down the formal abstract geometry that we know today.

Thales, an olive-oil merchant, lived from about 600 to 550 B.C. One of the unchanging properties of triangles that he discovered was that a triangle drawn in a semicircle (half a circle), with the diameter as a hypotenuse, will always be a right triangle.

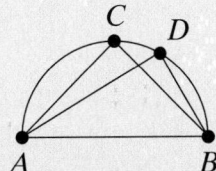

Around 540 B.C. a student of Thales, Pythagoras, founded a group that studied, among other things, mathematics. One of the rules of the *Pythagoreans* was never to eat beans! At first, they believed that the entire universe was made of only rational numbers, but working with right triangles convinced them that they could draw lines that have lengths equal to the square root of 2, the square root of 5, and so on.

1. What is the name of a teacher of Pythagoras?

2. What was the name of a group founded by Pythagoras?

3. What is the measure of $\angle C$?
   - (A) 360°
   - (B) 180°
   - (C) 90°
   - (D) 45°

4. Which term best describes $\overline{AC}$?
   - (E) leg
   - (F) sine
   - (G) hypotenuse
   - (H) tangent

5. If $AC = CB = 1$ in., what is AB?
   - (A) 2 in.
   - (B) $\sqrt{3}$ in.
   - (C) $\sqrt{2}$ in.
   - (D) 1 in.

6. If $AB = 6$ in. and $DB = 3$ in., what is AD?
   - (E) $3\sqrt{2}$ in.
   - (F) $3\sqrt{3}$ in.
   - (G) $6\sqrt{2}$ in.
   - (H) $6\sqrt{3}$ in.

7. If AB is $\sqrt{8}$ cm and $AC = CB$, what are AC and CB?

8. Which term does NOT apply to $\overline{AB}$?
   - (A) diameter
   - (B) hypotenuse
   - (C) leg
   - (D) line segment

9. How does the measure of $\angle D$ compare with the measure of $\angle C$?

10. What country was Thales from?

11. How long did Thales live?

12. What must be true of $\sqrt{2}$?
    - **I.** It is not a rational number.
    - **II.** A segment can have length $\sqrt{2}$.
    - **III.** It is equal to $\sqrt{5}$.
    - (E) I only
    - (F) I and II
    - (G) I and III
    - (H) II and III only

Picture Perfect

Applying Ratios Ancient Greeks realized that rectangles with certain dimensions were especially pleasing to the eye. A golden rectangle has sides that form the proportion $\frac{a}{b} = \frac{a+b}{a}$. The ratio of two sides of a golden rectangle is called the *golden ratio*. Artists make paintings with dimensions close to the golden ratio. Photographers often *crop*, or cut, their photographs to be golden rectangles.

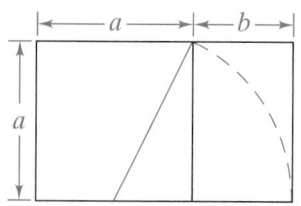

How to Make a Golden Rectangle

Start with a square with side length a. Open a compass the length from the midpoint of one side of the square to a corner on the opposite side. Make an arc. Extend the side containing the midpoint to intersect the arc. Make a rectangle using lengths b and a.

Golden Rectangle Proportion
a is to b as $(a + b)$ is to a.

The Parthenon
The front of the Parthenon, in Athens, Greece, approximates a golden rectangle.

x

$1.62x$

The Golden Rectangle in Art

Artist Sydney McGinley makes pastel paintings of flowers, such as *Pyramidal Fuschia*, using a golden rectangle to position the flowers within the painting.

The Villa Savoye

The Swiss architect Charles Le Corbusier designed the Villa Savoye, outside Paris, France, based on the golden rectangle, among other things. The house, built in 1930, looks different from each side.

Activity

1. a. Copy the table. For each rectangle, find the ratios $\frac{a}{b}$ and $\frac{a+b}{a}$. Write the ratios in decimal form, rounding to the nearest tenth. Write *yes* if the decimals are approximately equal.

b. Which rectangles are close to a golden rectangle? Explain.

Rectangle Dimensions (inches)

Side a	Side $a + b$	$\dfrac{a}{b}$	$\dfrac{(a+b)}{a}$	Golden Ratio?
5	8	$\frac{5}{3}=1.\overline{6}\approx 1.7$	$\frac{8}{5}=1.6$	Yes
3	4	■	■	■
6	10	■	■	■
14	22	■	■	■
12	16	■	■	■
15	24	■	■	■
18	26	■	■	■
21	33	■	■	■

2. Photo labs make prints in several sizes, including 3×5, 4×6, and 8×10. Which of these sizes is closest to a golden rectangle?

3. Open-Ended From the table, choose one pair of dimensions that do not form a golden rectangle. Change the value of a to a whole number that makes the rectangle closer to a golden rectangle. Justify your choice by showing your work.

4. Research Find at least three images from magazines or catalogs that you think approximate golden rectangles. Measure the images and calculate the ratio of length to width.

Go Online
PHSchool.com

For: Information about the golden ratio
Web Code: ade-1153

What You've Learned

 Assessment Framework

- **10.8.05:** In Chapter 3, you investigated measures of central tendency for sets of data.

- **6.8.03:** In Chapter 4, you simplified fractions by dividing the numerator and denominator by the GCF.

- **6.8.18:** In Chapter 5, you performed operations with fractions.

- **6.8.03:** In Chapter 6, you found the probability of events. You also wrote fractions and decimals as percents.

 Check Your Readiness **GO** **for Help** to the Lesson in green.

Finding the Median (Lesson 3-3)

Find the median.

1. $12, 14, 10, 9, 13, 12, 15, 12, 11$ **2.** $55, 53, 67, 52, 50, 49, 51, 52, 52$

3. $101, 100, 100, 105, 102, 101$ **4.** $0.2, 0.5, 0.11, 0.25, 0.34, 0.19$

Multiplying Fractions (Lesson 5-4)

Find each product.

5. $\frac{2}{3} \cdot \frac{1}{2}$ **6.** $\frac{7}{8} \cdot \frac{6}{7}$ **7.** $\frac{9}{10} \cdot \frac{8}{9}$ **8.** $\frac{5}{6} \cdot \frac{4}{5}$ **9.** $\frac{3}{4} \cdot \frac{2}{3}$ **10.** $\frac{7}{8} \cdot \frac{6}{7} \cdot \frac{5}{6}$

Finding Probability (Lesson 6-4)

Find the probability for one roll of a number cube.

11. $P(2)$ **12.** $P(5)$ **13.** $P(2 \text{ or } 5)$ **14.** $P(8)$

15. $P(1, 2, \text{ or } 3)$ **16.** $P(\text{less than } 1)$ **17.** $P(\text{not } 3)$ **18.** $P(\text{greater than } 4)$

A student is chosen at random from a class of 15 boys and 18 girls. Find each probability.

19. $P(\text{girl})$ **20.** $P(\text{boy})$ **21.** $P(\text{not a girl})$ **22.** $P(\text{not a boy})$

Fractions, Decimals, and Percents (Lesson 6-5)

Write each percent as a decimal, and each decimal or fraction as a percent.

23. 50% **24.** 36% **25.** 20% **26.** 5%

27. $\frac{1}{5}$ **28.** $\frac{7}{8}$ **29.** 0.28 **30.** 0.3

Data Analysis and Probability

Chapter

12

◀))**Key Vocabulary**

- box-and-whisker plot (p. 641)
- combination (p. 668)
- counting principle (p. 658)
- dependent events (p. 664)
- experimental probability (p. 673)
- histogram (p. 637)
- independent events (p. 662)
- line plot (p. 636)
- permutation (p. 667)
- quartiles (p. 641)
- random sample (p. 677)
- sample (p. 677)
- sample space (p. 658)
- simulation (p. 673)
- theoretical probability (p. 658)

What You'll Learn Next

 Assessment Framework

In this chapter, you will learn how to

- **10.8.03:** Use graphs to represent data.

- **10.8.06:** Find theoretical probability and experimental probability.

- **10.8.08:** Find permutations and combinations.

- Solve problems by doing simulations.

 Activity Lab Applying what you learn, on pages 692–693 you will solve problems about goal scoring in World Cup soccer.

12-1

Frequency Tables, Line Plots, and Histograms

 Assessment Framework

10.8.01 Read, interpret, and make predictions from data represented in a bar graph, line plot, Venn diagram, chart/table, line graph, scatterplot, circle graph, stem–and–leaf plot, or histogram.

✓ Check Skills You'll Need

Find the median and mode of each data set.

1. 6, 9, 9, 5, 9

2. 73, 78, 77, 73, 79

3. 300, 100, 200, 150, 300

4. 3, 5, 7, 9, 3, 4, 6, 3, 7

 for Help
Lesson 3-3

New Vocabulary

- frequency table
- line plot
- range
- histogram

1 **Using Frequency Tables and Line Plots**

Activity

Exploring Frequency Tables

Surveys Many people have favorite colors. Do people also have favorite numbers? Take a survey of your classmates.

1. Ask each person to choose an integer from 0 to 9. Use a table to record the responses.

2. Which number was chosen most frequently? How many times was each of the other numbers chosen?

3. Suppose you want to continue your survey. Looking back, would you use the same type of table you used for Question 1? Can you make improvements? Explain.

You can display data in a **frequency table,** which lists each data item with the number of times it occurs. Then you can use a **line plot**, which displays data with **X** marks above a number line.

1 EXAMPLE **Using a Line Plot**

A number cube was rolled 20 times. The results are at the right. Display the data in a frequency table. Then make a line plot.

| 5 | 2 | 5 | 4 | 1 | 6 | 5 | 2 | 5 | 1 |
| 3 | 6 | 1 | 3 | 4 | 5 | 3 | 5 | 3 | 4 |

	Use a tally mark for each result.	Count the tally marks and record the frequency.

Number	Tally	Frequency
1	III	3
2	II	2
3	IIII	4
4	III	3
5	⊬⊬I	6
6	II	2

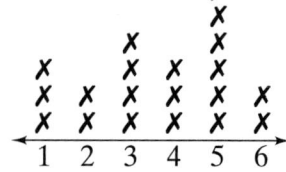

☑ Quick Check

1. Display the data below in a frequency table.

10 12 13 15 10 11 14 13 10 11 11 12 10 10 15

2 Using Histograms to Display Data

A **histogram** shows the frequencies of data items as a graph. The data are often grouped into intervals. The intervals are of equal size and do not overlap. The height of each bar shows the frequency of the data in a given interval.

2 EXAMPLE   Real-World 🌐 Problem Solving

Battery Life The results of testing 12 batteries of the same type are shown at the right. Use the data to make a histogram.

Hours of Battery Life

9	12	14	10	15	10
18	23	10	14	22	11

Step 1 Decide on the interval size. The data start at 9 hours and go to 24 hours. A possible interval choice is 4 hours.

Step 2 Make a frequency table.

Hours	Tally	Frequency
9–12	卌 I	6
13–16	III	3
17–20	I	1
21–24	II	2

Step 3 Make a histogram. Include a title and label the axes.

Hours of Battery Life

For: Histogram Activity
Use: Interactive Textbook, 12-1

☑ Quick Check

2. a. Display the data for battery life in a histogram with intervals of 3 hours.

b. Is the range of the data 14 or 4? Explain.

EXERCISES

For more exercises, see *Extra Skill and Word Problem Practice*.

Practice and Problem Solving

A Practice by Example

Example 1
(page 636)

Go for Help

Display each set of data in a frequency table and a line plot.

1. 1 4 0 3 0 1 3 2 2 4

2. 6 2 8 7 9 3 5 4 8 2 4 6 4 1

3. 10 30 20 30 50 10 40 30 50 40 30 50

4. 25 29 28 28 30 25 26 28 27 29 26 30

5. rolls of a number cube: 4 1 3 4 2 1 2 5 2 3 5 1 6 1 3 5 6

6. test scores: 100 90 70 60 95 65 85 70 70 75 80 85 75 70 100 90

Example 2
(page 637)

Draw a histogram for each frequency table.

7.

Interval	1–2	3–4	5–6	7–8
Frequency	7	10	4	5

8.

Interval	5–8	9–12	13–16
Frequency	12	8	2

9. A company asked its employees to keep track of the number of minutes they spend online checking e-mail each day. The responses are shown at the right.
   a. What intervals would you use to make a histogram?
   b. Make a frequency table for the data.
   c. Make a histogram.

Minutes Checking E–mail

25	35	24	27	42
45	36	38	62	84
72	33	44	27	54
28	33	65	71	24
54	47	36	71	29

B Apply Your Skills

10. Literature The numbers of letters in each of the first 25 words of *Alice's Adventures in Wonderland* by Lewis Carroll are shown below. Display the data in a histogram.
   4 3 10 5 3 9 2 3 4 5 2 7 2 3 6 2 3 4 3 2 6 7 2 2 4

11. The ages of drama club members are listed below. Display the data in a frequency table and find the range.
   14 16 14 16 14 13 12 15 16 12 12 15 14 15 15

12. The heights in inches of plants grown for a science project are listed below. Display the data in a histogram.
   25 25 20 25 16 20 25 30 25 31 26 28 30

13. Baseball In the World Series, the first team to win four games is the champion. Sometimes the series ends after four games, but it can last up to seven games. Make a frequency table of the data at the right and use the table to find the mode.

Number of World Series Games, 1970—2004

5	7	7	7	5	7	4	6	6	7	6	6
7	5	5	7	7	7	5	4	4	7	6	6
0	6	6	7	4	4	5	7	7	6	4	

Online
Homework Video Tutor
Visit: PHSchool.com
Web Code: ade-1201

A frequency table or line plot may allow you to readily "see" the mode and find the median. Find the mode and the median for the data set in each exercise.

14. Exercise 3

15. Exercise 4

16. Exercise 5

17. Exercise 6

 Challenge

18. Reasoning A magazine line plot shows results of a survey. Explain how to use the line plot to find each of the following:
a. the number of people who answered the survey.
b. the mode, median, and mean

19. Writing in Math Describe a set of data that would be easier to display with a frequency table than with a histogram.

ISAT

Test Prep

Multiple Choice

20. Below is a list of the ages of first-year teachers in one school system. What is the mode of the ages?
23, 42, 21, 25, 23, 24, 23, 24, 37, 23, 39, 51, 63, 24, 55
A. 23   **B.** 24   **C.** 37   **D.** 51

21. What is the range of the data below?
99.2, 101.5, 97.9, 102.1, 98.6, 100.4, 102.2, 99.9
F. 3.7   **G.** 3.9
H. 4.0   **J.** 4.3

Short Response

The line plot (right) represents the results of a class survey in which students were asked to name their favorite lunch.

22. a. How many students were surveyed?
b. How do you know?

23. a. What is the mode of the survey?
b. Explain your answer for part (a).

			X		
	X		X		
	X		X		X
X	X		X		X
X	X	X	X		X
X	X	X	X	X	X
X	X	X	X	X	X
Pizza	Spaghetti	Hamburgers	Chicken	Tacos	Subs

Mixed Review

 for Help

Lesson 11-7

24. Measurement The angle of elevation to a treetop from a point 10 ft out from the tree's base is 70°. Find the height of the tree.

Lesson 9-5

Given that $\triangle LMN \cong \triangle PQR$, complete each statement.

25. $\angle N \cong$ ■   **26.** $\overline{MN} \cong$ ■   **27.** $PQ =$ ■

Lesson 3-3

Find the mean, median, and mode for each data set.

28. 12 13 14 16 16 17 18 18   **29.** 8 15 22 9 11 16 20 10

Activity Lab
Histograms on a Graphing Calculator

Technology

For Use With Lesson 12-1

You can use a graphing calculator to make a histogram.

ACTIVITY

Make a histogram of the data below. Determine the size of the intervals and the frequency of the second interval.
10, 26, 18, 35, 14, 11, 17, 29, 31, 25, 27, 20, 19, 12, 13, 26

Step 1 Press **LIST** to find list L_1. Enter the data in L_1. (Remove any data already in L_1 by selecting and pressing L_1, then CLEAR ENTER.)

Step 2 In **PLOT**, enter 1 and select **On**. Select the Type of graph that looks like a histogram and ENTER.

Step 3 In the **ZOOM** menu, select "ZoomStat" and ENTER.

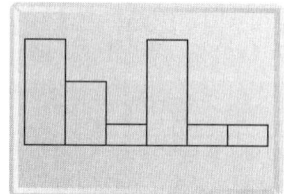

Step 4 Press TRACE and move the cursor across the histogram to determine the size of the intervals and the frequency of each interval.

The size of the interval is $20 - 15 = 5$. The frequency of the second interval is 3.

EXERCISES

Use a graphing calculator to make a histogram of the test grades of students shown below. Then answer the following questions.

98 92 76 84 93 82 74 68 85 91 77 83 94 97 72
88 70 84 87 82 91 77 93 88 86 81 85 92 82 78

1. What is the size of each interval?

2. Which interval has the greatest frequency? What is the frequency?

3. Which interval has the least frequency? What is the frequency?

4. Press WINDOW . Chance **XScl** to 4 and press GRAPH . Describe the change from the original graph.

640 Technology Histograms on a Graphing Calculator

Box-and-Whisker Plots

1   Making Box-and-Whisker Plots

A **box-and-whisker plot** displays the distribution of data items along a number line. **Quartiles** divide the data into four equal parts. The median is the middle quartile.

Box-and-Whisker Plot

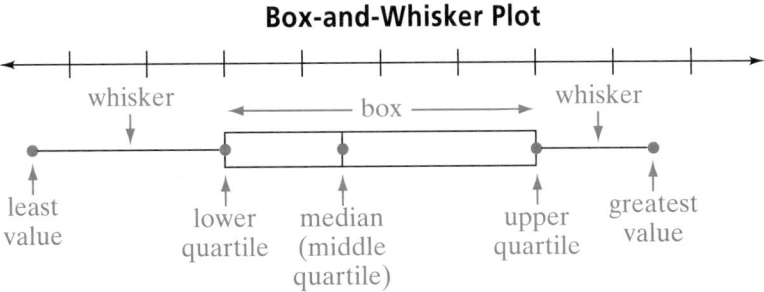

What You'll Learn
• To make box-and-whisker plots
• To analyze data in box-and-whisker plots

. . . And Why
To solve real-world problems involving large data sets

✓ Check Skills You'll Need

Find each median.

1. 12, 10, 11, 7, 9, 8, 10, 5

2. 4.5, 3.2, 6.3, 5.2, 5, 4.8, 6, 3.9

3. 55, 53, 67, 52, 50, 49, 51, 52, 52, 52

4. 101, 100, 100, 105, 102, 101

GO for Help
Lesson 3-3

◄)) New Vocabulary
• box-and-whisker plot
• quartiles

---

1 EXAMPLE   <u>Real-World</u> <u>Problem Solving</u>

Statistics **The table, below right, shows United States crops harvested from 1988 to 2000. Make a box-and-whisker plot.**

Step 1 Arrange the data in order from least to greatest. Find the median.

298 308 314 317 318 318 321 322 323 326 326 327 333

Step 2 Find the lower quartile and upper quartile, which are the medians of the lower and upper "halves."

298 308 314 317 318 318 321 322 323 326 326 327 333

lower quartile $= \dfrac{314 + 317}{2} = \dfrac{631}{2} = 315.5$

upper quartile $= \dfrac{326 + 326}{2} = \dfrac{652}{2} = 326$

Step 3 Draw a number line. Mark the least and greatest values, the median, and the quartiles. Draw a box from the first to the third quartiles. Mark the median with a vertical segment. Draw whiskers from the box to the least and greatest values.

Crops Harvested (millions of acres)

Crops Harvested

Year	Acres (millions)	Year	Acres (millions)
1988	298	1995	314
1989	318	1996	326
1990	322	1997	333
1991	318	1998	326
1992	317	1999	327
1993	308	2000	323
1994	321		

SOURCE: *Statistical Abstract of the United States.* Go to to **www.PHSchool.com** for a data update. Web Code: adg-9041

✓ Quick Check

1. Draw a box-and-whisker plot for the distances of migration of birds (thousands of miles): 5, 2.5, 6, 8, 9, 2, 1, 4, 6.2, 18, 7.

You can compare two sets of data by making two box-and-whisker plots below one number line.

---

2 EXAMPLE   Real-World 🌐 Problem Solving

Biology Use box-and-whisker plots to compare orca whale masses and hippopotamus masses.

Orca whale masses (kg)

3,900   2,750   2,600   3,100   4,200   2,600   3,700   3,000   2,200

Hippopotamus masses (kg)

1,800   2,000   3,000   2,500   3,600   2,700   1,900   3,100   2,300

Draw a number line for both sets of data. Use the range of data points to choose a scale.

Draw the second box-and-whisker plot below the first one.

✓ Quick Check

2. Compare annual video sales and CD sales by making two box-and-whisker plots below one number line.

videos (millions of units): 28, 24, 15, 21, 22, 16, 22, 30, 24, 17

CDs (millions of units): 16, 17, 22, 16, 18, 24, 15, 16, 25, 18

Real-World 🌐 Connection

DNA evidence suggests that whales and hippopotamuses are closely related genetically.

---

2 | Analyzing Box-and-Whisker Plots

Although you cannot see every data point in a box-and-whisker plot, you can use the quartiles and the greatest and least values to analyze and describe a data set.

③ EXAMPLE   Describing Data

Describe the data in the box-and-whisker plot.

Exam Scores

The highest score is 90 and the lowest is 50. At least half of the scores are within 10 points of the median, 75.

For: Box-and-Whisker Activity
Use: Interactive Textbook, 12-2

✓ Quick Check

3. Describe the data in each box-and-whisker plot.

a.   **b.**

You can compare box-and-whisker plots to analyze two sets of data.

④ EXAMPLE   Real-World 🌐 Problem Solving

Social Studies **The plots below compare the percents of the voting-age population who said they registered to vote in U.S. elections to the percents who said they voted. Which conclusion best reflects the data collected?**

Percents of Population Who Registered and Voted, 1990–2000

Ⓐ percent voted was about 15 less than percent registered
Ⓑ percent voted was about half the percent registered
Ⓒ percent voted was equal to the percent registered
Ⓓ percent voted was about 15 more than percent registered

The median of the percent who voted was about 50 and the median of the percent who registered was about 65: $65 - 50 = 15$. The answer is A.

Test-Taking Tip

Understand the data before you work on a problem. When you analyze a box-and-whisker plot, ask yourself questions such as "How many sets of data are displayed?"

✓ Quick Check

4. Use the box-and-whisker plots below. What conclusions can you draw about heights of Olympic basketball players?

Olympic Basketball Players' Heights (in.)

Men

Women

EXERCISES

For more exercises, see *Extra Skill and Word Problem Practice*.

Practice and Problem Solving

A Practice by Example

Example 1
(page 641)

GO for Help

1. Biology Use the data at the right to make a box-and-whisker plot for the maximum speeds of animals.

2. Make a box-and-whisker plot for this set of data:
16, 18, 59, 75, 30, 34, 25, 49, 27, 16, 21, 58, 71, 19, 50

Example 2
(page 642)

3. Compare the data sets by making two box-and-whisker plots below one number line.
set A: 3, 7, 9, 12, 2, 1, 6, 5, 4, 3, 7, 10, 13, 8, 1, 9
set B: 9, 8, 1, 7, 6, 3, 7, 9, 8, 6, 4, 7, 8, 9, 10, 10

Maximum Speeds of Animals for a Quarter Mile

Animal	Maximum Speed (mi/h)
Cheetah	70
Lion	50
Quarter horse	47.5
Coyote	43
Hyena	40
Rabbit	35
Giraffe	32
Grizzly bear	30
Cat (domestic)	30
Elephant	25
Squirrel	12

SOURCE: *The World Almanac*

Example 3
(page 643)

Answer each question for the data in the box-and-whisker plot below.

4. What are the highest and lowest prices for the CD players?

Prices of Portable CD Players ($)

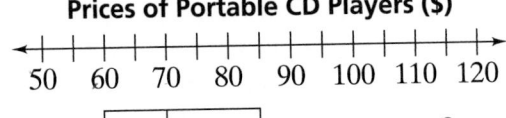

5. What is the lower quartile price? The median price? The upper quartile price?

6. About half of the prices are within what amount of the median?

Example 4
(page 643)

7. In Example 2 on page 642, what conclusions can you draw?

B Apply Your Skills

8. a. Olympics Compare the ages of male and female soccer players by making two box-and-whisker plots below one number line.

Ages of U.S. Olympic Soccer Team Players

men: 22, 21, 22, 26, 20, 26, 23, 21, 22, 22, 22, 22, 21, 22, 23, 21, 20, 22

women: 30, 27, 28, 25, 31, 24, 31, 24, 21, 23, 27, 18, 19, 24, 23, 20

b. Compare the box-and-whisker plots. What can you conclude?

9. Use the box-and-whisker plot below. What can you conclude about acreages of state parks?

Areas of State Parks (acres)

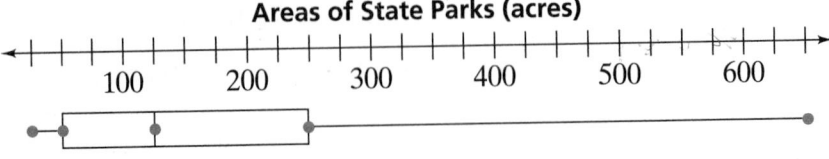

GO Online
Homework Video Tutor
Visit: PHSchool.com
Web Code: ade-1202

10. Writing in Math Explain how you can find the quartiles of a set of data.

11. **Error Analysis** A student made a box-and-whisker plot. The student marked the greatest and least data values and then divided the distance between those points into four equal parts. What error did the student make?

 Challenge

12. **Open-Ended** Write a set of data whose box-and-whisker plot has a long box and short whiskers.

13. **Reasoning** Can you find the mean, median, and mode of a set of data by looking at a box-and-whisker plot? Explain.

ISAT

Test Prep

Multiple Choice

For Exercises 14–16, use the table.

14. What is the median of the maximum life spans of the animals in the table?
    A. 18 yr   **B.** 31 yr
    C. 34 yr   **D.** 50 yr

15. What is the median of the maximum life spans of the animals if you exclude the mouse and chipmunk?
    F. 50 yr   **G.** 43 yr
    H. 26 yr   **J.** 18 yr

Short Response

16. **a.** Make a box-and-whisker plot to represent the maximum life spans.
    b. Identify and label the median, the lower and upper quartiles, and the least and greatest maximum life spans.

Animals' Maximum Life Spans

Animal	Years
Beaver	50
Black bear	36
Chimpanzee	53
Chipmunk	8
Elephant	77
Goat	18
Horse	50
Mouse	6
Squirrel	23
Tiger	26

Mixed Review

GO for Help

Lesson 12-1

Display each set of data in a frequency table.

17. 6 8 7 6 5 8 5 6 4 8 7 5
    4 7 6 8 6 7

18. 32 31 29 33 31 32 35 33
    32 31 32 30

Lesson 11-3

Find the distance between the points in each pair to the nearest tenth.

19. $D(3, -2), S(-3, 2)$

20. $A(0, 4), W(-7, -5)$

21. $Y(6, 4), K(-1, 3)$

22. $Z(9, 0), M(-8, 11)$

Lessons 4-9 and 5-5

23. Lawns can have 850 blades of grass per square foot.
    a. About how many blades of grass are in one square yard?
    b. The area of all lawns in the United States equals an area twice as large as that of Pennsylvania. Pennsylvania's area is 46,058 mi². Estimate the number of blades of grass in lawns in the United States. Write your answer in scientific notation. (*Hint:* A mile equals 5,280 feet.)

A **stem-and-leaf plot** organizes data by showing the items in order.
The leaf is the last digit to the right.
The stem is the remaining digit or digits.

stem⟶ 15.7 ⟵leaf

stem⟶ 32 ⟵leaf

Online active math

For: Stem-and-Leaf Plot Activity
Use: Interactive Textbook, 12-2b

1 EXAMPLE

Use the table at the right to construct a stem-and-leaf plot. Then find the median, mode, and range.

Choose the stems. For this data set, use the values in the tens place. Draw a line to the right of the stems.

stems ⟶
```
2|
3|
```

Leaves are single digits, so for this data set the leaves will be the values in the ones place.

```
2|9 8
3|7 8 7 3 9 7
```
⟵ leaves

Broadway Productions

```
2|8 9
3|3 7 7 7 8 9

2|8 means 28
```
⟵ key

Arrange the leaves on each stem from least to greatest. Include a title and a key that shows how to read your stem-and-leaf plot.

Broadway Productions

Season	New Shows
1993–1994	37
1994–1995	29
1995–1996	38
1996–1997	37
1997–1998	33
1998–1999	39
1999–2000	37
2000–2001	28

SOURCE: *The World Almanac.*

Since the data items are in order, the median is the midpoint. The median is the mean of the fourth and fifth values, or 37.

The mode corresponds to the most repeated leaf. The mode is 37.

The range is the difference of the greatest and least values, or 11.

Average Longevity

1. Biology Use the table at the right.
  a. Reasoning What number should you use as the stem for the kangaroo and the opossum?
  b. Construct a stem-and-leaf plot.
  c. Find the median.
  d. Find the mode.
  e. Find the range.

Animal	Years	Animal	Years
Grizzly bear	25	Hippopotamus	41
Kangaroo	7	Pig	10
Cow	15	Lion	15
Dog	12	Opossum	1
Giraffe	10	Cat	12
Gorilla	20	Zebra	15

SOURCE: *The World Almanac*

Make a stem-and leaf plot for each set of data. Then find the median, the mode, and the range.

2. 15, 22, 25, 10, 36, 15, 28, 35, 18

3. 47, 41, 60, 75, 85, 53, 57, 76, 79, 81, 84, 86

4. 785, 785, 776, 772, 792, 788, 761, 768, 768

5. 4.5, 4.3, 0.8, 3.5, 2.6, 1.4, 0.2, 0.8, 4.3, 6.0

A back-to-back stem-and-leaf plot uses two sets of data. The side-by-side display makes the data easier to compare.

2 EXAMPLE

Draw a back-to-back stem-and-leaf plot for the winning times in the Olympic 100-m dash. Find each median and mode.

Use seconds for the stem and tenths of seconds for the leaves. Put the leaves in ascending order starting at the stem.

Winning Times, 100-m Dash

Men's Times (tenths of second)	Stem (seconds)	Women's Times (tenths of second)
9 9 9 8	9	
3 2 1 1 0 0 0	10	5 8 8 9
	11	0 0 0 1 1 1 4

means 10.0 ◄— 0 | 10 | 5 —► means 10.5

The median of the times for men is 10.0 s. The median of the times for women is 11.0 s. The modes of the times for men are 9.9 s and 10.0 s. The modes of the times for women are 11.0 s and 11.1 s.

Winning Times, 100-m Dash (seconds)

Year	Men	Women
1960	10.2	11.0
1964	10.0	11.4
1968	9.9	11.0
1972	10.1	11.1
1976	10.1	11.1
1980	10.3	11.1
1984	10.0	11.0
1988	9.9	10.5
1992	10.0	10.8
1996	9.8	10.9
2000	9.9	10.8

SOURCE: *Sports Illustrated Sports Almanac*

Make a back-to-back stem-and-leaf plot for each pair of data sets. Then find each median and mode.

6. set A: 9.1, 8.2, 7.3, 6.4, 7.3, 8.5   set B: 7.6, 9.2, 8.2, 8.3, 9.7, 7.6

7. set C: 236, 237, 241, 250, 242   set D: 262, 251, 248, 243, 257

8. Annual video sales (millions):   Annual CD sales (millions):
   28, 24, 15, 21, 22, 16, 22, 30, 24, 17   16, 17, 22, 16, 18, 24, 15, 16, 25, 18

Use the stem-and-leaf plot at the right. The plot shows the time spent on homework by students in two classes.

9. Which numbers are the stems?

10. What is the least time spent for each set of data?

11. What is the median for each set of data?

12. What is the mode for each set of data?

13. What is the range for each set of data?

Time Spent on Homework (min)

Class A		Class B
7 4 3	6	1 1 3 5 5
9 9 8 5 4 4	7	0 2 2 4
5 2 1 0	8	4 5 8 9
7 6 6 4 2	9	3 6 7 9 9 9

means 63 ◄— 3 | 6 | 1 —► means 61

Using Graphs to Persuade

IL Assessment Framework

10.8.03 Create a bar graph, chart/table, line graph, or circle graph and solve a problem using the data in the graph for a given set of data.

1 ▸ **Using Breaks in Scales**

You can draw graphs of a data set in different ways in order to give different impressions.

You can use a break in the scale on one or both axes of a line graph or a bar graph. This lets you show more detail and emphasize differences. However, it can also give a distorted picture of the data.

☑ Check Skills You'll Need

Find the slope of $\overline{AB}$ in each graph.

1.

2.

GO for Help
Lesson 8-3

1 EXAMPLE Real-World ● Problem Solving

Population Which title would be more appropriate for the graph below: "Los Angeles Overwhelms Chicago" or "Populations of Chicago and Los Angeles"? Explain.

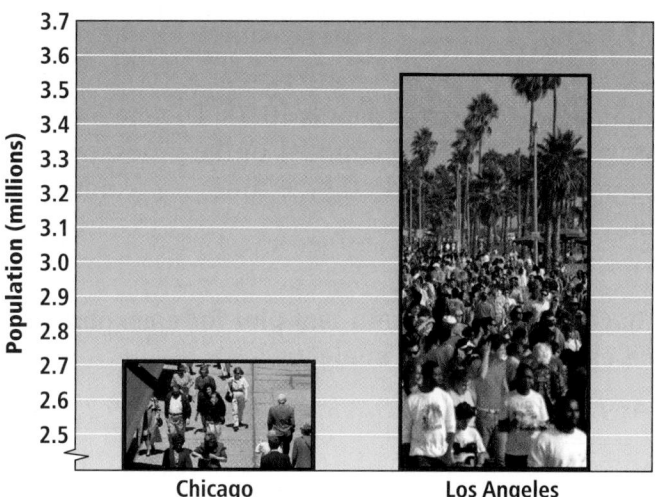

Because of the break in the vertical axis, the bar for Los Angeles appears to be more than three times as tall as the bar for Chicago. Actually, the population of Los Angeles is a little less than 3.6 million, and the population of Chicago is about 2.7 million. So the population of Los Angeles is about 1.3 times that of Chicago.

The title "Los Angeles Overwhelms Chicago" could be misleading. "Populations of Chicago and Los Angeles" better describes the information in the graph.

☑ Quick Check

1. Use the data in the graph in Example 1. Redraw the graph without a break.

Using Different Scales

You can use different scales or spacing along axes. This lets you emphasize (or de-emphasize) how changes in data are related.

2 **EXAMPLE** Real-World 🌎 Problem Solving

Cost of Living Study the graphs below. Which graph gives the impression of a sharper increase in price? Explain.

In the graph at the right, the months are much closer together, so the line appears to climb more rapidly. This graph suggests that prices are going up faster than suggested by the graph at the left.

✓ Quick Check

2. Use the data in the table at the right.

   a. Make a graph that suggests a rapid decrease in the total weight of fish caught.

   b. Make a graph that suggests a slow decrease in the total weight of fish caught.

   c. **Reasoning** A group is planning a campaign to protect the supply of fish. They are proposing a regulation that would limit the number of pounds of fish caught annually. Would they more likely use the graph from part (a) or part (b) in their proposal? Explain.

Fish Caught for Food in the U.S.

Year	Fish Caught (billions of pounds)
1993	8.2
1994	7.9
1995	7.7
1996	7.5

SOURCE: *Statistical Abstract of the United States.* Go to **www.PHSchool.com** for a data update. Web Code: adg-9041

There is a fine line between using graphs to persuade and using graphs to mislead.

Bar graphs can be misleading if their "bars" change in more than one dimension. This can happen when graphs use realistic images for the bars. These images make the graphs more interesting but also can give false impressions.

3 EXAMPLE   Real-World 🌐 Problem Solving

Reasoning What makes the graph misleading? Explain.

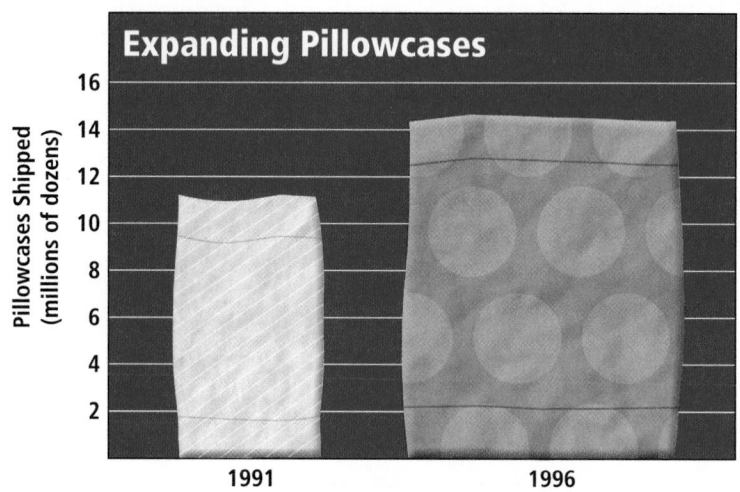

By reading the vertical axis, you can see that the number of pillowcases shipped increased by about one fourth.

However, the bar on the right has not only increased in height, but has also nearly doubled in width. The area of the second bar is more than two times the area of the first bar.

Because of this, you might get the impression that the increase was much greater than it really was.

✓ Quick Check

3. Use the data in the table below.

**Prices of Field-Grown Tomatoes
in the United States**

Year	Price of Tomatoes (cents per pound)
1990	86
1997	162

SOURCE: *Statistical Abstract of the United States.* Go to **www.PHSchool.com** for a data update. Web Code: adg-9041

a. Draw a graph that suggests that the price of tomatoes nearly doubled.

b. Draw a graph that suggests that the price of tomatoes more than doubled.

EXERCISES

For more exercises, see *Extra Skill and Word Problem Practice*.

Practice and Problem Solving

Ⓐ Practice by Example

Example 1
(page 648)

GO **for Help**

For Exercises 1–4, use the graph at the right.

1. Which magazine *appears* to have about twice the circulation of *Circuitry Today*?

2. Which magazine *actually* has twice the circulation of *Circuitry Today*?

3. Explain why the graph might mislead you.

4. Redraw the graph without a break in the horizontal axis.

Magazine Circulation

Example 2
(page 649)

Statistics **For Exercises 5–7, use the graph at the right.**

🌐 5. **School Computers** Does the graph suggest a rapid increase or a slow increase in the percent of students using a computer at school?

6. Redraw the graph. Change the horizontal scale to suggest a slower increase from 1989 to 1993.

7. Redraw the graph. Suggest a slower increase from 1989 to 1993 by changing the vertical scale.

Percent of Students Using Computers at School

Example 3 🌐
(page 650)

Food Service **For Exercises 8–10, use the graph below.**

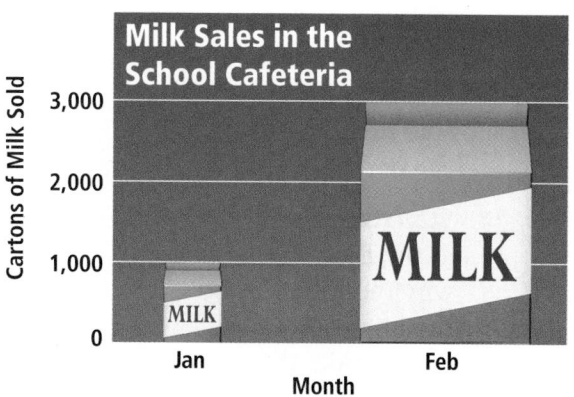

8. What impression does the graph give you about milk sales in the school cafeteria? Is the graph misleading? Explain.

9. Redraw the graph to represent the data accurately.

10. Redraw the graph to suggest that milk sales changed very little.

B Apply Your Skills

GO **for Help**

For a guide to reading the table and drawing the graph in Exercise 11, see page 654.

11. **a. Statistics** Use the data at the right. Draw a graph with an axis break to suggest that enrollment in 2000 was many times the enrollment in 1990.
    b. Draw a second graph of the data, without using a break. Choose a scale that suggests that enrollment did not increase much from 1990 to 2000.

U.S. College Enrollment

Year	Enrollment
1990	13.8 million
1995	14.2 million
2000	14.9 million

SOURCE: U.S. Education Department

For Exercises 12–14, use the graph at the right.

12. **Writing in Math** The graph suggests that the number of students per computer in elementary schools is three times the number of students per computer in high schools. Is this true? Explain.

13. What does the graph suggest is the ratio of middle school students per computer to high school students per computer? What is the actual ratio?

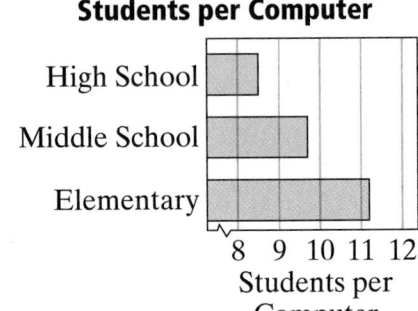

Average Number of Students per Computer

14. Redraw the graph without a break. Describe the effect this has on what the graph suggests.

Average Annual Tuition and Fees for Four-Year Public Colleges

Year	Tuition and Fees
1980–1981	$1,647
1990–1991	$2,529
2000–2001	$3,535

SOURCE: The College Board

15. Use the data at the left. Draw a line graph that gives the impression of a gradual increase in college tuition and fees from 1980 to 2001.

16. **Open-Ended** Find a graph in a newspaper or magazine that could be misleading. Explain how it could be misleading.

C Challenge

Percent of Milk Sold That Was Low-Fat

Year	Percent
1980	38%
1990	59%

17. Use the data at the left to make two different graphs. Draw one of the graphs to suggest that the percent of low-fat milk sold in 1990 was double the percent in 1980.

18. **Statistics** Use the graph at the right. Explain why the intervals on the horizontal axis could make the graph misleading.

19. Tell how to scale the x- and y-axes so that $\overline{AB}$ joining points $A(4, 2)$ and $B(8, 6)$ appears to have the slope given.

a. $\frac{1}{2}$ b. 1 c. 2

Home Ownership Rates, by Age

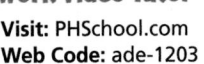

GO **Online**

Homework Video Tutor

Visit: PHSchool.com
Web Code: ade-1203

Multiple Choice   For Exercises 20 and 21, use the graph below.

20. The graph makes it appear that there are how many times as many students per teacher at North HS as there are at West HS?

Student-Teacher Ratios at Area High Schools

A. 2 times   **B.** 3 times
C. 4 times   **D.** 5 times

21. Why might this graph give a distorted picture of the data?
   F. The longest horizontal bar is on top.
   G. The vertical lines are evenly spaced.
   H. There is a break in the horizontal axis.
   J. The horizontal bars are different lengths.

Short Response   **22.** Use the table at the right to make two different line graphs.
   a. Draw one graph to suggest that sales more than doubled from 1996 to 1999.
   b. Draw the other graph to suggest that sales increased only slightly during the same period.

Annual Sales

Year	Sales
1996	$87 million
1997	$87 million
1998	$88 million
1999	$90 million

Mixed Review

Lesson 12-2

Make a box-and-whisker plot for each set of data.

23. 27, 25, 23, 29, 25, 28, 26, 27, 23, 21, 20, 24, 25, 28, 30, 19, 25

24. 2, 6, 3, 9, 15, 4, 9, 20, 6, 7, 2, 3, 8, 4, 1, 5, 6, 8, 5, 4, 9, 3, 2, 8, 7

25. 100, 95, 102, 101, 96, 100, 104, 115, 102, 108, 92, 97, 103, 106

Lessons 10-5

26. Geometry The Museum of Health and Medical Science in Houston, Texas, has one of the largest kaleidoscopes in the world. It is a cylinder 10 feet long and 22 inches in diameter. What is the surface area of the kaleidoscope?

Lesson 6-4

Find each probability for choosing a letter at random from the word STATISTICS.

27. P(vowel)   **28.** P(S)   **29.** P(not T)   **30.** P(A or C)

Analyzing Data Read the problems below. Then let Kayla's thinking guide you through the solution. Check your understanding with the exercise at the bottom of the page.

a. Statistics Use the data at the right. Draw a graph with a break to suggest that enrollment in 2000 was many times the enrollment in 1990.

b. Draw a second graph of the data without using a break. Choose a scale that suggests that enrollment did not increase much from 1990 to 2000.

U.S. College Enrollment

Year	Enrollment
1990	13.8 million
1995	14.2 million
2000	14.9 million

SOURCE: U.S. Education Department

What Kayla Thinks

Part (a) asks me to draw a graph with a break that makes enrollment in 2000 look *many times* the enrollment in 1990.

I'll use a bar graph. The table shows the 1990 enrollment was 13.8 million. I'll break the vertical scale right before 13.8 to make the 1990 bar look small.

The table shows a 2000 enrollment of 14.9 million. I'll use vertical intervals of 0.3. That makes the top mark 15.0.

The bar for 14.9 is as tall as possible. It looks nearly 4 times as tall as 1990!

Part (b) asks for no break. I'll scale by 2 on the vertical axis. This will make 1990 and 2000 almost the same height.

What Kayla Draws

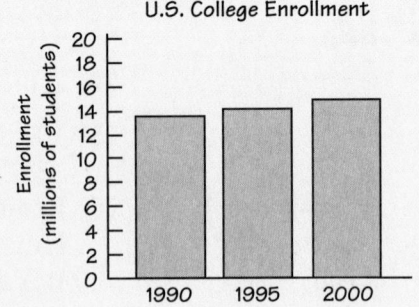

EXERCISE

1. Two months ago, the price for Technostar stock was $32. Last month it was $32.40. Now it is $32.80. Draw graphs suggesting each of the following about the stock price.

   a. a large increase   **b.** a small increase

Bar graphs, line graphs, and *circle graphs* are three common ways to represent data.

Sometimes you have to choose which type of graph to use to represent a set of data. Knowing the differences among the types of graphs can help you make the best choice.

You use a bar graph to compare amounts. One axis shows the categories and the other axis shows the amounts. A multiple-bar graph includes a key.

You use a line graph to show the changes in a set of data over a period of time. A multiple-line graph shows changes in more than one category of data. You can use a line graph to look for trends and make predictions.

Circle graphs show data as percents or fractions of a whole. The total must be 100% of 1. The angles at the center are central angles, and each angle is proportional to the percent or fraction of the total.

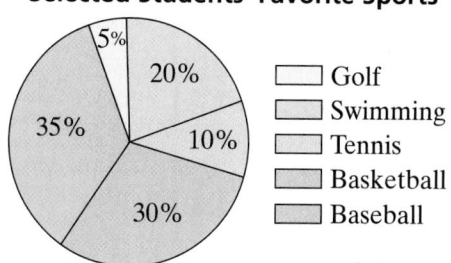

EXERCISES

1. **Multiple Choice** Choose the line graph that best represents the data in the table.

Montana's Resident Population (thousands)

Year	1999	2000	2001	2002	2003	2004
Population	883	904	906	911	918	927

Source: U.S. Census Bureau. Go to **www.PHSchool.com** for a data update. Web Code: adg-9041

   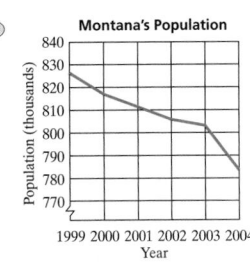

2. **Multiple Choice** Choose the circle graph that best represents the data in the table.

Favorite Books

Type of Book	Number of People
Adventure	15
Biography/Memoir	30
Romance	75
Science Fiction	60

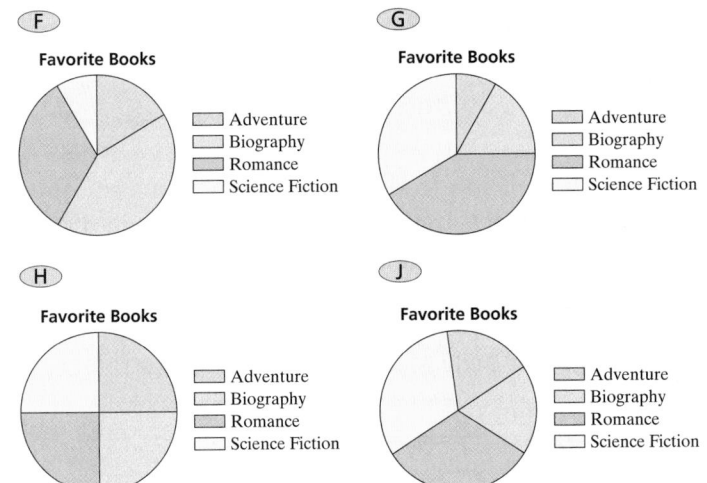

Choose a bar graph, line graph, or circle graph to display each set of data. Explain your choice.

3. **List and Sale Prices**

Item	List Price	Sale Price
Digital camera	$279	$223
Headphone radio	$40	$32
Smartphones	$195	$156

4. **Selected Costs of Owning a Car**

Category	Percent
Financing	52
Gas, oil, and maintenance	25
Insurance	20
Registration	3

Counting Outcomes and Theoretical Probability

 Assessment Framework

1 Counting Possible Choices

ctivity

Exploring Possible Outcomes

Congratulations! Your application to run the pizza stand at school home games has been accepted. Now you have to decide which pizzas to sell. You plan to offer two or three choices in each of three categories—size, crust, and topping. The more types of pizza the better, but you're limited by kitchen space to a total of 18 types.

1. Decide which types of pizza you will offer. Make a menu that shows your customers their options.

2. **Reasoning** Suppose you decide to offer three choices of size and three choices of crust. How many choices of toppings can you offer?

You can use a tree diagram to display and count possible choices.

1 EXAMPLE Drawing a Tree Diagram

A school team sells caps in two colors (blue or white), two sizes (child or adult), and two fabrics (cotton or polyester). Draw a tree diagram to find the number of cap choices.

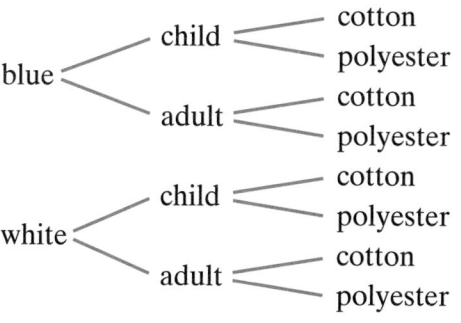

Each branch of the "tree" represents one choice—for example, blue–child–cotton.

There are 8 possible cap choices.

✓ Quick Check

1. Suppose the caps in Example 1 also come in black. Draw a tree diagram. How many cap choices are there?

10.8.06 Solve problems involving the probability of an event composed of repeated trials, compound events, or future events with or without replacement.

10.8.07 Represent all possible outcomes for simple or compound events.

✓ Check Skills You'll Need

A bag has 5 blue (B) chips, 4 red (R) chips, and 3 tan (T) chips. Find each probability for choosing a chip at random from the bag.

1. $P(R)$ 2. $P(\text{not } R)$
3. $P(B)$ 4. $P(R \text{ or } B)$
5. $P(T)$ 6. $P(B \text{ or } T)$

GO for Help
Lesson 6-4

🔊 **New Vocabulary**
- counting principle
- theoretical probability
- sample space

Vocabulary Tip

The <u>Counting</u> <u>Principle</u> is sometimes called the "Multiplication Counting Principle."

Key Concepts Counting Principle

If there are m ways of making one choice, and n ways of making a second choice, then there are $m \cdot n$ ways of making the first choice followed by the second.

The Counting Principle is particularly useful when a tree diagram would be too large to draw.

2 EXAMPLE Using the Counting Principle

How many two-letter monograms are possible?

first letter		second letter		**monograms**
possible choices		possible choices		possible choices
26	$\cdot$	26	$=$	676

There are 676 possible two-letter monograms.

Real-World ⊕ Connection

A monogram is made up of two or more letters, such as your initials.

☑ **Quick Check**

2. a. How many three-letter monograms are possible?
   b. How many five-letter license plates can be made if the letters O and I cannot be used?

2 Finding Probability by Counting Outcomes

You can count outcomes to help you find the **theoretical probability** of an event in which outcomes are equally likely.

Key Concepts Theoretical Probability

$$P(\text{event}) = \frac{\text{number of favorable outcomes}}{\text{number of possible outcomes}}$$

A **sample space** is a list of all possible outcomes. You can use a tree diagram to find a sample space. Then you can calculate probability.

3 EXAMPLE   Using a Tree Diagram

Use a tree diagram to find the sample space for tossing two coins.
Then find the probability of tossing two tails.

heads —— heads
       —— tails   **The tree diagram shows there**
tails —— heads   **are four possible outcomes, one**
      —— tails   **of which is tossing two tails.**

$$P(\text{event}) = \frac{\text{number of favorable outcomes}}{\text{number of possible outcomes}}$$ **Use the probability formula.**

$$P(\text{two tails}) = \frac{\text{number of two-tail outcomes}}{\text{number of possible outcomes}}$$

$$= \frac{1}{4}$$

The probability of tossing two tails is $\frac{1}{4}$.

✓ Quick Check

● **3.** You toss two coins. Find $P(\text{one head and one tail})$.

You can also use the Counting Principle to find probability.

4 EXAMPLE   Real-World 🌐 Problem Solving

Multiple Choice **Many people play lottery games without knowing
the probability of winning. In some state lotteries, the winning
number is made up of four digits chosen at random. Suppose a
player buys two tickets with different numbers. What is the
probability that the player has a winning ticket?**

Ⓐ $\frac{1}{5,040}$ Ⓑ $\frac{1}{5,000}$ Ⓒ $\frac{1}{2,520}$ Ⓓ $\frac{1}{40}$

First find the number of possible outcomes. For each digit, there
are 10 possible outcomes, 0 through 9.

1st digit outcomes		2nd digit outcomes		3rd digit outcomes		4th digit outcomes		total outcomes
10	·	10	·	10	·	10	=	10,000

Then find the probability when there are two favorable outcomes.

$$P(\text{winning ticket}) = \frac{\text{number of favorable outcomes}}{\text{number of possible outcomes}} = \frac{2}{10,000}$$

The probability is $\frac{2}{10,000}$, or $\frac{1}{5,000}$. The correct answer is B.

Test-Taking Tip
Remember that
theoretical probability
is a ratio. You can
write a probability as a
fraction, a decimal, or
a percent. Use the form
that makes the most
sense for the problem
you are solving.

✓ Quick Check

4. A lottery uses five digits chosen at random. Find the probability
of buying a winning ticket.

EXERCISES

For more exercises, see *Extra Skill and Word Problem Practice*.

Practice and Problem Solving

 Practice by Example

Example 1
(page 657)

 for Help

You can choose a burrito having one filling wrapped in one tortilla. Draw a tree diagram to count the number of burrito choices.

1. tortillas: flour or corn; fillings: beef, chicken, bean, cheese, or vegetable

2. tortillas: whole wheat flour, blue corn, or white corn; fillings: chicken, tofu, grilled fish, or vegetable

Example 2
(page 658)

There are four roads from Marsh to Taft and seven roads from Taft to Polk. Use the Counting Principle to find the number of routes below.

3. from Marsh to Polk through Taft

4. from Marsh to Polk after a new road opens from Marsh to Taft

Example 3
(page 659)

Use a tree diagram to find the sample space for tossing three coins. Then find each probability.

5. *P*(three heads)   **6.** *P*(two tails)   **7.** *P*(at least one head)

Example 4
(page 659)

Use the Counting Principle to help you find each probability.

8. Rolling a 3 on each of two number cubes

9. Lottery Choosing the three winning lottery numbers when the numbers are chosen at random from 1 to 50. Numbers can repeat.

 Apply Your Skills **10. Snacks** You can choose chocolate, strawberry, or vanilla frozen yogurt, and red, blue, or green sprinkles. A sundae has one yogurt flavor and two different colors of sprinkles. How many different kinds of sundaes can you order? List them.

Sweaters

Colors	Styles
Blue	Cardigan
Pink	Crewneck
Red	V-neck
Brown	
Black	

You have one sweater of each possible color and style in the table (left).

11. How many sweaters do you have?

12. What is the probability of choosing a brown sweater at random?

13. What is the probability of choosing a cardigan at random?

Find the probability of each event.

14. You toss tails and roll an even number (when you toss a coin and roll a number cube).

15. You roll two odd numbers and pick a vowel (when you roll two number cubes and pick a letter of the alphabet at random).

 Challenge

 Online
Homework Video Tutor
Visit: PHSchool.com
Web Code: ade-1204

16. Reasoning You have a bag containing an equal number of nickels, dimes, and quarters. You reach into the bag and choose a coin. Are all outcomes equally likely? Explain.

17. Writing in Math Write a problem (unlike any in this lesson) that you can solve using the Counting Principle. Then solve.

Multiple Choice

18. You are writing a three-digit number. The first digit must be 2 or 8. The second digit must be 1, 3, or 9. The third digit must be 4, 5, 6, 7, or 8. Which expression can you use to find how many different three-digit numbers you can write?

A. $2 \cdot 3 \cdot 5$
B. $5 \cdot 4 \cdot 3 \cdot 2 \cdot 1$
C. $(1 \cdot 2) + (2 \cdot 3) + (3 \cdot 5)$
D. $2 + 3 + 5$

19. An ice-cream vendor sells small or large cones and has chocolate, vanilla, rocky road, pecan, and strawberry flavors. To help a customer select a flavor and size, the vendor has a spinner. What is the probability that the spinner will choose a large strawberry for a customer?

F. $\frac{1}{14}$ **G.** $\frac{1}{10}$ **H.** $\frac{1}{7}$ **J.** $\frac{1}{3}$

Extended Response

20. You roll two number cubes. List all possible outcomes. Find the probability of each event. Show your work.
a. rolling a 1 and a 2
b. rolling the same numbers
c. rolling different numbers

Mixed Review

Lesson 12-1

Display each data set in a line plot. Find the range.

21. 3 4 5 4 7 7 3 6 5

22. 19 18 19 17 17 16 19 18 17 19

Lesson 11-3

Find the midpoint of a segment with the given endpoints.

23. $X(3, -2)$ and $Y(-3, 6)$ **24.** $A(-1, 0)$ and $B(2, 1)$

Checkpoint Quiz 1

Lessons 12-1 through 12-4

1. Display the data below in a frequency table.
47 51 50 52 50 47 48 50 49 51 48 52

2. Make a box-and-whisker plot for the data below.
31, 33, 74, 90, 44, 49, 40, 64, 42, 31, 36, 73, 86, 34, 46, 65

3. Open-Ended Use the data in the table.
a. Draw a graph that could be misleading. Explain.
b. Draw a second graph that is not misleading.

Year	Hourly Minimum Wage
1996	$4.75
1997	$5.15

SOURCE: *Wall Street Journal Almanac*

4. Olivia and Oliver each choose a number from 1 to 10 at random. What is the probability that both numbers are odd numbers?

12-5

Independent and Dapandent Events

 Assessment Framework

10.8.06 Solve problems involving the probability of an event composed of repeated trials, compound events, or future events with or without replacement.

 Check Skills You'll Need

Multiply.

1. $\frac{3}{5} \cdot \frac{1}{5}$ **2.** $\frac{1}{4} \cdot \frac{2}{4}$

3. $\frac{4}{10} \cdot \frac{2}{10}$ **4.** $\frac{5}{9} \cdot \frac{4}{8}$

5. $\frac{4}{7} \cdot \frac{3}{6}$ **6.** $\frac{9}{10} \cdot \frac{8}{9}$

GO for Help
Lesson 5-4

🔊 **New Vocabulary**

• independent events
• **dependent events**

1 | **Independent Events**

(A)ctivity

Exploring Probability in Games

You have four cards with an M written on them, two with an A, six with a T, and eight with an H.

1. You draw an M card at random and replace it. What is the probability that the next card you draw at random will also be an M card?

2. You draw an M card at random and do not replace the card. What is the probability that the next card you draw at random will also be an M card?

3. Make a table to find the probability of matching cards.

Probability **With** Replacement		Probability **Without** Replacement	
First Card	Second Card Matches	First Card	Second Card Matches
$P(M) = $ ■	$P(M) = $ ■	$P(M) = $ ■	$P(M) = $ ■
$P(A) = $ ■	$P(A) = $ ■	$P(A) = $ ■	$P(A) = $ ■
$P(T) = $ ■	$P(T) = $ ■	$P(T) = $ ■	$P(T) = $ ■
$P(H) = $ ■	$P(H) = $ ■	$P(H) = $ ■	$P(H) = $ ■

4. **Reasoning** For any letter, why is the probability for selecting the second card with replacement of the first card different from the probability of selecting the second card without replacement of the first card?

Suppose the numbers from 1 to 10 are written on 10 cards, one number to a card. You are interested in drawing one card at random and getting an even number, and then drawing a second card and getting an even number again.

If you *replace* your first card, the probability of getting an even number on the second card is unaffected.

Independent events are events for which the occurrence of one event *does not affect* the probability of the occurrence of the other.

Key Concepts	Probability of Independent Events

For two independent events A and B, the probability of both events occurring is the product of the probabilities of each event occurring.

$$P(A, \text{then } B) = P(A) \cdot P(B)$$

Real-World **Connection**

Bluebonnets (see Example 2) grow wild in the south-western United States.

1 EXAMPLE **Finding Probability for Independent Events**

You roll a number cube once. Then you roll it again. What is the probability that you get 2 on the first roll and a number greater than 4 on the second roll?

$$P(2) = \frac{1}{6} \qquad \text{There is one 2 among 6 numbers on a number cube.}$$

$$P(\text{greater than 4}) = \frac{2}{6} \qquad \text{There are two numbers greater than 4 on a number cube.}$$

$$P(2, \text{then greater than 4}) = P(2) \cdot P(\text{greater than 4})$$

$$= \frac{1}{6} \cdot \frac{2}{6}$$

$$= \frac{2}{36}, \text{ or } \frac{1}{18}$$

The probability is $\frac{1}{18}$.

 Quick Check

1. You toss a coin twice. Find the probability of getting two heads.

You can use fractions, decimals, or percents to represent probabilities and to find the probability of two events occurring.

2 EXAMPLE **Real-World** **Problem Solving**

Gridded Response **Under the best conditions, a wild bluebonnet seed has a 20% probability of growing. If you select two seeds at random, what is the probability that both will grow, under the best conditions?**

$$P(\text{a seed grows}) = 20\%, \text{ or } 0.20 \qquad \text{Write the percent as a decimal.}$$

$$P(\text{two seeds grow}) = P(\text{a seed grows}) \cdot P(\text{a seed grows})$$

$$= 0.20 \cdot 0.20 \qquad \text{Substitute.}$$

$$= 0.04 \qquad \text{Multiply.}$$

$$= 4\% \qquad \text{Write 0.04 as a percent.}$$

The probability that two seeds grow is 4%.

Test-Taking Tip

When your answer is a percent, grid the percent as a decimal. Grid .04, not 4.

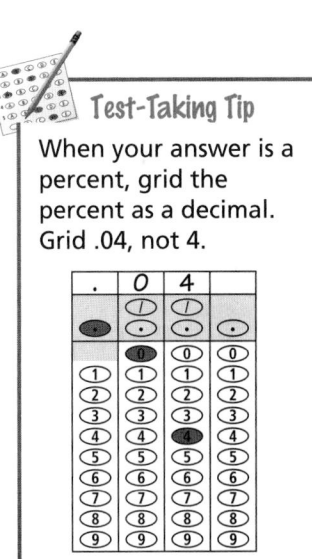

✓ Quick Check

2. **Botany** Chemically treated bluebonnet seeds have a 30% probability of growing. You select two such seeds at random. What is the probability that both will grow?

2 Dependent Events

Suppose you want to draw two even-numbered cards from cards showing numbers from 1 to 10. You draw one card. Then, *without replacing* the first card, you draw a second card. The probability of drawing an even number on the second card is affected.

Dependent events are events for which the occurrence of one event *affects* the probability of the occurrence of the other.

> **Key Concepts** | **Probability of Dependent Events**
>
> For two dependent events *A* and *B,* the probability of both events occurring is the product of the probability of the first event and the probability that, after the first event, the second event occurs.
>
> $$P(A, \text{then } B) = P(A) \cdot P(B \text{ after } A)$$

Online
active math

For: Probability Activity
Use: Interactive Textbook, 12-5

3 EXAMPLE — Finding Probability for Dependent Events

Three girls and two boys volunteer to represent their class at a school assembly. The teacher selects one name and then another from a bag containing the five students' names. What is the probability that both representatives will be girls?

$P(\text{girl}) = \frac{3}{5}$ **Three of five students are girls.**

$P(\text{girl after girl}) = \frac{2}{4}$ **If a girl's name is drawn, two of the four remaining students are girls.**

$P(\text{girl, then girl}) = P(\text{girl}) \cdot P(\text{girl after girl})$

$\qquad = \frac{3}{5} \cdot \frac{2}{4}$ **Substitute.**

$\qquad = \frac{6}{20}, \text{or } \frac{3}{10}$ **Simplify.**

The probability that both representatives will be girls is $\frac{3}{10}$.

✓ Quick Check

3. **a.** For Example 3, find $P(\text{boy, then girl})$.
   b. Find $P(\text{girl, then boy})$.

EXERCISES

For more exercises, see *Extra Skill and Word Problem Practice*.

Practice and Problem Solving

A Practice by Example

GO for Help

Example 1
(page 663)

œYou roll a number cube twice. What is the probability that you roll each pair of numbers?

1. 6, then 5

2. 6, then a number less than 4

3. 6, then 2 or 5

4. an even number, then 2 or 5

5. 1, then 1

6. an even number, then an odd number

Example 2
(page 663)

7. Weather Forecasting Weather forecasters are accurate 91% of the time when predicting precipitation for the day. What is the probability that a forecaster will make correct precipitation predictions two days in a row?

Example 3
(page 664)

You select a card at random from those below. Without replacing the card, you select a second card. Find each probability.

8. P, then G

9. E, then A

10. E, then a second vowel

11. G, then R or A

12. P or E, then A

13. a consonant, then a vowel

B Apply Your Skills

Are the events independent or dependent? Explain.

14. You select a card. Without putting the card back, you select a second card.

15. You roll a number cube. You roll it again.

16. Multiple Choice You roll two number cubes numbered 1 through 6. What is the probability of rolling a sum of 5?

(A) $\frac{2}{3}$　　　(B) $\frac{1}{9}$　　　(C) $\frac{1}{3}$　　　(D) $\frac{1}{6}$

You pick a marble from a bag containing 1 green marble, 4 red marbles, 2 yellow marbles, and 3 black marbles. You replace the first marble and then select a second one. Find each probability.

17. P(red, then yellow)

18. P(black, then black)

19. P(red, then black)

20. P(yellow, then black)

Gino has 5 blue socks and 4 black socks. He selects one sock at random. Without replacing the sock, he selects a second sock at random. Find each probability.

21. P(blue, then black)

22. P(black, then blue)

23. P(black, then black)

24. P(blue, then blue)

**GO Online
Homework Video Tutor**
Visit: PHSchool.com
Web Code: ade-1205

25. A refrigerator contains 12 orange drinks, 4 grape drinks, and 25 apple drinks. Ann is first in the line for drinks. Mark is second. What is the probability that Ann gets an apple drink and Mark gets a grape drink, if they are given drinks at random?

 Challenge **26.** On a multiple-choice test you randomly guess the answers to two questions. Each question has five choices.
   a. What is the probability that you get both answers correct?
   b. What is the probability that you get both answers incorrect?

27. Mrs. Kendall's wallet contains 3 one-dollar bills, 2 five-dollar bills, and 3 ten-dollar bills. She randomly selects one bill and then another. Find the probability that she selects the given bills.
   a. a one-dollar bill and then a ten-dollar bill
   b. a ten-dollar bill and then a five-dollar bill

ISAT

Test Prep

Multiple Choice **28.** There are 6 girls and 5 boys in a debate class. The teacher chooses two students at random to lead a class discussion. What is the probability of selecting a girl and then a boy?

   A. $\frac{30}{121}$ **B.** $\frac{3}{11}$ **C.** $\frac{36}{121}$ **D.** $\frac{6}{11}$

29. Mike asks Carolyn to pick a number at random from 1 to 100, and then asks Jamie to do the same. What is the probability that both girls will select 49?

   F. $\frac{1}{50}$ **G.** $\frac{1}{100}$ **H.** $\frac{1}{9,900}$ **J.** $\frac{1}{10,000}$

Short Response **30. a.** Exercise 29 involves two events. What are they?
   b. Are they independent or dependent? Explain.

31. In a game, Teri and Hector take turns choosing cards at random from a basket. Each card shows a "T" or "H". A player chooses a card, records the letter, and puts the card in a discard pile.
   a. Are the letters drawn independent or dependent events?
   b. Explain your answer.

Mixed Review

 Lesson 12-4 **32. Travel** From Compt there are four ways to get to Murch. From Murch there are five ways to get to Toll. How many ways are there from Compt to Toll through Murch?

Lesson 11-6 **For each triangle, find the sine, cosine, and tangent of angle *A*.**

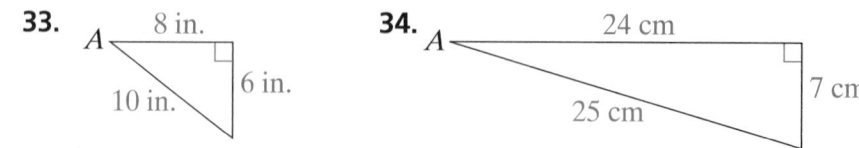

33. *A* — 8 in. — 6 in. — 10 in.   **34.** *A* — 24 cm — 7 cm — 25 cm

Permutations and Combinations

IL Assessment Framework

1 Permutations

An arrangement in which order is important is a **permutation.** For the letters O, P, S, and T, the permutations *STOP* and *POTS* are different because the order of the letters is different.

You can use the Counting Principle to find the number of possible permutations.

1 EXAMPLE Counting Permutations

Find the number of permutations possible for the letters O, P, S, and T.

1st letter	2nd letter	3rd letter	4th letter
4 choices	3 choices	2 choices	1 choice
4 ·	3 ·	2 ·	1 = 24

There are 24 permutations of the letters O, P, S, and T.

✔ Quick Check

1. Use the Counting Principle to find the number of permutations possible for the letters W, A, T, E, and R.

A track team has seven members. In how many ways could four team members line up for a relay race?

You can use *permutation notation* to represent this problem.

7 members ⌐ ⌐ Choose 4.

$$_7P_4 = 7 \cdot 6 \cdot 5 \cdot 4 = 840$$

          1st   2nd   3rd   4th
     member member member member

Four of seven team members could line up in 840 ways.

Key Concepts Permutation Notation

The expression $_nP_r$ stands for the number of permutations of n objects chosen r at a time.

10.8.08 Solve simple problems involving the number of ways objects can be arranged.

✓ Check Skills You'll Need

Use the Counting Principle to find the number of outcomes.

1. Roll 2 number cubes.

2. Choose three different letters.

3. Select a month and a day of the week.

4. Toss a coin 4 times.

GO for Help
Lesson 12-4

🔊 **New Vocabulary**
• permutation
• combination

GO ●nline

Video Tutor Help
Visit: PHSchool.com
Web Code: ada-0775

Graphing Calculator Hint
To evaluate $_9P_5$, press
9 nPr 5 [ENTER]. Find nPr
in the [MATH] **PRB** menu.

2 EXAMPLE **Simplifying Permutation Notation**

You have 9 books and want to display 5 on a shelf. How many different 5-book arrangements are possible?

9 books ⌐ ⌐ Choose 5.

$$_9P_5 = 9 \cdot 8 \cdot 7 \cdot 6 \cdot 5 = 15{,}120 \quad \textbf{Simplify.}$$

There are 15,120 arrangements possible.

✓ Quick Check

2. Simplify each expression.

   a. $_5P_2$ **b.** $_5P_3$ **c.** $_5P_4$ **d.** $_5P_5$

2   Combinations

Sometimes the order of items is not important. For instance, a ham and cheese sandwich is the same as a cheese and ham sandwich. An arrangement in which order does not matter is a **combination.**

3 EXAMPLE **Real-World** 🌐 **Problem Solving**

Inland Water

Country	Water Area (mi²)
Australia	26,610
Canada	291,573
Ethiopia	46,680
India	121,391
Tanzania	22,799
United States	79,541

SOURCE: *The Top 10 of Everything*

Geography **In how many ways could you choose two countries from the table when you write reports about inland water?**

Make an organized list of all the combinations.

AC   AE   AI   AT   AU   **Abbreviate by using the first**
      CE   CI   CT   CU   **letter of each country's name.**
            EI   ET   EU   **First, list all pairs containing**
                 IT   IU   **Australia. Continue until every**
                     TU   **pair of countries is listed.**

There are fifteen ways to choose two countries from the list of six.

✓ Quick Check

3. In how many ways could you choose three different items from a menu containing six items?

GO **Online**

Video Tutor Help
Visit: PHSchool.com
Web Code: ada-0775

┌───┐
Key Concepts   **Combination Notation**

The expression $_nC_r$ stands for the number of combinations of n objects chosen r at a time.
└───┘

In general, there are fewer combinations than permutations. To find the number of combinations, $_nC_r$, of r items chosen from n items, find the total number of permutations $_nP_r$, and then divide by the number of possible permutations, $_rP_r$, for any group of r items.

$$_nC_r = \frac{_nP_r}{_rP_r}.$$

4 EXAMPLE **Simplifying Combination Notation**

You have five choices of sandwich fillings. How many different sandwiches could you make by choosing three of the five fillings?

5 fillings ⌐ ⌐ Choose 3.

$$_5C_3 = \frac{_5P_3}{_3P_3}$$

$$= \frac{5 \cdot 4 \cdot 3}{3 \cdot 2 \cdot 1} = 10 \quad \textbf{Simplify.}$$

You could make 10 different sandwiches.

> **Graphing Calculator Hint**
> To evaluate $_5C_3$, press
> 5 nCr 3 ENTER. Find **nCr**
> in the MATH PRB menu.

✓ Quick Check

4. Simplify each expression.

   a. $_8C_2$ **b.** $_8C_3$ **c.** $_8C_4$ **d.** $_8C_5$

You can tell whether a problem requires permutations or combinations by asking yourself, *Does order matter?* If the answer is *yes*, use permutations. If it is *no*, use combinations.

5 EXAMPLE **Identifying Whether Order Is Important**

Tell which type of arrangement each problem involves. Explain.

a. How many different groups of three books could you choose from five books?

   Combinations; the order of the books selected does not matter.

b. In how many different orders could you play three CDs?

   Permutations; the order in which you play the CDs matters.

✓ Quick Check

5. Tell which type of arrangment is involved. Explain.

   a. A teacher selects a committee of 4 students from 25 students. How many different committees could the teacher select?

   b. Class officers are president, vice-president, secretary, and treasurer. From a class of 25 students, how many different groups of officers could students elect?

EXERCISES

For more exercises, see *Extra Skill and Word Problem Practice*.

Practice and Problem Solving

A Practice by Example

Example 1
(page 667)

Example 2
(page 668)

Use the Counting Principle to find the number of permutations possible for all the letters in each group.

1. S, I, T   **2.** P, L, U, S   **3.** W, O, R, L, D

Simplify each expression.

4. $_4P_2$ **5.** $_6P_4$ **6.** $_9P_4$ **7.** $_{10}P_8$

8. How many different arrangements of four books on a shelf could you make from eight books?

Example 3
(page 668)

In how many ways could you choose two different items from each group? Make an organized list of all the combinations.

9. C, A, T   **10.** M, A, T, H   **11.** V, A, L, U, E

Example 4
(page 669)

Simplify each expression.

12. $_4C_2$ **13.** $_6C_4$ **14.** $_9C_4$ **15.** $_{10}C_8$

16. Literature Louisa May Alcott published 13 novels during her lifetime. In how many ways could you select three of these books?

17. You have six choices of sandwich fillings. How many different sandwiches could you make by choosing three of the six fillings?

Example 5
(page 669)

Does each problem involve *permutations* or *combinations*? Explain.

18. In how many different ways could three students form a line?

19. In how many ways could you choose three shirts from seven shirts?

B Apply Your Skills

Find the number of possible 5-letter permutations of the given letters.

20. D, E, C, I, M, A, L   **21.** F, A, C, T, O, R   **22.** T, R, I, A, N, G, L, E

23. Use the different letters from your last name.
  a. Find the number of two-letter permutations.
  b. Find the number of two-letter combinations.

Simplify each expression.

24. $_6P_3$ **25.** $_6C_3$ **26.** $_2C_1$ **27.** $_2P_1$

28. $_{12}P_9$ **29.** $_{10}P_5$ **30.** $_{10}C_5$ **31.** $_{20}C_{19}$

C Challenge

32. Use the letters E, P, S, and T.
  a. How many possible arrangements of the letters are there?
  b. Add a second letter T to the list. How many distinct arrangements of the five letters are possible?

33. Writing in Math To open a combination lock, you turn a dial to match three whole numbers from 0 to 39. You alternate directions of the turns. Explain why 128,000 combinations are possible.

ISAT

Multiple Choice

34. What is the value of $_{10}C_2$?
    A. 45   **B.** 90   **C.** 180   **D.** 360

35. A teacher is organizing a class of 24 students into eight groups of three. In how many different ways could she form groups of three?
    F. 56   **G.** 2,024   **H.** 12,144   **J.** 735,471

Short Response

36. a. How many three-letter permutations are possible for the letters H, E, X, A, G, O, N?
    b. How many four-letter permutations are possible?

Mixed Review

GO for Help

Lesson 12-5

On each of five cards there is one of the letters A, B, C, D, and E. You select two cards. Find $P(A$, then $B)$ in each situation.

37. with first card replaced   **38.** with first card not replaced

Lessons 10-2 and 11-2

39. Find the area of the triangle at the right.

Lesson 6-9 **40. Consumer Issues** A coat is on sale for $80. Its original price was $120. What is the percent of discount?

10 in.   26 in.

Math at Work

Wildlife Statistician

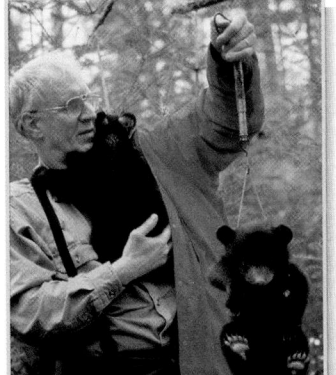

Wildlife statisticians study the growth or decline of plant and animal life in a geographical region. They make observations and collect data for a small portion, or sample, of an animal or plant population. Then they draw conclusions about the entire population. If you enjoy studying wildlife, this may be the job for you.

Go Online
PHSchool.com   **For:** Information about statisticians
        Web Code: adb-2031

A *simulation* is a model of a real-world event. You can toss coins or roll number cubes to simulate some events.

ACTIVITY

In the game "Two-Color Toss," two players take turns tossing three two-color counters. Player A gets a point if at least two red sides are showing. Otherwise, Player B gets a point.

1. Use three number cubes to simulate the game. Let the numbers 1, 2, and 3 represent "red" and the numbers 4, 5, and 6 represent "not red." Roll the number cubes ten times. Record your results in a table. What is the experimental probability of Player A winning the game based on these results?

2. Use three coins to simulate the game. Let heads represent "red" and tails represent "not red." Toss the coins ten times. What is the experimental probability of Player A winning the game based on these results?

3. **Writing in Math** Describe a spinner you could use to simulate Two-Color Toss. Explain how you would use it.

4. The simulations in Questions 1 and 2 allowed you to determine the experimental probability of winning Two-Color Toss.
   a. Calculate the theoretical probability that player A will win the game.
   b. Compare the theoretical probability to the experimental probability you collected through the simulations.

5. Combine your results from one of the simulations with those of other students in your class. When the experimental probability includes a greater number of samples, how does it compare to the theoretical probability? Explain.

6. **Reasoning** Is the game Two-Color Toss fair? Why or why not? Explain.

7. Suppose you change the rules of "Two-Color Toss" to include a third person. Player A gets a point if exactly two red sides are showing. Player B gets a point if exactly two yellow sides are showing. Player C gets a point if neither Player A nor Player B get a point. Conduct 25 simulations.
   a. Find the experimental probability that each player wins.
   b. Is the game fair? Explain.

Experimental Probability

IL Assessment Framework

1 Finding Experimental Probability

Experimental probability is probability based on experimental data.

> **Key Concepts** | Experimental Probability
>
> $$P(\text{event}) = \frac{\text{number of times an event occurs}}{\text{number of times experiment is done}}$$

10.8.06 Solve problems involving the probability of an event composed of repeated trials, compound events, or future events with or without replacement.

1 EXAMPLE   Real-World 🌐 Problem Solving

Medical Science   A medical study tests a new medicine on 3,500 people. It is effective for 3,010 people. Find the experimental probability that the medicine is effective. Then predict the number of people in a group of 6,000 for whom the medicine will be effective.

$$P(\text{event}) = \frac{\text{number of times an event occurs}}{\text{number of times experiment is done}}$$

$$= \frac{3,010}{3,500} = 0.86, \text{ or } 86\%$$

The medicine will be effective for $.86 \times 6,000 = 5,160$ people.

✓ Quick Check

1. Another medicine is effective for 1,183 of 2,275 people. Find the experimental probability that the medicine is effective. Then predict the number of people in a group of 4,500 for whom the medicine will be effective.

✓ Check Skills You'll Need

Write each decimal or fraction as a percent.

1. 0.8   **2.** 0.53   **3.** 0.625

4. $\frac{3}{5}$ **5.** $\frac{7}{12}$ **6.** $\frac{5}{8}$

GO for Help
Lesson 6-5

🔊 New Vocabulary
- experimental probability
- simulation

2 Using Simulations

A **simulation** is a model used to find experimental probability.

2 EXAMPLE   Using a Simulation

Simulate the correct guessing of true-false answers.

Toss a coin to simulate each guess. Heads represents a correct guess. The results of 50 trials are at the right.

$$P(\text{heads}) = \frac{\text{number of heads}}{\text{number of tosses}} = \frac{22}{50} = \frac{11}{25}$$

The experimental probability of guessing correctly is $\frac{11}{25}$.

```
HHTTT   THHTT
THTHH   HTTTH
TTHTT   THTHT
HHTTT   HTHHH
THTHT   THTHT
```

✓ Quick Check

2. a. In Example 2, compare the experimental probability with the theoretical probability.

    b. If you try the experiment 100 times, what is likely to happen to the experimental probability?

More Than One Way

Use theoretical and experimental probabilities to find a probability for correctly guessing all four answers on a four-question true-false quiz.

Nicole's Method

Each guess is independent. Find the probability of one correct guess. Then find the probability of four independent correct guesses.

$$P(\text{1 correct guess}) = \frac{1}{2}$$

$$P(\text{4 correct guesses}) = \frac{1}{2} \cdot \frac{1}{2} \cdot \frac{1}{2} \cdot \frac{1}{2} = \frac{1}{16}$$

The theoretical probability is $\frac{1}{16}$.

Daryl's Method

Simulate the problem by tossing a coin. Let heads stand for a correct guess and tails for an incorrect guess. Use the results of 120 tosses given at the left. Separate the results into 30 groups of 4. Count the groups with 4 heads. There are two.

HTTT	HTTT	HHHT	TTTT	TTHT	THTT
THHH	THHH	HTTT	TTHH	HTTT	HTHH
HTHH	THTT	TTHT	THTH	HHTT	THTH
HHHH	TTHT	HHHH	THTT	TTTH	HHHT
HHTT	HTTT	THTT	HHTT	HHTH	HTHH

Find the experimental probability.

$$P(\text{event}) = \frac{\text{number of times an event occurs}}{\text{number of times experiment is done}}$$

$$= \frac{2}{30} = \frac{1}{15}$$

The experimental probability is $\frac{1}{15}$.

120 Coin Tosses

```
HTTTHTTTHHHT
TTTTTHTTHTT
THHHTHHHHTTT
TTHHHTTTHTHH
HTHHTHTTTTHT
THTHHHTTTHTH
HHHHTTHTHHHH
THTTTTHHHHT
HHTTHTTTTHTT
HHTTHHTHHTHH
```

For Daryl's simulation, the experimental probability is a little greater than the theoretical probability.

Choose a Method

1. Which method would you use to solve the problem? Explain.

EXERCISES

Practice and Problem Solving

A Practice by Example

Example 1
(page 673)

for Help

A student randomly selected 68 vehicles in a large parking lot and noted the color of each. Use the results to find the experimental probability that a vehicle chosen at random in the lot is the given color. Write the probability as a percent, to the nearest tenth of a percent.

Color	Number of Vehicles
Black	9
Blue	10
Brown	13
Green	7
Red	12
White	11
Gray	6

1. red

2. white

3. black

4. blue or green

5. not black or gray

6. purple

Example 2
(page 673)

7. In a multiple-choice test, each item has four choices.
  a. Tell how to simulate the correct guessing of the correct choice.
  b. Carry out your simulation. What do you find for the experimental probability?
  c. Compare your result to the theoretical probability.

B Apply Your Skills

8. Multiple Choice Use the table of vehicle colors above. Predict the number of green cars you would expect to see if there were 125 cars in the parking lot.
  Ⓐ 8 cars   Ⓑ 10 cars   Ⓒ 12 cars   Ⓓ 13 cars

Students were surveyed about the numbers of pencils in their book bags. The table shows the results. Write each experimental probability as a fraction in simplest form.

Pencils in Students' Book Bags

Number of pencils	Number of students
0	4
1	16
2 or more	12

9. *P*(one pencil)

10. *P*(no pencils)

11. *P*(two or more pencils)

12. *P*(at least one pencil)

13. a. How would you find an experimental probability for tossing three coins and getting three heads?
  b. Reasoning How would you compare an experimental probability for getting three heads to the theoretical probability? Would you expect the probabilities to be equal? Explain.

14. Error Analysis A student wants to do a simulation to find a probability for correctly guessing a number from 1 to 5 two times in a row. He decides to roll a number cube 100 times, separating the results into 50 groups of two and letting a roll of 1 stand for a correct guess. Explain why the student's simulation will not give good results.

nline
Homework Video Tutor
Visit: PHSchool.com
Web Code: ade-1207

nline lesson quiz, PHSchool.com, **Web Code:** ada-1207

12-7 Experimental Probability **675**

15. Two players played a number-cube game. The table shows the results.
  a. Find P(A wins) and P(B wins).
  b. **Writing in Math** A *fair game* is one in which each player has the same chance of winning. Do you think the game that A and B played is fair? Explain.

Game Results

A Wins	B Wins
~~HHH~~ ~~HHH~~ ~~HHH~~ ~~HHH~~ ~~HHH~~ IIII	~~HHH~~ ~~HHH~~ ~~HHH~~ ~~HHH~~ ~~HHH~~ ~~HHH~~ ~~HHH~~ ~~HHH~~ ~~HHH~~ ~~HHH~~ II

C Challenge

16. a. Open-Ended Write an experimental probability problem that you can solve with a simulation. Your problem should be different from any in this lesson.
  b. Solve the problem.

Test Prep

Gridded Response

17. A baseball manufacturer checked 250 of its baseballs and found that 8 were defective. What is the experimental probability, to the nearest tenth of a percent, that a baseball is NOT defective?

18. Suki tosses two number cubes 100 times. In 19 of the tosses, the sum of the two cubes equals 7. What is Suki's experimental probability of getting a sum of 7 when tossing two number cubes?

19. A medical experiment finds that 232 out of 1,000 patients did NOT respond to the same medication. What is the experimental probability, to the nearest tenth of a percent, that a patient will respond to the medication?

Mixed Review

Lesson 12-6

Evaluate each expression.

20. $_4P_2$ **21.** $_{10}P_3$ **22.** $_4C_3$ **23.** $_6C_3$

Lesson 10-9

24. Geometry Find the volume of a spherical globe with a diameter of 0.9 m. Round to the nearest tenth.

Lesson 9-8

Geometry Write a rule to describe each translation.

25.

26.

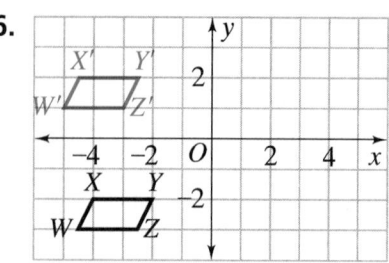

Random Samples and Surveys

1 | Choosing Samples for Surveys

How many books do you read each week? What are your hobbies? Statisticians use questions like these in surveys to get information about specific groups.

A **population** is a group about which you want information. A **sample** is a part of the population you use to make estimates about the population. The larger your sample, the more reliable your estimates will be.

For a **random sample** each member of the population has an equal chance to be selected. A random sample is likely to be representative of the whole population.

1 EXAMPLE | Real-World 🌐 Problem Solving

Recycling You want to find out whether students will participate if you start a recycling program at your school. Tell whether each survey plan describes a good sample.

a. **Interview every tenth teenager you see at a mall.**
   This sample will probably include students who do not go to your school. It is not a good sample because it is not taken from the population you want to study.

b. **Interview the students in your ecology class.**
   The views of students in an ecology class may not represent the views about recycling of students in other classes. This is not a good sample because it is not random.

c. **Interview every tenth student leaving a school assembly.**
   This is a good sample. It is selected at random from the population you want to study.

✓ Quick Check

1. Explain whether each plan describes a good sample.

   a. You want to know which bicycle is most popular. You plan to survey entrants in a bicycle race.
   b. You want to know how often teens rent videos. You plan to survey teens going into the local video rental store.
   c. You want to know the most popular breakfast cereal. You plan to survey people entering a grocery store.

What You'll Learn

- To choose a sample for a survey of a population
- To make estimates about populations

. . . And Why

To solve real-world problems involving recycling and quality control

✓ Check Skills You'll Need

Solve each proportion.

1. $\frac{8}{32} = \frac{n}{450}$

2. $\frac{7}{25} = \frac{n}{24,000}$

3. $\frac{2}{250} = \frac{n}{50,000}$

4. $\frac{4}{100} = \frac{n}{144,000}$

GO for Help
Lesson 6-2

🔊 New Vocabulary

- population
- sample
- random sample

You can use a sample to make an estimate about a population by writing and solving a proportion.

For: Population Activity
Use: Interactive Textbook, 12-8

2 **EXAMPLE** Real-World Problem Solving

Quality Control From 20,000 calculators produced, a manufacturer takes a random sample of 500 calculators. The sample has 3 defective calculators. Estimate the total number of defective calculators.

$$\frac{\text{defective sample calculators}}{\text{sample calculators}} = \frac{\text{defective calculators}}{\text{calculators}}$$ **Write a proportion.**

$$\frac{3}{500} = \frac{n}{20,000}$$ **Substitute.**

$$3(20,000) = 500n$$ **Write cross products.**

$$\frac{3(20,000)}{500} = \frac{500n}{500}$$ **Divide each side by 500.**

$$120 = n$$ **Simplify.**

Estimate: About 120 calculators are defective.

✓ Quick Check

2. Use the data in the table below.

Calculator Samples

Sample	Number Sampled	Number Defective
A	500	3
B	200	2
C	50	0

a. Using Sample B, how many of 20,000 calculators would you estimate to be defective?

b. **Reasoning** Would you expect an estimate based on Sample C to be more accurate or less accurate than one based on Sample B? Explain.

c. Explain why you would take a sample rather than counting or surveying an entire population.

In Example 2, you can think of the sample as giving an experimental probability ($\frac{3}{500} = 0.006$). Then you can multiply this probability by the total number of calculators ($0.006 \cdot 20,000$) to estimate the total number of defective calculators.

EXERCISES

For more exercises, see *Extra Skill and Word Problem Practice*.

Practice and Problem Solving

A Practice by Example

Example 1
(page 677)

GO for Help

Sports You want to find how popular basketball is at your school. State whether each survey plan describes a good sample. Explain.

1. Interview the 10 tallest students in the school.

2. Interview 20 students after picking their ID numbers at random.

3. Interview 30 students watching a basketball game.

Example 2
(page 678)

4. Quality Control A worker takes 100 eggs at random from a shipment of 120,000 eggs. The worker finds that four eggs are bad. Estimate the total number of bad eggs.

5. Estimation Of 75 pairs of jeans, 7 have flaws. Estimate how many of 24,000 pairs of jeans are flawed.

B Apply Your Skills

You want to find which restaurants in your city are most popular. State whether each survey plan describes a good sample. Explain.

6. Choose people to interview at random from the city phone book.

7. Interview every fifth person leaving a restaurant in the city.

8. Interview all the restaurant critics in the state.

GO **Online**
Homework Video Tutor
Visit: PHSchool.com
Web Code: ade-1208

9. Error Analysis Eight of the 32 students in your math class have a cold. The school population is 450. A student estimates that 112 students in the school have a cold.
 a. Why is your math class not representative of the population?
 b. Describe a survey plan you could use to better estimate the number of students who have a cold.

10. Reasoning You survey every fifth student leaving volleyball practice. Of those surveyed, 92% support a proposal to buy new bleachers for the gym. Should you report that there is overwhelming support for the proposal? Explain.

C Challenge

11. Open-Ended Describe a survey question, a population, and a sample you could use to make an estimate.

12. Writing in Math From 50,000 computer chips produced, you sample 250 chips and find that 0.8% are defective. Explain how you could estimate the total number of defective chips.

ISAT

Test Prep

Multiple Choice

13. Out of 6,000 radios tested, 12 are defective. What is the estimated total number of defective radios in a group of 250,000?
 A. 60   **B.** 120   **C.** 200   **D.** 500

14. All students at a local elementary school eat lunch at school. You want to find how many students bring their lunches. Which group would be a good sample?

F. students on one school bus   **G.** one first-grade classroom

H. the cafeteria workers   **J.** all third-grade classrooms

Short Response   For Exercises 15 and 16, **(a)** state whether each survey plan describes a good sample. **(b)** Explain your answer.

15. You want to find how often teens get haircuts. You plan to survey customers in a barbershop.

16. You want to find students' favorite foods. You plan to survey every fourth student leaving the library.

Mixed Review

Lesson 12-7

Use the survey data at the right. Write each experimental probability as a fraction.

17. P(no pets)   **18.** P(two or more pets)

19. P(one pet)   **20.** P(at least one pet)

Students' Pets	
Number of Pets	Number of Students
0	9
1	12
2 or more	5

Lesson 12-6   **21.** How many combinations of four flowers can you choose from a bouquet of one dozen different flowers?

Lesson 10-3   **Geometry** Find the area of each circle. Give the exact area and area rounded to the nearest whole number of units. Use 3.14 for π.

22. $r = 24$ cm   **23.** $d = 45$ in.   **24.** $r = 50$ mi

Checkpoint Quiz 2   Lessons 12-5 through 12-8

1. A bag contains 10 cards labeled 1–10. You draw one card and then another, without replacing the first card before drawing the second. Find the probability of drawing two even numbers.

2. a. A club of 20 students chooses a president and a vice-president. How many different outcomes are possible?

     b. A club of 20 students chooses two committee members. How many different committees may be chosen?

3. A hockey player attempts 15 goals and makes 2. Find the experimental probability of making a goal. Predict the number of goals the player will make in the next game if the player attempts 23 goals.

4. Of 450 oranges from a crop of 50,000 oranges, 85 are "premium." Estimate the number of premium oranges in the whole crop.

Using Random Numbers

Some calculators and computer programs can generate *random numbers*. You can use random numbers to simulate an event.

To make a list of random integers on a graphing calculator, highlight **randInt** in the MATH **PRB** menu. Press ENTER, and enter "0,9999." Press ENTER repeatedly for a list of four-digit random numbers. Note that the calculator suppresses any zeros at the front of a number. For example, 45 represents the four-digit number 0045.

EXAMPLE

There is a 30% probability of being stopped by a red light at each of four traffic lights. Use a simulation to find an experimental probability of being stopped by at least two red lights.

Use your calculator to generate 20 random 4-digit numbers.

There is a 30% chance of a red light, so let three of the ten digits represent a red light. For this simulation let 1, 2, and 3 represent a red light. Let 4, 5, 6, 7, 8, 9, and 0 represent a yellow or green light.

5186	8918	4275	4285
8124	9619	2517	9964
0912	2759	2329	1666
8938	0357	6755	2227
0201	6325	1905	6885

Any group with two or more of the digits 1, 2, or 3 represents being stopped by at least two red lights. There are seven such groups in this list.

• P(at least two red lights) $= \frac{7}{20}$, or 35%

EXERCISES

1. Use the information in the example. What is the experimental probability of being stopped by exactly three red lights? By four red lights?

2. What would be the result in the example if you had chosen 8, 9, and 0 instead of 1, 2, and 3 to represent red lights?

3. **a.** Make a new random number list by using randInt(0,999) in place of randInt(0,9999). How many digits are in each random number?
   b. How can you make a 6-digit random number?

4. **Writing in Math** Suppose the probability of being stopped by a red light at each of four lights is 50%. Describe how you would use random numbers to find the probability of getting a red light at two or more lights.

5. About 20% of high school students in the United States say they would like to be president. Use random numbers to find the probability that at least three of the next five high school students you see would like to be president.

Simulate the Problem

What You'll Learn

• To solve problems by simulation

. . . And Why

To solve real-world problems involving sports

✓ Check Skills You'll Need

Create a frequency table showing the number of times each letter of the alphabet appears in the sentence below.

A simulation is a model of a real experience.

 for Help
Lesson 12-1

Math Strategies in Action

Do you dream of flying your own airplane? Can you picture yourself in a space shuttle? Flight simulators help pilots train for real flying. Simulators are models of the real experience.

You can use simulations to investigate real-world problems. First develop a model, and then conduct an experiment.

EXAMPLE Real-World 🌎 Problem Solving

Basketball **As time is running out in the basketball game, your team is behind by one point. You are fouled and go to the free-throw line. If you miss the shot, your team loses. If you make it, the score is tied and you get another shot. If you miss the second shot, the game ends in a tie. If you make both shots, your team wins. Your average at free throws is four out of five. Simulate the situation and find an experimental probability for each event.**
a. You tie the game. b. You win the game. c. You tie or win the game.

Understand the Problem

Think about the problem.

1. Based on your average, what is the probability of making one free throw?

2. What methods could you use to simulate the problem?

Make a Plan

You can use a spinner to simulate the problem. Construct a spinner with five congruent sections. Make four of the sections blue and one of them red. The blue section represents *makes the shot* and the red section represents *misses the shot*. Each spin represents one shot.

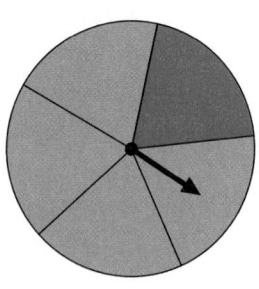

3. How many spins will you make for each experiment?

4. How many experiments will you do?

Carry Out the Plan

Use the results given in the table below. "B" stands for blue and "R" stands for red. Note that there is no second shot when the first shot is a miss (R).

Results of 100 Experiments

BR	BB	BB	BB	BB	BR	BB	BB	BB	BB
BR	BB	BR	BB	R	BB	R	BB	BR	BB
BB	BB	BB	R	BB	BB	BB	BB	BB	BB
BB	R	BB	BB	BB	BB	BB	BB	BB	BB
BB	R	BR	BR	BB	BB	BB	R	BB	BR
BB	BR	BB	BB	BB	R	BB	R	BB	BB
BB	R	BR	BB	BB	R	BB	BR	BB	R
BB	BB	BB	BB	BB	BB	BB	BR	BB	BB
BB	R	BR	BB	R	BB	BB	BB	R	BB
BR	BR	BB	R	BB	R	BB	BB	BB	BB

Make a frequency table.

Misses the first shot (R)	Makes the first shot and misses the second shot (BR)	Makes the first shot and makes the second shot (BB)
ЖЖ ЖЖ ЖЖ l	ЖЖ ЖЖ ЖЖ	ЖЖ ЖЖ ЖЖ ЖЖ ЖЖ ЖЖ ЖЖ ЖЖ ЖЖ ЖЖ ЖЖ ЖЖ ЖЖ llll

5. Find each experimental probability.
   a. Your team ties the game.
   b. Your team wins the game.
   c. Your team ties or wins the game.

Check the Answer

Simulations can give different results. You may find a different probability if you do another simulation. The more experiments you do, the closer the results of different simulations are likely to be.

✓ Quick Check

6. Continue the simulation with another 100 experiments. Combine the results with the results of the first 100 experiments.

7. Based on the second simulation, what is the probability that your team wins?

EXERCISES

For more exercises, see *Extra Skill and Word Problem Practice*.

Practice and Problem Solving

 A Practice by Example

GO for Help

Example
(page 682)

Solve by simulating the problem.

1. What is the experimental probability that exactly three children in a family of five children will be boys? Assume that $P(\text{boy}) = P(\text{girl})$.

2. You take a three-question multiple-choice test. Each question has four choices. You don't know any of the answers. What is the experimental probability that you will guess exactly two out of three correctly?

B Apply Your Skills

Solve using any strategy.

3. Thirteen of 25 students are going on a field trip. Six students are traveling in a van. What is the theoretical probability that a student chosen at random from those going on the trip is *not* traveling in the van?

4. A student draws a card at random from the cards below. What is the theoretical probability that the student will draw a card showing A or B?

Strategies

- Act It Out
- Draw a Diagram
- Guess, Check, Revise
- Look for a Pattern
- Make a Model
- Make a Table
- Simulate the Problem
- Solve by Graphing
- Use Multiple Strategies
- Work a Simpler Problem
- Work Backward
- Write an Equation
- Write a Proportion

5. Prices The original cost of a jacket is $72. During a sale, the store reduces the jacket price by 25%. After the sale, the store raises the reduced jacket price by 25%. What is the price of the jacket after it is increased?

6. Geometry A farmer uses 24 yd of fencing to make a rectangular pen. The pen is 6 yd longer than it is wide. What are the dimensions of the pen?

7. Reasoning The circumference of the peg is 3 in. Will the peg go through the hole? Explain.

 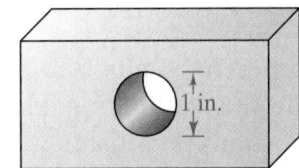

8. You toss five coins. What is the theoretical probability that you will get five heads?

GO **Online**
Homework Video Tutor

Visit: PHSchool.com
Web Code: ade-1209

9. Many sweepstakes contests have an elimination round. In the elimination round, half of the entrants are chosen at random to go on to the final round. Then one person is chosen as the winner. What is the theoretical probability that a person who enters a contest with 10,000 entrants will be the winner?

684 Chapter 12 Data Analysis and Probability

10. On a TV game show, you try to win a prize that is hidden behind one of three doors. After you choose a door, but before it is opened, the host opens one of the other doors, behind which there is no prize. You can then switch to the remaining closed door or stay with your original choice.

   a. Find the experimental probability of winning if your strategy is to stay with your original choice. (*Hint:* Simulate by using one marked index card and two unmarked index cards.)

   b. Find the experimental probability of winning if your strategy is to switch to the other door.

   c. **Writing in Math** Should you stay or switch in this game? Explain.

11. Each box of Tastycrunch cereal contains a prize. There are four possible prizes. The prizes are equally likely. You purchase 10 boxes of Tastycrunch. Simulate the problem to find the experimental probability that you will get all four prizes.

ISAT

Test Prep

Multiple Choice

12. Raul has 4 pairs of shoes to choose from each day. He wants to find the experimental probability of choosing his favorite pair of shoes at random. Which simulation should Raul use?
   A. Tossing a coin
   B. Rolling a number cube
   C. Spinning a spinner with 4 congruent sections
   D. Drawing chips from a bag with 8 different-colored chips

13. Angela conducts a simulation in which she gets a favorable outcome 230 times out of 500 trials. What is the experimental probability of a favorable outcome?
   F. 2.3%   **G.** 23%   **H.** 46%   **J.** 230%

14. Jerome constructs a spinner that has 5 congruent sections. He writes "yes" in one section and "no" in the other four sections. Jerome uses this spinner to simulate making free-throw shots. What experimental probability is he most likely to find?
   A. 1%   **B.** 5%   **C.** 20%   **D.** 80%

Mixed Review

GO for Help

Lesson 12-8 **15.** **Quality Control** Six out of every 80 wrenches are found to be defective. For a batch of 3,200 wrenches, estimate the number of wrenches that will *not* have any flaw.

Lesson 11-5 **16.** **Geometry** Each side of a square kite is to be 20 in. long. To the nearest inch, what length of wood do you need to make the diagonals?

Lesson 11-1 **Estimate to the nearest integer.**

   17. $\sqrt{15}$ **18.** $\sqrt{10}$ **19.** $\sqrt{50}$ **20.** $-\sqrt{82}$

In true/false questions, the entire statement must be true. Otherwise, the statement is false. A statement may be true for many cases and false for just one. This one case is called a *counterexample*. If you think a statement is false, try to find a counterexample.

1 EXAMPLE

True or False? The mean of a set of values is always different from the median of the same set of values.

Choose a simple example that has an odd number of values, and that is "evenly balanced" above and below the middle value.

   8, 10, 12, 14, and 16

Find the median: 8, 10, **12**, 14, 16
Find the mean: $(8 + 10 + 12 + 14 + 16) \div 5 = 12$

● This is a counterexample to the statement, so the statement is false.

2 EXAMPLE

Suppose two events are independent and the probability of each is less than 1. Is the following statement true or false? The probability that the two events occur is less than the probability of either event.

Since the events are independent, $P(A \text{ and } B) = P(A) \cdot P(B)$. $P(A)$ and $P(B)$ are both less than 1. The product of two (proper) fractions is less than either fraction. Test some cases:

   $\frac{1}{2} \times \frac{1}{4} = \frac{1}{8}$ $\frac{1}{8}$ is less than both $\frac{1}{2}$ and $\frac{1}{4}$.

   $\frac{3}{4} \times \frac{1}{2} = \frac{3}{8}$ $\frac{3}{8}$ is less than both $\frac{3}{4}$ and $\frac{1}{2}$.

● It seems likely that $P(A \text{ and } B) < P(A)$ and $P(A \text{ and } B) < P(B)$ are always true.

EXERCISES

Determine whether each statement is *true* or *false*. Explain.

1. The median of a data set is always one of the data values.

2. The number of permutations of two items from a data set is always two times the number of combinations when taking two objects at a time from the same data set.

3. In large data sets (1,000 or more values), the mean is always one of the data values.

Chapter Review

eic## Vocabulary Review

- **box-and-whisker plot** (p. 641)
- **combination** (p. 668)
- **counting principle** (p. 658)
- **dependent events** (p. 664)
- **experimental probability** (p. 673)
- **frequency table** (p. 636)
- **histogram** (p. 637)
- **independent events** (p. 662)
- **line plot** (p. 637)
- **permutation** (p. 667)
- **population** (p. 677)
- **quartiles** (p. 641)
- **random sample** (p. 677)
- **sample** (p. 677)
- **sample space** (p. 658)
- **simulation** (p. 673)
- **stem-and-leaf plot** (p. 646)
- **theoretical probability** (p. 658)

Choose the vocabulary term that correctly completes the sentence.

1. An arrangement in which order does not matter is a __?__ .

2. The part of a population used to make estimates about the entire population is a __?__ .

3. The ratio of the number of favorable outcomes to the number of possible outcomes is the __?__ of an event.

4. An arrangement in which order is important is a __?__ .

5. The difference between the greatest and the least values in a data set is the __?__ of the data set.

6. A listing of a data set that shows the number of times each data item occurs is a __?__ .

7. Events in which the first event *does* affect the second event are __?__ .

8. In a __?__ each member of the population has an equal chance of being selected.

Go Online
PHSchool.com

For: Vocabulary quiz
Web Code: adj-1251

Skills and Concepts

12-1 Objectives

▼ To display data in frequency tables and line plots (p. 636)

▼ To display data in histograms (p. 637)

You can show data in a **frequency table,** which lists each data item with the number of times it occurs, or a **line plot,** which displays data with **X** marks on a number line. A **histogram** shows the frequencies of data items as a graph.

Display each set of data in a frequency table and a line plot.

9. 11 10 12 10 12 11 13 12 11 9 12 10

10. 47 48 46 47 45 49 46 48 50 48 46 49

Draw a histogram for each frequency table.

11.

Interval	1–3	4–6	7–9	10–12
Frequency	6	4	5	2

12.

Interval	2–3	4–5	6–7	8–9
Frequency	2	8	6	7

12-2 Objectives

▼ To make box-and-whisker plots (p. 641)

▼ To analyze data in box-and-whisker plots (p. 642)

A **box-and-whisker plot** displays data items below a number line. **Quartiles** divide the data into four parts. The median is the middle quartile. You can compare two sets of related data by making two box-and-whisker plots on one number line.

Make a box-and-whisker plot for each set of data.

13. 6 9 6 5 8 2 3 9 4 8 5 7 12 9 4

14. 21 35 26 32 24 30 29 38 27 32 51

12-3 Objectives

▼ To recognize the use of breaks in the scales of graphs (p. 648)

▼ To recognize the use of different scales (p. 649)

A graph can give a different impression if a break is used in the scale. A graph can be misleading when a scale is distorted.

For Exercises 15 and 16, use the graph showing wheat production.

15. What does the graph suggest about U.S. wheat production?

16. Explain how you could redraw the graph so that production seems to be increasing dramatically.

12-4 Objectives

▼ To use a tree diagram and the Counting Principle to count possible choices (p. 657)

▼ To find theoretical probability by counting outcomes (p. 658)

A **sample space** is all the possible outcomes of an event. Use a tree diagram or the **Counting Principle** to count the number of outcomes. You can count outcomes to help find **theoretical probability.**

17. Volunteers have made a large number of sandwiches for a school party. The sandwiches come on white bread, on whole wheat bread, or on a roll. Each contains one of five fillings: turkey, chicken, egg salad, cheese, or peanut butter.
 a. How many different types of sandwich are possible?
 b. There are 20 of each type of sandwich. You receive one sandwich at random. Find the theoretical probability of getting a sandwich on bread with a meat filling.

12-5 Objectives

▼ To calculate probabilities of independent events (p. 662)

▼ To calculate probabilities of dependent events (p. 664)

Independent events are events for which the occurrence of one event does not affect the probability of the occurrence of the other. If A and B are independent events, the probability that both A and B occur is $P(A \text{ and } B) = P(A) \cdot P(B)$.

Dependent events are events for which the occurrence of one event affects the probability of the occurrence of the other. If A and B are dependent events, the probability that A and then B occur is $P(A, \text{ then } B) = P(A) \cdot P(B \text{ after } A)$.

You select a card at random from those at the right. Find the probability of each event.

18. You select E, replace the card, and then select V.

19. You select T, do not replace the card, and then select N.

12-6 Objectives

▼ To use permutations (p. 667)

▼ To use combinations (p. 668)

An arrangement in which order is important is a **permutation.** An arrangement in which order does not matter is a **combination.**

Tell whether each question is a *permutation* or a *combination* problem. Explain. Then find each answer.

20. In how many different ways can five people line up for a photo?

21. How many groups of three pens can you select from a box of twelve pens?

12-7 and 12-9 Objectives

▼ To find experimental probability (p. 673)

▼ To use simulations (p. 673)

▼ To solve problems by simulation (p. 682)

Experimental probability is based on experimental data. You can use a simulation to model real-world problems.

Use the survey data at the right. Write each experimental probability as a fraction in simplest form.

22. P(one notebook)

23. P(at least two notebooks)

24. You take a 3-question multiple-choice quiz. Each question has 3 choices. You don't know any of the answers. Use a simulation to find an experimental probability that you will guess exactly 2 out of 3 correctly.

Notebooks in Students' Lockers

Number of Notebooks	Frequency
0	1
1	9
2	6
3 or more	4

12-8 Objectives

▼ To choose a sample for a survey of a population (p. 677)

▼ To make estimates about populations (p. 678)

A **population** is a group about which you want information. A **sample** is a part of the population you use to make estimates for the population. In a **random sample** each member of the population has an equal chance to be selected.

You want to find the favorite brand of in-line skates in your town. Does each survey plan describe a good sample? Explain.

25. You interview students in your homeroom.

26. You interview every tenth student entering the building.

Chapter 12

Chapter Test

Go Online
PHSchool.com
For: Chapter test
Web Code: ada-1252

For Exercises 1 and 2, use the box-and-whisker plot.

Test Grades

1. What is the median grade on the test?

2. What is the range in grades?

3. Make a box-and-whisker plot for the data.
$75, 70, 80, 85, 85, 55, 60, 60, 65, 85, 75, 95, 50$

4. Use the data below.
$8, 4, 5, 1, 8, 4, 7, 9, 10, 5, 0, 5, 3, 4, 2$
   a. Display the data in a frequency table.
   b. Display the data in a line plot.
   c. Find the range of the data.

For Exercises 5 and 6, use the table. The table shows the money spent on movie tickets.

Year	Dollars (billions)
2001	9.0
2002	9.6
2003	9.9

5. Draw a graph that emphasizes the increase in money spent over time.

6. Draw a graph to suggest that the money spent has not changed much over time.

Use the word TRAIN. Find the probability of each event when a letter is drawn at random.

7. selecting an R, replacing it, and then selecting an N

8. selecting an R, not replacing it, and then selecting an N

9. a. Find the sample space for tossing 3 coins.
   b. Find the theoretical probability of tossing 2 heads and 1 tail.

Simplify each expression.

10. $_3P_2$

11. $_5C_2$

Find the number of three-letter permutations you can make using each group of letters.

12. F, O, U, R

13. L, U, N, C, H

A student has 4 blue shirts and 2 white shirts. He selects one shirt at random. Without replacing the shirt, he selects a second shirt at random. Find each probability.

14. $P(\text{blue, then white})$

15. $P(\text{white, then blue})$

16. $P(\text{blue, then blue})$

17. $P(\text{white, then white})$

For Exercises 18–21, use the table below. The table shows the colors of a random sample of the bicycles in a rack at school.

Color	Number of Bicycles
Black	9
Blue	10
Red	14

Find each experimental probability for a bicycle chosen at random from the rack. Write each probability as a percent, to the nearest tenth of a percent.

18. $P(\text{red})$

19. $P(\text{blue})$

20. $P(\text{black})$

21. How many bicycles would you expect to be black if there are 50 bicycles in the rack?

22. You roll a pair of number cubes once. What is the probability of rolling doubles?
   a. Find the sample space. Then find the theoretical probability.
   b. Use a simulation to find the experimental probability.
   c. **Writing in Math** For parts (a) and (b), how close should you expect your answers to be? Explain.

ISAT Test Prep

Multiple Choice

1. $\overleftrightarrow{MN} \parallel \overleftrightarrow{OP}$. Which angles are supplementary?

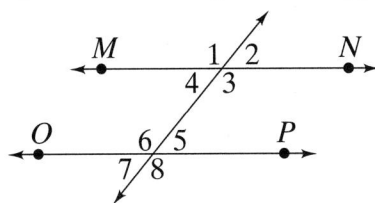

- Ⓐ ∠1 and ∠3
- Ⓑ ∠4 and ∠6
- Ⓒ ∠2 and ∠5
- Ⓓ ∠7 and ∠5

2. How many shaded triangles will exactly fill the trapezoid?

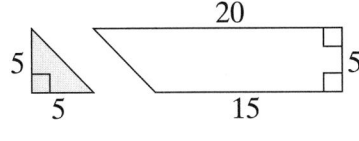

- Ⓔ four
- Ⓕ five
- Ⓖ six
- Ⓗ seven

3. Each of the six faces of a cube is painted either yellow or green. When the cube is tossed, the probability is $\frac{2}{3}$ that the cube will land with a green face up. How many faces are yellow?

- Ⓐ one
- Ⓑ two
- Ⓒ three
- Ⓓ four

Gridded Response

4. Simplify $_6P_3$.

5. A student has 3 blue T-shirts and 2 white T-shirts. He selects one T-shirt at random. Without replacing the T-shirt, he selects another T-shirt at random. What is the probability that the student will pick a white T-shirt and then a blue T-shirt?

6. A shoe manufacturer checks 150 pairs of walking shoes and finds three pairs to be defective. What is the estimated percent probability that a pair of walking shoes is defective?

Short Response

7. For the data listed below, **(a)** make a box-and-whisker plot. **(b)** Label the median and the lower and upper quartiles.

55, 50, 60, 65, 65, 35, 40, 40, 45, 65, 55, 75, 30, 35, 55, 60, 45, 55

8. Use the data in the table. Make a graph that suggests each situation.
   a. sales decreasing sharply
   b. sales staying about the same

Year	Sales (dollars)
1997	18.2 million
1998	17.9 million
1999	17.7 million
2000	17.5 million

In Exercises 9 and 10, (a) state whether each survey plan describes a good sample.
(b) Explain your reasoning.

9. To find how many people who buy stamps are buying them for a collection, you survey people in the post office.

10. To find how popular the U.S. women's soccer team is in your school, you survey all the girls in your English class.

11. ∠ABC is an acute angle.
   a. Write an inequality for *x*.
   b. Explain your answer for part (a).

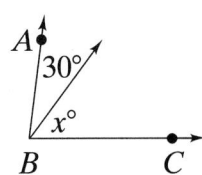

Extended Response

12. You roll two number cubes.
   a. What is $P(6, \text{then } 6)$?
   b. What is $P(\text{odd, then even})$?
   c. Suppose you roll the two number cubes 50 times in a simulation. You roll double 3s six times. What is the experimental probability of NOT getting double 3s?

Activity Lab

World Cup Soccer

Applying Data Analysis Anyone who has ever played soccer knows that controlling a rolling ball with your feet may be fun, but it isn't easy! Perhaps that's why the sport of soccer appeals to so many people of all ages all over the world. Soccer has been played in its current version since about 1863, and international competitions began before 1900. Today, Men's and Women's World Cup competitions are held every four years, one year apart.

Team Grin
Players from the United States women's soccer team pose with their gold medals after defeating China to win the 1999 Women's World Cup.

Final Gold
Mia Hamm (left) of the United States and Daniela Alves of Brazil get ready to kick the ball during the 2000 Women's Gold Cup Finals.

Go **O**nline
PHSchool.com

For: information about soccer
Web Code: ade-1253

FIFA World Cup™ Trophies

The Men's and Women's World Cup trophies are both made of gold. The United States won the FIFA Women's World Cup™ in 1999. Brazil won the Men's FIFA World Cup™ in 2002.

© 1998 FIFA

© 1974 FIFA

Following the Ball

Senegal midfielder Papa Bouba Diop (left) and Swedish forward Henrik Larsson go for the ball.

Activity

Use the table to answer the questions.

1. Make a line plot of the goals scored by the players.

2. What is the range of the data in the table?

3. Find the mean, median, and mode of the data. Which measure best represents the data? Explain.

4. **a.** Based on the data at the right, make a table showing the number of goals scored by each team.

   b. Find the mean and the mode of the data in your table.

   c. Why is the mean of this data different from the mean found in Exercise 3?

5. **Number Sense** Suppose you did not know which team won the 2002 FIFA World Cup™. From the data in the table, can you determine the top two teams? Explain.

2002 FIFA Men's World Cup™ Top Goal Scorers

Flag	Player	Team	Goals Scored
	Ronaldo	Brazil	8
	Rivaldo	Brazil	5
	Miroslav Klose	Germany	5
	Jon Dahl Tomasson	Denmark	4
	Christian Vieri	Italy	4
	Marc Wilmots	Belgium	3
	Pauleta	Portugal	3
	Papa Bouba Diop	Senegal	3
	Ilhan Mansiz	Turkey	3
	Robbie Keane	Ireland	3
	Michael Ballack	Germany	3
	Fernando Morientes	Spain	3
	Raul	Spain	3
	Henrik Larsson	Sweden	3

What You've Learned

Assessment Framework

In Chapter 1, you wrote rules for patterns using inductive reasoning.

● **8.8.03:** In Chapter 2, you learned to simplify variable expressions by combining like terms.

● **6.8.09:** In Chapter 4, you learned how to multiply powers in the same base by adding the exponents.

● **8.8.11:** In Chapter 8, you graphed linear functions by making a table of values to show ordered-pair solutions.

 Check Your Readiness **for Help** to the Lesson in green.

Evaluating Expressions (Lesson 1-3)

Evaluate each expression.

1. $8b$, for $b = 5$ **2.** $(-h)^5$, for $h = 2$ **3.** $19 - (n - 6)$, for $n = 8$

4. $4a + 4$, for $a = 6$ **5.** n^2, for $n = 0.8$ **6.** $55 - 3mn$, for $m = 2, n = 5$

7. $\frac{120}{s + r}$, for $s = 25$ and $r = 35$ **8.** $\frac{j - k}{9}$, for $j = 75$ and $k = 12$

Using the Distributive Property (Lesson 2-2)

Simplify each expression.

9. $(d - 4)3$ **10.** $5(3x + 1)$ **11.** $3(u - 8)$ **12.** $-4(-2y - 7)$

13. $4(-3d + 1)$ **14.** $10(5 - 3s)$ **15.** $-3(7 - 2w)$ **16.** $(9 - 2b)3$

Simplifying Variable Expressions (Lesson 2-3)

Simplify each expression.

17. $5a - 4 + 6a$ **18.** $x - 4x + 3x + 5$ **19.** $g + 4 - 3g + g$

20. $5t + 5s + 5t$ **21.** $9b - 3d + 7d - 2b$ **22.** $-4(9c) + 2(-4c) - c$

Equations With Two Variables (Lesson 8-2)

Find the y values of each equation for $x = -2, 0$, and 2.

23. $y = 3x - 4$ **24.** $y = -3x$ **25.** $y = 4x - 2$ **26.** $y = \frac{3}{5}x - 5$

27. $y = 6 - 2x$ **28.** $y = -\frac{1}{4}x - 8$ **29.** $y = \frac{1}{2}x$ **30.** $y = -3x - 1$

Nonlinear Functions and Polynomials

◀)) **Key Vocabulary**

- absolute value function (p. 703)
- arithmetic sequence (p. 696)
- binomial (p. 712)
- common difference (p. 696)
- common ratio (p. 697)
- geometric sequence (p. 697)
- monomial (p. 712)
- polynomial (p. 712)
- quadratic function (p. 702)
- sequence (p. 696)
- term (p. 696)
- trinomial (p. 712)

What You'll Learn Next

IL **Assessment Framework**

In this chapter, you will learn how to

- **8.8.01:** Use arithmetic and geometric sequences.
- Graph nonlinear functions.
- **8.8.03:** Perform operations with polynomials.
- Solve a problem using multiple strategies.

Activity Lab Applying what you learn, on pages 744–745 you will learn to solve problems about carbon-14 dating.

13-1

Patterns and Sequences

IL **Assessment Framework**

8.8.01 Analyze, extend, and create sequences or linear functions, and determine algebraic expressions to describe the nth term of a sequence.

✓ Check Skills You'll Need

Write a rule for each number pattern.

1. 60, 48, 36, 24, . . .

2. 7, 12, 17, 22, . . .

3. 6, 18, 54, 162, . . .

4. 60, 30, 15, $7\frac{1}{2}$, . . .

GO for Help
Lesson 1-7

◀)) **New Vocabulary**

• **sequence**
• **term**
• **arithmetic sequence**
• **common difference**
• **geometric sequence**
• **common ratio**

 Arithmetic Sequences

ctivity..................

Discovering a Pattern

You win a contest and can choose one of two options for 30 days.

Option A	Option B
You receive $500 the first day, $550 the second, $600 the third, $650 the fourth, and so on.	You receive $1 the first day, $2 the second, $4 the third, $8 the fourth, and so on.

1. Make a table of values for both options for the first 10 days.
   a. Which option gives you more money in 10 days?
   b. Which option would you choose for 30 days? Explain.

A **sequence** is a set of numbers that follow a pattern. Each number in the sequence is a **term** of the sequence. You find a term of an **arithmetic sequence** by *adding* a fixed number to the previous term. This fixed number is called the **common difference.**

Term Number	1st	2nd	3rd	4th
Arithmetic Sequence	2	6	10	14
Common Difference		+4	+4	+4

You can find the common difference for an arithmetic sequence by subtracting any term from the next term in the sequence.

1 EXAMPLE   Finding the Common Difference

What is the common difference in the sequence 4, 2, 0, −2, . . .?

4   2   0   −2   **Find the common difference.**
  −2   −2   −2

The common difference is −2.

✓ Quick Check

1. What is the common difference in each sequence?
   a. 8, 13, 18, 23, . . .   **b.** 12, 9, 6, 3, . . .

You can continue a sequence and write a rule to describe it.

2 EXAMPLE <u>Real-World</u> Problem Solving

A runner training for a race runs 2 mi the first day, $2\frac{1}{4}$ mi the second day, $2\frac{1}{2}$ mi the third day, and so on. Find the next three terms of the sequence. Then write a rule to describe the sequence.

Ⓐ $2, 2\frac{1}{4}, 2\frac{1}{2}$; *Start with 2 and add $\frac{1}{4}$ repeatedly.*

Ⓑ $2\frac{3}{4}, 3, 3\frac{1}{4}$; *Start with 2 and add $\frac{1}{4}$ repeatedly.*

Ⓒ $2\frac{3}{4}, 3, 3\frac{1}{4}$; *Start with 3 and add $\frac{1}{4}$ repeatedly.*

Ⓓ $3, 3\frac{1}{4}, 3\frac{1}{2}$; *Start with 3 and add $\frac{1}{4}$ repeatedly.*

$$2 \quad 2\frac{1}{4} \quad 2\frac{1}{2} \quad 2\frac{3}{4} \quad 3 \quad 3\frac{1}{4}$$
$$+\frac{1}{4} \ +\frac{1}{4} \ +\frac{1}{4} \ +\frac{1}{4} \ +\frac{1}{4}$$

Find the common difference. Use it to find the next three terms.

The next three terms are $2\frac{3}{4}, 3$, and $3\frac{1}{4}$. The rule for the sequence is *Start with 2 and add $\frac{1}{4}$ repeatedly.* The answer is B.

During a two-mile run, a runner's feet strike the ground about 3,000 times.

✓ Quick Check

2. Find the next three terms of each sequence. Then write a rule to describe the sequence.

a. $23, 19, 15, 11, \ldots$ **b.** $-6, -4\frac{2}{3}, -3\frac{1}{3}, -2, \ldots$

2 Geometric and Other Sequences

You find a term of a **geometric sequence** by *multiplying* the previous term by a fixed number called the **common ratio.**

Term Number	1st	2nd	3rd	4th
Geometric Sequence	2	6	18	54
Common Ratio		×3	×3	×3

You can find the common ratio for a geometric sequence by dividing any term by the previous term in the sequence.

3 EXAMPLE Finding the Common Ratio

Find the common ratio in the sequence $4, 8, 16, 32, \ldots$ Find the next three terms of the sequence. Then write a rule to describe the sequence.

$$4 \quad 8 \quad 16 \quad 32 \quad 64 \quad 128 \quad 256$$
$$\times 2 \ \times 2 \ \times 2 \ \times 2 \ \times 2 \ \times 2$$

Find the common ratio. Use it to find the next three terms.

The next three terms are $64, 128$, and 256. The rule for the sequence is *Start with 4 and multiply by 2 repeatedly.*

3. Find the common ratio and the next three terms of each sequence. Then write a rule to describe the sequence.

    a. $4, 12, 36, 108, \ldots$ **b.** $4, 2, 1, 0.5, \ldots$

Not every sequence is arithmetic or geometric. You can determine whether any sequence of numbers is arithmetic or geometric by looking for a common difference or a common ratio. For other sequences, you can look for patterns.

4 EXAMPLE   **Finding the Type of Sequence**

Tell whether each sequence is *arithmetic*, *geometric*, or *neither*. Find the next three terms of each sequence.

a. $4, 6, 8, 10, \ldots$

$$4 \quad 6 \quad 8 \quad 10 \quad 12 \quad 14 \quad 16$$
$$+2 \quad +2 \quad +2 \quad +2 \quad +2 \quad +2$$

There is a common difference of 2. The sequence is arithmetic. The next three terms are 12, 14, and 16.

b. $4, 6, 9, 13\frac{1}{2}, \ldots$

$$4 \quad 6 \quad 9 \quad 13\frac{1}{2} \quad 20\frac{1}{4} \quad 30\frac{3}{8} \quad 45\frac{9}{16}$$
$$\times\frac{3}{2} \quad \times\frac{3}{2} \quad \times\frac{3}{2} \quad \times\frac{3}{2} \quad \times\frac{3}{2} \quad \times\frac{3}{2}$$

The ratios for the first four terms are $\frac{6}{4}, \frac{9}{6}$, and $\frac{27}{18}$. These equal $\frac{3}{2}$, which is the common ratio. The sequence is geometric. The next three terms are $20\frac{1}{4}, 30\frac{3}{8}$, and $45\frac{9}{16}$.

c. $4, 6, 9, 13, \ldots$

$$4 \quad 6 \quad 9 \quad 13 \quad 18 \quad 24 \quad 31$$
$$+2 \quad +3 \quad +4 \quad +5 \quad +6 \quad +7$$

The sequence is neither arithmetic nor geometric. Following the pattern above, the next three terms are 18, 24, and 31.

✓ **Quick Check**

4. Tell whether each sequence is *arithmetic*, *geometric*, or *neither*. Then find the next three terms of the sequence.

    a. $3, 9, 27, 81, \ldots$ **b.** $10, 13, 18, 25, \ldots$
    c. $-12, 12, -12, 12, \ldots$ **d.** $50, 200, 350, 500, \ldots$

EXERCISES

For more exercises, see *Extra Skill and Word Problem Practice.*

Practice and Problem Solving

A Practice by Example

GO for Help

Example 1
(page 696)

What is the common difference of each arithmetic sequence?

1. $5, 4, 3, 2, \ldots$ **2.** $4, 11, 18, 25, \ldots$ **3.** $7, 1, -5, -11, \ldots$

4. $80, 60, 40, 20, \ldots$ **5.** $3, 9, 15, 21, \ldots$ **6.** $-6, -5, -4, -3, \ldots$

Example 2
(page 697)

Find the next three terms of each sequence. Then write a rule to describe the sequence.

7. $0, 5, 10, 15, \ldots$ **8.** $21, 15, 9, 3, \ldots$ **9.** $-11, -8, -5, -2, \ldots$

10. Exercising You begin doing 20 sit-ups every day in November. You do 32 sit-ups every day in December, 44 sit-ups every day in January, and so on. Find the next three terms of the sequence. Then write a rule to describe the sequence.

Example 3
(page 697)

Find the common ratio and the next three terms of each sequence. Then write a rule to describe the sequence.

11. $3, 6, 12, 24, \ldots$ **12.** $5, 1, \frac{1}{5}, \frac{1}{25}, \ldots$ **13.** $45, 90, 180, 360, \ldots$

14. $2, 3, 4\frac{1}{2}, 6\frac{3}{4}, \ldots$ **15.** $12, 4, 1\frac{1}{3}, \frac{4}{9}, \ldots$ **16.** $8, 40, 200, 1{,}000, \ldots$

Example 4
(page 698)

Tell whether each sequence is *arithmetic*, *geometric*, or *neither*. Find the next three terms of the sequence.

17. $1, 3, 9, 27, \ldots$ **18.** $10, 5, 0, -5, \ldots$ **19.** $4.5, 4, 3.5, 3, \ldots$

20. $2, 2, 4, 6, \ldots$ **21.** $-1, 3, -9, 27, \ldots$ **22.** $0, 5, 12, 21, \ldots$

23. Multiple Choice Is the sequence $4, 3\frac{1}{2}, 3, 2\frac{1}{2}, \ldots$ *arithmetic* or *geometric*? Find the common difference or common ratio.

  Ⓐ arithmetic; $\frac{1}{2}$ Ⓑ arithmetic; $-\frac{1}{2}$

  Ⓒ geometric; 2 Ⓓ geometric; $\frac{1}{2}$

B Apply Your Skills

Tell whether each sequence is *arithmetic* or *geometric*. If arithmetic, give the common difference. If geometric, give the common ratio.

24. $1, 1\frac{1}{2}, 2, 2\frac{1}{2}, \ldots$ **25.** $-3, -15, -75, \ldots$ **26.** $-4, 12, -36, 108, \ldots$

27. $5, 6.4, 7.8, 9.2, \ldots$ **28.** $5, 15, 45, 135, \ldots$ **29.** $8.3, 5.7, 3.1, 0.5, \ldots$

Find the next three terms of each sequence. Then write a rule to describe the sequence.

30. $1, 4, 16, 64, \ldots$ **31.** $3, 1, -1, -3, \ldots$ **32.** $2, 20, 200, 2{,}000, \ldots$

33. $9, 18, 36, 72, \ldots$ **34.** $25, 50, 75, 100, \ldots$ **35.** $6.5, 6.7, 6.9, 7.1, \ldots$

Tell whether each sequence is *arithmetic*, *geometric*, or *neither*. Find the next three terms of each sequence.

GO Online

Homework Video Tutor

Visit: PHSchool.com
Web Code: ade-1301

36. $\frac{1}{2}, \frac{5}{6}, 1\frac{1}{6}, 1\frac{1}{2}, \ldots$ **37.** $1, 10, 2, 20, \ldots$ **38.** $13, 12, 10, 7, \ldots$

39. $7, 7.03, 7.06, 7.09, \ldots$ **40.** $-\frac{1}{5}, -\frac{1}{10}, -\frac{1}{20}, -\frac{1}{40}, \ldots$

To review compound interest, see Lesson 7-8.

41. Savings You open a savings account with $2,000. The account earns 4% interest compounded semiannually.
  a. Write the balance in the savings account after each interest payment for two years.
  b. **Writing in Math** Does the pattern of balances form an arithmetic or geometric sequence? Explain.

 Challenge Evaluate each expression for $n = -2, -1, 0,$ and 1. Is the sequence formed *arithmetic*, *geometric*, or *neither*?

42. $3n$

43. $n(n + 1)$

44. 2^n

45. n^2

46. Patterns In the Fibonacci sequence $1, 1, 2, 3, 5, 8, \ldots$, you find each term (after the first two terms) by adding the two previous terms. Write the next three terms of the sequence.

ISAT

 Test Prep

Multiple Choice

47. If the first term of an arithmetic sequence is 35 and the fifth term is 67, what is the third term?
  A. 43   **B.** 51   **C.** 59   **D.** 75

48. If the rule for a sequence is "start with -7 and multiply by -2 repeatedly," what is the fourth term in the sequence?
  F. -112 **G.** -56 **H.** 56   **J.** 112

Short Response

Read the passage below before doing Exercises 49 and 50.

Population Watch

The population of the United States in 1980 was about 226 million, in 1985 it was about 238 million, in 1990 it was about 250 million, and in 1995 it was about 263 million.

49. What intervals of time are used with the given population data?

50. Which type of sequence, arithmetic or geometric, could you use to model the United States population data? Explain.

Mixed Review

Lesson 12-8

51. Surveys You want to find out which presidential candidate is most popular in your city. You plan to interview people who visit the city's art museum. State whether the survey plan describes a good sample. Explain your reasoning.

Lesson 9-6 **Find the circumference of each circle rounded to the nearest tenth.**

52. radius = 8.5 m   **53.** radius = 5 in.   **54.** diameter = 14 cm

Displaying Sequences

You can model rules for sequences mathematically and then display the sequences using graphing calculator tables. You can use the tables to find any term in a sequence.

1 ACTIVITY

Model the rule "Start with 23 and add −4 repeatedly" mathematically and then display the sequence in a calculator table.

Model: $23 + (-4)x$, or $23 - 4x$, with $x = 0, 1, 2, \ldots$

Display Method 1

Press [Y=] and enter $Y_1 = 23 - 4x$.

• In **TBLSET,** set TblStart = 0 and ΔTbl = 1, then press **TABLE.**

X	Y_1	
0	23	
1	19	
2	15	
3	11	
4	7	
5	3	
6	−1	

X=6

Move down in either column to see more terms of the sequence.

2 ACTIVITY

Model the rule "Start with 4 and multiply by 2 repeatedly" mathematically and then display the sequence in a calculator table. Find the sixth term.

Model: $4(2)^x$, with $x = 0, 1, 2, \ldots$

Display Method 2

Clear your home screen. In **STAT,** use the **OPS** menu. Select the **seq** operator, and [ENTER]. Then

enter seq(X,X,0,10) [STO▶] **STAT L₁** [ENTER]. In similar fashion,

enter seq(4(2)^X,X,0,10) [STO▶] **STAT L₂** [ENTER].

Press [LIST].

• The sixth term is when $x = 6$, or 256.

L1	L2	L3	1
0	4		
1	8		
2	16		
3	32		
4	64		
5	128		
6	256		

L1(7)=6

This list ends at 10.

EXERCISES

Use a graphing calculator table to display the first 11 terms of each sequence. Find the 11th term. Use Display Method 1 for some exercises and Display Method 2 for the others.

1. Start with 0 and add 5 repeatedly.

2. Start with 80 and subtract 30 repeatedly.

3. Start with 3 and add 6 repeatedly.

4. Start with −4 and multiply by −3 repeatedly.

5. $7, 7.3, 7.6, 7.9, \ldots$ **6.** $3, 1, -1, -3, \ldots$ **7.** $18 - 3x; x = 0, 1, 2, \ldots$ **8.** $6(3)^x$

9. In Activity 1, the model gives the desired sequence for x having values $0, 1, 2, \ldots$ Find a model using x that gives the same sequence for x having values $1, 2, 3, \ldots$

Graphing Nonlinear Functions

What You'll Learn

- To graph quadratic functions
- To graph absolute value functions

. . . And Why

To use nonlinear functions in modeling real-world situations, such as finding the area of an enclosed space

☑ **Check Skills You'll Need**

Find the y values of each equation for x = −2, 0, and 2.

1. $y = 5x - 1$

2. $y = \frac{1}{2}x + 3$

3. $y = 3x + 2$

4. $y = \frac{1}{4}x - 5$

 for Help
Lesson 8-2

◀)) **New Vocabulary**

- quadratic function
- absolute value function

1 Graphing Quadratic Functions

Activity..........

Graphing Data

You can graph the area of a square as a function of the length of a side of the square.

1. Copy and complete the table at the right.

2. Draw a graph of the data. Does your graph appear to be a linear function? Explain.

Side x	Area f(x)
1	1
2	■
3	■
4	■
5	■
6	36

In a **quadratic function,** the input variable is squared. The graph of a quadratic function is a U-shaped curve called a *parabola*. The curve may open upward or downward.

1 EXAMPLE   Graphing a Quadratic Function

For the function $y = 2x^2$, make a table with integer values of x from −2 to 2. Then graph the function.

Make a table.

x	$2x^2 = y$	(x, y)
−2	$2(-2)^2 = 8$	(−2, 8)
−1	$2(-1)^2 = 2$	(−1, 2)
0	$2(0)^2 = 0$	(0, 0)
1	$2(1)^2 = 2$	(1, 2)
2	$2(2)^2 = 8$	(2, 8)

Make a graph.

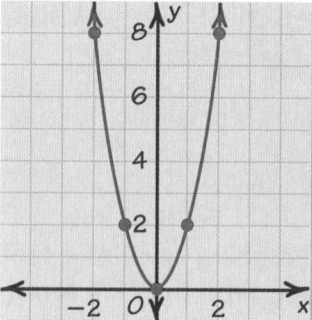

☑ Quick Check

1. For each function, make a table with integer values of x from −2 to 2. Then graph each function.

    a. $y = -2x^2$ **b.** $y = -x^2 + 3$

2 EXAMPLE Using a Graph to Solve a Problem

The function $A = 10x - x^2$, where x is the width in yards, gives the area A of a goat pen in square yards. Graph the function. Use the graph to find the width that gives the greatest area.

x	$10x - x^2 = y$	(x, y)
0	$10(0) - 0^2 = 0$	(0, 0)
1	$10(1) - 1^2 = 9$	(1, 9)
2	$10(2) - 2^2 = 16$	(2, 16)
3	$10(3) - 3^2 = 21$	(3, 21)
4	$10(4) - 4^2 = 24$	(4, 24)
5	$10(5) - 5^2 = 25$	(5, 25)
6	$10(6) - 6^2 = 24$	(6, 24)

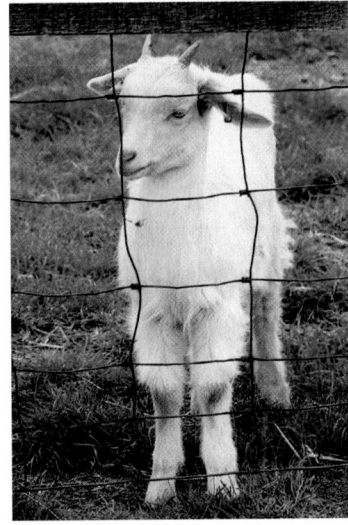

Real-World 🌐 **Connection**

A goat pen with width 5 yd and area 25 yd² must have length 5 yd.

The ordered pair $(5, 25)$ shows what appears to be the highest point. So the width 5 yards gives the greatest area.

✓ Quick Check

2. Graph each function.

   a. $y = 3x + x^2$ **b.** $y = 6x - x^2$

---

2 Graphing Absolute Value Functions

The equation $y = |x|$ is an **absolute value function.** The graph of $y = |x|$ is V-shaped.

Vocabulary Tip

Quadratic and absolute value functions are <u>nonlinear</u> <u>functions</u> because you cannot draw the graph of either in one line.

3 EXAMPLE Graphing an Absolute Value Function

Graph the function $y = |x|$.

x	$|x| = y$	(x, y)
-2	$|-2| = 2$	(-2, 2)
-1	$|-1| = 1$	(-1, 1)
0	$|0| = 0$	(0, 0)
1	$|1| = 1$	(1, 1)
2	$|2| = 2$	(2, 2)

Online active math

For: Nonlinear Functions Activity
Use: Interactive Textbook, 13-2

✓ Quick Check

3. Graph each function.

   a. $y = -|x| + 1$ **b.** $y = 2|x|$

EXERCISES

For more exercises, see *Extra Skill and Word Problem Practice*.

Practice and Problem Solving

A Practice by Example

GO for Help

Example 1
(page 702)

For each function, make a table with integer values of x from -2 to 2. Then graph the function.

1. $y = 4x^2$ **2.** $y = -x^2$ **3.** $y = -3x^2$ **4.** $y = x^2 + 1$

5. $y = -x^2 + 2$ **6.** $y = x^2 - 2$ **7.** $y = x^2 + 4$ **8.** $y = -x^2 + 3$

Example 2
(page 703)

Graph each function.

9. $y = x - x^2$ **10.** $y = 2x - x^2$ **11.** $y = 5x - x^2$ **12.** $y = 8x - x^2$

13. The function $A = 15x - x^2$, where x is the width in yards, gives the area A of a llama pen in square yards. Make a table with integer values from 0 to 10. Graph the function. Use the graph to find the width that gives the greatest area.

Example 3
(page 703)

For each function, make a table with integer values of x from -2 to 2. Then graph the function.

14. $y = 3|x|$ **15.** $y = |x| + 3$ **16.** $y = -3|x|$

17. $y = |x| - 4$ **18.** $y = -|x| - 1$ **19.** $y = -2|x|$

B Apply Your Skills

GO **O**nline
Homework Video Tutor
Visit: PHSchool.com
Web Code: ade-1302

State whether the graph of the function has a U shape or a V shape. Make a table with integer values of x from -2 to 2. Then graph the function.

20. $y = |x| + 1$ **21.** $y = x^2 - 8$ **22.** $y = 3x - x^2$

23. $y = -4x^2$ **24.** $y = -|x| - 3$ **25.** $y = 2x^2 - 2$

26. $y = -\frac{1}{2}|x|$ **27.** $y = |x| - 2$ **28.** $y = -x^2 + 5$

GO for Help

For a guide to reading and solving Exercise 29, see page 706.

29. a. Graph $y = x^2$, $y = 2x^2$, and $y = \frac{1}{2}x^2$ on the same coordinate plane.
   b. Describe how the coefficients of x^2 affect the graphs.

30. Writing in Math Describe how the graphs of the functions $y = x^2$, $y = 2x + x^2$, and $y = 2x - x^2$ are alike and how they are different.

31. Open-Ended Write an absolute value function of your own. Graph the function.

C Challenge

Writing in Math

How are quadratic and absolute value functions alike? How are they different?

32. Reasoning For the *cubing function*, $y = x^3$, make a table with integer values of x from -2 to 2. Then graph the function. Is the cubing function a quadratic function? Explain.

33. a. Geometry Make a table to show edge lengths and volumes of four cubes. Let the edge lengths be 1 m, 2 m, 3 m, and 4 m.
   b. Graph the ordered pairs from your table.
   c. Using your graph from part (b), estimate the volume of a cube with edge length 3.5 m.

Multiple Choice   For Exercises 34–36, use the graph at the right.

34. The graph shows what type of function?
  A. quadratic   **B.** linear
  C. area   **D.** absolute value

35. Which point is NOT on the graph?
  F. $(1, -2)$ **G.** $(-2, 0)$
  H. $(0, -2)$ **J.** $(1, -1)$

36. Which function matches the graph?
  A. $y = -2|x|$ **B.** $y = x^2 - 2$
  C. $y = |x - 2|$ **D.** $y = |x| - 2$

Short Response   **37.** For the function $y = -3x^2$, **(a)** make a table with integer values of x from -2 to 2.   **(b)** Graph the function.

Mixed Review

Lesson 13-1   **Find the next three terms of each sequence. Then write a rule to describe the sequence.**

38. $8, 4, 2, 1, \ldots$ **39.** $12, 27, 42, 57, \ldots$ **40.** $3, 4, 6, 9, \ldots$

Lesson 12-1   **41. Statistics** The table shows the prices of evening movies at 18 different theaters. Use the data to make a frequency table.

Costs of Movie Tickets

$7.00, $6.50, $7.50, $7.00, $7.50, $8.00,
$7.00, $8.50, $8.00, $6.00, $7.00, $7.50,
$8.00, $7.00, $7.50, $8.50, $7.50, $6.50

Math at Work

Systems Analyst

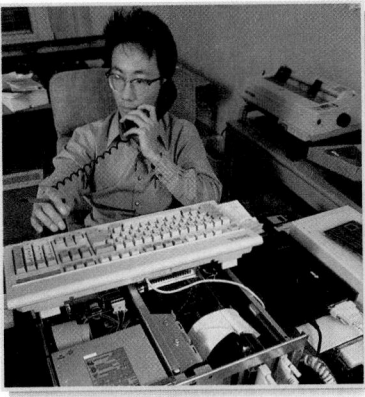

Systems analysts are responsible for upgrading hardware and designing and installing new software. They also respond to problems users have with hardware or software. Logic skills are necessary for writing programs and solving problems.

Systems analysts have backgrounds in computer programming. Since computer technology is constantly changing, they must continue their education throughout their careers.

Go Online
PHSchool.com   **For:** Information about systems analysts
Web Code: adb-2031

Understanding Math Problems Read the problem below. Then let Lily's thinking guide you through the solution. Check your understanding with the exercises at the bottom of the page.

a. Graph $y = x^2$, $y = 2x^2$, and $y = \frac{1}{2}x^2$ on the same coordinate plane.

b. Describe how the coefficients of x^2 affect the graphs.

What Lily Thinks

To graph the three functions, I need to make a table. Then I need to draw the graphs. That's part (a).

Now I need to describe how the coefficients of x^2 affect the graphs. First I'll tell how the graphs are alike. Then I'll describe how the graphs are different.

Now I'll tell how the functions are alike. And how the functions are different.

OK, I know the graphs get wider as the coefficients of x^2 decrease in value. That's what I'll write.

What Lily Writes

Graphs alike: All three graphs are parabolas. All contain (0, 0). All open upward.
Graphs differ: From the top down, they get wider.

Functions alike: All contain x^2.
Functions differ: x^2 has different coefficients.

As the coefficients of x^2 decrease in value, the parabolas get wider.

EXERCISES

1. For $y = -x^2$, $y = -2x^2$, and $y = -\frac{1}{2}x^2$, describe how the coefficients of x^2 affect the graphs of the functions.

2. a. Graph $y = x^2$, $y = x^2 + 2$, and $y = x^2 - 3$ on the same coordinate plane.

   b. Describe how the constants affect the graphs of the functions.

3. For $y = k|x|$, describe how the values of k affect the graphs.

Exponential Growth and Decay

1 | Exponential Growth

A function like $y = 2^x$ has input, or domain, values that are exponents. It models *exponential growth*. Its graph curves upward as input values increase.

1 EXAMPLE Real-World Problem Solving

Biology A warren of rabbits starts with one male and one female. The number of rabbits then doubles each month. The function $y = 2^x$ models the number of rabbits in the warren.

For the function $y = 2^x$, make a table with integer values of x from 2 to 5. Then graph the function.

x	2^x	y	(x, y)
2	2^2	4	(2, 4)
3	2^3	8	(3, 8)
4	2^4	16	(4, 16)
5	2^5	32	(5, 32)

✓ Quick Check

1. For the function $y = 3^x$, make a table with integer values of x from 1 to 4. Then graph the function.

You can multiply the power in a function by a number. For example, in $y = 0.25(4^x)$, the power 4^x is multiplied by 0.25.

What You'll Learn

- To use tables, rules, and graphs with functions modeling growth
- To use tables, rules, and graphs with functions modeling decay

. . . And Why

To model real-world situations involving population growth

✓ Check Skills You'll Need

Evaluate each expression.

1. 5^2 **2.** 4^3 **3.** 3^5 **4.** 2^8

GO for Help
Lesson 4-2

2 EXAMPLE **Graphing Exponential Growth**

For the function $y = 0.25(4)^x$, make a table with integer values of
x from 0 to 4. Then graph the function.

x	$0.25(4)^x$	y	(x, y)
0	$0.25(4)^0$	0.25	$(0, 0.25)$
1	$0.25(4)^1$	1	$(1, 1)$
2	$0.25(4)^2$	4	$(2, 4)$
3	$0.25(4)^3$	16	$(3, 16)$
4	$0.25(4)^4$	64	$(4, 64)$

✓ Quick Check

2. For the function $y = 0.5(2)^x$, make a table with integer values of
   x from 0 to 5. Then graph the function.

2 Exponential Decay

A function like $y = \left(\frac{1}{2}\right)^x$ models *exponential decay*. Its graph slopes
downward as input values increase.

3 EXAMPLE **Graphing Exponential Decay**

For $y = 60\left(\frac{1}{2}\right)^x$, make a table with integer values of x
from 0 to 5. Then graph the function.

x	$60(\frac{1}{2})^x$	y	(x, y)
0	$60(\frac{1}{2})^0$	60	$(0, 60)$
1	$60(\frac{1}{2})^1$	30	$(1, 30)$
2	$60(\frac{1}{2})^2$	15	$(2, 15)$
3	$60(\frac{1}{2})^3$	7.5	$(3, 7.5)$
4	$60(\frac{1}{2})^4$	3.75	$(4, 3.75)$
5	$60(\frac{1}{2})^5$	1.875	$(5, 1.875)$

Real-World 🌐 Connection

Doctors use the element
technetium to make
bone scans. Technetium
decays exponentially.
After 6 hours, only 15 mg
of a 30-mg dose remain.
After 12 hours, only
7.5 mg remain.

✓ Quick Check

3. For the function $y = 90\left(\frac{1}{3}\right)^x$, make a table with integer values
   of x from 0 to 5. Then graph the function.

EXERCISES

For more exercises, see *Extra Skill and Word Problem Practice*.

Practice and Problem Solving

A Practice by Example

Examples 1 and 2
(pages 707 and 708)

Make a table with integer values of x from 0 to 4. Then graph the function.

1. $y = 4^x$ **2.** $y = 5^x$ **3.** $y = 6^x$

4. $y = 0.4(2)^x$ **5.** $y = 0.5(4)^x$ **6.** $y = 0.2(5)^x$

7. Biology A bacteria culture starts with ten cells and doubles every hour. The function $y = 10(2)^x$ models the number of cells y in the culture after x hours. Make a table with integer values of x from 0 to 3. Then graph the function.

Example 3
(page 708)

Make a table with integer values of x from 0 to 5. Then graph the function.

8. $y = \left(\frac{1}{2}\right)^x$ **9.** $y = 30\left(\frac{1}{3}\right)^x$ **10.** $y = 100\left(\frac{1}{5}\right)^x$

B Apply Your Skills

Match each graph with an equation.

11.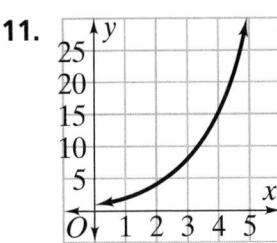

A. $y = 3^x$ **B.** $y = 2^x$

12.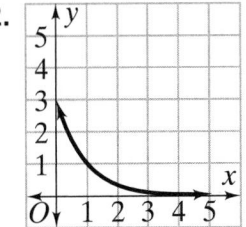

A. $y = 3\left(\frac{1}{3}\right)^x$ **B.** $y = 2\left(\frac{1}{2}\right)^x$

13. Multiple Choice You put $100 in a stock that increases in value by 20% each year. The function $v = 100(1.2)^x$ describes the value of the stock after x years. Evaluate the function for $x = 2$. What does the value represent?

Ⓐ 103.2; the value of the stock after 2 years
Ⓑ 120; the number of shares you own after 2 years
Ⓒ 144; the value of the stock after 2 years
Ⓓ 240; the number of shares you own after 2 years

Make a table with integer values of x from 0 to 4. Then graph the function.

14. $y = 2 \cdot 3^x$ **15.** $y = \frac{1}{5} \cdot 5^x$ **16.** $y = 6(0.5)^x$

17. $f(x) = \frac{1}{2} \cdot 2^x$ **18.** $g(x) = 20\left(\frac{1}{2}\right)^x$ **19.** $g(x) = 3 \cdot 2^x$

GO **O**nline
Homework Video Tutor
Visit: PHSchool.com
Web Code: ade-1303

Is the point (4, 16) on the graph of each function? Explain.

20. $y = 4x$ **21.** $y = 2^x$ **22.** $y = x^2$ **23.** $y = \left(\frac{1}{2}\right)^x$

Challenge

24. a. For the functions $y = 2x$, $y = x^2$, and $y = 2^x$, make tables with integer values of x from 0 to 5. Then graph the functions.

b. Writing in Math Describe how the graphs are similar. Describe how they are different.

25. Reasoning Without graphing, predict whether each function shows exponential growth or exponential decay. Justify your prediction.

a. $y = 5^x$ **b.** $y = \left(\frac{1}{2}\right)^x$ **c.** $y = 3(0.2)^x$ **d.** $y = 3(2)^x$

 ISAT

Test Prep

Gridded Response For the given equation, what is the value of y for $x = 2$?

26. $y = 0.2(3)^x$ **27.** $y = 3\left(\frac{1}{3}\right)^x$ **28.** $y = 3x^2 - 6$ **29.** $y = 4|x| - 1$

For Exercises 30 and 31, use the formula $B = p(1.03)^n$ to find the balance B (in dollars and cents) for a principal p invested at a compound interest rate of 3% for n years.

30. \$5 invested for 5 years **31.** \$2 invested for 10 years

Mixed Review

 GO for Help

Lesson 13-2 **Graph each function.**

32. $y = |x| + 2$ **33.** $f(x) = 3|x|$ **34.** $g(x) = -x^2 + 1$

Lesson 12-4 **35. Shopping** Janelle is buying a sweatshirt. She has a choice of red, purple, or green; zipper or no zipper; and hooded or not hooded. How many different sweatshirt choices does she have?

Lesson 11-3 **Find the midpoint of each segment with the given endpoints.**

36. $A(4, -6)$ and $B(-2, 5)$ **37.** $X(-3, -8)$ and $Y(1, 6)$

✓ **Checkpoint Quiz 1** **Lessons 13-1 through 13-3**

Find the next three terms of each sequence. Then write a rule to describe the sequence.

1. $100, 85, 70, 55, \ldots$ **2.** $17, 24, 31, 38, \ldots$ **3.** $13, 26, 52, 104, \ldots$

4. A geometric sequence begins with 3 and has common ratio 2. Write its first five terms.

For each function, make a table with integer values of x. (Use –2 to 2 for Ex. 5 and 6; use 0 to 4 for Ex. 7.) Then graph the function.

5. $y = \frac{1}{4}x^2$ **6.** $f(x) = \frac{1}{4}|x|$ **7.** $f(x) = 0.5(3)^x$

Nonlinear Functions and Graphing Calculators

For Use With Lesson 13-3

You can use a graphing calculator to graph nonlinear functions.
For the exponent 2, you can use the x^2 key or press $\wedge$ 2.

ACTIVITY

Graph $y = |3x|$.

Step 1 Press **Y=** **CLEAR**. Press **MATH**. In the
NUM menu, select **abs** then **ENTER**.
Enter $Y_1 = abs\,(3x)$.

Step 2 Set your viewing window.

Step 3 Press **GRAPH**.

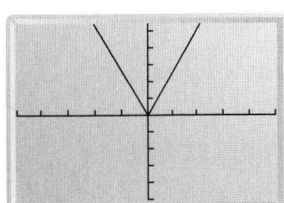

Step 4 Press **TABLE** to see solutions.

X	Y₁	
−4	12	
−3	9	
−2	6	
−1	3	
0	0	
1	3	
2	6	
X=2		

EXERCISES

**Graph each equation using a graphing calculator. For each function,
use TABLE and make a table on paper for integer values of x from
−5 to 5. Then sketch the graph.**

1. $y = |2x|$ **2.** $y = -|2x|$ **3.** $y = |2x| + 1$

4. $y = x^2 - 1$ **5.** $y = -x^2 - 1$ **6.** $y = 3(2)^x$

7. $y = -3(2)^x$ **8.** $y = 3\left(\frac{1}{2}\right)^x$ **9.** $y = -3\left(\frac{1}{2}\right)^x$

10. Compare your graphs for Exercises 1 and 2.
   a. Explain how they are related and why this is so.
   b. Compare the equations in Exercises 6 and 7. Should their graphs
      be related in the same way as in part (a)? Explain. Then check.

11. **Open-Ended** Write a nonlinear function that you can graph using
a graphing calculator. Graph your function. Make a table of values
and sketch your graph.

13-4   Polynomials

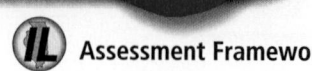 Assessment Framework

8.8.03 Simplify algebraic expressions.

☑ **Check Skills You'll Need**

Evaluate each expression.

1. $5n$ for $n = -8$

2. mn for $m = 6$ and $n = -4$

3. $x - 9$ for $x = 7$

4. $63 - 5x$ for $x = 7$

 for Help
Lesson 1-3

🔊 **New Vocabulary**

- monomial
- polynomial
- binomial
- trinomial

1   Identifying Polynomials

You have seen how mathematics uses algebraic expressions to represent real-world situations. Some of these expressions are monomials. A **monomial** is a real number, a variable, or a product of a real number and variables with whole-number exponents.

Monomials: 3 m $5xy$ $0.35bc^3$ $\frac{w}{9}$ $\frac{1}{4}p^2q$

Not monomials: $a - 8$ $\sqrt{m}$ y^{-1} (or $\frac{1}{y}$) $\frac{ab}{c}$

1 EXAMPLE   **Recognizing a Monomial**

Is the expression a monomial? Explain.

a. $7x^2y$ Yes, the expression is the product of the real number 7 and the variables x and y.

b. $8 + a$ No, the expression is a sum.

c. $\frac{a}{7y}$ No, the denominator contains a variable.

d. $\frac{5x}{4}$ Yes, the expression is the product of the real number $\frac{5}{4}$ and the variable x.

☑ **Quick Check**

1. Is the expression a monomial? Explain.

   a. $\frac{6}{m}$ **b.** $\frac{m}{6}$ **c.** 45 **d.** $mx + b$

A **polynomial** is a monomial or a sum or difference of monomials. We call the monomials that make up a polynomial its *terms*. You can name a polynomial by the number of its terms.

Polynomial	Number of terms	Examples
Monomial	1	$4,\ 32,\ x,\ 2x^2$
Binomial	2	$x - 3,\ 5x + 1,\ x^3 - x$
Trinomial	3	$x^2 + x + 1,\ x^4 - 2x - 5$

2 EXAMPLE   Naming a Polynomial

State whether the polynomial is a *monomial*, a *binomial*, or a *trinomial*.

a. $x - y$

binomial

b. $8xyz$

monomial

c. $y^2 + 8y + 18$

trinomial

✓ Quick Check

2. Is the polynomial a monomial, a binomial, or a trinomial?

    a. 10   **b.** $9x^2 + xy$ **c.** $8 - y$ **d.** $5 + x - 3y$

---

2 | Evaluating Polynomials

You evaluate polynomials by substituting values for the variables.

3 EXAMPLE   Evaluating a Polynomial

Evaluate each polynomial for $m = 8$ and $p = -3$.

a. $2mp$

$2mp = 2(8)(-3)$ **Replace *m* with 8 and *p* with −3.**

$= -48$ **Simplify.**

b. $3m - 2p$

$3m - 2p = 3(8) - 2(-3)$

$= 24 + 6$

$= 30$

Test-Taking Tip

When you simplify a long polynomial, apply the properties one at a time. Record your work clearly, so you can check your answer easily.

✓ Quick Check

3. Evaluate each polynomial for $x = -2$ and $y = 5$.

    a. $5xy$ **b.** $x + 3y$ **c.** $y^2 - 2y + x$

4 EXAMPLE   Real-World Problem Solving

Gridded Response The polynomial $-16t^2 + 140t$ gives the height, in feet, reached by fireworks in t seconds. If the fireworks explode 4 seconds after launch, at what height do they explode?

$-16t^2 + 140t$

$-16(4)^2 + 140(4)$ **Replace *t* with 4.**

304 **Simplify.**

The fireworks explode at 304 feet.

3	0	4	
⊘	⊘	⊘	⊘
⊙	⊙	⊙	⊙
①	①	①	①
②	②	②	②
●	③	③	③
④	④	④	●
⑤	⑤	⑤	⑤
⑥	⑥	⑥	⑥
⑦	⑦	⑦	⑦
⑧	⑧	⑧	⑧
⑨	⑨	⑨	⑨

Real-World Connection

During a twenty-minute show, fireworks technicians can set off as many as 6,000 different fireworks.

✓ Quick Check

4. Fireworks are set to explode 6 seconds after launch. At what height will they explode?

EXERCISES

For more exercises, see *Extra Skill and Word Problem Practice.*

Practice and Problem Solving

A Practice by Example

Example 1
(page 712)

Is the expression a monomial? Explain.

1. $2 + x$ **2.** $18ab^2$ **3.** $\frac{a}{3}$ **4.** $\frac{4}{b}$

5. 1 **6.** $0.82k$ **7.** $2x$ **8.** $-0.3y$

Example 2
(page 713)

State whether the polynomial is a *monomial,* a *binomial,* or a *trinomial.*

9. $3xy + 4y^2$ **10.** $5c - 2 + a$ **11.** $7y^2 + 2y - 9$

12. 658 **13.** $3x^2 + 2x$ **14.** 21

15. $7p^2$ **16.** $56 - x$ **17.** $a^2 + 7b - 3c$

Example 3
(page 713)

Evaluate each polynomial for $a = 2$ and $b = -4$.

18. $2ab$ **19.** $-4ab$ **20.** $7a + b$

21. $a - 3b$ **22.** $5a + 7b$ **23.** $ab^2 + 5$

24. $a^2 + 2b - 3$ **25.** $2a^2 - b + 4$ **26.** $10a + b^2 - 7$

Example 4
(page 713)

27. Sports The polynomial $-16t^2 + 32t + 4$ gives the height, in feet, that a tossed ball reaches in t seconds. If the ball reaches a maximum height after one second, what is that height?

B Apply Your Skills

Is the expression a monomial? Explain.

28. pq^{-3} **29.** 0 **30.** $\frac{3}{p}$ **31.** $10bc + b$

State whether the polynomial is a *monomial,* a *binomial,* a *trinomial* or *none* of these.

32. $4.5 + 3.7m$ **33.** $2x - 4^{-1}$ **34.** -42 **35.** $x^2 + 7x + 4$

36. $3a^2 - 6a^{-3}$ **37.** $15 + w$ **38.** abc **39.** $b^2 + \frac{2}{b} - 3$

40. Open-Ended Write a polynomial with four terms.

41. Geometry You can write the formula for the area of a trapezoid as $A = \frac{1}{2}b_1h + \frac{1}{2}b_2h$. What kind of polynomial is $\frac{1}{2}b_1h + \frac{1}{2}b_2h$?

42. a. Writing in Math Name other words with the prefixes *mono, bi, tri,* and *poly.* How do the prefixes help you understand the meanings of the words?
    b. What would you call a polynomial with four terms?

GO **O**nline
Homework Video Tutor
Visit: PHSchool.com
Web Code: ade-1304

Evaluate each polynomial for $x = -5$ and $y = 3$.

43. $2x + 2y$ **44.** $7 + x^2y$ **45.** $7y^2 + 6x - 20$

46. $xy - y$ **47.** $x^2 + 2x - 3$ **48.** $\frac{x^2}{5} + x$

C **Challenge** **Reasoning** Tell why each expression is not a polynomial.

49. $x^2 + 2x + \frac{1}{x}$ **50.** $2ab + b^2 + \sqrt{a}$ **51.** $(y^2 + 4) \div y$

 52. a. Public Schools The polynomial $34x^2 - 945x + 46{,}971$ models U.S. public school enrollment, in thousands, from 1970 to 1998. The value of x for 1970 is 1 and the value of x for 1998 is 29. How many students were enrolled in public schools in 1970? In 1998?

   b. Use the polynomial to predict enrollment in 2010.

53. Geometry A polygon is convex if no diagonal has points outside the polygon. The polynomial $\frac{n^2}{2} - \frac{3n}{2}$ gives the number of diagonals that you can draw in a convex polygon with n sides. How many diagonals does a 20-sided convex polygon have?

ISAT

Test Prep

Multiple Choice **54.** Which of the following statements is NOT true?
   A. A monomial is a polynomial.
   B. A binomial is a sum or difference of two monomials.
   C. A polynomial must have more than one term.
   D. An integer is a monomial.

55. The area of a trapezoid is $\frac{1}{2}b_1h + \frac{1}{2}b_2h$, where h is the height and b_1 and b_2 are the lengths of the bases. What is the area of a trapezoid with height 13 in., one base 4 in., and the other base twice as long?
   F. 39 in.^{2} **G.** 52 in.^{2} **H.** 78 in.^{2} **J.** 130 in.^{2}

Short Response **56.** Is $\frac{4}{x}$ a monomial? Explain.

57. a. Write an example of a monomial, a binomial, and a trinomial.
   b. Explain why each is that type of polynomial.

Mixed Review

GO for Help

Lesson 13-3 For each function make a table with integer values of x from 1 to 4. Then graph each function.

58. $y = 2 \cdot 2^x$ **59.** $f(x) = \frac{1}{3} \cdot 3^x$ **60.** $y = 18(0.2)^x$

Lesson 11-7 **61. Navigation** A plane is flying 6.3 mi above the ground. The angle of depression to an airport is 14°. How far is the plane from the airport (in ground distance)?

Lesson 2-3 Simplify each expression.

62. $m + 5 + 3m$ **63.** $2y - 1 + 6x + 5$ **64.** $4a + 10b - 7a - 2$

Just as you can get information about a polynomial by counting the number of terms, you can get other information by looking at the exponents. The *degree of a term* is the sum of the exponents of the variables in the term. The *degree of a polynomial* is the greatest degree of its terms.

polynomial $\longrightarrow x^3 + 4x^2 + xy - 5x + 9 \longleftarrow$ The degree of a nonzero constant is zero.

degree of each term $\longrightarrow$ 3 2 2 1 0

Degree of the polynomial is 3.

1 EXAMPLE

Identify each polynomial by name and by degree.

a. $2 - a$

0 1 $\longleftarrow$ degree of each term

Greatest degree of the two terms is 1.

The polynomial is a binomial of degree 1.

b. $3y^3x$

4 $\longleftarrow$ Add the exponents: $3 + 1 = 4$.

Degree of the one term is 4.

The polynomial is a monomial of degree 4.

c. $5x^2 + x + 4$

2 1 0 $\longleftarrow$ degree of each term

Greatest degree of the three terms is 2.

The polynomial is a trinomial of degree 2.

When you write a polynomial with the terms in order of decreasing degree, the polynomial is in *standard form*. If you need to move terms to do this, you can first write subtractions as additions and then use the Commutative Property of Addition. For example, first write $4 - x^2$ as $4 + (-x^2)$. Then rewrite the polynomial as $-x^2 + 4$.

EXAMPLE

Write each polynomial in standard form.

a. $x^4 + 2 - x^2$

  4 0 2 ◄—— degree of each term

  standard form: $x^4 - x^2 + 2$

b. $-2y + y^3 + y^2 - 3$

  1 3 2 0 ◄—— degree of each term

  standard form: $y^3 + y^2 - 2y - 3$

When you simplify a polynomial, write your result in standard form.

3 **EXAMPLE**

Simplify each polynomial.

a. $5a + a^2 + 3a^2 + 2$

$5a + (1 + 3)a^2 + 2$	**Combine like terms.**
$5a + 4a^2 + 2$	**Simplify.**
$4a^2 + 5a + 2$	**Write in standard form.**

b. $3x - 8x + 2x^2 + 4x^2$

$(3 - 8)x + (2 + 4)x^2$

$-5x + 6x^2$

$6x^2 - 5x$

EXERCISES

Identify each polynomial by name and by degree.

1. $9c + 5$
2. $12a^2b$
3. $6x^2 - 3x + 2$
4. p^2q^3
5. $d^4 + 6d$
6. $4a^3 + 8a^2 - 11$
7. $24x^3yz$
8. $15x - 2x^2$

Write each polynomial in standard form.

9. $8 + 5a$
10. $3y^2 + 16 + y$
11. $2c + 4c^2 - 7$
12. $5x - 4x^2 + 3$
13. $2b^2 - 2 + b^3 - b$
14. $11 + 6y^2 - y$
15. $4x^4 + 4x^5 + x^2 + 2x^3$
16. $p^6 - 4 + p + p^2 - 7p^3$
17. $9a - 5 + 6a^3 - 5a^2$

Simplify each polynomial.

18. $x + 3x^2 + x^2$
19. $3a + 5a^2 + 2a + 6$
20. $4m^2 + m^2 + 10 + 4m$
21. $6p - 5p^2 + 4p + 3p^2$
22. $c + 9c^2 - 7c - 8$
23. $-2x^2 + 5 + 3x^2 + 2x + 3$
24. $3b + 1 + 7b^2 - 3b - 2b^2$
25. $5m^3 + 8m^2 + 11m + 14$
26. $3a^4 - 5a^6 - 9a + 6$
27. $-11 - y^2 - 8y + 2y$
28. $6p + 8p^2 + 5p + 7p^2$
29. $22x + 18x^2 + 6 + 4x$

13-5

Adding and Subtracting Polynomials

IL Assessment Framework

8.8.03 Simplify algebraic expressions.

 Check Skills You'll Need

Simplify each expression.

1. $5x - 7 - 3x$

2. $a + 3b + 4a - 7b$

3. $8m - 4n - 7m - 8n$

4. $2x + 3y - 7 - 8x + 2$

GO for Help
Lesson 2-3

---

1 **Adding Polynomials**

In Chapter 2, you saw models for variables and numbers. You can also model the square, x^2, of a variable x.

x^2 x 1 -1

You can use models or properties to add polynomials.

1 **EXAMPLE** **Adding Polynomials**

Simplify $(2x^2 + 3x - 1) + (x^2 + x - 3)$.

Method 1 Add using tiles.

$2x^2 + 3x - 1$

$x^2 + x - 3$

The sum is $3x^2$ $+$ $4x$ $-$ 4

Method 2 Add by combining like terms.

$(2x^2 + 3x - 1) + (x^2 + x - 3)$

$= (2x^2 + x^2) + (3x + x) - 1 - 3$ Use the Commutative and Associative Properties of Addition to group like terms.

$= (2 + 1)x^2 + (3 + 1)x - 1 - 3$ Use the Distributive Property to combine like terms.

$= 3x^2 + 4x - 4$ Simplify.

Vocabulary Tip

Like terms are terms with the same variable(s), raised to the same power(s). You combine like terms by adding coefficients.

$3b + 12b = (3 + 12)b$
$= 15b$

Quick Check

1. Simplify.

   a. $(7d^2 + 7d) + (2d^2 + 3d)$

   b. $(x^2 + 2x + 5) + (3x^2 + x + 12)$

You can also add polynomials in a column by aligning like terms and then adding their coefficients.

GO **Online**

Video Tutor Help
Visit: PHSchool.com
Web Code: ada-0775

2 EXAMPLE   **Aligning Like Terms**

Find the sum of $z^2 + 5z + 4$ and $2z^2 - 5$.

$$\begin{array}{r} \text{Align like terms.} \\ z^2 + 5z + 4 \\ +\ 2z^2 \qquad -\ 5 \\ \hline 3z^2 + 5z - 1 \end{array}$$ **Add the terms in each column.**

✓ Quick Check

2. Simplify each sum.

a. $\begin{array}{r} 4x + 9y \\ +\ \ 3x - 5y \\ \hline \end{array}$

b. $\begin{array}{r} a^2 + 6a - 4 \\ +\ \ 8a^2 - 8a \\ \hline \end{array}$

c. $(4g^2 - 2g + 2) + (2g^2 - 3)$
d. $(-2t^2 + t + 5) + (2t + 4)$

---

2   Subtracting Polynomials

You subtract polynomials by adding the opposite of each term in the second polynomial.

3 EXAMPLE   **Subtracting Polynominals**

Simplify $(5x^2 + 10x) - (3x - 12)$.

$(5x^2 + 10x) - (3x - 12)$

$= 5x^2 + 10x - 3x + 12$ **Write the opposite of each term in the second polynomial.**

$= 5x^2 + (10x - 3x) + 12$ **Group like terms.**

$= 5x^2 + (10 - 3)x + 12$ **Use the Distributive Property.**

$= 5x^2 + 7x + 12$ **Simplify.**

> **Test-Taking Tip**
> After you have written the sum or difference of two polynomials, make a mental check of your work, term by term.

✓ Quick Check

3. Simplify each difference.

a. $(7a^2 - 2a) - (5a^2 + 3a)$
b. $(10z^2 + 6z + 5) - (z^2 - 8z + 7)$
c. $(3w^2 + 8 + v) - (5w^2 - 3 - 7v)$

Practice and Problem Solving

A Practice by Example

Example 1
(page 718)

 for Help

Write the sum modeled in each exercise. Then simplify the sum.

1.

2.

Add by combining like terms.

3. $(x^2 + 3x + 1) + (x^2 + x + 6)$ 4. $(x^2 + 5x + 2) + (3x^2 + x + 1)$

5. $(3x + 2) + (-4x + 3)$ 6. $(5x^2 + 3x + 7) + (7x - 2)$

Example 2
(page 719)

Simplify each sum.

7. $\;\; 5a + 7b$
$\underline{+\;\; -3a + 2b}$

8. $\;\; x^2 + 4x - 2$
$\underline{+\;\; 8x^2 - 3x + 7}$

9. $\;\; x^4 + 3x^3 - x^2 + x - 2$
$\underline{+ \;\; 7x^3 + x^2 - 5x - 9}$

10. $\;\; xy + 5x - 2y + 4$
$\underline{+\;\; 2xy - 3x - 3y - 8}$

11. $\;\; x^3 + 5x^2 + 3x - 2$
$\underline{+\;\; x^3 \;\; - 2x + 6}$

12. $\;\; 4x^2 - 5xy \;\; + 7$
$\underline{+\;\; 8x^2 + 3xy - 3y - 4}$

Example 3
(page 719)

Simplify each difference.

13. $(5x + 9) - (2x + 1)$

14. $(-11a^2 + 2a - 1) - (7a^2 + 4a)$

15. $(3x - 2y) - (5x + 4y)$

16. $(2x^2 + 3x - 7) - (x^2 - 6x - 9)$

17. $(ab - 4) - (3ab - 6)$

18. $(-4x^2 + x - 1) - (x^2 - x + 8)$

B Apply Your Skills

Simplify each sum or difference.

19. $(x^2 - 3x - 9) - (5x - 4)$

20. $(13a^2 - 3a) + (2a^2 + 5a)$

21. $(2x^2 + 3x) + (x^2 + 2x)$

22. $(8j - 3k + 6m) - (-2j + 3m)$

23. $(w^2 + 5w) + (2w - 6)$

24. $(3x^2 + x + 7) - (2x^2 + x + 2)$

25. $(6y - 8) - (2y + 7)$

26. $(x^2 + 3x + 5) + (x^2 + x + 2)$

27. **a.** Write an expression for the sum of three consecutive integers. Let x be the first integer. Then simplify the expression.
    b. What three consecutive integers have the sum 108?

Geometry **Write the perimeter of each figure as a polynomial. Simplify.**

28.

29.

30.

31.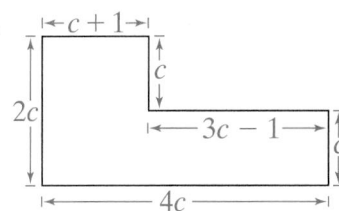

$$5x^2 + 4x - 3$$
$$- \quad 2x^2 - x$$
$$\overline{\quad 3x^2 + 3x - 3 \quad}$$

32. Error Analysis Tian simplified $(5x^2 + 4x - 3) - (2x^2 - x)$ as shown at the left. What is his error?

33. The perimeter of a triangle is $11y - 2$. Two of the sides are represented by the expressions $3y - 1$ and $3y + 1$. Write an expression for the third side.

Geometry **Find each missing length.**

34. perimeter $= 11x + 6$

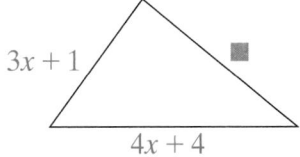

35. perimeter $= 12b - 2$

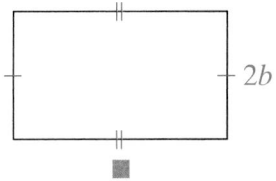

36. perimeter $= 5m^2 + 3m$

37. perimeter $= 6a + 3$

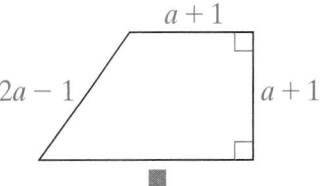

38. Writing in Math How is the process for adding two polynomials like the process for adding two integers? How is it different?

C **Challenge**

39. Reasoning Justify each step.
$$(x^2 + 2x + 1) - (2x^2 - 3x - 4)$$
$$(x^2 + 2x + 1) + (-2x^2) + 3x + 4$$
$$(x^2 + -2x^2) + (2x + 3x) + (1 + 4)$$
$$(1 + -2)x^2 + (2 + 3)x + (1 + 4)$$
$$-x^2 + 5x + 5$$

40. Do Exercise 27 by letting x be the second integer.

41. a. Geometry The volume of a cube is $(3x^3 + 9)$ in.^{3}. A smaller cube with volume $(x^3 - 3)$ in.^{3} is cut out of the cube. Write a polynomial for the remaining volume.
  b. Evaluate your polynomial for $x = 2$.
  c. Reasoning When $x = 2$, will the large cube fit into a 5 in.-by-4 in.-by-6 in. box? Explain. (*Hint:* Recall cube roots, p. 591.)

42. a. What polynomial is the opposite of $2x^2 + 3x - 5$?
  b. What is the sum of $2x^2 + 3x - 5$ and its opposite?

Test Prep

Multiple Choice For Exercises 43 and 44 assume x is an integer.

43. What is the sum of x and the next two integers?
  A. $+$ $+$ **B.** $+$ $+$ $+$ $+$
  C. $+$ $+$ **D.** $+$ $+$ $+$ $+$

44. What is the sum of x and the previous two integers?
  F. $+$ $-$ $+$ $-$ **G.** $-$ $-$ $-$ $-$
  H. $+$ $+$ $+$ $+$ **J.** $+$ $+$

45. What is the perimeter of the given figure?
  A. $+$ **B.** $+$
  C. $+$ **D.** $+$

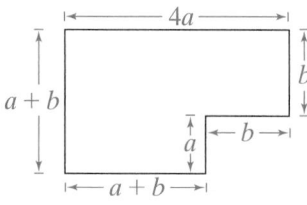

Short Response

46. The perimeter of the given figure is $8x^2 + 4$.
  a. What is the missing length?
  b. If $= 3$ cm, what is the perimeter of the figure?

Mixed Review

 for Help

Lesson 13-4   **Evaluate each polynomial for $a = 2$, $b = -1$, and $c = \frac{1}{2}$.**

47. $8ab + 1$ **48.** $5 + 4ab - c$ **49.** $a^2 + ab + b^2$

Lesson 10-2   **Find the area of each figure.**

50.

51.

52.

Lesson 3-6 🌐 **53. Charity** A student participated in a walk for charity. His friends pledged a total of $3.20 for each mile he walked. The student earned $22.40 for the charity. How many miles did he walk?

Multiplying a Polynomial by a Monomial

13-6

 Assessment Framework

8.8.03 Simplify algebraic expressions.

1 Using an Area Model

You can model the product of a monomial and a polynomial using algebra tiles. You can find the area of a rectangle that is $2x$ units long and $(x + 4)$ units wide by counting the tiles.

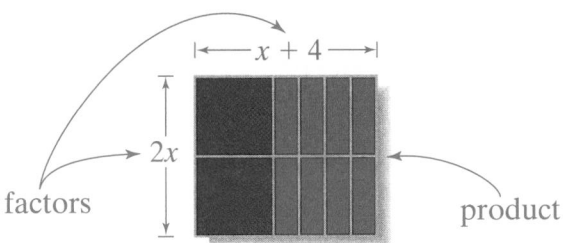

factors   product

The area is $2x^2 + 8x$. So $2x(x + 4) = 2x^2 + 8x$.

You can also use the Distributive Property to simplify a product of a monomial and a polynomial. Multiply each term of the polynomial by the monomial.

✓ Check Skills You'll Need

Simplify each expression.

1. $7(v + 3)$

2. $3(u - 8)$

3. $-5(6 - 3t)$

4. $(p + 8)9$

GO for Help
Lesson 2-3

1 EXAMPLE   Real-World Problem Solving

Multiple Choice **What is the area of the garden? All measurements are in feet.**

Ⓐ $(3x - 5)$ ft^2
Ⓑ $(2x^2 - 10x)$ ft^2
Ⓒ $(2x^2 - 5)$ ft^2
Ⓓ $(x^3 - 10x)$ ft^2

$$A = \ell w = 2x(x - 5) \qquad \textbf{Substitute.}$$
$$= 2x(x) - 2x(5) \quad \textbf{Use the Distributive Property.}$$
$$= 2x^2 - 10x \qquad \textbf{Simplify.}$$

The area of the garden is $(2x^2 - 10x)$ ft^2. The answer is B.

✓ Quick Check

1. Simplify each product.

   a. $3x(x + 4)$ **b.** $-x(2x - 3)$

Test-Taking Tip

When you multiply a polynomial by a monomial with a negative sign, remember to distribute the negative sign to each term of the polynomial.

You can often use other properties to simplify the product of a monomial and a polynomial.

2 EXAMPLE **Simplifying a Product**

Simplify $3x^2(8x^2 - 5x + 2)$.

$3x^2(8x^2 - 5x + 2)$

$= 3x^2(8x^2) + 3x^2(-5x) + 3x^2(2)$ **Use the Distributive Property.**

$= (3)(8)x^{2+2} + (3)(-5)x^{2+1} + (3)(2)x^2$ **Use the Commutative Property of Multiplication.**

$= (3)(8)x^4 + (3)(-5)x^3 + (3)(2)x^2$ **Add exponents.**

$= 24x^4 - 15x^3 + 6x^2$ **Simplify.**

> **Problem Solving Hint**
> To multiply powers with the same base, add exponents.

✓ **Quick Check**

2. Simplify each product.

   a. $x(x^2 + 2x + 4)$ **b.** $2a^2(2a^3 - 3a^2 + 3)$

---

2   Writing a Polynomial as a Product

You can sometimes use the Distributive Property to write a polynomial as the product of two factors. First, find the GCF of all the terms of the polynomial and then use it as one of the factors.

3 EXAMPLE **Finding Factors of a Polynomial**

Write $6x^3 + 3x^2 + 9x$ as a product of two factors.

$\left.\begin{array}{l} 6x^3 = 2 \cdot 3 \cdot x \cdot x \cdot x \\ 3x^2 = 3 \cdot x \cdot x \\ 9x = 3 \cdot 3 \cdot x \end{array}\right\}$ **Write the prime factorization of each term.**

$\text{GCF} = 3x$ **Find the GCF.**

Write each term as the product of $3x$ and another factor.

$6x^3 = 3x \cdot 2x^2$ $3x^2 = 3x \cdot x$ $9x = 3x \cdot 3$

$6x^3 + 3x^2 + 9x = 3x(2x^2 + x + 3)$ **Use the Distributive Property.**

✓ **Quick Check**

3. Use the GCF of the terms to write each polynomial as the product of two factors.

   a. $2x^2 + x$ **b.** $2b^3 + 6b^2 - 12b$

> **GO for Help**
> For a guide to prime factorization, see Lesson 4-3.

EXERCISES

For more exercises, see *Extra Skill and Word Problem Practice*.

Practice and Problem Solving

A Practice by Example

Example 1
(page 723)

 for Help

Simplify each product. Use an area model as needed.

1. $3x(x + 1)$

2. $x(x + 5)$

3. $2x(x + 3)$

4. $3y(y + 7)$

5. $2x(3x + 1)$

6. $2x(x + 6)$

7. $3x(3x - 1)$

8. $3x(2x + 4)$

9. $7c(4 + c)$

10. City Property Find the area of the city lot shown. All measurements are in feet.

$3x$

$x-45$

11. Sports The length of an Olympic-size pool is 50 meters. If x represents the width of one lane, what is the area of a pool with five lanes?

Example 2
(page 724)

Simplify each product.

12. $5x(-3x^2 + 2x)$

13. $x(5x^2 + x - 4)$

14. $3a(a^2 + 2a + 1)$

15. $3b(2b^2 - b + 4)$

16. $a^3(a + a^2 + 5)$

17. $-3(2c^2 - 3c - 1)$

18. $5c(c + 5 - c^2)$

19. $4x^2(x^3 + x^2 - x)$

20. $7b^2(2b^2 + b - 3)$

Example 3
(page 724)

Use the GCF of the terms to write each polynomial as the product of two factors.

21. $3d^4 + d^2$

22. $4y^3 - 8y^2 - 12y$

23. $10x^5 - 5x^3 + 10x$

24. $7x^2 - 14x$

25. $14a^2 + 7a - 7$

26. $24y^3 + 6y^2 - 20y$

27. $7p^2 + p$

28. $5z^2 - 20z$

29. $15x^3 + 4x^2 - 7x$

B Apply Your Skills

Simplify each product.

30. $3y(4y - 1)$

31. $a(a^2 + 3)$

32. $-14a(a^2 + 3a - 4)$

33. $\frac{1}{2}b(b - 8)$

34. $-8y(2y + 3)$

35. $6y^2\left(y^2 - 2y - \frac{1}{3}\right)$

36. $12x^2(5x + 2)$

37. $x(2x - 5)$

38. $17y(2y^2 - 8y + 9)$

39. Open-Ended Write a monomial and a polynomial with 4 terms. Multiply them and then simplify the product.

40. Open-Ended Write a polynomial whose terms have a GCF ≠ 1. Then write the polynomial as the product of two factors.

41. Multiple Choice Write the polynomial $2m^3n - 6m^2n^2 + 8mn$ as the product of two factors.

Ⓐ $-2mn(m + 3mn - 4)$

Ⓑ $-2(m^3n + 3m^2n^2 - 4mn)$

Ⓒ $2mn(m - 3mn + 4)$

Ⓓ $2mn(m^2 - 3mn + 4)$

GO **Online**
Homework Video Tutor
Visit: PHSchool.com
Web Code: ade-1306

Write each polynomial as the product of two factors.

42. $-9b^2 - 3b$

43. $4x^5 - 4x^4 + 8x^2$

44. $18g^7 - 6g^4 + 3g^2$

45. $2a^3 - 6a^2 - 4a$

46. $6y^6 + 32y^4 - y^3$

47. $4m^9 + 6m^5 - 2m^2$

C Challenge

Simplify each product.

48. $4z(2z^6 - 3z^5 - 12z^2 + 8)$ **49.** $-3xy(2x^2y + xy + y^2 - 3)$

Geometry In Exercises 50–55, write an expression to represent the area of each figure. Then simplify the expression.

50.   **51.**

Writing in Math

Explain how to use the GCF to write the polynomial $15a^3 + 20a^2 + 45a$ as the product of two factors.

52. The width of a rectangle is 7 more than $\frac{1}{2}$ its length.

53. The length of a rectangle is 5 less than 4 times its width.

54. The base length of a triangle is $8x$. The triangle's height is twice the base length plus 5.

55. The height of an isosceles triangle is 3 less than $\frac{1}{3}$ its base.

ISAT

Test Prep

Multiple Choice

56. The length of a rectangular table is 35 inches greater than twice the width. If x is the width, what is the area of the table?
   A. $2x^2 + 35x$ **B.** $x + 35$ **C.** $2x + 35$ **D.** $2x^2 + 35$

57. Which polynomial is the simplified form of $-3y(-6y^2 - 5y + 1)$?
   F. $18y^3 - 15y^2 - 3y$ **G.** $18y^2 + 15y - 3$
   H. $18y^3 + 15y^2 - 3y$ **J.** $18y^2 - 15y - 3$

Extended Response

58. The length of a rectangle is 2 inches more than the width w.
   (a) What expression in terms of w could you use for the length of the rectangle?   **(b)** Explain.   **(c)** Draw a diagram of the rectangle and label it.   **(d)** Find the area.

Mixed Review

Lesson 13-5   **Find each sum or difference.**

59. $(2x + 8) + (3x^2 + 5x - 2)$

60. $(-7x^2 - 8x + 4) - (2x^2 - 3x - 9)$

Lesson 12-1   **Display each set of data in a line plot.**

61. $1.7, 2.1, 1.9, 2.1, 2.2, 2.4,$ **62.** $13, 17, 15, 14, 12, 14,$
       $2.3, 2.1, 1.9$ $11, 13, 15$

Lesson 5-6 🌐 **63. Banking** A college student received a bank statement. The new balance was $200. It showed deposits of $400, interest of $1, and checks totaling $650. What was the beginning balance?

Multiplying Binomials

IL Assessment Framework

8.8.03 Simplify algebraic expressions.

1 Using Models

You can use tiles to model the product of two binomials.

1 EXAMPLE Using a Model

Simplify $(x + 2)(x + 4)$.

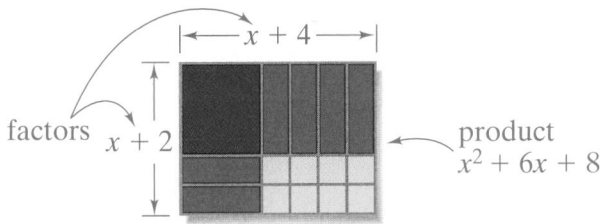

$$(x + 2)(x + 4) = x^2 + 6x + 8$$

The area is $x^2 + 6x + 8$.

✓ Quick Check

1. Simplify each product using models.

  a. $(x + 2)(x + 3)$ **b.** $(y + 1)(y + 4)$

✓ **Check Skills You'll Need**
Simplify each expression.

1. $-2(2x + 1)$

2. $3(7 + 4y)$

3. $(2a - b)5$

4. $(3m - 2n)4$

GO for Help
Lesson 2-2

---

2 Multiplying Binomials

To simplify the product of two binomials, you can think of one binomial as a single expression and use the Distributive Property. Then you use the Distributive Property a second time.

2 EXAMPLE Multiplying Two Binomials

Simplify $(x + 4)(x - 3)$.

$(x + 4)(x - 3)$
$= x(x - 3) + 4(x - 3)$ **Use the Distributive Property.**
$= x^2 - 3x + 4x - 12$ **Use the Distributive Property again!**
$= x^2 + x - 12$ **Simplify.**

Check $(x + 4)(x - 3) = (x + 4)x - (x + 4)3$
$= x^2 + 4x - 3x - 12$
$= x^2 + x - 12$

✓ Quick Check

2. Simplify each product.

   a. $(x + 2)(x - 5)$ **b.** $(m + 2)(2m + 3)$

More Than One Way

Write a polynomial to express the area of the square at the right.

$(2x + 1)$ in.

Eric's Method

Use a model.

The area of the square is $(4x^2 + 4x + 1)$ in.^{2}.

Jasmine's Method

Use the formula for the area of a square and the Distributive Property.

$$\text{Area} = \text{side}^2$$
$$A = (2x + 1)^2$$
$$= (2x + 1)(2x + 1)$$
$$= 2x(2x + 1) + 1(2x + 1)$$
$$= 2x(2x) + 2x(1) + 1(2x) + 1(1)$$
$$= 4x^2 + 2x + 2x + 1$$
$$= 4x^2 + 4x + 1$$

The area of the square is $(4x^2 + 4x + 1)$ in.^{2}.

Choose a Method

1. Which method do you prefer to use? Explain.

2. Which method would you use to simplify $(3x + 4)(3x + 4)$?

EXERCISES

For more exercises, see *Extra Skill and Word Problem Practice.*

Practice and Problem Solving

A Practice by Example

Example 1
(page 727)

GO for Help

Simplify each product using models. Sketch and label your models.

1. $(x + 2)(x + 1)$ **2.** $(y + 2)(y + 2)$ **3.** $(w + 3)(w + 1)$

4. $(k + 3)(k + 4)$ **5.** $(x + 4)(x + 5)$ **6.** $(m + 9)(m + 3)$

7. $(s + 3)(s + 6)$ **8.** $(t + 2)(t + 5)$ **9.** $(m + 1)(m + 6)$

Example 2
(page 727)

Simplify each product using the Distributive Property.

10. $(x + 2)(x - 1)$ **11.** $(c + 7)(c + 9)$ **12.** $(x - 5)(x + 3)$

13. $(a - 4)(a - 2)$ **14.** $(x + 5)(x + 5)$ **15.** $(b + 6)(b - 6)$

16. $(c + 3)(c - 4)$ **17.** $(x + 3)(x - 2)$ **18.** $(y + 3)(y + 8)$

B Apply Your Skills

19. Multiple Choice What is the area of the rectangle at the right?
   Ⓐ $7n - 4$ Ⓑ $12n - 5$
   Ⓒ $12n^2 - 11n - 5$ Ⓓ $12n^2 - 5$

$4n - 5$
$3n + 1$

Find the area of each rectangle.

20.

$2c + 4$
$5c + 3$

21.

$3x + 3$
$3x - 3$

GO Online
Homework Video Tutor
Visit: PHSchool.com
Web Code: ade-1307

Simplify each product.

22. $(x + 4)(2x + 1)$ **23.** $(n - 16)(n + 20)$ **24.** $(x + 2)(x + 8)$

25. $(b + 1)^2$ **26.** $(m - 8)(m - 3)$ **27.** $(2a + b)(4c - 2d)$

28. $(3c + 1)(2c - 4)$ **29.** $(3 + x)(5 - x)$ **30.** $\left(\frac{1}{2}x + 9\right)(4x + 8)$

31. Error Analysis A student simplifies $(x + 5)(x - 3)$ as shown at the right. Find the error in the student's work.

$(x + 5)(x - 3)$
$x(x - 3) + 5(x - 3)$
$x^2 - 3x + 5x - 3$
$x^2 + 2x - 3$

32. Writing in Math Explain the similarities between multiplying two binomials and multiplying a polynomial by a monomial.

C Challenge

Patterns Simplify the expressions. What pattern do you see?

33. $(y + 2)^2, (y + 3)^2, (y + 4)^2$

34. $(y + 1)(y - 1), (y + 2)(y - 2), (y + 5)(y - 5)$

35. Geometry The base of a parallelogram is $(w + 5)$ cm. The height is 2 cm less than the base. Find the area of the parallelogram.

36. Suppose x is an odd integer. What is the product of x and the next two odd integers?

nline lesson quiz, PHSchool.com, Web Code: ada-1307   **13-7** Multiplying Binomials   **729**

Test Prep

Multiple Choice

37. Suppose m is an even integer. What is the product of the next two consecutive even integers?

A. $m^2 + 3m + 2$　　　　　　**B.** $m^2 + 6m + 8$

C. $m^2 + 2m$　　　　　　　**D.** $2m + 6$

38. If the length of a rectangular picture is $(2x + 3)$ inches and the width is $(x - 4)$ inches, which expression represents the area of the picture?

F. $(2x^2 + 5x - 12)$ in.^{2}　　　**G.** $(2x^2 + 3x - 12)$ in.^{2}

H. $(2x^2 - 8x - 12)$ in.^{2}　　　**J.** $(2x^2 - 5x - 12)$ in.^{2}

Short Response

39. a. Simplify $(3c - 1)(4c + 2)$ using the Distributive Property.

　　b. Justify each step in part (a).

Mixed Review

Lesson 13-6

Find each product.

40. $7a(a + 5b + 2c)$　　　　　**41.** $-3xy(2x + 9y - 6)$

42. $8m^2(-4m^3 + mp + 2p^4)$　　**43.** $2pq(5p + 8pq + 2)$

Lesson 12-6

44. Does the problem below require *permutations* or *combinations*? Explain.

　　　You select three colors from a choice of eight colors to paint a picture. How many 3-color choices are possible?

Lesson 12-2

Make a box-and-whisker plot for the data.

45. $8, 9, 27, 39, 14, 17, 13, 25, 15, 8, 11, 29, 36, 10, 15, 25$

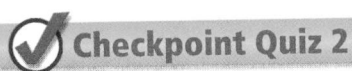 **Checkpoint Quiz 2**　　　　　　　**Lessons 13-4 through 13-7**

Tell whether each polynomial is a *monomial*, a *binomial*, or a *trinomial*.

1. 178　　　　**2.** $x + 15y$　　　**3.** $7pq$　　　**4.** $m^2 + 4m - 12$

Evaluate each polynomial for $x = -1$ and $y = 3$.

5. $5x - y$　　　**6.** $x + 3y$　　　**7.** $-7x + x^2y$　　**8.** $4y^2 + 11x - 16$

Simplify each expression.

9. $(4a - b) + (3a - 5b)$　　　　**10.** $(x^2 + 7x - 4) + (x^2 + 9)$

11. $(g + 6)(g + 4)$　　　　　　**12.** $3m(-6m - 2m^2p - 10p)$

13. Open-Ended Write a binomial expression for the length of a side of a square. Use it to write a polynomial for the area of the square.

You can sometimes write a trinomial as the product of two binomial factors. You can use algebra tiles to find the factors. Use tiles to form a rectangle. The lengths of the sides of the rectangle are the factors of the trinomial.

EXAMPLE

Write $x^2 + 4x + 3$ as the product of two binomial factors.

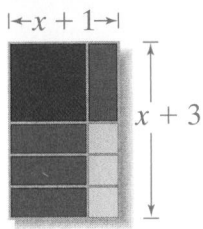

$x^2 + 4x + 3$

Model the trinomial.

|←x + 1→|

$x + 3$

Use the tiles to form a rectangle. The length is $(x + 3)$ and the width is $(x + 1)$.

• $x^2 + 4x + 3 = (x + 3)(x + 1)$

EXERCISES

Use tiles to find binomial factors of each trinomial.

1. $x^2 + 2x + 1$ **2.** $x^2 + 5x + 6$ **3.** $x^2 + 7x + 10$

4. $x^2 + 6x + 5$ **5.** $x^2 + 4x + 4$ **6.** $x^2 + 5x + 4$

7. $x^2 + 9x + 8$ **8.** $2x^2 + 5x + 3$ **9.** $2x^2 + 7x + 3$

10. $2x^2 + 9x + 4$ **11.** $2x^2 + 9x + 9$ **12.** $2x^2 + 9x + 10$

13. Reasoning Complete $x^2 + \blacksquare x + 12$ with three different integers so that each trinomial has two binomial factors. For each trinomial, write the binomial factors.

14. a. What two numbers have a sum of 11 and a product of 30?
    b. Reasoning Use your answer to part (a) to find the binomial factors of $x^2 + 11x + 30$.

15. $(x + 3)^2 = x^2 + 6x + 9$ is a *perfect-square trinomial.* What properties of a trinomial would reveal it as a perfect-square trinomial? Show how a perfect-square trinomial can be factored.

Use Multiple Strategies

What You'll Learn

- To solve problems by combining strategies

. . . And Why

To solve problems about building a kite

 Check Skills You'll Need

Write an equation for each statement.

1. Seven times the opposite of twelve is negative 84.

2. Eleven times a number is 132.

3. A number divided by 45 is three.

4. A number squared is 64.

GO for Help
Lesson 2-4

1 Combining Strategies

Math Strategies in Action
After a natural disaster such as an earthquake, a tornado, or a flood, relief workers help to rescue survivors. They also bring food, clothing, and blankets to people who need them. Relief organizers use multiple strategies as they plan and coordinate their efforts.

In many situations in your own life, you have already combined multiple strategies. Remember when you learned how to ride a bike or fly a kite. The more you practiced, the less you had to think about the steps required to be successful.

In mathematics, you can combine strategies to solve problems. The more strategies you learn and the more you use them, the better problem solver you will be. Solving problems can become as easy as riding a bike or flying a kite!

EXAMPLE Real-World Problem Solving

Hobbies Suppose you receive instructions for building a kite. The writer of the instructions presents them as a puzzle:

> I fly above the clouds with my tail flowing behind me.
> My tail is 12 ft plus twice my length. Together, our length is 21 ft. How long am I? How long is my tail?

Understand the Problem

Read the problem carefully.

1. What do you want to find?

2. What is the relationship between the length of the kite's tail and the length of the kite's body?

Make a Plan

To get a visual picture of the problem, draw a diagram. Then write an equation to solve the problem.

Carry Out the Plan

Draw a diagram.

Let b = length of the body of the kite.

Write an equation.

$3b + 12 = 21$	**Use the diagram to write an equation.**
$3b + 12 - 12 = 21 - 12$	**Subtract 12 from each side.**
$3b = 9$	**Simplify.**
$\dfrac{3b}{3} = \dfrac{9}{3}$	**Divide each side by 3.**
$b = 3$	

The kite is 3 ft long. Now find the length of the tail.

length of tail = $2b + 12$	**Use the diagram to write an expression for the length of the tail.**
$= 2(3) + 12$	**Replace b with the length of the kite's body.**
$= 18$	**Simplify.**

The tail is 18 ft long.

Check the Answer

It is always good procedure to check your result in the context of the original problem.

✓ Quick Check

3. The original problem says that the tail must be 12 ft plus twice the length of the kite's body. Show that the lengths found meet this condition.

4. The length of the kite's body plus the length of its tail must be 21 ft. Show that the lengths found meet this condition.

EXERCISES

For more exercises, see *Extra Skill and Word Problem Practice*.

Practice and Problem Solving

 Practice by Example

Example 1
(page 732)

Combine multiple strategies to solve each problem.

1. Travel A bus traveling 40 mi/h left Freetown at noon. A car following the bus at 60 mi/h left Freetown at 1:30 P.M.
   a. At what time did the car catch up with the bus?
   b. How many miles were the car and the bus from Freetown when the car caught up with the bus?

2. Chess A student playing a computer chess game gets 5 points every time he wins a round. The computer gets 3 points every time it wins a round. They play 64 rounds and end with a tied score. How many rounds did the computer win?

3. (Algebra) A kite and its tail total 36 ft in length. The tail is five times the length of the body. How long is the kite's tail?

 Apply Your Skills

Solve using any strategy.

4. A student has $8 to spend on a phone call. The cost of a call is $.34 for the first minute and $.24 for each additional minute. How long can the student talk on the phone?

5. Painting A painter places an 8.5-ft-long ladder against a wall. The bottom of the ladder is 4 ft from the base of the wall. How high up the wall does the ladder reach?

6. Geometry A room has a floor area of 1,025 ft^2 and a 10-ft-high ceiling. The Housing Code requires at least 200 ft^3 per person. What is the maximum number of people allowed in the room?

7. Pets A student weighs her hamsters two at a time. Sandy and White Ears weigh 209 g together. White Ears and Sport weigh 223 g together. Sandy and Sport weigh 216 g together. How much does each hamster weigh?

8. Geometry There are 27 white cubes assembled to form a large cube. The outside surface of the large cube is painted red. The large cube is then separated into the 27 smaller cubes. How many of the small cubes will have red paint on exactly the following number of faces?
   a. three faces   **b.** two faces   **c.** one face   **d.** no face

9. You decide to purchase a new telephone. You can choose from 8 different models, 2 different cord lengths, and 4 different colors. How many possible choices do you have?

10. Geometry A lot measures 50 ft by 100 ft. The house on the lot measures 25 ft by 50 ft. What is the area of the lawn?

11. (Algebra) A student spends $\frac{1}{3}$ of her money on a movie and $\frac{1}{4}$ of the remaining amount on a snack after the movie. She now has $12 left. How much money did she have originally?

Strategies

- Act It Out
- Draw a Diagram
- Guess, Check, Revise
- Look for a Pattern
- Make a Model
- Make a Table
- Simulate the Problem
- Solve by Graphing
- Use Multiple Strategies
- Work a Simpler Problem
- Work Backward
- Write an Equation
- Write a Proportion

Homework Video Tutor

Visit: PHSchool.com
Web Code: ade-1308

 Challenge

🌐 **12. Salaries** A clerk starts working at a beginning salary of $10,400 with an annual increase of $400. An assistant clerk who starts at the same time has a starting salary of $9,600 per year with an annual increase of $600.
   a. Who earns more after 3 years?
   b. After how many years will the assistant be earning more money than the clerk?

13. Geometry You have three pieces of string, each 60 cm long. You form a circle with one piece, a square with another, and an equilateral triangle with the third piece. How do the areas of the three figures compare? Explain.

14. Each face of a cube can be painted either red or yellow. How many different ways can you paint the cube?

ISAT

Test Prep

Multiple Choice

15. What is the product of $(x - 3)(x + 3)$?
   A. $x^2 + 6x - 9$ **B.** $x^2 - 6x + 9$
   C. $x^2 - 9$ **D.** $x^2 + 9$

16. A house lot measures 75 ft by 100 ft. It is all lawn except for the house on the lot. The house measures 30 ft by 50 ft. What is the area of the lawn?
   F. 1,500 ft^2 **G.** 6,000 ft^2 **H.** 7,500 ft^2 **J.** 8,000 ft^2

Short Response

17. A square has a perimeter of 24 inches and a rectangle has an area of 36 sq. inches. **(a)** Which figure has the greater area? **(b)** Explain.

18. Aaron receives his allowance of $25. He spends $\frac{1}{5}$ of it on food, $\frac{1}{4}$ of it on magazines, and $\frac{11}{20}$ of it on movies. **(a)** How much of his allowance does Aaron have left? **(b)** Show your work.

Mixed Review

 for Help

Lesson 13-7

Simplify each product.

19. $(x + 1)(x - 3)$ **20.** $(d + 2)(2d + 5)$ **21.** $(x + 3)^2$

Lesson 12-6

Make a list to find the number of two-letter combinations you can form from each group of letters.

22. G, O, A, T   **23.** A, P, E   **24.** H, Y, E, N, A

Lesson 5-1 🌐 **25. Jogging** A boy jogs in the park every other day. His sister jogs every third day. They both jogged together on April 2. On how many more of the 30 days in April will they jog together if they maintain this schedule?

Using Mental Math

You can solve many problems quickly using mental math and proven "shortcut" methods. One well-known shortcut is the FOIL method for multiplying binomials. With it, you multiply each term of the first binomial with each term of the second binomial, just as you did when you used the Distributive Property in Lesson 13-7.

EXAMPLE

Simplify the product $(2x + 3)(x + 6)$.

Think First terms, Outer terms,
        Inner terms, Last terms.
Notice that the first letters spell FOIL.

First Last

$(2x+3)(x+6)$

Inner

Outer

Identify the *First* terms in each binomial. Multiply them.	$2x$ and x $2x \cdot x =$	$2x^2$
Identify the *Outer* terms. Multiply them. Identify the *Inner* terms. Multiply them.	$2x$ and 6 $2x \cdot 6 = 12x$ 3 and x $3 \cdot x = 3x$	
Add the outer and inner products.	$12x + 3x =$	$15x$
Identify the *Last* terms in each binomial. Multiply them.	3 and 6 $3 \cdot 6 =$	18

● Your FOIL result will look like this: $(2x + 3)(x + 6) = 2x^2 + 15x + 18$

EXERCISES

Use FOIL and mental math to simplify the following.

1. $(x + 2)(x + 3)$ **2.** $(x + 6)(x + 6)$ **3.** $(x + 3)(x + 4)$

4. $(x + 2)^2$ **5.** $(x - 8)(x - 2)$ **6.** $(x - 6)(x - 3)$

7. $(x - 5)(x - 5)$ **8.** $(x - 4)^2$ **9.** $(x - 9)(x + 9)$

10. $(x + 4)(x - 7)$ **11.** $(x - 5)(x + 8)$ **12.** $(x + 6)(x - 6)$

13. $(2x + 2)(x + 6)$ **14.** $(7x + 7)(x + 3)$ **15.** $(6x - 5)(4x - 10)$

16. $(3x + 1)^2$ **17.** $(5x - 2)(4x + 3)$ **18.** $(8x + 5)(3x - 1)$

19. $(6x + 5)(4x - 10)$ **20.** $(3x - 2)(4x + 3)$ **21.** $(4x + 6)(4x - 6)$

22. $(3 - 3x)(5 + 4x)$ **23.** $(7 + 2x)(1 - x)$ **24.** $\left(\frac{1}{2}x + 5\right)(4x + 10)$

Chapter Review

Vocabulary Review

🔊 **absolute value function** (p. 703)
arithmetic sequence (p. 696)
binomial (p. 712)
common difference (p. 696)

common ratio (p. 697)
geometric sequence (p. 697)
monomial (p. 712)
polynomial (p. 712)

quadratic function (p. 702)
sequence (p. 696)
term (p. 696)
trinomial (p. 712)

Match the vocabulary terms on the right with their descriptions on the left.

1. A monomial or a sum or difference of monomials

2. The graph of this is a parabola.

3. A sequence in which you find the terms by adding a fixed number to previous terms

4. An equation of the type $y = |x|$

5. A polynomial with two terms

6. A polynomial with three terms

7. Each number in a sequence

8. A set of numbers that follow a pattern

9. A real number, a variable, or a product of a real number and variables with whole-number exponents

a. arithmetic sequence
b. binomial
c. monomial
d. polynomial
e. quadratic function
f. absolute value function
g. term
h. trinomial
i. sequence

Go Online
PHSchool.com

For: Vocabulary quiz
Web Code: adj-1351

Skills and Concepts

13-1 Objectives

▼ To describe number patterns with arithmetic sequences (p. 696)

▼ To describe number patterns with geometric sequences (p. 697)

A **sequence** is a set of numbers that follow a pattern. Each number in the sequence is a **term** of the sequence. You find a term of an **arithmetic sequence** by adding a fixed number, called the **common difference,** to the previous term.

You find a term of a **geometric sequence** by multiplying the previous term by a fixed number. This fixed number is the **common ratio.**

Find the next three terms of each sequence. Then write a rule to describe the sequence.

10. $1, 5, 9, 13, \ldots$

11. $-60, -30, -15, -7.5, \ldots$

12. $100, 107, 114, 121, \ldots$

13. $0, -5, -10, -15, \ldots$

14. $26, 15, 4, -7, \ldots$

15. $\frac{1}{10}, \frac{1}{2}, 2\frac{1}{2}, 12\frac{1}{2}, \ldots$

**Tell whether each sequence is *arithmetic, geometric,* or *neither.*
Find the next three terms of the sequence.**

16. $9, 13, 17, 21, \ldots$

17. $-8, -4, -2, -1, \ldots$

18. $3, 4, 5, 6, \ldots$

19. $-22, -11, 0, 11, \ldots$

20. $10, 1, 20, 2, \ldots$

21. $\frac{1}{200}, \frac{1}{100}, \frac{1}{50}, \frac{1}{25}, \ldots$

22. Open-Ended Describe a situation that you can represent with an arithmetic sequence. Write a sequence of numbers for that situation and identify the common difference.

13-2 and 13-3 Objectives

▼ To graph quadratic functions (p. 702)

▼ To graph absolute value functions (p. 703)

▼ To use tables, rules, and graphs with functions modeling growth (p. 707)

▼ To use tables, rules, and graphs with functions modeling decay (p. 708)

Two types of nonlinear functions are **quadratic functions** and **absolute value functions.** The graph of a quadratic function is a U-shaped curve called a *parabola* that opens upward or downward. The graph of an absolute value function is V-shaped.

A function like $y = 2^x$ models *exponential growth.* Its graph curves upward as input values increase. A function like $y = \left(\frac{1}{2}\right)^x$ models *exponential decay.* Its graph slopes downward as input values increase.

**For each function, make a table with integer values of x from -2 to 2.
Then graph the function.**

23. $y = \frac{1}{2}x^2$ **24.** $y = 2|x|$ **25.** $y = |x| + 1$ **26.** $y = x^2 + 5$

27. $y = -|x|$ **28.** $y = \frac{1}{2}|x|$ **29.** $y = -x^2 - 3$ **30.** $y = -x^2 + 4$

**For each function, make a table with integer values of x from 0 to 4.
Then graph the function.**

31. $y = \left(\frac{1}{4}\right)^x$ **32.** $y = \frac{1}{2} \cdot 2^x$ **33.** $y = 3^x$ **34.** $y = \left(\frac{1}{2}\right)^x$

13-4 Objectives

▼ To identify polynomials (p. 712)

▼ To evaluate polynomials (p. 713)

A **monomial** is a real number, a variable, or a product of a real number and variables with whole-number exponents. A **polynomial** is a monomial or a sum or difference of monomials. You can name a polynomial by the number of its terms. A **binomial** has two terms and a **trinomial** has three terms.

**Tell whether each polynomial is a *monomial,* a *binomial,*
or a *trinomial.***

35. $3x$ **36.** $2x^2 - 1$ **37.** $\frac{2}{3}x$ **38.** $x^4 - x^3 + 2$ **39.** 15

40. mn **41.** $z^2 + z$ **42.** $7d + f$ **43.** $-2x^2 - 12$ **44.** $3 + 2x - x^2$

Evaluate each polynomial for $x = -3$ and $y = 2$.

45. y^5 **46.** $x^2 - y$ **47.** $y^2 - x - 1$ **48.** $2xy$ **49.** $3 - xy$

13-5 Objectives

▼ To add polynomials (p. 718)

▼ To subtract polynomials (p. 719)

You can add polynomials by using models, combining like terms, or aligning like terms vertically and then adding their coefficients. You can subtract polynomials by adding the opposite of each term in the second polynomial.

Simplify each sum or difference.

50. $(a^2 + a + 1) + (2a^2 + a + 7)$

51. $(m^2 - 5m - 2) + (3m^2 + 3m - 10)$

52. $(3x^2 - 4) + (x^2 - 2x + 6)$

53. $(7p - 5q + 2) - (3p + 2q + 4)$

54. $(10w^2 + 6w) - (7w^2 - 3w + 5)$

55. $(9x - 3y) - (3x - 9y)$

13-6 and 13-7 Objectives

▼ To use an area model for multiplication (p. 723)

▼ To write a polynomial as the product of a monomial and a polynomial (p. 724)

▼ To use models in multiplying binomials (p. 727)

▼ To multiply two binomials (p. 727)

You can use properties to simplify the product of a monomial and a polynomial. You can sometimes use the Distributive Property to write a polynomial as the product of two factors.

You can use tiles to model the product of two binomials. When you use the Distributive Property to find the product of two binomials, you use the Distributive Property twice.

Simplify each product.

56. $a(2a + 5)$ **57.** $4c(3c - 7)$ **58.** $-6y(5y + 3)$

59. $3x(x^2 - x - 5)$ **60.** $x^2(x + 7)$ **61.** $2x^2(x^2 - 3x - 6)$

62. $(x + 3)(x + 4)$ **63.** $(x + 1)(x - 5)$ **64.** $(x - 2)(x - 4)$

Use the GCF of the terms to write each expression as the product of two factors.

65. $x^2 - x$ **66.** $9p^2 + 27$ **67.** $3x^3 - 9x^2 + 6x$

68. $5b^5 + 20b^3 - 30$ **69.** $8x^3 + 2x^2 + 4x$ **70.** $28a^2 - 4ab$

13-8 Objectives

▼ To solve problems by combining strategies (p. 732)

You can combine multiple strategies to solve problems.

71. A gardener plans to use 196 feet of fencing to enclose a garden. What is the largest possible area of the garden?

72. Explain your choice of strategies for Exercise 71.

Chapter Test

Go Online
PHSchool.com
For: Chapter test
Web Code: ada-1352

Find the next three terms of each sequence. Then write a rule to describe the sequence.

1. $5, 8, 11, 14, \ldots$
2. $-1.5, -3, -6, \ldots$
3. $50, 10, 2, 0.4, \ldots$
4. $100, 93, 86, 79, \ldots$

Tell whether each sequence is *arithmetic*, *geometric*, or *neither*. Find the next three terms of the sequence.

5. $5, 2, -1, -4, \ldots$
6. $1, 1, 2, 3, 5, \ldots$
7. $15, 13, 11, 9, \ldots$
8. $-48, -12, -3, \ldots$
9. $2, 4, 8, 16, \ldots$
10. $0, 7, 14, 21, \ldots$

For each function, make a table with integer values of x from -2 to 2. Then graph the function.

11. $y = x^2$
12. $y = x^2 - 1$
13. $y = -x^2 + 1$
14. $y = -x^2 - 2$
15. $y = |x| - 1$
16. $y = \frac{1}{2}|x|$

For each function, make a table with integer values of x from 0 to 4. Then graph the function.

17. $y = 2^x$
18. $y = 3^x$
19. $y = 2\left(\frac{1}{2}\right)^x$
20. $y = \left(\frac{1}{3}\right)^x$

Tell whether each polynomial is a *monomial*, a *binomial*, or a *trinomial*.

21. $4x - 1$
22. $c^2 + c + 1$
23. xyz
24. $a^5 - 7$
25. $h^4 - h^3 - h$
26. ab

Evaluate each polynomial for $x = 4$ and $y = 10$.

27. $x + y$
28. $y - x^2$
29. $xy - 15$
30. $x^2 + xy - y^2$

31. **Open-Ended** Write a polynomial with two different variables. Assign a value to each variable. Evaluate your polynomial for those values.

Simplify each sum or difference.

32. $(x^2 + 4x + 3) + (x^2 - 3x + 7)$
33. $(2x^2 - 3) + (x + 4)$
34. $(3x^2 + 2x + 4) + (x^2 + 3)$
35. $(x^2 + 10x + 9) - (x^2 + x + 1)$
36. $(3x^2 - x + 3) - (2x^2 - 2x - 4)$
37. $(2x^2 - 4x) - (x^2 - 3x - 5)$

Simplify each product.

38. $x(x - 4)$
39. $2x(x^2 - x + 2)$
40. $x^2(3x^2 + 2x - 5)$
41. $(x + 2)(x + 4)$
42. $(x + 1)(x + 5)$
43. $(x + 3)(x - 1)$
44. $(x + 2)(x - 4)$
45. $(x - 1)(x - 6)$
46. $(x - 2)(x - 3)$

Write each expression as the product of a monomial and a polynomial.

47. $2x^3 + 4x^2 + 12x$
48. $x^2 - x$
49. $9x^3 - 18x^2 - 3x$

50. **Writing in Math** Explain how you can use the Distributive Property to write the expression $3x^2 + 6x$ as the product of a monomial and a polynomial.

51. A customer gives a clerk a $100 bill for a $76 purchase. In how many ways can the clerk give change using $20, $10, $5, and $1 bills?

ISAT Test Prep

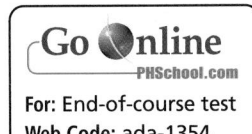

For: End-of-course test
Web Code: ada-1354

Multiple Choice

1. What is the solution of $-3x + 1 < 25$?
- (A) $x > 8$
- (B) $x < -8$
- (C) $x > -8$
- (D) $x < 8$

2. 32% of b is 8,000. What is b?
- (E) 250
- (F) 2,560
- (G) 25,000
- (H) 25,600

3. What is the distance Joe traveled if he drove for $2\frac{1}{2}$ h at a rate of 62 mi/h?
- (A) 24.8 mi
- (B) 124 mi
- (C) 154 mi
- (D) 155 mi

4. Which decimal is between $(-0.1)^2$ and 0.05?
- (E) 0.03
- (F) 0.2
- (G) 0.3
- (H) -0.02

5. What is $\dfrac{a^5b^3c}{a^6b^2}$ if $a = 2$, $b = -3$, and $c = -4$?
- (A) -6
- (B) -2
- (C) 6
- (D) 12

6. An artist created this scale drawing of a lighthouse. About how tall is the actual lighthouse? Use your centimeter ruler.

Scale:
1 cm = 12 m
- (E) 36 m
- (F) 48 m
- (G) 72 m
- (H) 120 m

7. Which ordered pair is a solution of $x - 2y = 3$ and $3x + y = 2$?
- (A) $(1, -1)$
- (B) $(-1, 1)$
- (C) $(3, 2)$
- (D) $\left(2, -\frac{1}{2}\right)$

8. What number is next in the pattern?
$-1, \sqrt{1}, -2, \sqrt{4}, -3, \ldots$
- (E) $\sqrt{3}$
- (F) $\sqrt{5}$
- (G) $\sqrt{7}$
- (H) $\sqrt{9}$

9. In $\triangle ABC$, $m\angle A = 55°$, and $m\angle C = 15°$. What type of triangle is $\triangle ABC$?
- (A) acute
- (B) equilateral
- (C) right
- (D) obtuse

10. If $\triangle ABC \sim \triangle DEF$. What is AC?
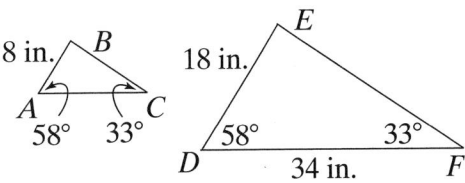
- (E) 15.11 in.
- (F) 17.25 in.
- (G) 24 in.
- (H) 76.5 in.

11. $ABCD$ is a rectangle. Which statement is NOT true?
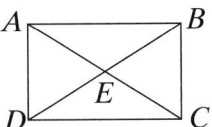
- (A) $\overline{AC} \cong \overline{DB}$
- (B) $\angle ADC \cong \angle CBA$
- (C) $\triangle DAE \cong \triangle BCE$
- (D) $\angle CBD \cong \angle DAB$

12. A cone has $r = 4$ and $h = 12$. What is its volume?
- (E) 16π
- (F) 64π
- (G) 96π
- (H) 192π

13. Which inequality represents *The number t is at least 35*?
- (A) $t > 35$
- (B) $t < 35$
- (C) $t \geq 35$
- (D) $t \leq 35$

14. What is the area of the shaded region?

- (E) 2.4 ft^2
- (F) 3.4 ft^2
- (G) 4.2 ft^2
- (H) 4.3 ft^2

15. What is the area of $\triangle CDE$?
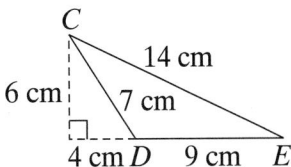
- (A) 12 cm^2
- (B) 27 cm^2
- (C) 36 cm^2
- (D) 39 cm^2

16. A bicycle company makes 3 different bicycle styles. Each style comes in 4 colors. Each style is made in 6 frame sizes with a choice of 2 types of seat. The bicycle shop would like to order one of each type of bicycle. How many bicycles is that?
- (E) 60 bicycles
- (F) 120 bicycles
- (G) 144 bicycles
- (H) 240 bicycles

17. In a box filled with 60 colored chips, $\frac{1}{6}$ are blue, $\frac{1}{12}$ are white, $\frac{1}{4}$ are yellow, and $\frac{1}{2}$ are purple. What is the probability of picking at random a purple chip or a white chip?
- (A) $\frac{1}{24}$
- (B) $\frac{7}{12}$
- (C) $\frac{3}{5}$
- (D) $\frac{2}{3}$

18. If the first term in an arithmetic sequence is 15 and the fifth term is 39, what is the fourth term in the sequence?
- (E) 32
- (F) 33
- (G) 34
- (H) 35

19. What is the simplest form $6z(4 - 2z^2)$?
- (A) $24z - 12z^3$
- (B) $24z - 12z^2$
- (C) $24z - 2z^2$
- (D) $24z + 12z^3$

20. Which expression is represented by the model shown below?

- (E) $2(x^2 + 2x) + 3$
- (F) $2x^2 + 2 + 3^2$
- (G) $x^2 + 2x + 3$
- (H) $2x^2 + 2x + 3$

21. What is $(x^4 + 2x^3 - x^2 + x - 3) + 6x^3 + x^2 - 4x - 8$?
- (A) $x^4 + 4x^3 - 2x^2 - 5x - 5$
- (B) $x^4 + 8x^3 - 4x - 5$
- (C) $x^4 + 8x^3 + 2x^2 - 3x - 11$
- (D) $x^4 + 8x^3 - 3x - 11$

22. What is $(5r - 4s) - (2r - s)$?
- (E) $10r - 4s$
- (F) $3r - 3s$
- (G) $10r^2 - 4s^2$
- (H) $3r - 5s$

23. Which phrase best describes the expression $9xyz$?
- (A) monomial
- (B) binomial
- (C) trinomial
- (D) polynomial

24. Which equation matches the graph?

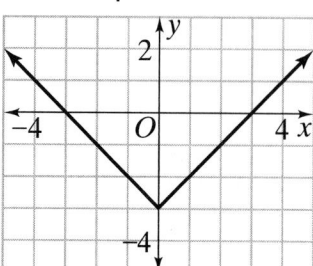

- (E) $y = |x| - 3$
- (F) $y = x^2 - 3$
- (G) $y = -3|x|$
- (H) $y = |x - 3|$

25. A submarine dove to a depth of 540 ft, then rose 84 ft. Which integer represents the final depth of the submarine?
- (A) -624
- (B) -456
- (C) 456
- (D) 624

26. Which property does $7(w + 8) = 7w + 56$ show?
- (E) Commutative Property of Addition
- (F) Associative Property of Multiplication
- (G) Identity Property of Addition
- (H) Distributive Property

27. Which of the following equations would you use to find out how far a satellite will travel in 2 minutes if it is traveling at a rate of 8 km per second?
- (A) $d = 8(120)$
- (B) $d = \frac{8}{120}$
- (C) $d = 8(2)$
- (D) $d = \frac{8}{2}$

28. What is the GCF of $18x^3y^4$ and $48xy^5$?
- (E) $12xy^4$
- (F) $12x^2y$
- (G) $6xy^4$
- (H) $6x^2y$

29. Which of the following is the simplified form of $\left(\frac{3a}{6b}\right)^3$?
- (A) $\frac{a^3}{2b^3}$
- (B) $\frac{a^3}{6b^3}$
- (C) $\frac{a^3}{8b^2}$
- (D) $\frac{a^3}{8b^3}$

30. Which of the following is a rule for the function described in the table?

x	$f(x)$
-2	-7
0	-3
2	1
4	5

E. $f(x) = 2x - 3$ F. $f(x) = 3x - 2$
G. $f(x) = 2x + 3$ H. $f(x) = 3x + 2$

31. Between which two integers is the value of $\sqrt{70}$?

A. 3 and 4   B. 8 and 9
C. 36 and 49   D. 64 and 81

32. Which polynomial is the product of the binomials $(x + 2)$ and $(x - 13)$?

E. $x^2 + 15x + 26$ F. $x^2 - 11x - 26$
G. $x^2 - 11x + 26$ H. $x^2 - 15x - 26$

Gridded Response

33. If $m\angle 2 = 110°$, what is $m\angle 3$ in degrees?

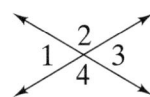

34. Small pieces of paper with the letters SKATES are placed in a bag. What is the probability of selecting a T from the bag at random, not replacing it, and then selecting an A?

35. A truck leaves a rest stop and travels at a steady rate of 65 mi/h. Later, a car leaves the rest stop, travels at a steady rate of 75 mi/h, and catches up with the truck in 3.25 hours. For how many hours had the truck been traveling?

36. What is the surface area of the figure to the nearest whole number of square feet?

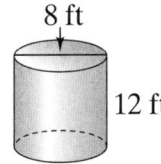

8 ft

12 ft

Short Response

37. An agent made a $7,500 commission for selling a house. The commission rate is 6%.
a. What was the price of the house?
b. If the commission rate is raised to 7%, what commission would the agent make for the house price in part (a)?

In Exercises 38 and 39, **(a) write the perimeter of each figure as a polynomial. (b) Then simplify.**

38.

$5b$

39.

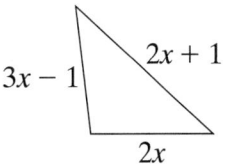

$3x - 1$ $2x + 1$

$2x$

40. A salesperson receives a 5% commission for each computer sold. **(a)** Is the value of the commission a function of the final sales price of each computer?   **(b)** Explain.

Extended Response

For each function, **(a) make a table with integer values of x from 0 to 4. (b) Graph the function. (c) What exponential change does the graph show, growth or decay? Explain your answer.**

41. $y = 3^x$ **42.** $y = 20\left(\frac{1}{2}\right)^x$

43. Two electronics stores have the same television model on sale. The price of the television at Store A is $299 before a 25% discount. The price of the television at Store B is $279 before a 20% discount.
a. Which store has the greater discount?
b. Which store has the lower sale price?
c. What is the difference between the two sale prices?

Activity Lab

Carbon Dating

Applying Algebra Have you ever wondered how a scientist can estimate the age of a fossil? When an organism is alive, it maintains carbon-14 in the same proportion as the atmosphere. When the organism dies, it stops replenishing its carbon-14. A scientist finds the amount of carbon-14 currently present in the fossil and calculates how long the amount that was present at death has been decaying.

Amber Insects
Sometimes bees, flies, and other insects get stuck in the sap from a tree. Over time, the sap hardens and turns into amber.

How Old Is That?
Carbon-14 has a half-life of 5,730 years. Scientists use it to determine the age of bone, cloth, wood, and plant fibers.

Mammoth Model
The "woolly mammoth" was about 11 ft tall and weighed 4 to 6 tons, the same as an African elephant today, but had very small ears, a sloping back, and much longer tusks.

Shoulder hump

Mammoth hair was up to 3 ft long.

744

Activity

1. Copy and complete the table. *1–4. See margin.*

2. **Estimation** About how old is a fossil that has 40% carbon-14 present?

3. **Estimation** What percent of carbon-14 would you hope to find in a fossil that you think is 20,000 years old?

4. **Reasoning** Why do you think carbon-14 dating works only on fossils less than 60,000 years old?

Carbon-14 Dating

Percent of Carbon-14 Present	Age of Fossil (years)
100	0
50	5,730
■	11,460
12.5	■
■	22,920
3.125	■
■	34,380
0.78125	■

Remains of the Mammoth

Scientists have found several frozen mammoths, complete with hide and hair, in the frozen ground of Siberia and Alaska.

Go Online
PHSchool.com

For: Information about fossils
Web Code: ade-1353

Chapter Projects

Cure for the Common Code

A special sculpture stands outside the headquarters of the United States Central Intelligence Agency (CIA) in Langley, Virginia. Carved in the copper sculpture is a message in secret code. The code is so complex that for many years even CIA agents could not figure it out. The sculptor, James Sandborn, provided the secret agents with a challenge they could appreciate.

Chapter 1 *Algebraic Expressions and Integers*

Invent a Secret Code For the chapter project, you will decode computer writing and write in a code used by Julius Caesar. Then you'll invent a code of your own.

Go Online
PHSchool.com

For: Information about secret codes
Web Code: add-0161

DON'T LOSE YOUR

Chapter 2 *Solving One-Step Equations and Inequalities*

Have you ever used a balance in your science class? Balances make very precise measurements in science, industry, and government. The United States Mint, for example, ensures that the coins it produces meet exact specifications. You can make your own version of a balance and use it to compare the masses of different objects.

Make a Balance Scale For the chapter project, you will make a simple balance scale. You will use it to write and solve equations and inequalities for the masses of different coins.

Go Online
PHSchool.com

For: Information about balances
Web Code: add-0161

CURRENCY EVENTS

Chapter 3 *Decimals and Equations*

When you are shopping, of course you want to know how much an item costs before you decide to buy it! When you travel in another country, you need to "translate" the cost into its value in U.S. dollars.

Compare Currencies For the chapter project, you will research currency exchange rates and calculate prices in different currencies. You will make a poster that shows prices in U.S. dollars and in the currencies of three other countries.

Go Online
PHSchool.com

For: Information about currencies
Web Code: add-0161

TIME AFTER TIME

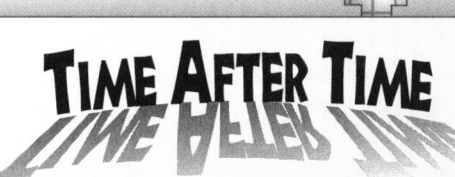

Chapter 4 *Factors, Fractions, and Exponents*

On the morning of the summer solstice, the sun rises directly over one of the stones at Stonehenge in southern England. Just as a sundial tells the time of day, Stonehenge tells the time of year.

A calendar may involve several astronomical events. For example, our day is based on Earth's rotation, whereas our year is based on Earth's movement around the sun. Over the centuries, people have come up with many different calendars.

Design a Calendar For the chapter project, you will investigate calendars and adjustments to calendars. Then you will design your own calendar. Your final project will be a sample and an explanation of your calendar.

Go Online
PHSchool.com

For: Information about calendars
Web Code: add-0161

If the Shoe Fits

What size shoe do you wear? As you grow, your shoe size can change rapidly. If your foot grows half an inch, does that mean you should get shoes that are a half-size larger?

The scale we use for sizing shoes is from the *duodecimal*, or base 12, number system. For that reason, a size chart could come in handy.

Make a Comparison Chart For the chapter project, you will make measurements and calculations that relate women's shoe sizes, men's shoe sizes, and shoe lengths. Your final project will be a convenient comparison chart that you can distribute to your friends and family and to shoe stores.

Go Online
PHSchool.com

For: Information about shoe sizes
Web Code: add-0161

STRING BAND

Guitars, fiddles, harps . . . people have been enjoying stringed instruments for thousands of years. The music from a stringed instrument follows rules of mathematics that you will learn in this chapter.

Make a Musical Instrument For the chapter project, you will construct and play a simple stringed instrument. You will make measurements that can be applied to a real instrument. Your final project will consist of drawings that show how to play notes on both instruments.

Go Online
PHSchool.com

For: Information about stringed instruments
Web Code: add-0161

The Intensity of DENSITY

Have you ever wondered why some objects sink while others float? People float in the salt water of the Dead Sea. Pebbles sink when tossed into a river. The densities of a liquid and an object influence whether the object sinks or floats in the liquid. Similarly, the densities of two liquids influence whether they combine or separate.

Chapter 7 *Solving Equations and Inequalities*

Find the Densities of Liquids For the chapter project, you will measure the masses and volumes of several liquids. You will use your measurements and an equation to calculate the density of each liquid.

Go Online
PHSchool.com

For: Information about densities
Web Code: add-0161

Rental Math

Your school is planning its graduation ceremony. Hundreds of people will be coming, and they need places to sit. Your school has some chairs, but not enough for this crowd! Better call a rental company.

Chapter 8 *Linear Functions and Graphing*

Compare Prices For the chapter project, you will research the cost of renting folding chairs. You do not yet know how many chairs you will need, so you will investigate the price per chair, as well as delivery charges. For your report to the graduation committee, you will write and graph equations to show the total costs of renting chairs from different companies.

Go Online
PHSchool.com

For: Information about chair rentals
Web Code: add-0161

Chapter 9 *Spatial Thinking*

A mysterious map has come into your possession. The map shows the Sea Islands off the coast of Georgia. But that's not all! The map also contains three clues that tell where a treasure is supposedly buried.

Draw a Treasure Map Your project for this chapter will be to find the location of the treasure. Trace the map provided, and then add to the drawing by following the clues in the activities.

For: Information about treasure maps
Web Code: add-0161

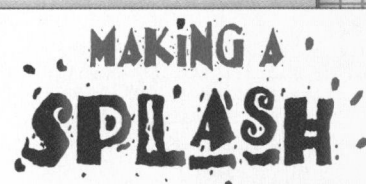

MAKING A SPLASH

Chapter 10 *Area and Volume*

When you jump into a pool or step into a bathtub, you cause the water level to rise. That's an example of water displacement. The volume of water displaced is equal to the volume of the object submerged—you.

Use Water Displacement to Find Volume For your chapter project, you will build a prism and a cylinder. You will calculate their volumes by using formulas. Then you will find their volumes by using water displacement.

For: Information about water displacement
Web Code: add-0161

Tree Angles

A giant sequoia in California is the largest living thing on Earth. It weighs about as much as 15 blue whales. What is the largest tree in your neighborhood? Maybe it is the largest of its species. You could nominate it to be in the National Register of Big Trees.

Measure a Big Tree The National Register of Big Trees has a formula to compare the sizes of trees of the same species: Big Tree Points = $C + H + \frac{S}{4}$, where C is the

circumference in inches of the trunk at $4\frac{1}{2}$ feet above the ground, H is the tree's height in feet, and S is the average spread in feet of the tree's crown of branches.

For the chapter project, you will measure a tree and calculate its score in Big Tree Points.

Go Online
PHSchool.com

For: Information about tree sizes
Web Code: add-0161

The Good Times POll

Do you participate in an organized extracurricular activity, such as a sport or a club? How much time do you devote to such activities each week? How does the amount of time you spend compare to the averages for students in your class and your school?

Conduct a Survey For the chapter project, you will do a survey of your class and a survey of your school. You will use statistical measures and graphs to analyze and display the results.

Go Online
PHSchool.com

For: Information about surveys
Web Code: add-0161

PRISM BUILDING

The prismatic shapes of tall buildings can be described using mathematical expressions such as $(a + b)^3$. Is $(a + b)^3$ equal to $a^3 + b^3$? No, but many students make that mistake. Sometimes it helps to have a concrete representation of a mathematical expression.

Make a 3-D Polynomial Model For the chapter project, you will make a three-dimensional model of a polynomial. You will analyze the model and its parts. You will use the model to see how polynomials can represent real-world objects.

Go Online
PHSchool.com

For: Information about polynomials
Web Code: add-0161

Chapter 1 Extra Practice: Skills and Word Problems

● **Lesson 1-1** Write a variable expression for each word phrase.

1. 6 less than x

2. y less than 12

3. the sum of z and 2

4. a number m increased by 34

5. the product of 8 and p

6. t divided by 5

● **Lesson 1-2** Simplify each expression.

7. $15 + 20 \cdot 3$

8. $46 - 4(2 + 8)$

9. $16 \div 4 + 10 \div 2$

10. $100 \div (30 + 20)$

11. $5(8 + 4) \div 6 \div 2$

12. $9 \cdot 6 - 12 \div 2$

● **Lesson 1-3** Evaluate each expression.

13. $3x + 6$, for $x = 12$

14. $15a - 2a$, for $a = 20$

15. $38 - 3y$, for $y = 9$

16. $25 - (t + 18)$, for $t = 7$

17. $\frac{x + y}{10}$, for $x = 35$ and $y = 65$

● **Lesson 1-4** Compare. Use >, <, or = to complete each statement.

18. $-12 \ \blacksquare\ -9$

19. $|-4| \ \blacksquare\ |4|$

20. $-|-7| \ \blacksquare\ |-7|$

21. $0 \ \blacksquare\ -100$

● **Lessons 1-5 and 1-6** Simplify each expression.

22. $-56 + 60$

23. $18 + (-25)$

24. $-34 + (-36)$

25. $19 - (-5)$

26. $80 - (-125)$

27. $-82 - (-50)$

28. $-7 + 35 + (-22)$

29. $-44 - 20 - 80$

30. $-8 + (-13) - (24)$

● **Lesson 1-7** Write a rule for continuing each pattern. Find the next three numbers in the pattern.

31. $-12, -3, 6, 15, 24, \ldots$

32. $0.15, 0.3, 0.45, 0.6, \ldots$

33. $1, 1, 2, 3, 5, 8, 13, \ldots$

● **Lesson 1-9** Simplify each expression.

34. $-4 \cdot 12$

35. $-15(-8)$

36. $30 \cdot (-5)$

37. $-1(-2)(-3)(-4)$

38. $-78 \div (-3)$

39. $-150 \div 25$

40. $\frac{120}{-15}$

41. $-1{,}125 \div (-125)$

● **Lesson 1-10** Draw a coordinate plane. Graph each point.

42. $A(0, 9)$

43. $B(-3, -5)$

44. $C(-9, 5)$

45. $D(7, 2)$

46. $E(0, 0)$

47. $F(8, 0)$

48. $G(7, -8)$

49. $H(1, 1)$

50. $K(-2, -2)$

● **Lesson 1-1 Write an expression for each statement.**

51. Shari has *g* gel pens, and Jennifer has 8 fewer gel pens.

52. A stock starts Friday at a price *p*, and ends the day $2.50 higher.

● **Lesson 1-2 Write and simplify a numerical expression for the phrase.**

53. the quotient of twenty-eight and seven, minus two

● **Lesson 1-3 Write an expression for each statement. Then evaluate it for the given value.**

54. A video store pays $30 for each movie *m* that it purchases. How much does it pay for 15 movies?

55. A pizza store charges $3 for delivery and $10 per pizza *p*. How much does it cost to have three pizzas delivered?

● **Lesson 1-4 Write an expression to represent each quantity.**

56. a payment of *d* dollars on a credit card with a balance of $165

57. The temperature on top of a mountain is 4°C lower than the temperature *t* at the base of the mountain.

● **Lessons 1-5 and 1-6 Write a numerical expression for each statement. Then find the sum or difference.**

58. Your savings account had a balance of $175 before you deposited $250.

59. A hot-air balloon descends 450 ft from a height of 1,000 ft.

● **Lesson 1-7 Is each conjecture correct or incorrect? If incorrect, give a counterexample.**

60. The difference of two numbers is always less than their sum.

61. The sum of two numbers is always greater than zero.

● **Lesson 1-8 Look for a pattern to help you solve the problem.**

62. You owe a friend $42. You repay the friend $2 the first day, $4 the second day, $6 the third day, and so on. How many days will you take to pay your friend back?

● **Lesson 1-9 Simplify each expression.**

63. thirty-six divided by three

64. four times six, divided by twelve

● **Lesson 1-10 Write the coordinates of each point.**

65. three units left of the *y*-axis and six units below the *x*-axis

66. five units right of the *y*-axis and two units above the *x*-axis

Extra Practice: Skills and Word Problems

● **Lesson 2-1 Simplify each expression. Justify each step.**

1. $99 + (-46) + (-99) + 45$

2. $225 + 320 + 75$

3. $18 + 12 + (-25) + 13$

4. $5 \cdot 678 \cdot 2$

5. $58 \cdot 2 \cdot 50$

6. $20 \cdot 4 \cdot 5 \cdot 25$

● **Lessons 2-2 and 2-3 Use the Distributive Property to simplify.**

7. $7(5) - 3(5)$

8. $3 \cdot 6 + 7 \cdot 6$

9. $15 \cdot 32 - 12 \cdot 32$

10. $7b + 25 - 4b$

11. $3(a - 2c)$

12. $3q + 2(q + 1)$

13. $-3(4y - 1) + 5(7 - y)$

14. $41 - 2(m + 1) - m$

15. $12 + 5x - 2(3x + 5)$

● **Lesson 2-4 Write an equation for each sentence. Is each equation *true*, *false*, or an *open sentence*?**

16. Twice the sum of a number and one is twenty-two.

17. Negative three divided by negative one is three.

18. Forty-five plus five equals negative fifty.

● **Lessons 2-5 and 2-6 Solve each equation.**

19. $40 + x = 25$

20. $-5 = y - 12$

21. $z + (-23) = -47$

22. $14 = a - 9$

23. $t - 453 = -520$

24. $78 = b + 100$

25. $4k = 96$

26. $300 = -15j$

27. $-12c = 180$

28. $\frac{d}{7} = -14$

29. $-4 = \frac{w}{6}$

30. $\frac{k}{-9} = -20$

● **Lesson 2-8 Graph the solutions of each inequality.**

31. $x > -12$

32. $y \leq 3$

33. $0 \geq z$

34. $p < -9$

35. $7 < n$

36. $f \leq -3$

● **Lessons 2-9 and 2-10 Solve each inequality.**

37. $a + 3 < -1$

38. $-2 > b - 4$

39. $5 + x > -8$

40. $-12 < -2 + y$

41. $w - 32 \leq 15$

42. $-20 \geq z - 13$

43. $\frac{c}{5} \leq -3$

44. $8p \geq -96$

45. $0 < 8r$

46. $\frac{t}{-6} < -3$

47. $\frac{a}{11} > -22$

48. $-12k \geq -144$

● **Lesson 2-1** **Name each property shown.**

  49. Seven plus twelve equals twelve plus seven.

  50. Thirty-four times one is thirty-four.

● **Lesson 2-2** **Use the Distributive Property to solve each problem.**

  51. A sports stadium holds 14,600 people. There are eight home games in a season. Find the total number of people who could attend home games in one season.

  52. Janet drives 36 miles Monday through Friday to work and back. How many miles does she drive in one week?

● **Lesson 2-3** **Write and simplify a variable expression.**

  53. A family ordered four dinners at d dollars each and a $7 side dish from a local restaurant. There is a $3 delivery charge.

● **Lesson 2-4** **Write an equation to solve each problem.**

  54. Michelle wants to run a total of 15 miles per week. She runs 3 miles each day d that she runs. Will she meet her goal by running 5 days per week?

  55. Suppose you want to save $105. You put $15 per week w into a savings account. Will you have $105 in 6 weeks?

● **Lessons 2-5 and 2-6** **Write and solve an equation.**

  56. Jake bought five books at a yard sale. He now has 44 books. How many books did Jake have before?

  57. A painter pays $15 per can of paint. How many cans of paint can she buy with $165?

● **Lesson 2-7** **Use *Guess, Check, and Revise* to solve each problem.**

  58. Sara bought some tapes for $8 each and some books for $5 each. She paid a total of $39. How many of each did she buy?

  59. The sum of the ages of two brothers is 22 and the product of their ages is 120. How old are the brothers?

● **Lesson 2-8** **Write and graph an inequality for each sentence.**

  60. A number d plus fifteen is no more than 12.

  61. Seven times a number p is more than forty-two.

● **Lessons 2-9 and 2-10** **Write and solve an inequality.**

  62. Four times a number r is no more than sixty-five.

  63. You want to save at least $100. How much do you need to save if you start with $37?

Extra Practice: Skills and Word Problems

● **Lesson 3-1** Estimate. State the method you used.

1. $5.35 + 7.953$

2. $25.68 - 3.7$

3. $6.877 + 3.521 + 8.5$

4. $103.890 - 25.6$

5. $42.875 + 36.982 + 45.7$

6. $42.651 - 12.8$

● **Lesson 3-2** Estimate each product or quotient.

7. $9.5(12.31)$

8. $24.8 \div 5.03$

9. $2.8 \cdot 6.11$

10. $-5.78 \div 1.95$

11. $(-2.468)(-9.031)$

12. $-19.32 \div 4.025$

● **Lesson 3-3** Find the mean, median, and mode. When the answer is not an integer, round to the nearest tenth. Identify any outliers.

13. 10 13 10 15 12 11 12 19 14

14. 85 86 80 85 90 90 50 88

15. $25 $30 $32 $28 $30 $15 $28 $30

16. 6.2 4.5 4.8 12.3 5.7 4.8 6.0

● **Lesson 3-4** Evaluate each formula for the values given.

17. perimeter of a rectangle: $P = 2\ell + 2w$ when $\ell = 45$ yd and $w = 20$ yd

18. circumference of a circle: $C = 2\pi r$ when $r = 6.8$ in.; use 3.14 for π

19. distance traveled: $d = rt$ when $r = 50$ mi/h and $t = 3.5$ h

20. perimeter of a square: $P = 4s$ when $s = 12$ cm

● **Lessons 3-5 and 3-6** Solve each equation.

21. $t + 4.5 = 17.2$

22. $15.5 + y = 10.5$

23. $x - 70.2 = 23.6$

24. $1.2b = 6$

25. $c \div 5.3 = 12$

26. $-21.2 = p - 12.7$

27. $f \div 5.25 = 7.8$

28. $6.4m = 38.4$

29. $-3.1 = -31a$

30. $h + 25.8 = 76$

31. $101.5 = j - 82.8$

32. $-50.8 = d + 36.2$

33. $4.5v = 13.5$

34. $s \div 10.5 = 42$

35. $26.2 = z - 6.55$

● **Lesson 3-7** Complete each statement.

36. 0.95 m $= \blacksquare$ cm

37. 250 mL $= \blacksquare$ L

38. 2.5 kg $= \blacksquare$ g

39. 60 g $= \blacksquare$ kg

40. 0.54 L $= \blacksquare$ mL

41. 5.62 m $= \blacksquare$ cm

42. 58 cm $= \blacksquare$ m

43. 564 mm $= \blacksquare$ m

44. 345 g $= \blacksquare$ mg

45. 36 mg $= \blacksquare$ g

46. 234 cm $= \blacksquare$ m

47. 567 mg $= \blacksquare$ g

● **Lessons 3-1 and 3-2 Estimate each amount.**

48. Four packages of ground beef weigh 1.94 lb, 1.82 lb, 2.21 lb, and 2.03 lb.

49. You buy three items that cost $4.85, $7.45, and $8.99.

50. Your class is on a field trip. Thirty students buy lunches that cost $4.95 each.

51. A car holds 12 gallons of gasoline. Gas costs $2.29/gal. About how much will it cost to fill the car up?

52. A fund drive for a charity raised $2,450. If 120 people donated, about how much did each person donate on average?

● **Lesson 3-3 Find the mean, median, mode, and range of each group of data. Then identify which measure of central tendency best describes the data set.**

53. The daily balance in a checking account for 5 days is $30, $42, $25, $25, $34.

54. The heights in centimeters of ten people are 168, 160, 164, 166, 180, 178, 165, 166, 160, and 166.

● **Lesson 3-4 Use the distance formula $d = rt$ (where d is the distance, r is rate, or speed, and t is time spent traveling) to answer each question.**

55. The length of Michelle's commute to work is 35 mi. It takes her 54 min to get to work. What is her average speed?

56. Sam runs 6 mi/h. How many minutes will it take him to run 4 mi?

57. A train travels 70 mi/h. How far does it travel in 45 min?

● **Lesson 3-5 and 3-6 Write and solve an equation.**

58. Karenna spent $8.75 at a video store. She had $16.65 when she left the video store. How much money, m, did she start with?

59. At the deli, 1.5 lb of turkey cost $5.64. What is the cost per pound, c, of the turkey?

● **Lesson 3-7 Convert each unit.**

60. A bag of potato chips has 400 mg of sodium per serving. How many grams of sodium does it have?

61. Julius is training to run a 10-km race. How many meters long is the race?

● **Lesson 3-8 Solve the problem by *Acting It Out*.**

62. A class has 15 students. How many handshakes are there if each person in the class shakes hands once with everyone else?

Extra Practice: Skills and Word Problems

● **Lesson 4-1** List all the factors of each number.

1. 60   **2.** 45   **3.** 64   **4.** 46   **5.** 36   **6.** 100

● **Lesson 4-2** Evaluate each expression.

7. x^2, for $x = 8$ **8.** $-2v^3$, for $v = 2$ **9.** $5t^2 - 4$, for $t = 4$

10. $a^3 + 10$, for $a = -5$ **11.** mn^2, for $m = 3$ and $n = 4$ **12.** $6(2r - 4)^2$, for $r = 7$

● **Lesson 4-3** Is each number *prime*, *composite*, or *neither*? For each composite number, write the prime factorization. Use exponents where possible.

13. 25   **14.** 36   **15.** 47   **16.** 38   **17.** 1   **18.** 117

Find the GCF.

19. 20, 30   **20.** 8, 12, 18   **21.** $5x, 40x$ **22.** $6y, 108$

● **Lesson 4-4** Write in simplest form.

23. $\frac{12}{20}$ **24.** $\frac{4}{20}$ **25.** $\frac{35}{80}$ **26.** $\frac{18}{36}$

27. $\frac{13}{52}$ **28.** $\frac{75}{100}$ **29.** $\frac{16}{50}$ **30.** $\frac{5x}{65x^2}$

31. $\frac{3x^2}{45x}$ **32.** $\frac{50a^2}{5a}$ **33.** $\frac{36x}{16}$ **34.** $\frac{100pq}{625q}$

● **Lesson 4-6** Graph each rational number on one number line.

35. 0.2   **36.** $\frac{3}{10}$ **37.** -2 **38.** -1 **39.** $-\frac{1}{2}$

Evaluate each expression for $a = 10$ and $b = -4$. Write in simplest form.

40. $\frac{a + b}{a}$ **41.** $\frac{b}{a}$ **42.** $\frac{a - b}{3a}$ **43.** $\frac{b^2}{a^2}$

● **Lessons 4-7 and 4-8** Simplify each expression.

44. $8a^2 \cdot 3a^4$ **45.** $3y^2 \cdot 2y^3$ **46.** $(p^5)^6$ **47.** $(x^3)(y)(x^5)$

48. $\frac{6x^2}{2x^5}$ **49.** $\frac{18t^{20}}{6t^5}$ **50.** $\frac{b^2}{b^3}$ **51.** 12^0

● **Lesson 4-9** Multiply. Express each result in scientific notation.

52. $(5 \times 10^4)(8 \times 10^9)$ **53.** $(1.1 \times 10^6)(6 \times 10^{10})$ **54.** $(3 \times 10^{12})(4 \times 10^8)$

● **Lesson 4-1 Use divisibility rules to answer each question.**

55. A restaurant serves a 12-piece appetizer. What sizes of groups can split the appetizer evenly?

56. How many six-slice pizzas must you order for five people to get the same number of slices with none left over?

● **Lesson 4-2 Write a variable expression.**

57. seven minus *j* times *j* plus four

● **Lesson 4-3 Solve each problem.**

58. A teacher divides 27 students into groups of at least two students. All the groups are the same size. What is the greatest possible number of groups?

59. Lucia is reading a book with 25 chapters. She reads the same number of chapters each day. Can she finish the book in exactly six days? Explain.

● **Lesson 4-4 Write a fraction in simplest form for each statement.**

60. A chef used four eggs from a carton of twelve.

61. Twenty-five of thirty students went on a field trip.

● **Lesson 4-5 Solve by simplifying each problem.**

62. Thirty-two teams are going to play in a single-elimination tournament. How many games will be played in the tournament?

63. How many digits are used to write the numbers 90 through 110?

● **Lesson 4-6 Use the acceleration formula, $a = \frac{f - i}{t}$ (where *a* is acceleration, *f* is final speed, *i* is initial speed, and *t* is time) to answer each question.**

64. A car goes from an initial speed of 46 ft/s to a final speed of 71 ft/s in 5 s. What is the acceleration?

65. A bicyclist went from a complete stop to 18 ft/s in 6 s. What was her acceleration?

● **Lessons 4-7 and 4-8 Write an exponential expression for each phrase. Then simplify.**

66. *x* cubed to the fourth power

67. four times *y* to the fourth power divided by *y* squared

● **Lesson 4-9 Write the population in scientific notation.**

68. The population of the United States increased by approximately 32,700,000 people between 1990 and 2000.

Chapter 5 Extra Practice: Skills and Word Problems

Lesson 5-1 Find the LCM of each group of numbers or expressions.

1. $15, 30$

2. $4, 8, 10$

3. $8x, 12y$

4. $3t^2, 5t$

Compare. Use $>$, $<$, or $=$ to complete each statement.

5. $\frac{5}{8} \blacksquare \frac{3}{5}$

6. $\frac{3}{10} \blacksquare \frac{1}{3}$

7. $\frac{3}{4} \blacksquare \frac{6}{8}$

8. $-\frac{1}{5} \blacksquare -\frac{1}{4}$

Lesson 5-2 Write each fraction or mixed number as a decimal.

9. $\frac{7}{8}$

10. $2\frac{3}{5}$

11. $\frac{3}{11}$

12. $\frac{16}{5}$

13. $-\frac{7}{10}$

14. $-2\frac{1}{9}$

Write each decimal as a fraction or mixed number in simplest form.

15. 1.3

16. 0.605

17. $0.\overline{6}$

18. $-0.\overline{15}$

19. 0.35

20. 5.4

Lesson 5-3 Add or subtract.

21. $\frac{2}{5} + \frac{3}{5}$

22. $3\frac{3}{4} - 1\frac{5}{6}$

23. $-\frac{5}{8} + \frac{1}{4}$

24. $\frac{10}{x} - \frac{12}{x}$

25. $\frac{1}{2} - \frac{3}{4}$

26. $4\frac{5}{6} + 5\frac{2}{9}$

27. $\frac{5}{t} + \frac{3}{4}$

28. $5\frac{1}{3} - \frac{7}{8}$

Lesson 5-4 Find each product or quotient.

29. $\frac{3}{5} \cdot \frac{2}{3}$

30. $\frac{5}{6} \div 1\frac{2}{3}$

31. $-\frac{7}{10} \cdot 1\frac{3}{7}$

32. $\frac{5y}{6} \div \frac{2y}{3}$

33. $-\frac{2}{3} \cdot \left(-\frac{9}{22}\right)$

34. $10\frac{5}{8} \div \frac{5}{8}$

35. $\frac{5x}{7} \cdot \frac{1}{5}$

36. $\left(-\frac{1}{2}\right)\left(-\frac{3}{4}\right)$

37. $\frac{2}{5} \div \left(-\frac{1}{5}\right)$

38. $\frac{6}{7} \cdot \frac{3}{7}$

Lesson 5-5 Complete each statement.

39. 60 in. $= \blacksquare$ ft

40. 15 qt $= \blacksquare$ pt

41. 4 lb $= \blacksquare$ oz

Lessons 5-7 and 5-8 Solve each equation.

42. $\frac{3}{5} + a = 1\frac{2}{3}$

43. $b - 3\frac{1}{2} = 5$

44. $-\frac{4}{5}c = \frac{7}{10}$

45. $5d = \frac{3}{4}$

46. $1\frac{4}{7} = f + \frac{3}{14}$

47. $\frac{7}{8} = g - \frac{2}{3}$

Lesson 5-9 Simplify each expression.

48. $(8a^3)^2$

49. $(x^2y^3)^4$

50. $(-2v)^3$

51. $(abc^3)^5$

52. $(f^2g^3)^6$

53. $(2xy)^3$

54. $\left(\frac{2}{5}\right)^3$

55. $\left(\frac{2c}{d^3}\right)^2$

56. $\left(\frac{3t}{4v}\right)^2$

57. $\left(\frac{1}{4}\right)^3$

● **Lesson 5-1 Use the LCM to answer each question.**

58. A store sells T-shirts in packages of three, and pairs of socks in packages of five. What is the least number of packages you can buy to have equal numbers of pairs of socks and T-shirts?

59. Pietro and Nancy are working on class projects. One week before it is due, Pietro has completed $\frac{5}{7}$ of his project, and Nancy has completed $\frac{2}{3}$ of her project. Who has completed more?

● **Lesson 5-2 Write a fraction to answer each question.**

60. A $20 shirt is on sale for $16. What fraction of the original price is the sale price?

61. Steve found a dime and a quarter on the ground. What fraction of a dollar did he find?

● **Lessons 5-3 and 5-4 Write and simplify an expression.**

62. the quotient of one half and two fifths

63. Suppose you are packing a box that measures $1\frac{3}{4}$ ft by $1\frac{1}{2}$ ft. How much longer is the box than it is wide?

● **Lesson 5-5 Use dimensional analysis to answer each question.**

64. In gym class you are going to run a half-mile. How many feet will you run?

65. Jacques has a gallon jug of milk that is $\frac{1}{4}$ full. How many cups of milk does he have?

● **Lesson 5-6 Work backward to solve each problem.**

66. Suppose you want to finish running some errands by 4:00 P.M. Shopping will take 20 min. Eating will take 25 min. You will meet with a friend for 15 min. And your travel time will be a total of 20 min. When should you start your errands?

67. Molly has $3.50. She spent $5, $6.50, and $3.20. How much money did Molly have originally?

● **Lesson 5-7 and 5-8 Write and solve an equation.**

68. You have read $\frac{2}{7}$ of a book. How much of the book remains?

69. A building is made of bricks that are $\frac{3}{5}$ ft tall. The building is 60 bricks high. Find the height of the building, h.

● **Lesson 5-9 Use the formula for volume of a cube, $V = s^3$.**

70. Find the volume of a cube with side length $5d$ cm.

Extra Practice: Skills and Word Problems

● **Lesson 6-1** Write each ratio as a fraction in simplest form.

1. $15 : 30$ **2.** 25 to 10   **3.** 4 out of 16   **4.** $\frac{15}{35}$

Find each unit rate.

5. 40 mi/h = ■ ft/s   **6.** 8 cm/s = ■ m/h   **7.** 5.5 qt/min = ■ gal/h

● **Lesson 6-2** Solve each proportion. Round to the nearest tenth where necessary.

8. $\frac{3}{5} = \frac{a}{60}$ **9.** $\frac{8}{7} = \frac{96}{b}$ **10.** $\frac{8}{c} = \frac{40}{85}$ **11.** $\frac{d}{36} = \frac{2}{3}$

12. $\frac{105}{200} = \frac{x}{40}$ **13.** $\frac{8}{15} = \frac{y}{50}$ **14.** $\frac{z}{40} = \frac{11}{15}$ **15.** $\frac{t}{2} = \frac{1.5}{8}$

● **Lesson 6-3** The scale of a map is 4 in. : 25 mi. Find the actual distance for each map distance. Round to the nearest tenth where necessary.

16. 10 in.   **17.** 5.5 in.   **18.** $\frac{1}{2}$ in.   **19.** 3 in.

● **Lesson 6-4** Find each probability for one roll of a number cube. Then find the odds in favor of the event.

20. $P(4)$ **21.** $P(8)$ **22.** $P(\text{even number})$ **23.** $P(1 \text{ or } 2)$

● **Lesson 6-5** Write each percent as a fraction in simplest form and as a decimal.

24. 10%   **25.** 200%   **26.** 6%   **27.** 1.75%   **28.** 8.5%

Write each number as a percent. Where necessary, round to the nearest tenth of a percent.

29. 0.15   **30.** 1.2   **31.** $\frac{5}{12}$ **32.** $\frac{1}{8}$ **33.** 0.345

● **Lessons 6-6 and 6-7** Solve each percent problem by using a proportion or an equation.

34. Find 12% of 80.   **35.** 30% of x is 12. What is x?

36. What percent of 50 is 2.5?   **37.** Find 30% of 121.

● **Lesson 6-8** Find each percent of change. Tell whether the change is an increase or a decrease.

38. 120 to 80   **39.** 40 to 100   **40.** 175 to 231   **41.** $4 to $3.50

● **Lesson 6-9** Find each sale price.

42. regular price, $100; discount, 20%   **43.** regular price, $60; discount, 25%

● **Lesson 6-1** **Find the unit rate.**

44. A person runs 40 yd in 6 s.

45. A car backs up 15 ft in 5 s.

● **Lessons 6-2 and 6-3** **Use a proportion to answer each question.**

46. An athlete measures her heart rate while exercising. Her heart beats 32 times in 15 seconds. Find her heart rate per minute.

47. A map has a scale of 1 cm : 5 km. Two cities are 4.5 cm apart on the map. What is the actual distance between the cities?

48. A car is 15 ft long. A model of the car has a scale of 1 in. : 2 ft. How long is the model?

● **Lesson 6-4** **Find each probability.**

49. A bag contains 3 red marbles, 5 green marbles, and 2 blue marbles. You choose a marble at random. Find P(blue).

50. Jack has 4 white shirts, 3 black shirts, and 2 blue shirts. He selects a shirt at random. Find the probability he will select a black shirt.

● **Lesson 6-5** **Write a percent to represent each situation.**

51. Three students of a class of 25 are absent.

52. A baseball player has a batting average of 0.275.

● **Lesson 6-6** **Write and solve a proportion.**

53. Out of 120 people who saw a movie, 40% of them enjoyed it. How many people liked the movie?

● **Lesson 6-7** **Write and solve an equation.**

54. Forty-five percent of a number n is eighty.

55. Find the final price of a $25 item after 6% sales tax.

● **Lesson 6-8** **Find each percent of change.**

56. Last year 150 people attended a school dance. This year 175 people attended.

57. A bicycle sold for $200 last month. The same model was on sale for $170 this month.

● **Lesson 6-9** **Find each selling price.**

58. A $12 DVD is marked up 15%.

59. A $65 pair of shoes is discounted 20%.

● **Lesson 6-10** **Make a table to solve the problem.**

60. An investment account returns 7% each year. An investor deposits $2,500 into the account. Find the balance in the account at the end of each of the next ten years.

Extra Practice: Skills and Word Problems

- **Lessons 7-1, 7-2, 7-3, and 7-5** Solve and check each equation.

1. $10 - 5x = 15$

2. $3y + 17 = -13$

3. $62 = -12z + 14$

4. $6x - 2x = 12$

5. $t + 5 - 2t = -10$

6. $24 = 2(b - 2) - 4b$

7. $5 - 2(y - 5) = 27$

8. $-56a + 90 + 58a = 92$

9. $8 = 3(c + 8)$

10. $8 - \frac{t}{2} = 53$

11. $75 = \frac{m}{3} + 10$

12. $\frac{3}{5}p + 18 = 24$

13. $0.05x - 0.08 + x = 0.97$

14. $2.5y + 3.5 = -1.5$

15. $6.3p + 1.2p = 22.5$

16. $2x + 6 = 5x$

17. $3a + 2 = a - 8$

18. $3(b - 2) = 9b$

19. $8(f + 3) = 10f - 32$

20. $\frac{1}{4}(x - 8) = \frac{3}{4}x$

21. $4(w - 2.1) = w + 0.6$

- **Lesson 7-6** Solve and graph each inequality.

22. $3x + 18 > 12$

23. $4 + 9a \geq -23$

24. $10.5 < -4y + 2.5$

25. $19 - 3x \geq -2$

26. $-5(a - 3) \leq 45$

27. $\frac{1}{2}(t - 6) \leq 22$

28. $\frac{y}{4} - 6 < -9$

29. $-31.4 \leq 2x + 1$

30. $5.8 > 1 + 0.2m$

- **Lesson 7-7** Solve for the variable indicated in red.

31. $s = p + c$

32. $x + y = 180$

33. $a - b = c$

34. $I = prt$

- **Lesson 7-8** Find the simple interest.

35. $450 deposited at an interest rate of 2% for 4 years

36. $3,000 deposited at an interest rate of 3% for 10 years

37. $10,000 deposited at an interest rate of 9% for 5 years

Find each balance.

38. $9,000 at 6% compounded annually for 5 years

39. $25,000 at 7% compounded semiannually for 10 years

40. $12,000 at 3% compounded semiannually for 8 years

41. $1,000 at 4% compounded annually for 10 years

42. $500 at 1.5% compounded annually for 4 years

43. $2,000 at 5% compounded semiannually for 2 years

Lessons 7-1, 7-2, 7-3, 7-4, and 7-5 Write and solve an equation.

44. Three fourths of a number n plus four is ten.

45. Negative three times a number n plus four equals two times the number n minus six.

46. Darryl had $265 in his checking account. He spent $60 dollars and deposited d dollars each week for 5 weeks. His final balance was $330. Find the amount of money he deposited each week.

47. Lila has a collection of 85 coins. She adds six coins to the collection and gives away two coins from the collection each week. Find the number of coins in her collection after 8 weeks.

48. Mr. Maxwell's phone service costs $40 per month plus $.10 for each minute of long-distance calls. His bill for January was $52.20. How many long-distance minutes did he use?

49. Suppose you have $70 in your savings account. If you deposit $20 each week, in how many weeks will you have $250?

50. A car rental company charges $20 per day plus $.15 per mile. The bill for two days was $49.75. How many miles did the customer drive?

51. Jane leaves school and walks home at a rate of 4 mi/h. 15 minutes later, Bill finds a book that Jane forgot and runs at a rate of 8 mi/h. How many minutes will it take Bill to catch up with Jane?

Lesson 7-6 Write and solve an inequality.

52. A student received grades of 75, 90, and 83 on three math tests. What grade does the student need on the fourth test to have an average test score of at least 85?

Lesson 7-7 Use the distance formula $d = rt$, where d is distance, r is rate, or speed, and t is time spent traveling.

53. A car travels 35 miles in 50 minutes. What is the speed of the car in mi/h?

54. A runner signed up for a 10-mile race. How long will it take the runner to complete the race if he runs at a rate of 8 mi/h?

Lesson 7-8 Use the compound interest formula $B = p(1 + r)^n$, where B is the final balance, p is the principal, r is the interest rate for each period, and n is the number of interest periods.

55. Ms. Simpson takes out a $1,200 loan that charges 8% interest compounded annually. Suppose she makes no payments on the loan for 6 years. Find the balance after 6 years.

56. A savings account with a balance of $150 earns 2% interest compounded semiannually. No deposits or withdrawals are made. Find the balance in the account after 5 years.

● **Lesson 8-1 Is each relation a function? Explain.**

1. $\{(3, 5), (4, 7), (4, 8), (6, 10)\}$ **2.** $\{(0, -1), (1, 3), (-2, 4), (3, 6)\}$

3. $\{(4, 5), (5, 2), (1, -3), (-2, -3), (0, 2)\}$ **4.** $\{(1.5, 0.6), (1.5, 1.1), (2, 1.9), (1, 3.2)\}$

● **Lesson 8-2 Find the solution of each equation for $x = -3, 0$, and 2.**

5. $y = 3x - 2$ **6.** $y = 2x + 5$ **7.** $y = \frac{1}{2}x + 8$ **8.** $x = 3 - y$

9. $y = -4$ **10.** $2y = 6x - 10$ **11.** $x - 2y = 3$ **12.** $y = -x - 1.5$

● **Lesson 8-3 Find the slope and y-intercept of the graph of each equation.**

13. $y = 5x - 4$ **14.** $y = 10 - 3x$ **15.** $2y = 3x + 12$ **16.** $4x + y = 16$

17. $y = \frac{3}{5}x - 1$ **18.** $12x - 6y = 30$ **19.** $y = x - \frac{1}{2}$ **20.** $x - y = -2$

Graph each line.

21. slope 3, through $(0, -5)$ **22.** slope -1, through $(3, 5)$ **23.** no slope, through $(2, -1)$

24. $y = 2x + 1$ **25.** $x + y = 4$ **26.** $y = \frac{1}{2}x - 1$

● **Lesson 8-4 Write a rule for each linear function.**

27.

x	y
0	−1
1	2
2	5
3	8

28.

x	y
−1	4
0	6
1	8
2	10

29.

x	y
−2	−6
0	4
2	14
4	24

30. The graph has slope $-\frac{1}{2}$ and y-intercept 3.

31. The graph has slope 2 and contains the point $(-1, 1)$.

32. The graph contains the points $(-3, -2)$ and $(3, 0)$.

● **Lesson 8-5 Use the table to complete Exercises 33 and 34.**

33. Make a scatter plot of (time studying, test grade).

34. Is there a positive correlation, negative correlation, or no correlation between the sets of data? Explain.

Study Time

Time Spent Studying (minutes)	40	30	20	50	75
Test Grade	85	80	60	80	90

● **Lessons 8-7 and 8-8 Solve each system by graphing.**

35. $y = x + 3$
$3x - y = 1$

36. $x + y = -7$
$x - y = 1$

37. $y > 2x - 4$
$y < -3x + 6$

38. $x + y < 10$
$x - y < -5$

● **Lesson 8-1 Is each relation a function? Explain.**

39. Is the number of miles driven a function of the amount of gasoline used?

40. Is the time it takes to build a house a function of the number of people working on it?

● **Lesson 8-2 Use the formula $F = \frac{9}{5}C + 32$, where F is the temperature in Fahrenheit and C is the temperature in Celsius.**

41. The boiling point of a chemical is 35°C. Find the equivalent temperature in degrees Fahrenheit.

● **Lesson 8-3 Find each slope.**

42. The top of a roof is 8 ft higher than the edge, 6 feet away.

43. An airplane climbs 2,000 ft over a distance of 10 miles.

● **Lesson 8-4 Write a function for the situation.**

44. A ski trail has a slope of $-\frac{2}{3}$. Write a function for the distance d traveled forward for the height h traveled down.

● **Lesson 8-5 Would you expect a *positive correlation*, a *negative correlation*, or *no correlation* between each pair of data sets? Explain.**

45. grades on homework and grades on tests

46. price of a television and number sold

● **Lesson 8-6 Solve each problem by graphing.**

47. A car gets 28 mi/gal in highway driving. How many gallons of gasoline does the car need to drive 150 mi?

48. A builder constructs a skateboard ramp with a slope of $\frac{1}{8}$. Find the length of a ramp that increases 5 ft in height.

● **Lesson 8-7 Write and solve a system of equations.**

49. A bag contains red and blue marbles. There are 20 fewer blue marbles than red marbles, and twice as many red marbles as blue marbles. How many marbles are in the bag?

50. A phone company offers two service plans. One plan costs $10 per month and $.09 per minute. The other plan costs $15 per month and $.05 per minute. For what number of minutes will the cost of the plans be the same?

● **Lesson 8-8 Write and graph a linear inequality.**

51. A grocery store charges $3/lb for chicken and $5/lb for beef. How many pounds of each can you buy for less than $15?

● **Lesson 9-1** Use the figure at the right.

1. Name the line in three ways.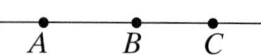

2. Name four different rays.

Use the figure at the right. Name each of the following.

3. four segments that intersect $\overline{MR}$

4. three segments parallel to $\overline{MR}$

5. three segments skew to $\overline{MR}$

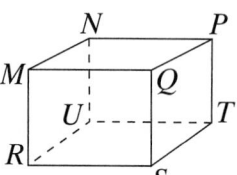

● **Lesson 9-2** In the figure at the right, $x \parallel y$.

6. List all angles that are congruent to $\angle 1$.

7. If $m\angle 5 = 67°$, what are the measures of the other angles?

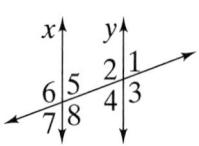

● **Lesson 9-3** Classify each figure.

8.

9.

10.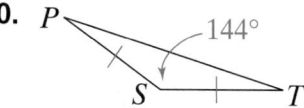

● **Lesson 9-5**

11. $\triangle XYZ \cong \triangle STU$. Which of the following must be true?
   a. $\overline{YZ} \cong \overline{TU}$ **b.** $\angle X \cong \angle T$ **c.** $\overline{ZX} \cong \overline{TS}$
   d. $\angle YZX \cong \angle STU$ **e.** $\triangle YZX \cong \triangle UTS$

● **Lesson 9-6** Find the circumference of each circle with the given radius or diameter. Use 3.14 for π. Round to the nearest tenth.

12. radius = 4 in.   **13.** diameter = 25 ft   **14.** radius = 7.8 cm   **15.** diameter = 100 m

● **Lesson 9-7** Draw $\triangle XYZ$ with acute $\angle Y$.

16. Construct the angle bisector of $\angle Y$.   **17.** Construct a bisector of $\overline{XY}$.

● **Lessons 9-8, 9-9 and 9-10** Graph the image of $\triangle CDG$ with vertices $C(1, 3)$, $D(3, 5)$, and $G(5, 1)$ after each transformation.

18. 3 units left, 2 units down   **19.** reflected over the x-axis   **20.** rotated 90° about the origin

● **Lesson 9-1** Use *always*, *sometimes*, or *never* to complete each statement.

21. Parallel lines are __?__ in the same plane.

22. Skew lines __?__ intersect.

● **Lesson 9-2**

23. Two roads intersect. One corner of the intersection has an angle of 65°. Find the measure of the adjacent angle.

● **Lesson 9-3** **Find each perimeter.**

24. A pond in the shape of a regular hexagon has a side length of 3 ft.

25. A plaza forms an isosceles triangle with two congruent sides 25 yd long, and the third side 10 yd long.

● **Lesson 9-4** **Solve by drawing a diagram.**

26. Tom leaves his house and walks 3 blocks east, 6 blocks south, 2 blocks east, 4 blocks north, and 4 blocks west. How many blocks and in which direction(s) does Tom need to walk to get home?

● **Lesson 9-5**

27. Suppose you draw a diagonal line in the sand between opposite corners in a rectangular sandbox. Does the line form two congruent triangles? Explain.

● **Lesson 9-6** **Find the circumference.**

28. A circular flower garden has a radius of 12 ft.

● **Lesson 9-7** **Construct the figure.**

29. Draw $\angle DEF$. Then construct the angle bisector $\overrightarrow{EG}$.

● **Lesson 9-8** **Write the translation in arrow notation.**

30. A city is moving a historic building. The building is 1.5 mi east and 2 mi south of the center of town. It is moving to a point 1 mi west and 0.4 mi south of the center of town.

● **Lesson 9-9** **Decide whether the statement is *always* true, *sometimes* true, or *never* true. Explain.**

31. The image of a point reflected over a vertical line will have the same *y*-coordinate.

● **Lesson 9-10**

32. Do isosceles triangles have rotational symmetry? Do equilateral triangles? Explain.

Extra Practice: Skills and Word Problems

● **Lessons 10-1 and 10-2** Find the area of each figure.

1.

2.

3.

4.

5.

6.

● **Lesson 10-3** Find the area of each figure. Give an exact answer, and an approximate answer to the nearest tenth using 3.14 for π.

7.

8.

9.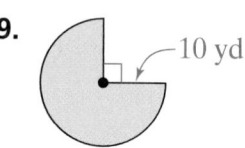

● **Lesson 10-4**

10. Draw a net to represent a rectangular box that is 3 ft long, 5 ft wide, and 2 ft high. Label dimensions on the net and find the surface area.

● **Lessons 10-5, 10-6, 10-7, and 10-9** Find the surface area and volume of each space figure, to the nearest tenth. Use 3.14 for π.

11.

12.

13.

14.

15.

16.

17.

18.

19.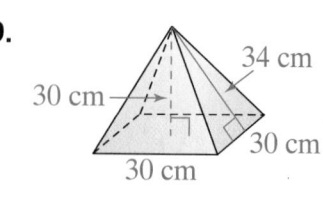

● **Lessons 10-1, 10-2, and 10-3** **Find the area of each figure.**

20. a rectangular football field 360 ft long by 160 ft wide

21. a pool shaped like a parallelogram with a base of 30 yd and a height of 12 yd

22. the square infield of a baseball diamond, 90 ft on each side

23. a triangular garden with a base of 15 m and a height of 20 m

24. a water treatment plant with circular pools 125 ft in diameter

25. a circular fountain with a radius of 6 m

● **Lesson 10-4** **Write the most precise name for each space figure with the given properties.**

26. three lateral surfaces that are triangles

27. one surface with no vertexes or bases, all points equidistant from point p

28. two hexagonal bases and six lateral surfaces

● **Lessons 10-5 and 10-6** **Find the surface area of each figure.**

29. a can of soup with a diameter of 4 in. and a height of 5 in.

30. a sugar cube with a side length of 1.5 cm

31. a sculpture shaped like an oblique rectangular prism with a width of 7 yd, a length of 9 yd, and a height of 4 yd

32. a ball with a diameter of 25 cm

33. a silo formed by a cylinder with a height of 150 ft and a half sphere with a radius of 35 ft

● **Lessons 10-7 and 10-9** **Find the volume of each figure.**

34. a racquetball court shaped like a rectangular prism with length 30 ft, width 20 ft, and height 40 ft

35. a hockey puck 1 in. thick and 3 in. in diameter

36. a globe with a diameter of 20 cm

● **Lesson 10-8** **Solve by making a model.**

37. Can you make a topless cube that has a volume of 125 in.^{3} by cutting the corners off a piece of cardboard 15 in. by 15 in.? Explain.

38. Suppose you cut 5-cm squares out of the corners of a 20 cm-by-30 cm piece of cardboard to make a box with no top. How much wrapping paper will you need to cover the box?

Chapter 11 Extra Practice: Skills and Word Problems

● **Lesson 11-1** Simplify each square root.

1. $\sqrt{4}$ **2.** $\sqrt{100}$ **3.** $-\sqrt{36}$ **4.** $\sqrt{121}$ **5.** $\sqrt{25}$

Estimate to the nearest integer.

6. $\sqrt{50}$ **7.** $\sqrt{12}$ **8.** $\sqrt{40}$ **9.** $\sqrt{105}$ **10.** $\sqrt{55}$

Identify each number as rational or irrational.

11. $\sqrt{9}$ **12.** 0.6 **13.** $\sqrt{5}$ **14.** $0.\overline{6}$ **15.** $0.010010001\ldots$

● **Lesson 11-2** Find each missing length, to the nearest tenth of a unit.

16.   **17.**   **18.**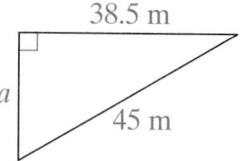

● **Lesson 11-3** Find the distance between each pair of points. Round to the nearest tenth.

19. $(4, 6), (8, 2)$ **20.** $(0, -4), (-5, 1)$ **21.** $(20, -5), (10, -8)$

Find the midpoint of each segment with the given endpoints.

22. $A(5, 4)$ and $B(3, 0)$ **23.** $C(-2, -4)$ and $D(3, 1)$ **24.** $E(-1, 5)$ and $F(2, -1)$

● **Lesson 11-5** Find the missing lengths.

25.   **26.**   **27.**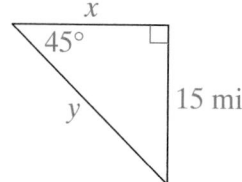

● **Lessons 11-6 and 11-7** Find each value. Round to four decimal places.

28. $\sin 10°$ **29.** $\tan 85°$ **30.** $\cos 33°$

31. $\tan 5°$ **32.** $\sin 78°$ **33.** $\cos 65°$

34. $\cos 52°$ **35.** $\tan 50°$ **36.** $\sin 30°$

37. A right triangle has one leg of 10 cm and an angle whose measure is 25°. What lengths are possible for the other leg and the hypotenuse, to the nearest tenth?

● **Lesson 11-1** Use the formula $d = \sqrt{1.5h}$, where h is the height above ground in feet and d is the distance to the horizon in miles.

38. At the top of a Ferris wheel, Jose is 395 ft above the ground. About how far can Jose see to the horizon?

39. The observation deck of a skyscraper is 950 ft above the ground. About how far can Suzette see from the deck?

● **Lesson 11-2** Use the Pythagorean Theorem to answer each question.

40. The top of a straight slide is 3 m above the ground. The end of the slide is 4 m from the ladder. How long is the slide?

41. Three friends are trying to stand at the points of a right triangle. The distances between them are 10 yd, 24 yd, and 29 yd. Did they form a right triangle? Explain.

● **Lesson 11-3** Use the distance formula, $d = \sqrt{(x_2 - x_1)^2 + (y_2 - y_1)^2}$.

42. Samir's house is 3 miles east and 2 miles south of his school. Find the shortest distance between his house and the school.

● **Lesson 11-4** Write and solve a proportion.

43. LaTanya is using a mirror to measure the height of a tree indirectly. She positions the mirror 0.75 m away from her on the ground so that she can see the top of the tree. Her eyes are 1.5 m above the ground. The tree is 10 m behind her. How tall is it?

● **Lesson 11-5** Use the properties of special triangles.

44. A flea market fills a town square that is 80 yd long on each side. What is the diagonal distance across the flea market?

45. Julia is constructing a 30°-60°-90° triangle. She draws the short leg 5 in. long. Find the lengths of the long leg and the hypotenuse.

● **Lesson 11-6** Use sine, cosine, or tangent.

46. Jasper is standing 60 ft away from a tree. The top of the tree is at a 35° angle to him. Find the height of the tree.

● **Lesson 11-7** Use angles of elevation or depression.

47. An Instrument Landing System brings airplanes to a runway at an angle of 3°. How high is an airplane on an ILS when it is 6,000 ft from the runway?

48. An airplane departing an airport is required to climb at an angle of at least 5°. How high will the airplane be when it has travelled 5 miles?

Chapter 12 · Extra Practice: Skills and Word Problems

● **Lesson 12-1 Display each set of data in a frequency table. Then draw a line plot for each frequency table. Find the range.**

1. 21 22 20 21 21 20 23 22 21 21

2. 95 100 95 95 90 80 85 80 95 100

● **Lesson 12-2 Use box-and-whisker plots to compare data sets. Use a single number line.**

3. 1st set: 26 60 36 44 62 24 29 50 37 52 40 41 18 39 64 42
2nd set: 78 22 29 67 10 62 50 72 8 63 35 80 52 60 18 65 61

● **Lesson 12-3 Use the graph at the right for Exercises 4 and 5.**

4. The graph suggests that the number of farms in 1982 was three times the number in 1992. Is this true? Explain.

5. Redraw the graph without a break.

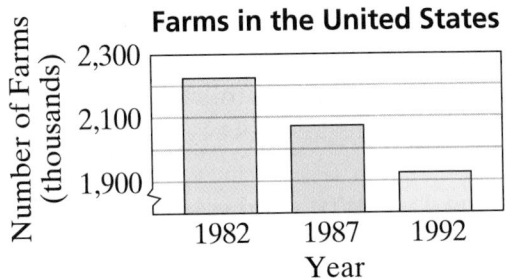

● **Lesson 12-4**

6. A menu shows that you can pick one vegetable from four choices, one potato dish from five choices, and one main dish from two choices. How many different choices of meals do you have?

● **Lesson 12-5 You select letters at random from the word MATHEMATICS.**

7. Find the probability that you select A and then, after replacing A, select T.

8. Find the probability that you select A and then, without replacing A, select T.

● **Lesson 12-6 Simplify each expression.**

9. $_3C_2$ **10.** $_3P_2$ **11.** $_5P_2$ **12.** $_7C_3$ **13.** $_{10}C_3$ **14.** $_8P_3$

● **Lessons 12-7 and 12-8 Some students were surveyed about the number of books in their lockers. The table shows the results.**

15. Find the experimental probability that a locker will have 3 books.

16. In a school of 600 students, how many lockers would you expect to have one book?

Number of Books in Students' Lockers

Number of Books	1	2	3	4	5
Number of Students	12	21	10	7	10

Lesson 12-1 Display the data in a line plot.

17. A class survey asked students how many pens they had. Five people had one pen, 8 people had two pens, 4 people had three pens, 2 people had four pens, and 3 people had no pens.

Lesson 12-2 Make a box-and-whisker plot for each set of data.

18. ages of members of the drama club: 13, 18, 16, 13, 14, 14, 14, 15, 18, 17, 15, 16, 16, 15, 16, 16, 14, 14, 17, 17, 19

19. number of students in various clubs: 5, 20, 30, 12, 10, 15, 20, 6, 10, 8, 9, 17, 18, 4, 22, 27

Lesson 12-3 Use the table for Exercises 20 and 21.

20. Make a graph that shows a sharp increase in ticket prices.

21. Make a graph that shows relatively little change in ticket prices.

Average Major League Baseball Ticket Prices

Year	Price
1999	$15.00
2000	$16.81
2001	$17.64
2002	$18.30
2003	$19.01
2004	$19.82

SOURCE: Team Marketing Report

Lesson 12-4 Find the probability.

22. A cafeteria makes sandwiches on white or wheat bread, with ham, turkey, or roast beef, and with mayonnaise or mustard. What is the probability of selecting turkey on wheat with mustard at random?

Lesson 12-5 Identify the events as *dependent* or *independent*. Then find each probability.

23. You roll an even number on a number cube, and then you toss a coin and get heads.

24. A bag contains 6 blue marbles, 4 red marbles, and 5 green marbles. You select a blue marble, keep it, and then select a red marble.

Lesson 12-6 Find the number of possibilities.

25. Four candidates run for club president and five run for vice-president.

26. You take 5 out of 12 shirts with you on vacation.

Lessons 12-7 and 12-9 Find each probability by simulating the problem.

27. rolling 3 on a number cube and tossing heads on a coin

28. rolling two evens and an odd on a toss of three number cubes

Lesson 12-8

29. In a class of 50 students, 15 missed two or fewer days of class last year. Estimate how many students missed two or fewer days in the school population of 1,500.

Extra Practice: Skills and Word Problems

● **Lesson 13-1** Find the next three terms of each sequence. Then write a rule to describe each sequence.

1. $100, 80, 60, 40, \ldots$

2. $6, 12, 18, 24, \ldots$

3. $8, 16, 24, 32, \ldots$

4. $50, 500, 5,000, 50,000, \ldots$

5. $-5, 25, -125, 625, \ldots$

6. $50, 10, -30, -70, \ldots$

● **Lesson 13-2** Graph each function, for x values from -2 to 2.

7. $y = x^2 - 1$

8. $y = -x^2 + 6$

9. $y = |x| - 3$

10. $y = -|x| + 2$

11. $y = -3x^2$

12. $y = -3|x| - 1$

13. $y = 2x^2 - 2$

14. $y = \frac{1}{2}|x|$

● **Lesson 13-3** For each function, make a table with integer values of x from 0 to 4. Then graph each function.

15. $y = 4^x$

16. $y = \frac{1}{2} \cdot 10^x$

17. $y = 10(0.5)^x$

18. $y = 2^x$

● **Lesson 13-4** Tell whether each polynomial is a *monomial*, a *binomial*, or a *trinomial*.

19. $2x^2 - 3x - 1$

20. $3xy$

21. $5x^3 - 15$

22. $10 - 2x + 5y$

23. xyz^2

24. $56 - y$

25. $3ab - a^2 - b$

26. 80

● **Lesson 13-5** Simplify each sum or difference.

27. $(5y - 12) + (2y + 10)$

28. $(x^2 + 3x + 4) + (2x^2 + x + 6)$

29. $(x^2 - 7x + 2) + (-x^2 + 6x - 2)$

30. $(4a^2 - 3a - 2) - (2a^2 + 5a + 10)$

31. $(5x - 3) + (6x^2 - 9)$

32. $(15y^2 + 12y) - (12y^2 - 20)$

33. $(3ab + a^2 + b^2) - (a^2 - 3b^2 - 5ab)$

34. $(10t - t^2 - 15) + (3t^2 + 12)$

● **Lessons 13-6 and 13-7** Simplify each product.

35. $2x(5x^2 + 6)$

36. $y^2(x + y)$

37. $6t^2(2t^2 - 3 + 8t)$

38. $(x - 8)(x + 1)$

39. $(y + 6)(2y + 4)$

40. $3b(5ab + 2ab^2 + 6b)$

Use the GCF of the terms to write each expression as the product of two factors.

41. $4x^2 - 12$

42. $5z^2 - 20z + 30$

43. $2a^2b - 4a + 6b$

44. $t^2 - 3t$

45. $6xy + 2x + 3x^2y$

46. $5w^3 + 6w^2 - 3w$

● **Lesson 13-1** **Find the next three terms of each sequence.**

47. Eduardo does 10 push-ups per day one week, 15 push-ups per day the next week, and 20 push-ups per day the following week.

48. You save $8 in January, $12 in February, and $18 in March.

● **Lesson 13-2** **Graph the function to answer each question.**

49. The formula $A = 12x - x^2$ models the area of a garden with a width of x ft. What width gives the greatest area?

50. The formula $h = -16t^2 + 200$ models the height h of a dropped ball that takes t seconds to reach the ground. Suppose you drop a ball from 200 feet. In approximately how many seconds will the ball hit the ground?

● **Lesson 13-3** **Graph each function.**

51. The formula $y = 25(2)^x$ models the number of cells y in a bacteria culture after x days.

52. You deposit $500 in a savings account earning 5% interest each year. The formula $b = 500(1.05)^y$ models the balance b in the account after y years.

● **Lesson 13-4** **Evaluate the polynomial.**

53. The polynomial $x^2 + 10x$ models the area of a greenhouse 10 m longer than it is wide. The greenhouse is 8 m wide. Find its area.

● **Lesson 13-5** **Write and simplify a polynomial expression.**

54. To make a flying ring, Lily cut out a circle with area $(2x + 4)$ cm^2 from the center of a plastic circle with area $(5x - 6)$ cm^2. Find the surface area of her flying ring.

● **Lessons 13-6 and 13-7** **Find each area. Use 3.14 for π.**

55. A rectangular soccer field is $4x$ m long and $(2x + 12)$ m wide.

56. A cornfield is shaped like a trapezoid with bases of $(5p + 2)$ m and $(2p - 4)$ m and a height of $3p$ m.

57. A circular pool has a radius of $(4c - 2)$ ft.

● **Lesson 13-8** **Solve by using multiple strategies.**

58. A rectangular playing field is three times as long as it is wide. Its area is 507 m^2. Find the perimeter of the playing field.

Skills Handbook

Skills Handbook

Comparing and Ordering Whole Numbers

The numbers on a number line are in order from least to greatest.

298 299 300 301 302 303 304 305 306

You can use a number line to compare whole numbers. Use the symbols > (is greater than) and < (is less than).

1 EXAMPLE

Use > or < to compare the numbers.

a. **303 ■ 299**
303 is to the right of 299.
303 > 299

b. **301 ■ 305**
301 is to the left of 305.
301 < 305

The value of a digit depends on its place in a number. Compare digits starting from the left.

2 EXAMPLE

Use > or < to compare the numbers.

a. **12,060,012,875 ■ 12,060,012,675**
8 hundreds > 6 hundreds, so
12,060,012,875 > 12,060,012,675.

b. **465,320 ■ 4,653,208**
0 millions < 4 millions, so
465,320 < 4,653,208.

EXERCISES

Use > or < to compare the numbers.

1. 3,660 ■ 360   **2.** 74,328 ■ 74,238   **3.** 88,010 ■ 8,101   **4.** 87,524 ■ 9,879

5. 295,286 ■ 295,826   **6.** 829,631 ■ 842,832   **7.** 932,401 ■ 932,701 **8.** 60,000 ■ 500,009

9. 1,609,372,002 ■ 609,172,002   **10.** 45,248,315,150 ■ 45,283,718,150

Write the numbers from least to greatest.

11. 3,747; 3,474; 3,774; 3,347; 3,734   **12.** 70,903; 70,309; 73,909; 73,090

13. 32,056,403; 302,056,403; 30,265,403; 30,256,403 **14.** 884,172; 881,472; 887,142; 881,872

Skills Handbook **779**

Rounding Whole Numbers

You can use number lines to help you round numbers.

1 EXAMPLE

a. Round 7,510 to the nearest thousand.

7,510 is between 7,000 and 8,000
and closer to 8,000.
7,510 rounds to 8,000.

b. Round 237 to the nearest ten.

237 is between 230 and 240
and closer to 240.
237 rounds to 240.

To round a number to a particular place, look at the digit to the right
of that place. If the digit is less than 5, round down. If the digit is 5 or
greater, round up.

2 EXAMPLE

Round to the place of the underlined digit.

a. 3,4_6_3,280

The digit to the right of the 6 is 3, so
3,463,280 rounds down to 3,460,000.

b. 28_9_,543

The digit to the right of the 9 is 5, so
289,543 rounds up to 290,000.

EXERCISES

Round to the nearest ten.

1. 42   **2.** 89   **3.** 671   **4.** 3,482   **5.** 7,029   **6.** 661,423

Round to the nearest thousand.

7. 5,800   **8.** 3,100   **9.** 44,280   **10.** 9,936   **11.** 987   **12.** 313,591

13. 5,641   **14.** 37,896   **15.** 82,019   **16.** 808,155   **17.** 34,501   **18.** 650,828

Round to the place of the underlined digit.

19. 68,_8_52   **20.** _4_51,006   **21.** 3,40_7_,481   **22.** 2_8_,512,030   **23.** 71,2_2_5,003

24. 96,_4_49   **25.** 4_0_1,223   **26.** _8_,902   **27.** 3,6_7_7   **28.** 2,551,_7_50

29. 6_8_,663   **30.** 70_1_,803,229   **31.** 56_5_,598   **32.** 32,_8_10   **33.** 1,_4_46,300

Multiplying Whole Numbers

When you multiply by a two-digit number, first multiply by the ones and then multiply by the tens. Add the products.

Skills Handbook

1 EXAMPLE

Multiply 62 × 704.

Step 1	Step 2	Step 3
704	704	704
× 62	× 62	× 62
——	——	——
1408	1408	1 408
	42240	+ 42 240
		————
		43,648

2 EXAMPLE

Find each product.

a. 93 × 6

```
   93
 ×  6
 ----
  558
```

b. 25 × 48

```
   48
 × 25
 ----
  240
+ 960
-----
1,200
```

c. 80 × 921

```
    921
 ×   80
 ------
 73,680
```

EXERCISES

Find each product.

1. 74 × 6   **2.** 35 × 9   **3.** 53 × 7   **4.** 80 × 8   **5.** 98 × 4   **6.** 65 × 8

7. 512 × 3   **8.** 407 × 9   **9.** 225 × 6   **10.** 340 × 5   **11.** 816 × 7   **12.** 603 × 3

13. 70 × 36   **14.** 41 × 55   **15.** 38 × 49   **16.** 601 × 87   **17.** 271 × 34   **18.** 450 × 67

19. 6 × 82   **20.** 405 × 5   **21.** 81 × 9   **22.** 3 × 274   **23.** 552 × 4

24. 60 × 84   **25.** 52 × 17   **26.** 31 × 90   **27.** 78 × 52   **28.** 43 × 66

29. 826 × 3   **30.** 702 × 4   **31.** 8 × 180   **32.** 6 × 339   **33.** 781 × 7

Dividing Whole Numbers

First estimate the quotient by rounding the divisor, the dividend, or both. When you divide, after you bring down a digit, you must write a digit in the quotient.

EXAMPLE

Find each quotient.

a. 741 ÷ 8

Estimate:

$720 \div 8 \approx 90$

$$
\begin{array}{r}
92 \text{ R5} \\
8\overline{)741} \\
-72 \\
\hline
21 \\
-16 \\
\hline
5
\end{array}
$$

b. 838 ÷ 43

Estimate:

$800 \div 40 \approx 20$

$$
\begin{array}{r}
19 \text{ R21} \\
43\overline{)838} \\
-43 \\
\hline
408 \\
-387 \\
\hline
21
\end{array}
$$

c. 367 ÷ 9

Estimate:

$360 \div 9 \approx 40$

$$
\begin{array}{r}
40 \text{ R7} \\
9\overline{)367} \\
-360 \\
\hline
7
\end{array}
$$

EXERCISES

Divide.

1. $4\overline{)61}$
2. $8\overline{)53}$
3. $7\overline{)90}$
4. $3\overline{)84}$
5. $6\overline{)81}$

6. $6\overline{)469}$
7. $3\overline{)653}$
8. $8\overline{)645}$
9. $9\overline{)231}$
10. $4\overline{)415}$

11. $60\overline{)461}$
12. $40\overline{)213}$
13. $70\overline{)517}$
14. $30\overline{)432}$
15. $80\overline{)276}$

16. $43\overline{)273}$
17. $52\overline{)281}$
18. $69\overline{)207}$
19. $38\overline{)121}$
20. $81\overline{)433}$

21. $94\overline{)1,368}$
22. $62\overline{)1,147}$
23. $55\overline{)2,047}$
24. $85\overline{)1,450}$
25. $46\overline{)996}$

26. $94 \div 4$
27. $66 \div 9$
28. $90 \div 5$
29. $69 \div 6$
30. $58 \div 8$

31. $323 \div 5$
32. $849 \div 7$
33. $404 \div 8$
34. $934 \div 3$
35. $619 \div 6$

36. $777 \div 50$
37. $528 \div 20$
38. $443 \div 70$
39. $312 \div 40$
40. $335 \div 60$

41. $382 \div 72$
42. $580 \div 68$
43. $279 \div 43$
44. $232 \div 27$
45. $331 \div 93$

46. $614 \div 35$
47. $423 \div 28$
48. $489 \div 15$
49. $1,134 \div 51$
50. $1,103 \div 26$

Decimals and Place Value

Each digit in a whole number or a decimal has both a place and a value. The value of any place is one tenth the value of the place to its left. The chart below can help you read and write decimals.

Billions	Hundred millions	Ten millions	Millions	Hundred thousands	Ten thousands	Thousands	Hundreds	Tens	Ones	.	Tenths	Hundredths	Thousandths	Ten-thousandths	Hundred-thousandths	Millionths
2	4	0	1	2	6	2	8	3	0	.	7	5	0	1	9	1

EXAMPLE

a. **What is the value of the digit 8 in the number above?**
The digit 8 is in the hundreds place. So, its value is 8 hundreds.

b. **Write 2.006 in words.**
The digit 6 is in the thousandths place. So, 2.006 is read two and six thousandths.

c. **Write five and thirty-four ten-thousandths as a decimal.**
Ten-thousandths is 4 places to the right of the decimal point. So, the decimal will have 4 places after the decimal point. The answer is 5.0034.

EXERCISES

Use the chart above. Write the value of each digit.

1. the digit 9
2. the digit 7
3. the digit 5
4. the digit 6
5. the digit 4
6. the digit 3

Write a decimal for the given words.

7. forty-one ten-thousandths
8. eighteen and five hundred four thousandths
9. eight millionths
10. seven and sixty-three hundred-thousandths
11. thirteen thousandths
12. sixty-five and two hundred one thousandths

Write each decimal in words.

13. 0.06
14. 4.7
15. 0.00011
16. 0.9
17. 0.012
18. 0.000059
19. 0.0042
20. 6.020

Comparing and Ordering Decimals

To compare two decimals, use the symbols > (is greater than),
< (is less than), or = (is equal to). When you compare, start at the left
and compare the digits.

1 EXAMPLE

Use >, <, or = to compare the decimals.

a. 0.1 ■ 0.06
1 tenth > 0 tenths, so
0.1 > 0.06.

b. 2.4583 ■ 2.48
5 hundredths < 8 hundredths,
so 2.4583 < 2.48.

c. 0.30026 ■ 0.03026
3 tenths > 0 tenths, so
0.30026 > 0.03026.

2 EXAMPLE

Draw number lines to compare the decimals.

a. 0.1 ■ 0.06

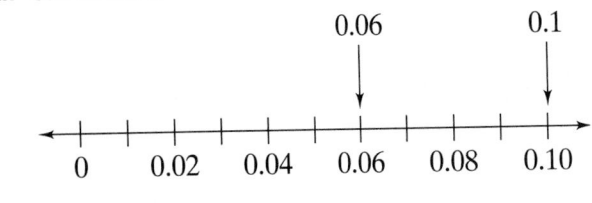

0.1 > 0.06

b. 2.4583 ■ 2.48

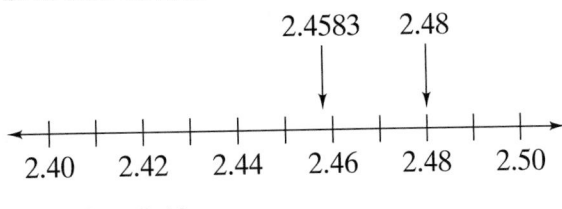

2.4583 < 2.48

EXERCISES

Use >, <, or = to compare the decimals. Draw number
lines if you wish.

1. 0.003 ■ 0.02
2. 84.2 ■ 842
3. 0.162 ■ 0.106
4. 0.0659 ■ 0.6059
5. 2.13 ■ 2.99
6. 3.53 ■ 3.529
7. 2.01 ■ 2.010
8. 0.00072 ■ 0.07002
9. 0.458 ■ 0.4589
10. 8.627 ■ 8.649
11. 0.0019 ■ 0.0002
12. 0.19321 ■ 0.19231

Write the decimals in order from least to greatest.

13. 2.31, 0.231, 23.1, 0.23, 3.21
14. 1.02, 1.002, 1.2, 1.11, 1.021
15. 0.02, 0.002, 0.22, 0.222, 2.22
16. 55.5, 555.5, 55.555, 5.5555
17. 0.07, 0.007, 0.7, 0.71, 0.72
18. 2.78, 2.7001, 2.701, 2.71, 2.7
19. 7, 7.3264, 7.3, 7.3246, 7.0324
20. 0.0101, 0.0099, 0.011, 0.00019

Rounding

When you round to a particular place, look at the digit to the right of that place. If it is 5 or greater, you increase the digit in the place you are rounding to by 1. If it is less than 5, you leave the digit in the place you are rounding to unchanged.

EXAMPLE

a. **Round 1.627 to the nearest whole number.**
   The digit to the right of the units place is 6, so 1.627 rounds up to 2.

b. **Round 12,034 to the nearest thousand.**
   The digit to the right of the thousands place is 0, so 12,034 rounds down to 12,000.

c. **Round 2.7195 to the nearest hundredth.**
   The digit to the right of the hundredths place is 9, so 2.7195 rounds up to 2.72.

d. **Round 0.060521 to the nearest thousandth.**
   The digit to the right of the thousandths place is 5, so 0.060521 rounds up to 0.061.

EXERCISES

Round to the nearest thousand.

1. 105,099   **2.** 10,400   **3.** 79,527,826   **4.** 79,932   **5.** 4,312,349

Round to the nearest whole number.

6. 135.91   **7.** 3.001095   **8.** 96.912   **9.** 101.167   **10.** 299.9

Round to the nearest tenth.

11. 82.01   **12.** 4.67522   **13.** 20.397   **14.** 399.95   **15.** 129.98

Round to the nearest hundredth.

16. 13.458   **17.** 96.4045   **18.** 0.699   **19.** 4.234   **20.** 12.09531

Round to the place of the underlined digit.

21. 7.0<u>6</u>15   **22.** <u>5</u>.77125   **23.** 1,5<u>2</u>2   **24.** 0.919<u>5</u>2   **25.** 4.<u>2</u>43

26. 2<u>3</u>6.001   **27.** <u>3</u>52   **28.** 3.4953<u>6</u>6   **29.** 8.<u>0</u>7092   **30.** <u>0</u>.6008

31. 4<u>0</u>9   **32.** 23,<u>9</u>51,888   **33.** 2.5<u>7</u>84   **34.** 8<u>6</u>2   **35.** 19.<u>3</u>2

36. <u>9</u>18   **37.** 7,<u>7</u>35   **38.** 25.66<u>0</u>47   **39.** 9<u>8</u>3,240,631   **40.** <u>2</u>7

41. 0.0037<u>7</u>1   **42.** 0.<u>0</u>649   **43.** 12.<u>7</u>77   **44.** 1,75<u>9</u>,230   **45.** 2<u>0</u>,908

Adding and Subtracting Decimals

You add or subtract decimals just as you do whole numbers. You line up the decimal points and then add or subtract. If you wish, you can use zeros to make the columns even.

EXAMPLE

Find each sum or difference.

a. **37.6 + 8.431**

$$\begin{array}{r} 37.6 \\ + \ 8.431 \end{array} \rightarrow \begin{array}{r} 37.600 \\ + \ 8.431 \\ \hline 46.031 \end{array}$$

b. **8 − 4.593**

$$\begin{array}{r} 8 \\ - \ 4.593 \end{array} \rightarrow \begin{array}{r} 8.000 \\ - \ 4.593 \\ \hline 3.407 \end{array}$$

c. **8.3 + 2.99 + 17.5**

$$\begin{array}{r} 8.3 \\ 2.99 \\ + \ 17.5 \end{array} \rightarrow \begin{array}{r} 8.30 \\ 2.99 \\ + \ 17.50 \\ \hline 28.79 \end{array}$$

EXERCISES

Find each sum or difference.

1. $\begin{array}{r} 39.7 \\ - \ 36.03 \end{array}$

2. $\begin{array}{r} 1.08 \\ - \ 0.9 \end{array}$

3. $\begin{array}{r} 6.784 \\ + \ 0.528 \end{array}$

4. $\begin{array}{r} 5.01 \\ - \ 0.87 \end{array}$

5. $\begin{array}{r} 13.02 \\ + \ 23.107 \end{array}$

6. $\begin{array}{r} 8.634 \\ + \ 1.409 \end{array}$

7. $\begin{array}{r} 2.1 \\ - \ 0.5 \end{array}$

8. $\begin{array}{r} 8.23 \\ - \ 3.1 \end{array}$

9. $\begin{array}{r} 1.05 \\ + \ 12.9 \end{array}$

10. $\begin{array}{r} 2.6 \\ + \ 0.003 \end{array}$

11. $\begin{array}{r} 0.1 \\ 58.21 \\ + \ 1.9 \end{array}$

12. $\begin{array}{r} 12.2 \\ 3.06 \\ + \ 0.5 \end{array}$

13. $\begin{array}{r} 9.42 \\ 3.6 \\ + \ 21.003 \end{array}$

14. $\begin{array}{r} 15.22 \\ 7.4 \\ + \ 8.125 \end{array}$

15. $\begin{array}{r} 3.7 \\ 20.06 \\ + \ 16.19 \end{array}$

16. 76.39 − 8.47
17. 8.7 + 17.03
18. 32.403 + 12.06
19. 20.5 + 11.45

20. 8.9 − 4.45
21. 1.245 + 5.8
22. 3.9 + 6.57
23. 14.81 − 8.6

24. 11.9 − 2.06
25. 3.45 + 4.061
26. 8.29 + 4.3
27. 7.06 − 4.235

28. 6.02 + 4.005
29. 7.05 − 3.5
30. 1.18 + 3.015
31. 2.304 − 0.87

32. 5.002 − 3.45
33. 6.8 + 3.57
34. 0.23 + 0.091
35. 0.5 − 0.18

36. 8.3 + 2.99 + 17.52
37. 9.5 + 12.32 + 6.4
38. 4.521 + 1.8 + 3.07

39. 3.602 + 9.4 + 24
40. 11.6 + 8.05 + 5.13
41. 7.023 + 1.48 + 3.9

42. 57 + 0.6327 + 189.007
43. 741 + 6.08 + 0.0309
44. 0.045 + 16.32 + 8.6

45. 4.27 + 6.18 + 0.91
46. 3.856 + 14.01 + 1.72
47. 11.45 + 3.79 + 23.861

Multiplying Decimals

Multiply decimals as you would whole numbers. Then place the decimal point in the product. To do this, add the number of decimal places in the factors.

Skills Handbook

① EXAMPLE

Multiply 0.068 × 2.3.

Step 1   Multiply.

$$
\begin{array}{r}
0.068 \\
\times\ 2.3 \\
\hline
204 \\
+\ 1360 \\
\hline
1564
\end{array}
$$

Step 2   Place the decimal point.

$$
\begin{array}{r}
0.068 \\
\times\ 2.3 \\
\hline
204 \\
+\ 1360 \\
\hline
0.1564
\end{array}
$$

← three decimal places
← one decimal place

← four decimal places

② EXAMPLE

Find each product.

a. 3.12 × 0.9

$$
\begin{array}{r}
3.12 \\
\times\ 0.9 \\
\hline
2.808
\end{array}
$$

b. 5.75 × 42

$$
\begin{array}{r}
5.75 \\
\times\ 42 \\
\hline
11\ 50 \\
+\ 230\ 00 \\
\hline
241.50
\end{array}
$$

c. 0.964 × 0.28

$$
\begin{array}{r}
0.964 \\
\times\ 0.28 \\
\hline
7712 \\
+\ 19280 \\
\hline
0.26992
\end{array}
$$

EXERCISES

Multiply.

1. $\begin{array}{r} 1.48 \\ \times\ 3.6 \\ \hline \end{array}$
  2. $\begin{array}{r} 191.2 \\ \times\ 3.4 \\ \hline \end{array}$
  3. $\begin{array}{r} 0.05 \\ \times\ 43 \\ \hline \end{array}$
  4. $\begin{array}{r} 0.27 \\ \times\ 5 \\ \hline \end{array}$
  5. $\begin{array}{r} 1.36 \\ \times\ 3.8 \\ \hline \end{array}$

6. $\begin{array}{r} 6.23 \\ \times\ 0.21 \\ \hline \end{array}$
  7. $\begin{array}{r} 0.512 \\ \times\ 0.76 \\ \hline \end{array}$
  8. $\begin{array}{r} 0.04 \\ \times\ 7 \\ \hline \end{array}$
  9. $\begin{array}{r} 0.136 \\ \times\ 8.4 \\ \hline \end{array}$
  10. $\begin{array}{r} 3 \\ \times\ 0.05 \\ \hline \end{array}$

11. 2.07 × 1.004

12. 0.12 × 6.1

13. 3.2 × 0.15

14. 0.74 × 0.23

15. 2.6 × 0.14

16. 0.77 × 51

17. 9.3 × 0.706

18. 71.13 × 0.4

19. 0.42 × 98

20. 6.3 × 85

21. 45 × 0.028

22. 76 × 3.3

23. 9 × 1.35

24. 4.56 × 7

25. 5 × 2.41

26. 704 × 0.3

27. 8.003 × 0.6

28. 42.2 × 0.9

29. 0.6 × 30.02

30. 0.05 × 11.8

Zeros in a Product

When you multiply with decimals, you may have to write one or more zeros to the left of a product before you can place the decimal point.

① EXAMPLE

Multiply 0.06 × 0.015.

Step 1 Multiply.

```
  0.015
× 0.06
─────
   90
```

Step 2 Place the decimal point.

```
  0.015
× 0.06
───────
0.00090
```
← The product should have 5 decimal places, so you must write three zeros before placing the decimal point.

② EXAMPLE

a. 0.02 × 1.3

```
    1.3
× 0.02
──────
  0.026
```

b. 0.012 × 2.4

```
      2.4
× 0.012
───────
       48
+   240
───────
  0.0288
```

c. 0.022 × 0.051

```
     0.051
×  0.022
─────────
       102
+   1020
─────────
 0.001122
```

EXERCISES

Multiply.

1.
```
  0.03
× 0.9
```

2.
```
  0.06
× 0.5
```

3.
```
   2.4
× 0.03
```

4.
```
      7
× 0.01
```

5.
```
  0.05
× 0.05
```

6.
```
  0.016
× 0.12
```

7.
```
  0.031
× 0.08
```

8.
```
  0.03
× 0.2
```

9.
```
   0.27
× 0.033
```

10.
```
  0.014
× 0.25
```

11. 0.003×0.55

12. 0.01×0.74

13. 0.47×0.08

14. 0.76×0.1

15. 0.3×0.27

16. 0.19×0.05

17. 0.018×0.04

18. 0.43×0.2

19. 0.03×0.03

20. 4.003×0.02

21. 0.5×0.08

22. 0.06×0.7

23. 0.047×0.008

24. 0.05×0.06

25. 0.03×0.4

26. 0.05×0.036

27. 0.4×0.23

28. 0.3×0.017

29. 0.3×0.24

30. 0.67×0.09

31. 3.02×0.006

32. 0.31×0.08

33. 0.14×0.05

34. 0.07×0.85

Dividing Decimals by Whole Numbers

When you divide a decimal by a whole number, the decimal point in the quotient goes directly above the decimal point in the dividend. You may need extra zeros to place the decimal point.

1 EXAMPLE

Divide 2.432 ÷ 32.

Step 1 Divide.

```
        76
32)2.432
   - 2 24
      192
    - 192
        0
```

Step 2 Place the decimal point.

```
     0.076    ← Put extra zeros to the left.
32)2.432        Then place the decimal point.
   - 2 24
      192
    - 192
        0
```

2 EXAMPLE

a. 37.6 ÷ 8

```
     4.7
  8)37.6
   - 32
      5 6
    - 5 6
        0
```

b. 39.33 ÷ 69

```
      0.57
 69)39.33
    - 34 5
       4 83
     - 4 83
         0
```

c. 4.482 ÷ 54

```
      0.083
 54)4.482
    - 4 32
       162
     - 162
         0
```

EXERCISES

Divide.

1. 7)17.92   **2.** 5)16.5   **3.** 9)6.984   **4.** 6)91.44   **5.** 4)35.16

6. 56)8.848   **7.** 22)2.42   **8.** 26)1,723.8   **9.** 83)15.272   **10.** 39)26.91

11. $14.49 \div 7$ **12.** $10.53 \div 9$ **13.** $17.52 \div 2$ **14.** $37.14 \div 6$

15. $0.1352 \div 8$ **16.** $0.0324 \div 9$ **17.** $0.0882 \div 6$ **18.** $0.8682 \div 6$

19. $12.342 \div 22$ **20.** $29.792 \div 32$ **21.** $22.568 \div 26$ **22.** $11.340 \div 36$

23. $45.918 \div 18$ **24.** $79.599 \div 13$ **25.** $58.5 \div 15$ **26.** $74.664 \div 12$

27. $21.0 \div 84$ **28.** $89.378 \div 67$ **29.** $0.0672 \div 48$ **30.** $171.031 \div 53$

Multiplying and Dividing by Powers of Ten

You can use shortcuts to multiply or divide by powers of ten.

When you multiply by	Move the decimal point	When you divide by	Move the decimal point
10,000	4 places to the right	10,000	4 places to the left
1,000	3 places to the right	1,000	3 places to the left
100	2 places to the right	100	2 places to the left
10	1 place to the right	10	1 place to the left
0.1	1 place to the left	0.1	1 place to the right
0.01	2 places to the left	0.01	2 places to the right
0.001	3 places to the left	0.001	3 places to the right

EXAMPLE

Multiply or divide.

a. 0.7×0.001

Move the decimal point 3 places to the left.

0.000.7

$0.7 \times 0.001 = 0.0007$

b. $0.605 \div 100$

Move the decimal point 2 places to the left.

0.00.605

$0.605 \div 100 = 0.00605$

EXERCISES

Multiply or divide.

1. $10,000 \times 0.056$ **2.** 0.001×0.09 **3.** 5.2×10 **4.** $0.03 \times 1,000$

5. $236.7 \div 0.1$ **6.** $45.28 \div 10$ **7.** $0.9 \div 1,000$ **8.** $1.07 \div 0.01$

9. 100×0.08 **10.** $1.03 \times 10,000$ **11.** 1.803×0.001 **12.** 4.1×100

13. $13.7 \div 0.001$ **14.** $203.05 \div 0.01$ **15.** $4.7 \div 10$ **16.** $0.05 \div 100$

17. 23.6×0.01 **18.** $1,000 \times 0.12$ **19.** 0.41×0.001 **20.** 0.01×6.2

21. $42.3 \div 0.1$ **22.** $0.4 \div 10,000$ **23.** $5.02 \div 0.01$ **24.** $16.5 \div 100$

25. $0.27 \div 0.01$ **26.** 1.05×0.001 **27.** 10×0.04 **28.** $2.09 \div 100$

29. 0.65×0.1 **30.** $0.03 \div 100$ **31.** $2.6 \div 0.1$ **32.** $12.6 \times 10,000$

33. $0.3 \div 1,000$ **34.** 0.01×6.7 **35.** 100×0.158 **36.** $23.1 \div 10$

Dividing Decimals by Decimals

To divide with a decimal divisor, multiply it by the smallest power of ten that will make the divisor a whole number. Then multiply the dividend by that same power of ten.

⬤ EXAMPLE

Find each quotient.

a. 3.348 ÷ 6.2
Multiply by 10.

$$
\begin{array}{r}
0.54 \\
6.2\overline{)3\,3.48} \\
-3\ 1\ 0 \\
\hline
2\ 48 \\
-2\ 48 \\
\hline
0
\end{array}
$$

b. 2.4885 ÷ 0.35
Multiply by 100.

$$
\begin{array}{r}
7.11 \\
0.35\overline{)2.48.85} \\
-2\ 45 \\
\hline
3\ 8 \\
-3\ 5 \\
\hline
35 \\
-35 \\
\hline
0
\end{array}
$$

c. 0.0576 ÷ 0.012
Multiply by 1,000.

$$
\begin{array}{r}
4.8 \\
0.012\overline{)0.057.6} \\
-48 \\
\hline
96 \\
-96 \\
\hline
0
\end{array}
$$

EXERCISES

Divide.

1. $3.2\overline{)268.8}$ **2.** $1.9\overline{)123.5}$ **3.** $0.3\overline{)135.6}$ **4.** $2.3\overline{)170.2}$ **5.** $7.9\overline{)252.8}$

6. $5.7\overline{)10.26}$ **7.** $2.3\overline{)71.53}$ **8.** $3.1\overline{)16.12}$ **9.** $7.8\overline{)24.18}$ **10.** $6.3\overline{)14.49}$

11. $134.42 \div 5.17$ **12.** $89.96 \div 3.46$ **13.** $160.58 \div 5.18$ **14.** $106.59 \div 6.27$

15. $62.4 \div 3.9$ **16.** $260.4 \div 8.4$ **17.** $316.8 \div 7.2$ **18.** $162.4 \div 2.9$

19. $1.512 \div 0.54$ **20.** $3.225 \div 0.43$ **21.** $2.484 \div 0.69$ **22.** $511.5 \div 5.5$

23. $0.992 \div 0.8$ **24.** $4.53 \div 0.05$ **25.** $3.498 \div 0.06$ **26.** $59.2 \div 0.8$

27. $2.198 \div 0.07$ **28.** $14.28 \div 0.7$ **29.** $1.98 \div 0.5$ **30.** $26.36 \div 0.04$

31. $3.922 \div 7.4$ **32.** $23.52 \div 0.98$ **33.** $71.25 \div 7.5$ **34.** $114.7 \div 3.7$

35. $0.832 \div 0.52$ **36.** $1.125 \div 0.09$ **37.** $9.666 \div 2.7$ **38.** $1.456 \div 9.1$

39. $0.4374 \div 1.8$ **40.** $2.3414 \div 0.46$ **41.** $0.07224 \div 0.021$ **42.** $0.1386 \div 0.18$

43. $0.16926 \div 0.091$ **44.** $0.6042 \div 5.3$ **45.** $2.3374 \div 0.62$ **46.** $1.0062 \div 0.078$

Zeros in Decimal Division

When you are dividing by a decimal, sometimes you need to use extra zeros in the dividend or the quotient, or both.

1 EXAMPLE

Divide 0.045 ÷ 3.6.

Step 1 Multiply by 10.

$$3.6\overline{)0.0.45}$$

Step 2 Divide.

$$\begin{array}{r} 125 \\ 3.6\overline{)0.0.4500} \\ -36 \\ \hline 90 \\ -72 \\ \hline 180 \\ -180 \\ \hline 0 \end{array}$$

Step 3 Place the decimal point.

$$\begin{array}{r} 0.0125 \\ 3.6\overline{)0.0.4500} \\ -36 \\ \hline 90 \\ -72 \\ \hline 180 \\ -180 \\ \hline 0 \end{array}$$

2 EXAMPLE

Find each quotient.

a. **0.4428 ÷ 8.2**
Multiply by 10.
$$\begin{array}{r} 0.054 \\ 8.2\overline{)0.4.428} \end{array}$$

b. **0.00434 ÷ 0.07**
Multiply by 100.
$$\begin{array}{r} 0.062 \\ 0.07\overline{)0.00.434} \end{array}$$

c. **0.00306 ÷ 0.072**
Multiply by 1,000.
$$\begin{array}{r} 0.0425 \\ 0.072\overline{)0.003.0600} \end{array}$$

EXERCISES

Divide.

1. $0.05\overline{)0.0023}$

2. $0.02\overline{)0.000162}$

3. $0.12\overline{)0.009}$

4. $2.5\overline{)0.021}$

5. $0.0019 \div 0.2$

6. $0.9 \div 0.8$

7. $0.000175 \div 0.07$

8. $0.142 \div 0.04$

9. $0.0017 \div 0.02$

10. $0.003 \div 0.6$

11. $0.0105 \div 0.7$

12. $0.034 \div 0.05$

13. $0.00056 \div 0.16$

14. $0.0612 \div 7.2$

15. $0.217 \div 3.1$

16. $0.052 \div 0.8$

17. $0.000924 \div 0.44$

18. $0.05796 \div 0.63$

19. $0.00123 \div 8.2$

20. $0.0954 \div 0.09$

21. $0.0084 \div 1.4$

22. $0.259 \div 3.5$

23. $0.00468 \div 0.52$

24. $0.104 \div 0.05$

25. $0.00063 \div 0.18$

26. $0.011 \div 0.25$

27. $0.3069 \div 9.3$

28. $0.00045 \div 0.3$

Writing Equivalent Fractions

If you multiply or divide both the numerator and the denominator of a fraction by the same number, you get an equivalent fraction.

1 EXAMPLE

a. Find the missing number in $\frac{5}{6} = \frac{20}{\blacksquare}$.

$$\frac{5}{6} = \frac{20}{\blacksquare}$$ (×4)

$$\frac{5}{6} = \frac{20}{24}$$ (×4)

b. Find the missing number in $\frac{12}{30} = \frac{\blacksquare}{15}$.

$$\frac{12}{30} = \frac{\blacksquare}{15}$$ (÷2)

$$\frac{12}{30} = \frac{6}{15}$$ (÷2)

To write a fraction in simplest form, divide both the numerator and the denominator by the greatest common factor.

2 EXAMPLE

a. Write $\frac{6}{15}$ in simplest form.

3 is the greatest common factor.

$$\frac{6}{15} = \frac{6 \div 3}{15 \div 3} = \frac{2}{5}$$

The simplest form of $\frac{6}{15}$ is $\frac{2}{5}$.

b. Write $\frac{36}{42}$ in simplest form.

6 is the greatest common factor.

$$\frac{36}{42} = \frac{36 \div 6}{42 \div 6} = \frac{6}{7}$$

The simplest form of $\frac{36}{42}$ is $\frac{6}{7}$.

EXERCISES

Find each missing number.

1. $\frac{1}{3} = \frac{\blacksquare}{6}$
2. $\frac{3}{4} = \frac{\blacksquare}{16}$
3. $\frac{18}{30} = \frac{6}{\blacksquare}$
4. $\frac{2}{3} = \frac{\blacksquare}{21}$
5. $\frac{3}{4} = \frac{9}{\blacksquare}$

6. $\frac{3}{10} = \frac{9}{\blacksquare}$
7. $\frac{4}{5} = \frac{\blacksquare}{30}$
8. $\frac{2}{3} = \frac{8}{\blacksquare}$
9. $\frac{33}{55} = \frac{\blacksquare}{5}$
10. $\frac{27}{72} = \frac{9}{\blacksquare}$

11. $\frac{2}{3} = \frac{\blacksquare}{24}$
12. $\frac{11}{12} = \frac{55}{\blacksquare}$
13. $\frac{3}{5} = \frac{18}{\blacksquare}$
14. $\frac{60}{72} = \frac{10}{\blacksquare}$
15. $\frac{7}{8} = \frac{\blacksquare}{24}$

Write each fraction in simplest form.

16. $\frac{12}{36}$
17. $\frac{25}{30}$
18. $\frac{14}{16}$
19. $\frac{27}{36}$
20. $\frac{21}{35}$
21. $\frac{40}{50}$

22. $\frac{24}{40}$
23. $\frac{32}{64}$
24. $\frac{15}{45}$
25. $\frac{27}{63}$
26. $\frac{44}{77}$
27. $\frac{45}{75}$

28. $\frac{60}{72}$
29. $\frac{77}{84}$
30. $\frac{12}{24}$
31. $\frac{24}{32}$
32. $\frac{7}{21}$
33. $\frac{18}{42}$

Mixed Numbers and Improper Fractions

A fraction, such as $\frac{10}{7}$, in which the numerator is greater than or equal to the denominator is an improper fraction. You can write an improper fraction as a mixed number that shows the sum of a whole number and a fraction.

Sometimes it is necessary to do the opposite and write a mixed number as an improper fraction.

EXAMPLE

a. Write $\frac{11}{5}$ as a mixed number.

$$\frac{11}{5} \rightarrow \begin{array}{r} 2 \\ 5\overline{)11} \\ -10 \\ \hline 1 \end{array} \quad \begin{array}{l} \leftarrow \text{whole number} \\ \\ \\ \leftarrow \text{remainder} \end{array}$$

$\frac{11}{5} = 2\frac{1}{5} \quad \leftarrow$ whole number $+ \dfrac{\text{remainder}}{\text{denominator}}$

b. Write $2\frac{5}{6}$ as an improper fraction.

$$2\frac{5}{6} = 2 + \frac{5}{6}$$

$$= \frac{12}{6} + \frac{5}{6} \quad \leftarrow \text{Write 2 as } \frac{12}{6}.$$

$$= \frac{12 + 5}{6} \quad \leftarrow \text{Add the numerators.}$$

$$2\frac{5}{6} = \frac{17}{6}$$

EXERCISES

Write each improper fraction as a mixed number.

1. $\frac{7}{5}$
2. $\frac{9}{2}$
3. $\frac{13}{4}$
4. $\frac{21}{5}$
5. $\frac{13}{10}$
6. $\frac{49}{5}$

7. $\frac{21}{8}$
8. $\frac{13}{7}$
9. $\frac{17}{5}$
10. $\frac{49}{6}$
11. $\frac{17}{4}$
12. $\frac{5}{2}$

13. $\frac{27}{5}$
14. $\frac{12}{9}$
15. $\frac{30}{8}$
16. $\frac{37}{12}$
17. $\frac{8}{6}$
18. $\frac{19}{12}$

19. $\frac{45}{10}$
20. $\frac{15}{12}$
21. $\frac{11}{2}$
22. $\frac{20}{6}$
23. $\frac{34}{8}$
24. $\frac{21}{9}$

Write each mixed number as an improper fraction.

25. $1\frac{1}{2}$
26. $2\frac{2}{3}$
27. $1\frac{1}{12}$
28. $3\frac{1}{5}$
29. $2\frac{2}{7}$
30. $4\frac{1}{2}$

31. $2\frac{7}{8}$
32. $1\frac{2}{9}$
33. $5\frac{1}{5}$
34. $4\frac{7}{9}$
35. $9\frac{1}{4}$
36. $2\frac{3}{8}$

37. $7\frac{7}{8}$
38. $1\frac{5}{12}$
39. $3\frac{3}{7}$
40. $6\frac{1}{2}$
41. $3\frac{1}{10}$
42. $4\frac{6}{7}$

Adding and Subtracting Fractions With Like Denominators

When you add or subtract fractions with the same denominator, add or subtract the numerators and then write the answer over the denominator.

1 EXAMPLE

Add or subtract. Write each answer in simplest form.

a. $\frac{5}{8} + \frac{7}{8}$

$$\frac{5}{8} + \frac{7}{8} = \frac{5+7}{8}$$
$$= \frac{12}{8} = 1\frac{4}{8} = 1\frac{1}{2}$$

b. $\frac{11}{12} - \frac{2}{12}$

$$\frac{11}{12} - \frac{2}{12} = \frac{11-2}{12}$$
$$= \frac{9}{12} = \frac{3}{4}$$

To add or subtract mixed numbers, add or subtract the fractions first. Then add or subtract the whole numbers.

2 EXAMPLE

Add or subtract. Write each answer in simplest form.

a. $3\frac{4}{6} + 2\frac{5}{6}$

$$\begin{array}{r} 3\frac{4}{6} \\ + 2\frac{5}{6} \\ \hline 5\frac{9}{6} = 5 + 1 + \frac{3}{6} = 6\frac{1}{2} \end{array}$$

b. $6\frac{1}{4} - 1\frac{3}{4}$

$$6\frac{1}{4} \rightarrow \quad 5\frac{5}{4} \quad \leftarrow \text{Rewrite 1 unit as } \frac{4}{4} \text{ and add it to } \frac{1}{4}.$$

$$\begin{array}{r} -1\frac{3}{4} \quad -1\frac{3}{4} \\ \hline 4\frac{2}{4} = 4\frac{1}{2} \end{array}$$

EXERCISES

Add or subtract. Write each answer in simplest form.

1. $\frac{4}{5} + \frac{3}{5}$
2. $\frac{2}{6} - \frac{1}{6}$
3. $\frac{2}{7} + \frac{2}{7}$
4. $\frac{7}{8} + \frac{2}{8}$
5. $1\frac{2}{5} - \frac{1}{5}$

6. $\frac{3}{6} - \frac{1}{6}$
7. $\frac{6}{8} - \frac{3}{8}$
8. $\frac{2}{9} + \frac{1}{9}$
9. $\frac{4}{5} - \frac{1}{5}$
10. $\frac{5}{9} + \frac{7}{9}$

11. $9\frac{1}{3} - 8\frac{1}{3}$
12. $8\frac{6}{7} - 4\frac{2}{7}$
13. $3\frac{1}{10} + 1\frac{3}{10}$
14. $2\frac{2}{9} + 3\frac{4}{9}$

15. $4\frac{5}{12} - 3\frac{1}{12}$
16. $9\frac{5}{9} + 6\frac{7}{9}$
17. $5\frac{7}{8} + 2\frac{3}{8}$
18. $4\frac{4}{7} - 2\frac{1}{7}$

19. $9\frac{3}{4} + 1\frac{3}{4}$
20. $8\frac{2}{3} - 4\frac{1}{3}$
21. $8\frac{7}{10} + 2\frac{3}{10}$
22. $1\frac{4}{5} + 3\frac{3}{5}$

23. $7\frac{1}{5} - 2\frac{3}{5}$
24. $4\frac{1}{3} - 1\frac{2}{3}$
25. $4\frac{3}{8} - 3\frac{5}{8}$
26. $5\frac{1}{12} - 2\frac{7}{12}$

Multiplying and Dividing Fractions

To multiply fractions, multiply the numerators and the denominators.
To divide fractions, multiply by the reciprocal of the divisor.

EXAMPLE

Multiply. Write each answer in simplest form.

a. $\frac{8}{9} \times \frac{3}{10} = \frac{\overset{4}{8}}{\underset{3}{9}} \times \frac{\overset{1}{3}}{\underset{5}{10}} = \frac{4}{15}$

b. $3\frac{1}{8} \times 1\frac{3}{4} = \frac{25}{8} \times \frac{7}{4}$

$= \frac{175}{32} = 5\frac{15}{32}$ ← Rewrite as a mixed number.

Divide. Write each answer in simplest form.

c. $\frac{2}{3} \div \frac{4}{5} = \frac{2}{3} \times \frac{5}{4}$

$= \frac{\overset{1}{2}}{3} \times \frac{5}{\underset{2}{4}} = \frac{5}{6}$

d. $3\frac{1}{8} \div 1\frac{3}{4} = \frac{25}{8} \div \frac{7}{4}$

$= \frac{25}{\underset{2}{8}} \times \frac{\overset{1}{4}}{7} = \frac{25}{14} = 1\frac{11}{14}$ ← Rewrite as a mixed number.

EXERCISES

Multiply. Write each answer in simplest form.

1. $\frac{3}{4} \times \frac{3}{5}$

2. $\frac{2}{3} \times \frac{3}{4}$

3. $6 \times \frac{2}{3}$

4. $\frac{3}{4} \times \frac{5}{6}$

5. $\frac{5}{8} \times \frac{2}{3}$

6. $\frac{9}{16} \times \frac{2}{3}$

7. $\frac{3}{10} \times \frac{2}{15}$

8. $\frac{3}{4} \times \frac{1}{6}$

9. $\frac{1}{4} \times \frac{5}{20}$

10. $\frac{9}{10} \times \frac{1}{3}$

11. $1\frac{1}{3} \times 2\frac{2}{3}$

12. $\frac{3}{5} \times 2\frac{3}{4}$

13. $2\frac{1}{4} \times 3\frac{1}{3}$

14. $\frac{1}{4} \times 3\frac{1}{3}$

15. $6\frac{1}{4} \times 7$

16. $1\frac{3}{4} \times 2\frac{1}{5}$

17. $2\frac{3}{4} \times \frac{1}{2}$

18. $3\frac{4}{5} \times 2\frac{1}{3}$

Divide. Write each answer in simplest form.

19. $\frac{5}{8} \div \frac{5}{7}$

20. $\frac{5}{7} \div \frac{5}{8}$

21. $\frac{3}{4} \div \frac{6}{11}$

22. $\frac{1}{9} \div \frac{1}{9}$

23. $\frac{1}{9} \div 9$

24. $\frac{9}{10} \div \frac{3}{5}$

25. $\frac{2}{3} \div \frac{1}{9}$

26. $\frac{4}{5} \div \frac{5}{6}$

27. $\frac{1}{5} \div \frac{8}{9}$

28. $\frac{7}{8} \div \frac{1}{3}$

29. $4\frac{1}{5} \div 2\frac{2}{5}$

30. $6\frac{1}{4} \div 4\frac{3}{8}$

31. $2\frac{1}{3} \div 5\frac{5}{6}$

32. $1\frac{1}{2} \div 4\frac{1}{2}$

33. $15\frac{2}{3} \div 1\frac{1}{3}$

34. $10\frac{1}{3} \div 2\frac{1}{5}$

35. $6\frac{1}{4} \div 1\frac{3}{4}$

36. $6\frac{2}{3} \div 3\frac{1}{8}$

Working With Integers

Quantities less than zero can be written using negative integers. For example, a temperature of 5 degrees below zero can be written as -5. Positive integers are used for quantities greater than zero.

1 EXAMPLE

Write an integer for each situation.

a. **10 degrees above zero**
$+10$, or 10

b. **a loss of \$20**
-20

c. **15 yards lost**
-15

A number line can be used to compare integers. The integer to the right is greater.

2 EXAMPLE

Compare. Use >, <, or = to complete each statement.

a. **0 ▣ −3**
0 is to the right, so it is greater.
$0 > -3$

b. **−2 ▣ −6**
-2 is to the right, so it is greater.
$-2 > -6$

c. **−7 ▣ 3**
-7 is to the left, so it is less.
$-7 < 3$

EXERCISES

Write an integer for each situation.

1. 6 yards gained
2. 10 yards lost
3. 5 steps forward
4. 4 steps backward
5. find \$3
6. lose \$8
7. 12 floors up
8. 4 floors down

Compare. Use >, <, or = to complete each statement.

9. 0 ▣ −1
10. −9 ▣ 0
11. −3 ▣ 3
12. 7 ▣ −3
13. 0 ▣ 1

14. 3 ▣ 0
15. 1 ▣ −4
16. −2 ▣ −9
17. 6 ▣ −1
18. 3 ▣ −10

19. −7 ▣ 3
20. 4 ▣ 6
21. −16 ▣ −25
22. −15 ▣ −12
23. 7 ▣ −8

24. 2 ▣ 3
25. −7 ▣ −8
26. 35 ▣ −40
27. −30 ▣ −20
28. 25 ▣ −25

29. 9 ▣ −9
30. −6 ▣ −5
31. −23 ▣ −15
32. −17 ▣ −19
33. −15 ▣ −25

Skills Handbook

Tables

Table 1 Measures

Metric

Length

10 millimeters (mm) = 1 centimeter (cm)

100 cm = 1 meter (m)

1,000 m = 1 kilometer (km)

Area

100 square millimeters (mm^2) =
  1 square centimeter (cm^2)

10,000 cm^2 = 1 square meter (m^2)

1,000,000 m^2 = 1 square kilometer (km^2)

Volume

1,000 cubic millimeters (mm^3) =
  1 cubic centimeter (cm^3)

1,000,000 cm^3 = 1 cubic meter (m^3)

Mass

1,000 milligrams (mg) = 1 gram (g)

1,000 g = 1 kilogram (kg)

Volume (Capacity)

1,000 milliliters (mL) = 1 liter (L)

1 mL = 1 cm^3

Customary

Length

12 inches (in.) = 1 foot (ft)

3 ft = 1 yard (yd)

36 in. = 1 yd

5,280 ft = 1 mile (mi)

1,760 yd = 1 mi

Area

144 square inches ($in.^2$) = 1 square foot (ft^2)

9 ft^2 = 1 square yard (yd^2)

4,840 yd^2 = 1 acre

Volume

1,728 cubic inches ($in.^3$) = 1 cubic foot (ft^3)

27 ft^3 = 1 cubic yard (yd^3)

Weight

16 ounces (oz) = 1 pound (lb)

2,000 lb = 1 ton (t)

Volume (Capacity)

8 fluid ounces (fl oz) = 1 cup (c)

2 c = 1 pint (pt)

2 pt = 1 quart (qt)

4 qt = 1 gallon (gal)

Time

1 minute (min) = 60 seconds (s)

1 hour (h) = 60 min

1 day (d) = 24 h

1 year (yr) = 365 d

Table 2 📖 Reading Math Symbols

$>$	is greater than	p. 104
$<$	is less than	p. 104
$\geq$	is greater than or equal to	p. 104
$\leq$	is less than or equal to	p. 104
$=$	is equal to	p. 82
$\neq$	is not equal to	p. 82
$\approx$	is approximately equal to	p. 130
$\stackrel{?}{=}$	is this statement true?	p. 83
$+$	plus (addition)	p. 5
$-$	minus (subtraction)	p. 5
$\times, \cdot$	times (multiplication)	p. 5
$\div, \overline{)}$	divide (division)	p. 5
$\sqrt{x}$	nonnegative square root of x	p. 588
$^{\circ}$	degrees	p. 468
$\%$	percent	p. 314
$(\ )$	parentheses for grouping	p. 9
$|a|$	absolute value of a	p. 19
$a:b, \frac{a}{b}$	ratio of a to b	p. 292
(a, b)	ordered pair with x-coordinate a and y-coordinate b	p. 52
$\cong$	is congruent to	p. 469
$\sim$	is similar to	p. 303
$\parallel$	is parallel to	p. 463
π	pi, an irrational number approximately equal to 3.14	p. 490
$f(n)$	function value at n, f of n	p. 422
b	y-intercept	p. 417
m	slope of a line	p. 417
$-a$	opposite of a	p. 19
$\frac{1}{a}$	reciprocal of a	p. 254
a^n	nth power of a	p. 186
d	diameter	p. 491
	distance	pp. 145, 598
A'	image of A, A prime	p. 501

A	Area	p. 526
b_1, b_2	base lengths of a trapezoid	p. 534
b	base length	p. 527
h	height	p. 527
p or P	perimeter	p. 146
ℓ	length	p 146
	slant height	p. 558
w	width	p. 146
C	circumference	p. 490
S.A.	surface area	p. 551
L.A.	lateral area	p. 552
B	area of a base	p. 551
V	volume	p. 563
r	rate	p. 145
	radius	p. 491
$\overline{AB}$	segment AB	p. 462
$\overrightarrow{AB}$	ray AB	p. 462
$\overleftrightarrow{AB}$	line AB	p. 462
$\triangle ABC$	triangle with vertices A, B, and C	p. 303
$\angle A$	angle with vertex A	p. 468
$\angle ABC$	angle with sides $\overrightarrow{BA}$ and $\overrightarrow{BC}$	p. 468
$m\angle ABC$	measure of angle ABC	p. 469
AB	length of segment $\overline{AB}$	p. 462
$\sin A$	sine of $\angle A$	p. 614
$\cos A$	cosine of $\angle A$	p. 614
$\tan A$	tangent of $\angle A$	p. 614
$P(\text{event})$	probability of an event	p. 309
$_nP_r$	number of permutations of n things taken r at a time	p. 667
$_nC_r$	number of combinations of n things taken r at a time	p. 668
$\wedge$	raised to a power (in software or a calculator)	p. 213

Table 3 Squares and Square Roots

N	N^2	$\sqrt{N}$	N	N^2	$\sqrt{N}$
1	1	1	51	2,601	7.141
2	4	1.414	52	2,704	7.211
3	9	1.732	53	2,809	7.280
4	16	2	54	2,916	7.348
5	25	2.236	55	3,025	7.416
6	36	2.449	56	3,136	7.483
7	49	2.646	57	3,249	7.550
8	64	2.828	58	3,364	7.616
9	81	3	59	3,481	7.681
10	100	3.162	60	3,600	7.746
11	121	3.317	61	3,721	7.810
12	144	3.464	62	3,844	7.874
13	169	3.606	63	3,969	7.937
14	196	3.742	64	4,096	8
15	225	3.873	65	4,225	8.062
16	256	4	66	4,356	8.124
17	289	4.123	67	4,489	8.185
18	324	4.243	68	4,624	8.246
19	361	4.359	69	4,761	8.307
20	400	4.472	70	4,900	8.367
21	441	4.583	71	5,041	8.426
22	484	4.690	72	5,184	8.485
23	529	4.796	73	5,329	8.544
24	576	4.899	74	5,476	8.602
25	625	5	75	5,625	8.660
26	676	5.099	76	5,776	8.718
27	729	5.196	77	5,929	8.775
28	784	5.292	78	6,084	8.832
29	841	5.385	79	6,241	8.888
30	900	5.477	80	6,400	8.944
31	961	5.568	81	6,561	9
32	1,024	5.657	82	6,724	9.055
33	1,089	5.745	83	6,889	9.110
34	1,156	5.831	84	7,056	9.165
35	1,225	5.916	85	7,225	9.220
36	1,296	6	86	7,396	9.274
37	1,369	6.083	87	7,569	9.327
38	1,444	6.164	88	7,744	9.381
39	1,521	6.245	89	7,921	9.434
40	1,600	6.325	90	8,100	9.487
41	1,681	6.403	91	8,281	9.539
42	1,764	6.481	92	8,464	9.592
43	1,849	6.557	93	8,649	9.644
44	1,936	6.633	94	8,836	9.695
45	2,025	6.708	95	9,025	9.747
46	2,116	6.782	96	9,216	9.798
47	2,209	6.856	97	9,409	9.849
48	2,304	6.928	98	9,604	9.899
49	2,401	7	99	9,801	9.950
50	2,500	7.071	100	10,000	10

Table 4 Trigonometric Ratios

Angle	Sine	Cosine	Tangent	Angle	Sine	Cosine	Tangent
1°	0.0175	0.9998	0.0175	46°	0.7193	0.6947	1.0355
2°	0.0349	0.9994	0.0349	47°	0.7314	0.6820	1.0724
3°	0.0523	0.9986	0.0524	48°	0.7431	0.6691	1.1106
4°	0.0698	0.9976	0.0699	49°	0.7547	0.6561	1.1504
5°	0.0872	0.9962	0.0875	50°	0.7660	0.6428	1.1918
6°	0.1045	0.9945	0.1051	51°	0.7771	0.6293	1.2349
7°	0.1219	0.9925	0.1228	52°	0.7880	0.6157	1.2799
8°	0.1392	0.9903	0.1405	53°	0.7986	0.6018	1.3270
9°	0.1564	0.9877	0.1584	54°	0.8090	0.5878	1.3764
10°	0.1736	0.9848	0.1763	55°	0.8192	0.5736	1.4281
11°	0.1908	0.9816	0.1944	56°	0.8290	0.5592	1.4826
12°	0.2079	0.9781	0.2126	57°	0.8387	0.5446	1.5399
13°	0.2250	0.9744	0.2309	58°	0.8480	0.5299	1.6003
14°	0.2419	0.9703	0.2493	59°	0.8572	0.5150	1.6643
15°	0.2588	0.9659	0.2679	60°	0.8660	0.5000	1.7321
16°	0.2756	0.9613	0.2867	61°	0.8746	0.4848	1.8040
17°	0.2924	0.9563	0.3057	62°	0.8829	0.4695	1.8807
18°	0.3090	0.9511	0.3249	63°	0.8910	0.4540	1.9626
19°	0.3256	0.9455	0.3443	64°	0.8988	0.4384	2.0503
20°	0.3420	0.9397	0.3640	65°	0.9063	0.4226	2.1445
21°	0.3584	0.9336	0.3839	66°	0.9135	0.4067	2.2460
22°	0.3746	0.9272	0.4040	67°	0.9205	0.3907	2.3559
23°	0.3907	0.9205	0.4245	68°	0.9272	0.3746	2.4751
24°	0.4067	0.9135	0.4452	69°	0.9336	0.3584	2.6051
25°	0.4226	0.9063	0.4663	70°	0.9397	0.3420	2.7475
26°	0.4384	0.8988	0.4877	71°	0.9455	0.3256	2.9042
27°	0.4540	0.8910	0.5095	72°	0.9511	0.3090	3.0777
28°	0.4695	0.8829	0.5317	73°	0.9563	0.2924	3.2709
29°	0.4848	0.8746	0.5543	74°	0.9613	0.2756	3.4874
30°	0.5000	0.8660	0.5774	75°	0.9659	0.2588	3.7321
31°	0.5150	0.8572	0.6009	76°	0.9703	0.2419	4.0108
32°	0.5299	0.8480	0.6249	77°	0.9744	0.2250	4.3315
33°	0.5446	0.8387	0.6494	78°	0.9781	0.2079	4.7046
34°	0.5592	0.8290	0.6745	79°	0.9816	0.1908	5.1446
35°	0.5736	0.8192	0.7002	80°	0.9848	0.1736	5.6713
36°	0.5878	0.8090	0.7265	81°	0.9877	0.1564	6.3138
37°	0.6018	0.7986	0.7536	82°	0.9903	0.1392	7.1154
38°	0.6157	0.7880	0.7813	83°	0.9925	0.1219	8.1443
39°	0.6293	0.7771	0.8098	84°	0.9945	0.1045	9.5144
40°	0.6428	0.7660	0.8391	85°	0.9962	0.0872	11.4301
41°	0.6561	0.7547	0.8693	86°	0.9976	0.0698	14.3007
42°	0.6691	0.7431	0.9004	87°	0.9986	0.0523	19.0811
43°	0.6820	0.7314	0.9325	88°	0.9994	0.0349	28.6363
44°	0.6947	0.7193	0.9657	89°	0.9998	0.0175	57.2900
45°	0.7071	0.7071	1.0000				

Tables

Formulas and Properties

Geometric Formulas

Perimeter and Circumference

Rectangle

$P = 2\ell + 2w$

Circle

$C = \pi d$ or $C = 2\pi r$

Area

Square

$A = s^2$

Parallelogram and Rectangle

$A = bh$

Triangle

$A = \frac{1}{2}bh$

Trapezoid

$A = \frac{1}{2}h(b_1 + b_2)$

Circle

$C = \pi r^2$

Triangle Formulas

Pythagorean Theorem

In a right triangle with legs of lengths a and b and hypotenuse of length c, $a^2 + b^2 = c^2$.

Trigonometric Ratios

$\text{sine of } \angle A = \dfrac{\text{length of leg opposite } \angle A}{\text{length of hypotenuse}}$

$\text{cosine of } \angle A = \dfrac{\text{length of leg adjacent to } \angle A}{\text{length of hypotenuse}}$

$\text{tangent of } \angle A = \dfrac{\text{length of leg opposite } \angle A}{\text{length of leg adjacent to } \angle A}$

Triangle Angle Sum

For any $\triangle ABC$,

$m\angle A + m\angle B + m\angle C = 180°.$

Surface Area

Rectangular Prism

L.A. $= ph$

S.A. $=$ L.A. $+ 2B$

Cylinder

L.A. $= 2\pi rh$

S.A. $=$ L.A. $+ 2B$

Pyramid

L.A. $= \frac{1}{2}p\ell = n\left(\frac{1}{2}b\ell\right)$, where n is the number of faces

S.A. $=$ L.A. $+ B$

Cone

L.A. $= \pi r\ell$

S.A. $=$ L.A. $+ B$

Sphere

S.A. $= 4\pi r^2$

Volume

Prism

$V = Bh$

Cylinder

$V = Bh$, or $\pi r^2 h$

Pyramid

$V = \frac{1}{3}Bh$

Cone

$V = \frac{1}{3}Bh$, or $\frac{1}{3}\pi r^2 h$

Sphere

$V = \frac{4}{3}\pi r^3$

Properties of Real Numbers

Unless otherwise stated, $a, b, c,$ and d are real numbers.

Identity Properties

Addition	$a + 0 = a$ and $0 + a = a$
Multiplication	$a \cdot 1 = a$ and $1 \cdot a = a$

Commutative Properties

Addition	$a + b = b + a$
Multiplication	$a \cdot b = b \cdot a$

Associative Properties

Addition	$(a + b) + c = a + (b + c)$
Multiplication	$(a \cdot b) \cdot c = a \cdot (b \cdot c)$

Inverse Properties

Addition

$a + (-a) = 0$ and $-a + a = 0$

Multiplication

$a \cdot \frac{1}{a} = 1$ and $\frac{1}{a} \cdot a = 1 (a \neq 0)$

Distributive Properties

$a(b + c) = ab + ac \qquad (b + c)a = ba + ca$

$a(b - c) = ab - ac \qquad (b - c)a = ba - ca$

Properties of Equality

Addition	If $a = b$, then $a + c = b + c$.
Subtraction	If $a = b$, then $a - c = b - c$.
Multiplication	If $a = b$, then $a \cdot c = b \cdot c$.
Division	If $a = b$, and $c \neq 0$, then $\frac{a}{c} = \frac{b}{c}$.
Substitution	If $a = b$, then b can replace a in any expression.
Reflexive	$a = a$
Symmetric	If $a = b$, then $b = a$.
Transitive	If $a = b$ and $b = c$, then $a = c$.

Zero-Product Property

If $ab = 0$ then $a = 0$ or $b = 0$.

Zero Property of Multiplication

$a \cdot 0 = 0 \cdot a = 0$

Cross Product Property

$\frac{a}{b} = \frac{c}{d}$ is equivalent to $ad = bc$.

Closure Properties

$a + b$ is a unique real number.

ab is a unique real number.

Density Property

Between any two rational numbers, there is at least one other rational number.

Properties of Inequality

Addition	If $a > b$, then $a + c > b + c$.
	If $a < b$, then $a + c < b + c$.
Subtraction	If $a > b$, then $a - c > b - c$.
	If $a < b$, then $a - c < b - c$.

Multiplication

If $a > b$ and $c > 0$, then $ac > bc$.

If $a < b$ and $c > 0$, then $ac < bc$.

If $a > b$ and $c < 0$, then $ac < bc$.

If $a < b$ and $c < 0$, then $ac > bc$.

Division

If $a > b$ and $c > 0$, then $\frac{a}{c} > \frac{b}{c}$.

If $a < b$ and $c > 0$, then $\frac{a}{c} < \frac{b}{c}$.

If $a > b$ and $c < 0$, then $\frac{a}{c} < \frac{b}{c}$.

If $a < b$ and $c < 0$, then $\frac{a}{c} > \frac{b}{c}$.

Transitive	If $a > b$ and $b > c$, then $a > c$.
Comparison	If $a = b + c$ and $c > 0$, then $a > b$.

Properties of Exponents

For $a \neq 0$ and any integers m and n:

Zero Exponent	$a^0 = 1$
Negative Exponent	$a^{-n} = \frac{1}{a^n}$
Product of Powers	$a^m \cdot a^n = a^{m+n}$
Quotient of Powers	$\frac{a^m}{a^n} = a^{m-n}$
Power of a Power	$(a^m)^n = a^{m \cdot n}$

English/Spanish Illustrated Glossary

A

Absolute value (p. 19)   Absolute value is the distance of a number from zero on a number line. You write *the absolute value* of −3 as $|-3|$.

Valor absoluto (p. 19)   El valor absoluto de un número es la distancia desde cero hasta ese número en una recta numérica. Escribe "el valor absoluto de 23" como $|-3|$.

The absolute value of −3 is 3 because −3 is 3 units from zero on a number line.

Absolute value function (p. 703)   An absolute value function is a function with a graph that is V-shaped and opens up or down.

EXAMPLE   The absolute value function $y = |x| - 3$ has the graph shown here.

Función de valor absoluto (p. 703)   Una función de valor absoluto es una función con una gráfica en forma de V abierta hacia arriba o hacia abajo.

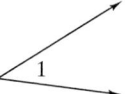

Acute angle (p. 468)   An acute angle is an angle with a measure less than 90°.

EXAMPLE $0° < m\angle 1 < 90°$

Ángulo agudo (p. 468)   Un ángulo agudo es cualquier ángulo que mide menos de 90°.

Acute triangle (p. 474)   An acute triangle is a triangle with three acute angles.

EXAMPLE $\angle 1, \angle 2,$ and $\angle 3$ are acute.

Acutángulo (p. 474)   Acutángulo es un triángulo que tiene sus tres ángulos agudos.

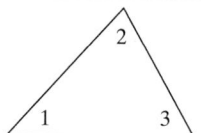

Addition Property of Equality (p. 90)   If $a = b$ then $a + c = b + c$.

Propiedad aditiva de la igualdad (p. 90)   Si $a = b$, entonces $a + c = b + c$.

$8 = 2(4)$, so $8 + 3 = 2(4) + 3$

Addition Property of Inequality (p. 109)   If $a > b$, then $a + c > b + c$. If $a < b$, then $a + c < b + c$.

Propiedad aditiva de la desigualdad (p. 109)   Si $a > b$, entonces $a + c > b + c$. Si $a < b$, entonces $a + c < b + c$.

$7 > 3$, so $7 + 4 > 3 + 4$
$2 < 5$, so $2 + 6 < 5 + 6$

Additive identity (p. 69)   The additive identity is zero. When you add a number and 0, the sum equals the original number.

$a + 0 = a$

Identidad aditiva (p. 69)   La identidad aditiva es cero. Cuando se suman un número y 0, la suma es idéntica al número original.

Additive inverses (p. 24)   Additive inverses are two numbers with a sum of zero.

23 and -23 are additive inverses because $-23 + 23 = 0$.

Inversos aditivos (p. 24)   Se llaman inversos aditivos a los números cuya suma es igual a cero.

Adjacent angles (p. 469)   Adjacent angles are two angles that share a vertex and a side but no points in their interiors.

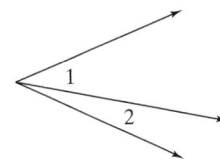

$\angle 1$ and $\angle 2$ are adjacent angles.

Ángulos adyacentes (p. 469)   Ángulos adyacentes son dos ángulos que tienen un mismo vértice y un lado común, pero no tienen puntos interiores comunes.

Alternate interior angles (p. 470)   Alternate interior angles are angles between two lines and on opposite sides of a transversal.

EXAMPLE $\angle 2$ and $\angle 3$ are alternate interior angles. $\angle 1$ and $\angle 4$ are also alternate interior angles.

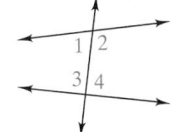

Ángulos alternos internos (p. 470)   Ángulos alternos internos son los pares de ángulos no adyacentes, ambos interiores, en lados opuestos de una transversal.

Altitude (p. 527)   An altitude is any segment perpendicular to the line containing the base of a figure, and drawn from the side opposite the base.

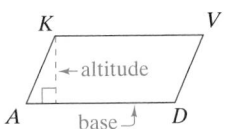

Altura (p. 527)   La altura es cualquier segmento perpendicular a la recta de la base de la figura y se dibuja desde el lado opuesto a la base.

Angle (p. 468)   An angle is a figure formed by two rays with a common endpoint.

EXAMPLE $\angle 1$ is made up of $\overrightarrow{GP}$ and $\overrightarrow{GS}$ with common endpoint G.

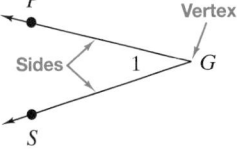

Ángulo (p. 468)   Un ángulo es una figura formada por dos rayos que parten de un origen común.

Angle bisector (p. 497)   An angle bisector is a ray that divides a given angle into two congruent angles, each half the size of the given angle.

EXAMPLE $\overrightarrow{BD}$ is the angle bisector of $\angle ABC$.

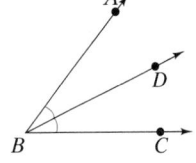

Bisectriz de un ángulo (p. 497)   La bisectriz de un ángulo es el rayo que divide un ángulo dado en dos ángulos congruentes, cada uno de los cuales tiene la mitad de tamaño que el ángulo dado.

English/Spanish Glossary

Angle of depression (p. 622)   An angle of depression is an angle formed by a horizontal line and a line of sight below it.

EXAMPLE $\angle XYZ$ is an angle of depression.

Ángulo de depresión (p. 622)   Un ángulo de depresión es un ángulo que está formado por una recta horizontal y una línea de visión por debajo de ella.

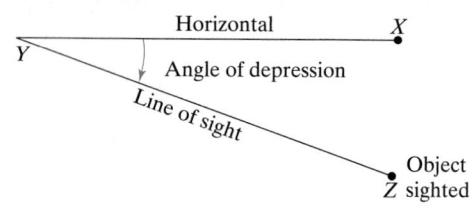

Angle of elevation (p. 620)   An angle of elevation is an angle formed by a horizontal line and a line of sight above it.

EXAMPLE $\angle ABC$ is an angle of elevation.

Ángulo de elevación (p. 620)   Una ángulo de elevación es un ángulo que está formado por una recta horizontal y una línea de visión por arriba de ella.

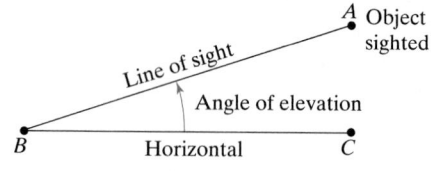

Angle of rotation (p. 511)   See *Rotation.*

Ángulo de rotación (p. 511)   Ver *Rotation.*

Area (p. 526)   The area of a figure is the number of square units it encloses.

EXAMPLE $b = 4$ ft and $h = 6$ ft, so the area is 24 ft^2.

Área (p. 526)   El área de una figura es el número de unidades cuadradas en su interior.

Each square equals 1 ft^2.

Arithmetic sequence (p. 696)   An arithmetic sequence is a sequence of numbers in which each term after the first is the result of adding a fixed number (called the common difference) to the previous term.

Progresión aritmética (p. 696)   Una progresión aritmética es una sucesión de números en la que cada término después del primero resulta de la suma de un mismo número (llamado diferencia común) al término anterior.

The sequence 4, 10, 16, 22, 28, 34, . . . is an arithmetic sequence. The common difference is 6.

Associative Properties of Addition and Multiplication (p. 68)
For any numbers a, b, and $c, (a + b) + c = a + (b + c)$ and $(ab)c = a(bc)$.

Propiedad asociativa de la suma y de la multiplicación (p. 68)   Para cualesquiera números a, b y $c, (a + b) + c = a + (b + c)$ y $(ab)c = a(bc)$.

$(2 + 7) + 3 = 2 + (7 + 3)$
$(9 \cdot 4)5 = 9(4 \cdot 5)$

Balance (p. 387)   The balance in an account is the principal plus the earned interest.

Balance (p. 387)   El balance de una cuenta es el capital más el interés ganado.

See *Compound interest.*

Bar graph (p. 103) A bar graph is a graph that compares amounts.

EXAMPLE This bar graph compares the numbers of students in grades 6, 7, and 8.

Gráfica de barras (p. 103) Una gráfica de barras es una gráfica que compara cantidades.

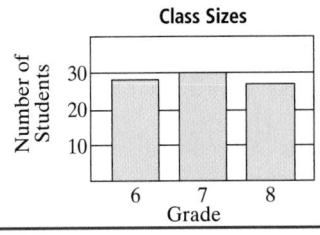

Base (p. 184) The base is the repeated factor of a number written in exponential form.

Base (p. 184) La base es el factor repetido de un número que se escribe en forma exponencial.

$$5^4 = 5 \cdot 5 \cdot 5 \cdot 5$$
5 is the base.

Bases of three-dimensional figures (p. 545) See *Cone, Cylinder, Prism,* and *Pyramid.*

Bases de figuras tridimensionales (p. 545) Ver *Cone, Cylinder, Prism* y *Pyramid.*

Bases of two-dimensional figures (pp. 526, 531) See *Parallelogram, Triangle,* and *Trapezoid.*

Bases de figuras bidimensionales (p. 526, 531) Ver *Parallelogram, Triangle,* y *Trapezoid.*

Binomial (p. 712) A binomial is a polynomial with two terms.

Binomio (p. 712) Un binomio es un polinomio con dos términos.

$3x^2 - 1$ is a binomial.

Box-and-whisker plot (p. 641) A box-and-whisker plot is a graph that shows the distribution of data along a number line. Quartiles divide the data into four equal parts.

EXAMPLE The box-and-whisker plot at the right is for the data
16 19 26 27 27 29 30 31 34 35 37 39 40.

The lower quartile is 26.5. The median is 30. The upper quartile is 36.

Gráfica de caja y brazos (p. 641) Una gráfica de caja y brazos presenta la distribución de datos en una recta numérica. Los cuartiles dividen los datos en cuatro partes iguales.

Center of rotation (p. 511) See *Rotation.*

Centro de rotación (p. 511) Ver *Rotation.*

Central angle (p. 491) A central angle is an angle whose vertex is the center of a circle.

Ángulo central (p. 491) Un ángulo central es un ángulo cuyo vértice está en el centro del círculo.

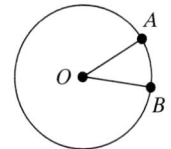

$\angle AOB$ is a central angle.

Chord (p. 490) A chord of a circle is a segment whose endpoints are on the circle.

EXAMPLE $\overline{AB}$ is a chord of circle O.

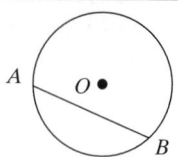

Cuerda (p. 490) Una cuerda es un segmento cuyos extremos se hallan en un círculo.

Circle (p. 490) A circle is the set of all points in a plane that are equidistant from a given point, called the center.

EXAMPLE Circle O

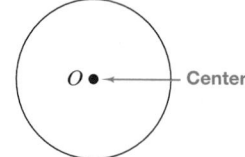

Círculo (p. 490) Un círculo es un conjunto de puntos en un plano que se hallan a la misma distancia de un punto dado llamado el centro.

Circle graph (p. 491) A circle graph is a graph that represents parts of a whole. The total must be 100% or 1.

EXAMPLE This circle graph represents the different types of the plays that William Shakespeare wrote.

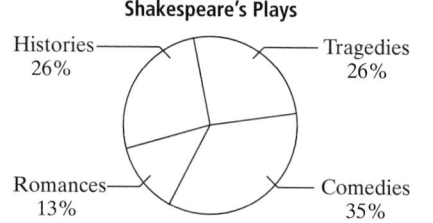

Shakespeare's Plays

Gráfica circular (p. 491) Una gráfica circular es la gráfica que representa partes de un todo. El total debe ser cien por ciénto o uno.

Circumference (p. 490) Circumference is the distance around a circle. You calculate the circumference of a circle by multiplying the diameter by π.

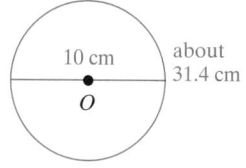

Circunferencia (p. 490) La circunferencia es la distancia alrededor de un círculo. La circunferencia de un círculo se calcula multiplicando el diámetro por π.

The circumference of the circle is 10π cm, or approximately 31.4 cm.

Coefficient (p. 78) A coefficient is a number that multiplies a variable.

In the expression $2x + 3y - 16$, 2 is the coefficient of x and 3 is the coefficient of y.

Coeficiente (p. 78) Coeficiente es el número que multiplica una variable.

Combination (p. 668) A combination is a group of items in which the order of the items is *not* important. You can use the notation $_nC_r$ to express the number of combinations of n objects chosen r at a time.

The combination (pots and pans) is the same as the combination (pans and pots).

Combinación (p. 668) Una combinación es un conjunto de datos en el cual el orden de sus componentes no es importante. Se puede usar la notación $_nC_r$ para expresar el número de combinaciones de n objetos elegidos r veces a la vez.

Commission (p. 325) Commission is pay that is equal to a percent of sales.

Comisión (p. 325) Una comisión es un pago que equivale a un porcentaje de las ventas.

A saleswoman received a 5% commission on sales of $120. Her commission was $6.

Common difference (p. 696) See *Arithmetic sequence.*

Diferencia común (p. 696) Ver *Arithmetic sequence.*

Common ratio (p. 697) See *Geometric sequence.*

Razón común (p. 697) Ver *Geometric sequence.*

Commutative Properties of Addition and Multiplication (p. 68) For any numbers a and b, $a + b = b + a$ and $ab = ba$.

Propiedad conmutativa de la suma (p. 68) Para cualquier número a y b, $a + b = b + a$, y $ab = ba$.

$6 + 4 = 4 + 6$
$9 \cdot 5 = 5 \cdot 9$

Compass (p. 495) A compass is a geometric tool used to draw circles and arcs.

Compás (p. 495) Un compás es un instrumento de geometría que se emplea para trazar círculos y arcos.

Compatible numbers (p. 135) Compatible numbers are numbers that are close in value to the numbers you want to add, subtract, multiply, or divide, and for which the operation is easy to perform mentally. Estimating sums, differences, products, and quotients is easy to do mentally when you use compatible numbers.

Números compatibles (p. 135) Los números compatibles son aquéllos con un valor cercano a los números que deseas sumar, restar, multiplicar o dividir, y con los cuales es fácil hacer los cáculos mentalmente. Cuando calculas sumas, diferencias, productos y cocientes, te resulta más fácil utilizar números compatibles.

Estimate $151 \div 14.6$.

$151 \approx 150$
$14.6 \approx 15$
$150 \div 15 = 10$
$151 \div 14.6 \approx 10$

For $155 \div 14.6$, 150 and 15 are compatible numbers.

Complement of an event (p. 310) The complement of an event is the opposite of that event. The probability of an event plus the probability of its complement equals 1.

Complemento de un suceso (p. 310) El complemento de un suceso es el opuesto de ese suceso. La probabilidad de un suceso más la probabilidad de su complemento es igual a 1.

The event *no rain* is the complement of the event *rain.*

English/Spanish Glossary

Complementary angles (p. 469)   Complementary angles are two angles whose measures add to 90°.

EXAMPLE $\angle BCA$ and $\angle CAB$ are complementary angles.

Ángulos complementarios (p. 469)   Dos ángulos son complementarios cuando la suma de sus medidas es 90°.

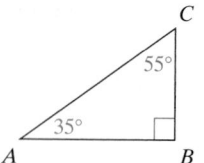

Composite number (p. 190)   A composite number is an integer greater than 1 with more than two positive factors.

Número compuesto (p. 190)   Un número compuesto es el número entero mayor que uno, que tiene más de dos factores positivos.

24 is a composite number that has 1, 2, 3, 4, 6, 8, 12, and 24 as factors.

Compound inequalities (p. 381)   Compound inequalities are two inequalities joined by the word *and* or the word *or*.

Desigualdades compuestas (p. 381)   Desigualdades compuestas son dos desigualdades que están enlazadas por medio de una *y* o una *o*.

$x > 4$ and $x \le 6$

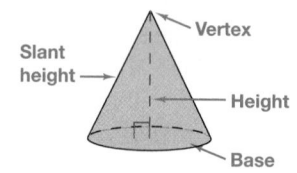

$x \le -2$ or $x > 3$

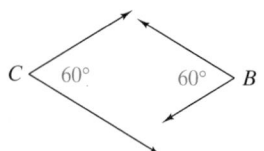

Compound interest (p. 387)   Compound interest is interest paid on both the principal and the interest earned in previous interest periods. You can use the formula $B = p(1 + r)^n$ where B is the final balance, p is the principal, r is the interest rate for each interest period, and n is the number of interest periods.

Interés compuesto (p. 387)   Interés compuesto es el interés pagado sobre el principal y sobre el interés ganado en previos períodos de interés. Para calcular el interés compuesto, se puede usar la formula $B = p(1 + r)^n$, en donde B es el balance en la cuenta, p es el principal, r es la tasa de interés para cada período y n es el número de períodos de interés.

You deposit $500 in an account earning 5% annual compound interest. The balance after six years is $500(1 + 0.05)^6$, or $670.05. The compound interest is $670.05 - 500$, or $170.05.

Cone (p. 545)   A cone is a space figure with one circular base and one vertex.

Cono (p. 545)   Un cono es una figura tridimensional con una base circular y un vértice.

Congruent angles (p. 469)   Congruent angles are angles that have the same measure.

EXAMPLE $\angle B \cong \angle C$

Ángulos congruentes (p. 469)   Ángulos congruentes son los ángulos que tienen la misma medida.

Congruent figures (p. 484) Congruent figures are figures that have the same size and shape. Congruent polygons have congruent corresponding sides and congruent corresponding angles. The symbol $\cong$ means "is congruent to."

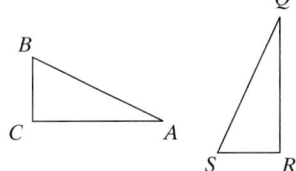

EXAMPLE $\overline{AB} \cong \overline{QS}$, $\overline{BC} \cong \overline{SR}$, and $\overline{AC} \cong \overline{QR}$.

$\angle A \cong \angle Q$, $\angle B \cong \angle S$, and $\angle C \cong \angle R$.

Triangles ABC and QSR are congruent.

$\triangle ABC \cong \triangle QSR$

Figuras congruentes (p. 484) Figuras congruentes son las figuras que tienen el mismo tamaño y la misma forma. Los polígonos congruentes tienen lados correspondientes congruentes y ángulos correspondientes congruentes. El símbolo $\cong$ significa "es congruente con."

Congruent segments (p. 495) Congruent segments are segments that have the same length.

$$\overline{AB} \cong \overline{WX}$$

Segmentos congruentes (p. 495) Segmentos congruentes son aquéllos que tienen la misma longitud.

Conjecture (p. 35) A conjecture is a conclusion reached through inductive reasoning.

A dropped piece of toast always lands with its buttered side down.

Conjetura (p. 35) Una conjetura es una conclusión obtenida usando el razonamiento inductivo.

Consecutive integers (p. 357) Consecutive integers are a sequence of integers obtained by counting by ones from any integer.

Three consecutive integers are $-5, -4$, and -3.

Numeros enteros consecutivos (p. 357) Los números enteros consecutivos son una sucesión de enteros que se obtiene al contar en unidades comenzando en cualquier entero.

Constant (p. 78) A constant is a term that has no variable.

In the expression $4x - 13y + 17$, 17 is the constant.

Constante (p. 78) Constante es un término que no tiene variable.

Coordinate plane (p. 52)   The coordinate plane is the plane formed by two number lines that intersect at their zero points. The horizontal number line is called the *x*-axis. The vertical number line is called the *y*-axis. The two axes meet at the origin, $O(0, 0)$, and divide the coordinate plane into four quadrants.

Plano de coordenadas (p. 52)   El plano de coordenadas está formado por la intersección de una recta numérica horizontal, llamada el eje de *x*, y una recta numérica vertical, llamada el eje de *y*. Los dos ejes se intersecan en el origen, $O(0, 0)$, y divide el plano de coordenadas en cuatro cuadrantes.

Coordinates (p. 52)   Coordinates are ordered pairs (x, y) that identify points in a coordinate plane. The *x*-coordinate (the first coordinate) shows the horizontal position. The *y*-coordinate (the second coordinate) shows the vertical position.

Coordenadas (p. 52)   Las coordenadas son pares ordenados (x, y), que identifican puntos en el plano de coordenadas. La coordenada *x*, (la primera coordenada) muestra la posición horizontal. La coordenada *y* (la segunda coordenada) muestra la posición vertical.

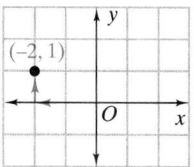

The ordered pair $(-2, 1)$ describes the point that is found by moving 2 units to the left from the origin and one unit up from the *x*-axis.

Correlation (p. 429)   A correlation is a relation between two sets of data. The data have a *positive correlation* if, as one set of values increases, the other set tends to increase. The data have a *negative correlation* if, as one set of values increases, the other set tends to decrease. The data have little or *no correlation* if the values show no relationship.

Correlación (p. 429)   Una correlación es la relación que hay entre dos conjuntos de datos. Los datos tienen una *correlación positiva* si, a medida que aumenta un conjunto de valores, el otro conjunto tiende a aumentar. Los datos tienen una *correlación negativa* si, a medida que aumenta un conjunto de valores, el otro conjunto tiende a disminuir. Los datos tienen correlación débil o *no tienen correlación* si los valores no muestran relación entre ellos.

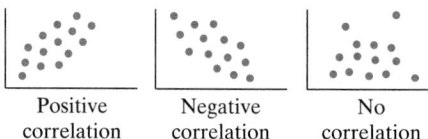

Corresponding angles (p. 470)   Corresponding angles are pairs of nonadjacent angles that lie on the same side of a transversal of two lines and in corresponding positions.

EXAMPLE $\angle 1$ and $\angle 3$ are corresponding angles.
$\angle 2$ and $\angle 4$ are corresponding angles.

Ángulos correspondientes (p. 470)   Ángulos correspondientes son los pares de ángulos no adyacentes, uno interior y el otro exterior, en el mismo lado de la transversal.

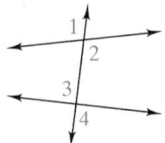

Corresponding angles of polygons (p. 484)   Corresponding angles are matching angles of similar or congruent figures.

Ángulos correspondientes de polígonos (p. 484)   Ángulos correspondientes son los ángulos equivalentes de figuras semejantes o congruentes.

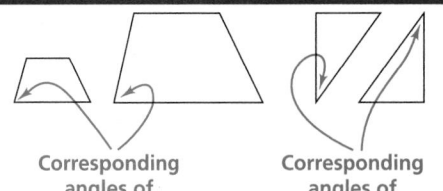

Corresponding angles of similar trapezoids

Corresponding angles of congruent triangles

Corresponding sides of polygons (p. 484)   Corresponding sides are matching sides of similar or congruent figures.

Lados correspondientes de polígonos (p. 484)   Lados correspondientes son los lados equivalentes de figuras semejantes o congruentes.

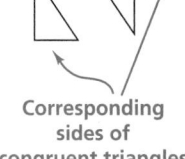

Corresponding sides of similar polygons

Corresponding sides of congruent triangles

Cosine (p. 614)   See *Trigonometric ratios*.

Razón coseno (p. 614)   Ver *Trigonometric ratios*.

Counterexample (p. 37)   A counterexample is an example that proves a statement false.

Contraejemplo (p. 37)   Contraejemplo es todo ejemplo que pruebe la falsedad de un enunciado.

Statement: Motor vehicles have four wheels.

Counterexample: A motorcycle is a motor vehicle with two wheels.

Counting Principle (p. 658)   If there are m ways of making one choice and n ways of making a second choice, then there are $m \times n$ ways of making the first choice followed by the second.

Principio de conteo (p. 658)   Si hay m maneras de realizar una elección y n maneras de realizar una segunda elección, por lo tanto hay $m \times n$ maneras de realizar la primera elección seguida de la segunda elección.

There are 26 possible choices for each letter of a monogram. Thus, there are $26 \cdot 26$, or 676, possible two-letter monograms.

Cross products (p. 298)   Cross products are products formed from a proportion. They are the product of the numerator of the first ratio and the denominator of the second ratio, and the product of the denominator of the first ratio and the numerator of the second ratio. For a proportion, these products are equal.

Productos cruzados (p. 298)   Los productos cruzados son los productos formados a partir de una proporción. Son el producto del numerador de la primera razón y del denominador de la segunda razón, y el producto del denominador de la primera razón y del numerador de la segunda razón. Para una proporción, estos productos son iguales.

The cross products for the proportion $\frac{3}{4} = \frac{6}{8}$ are $3 \cdot 8$ and $4 \cdot 6$.
$3 \cdot 8 = 24$ and $4 \cdot 6 = 24$.

English/Spanish Glossary

Cross section (p. 550) A cross section is the intersection of a plane and a space figure.

Sección de corte (p. 550) Una sección de corte es la intersección de un plano y una figura tridimensional.

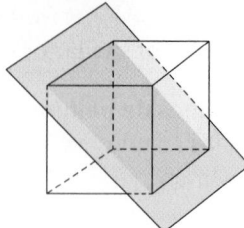

Cube (p. 546) A cube is rectangular prism with six congruent faces.

Cubo (p. 546) Un cubo es un prisma rectangular con seis caras congruentes.

Cube root (p. 591) The cube root of a given number is a number whose third power is the given number. The symbol for the cube root of a number is $\sqrt[3]{\ }$.

Raíz cúbica (p. 591) La raíz cúbica de un número dado es un número cuya tercera potencia es el número dado. El símbolo de la raíz cúbica de un número es $\sqrt[3]{\ }$.

$\sqrt[3]{8} = 2$ because $2^3 = 8$.

$\sqrt[3]{-8} = -2$ because $(-2)^3 = -8$.

Cubic unit (p. 563) A cubic unit is the amount of space occupied by a cube with edges one unit long.

Unidad cúbica (p. 563) Una unidad cúbica es el espacio que ocupa un cubo cuyos lados tienen una unidad de longitud.

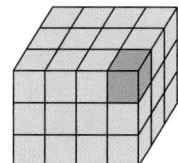

Cylinder (p. 545) A cylinder is a space figure with two circular, parallel, and congruent bases.

Cilindro (p. 545) Un cilindro es una figura tridimensional con dos bases circulares, paralelas y congruentes.

Decagon (p. 478) A decagon is a polygon with ten sides.

Decágono (p. 478) Un decágono es un polígono que tiene diez lados.

See *Polygon*.

Deductive reasoning (p. 79) Deductive reasoning is the process of reasoning logically from given facts to a conclusion.

EXAMPLE Deductive reasoning is used to simplify the expression $4c + 3(3 + c)$.

Razonamiento deductivo (p. 79) El razonamiento deductivo es el proceso de razonar lógicamente para llegar a una conclusión a partir de datos dados.

$$4c + 3(3 + c) = 4c + 9 + 3c$$
$$= 4c + 3c + 9$$
$$= (4 + 3)c + 9$$
$$= 7c + 9$$

Dependent events (p. 664) Dependent events are events for which the occurrence of one event affects the probability of the occurrence of the other.

Sucesos dependientes (p. 664) Cuando el resultado de un seceso afecta el resultado de un segundo suceso, los sucesos son dependientes.

A bag contains 10 pieces of paper and on each piece is a different number from 1 to 10. A paper is picked and not returned to the bag. The probability of the outcome of the second pick is dependent on the outcome of the first pick.

Diagonal (p. 480) A diagonal of a polygon is a segment that connects two nonconsecutive vertices.

Diagonal (p. 480) Una diagonal de un polígono es un segmento que conecta dos vértices no consecutivos.

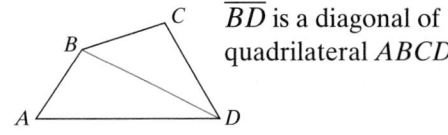

$\overline{BD}$ is a diagonal of quadrilateral *ABCD*.

Diameter (p. 490) A diameter of a circle is a chord that passes through the center of the circle.

EXAMPLE $\overline{RS}$ is a diameter of circle *O*.

Diámetro (p. 490) Un diámetro de un círculo es una cuerda que pasa a través del centro de un círculo.

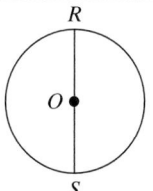

Dilation (p. 308) A dilation is a transformation that results in a size change. The scale factor, *r*, describes the size of the change from the original figure to its image. If $r > 1$, the dilation is an enlargement. If *r* is positive and $r < 1$, the dilation is a reduction.

Dilatación (p. 308) Una dilatación es una transformación que da como resultado un cambio de tamaño. El factor de escala *r* describe el tamaño del cambio de la figura original a su reproducción. Si $r > 1$, la dilatación es un agrandamiento. Si $r < 1$, la dilatación es una reducción.

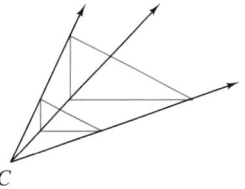

The blue triangle is an enlargement of the red triangle. The red triangle is a reduction of the blue triangle.

Dimensional analysis (p. 258) Dimensional analysis is a process of analyzing units to decide which conversion factors to use.

Análisis dimensional (p. 258) El análisis dimensional es el proceso de analizar unidades para decidir qué factores de conversión usar.

$0.5 \text{ mi} = \frac{0.5 \text{ mi}}{1} \cdot \frac{5{,}280 \text{ ft}}{1 \text{ mi}} = 2{,}640 \text{ ft}$

Discount (p. 333) A discount is the amount by which a price is decreased.

Descuento (p. 333) Descuento es la cantidad en la cual un precio es reducido.

The price of a $10 book is reduced by a discount of $1.50 to sell for $8.50.

English/Spanish Glossary

Glossary **815**

Distance Formula (p. 598)   The distance d between any two points (x_1, y_1) and (x_2, y_2) is $d = \sqrt{(x_2 - x_1)^2 + (y_2 - y_1)^2}$.

Fórmula de distancia (p. 598)   La distancia d entre cualesquiera dos puntos (x_1, y_1) y (x_2, y_2) es $d = \sqrt{(x_2 - x_1)^2 + (y_2 - y_1)^2}$.

The distance between $(6, 3)$ and $(1, 9)$ is d:
$$d = \sqrt{(1 - 6)^2 + (9 - 3)^2}$$
$$= \sqrt{(-5)^2 + 6^2}$$
$$= \sqrt{61}$$
$$\approx 7.8$$

Distributive Property (p. 73)   For any numbers a, b, and c, $a(b + c) = ab + ac$ and $a(b - c) = ab - ac$.

Propiedad distributiva (p. 73)   Para cualquier número a, b y c, $a(b + c) = ab + ac$ y $a(b - c) = ab - ac$

$$2\left(3 + \tfrac{1}{2}\right) = 2 \cdot 3 + 2 \cdot \tfrac{1}{2}$$
$$8(5 - 3) = 8(5) - 8(3)$$

Divisible (p. 180)   Divisible means that the remainder is 0 when you divide one integer by another.

Divisible (p. 180)   Un número entero es divisible por otro número si el residuo es cero.

15 is divisible by 5 because $15 \div 5 = 3$ with remainder 0.

Division Property of Equality (p. 94)   If $a = b$ and $c \neq 0$, then $\frac{a}{c} = \frac{b}{c}$.

Propiedad de igualdad en la división (p. 94)   Si $a = b$ y $c \neq 0$, entonces $\frac{a}{c} = \frac{b}{c}$.

$6 = 3(2)$, so $\frac{6}{3} = \frac{3(2)}{3}$

Division Properties of Inequality (p. 112)   If $a < b$ and c is positive, then $\frac{a}{c} < \frac{b}{c}$. If $a > b$ and c is positive, then $\frac{a}{c} > \frac{b}{c}$.
If you divide each side of an inequality by a negative number, you reverse the inequality symbol.

If $a < b$ and c is negative, then $\frac{a}{c} > \frac{b}{c}$.

If $a > b$ and c is negative, then $\frac{a}{c} < \frac{b}{c}$.

Propiedad de división de la desigualdad (p. 112)   Si $a < b$ y c es positivo, entonces $\frac{a}{c} < \frac{b}{c}$. Si $a > b$ y c es positivo, entonces $\frac{a}{c} > \frac{b}{c}$.
Si se divide cada lado de una desigualdad por un número negativo, se invierte la dirección del símbolo de desigualdad.

Si $a < b$, y c es negativo, entonces $\frac{a}{c} > \frac{b}{c}$.

Si $a > b$, y c es negativo, entonces $\frac{a}{c} < \frac{b}{c}$.

$3 < 6$, so $\frac{3}{3} < \frac{6}{3}$

$8 > 2$, so $\frac{8}{2} > \frac{2}{2}$

$6 < 12$, so $\frac{6}{-3} > \frac{12}{-3}$

$16 > 8$, so $\frac{16}{-4} < \frac{8}{-4}$

Domain (p. 404)   A domain is the set of first coordinates of the ordered pairs of a relation.

Dominio (p. 404)   Un dominio es el conjunto que comprende todas las primeras coordenadas de los pares ordenados de una relación.

In the relation $\{(0, 1), (-3, 2), (0, 2)\}$, the domain is $\{0, -3\}$.

Edge (p. 545)   An edge is the intersection of two faces of a space figure.

Arista (p. 545)   Un arista es el segmento en donde se intersecan dos caras de una figura tridimensional.

Equation (p. 82)   An equation is a mathematical sentence with an equal sign, =. An equation says that the side to the left of the equal sign has the same value as the side to the right of the equal sign.

$2(6 + 17) = 46$

Ecuación (p. 82)   Una ecuación es un enunciado matemático que contiene un signo igual, =. Una ecuacíon dice que el lado izquierdo del signo igual tiene el mismo valor que el lado derecho del signo igual.

Equilateral triangle (p. 474)   An equilateral triangle is a triangle with three congruent sides.

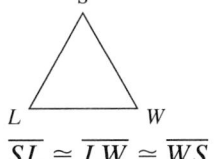

Triángulo equilátero (p. 474)   Un triángulo es equilátero cuando sus tres lados son congruentes.

$\overline{SL} \cong \overline{LW} \cong \overline{WS}$

Equivalent fractions (p. 196)   Equivalent fractions are fractions that describe the same part of a whole.

$\frac{3}{4}$ and $\frac{6}{8}$

Fracciones equivalentes (p. 196)   Fracciones equivalentes son fracciones que describen la misma parte de un todo.

Evaluate an expression (p. 14)   To evaluate an expression is to replace each variable with a number, and then follow the order of operations.

To evaluate the expression $3x + 2$ for $x = 4$, substitute 4 for x.
$3x + 2 = 3(4) + 2 = 12 + 2 = 14$

Evaluación de una expresión (p. 14)   Una expresión se evalúa, sustituyendo cada variable con un número. Luego se sigue el órden de las operaciones.

Event (p. 309)   An event is any outcome or group of outcomes.

In a game that includes tossing a coin and rolling a number cube, *tossing heads and rolling a 2* is an event.

Suceso (p. 309)   Un suceso es cualquier resultado o grupo de resultados.

Experimental probability (p. 673)   See *Probability*.

Probabilidad experimental (p. 673)   Ver *Probability*.

Exponent (p. 186)   An exponent is a number that shows how many times a base is used as a factor.

$3^4 = 3 \cdot 3 \cdot 3 \cdot 3$

4 is the exponent.

Exponente (p. 186)   Un exponente es un número que indica las veces que una base se usa como factor.

English/Spanish Glossary

Exponential decay (p. 708)   Exponential decay is any function of the form $y = b^x$, where $0 < b < 1$. The graph of the function slopes downward as input values increase.

EXAMPLE   The function $y = 10\left(\frac{1}{2}\right)^x$ is graphed for integer values of x from 1 to 5.

Decremento exponencial (p. 708)   Decremento exponencial es cualquier función de la forma $y = b^x$, donde $0 < b < 1$. La gráfica de la función tiene pendiente hacia abajo a medida que aumentan los valores de entrada.

Exponential growth (p. 707)   Exponential growth is any function of the form $y = b^x$, where $b > 1$. The graph of the function curves upward as input values increase.

EXAMPLE   The function $y = 2^x$ is graphed for integer values of x from 0 to 4.

Incremento exponencial (p. 707)   Incremento exponencial es cualquier función de la forma $y = b^x$, donde $b > 1$. La gráfica de la función se curva hacia arriba a medida que aumentan los valores de entrada.

Face (p. 545)   A face is a surface of a space figure.

Cara (p. 545)   Cara es la superficie plana de una figura tridimensional.

Factor (p. 181)   A factor of a nonzero integer is an integer that divides the nonzero integer with remainder zero.

1, 2, 3, 4, 6, 9, 12, 18, and 36 are factors of 36.

Factor (p. 181)   Un número entero es factor de otro número entero distinto de cero, cuando lo divide y el residuo es cero.

Formula (p. 145)   A formula is an equation that shows a relationship between quantities that are represented by variables.

The formula $P = 4s$ gives the perimeter of a square in terms of the length s of a side.

Fórmula (p. 145)   Una fórmula es una ecuación que muestra una relación entre las cantidades que representan las variables.

Frequency table (p. 636)   A frequency table is a list of items that shows the number of times, or frequency, with which they occur.

EXAMPLE   This frequency table shows the number of household telephones for the students in one school class.

Tabla de frecuencia (p. 636)   Una tabla de frecuencia registra el número de veces, o frecuencia, con que se ha producido un determinado tipo de resultado.

Household Telephones

Phones	Tally	Frequency
1	⳾⳾⳾ |||	8
2	⳾⳾⳾		6
3						4

Front-end estimation (p. 130) Front-end estimation is a way to estimate a sum. First add the front-end digits. Round to estimate the sum of the remaining digits. Then combine estimates.

Estimate \$3.49 + \$2.29.
$3 + 2 = 5$
$0.49 + 0.29 \approx 0.50 + 0.30 = 0.80$
$\$3.49 + \$2.29 \approx \$5 + \$0.80 = \$5.80$

Estimación por la izquierda (p. 130) La estimación por la izquierda se emplea para estimar sumas. Primero, se suman los dígitos delanteros. Luego, se redondea para estimar la suma de los dígitos restantes. Por último se combinan las estimaciones.

Function (p. 404) A function is a relationship in which each member of the domain is paired with exactly one member of the range. A number of the domain is an input and the related number of the range is an output.

Earned income is a function of the number of hours worked (n). If you earn \$5/h, then your income is expressed by the function $f(n) = 5n$.

Función (p. 404) Una función es una relación en la que a cada miembro de un dominio le corresponde exactamente un miembro dominio. Un número del dominio es el valor de entrada y el número relacionado del dominio es el valor de salida.

Function notation (p. 422) Function notation is notation that represents a function as $f(x)$ instead of y.

$f(x) = -2x + 1$

Notación de una función (p. 422) La notación de una función es aquélla que representa una función $f(x)$ en vez de y.

Function rule (p. 422) A function rule is an equation that describes a function.

$y = 2x + 5, f(x) = -4x + 3$

Regla de una función (p. 422) La regla de una función es la ecuación que describe una función.

Geometric sequence (p. 697) A geometric sequence is a sequence of numbers in which each term after the first is the result of multiplying the previous term by a fixed number (called the common ratio).

The sequence $1, 3, 9, 27, 81, \ldots$ is a geometric sequence. The common ratio is 3.

Progresión geométrica (p. 697) Una progresión geométrica es una sucesión de números en la que cada término, después del primero, es el resultado de la multiplicación del término anterior por un número fijo (llamando razón común).

Greatest common factor (GCF) (p. 191) The greatest common factor of two or more numbers is the greatest factor that the numbers have in common.

The greatest common factor (GCF) of 12 and 30 is 6.

Máximo común divisor (MCD) (p. 191) El máximo común divisor de dos o más números es el mayor divisor que los números tienen en común.

English/Spanish Glossary

Greatest possible error (p. 262)   The greatest possible error of a measurement is half the unit used for measuring.

The measurement 400 kg is rounded to the nearest hundred kilograms. So, the greatest possible error is 50 kg.

Máximo error posible (p. 262)   El máximo error posible de una medida es la mitad de la unidad usada para medir.

Height of a three-dimensional figure (pp. 552, 553, 572)
See *Cone*, *Cylinder*, *Prism*, and *Pyramid*.

Altura de figuras tridimensionales (pp. 552, 553, 572)
Ver *Cone, Cylinder, Prism* y *Pyramid*.

Height of a two-dimensional figure (pp. 527, 533 535)
See *Parallelogram*, *Triangle*, and *Trapezoid*.

Altura de figuras bidimensionales (pp. 527, 533, 535)
Ver *Parallelogram, Triangle* y *Trapezoid*.

Hexagon (p. 476)   A hexagon is a polygon with six sides.

See *Polygon*.

Hexágono (p. 476)   Un hexágono es un polígono que tiene seis lados.

Histogram (p. 637)   A histogram is a bar graph in which the heights of the bars give the frequencies of the data. There are no spaces between bars.

EXAMPLE This histogram gives the frequencies of board-game purchases at a local toy store.

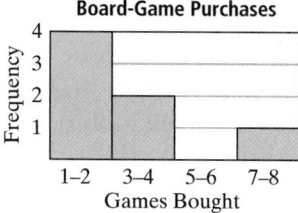

Histograma (p. 637)   Un histograma es una gráfica de barras en la cual la altura de las barras representa la frecuencia de los datos. No hay espacio entre las barras.

Hypotenuse (p. 592)   In a right triangle, the hypotenuse is the longest side, which is opposite the right angle.

See *Right triangle*.

Hipotenusa (p. 592)   La hipotenusa es el lado más largo de un triángulo rectángulo. Es el lado opuesto al ángulo recto.

Identity Properties of Addition and Multiplication (p. 69)   For any number a, the sum of a and 0 is a. The product of a and 1 is 1.

$a + 0 = a$
$a \cdot 1 = a$

Propiedad de identidad de la suma y de la multiplicación (p. 69)
La suma de cero y cualquier número a es a. El producto de cualquier número a y uno es a.

Image (p. 501) An image is the result of the transformation of a point, line, or figure to a new set of coordinates.

See *Transformation*.

Imagen (p. 501) Una imagen es el resultado de la transformación de un punto, una recta o una figura a un nuevo conjunto de coordenadas.

Improper fraction (p. 248) An improper fraction is a fraction with a numerator that is greater than or equal to the denominator.

$\frac{24}{15}$ and $\frac{16}{16}$ are improper fractions.

Fracción impropia (p. 248) Una fracción impropia es una fracción cuyo numerador es mayor o igual que su denominador.

Independent events (p. 662) Two events are independent events if the occurrence of one event does not affect the probability of the occurrence of the other.

When a number cube is rolled twice, the events rolling 6 and then rolling 3 are independent.

Sucesos independientes (p. 662) Dos sucesos son independientes si el acontecimiento de uno no afecta la probabilidad de que el otro suceso ocurra.

Indirect measurement (p. 304) Indirect measurement is a method of determining length or distance without measuring directly.

EXAMPLE By using the distances shown in the diagram and using properties of similar figures, you can find the height of the taller tower.

$\frac{240}{540} = \frac{x}{1,192} \rightarrow x \approx 529.8$ ft

Medición indirecta (p. 304) La medición indirecta es un método para determinar la longitud o distancia sin medir directamente.

Inductive reasoning (p. 35) Inductive reasoning is making conclusions based on patterns you observe.

By inductive reasoning, the next number in the pattern $2, 4, 6, 8, \ldots$ is 10.

Razonamiento inductivo (p. 35) El razonamiento inductivo es sacar conclusiones a partir de patrones observados.

Inequality (p. 104) An inequality is a sentence that uses one of the symbols $>, <, \geq, \leq,$ or $\neq$.

$0 \leq 2, k > -3, 10 < t$

Desigualdad (p. 104) Una desigualdad es un enunciado que usa uno de los siguientes símbolos $>, <, \geq, \leq,$ o $\neq$.

Integer (p. 19) The integers are the whole numbers and their opposites.

$-45, 0,$ and 289 are integers.

Números enteros (p. 19) Los números enteros son el conjunto de los números enteros positivos (naturales) y sus opuestos.

English/Spanish Glossary

Interest (p. 386) See *Compound interest* and *Simple interest*.

Interés (p. 386) Ver *Compound interest* y *Simple interest*.

Interest rate (p. 386) An interest rate is the percentage of the balance that an account or investment earns in a fixed period of time.

Tasa de interés (p. 386) Una tasa de interés es el porcentaje del saldo que gana una cuenta o inversión durante un período fijo.

A savings account pays $2\frac{1}{4}\%$ per year.

Inverse operations (p. 88) Inverse operations are operations that undo each other.

Operaciones inversas (p. 88) Operaciones inversas son las operaciones que se cancelan una a la otra.

Multiplication and division are inverse operations.

Irrational number (p. 589) An irrational number is a number whose decimal form neither terminates nor repeats.

Número irracional (p. 589) Un número irracional es aquél cuyas cifras decimales son infinitas y no se repiten.

The number π, which is approximately equal to 3.141592654, is an irrational number.

Isosceles triangle (p. 474) An isosceles triangle is a triangle with at least two congruent sides.

EXAMPLE $\overline{LM} \cong \overline{LB}$

$\triangle MLB$ is an isosceles triangle.

Triángulo isósceles (p. 474) Un triángulo isósceles es aquel que tiene al menos dos lados congruentes.

Lateral area (p. 552) The lateral area of a prism is the sum of the areas of the lateral faces.

Área lateral (p. 552) El área lateral de un prisma es la suma de las áreas de las caras laterales.

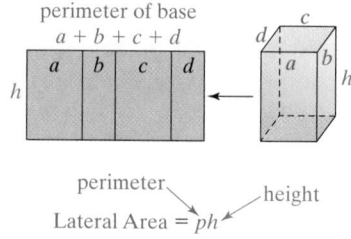

Lateral face (p. 545) See *Prism* and *Pyramid*.

Cara lateral (p. 545) Ver *Prism* y *Pyramid*.

Least common denominator (LCD) (p. 238)   The least common denominator of two or more fractions is the least common multiple (LCM) of their denominators.

The least common denominator (LCD) of the fractions $\frac{3}{8}$ and $\frac{7}{10}$ is $2 \cdot 2 \cdot 2 \cdot 5$, or 40.

Mínimo común denominador (mcd) (p. 238)   El mínimo común denominador de dos o más fracciones es el mínimo común múltiplo (mcm) de sus denominadores.

Least common multiple (LCM) (p. 236)   The least common multiple of two or more numbers is the least number that is a common multiple.

The least common multiple (LCM) of 6 and 15 is $2 \cdot 3 \cdot 5$, or 30.

Mínimo común múltiplo (mcm) (p. 236)   El número menor que es múltiplo común de dos o más números es el mínimo común múltiplo.

Legs of a right triangle (p. 592)   The legs of a right triangle are the two shorter sides of the triangle.

See *Right triangle*.

Catetos de un triángulo rectángulo (p. 592)   Los catetos de un triángulo rectángulo son los lados más cartos del triángulo.

Like terms (p. 78)   Like terms are terms with the same variable(s), raised to the same power(s).

EXAMPLE $3b$ and $12b$ are like terms. Like terms can be combined by using the Distributive Property.

$$3b + 12b = (3 + 12)b$$
$$= 15b$$

Términos semejantes (p. 78)   Términos semejantes son aquellos que tienen la o las mismas variables elevadas a las mismas potencias.

Line (p. 462)   A line is a series of points that extends in opposite directions without end.

EXAMPLE $\overleftrightarrow{AB}, \overleftrightarrow{BA}$, or n represent a line.

Recta (p. 462)   Una recta es una serie de puntos que se extiende infinitamente en direcciones opuestas.

Line graph (p. 102)   A line graph is a graph that shows a relationship between two quantities.

EXAMPLE This line graph shows the change in the number of listeners to station KLZR during the day.

EXAMPLE This multiple line graph represents seasonal air conditioner and snowblower sales (in thousands) for a large chain of stores.

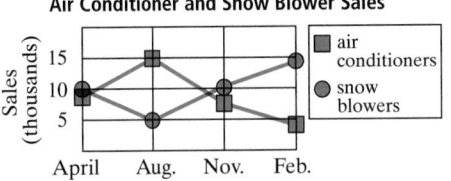

Gráfica lineal (p. 102)   Una gráfica lineal representa la relación que existe entre dos cantidades.

Line of reflection (p. 508)   A line of reflection is a line across which a figure is reflected.

See *Reflection*.

Eje de reflexión (p. 508)   Un eje de reflexión es una recta sobre la cual una figura es reflejada.

Line of symmetry (p. 507)   A line of symmetry is a line that divides a figure with reflectional symmetry into two congruent halves.

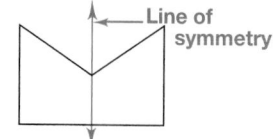

Eje de simetría (p. 507)   Un eje de simetría es una recta que divide una figura que tiene simetría de reflexión en dos mitades congruentes.

Line plot (p. 637)   A line plot is a graph that displays data by using X's above a number line.

EXAMPLE This line plot shows the numbers of girls on a field hockey team who are at the indicated heights.

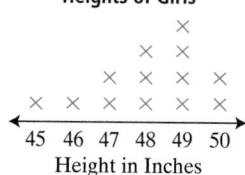

Diagrama de puntos (p. 637)   Un diagrama de puntos es una gráfica que muestra datos marcando una X sobre una recta numérica.

Linear equation (p. 410)   A linear equation is any equation whose graph is a line.

EXAMPLE $y = \frac{1}{2}x + 3$ is linear because its graph is a line.

Ecuación lineal (p. 410)   Una ecuación lineal es cualquier ecuación cuya gráfica de todas sus soluciones es una recta.

Linear inequality (p. 445)   A linear inequality is a number sentence in which the equal sign of a linear equation is replaced with $>, <, \geq$, or $\leq$.

$y \geq 2x + 3$
$y < -4x - 1$

Desigualdad lineal (p. 445)   Una desigualdad lineal es una proposición numérica en la cual el signo igual de una ecuación lineal se reemplaza con un signo $>, <, \geq$ o $\leq$.

Lower quartile (p. 641)   The lower quartile is the median of the lower half of a data set.

See *Box-and-whisker plot*.

Cuartil inferior (p. 641)   El cuartil inferior es la mediana de la mitad inferior del conjunto de datos.

Markup (p. 333)   Markup is the amount of increase in price. Markup is added to the cost of merchandise to arrive at the selling price.

A store buys a coat for $60 and sells it for $100. The markup is $40.

Sobrecosto (p. 333)   El sobrecosto es la cantidad que se aumenta en precio. El sobrecosto se agrega al costo de la mercadería y eso da el precio de venta.

Mean (p. 139)   The mean of a collection of the data items divided by the number of data items.

Media (p. 139)   La media de un conjunto de datos resulta de la suma de los datos dividida entre el número de componentes de los datos.

The mean temperature (°F) for the temperatures 44, 52, 48, 55, 61, 67, and 58 is 55.

Measures of central tendency (p. 139)   Measures of central tendency in statistics are *mean*, *median*, and *mode*.

Medidas de tendencia central (p. 139)   En estadistia, la *media*, la *mediana* y la *moda* son medidas de tendencia central en la estadística.

See *Mean*, *Median*, and *Mode*.

Median (p. 139)   The median of a collection of data is the middle number when there is an odd number of data items and they are written in order. For an even number of data items, the median is the mean of the two middle numbers.

Mediana (p. 139)   La mediana es el número central de un conjunto de datos, cuando hay un número impar de datos y éstos están dispuestos en orden. Si hay un número par de datos, la mediana es la media de los dos números centrales.

The median temperature (°F) for the temperatures 44, 48, 52, 55, 58, 61, and 67 is 55.

Midpoint Formula (p. 600)   The midpoint of a line segment with endpoints $A(x_1, y_1)$ and $B(x_2, y_2)$ is $\left(\frac{x_1 + x_2}{2}, \frac{y_1 + y_2}{2}\right)$.

Fórmula del punto medio (p. 600)   El punto medio de un segmento con puntos extremos $A(x_1, y_1)$ y $B(x_2, y_2)$ es $\left(\frac{x_1 + x_2}{2}, \frac{y_1 + y_2}{2}\right)$.

The midpoint of $A(-3, 2)$ and $B(7, -2)$ is $\left(\frac{-3 + 7}{2}, \frac{2 + -2}{2}\right)$, or $(2, 0)$.

Mixed number (p. 241)   A mixed number is the sum of a whole number and a fraction.

Número mixto (p. 241)   Un número mixto es la suma de un número entero y una fracción.

$3\frac{11}{16}$ is a mixed number.
$3\frac{11}{16} = 3 + \frac{11}{16}$

Mode (p. 139)   The mode of a collection of data is the data item that occurs most often. There can be no mode, one mode, or more than one mode.

Moda (p. 139)   La moda de un conjunto de datos es el dato que se presenta con mayor frecuencia. Puede no haber moda, una moda o más de una moda.

The mode of the collection of numbers 3, 4, 1, 3, 2, 2, 5, 3 is 3.

English/Spanish Glossary

	EXAMPLES

Monomial (p. 712)   A monomial is a real number, a variable, or a product of a real number and variables with whole number exponents.

$5x$, -4, and y^3 are all monomials.

Monomio (p. 712)   Un monomio es un número real, una variable o el producto de un número real y variables con exponentes que sean números enteros.

Multiple (p. 236)   A multiple of a number is the product of that number and any nonzero whole number.

The multiples of 13 are 13, 26, 39, 52, and so on.

Múltiplo (p. 236)   El múltiplo de un número es el producto de dicho número y cualquier otro número entero distinto de cero.

Multiple line graph (p. 102)   A multiple line graph is a graph that shows more than one data set changing over time.

See *Line graph.*

Gráfica multilineal (p. 102)   Una gráfica multilineal representa las variaciones de más de un conjunto de datos en el tiempo.

Multiplication Property of Equality (p. 95)   If $a = b$, then $ac = bc$.

$12 = 3(4)$, so $12 \cdot 2 = 3(4) \cdot 2$

Propiedad multiplicativa de la igualdad (p. 95)   Si $a = b$, entonces $ac = bc$.

Multiplication Properties of Inequality (p. 113)   If $a < b$, and c is positive, then $ac < bc$. If $a > b$, and c is positive, then $ac > bc$.

$3 < 4$, so $3(5) < 4(5)$
$7 > 2$, so $7(6) > 2(6)$

If you multiply each side of an inequality by a negative number, you reverse the inequality symbol.

If $a < b$, and c is negative, then $ac > bc$. If $a > b$, and c is negative, then $ac < bc$.

$6 < 9$, so $6(-2) > 9(-2)$
$7 > 5$, so $7(-3) < 5(-3)$

Propiedad multiplicativa de la desigualdad (p. 113)   Si $a < b$, y c es positivo, entonces $ac < bc$. Si $a > b$, y c es positivo, entonces $ac > bc$. Si se multiplica cada lado de una desigualdad por un número negativo, se invierte la dirección del signo de la desigualdad. Si $a < b$, y c es negativo, entonces $ac > bc$. Si $a > b$, y c es negativo, entonces $ac < bc$.

Multiplicative identity (p. 69)   The multiplicative identity is 1. For any number a, the product of a and 1 is a.

$a \cdot 1 = a$

Identidad multiplicativa (p. 69)   La identidad multiplicativa es 1. Cuando se multiplica un número por uno, el producto es igual al número original.

Multiplicative inverse (p. 254)   The multiplicative inverse of a number is its reciprocal.

The multiplicative inverse of $\frac{4}{9}$ is $\frac{9}{4}$.

Inverso multiplicativo (p. 254)   El inverso multiplicativo de un número es su recíproco.

Negative correlation (p. 429) See *Correlation*.

Correlación negativa (p. 429) Ver *Correlation*.

Net (p. 546) A net is a pattern that can be folded to form a space figure.
EXAMPLE This net can be folded to form a cube.

Plantilla (p. 546) Una plantilla es un patrón que se puede doblar para formar una figura tridimensional.

No correlation (p. 429) See *Correlation*.

Sin correlación (p. 429) Ver *Correlation*.

Obtuse angle (p. 468) An obtuse angle is an angle with a measure greater than 90° and less than 180°.

Ángulo obtuso (p. 468) Un ángulo obtuso es un ángulo que mide más de 90° y menos de 180°.

Obtuse triangle (p. 474) An obtuse triangle is a triangle with one obtuse angle.
EXAMPLE $\triangle NJX$ is an obtuse triangle, since $\angle J$ is an obtuse angle.

Triángulo obtusángulo (p. 474) Un triángulo es obtusángulo cuando contiene un ángulo obtuso.

Octagon (p. 480) An octagon is a polygon with eight sides.

See *Polygon*.

Octágono (p. 480) Un octágono es un polígono que tiene ocho lados.

Odds (p. 311) Odds are a ratio that describe the likelihood of an event. Odds in favor of an event $= \frac{\text{number of favorable outcomes}}{\text{number of unfavorable outcomes}}$.

For the toss of a coin, the odds in favor of tossing heads are 1 to 1.

Posibilidades (p. 311) Las posibilidades son la razón que describe la probabilidad de que ocurra un suceso. Posibilidades favorables de que ocurra un evento $= \frac{\text{número de sucesos favorables}}{\text{número de resultados no favorables}}$.

Open sentence (p. 82) An open sentence is an equation with one or more variables.

$3a = 5a + 8$

Proposición abierta (p. 82) Una proposición abierta es una ecuación con una o más variables.

English/Spanish Glossary

Opposites (p. 19)   Opposites are numbers that are the same distance from zero on the number line but in opposite directions.

Números opuestos (p. 19)   Números opuestos son los números que se hallan a la misma distancia de cero en una recta, numérica pero en direcciones opuestas.

-17 and 17 are opposites because they are both 17 units from zero on the number line.

Order of operations (pp. 9, 187)
1. Work inside grouping symbols.
2. Simplify any terms with exponents.
3. Multiply and divide in order from left to right.
4. Add and subtract in order from left to right.

Orden de las operaciones (pp. 9, 187)
1. Efectúa las operaciones que están dentro de los signos de agrupación.
2. Trabaja con los exponentes.
3. Multiplica y divide en orden de izquierda a derecha.
4. Suma y resta en orden de izquierda a derecha.

$2^3(7 - 4) = 2^3(3) = 8 \cdot 3 = 24$

Ordered pair (p. 52)   An ordered pair is a pair of numbers that gives the location of a point in a coordinate plane. The first number is the x-coordinate and the second number is the y-coordinate.

Par ordenado (p. 52)   Un par ordenado es un par de números que describe la localización de un punto en un plano de coordenadas. El primer número es la coordenada x y el segundo número es la coordenada y.

See *Coordinates*.

Origin (p. 52)   The origin is the intersection of the x-axis and the y-axis in a coordinate plane. The ordered pair $(0, 0)$ describes the origin.

Origen (p. 52)   El origen el punto de intersección de los ejes de x y de y en un plano de coordenadas. El par ordenado $(0, 0)$ describe el origen.

See *Coordinate plane*.

Outcomes (p. 309)   Outcomes are the possible results of an action.

Resultados (p. 309)   Se llama resultados a los posibles efectos o consecuencias de una acción.

Heads is an outcome of tossing a coin.

Outlier (p. 140)   An outlier is a data value that is much higher or lower than the other data values in a collection of data.

Extremo (p. 140)   Un extremo es el valor de un conjunto de datos que es mucho mayor o menor que el resto de los datos.

An outlier in the data $1, 1, 2, 3, 4, 4, 6, 7, 7, 52$ is 52.

Parabola (p. 706) A parabola is the graph of a quadratic function. It is U-shaped.

EXAMPLE This parabola is the graph of the equation $y = x^2 - 2$.

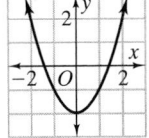

Parábola (p. 706) Una parábola es la gráfica de una ecuación cuadrática. Tiene la forma de U.

Parallel lines (p. 463) Parallel lines are lines that lie in the same plane and do not intersect. The symbol $\parallel$ means "is parallel to."

EXAMPLE $\overleftrightarrow{EF} \parallel \overleftrightarrow{HI}$

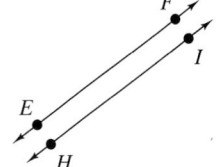

Rectas paralelas (p. 463) Rectas paralelas son las rectas que se encuentran en un mismo plano y no se cortan. El símbolo de dos rectas verticales paralelas significa "es paralelo a".

Parallelogram (p. 475) A parallelogram is a quadrilateral with both pairs of opposite sides parallel.

EXAMPLE $KVDA$ is a parallelogram.

$\overline{KV} \parallel \overline{AD}$ and $\overline{AK} \parallel \overline{DV}$.

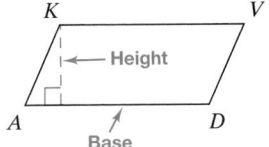

Paralelogramo (p. 475) Un paralelogramo es un cuadrilátero en el cual los lados opuestos son paralelos.

Pentagon (p. 476) A pentagon is a polygon with five sides.

See *Polygon*.

Pentágono (p. 476) Un pentágono es un polígono que tiene cinco lados.

Percent (p. 314) A percent is a ratio that compares a number to 100. The symbol for percent is %.

$\dfrac{50}{100} = 50\%$

Porcentaje (p. 314) Un porcentaje es una razón que compara un número con cien. El símbolo de porcentaje es %.

Percent of change (p. 329) Percent of change is the percent something increases or decreases from its original amount.

A school's population increases from 500 to 520 students. The percent of change is $\dfrac{520 - 500}{500} = 4\%$.

Porcentaje de cambio (p. 329) El porcentaje de cambio es el porcentaje en que algo aumenta o disminuye en relación con su valor original.

Perfect square (p. 588) A perfect square is the square of an integer.

$3^2 = 9$, so 9 is a perfect square.

Cuadrado perfecto (p. 588) Un cuadrado perfecto es un número natural que es igual a la segunda potencia de un número entero.

Perimeter (p. 146)   The perimeter of a figure is the distance around the figure. To find the perimeter of a rectangle, find the sum of the lengths of all its sides, or use the formula $P = 2\ell + 2w$.
EXAMPLE The perimeter of $ABCD$ is 12 ft.

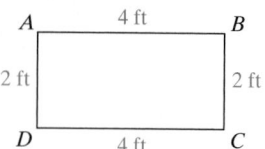

Perímetro (p. 146)   El perímetro de una figura es la suma de las longitudes de sus lados. Para hallar el perímetro de un rectángulo, halla la suma de los largos de todos los lados o usa la fórmula $P = 2\ell + 2w$.

Permutation (p. 667)   A permutation is an arrangement of items in a particular order. You can use the notation $_nP_r$ to express the number of permutations of n objects chosen r at a time.

The seating plans (Judith, Ann, Adrian) and (Ann, Judith, Adrian) are two different permutations.

Permutación (p. 667)   Una permutación es una colocación de objetos en un determinado orden. Se puede usar la notación $_nP_r$ para expresar el número de permutaciónes de n objetos elegidos r a la vez.

Perpendicular bisector (p. 496)   A perpendicular bisector is a line, segment, or ray that is perpendicular to a segment at its midpoint.
EXAMPLE $\overleftrightarrow{FG}$ is the perpendicular bisector of $\overline{DE}$.

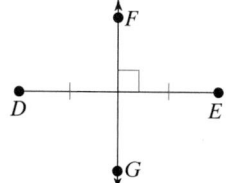

Mediatriz (p. 496)   Una mediatriz es una recta, segmento o rayo que es perpendicular a un segmento en su punto medio.

Perpendicular lines (p. 496)   Perpendicular lines are lines that intersect to form right angles.

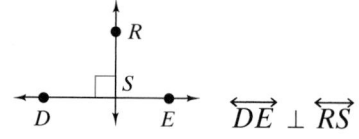

Rectas perpendiculares (p. 496)   Rectas perpendiculares son aquellas que se cortan para formar ángulos rectos.

Pi (p. 492)   Pi (π) is the name for the ratio of the circumference C to the diameter d of a circle.

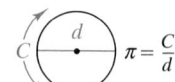

Pi (p. 492)   Pi (π) es el nombre de la razón de la circunferencia C al diámetro d de un círculo.

Plane (p. 462)   A plane is a flat surface that has no thickness and extends without end in the directions of all the lines it contains.

Plano (p. 462)   Un plano es una superficie plana que no tiene grosor y que se extiende indefinidamente en las direcciónes de todas las líneas que contiene.

$ABCD$ or M is a plane.

Point (p. 462)   A point is a location in space that has no size.

$\cdot A$

Punto (p. 462)   Un punto es una posición en el espacio. No tiene dimensiones, solamente tiene localización.

A is a point.

Polygon (p. 474) A polygon is a closed plane figure with at least three sides.

Polígono (p. 474) Un polígono es una figura plana cerrada formada por tres o más lados.

Polynomial (p. 712) A polynomial is a monomial or a sum or difference of monomials.

Polinomio (p. 712) Un polinomio es un monomio o la suma o la diferencia de dos o más monomios.

$4x^2 - 3x + 7$ is a polynomial.

Population (p. 677) A population is a group about which you want information.

Población (p. 677) Una población es un grupo sobre el cual se reúne información.

See *Sample*.

Positive correlation (p. 429) See *Correlation*.

Correlación positiva (p. 429) Ver *Correlation*.

Power (p. 186) A power is any expression in the form a^n. *Power* is also used to refer to the exponent.

Potencia (p. 186) Una potencia es cualquier expresión de la forma a^n. La potencia también se usa para referirse al exponente.

5^4 is a power and can be read as "five to the fourth power."

Precision in measurement (p. 164) The precision of a measurement is its exactness. A measurement cannot be more precise than the precision of the measuring tool used.

Precisión de una medición (p. 164) La precisión de una medición se refiere a su grado de exactitud. Una medida no puede ser más precisa que la precisión del instrumento de medida utilizado.

A hundredth of a meter is a smaller unit than a tenth of a meter. So, 2.72 m is more precise than 2.7 m.

Prime factorization (p. 191) The prime factorization of a number is the expression of the number as the product of its prime factors.

Descomposición en factores primos (p. 191) La descomposición en factores primos de un número es la expresión de dicho número como el producto de sus factores primos.

The prime factorization of 30 is $2 \cdot 3 \cdot 5$.

Prime number (p. 190) A prime number is an integer greater than 1 with only two positive factors, 1 and itself.

Número primo (p. 190) Un número primo es un número natural que tiene exactamente dos factores positivos, 1 y él mismo.

13 is a prime number because its only factors are 1 and 13.

Principal (p. 386)   The principal is the initial amount of an investment or loan.

See *Simple interest.*

Capital (p. 386)   El capital es el monto inicial de una inversión o préstamo.

Prism (p. 545)   A prism is a space figure with two parallel and congruent polygonal faces, called bases, and lateral faces that are parallelograms. A prism is named for the shape of its base.

Prisma (p. 545)   Un prisma es una figura tridimensional con dos caras poligonales congruentes y paralelas llamadas bases, y caras laterales paralelas. Un prisma recibe su nombre de acuerdo a la forma de las bases.

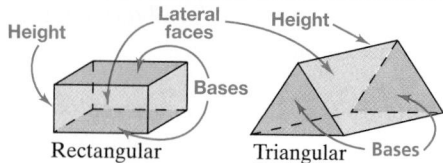

Rectangular   Triangular

Probability (p. 309)   The *theoretical probability* of an event E is $P(E) = \frac{\text{number of favorable outcomes}}{\text{number of possible outcomes}}$ when outcomes are equally likely. The *experimental probability* of an event E is $P(E) = \frac{\text{number of times an event occurs}}{\text{number of times experiment is done}}$. Experimental probability is based on experimental data.

Probabilidad (p. 309)   La *probabilidad teorica* de un suceso E es $P(E) = \frac{\text{número de resultados favorables}}{\text{número de resultados posibles}}$ cuando los resultados tienen la misma posibilidad de producirse.

La *probabilidad experimental* de un suceso E es $P(E) = \frac{\text{número de veces que ocurre un suceso}}{\text{número de veces que se realiza un experimento}}$. La probabilidad experimental se basa en datos experimentales.

The theoretical probability of spinning the number 4 is $\frac{1}{8}$.

In 100 trials, you spin the number 4 ten times. The experimental probability of spinning 4 is $\frac{10}{100}$, or $\frac{1}{10}$.

Proportion (p. 298)   A proportion is an equality of two ratios.

$\frac{3}{12} = \frac{12}{48}$ is a proportion.

Proporción (p. 298)   Una proporción es una igualdad de dos razones.

Pyramid (p. 545)   A pyramid is a space figure with triangular faces that meet at a vertex, and a base that is a polygon. A pyramid is named for the shape of its base.

Pirámide (p. 545)   Una pirámide es una figura tridimensional con caras triangulares que convergen en un vértice, y una base que es un polígono. Una pirámide recibe su nombre de acuerdo a la forma de la base.

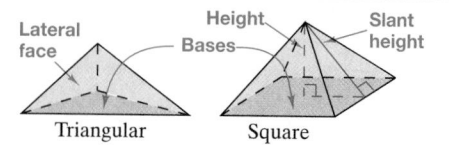

Triangular   Square

Pythagorean Theorem (p. 592)   In any right triangle, the sum of the squares of the lengths of the legs (a and b) is equal to the square of the length of the hypotenuse (c): $a^2 + b^2 = c^2$.

Teorema de Pitágoras (p. 592)   Para cualquier triángulo rectángulo, la suma del cuadrado de las longitudes de los catetos (a y b) es igual al cuadrado de la longitud de la hipotenusa (c): $a^2 + b^2 = c^2$.

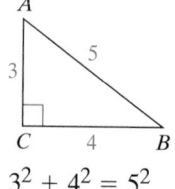

$3^2 + 4^2 = 5^2$

Quadrants (p. 52) Quadrants are the four regions determined by the *x*- and *y*-axes of the coordinate plane.

See *Coordinate plane.*

Cuadrantes (p. 52) El eje de *x* y el eje de *y* dividen el plano de coordenadas en cuatro regiones llamadas cuadrantes.

Quadratic function (p. 702) A quadratic function is a function based on squaring the input variable. The graph of a quadratic function is a parabola.

See *Parabola.*

Función cuadrática (p. 702) Una función cuadrática es la función que tiene una variable elevada a la segunda potencia. La gráfica de una función cuadrática es una párabola.

Quadrilateral (p. 475) A quadrilateral is a polygon with four sides.

See *Polygon.*

Cuadrilátero (p. 475) Un cuadrilátero es un polígono con cuatro lados.

Quartiles (p. 641) Quartiles are numbers that divide a data set into four equal parts.

See *Box-and-whisker plot.*

Cuartiles (p. 641) Los cuartiles son números que dividen un conjunto de datos en cuatro partes iguales.

Radius (plural is radii) (p. 492) A radius of a circle is a segment that has one endpoint at the center of the circle and the other endpoint on the circle.
EXAMPLE $\overline{OA}$ is a radius of circle *O*.

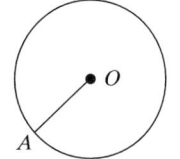

Radio (p. 492) El radio de un círculo es un segmento que tiene un extremo en el centro y el otro en el círculo.

Random sample (p. 677) A random sample is a sample of a population for which each member of the population has an equal chance of being selected.

For the population *customers at a mall*, a random sample could be every 20th customer entering for a 2-hour period.

Muestra aleatoria (p. 677) Una muestra aleatoria es una muestra de una población, de la cual cada miembro tiene la misma probabilidad de ser escogido.

Range of a relation (p. 404) A range is the set of second coordinates of the ordered pairs of a relation.

In the relation $\{(0, 1), (-3, 2), (0, 2)\}$, the range is $\{1, 2\}$.

Recorrido de una relación (p. 404) Un recorrido es el conjunto que comprende todas las segundas coordenadas de los pares ordenados de una relación.

English/Spanish Glossary

Range of a set of data (p. 139)   The range is the difference between the greatest and least values in a set of data.

The range of the data 7 9 15 3 18 2 16 14 14 20 is $20 - 2 = 18$.

Amplitud de un conjunto de datos (p. 139)   La amplitud es la diferencia entre los valores mayor y menor de un conjunto de datos.

Rate (p. 293)   A rate is a ratio that compares quantities measured in different units.

A student typed 1,100 words in 50 minutes for a typing rate of 1,100 words per 50 minutes, or 22 words/minute.

Tasa (p. 293)   Una tasa es una razón que compara dos cantidades medidas en unidades diferentes.

Ratio (p. 292)   A ratio is a comparison of two quantities by division.

There are three ways to write a ratio: 72 to 100, $72 : 100$, and $\frac{72}{100}$.

Razón (p. 292)   Una razón es la comparación de dos números mediante una división.

Rational number (p. 205)   A rational number is any number you can write as a quotient of two integers $\frac{a}{b}$, where b is not zero.

$\frac{3}{5}, -8, 8.7, 0.333\ldots, -5\frac{3}{11}, 0$, and $\frac{17}{4}$ are rational numbers.

Número racional (p. 205)   Un número racional es cualquier número que puede escribirse como el cociente de dos enteros $\frac{a}{b}$, donde b es distinto de cero.

Ray (p. 462)   A ray is a part of a line. It has exactly one endpoint. Its endpoint is named first.

$\overrightarrow{SW}$ represents a ray.

Rayo (p. 462)   Un rayo es una parte de una recta. Tiene exactamente un extremo. El extremo se nombre primero.

Real number (p. 589)   A real number is a rational number or an irrational number.

$3, -5.25, 3.141592653\ldots$, and $\frac{7}{8}$ are real numbers.

Números reales (p. 589)   Un número real es un número racional o un número irracional.

Reciprocal (p. 254)   Reciprocals are two numbers with a product of 1.

$\frac{4}{9}$ and $\frac{9}{4}$ are reciprocals.

$\frac{4}{9} \cdot \frac{9}{4} = 1$.

Recíprocos (p. 254)   Dos números son recíprocos cuando su producto es 1.

Rectangle (p. 475)   A rectangle is a parallelogram with four right angles.

EXAMPLE $RSWH$ is a rectangle.

Rectángulo (p. 475)   Un rectángulo es un paralelogramo con cuatro ángulos rectos.

Reflection (p. 508) A reflection is a transformation that flips a figure over a line of reflection.

EXAMPLE $K'L'M'N'$ is the reflection of $KLMN$ across the y-axis. The y-axis is the line of reflection.

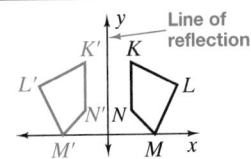

Reflexión (p. 508) Una reflexión es una transformación que invierte una figura a través de un eje de reflexión.

Reflectional symmetry (p. 507) A figure has reflectional symmetry when one half of the figure is a mirror image of the other half. The line of reflection is also called the line of symmetry.

Simetría de reflexión (p. 507) Una figura tiene simetría de reflexión cuando la mitad de la figura es una imagen refleja de la otra mitad. El eje de reflexión también se llama eje de simetría.

Regular polygon (p. 476) A regular polygon is a polygon with all its sides congruent and all its angles congruent.

EXAMPLE $ABDFEC$ is a regular hexagon.

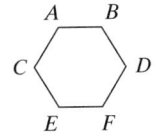

Polígono regular (p. 476) Un polígono regular tiene todos sus lados congruentes y todos sus ángulos son congruentes.

Relation (p. 404) A relation is a set of ordered pairs.

$\{(0, 2), (-3, 2), (0, 1)\}$ is a relation.

Relación (p. 404) Una relación es un conjunto de pares ordenados.

Relatively prime (p. 194) Two numbers are relatively prime if their GCF is 1.

9 and 20 are relatively prime.

Números primos entre sí (p. 194) Dos números son primos entre sí, si su máximo conúm divisor es 1.

Repeating decimal (p. 242) A repeating decimal is a decimal in which the same block of digits repeats without end. The symbol for a repeating decimal is a bar drawn over the digit or digits that repeat.

$0.8888 \ldots = 0.\overline{8}$

Decimal periódico (p. 242) Un decimal periódico es un decimal cuyos dígitos se repiten indefinidamente. El símbolo de un decimal periódico es una raya trazada encima del dígito o dígitos que se repiten.

Rhombus (p. 475) A rhombus is a parallelogram with four congruent sides.

EXAMPLE $GHJI$ is a rhombus.
$$GH = HJ = IJ = GI$$

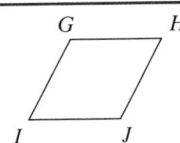

Rombo (p. 475) Un rombo es un paralelogramo con cuatro lados congruentes.

English/Spanish Glossary

Right angle (p. 468)   A right angle is an angle with a measure of 90°.
EXAMPLE $\angle CDE$ is a right angle.

Ángulo recto (p. 468)   Un ángulo recto es un ángulo que mide 90°.

Right triangle (p. 474)   A right triangle is a triangle with one right angle.
EXAMPLE $\triangle ABC$ is a right triangle, since $\angle B$ is a right angle.

Triángulo rectángulo (p. 474)   Un triángulo rectángulo es aquél que posee un ángulo recto.

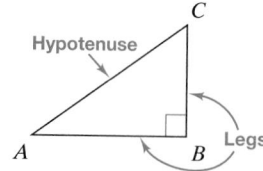

Rotation (p. 511)   A rotation is a transformation that turns a figure about a fixed point, called the center of rotation. The angle measure of the rotation is the angle of rotation.
EXAMPLE The image of $\triangle PQR$ after a 90° rotation is $\triangle PQ'R'$. Point P is the center of rotation.

Rotación (p. 511)   Una rotación es una transformación en la cual una figura se mueve sin deformación alrededor de un punto fijo, llamado centro de rotación. La medida del ángulo de la rotación es el ángulo de rotación.

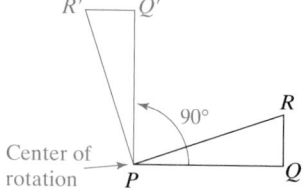

Rotational symmetry (p. 512)   A figure has rotational symmetry if the figure can be rotated 180° or less and match the original figure.

Simetría rotacional (p. 512)   Una figura tiene simetría rotacional si la figura se puede rotar 180° o menos y coincide exactamente con la figura original.

This figure has 60° rotational symmetry.

Sample (p. 677)   A sample is a part of a population.

Muestra (p. 677)   Una muestra es una parte de una población.

A class of 25 students is a sample of the population of a large school.

Sample space (p. 658)   A sample space is all possible outcomes of an experiment.

Espacio muestral (p. 658)   Un espacio muestral es el conjunto de todos los resultados posibles de un experimento.

The sample space for tossing two coins is HH, HT, TH, TT.

Scale drawing (p. 304)   A scale drawing is an enlarged or reduced drawing that is similar to an actual object or place.

Dibujo a escala (p. 304)   Un dibujo a escala es un dibujo aumentado o reducido que es similar al objeto o lugar real.

A map is a scale drawing.

Scalene triangle (p. 474)   A scalene triangle is a triangle with no congruent sides.

EXAMPLE $\triangle NPO$ is a scalene triangle.

Triángulo escaleno (p. 474)   Un triángulo escaleno es un triángulo que no tiene lados congruentes.

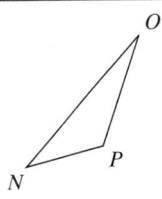

Scatter plot (p. 427)   A scatter plot is a graph that displays data from two related sets as ordered pairs.

EXAMPLE This scatter plot displays the amount various companies spent on advertising (in dollars) versus product sales (in thousands of dollars).

Diagrama de dispersión (p. 427)   Un diagrama de dispersión es una gráfica que muestra datos de dos conjuntos relacionados, como pares ordenados.

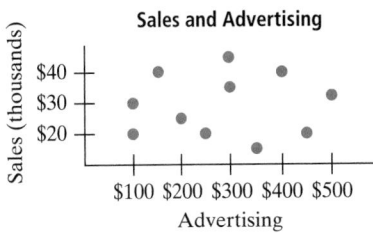

Scientific notation (p. 219)   Scientific notation is a way of expressing a number. A number is expressed in scientific notation when it is written as the product of a number greater than or equal to 1 and less than 10, and a power of 10.

Notación científica (p. 219)   La notación científica es una forma de expresar un número. Un número se expresa en notación científica cuando se escribe como el producto de un número mayor o igual a 1 y menor que 10 y el segundo es una potencia de 10.

In scientific notation, 37,000,000 is written as 3.7×10^7.

Segment (p. 462)   A segment is part of a line. It has two endpoints.

Segmento (p. 462)   Un segmento es parte de una recta. Tiene dos puntos extremos.

$\overline{CB}$ represents the segment shown.

Segment bisector (p. 496)   A segment bisector is a line, segment, or ray that separates a segment into two congruent segments.

Mediatriz de un segmento (p. 496)   La mediatriz de un segmento es una recta, segmento o rayo que divide el segmento en dos segmentos congruentes.

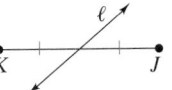

Line ℓ bisects $\overline{KJ}$.

Sequence (p. 696)   A sequence is a set of numbers that follow a pattern.

Progresión (p. 696)   Una progresión es un conjunto de números que sigue un patrón.

$2, 2.3, 2.34, 2.345, \ldots$

Side (pp. 468, 474)   See *Angle* and *Polygon*.

Cara (pp. 468, 474)   Ver *Angle* y *Polygon*.

English/Spanish Glossary

Significant digits (p. 164)   Significant digits are the digits that represent an actual measurement.

Dígitos significativos (p. 164)   Dígitos significativos son los dígitos que representan una medida real.

Similar figures (p. 303)   Similar figures are figures with corresponding angles that have equal measures and corresponding sides that have proportional lengths. The symbol ~ means "is similar to."

EXAMPLE $\triangle ABC \sim \triangle RTS$

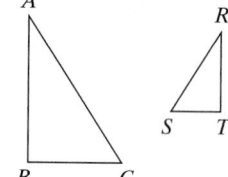

Figuras semejantes (p. 303)   Figuras semejantes son figuras con ángulos correspondients que tienen la misma medida y lados correspondientes que tienen longitudes proporcionales. El símbolo ~ significa "es semejante a."

Simple interest (p. 386)   Simple interest is interest paid only on the principal, the initial amount of money invested or borrowed. The formula for simple interest is $I = prt$, where I is the interest, p is the principal, r is the interest rate per year, and t is the time in years.

The simple interest on $1,000 at 5% for 2 years is $1,000 · 0.05 · 2, or $100.

Interés simple (p. 386)   Interés simple es aquel que se paga sólo por el capital, el monto inicial de dinero que se invierte o se pide prestado. La fórmula de interés simple es $I = prt$, donde I es el interés, p es el capital, r es la tasa de interés anual y t es el tiempo en años.

Simplest form of a fraction (p. 196)   The simplest form of a fraction is the form in which the only common factor of the numerator and denominator is 1.

The simplest form of the fraction $\frac{15}{20}$ is $\frac{3}{4}$.

Mínima expresión de una fracción (p. 196)   La mínima expresión de una fracción es la expresión en que el único factor común del numerador y del denominador es 1.

Simplify a variable expression (p. 78)   To simplify a variable expression is to replace it with an equivalent expression having as few terms as possible.

$2x + 5 + 4x$ simplifies to $6x + 5$.

Simplificar una expresión variable (p. 78)   Se simplifica una expresión variable al reemplazarla con una expresión equivalente que tiene el menor número posible de términos.

Simulation (p. 673)   A simulation is a model used to find experimental probability.

Your baseball team has an equal chance of winning or losing each of its next five games. You can toss a coin to simulate the outcomes of the next five games.

Simulación (p. 673)   Una simulación es un modelo que se usa para hallar la probabilidad experimental.

Sine (p. 614)   See *Trigonometric ratios*.

Razón del seno (p. 614)   Ver *Trigonometric ratios*.

Skew lines (p. 463)   Skew lines are lines in space that do not intersect and are not parallel. They do not lie in the same plane. Skew segments must be parts of skew lines.

Rectas cruzadas (p. 463)   Las rectas cruzadas son rectas en el espacio, que no se intersecan y que no son paralelas. No están en el mismo plano. Los segmentos cruzados son partes de rectas cruzadas.

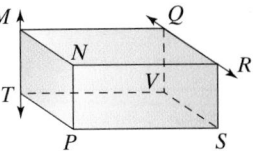

$\overleftrightarrow{MT}$ and $\overleftrightarrow{QR}$ are skew lines.

Slant height (p. 558)   See *Cone* and *Pyramid*.

Altura inclinada (p. 558)   Ver *Cone* y *Pyramid*.

Slope (p. 415)   Slope is a ratio that describes the tilt of a line.

$$\text{slope} = \frac{\text{vertical change}}{\text{horizontal change}} = \frac{\text{difference in } y\text{-coordinates}}{\text{difference in } x\text{-coordinates}}$$

Pendiente (p. 415)   La pendiente de una recta es la razón que describe su inclinación.

$$\text{Pendiente} = \frac{\text{variación vertical}}{\text{variación horizontal}} = \frac{\text{diferencia en las coordenadas } y}{\text{diferencia en las coordenadas } x}$$

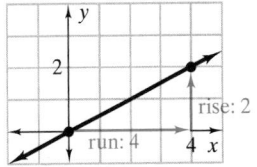

The slope of the given line is $\frac{2}{4}$, or $\frac{1}{2}$.

Slope-intercept form of an equation (p. 417)   The slope-intercept form of an equation is $y = mx + b$, where m is the slope and b is the y-intercept of the line.

Forma pendiente-intercepto de una ecuación (p. 417)   La forma pendiente-intercepto de una ecuación es $y = mx + b$ donde m es la pendiente y b es el intercepto en y de la recta.

The equation $y = 2x + 1$ is in slope-intercept form with $m = 2$ and $b = 1$.

Solid (p. 546)   A solid is a three-dimensional figure.

Sólido (p. 546)   Un sólido es una figura tridimensional.

See *Space figure*.

Solution (p. 83)   A solution is any value or values that make an equation or an inequality true.

Solución (p. 83)   Una solución es cualquier valor o valores que hacen verdadera una ecuación o una desigualdad.

4 is the solution of $x + 5 = 9$.

$(8, 4)$ is a solution of $y = -1x + 12$ because $4 = -1(8) + 12$.

-4 is a solution of $2x < -3$, because $2 \cdot -4 < -3$.

$(-1, 3)$ is a solution of $y > x - 4$, because $3 > -1 - 4$.

Space figure (p. 545)   A space figure is a three-dimensional figure, or solid.

EXAMPLE   A cylinder, a cone, and a prism are space figures.

Cuerpo geométrico (p. 545)   Un cuerpo geométrico es una figura tridimensional o sólido.

English/Spanish Glossary

Sphere (p. 545)   A sphere is the set of points in space that are a given distance from a point, called the center.

Esfera (p. 545)   Una esfera es el conjunto de todos los puntos del espacio que se hallan a una misma distancia de un punto dado llamado el centro.

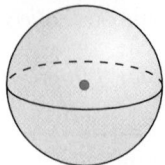

Square (p. 475)   A square is a parallelogram with four right angles and four congruent sides.

EXAMPLE $QRTS$ is a square.
$\angle Q, \angle R, \angle T,$ and $\angle S$ are right angles.
$QR = RT = ST = SQ$

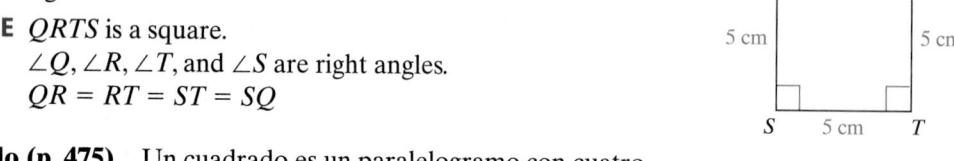

Cuadrado (p. 475)   Un cuadrado es un paralelogramo con cuatro ángulos rectos y cuatro lados congruentes.

Square root (p. 588)   The square root of a given number is a number that when multiplied by itself equals the given number.

The symbol for the nonnegative square root of a number is $\sqrt{}$.

$\sqrt{25} = 5$ because $5^2 = 25$.

Raíz cuadrada (p. 588)   La raíz cuadrada de un número dado es un número que cuando es multiplicado por sí mismo, es igual al número dado.

Standard form (p. 716)   Standard form of a polynomial is the form in which the terms are in order of decreasing degree.

$3y^2 + 8y - 2$ is in standard form.

Forma general de un polinomio (p. 716)   Un polinomio está en forma general cuando sus términos están en orden descendente.

Standard notation (p. 220)   Standard notation is the usual form for representing a number.

The standard notation of 8.9×10^5 is 890,000.

Notación normal (p. 220)   La notación normal es la forma común de representar un número.

Stem-and-leaf plot (p. 646)   A stem-and-leaf plot is a display that shows numeric data arranged in order. The leaf of each data item is its last digit. The stem is its other digits. The stems are stacked in order and the leaves are arranged in order to the side of each stem.

EXAMPLE This stem-and-leaf plot displays recorded times in a race. The stem records the whole number of seconds. The leaf represents tenths of a second. So, 27 | 7 represents 27.7 seconds.

27 | 7 means 27.7.

Diagrama de tallo y hojas (p. 646)   Un diagrama de tallo y hojas es una representación que muestra datos numéricos en orden de valor relativo. La hoja de cada dato es su último dígito. El tallo son sus otros dígitos. Los tallos están organizados en columnas ordenadas y las hojas están organizadas en orden al lado de cada tallo.

Straight angle (p. 468) A straight angle is an angle with a measure of 180°.

Ángulo llano (p. 468) Un ángulo llano es un ángulo cuya medida es 180°.

Subtraction Property of Equality (p. 88) If $a = b$, then $a - c = b - c$.

$10 = 2(5)$, so $10 - 5 = 2(5) - 5$

Propiedad sustrativa de la igualdad (p. 88) Si $a = b$, entonces $a - c = b - c$.

Subtraction Property of Inequality (p. 108) If $a > b$, then $a - c > b - c$. If $a < b$, then $a - c < b - c$.

$7 > 4$, so $7 - 3 > 4 - 3$
$6 < 9$, so $6 - 2 < 9 - 2$

Propiedad sustractiva de la desigualdad (p. 108) Si $a > b$, entonces $a - c > b - c$. Si $a < b$, entonces $a - c < b - c$.

Supplementary angles (p. 469) Supplementary angles are two angles whose measures add to 180°.

$\angle A$ and $\angle D$ are supplementary.

Ángulos suplementarios (p. 469) Dos ángulos son suplementarios si la suma de sus medidas es 180°.

Surface area (p. 551) Surface area is the sum of the areas of the base(s) and lateral faces of a space figure.

EXAMPLE The surface area of the prism is the sum of the areas of its faces.
$(12 + 12 + 12 + 12 + 9 + 9)$ in.^{2} = 66 in.^{2}

Each square = 1 in.^{2}

Área total (p. 551) El área total es la suma de las áreas de la o las bases y de las caras laterales de una figura tridimesional.

System of linear equations (p. 439) A system of linear equations is two or more linear equations.

$y = 3x + 1$ and $y = -2x - 3$ form a system of linear equations.

Sistema de ecuaciones lineales (p. 439) Dos o más ecuaciones lineales forman un sistema de ecuaciones lineales.

System of linear inequalities (p. 447) A system of linear inequalities is two or more linear inequalities.

$y \geq 3x + 1$ and $y < -2x - 3$ form a system of linear inequalities.

Sistema de desigualdades lineales (p. 447) Dos o más desigualdades lineales forman un sistema de desigualdades lineales.

Tangent (p. 614) See *Trigonometric ratios.*

Tangente (p. 614) Ver *Trigonometric ratios.*

English/Spanish Glossary

Term of an expression (p. 78)   A term is a number, a variable, or the product of a number and variable(s).

The expression $7x + 12 + (-9y)$ has three terms: $7x$, 12, and $-9y$.

Término de una expresión (p. 78)   Un término es un número, una variable o el producto de un número y una o mas variables.

Term of a sequence (p. 696)   A term of a sequence is any number in the sequence.

$1, 2, 3, 4, \ldots$

EXAMPLE   In this sequence, 1 is the first term, 2 is the second term, 3 is the third term, and 4 is the fourth term.

Término de una progresión (p. 696)   Un término de una progresión es cualquier número de la progresión.

Terminating decimal (p. 241)   A terminating decimal is a decimal with a finite number of digits.

Both 0.6 and 0.7265 are terminating decimals.

Decimal finito (p. 241)   Un decimal finito es un decimal que tiene un número finito de digitos.

Tessellation (p. 515)   A tessellation is a repeated pattern of figures that completely covers a plane without gaps or overlaps.

Teselación (p. 515)   Una teselación es un patrón repetido de figuras que cubre completamente un plano sin dejar espacios ni sobreponerse.

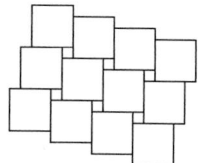

This tessellation consists of small squares and large squares.

Theoretical Probability (p. 658)   See *Probability*.

Probabilidad teórica (p. 658)   Ver *Probability*.

Three-dimensional figure (p. 545)   A three-dimensional figure is a figure that does not lie in a plane.

See *Space figure*.

Figura tridimensional (p. 545)   Una figura tridimensional es una figura que no está situada en un plano.

Transformation (p. 501)   A transformation is a change of position or size of a figure. Four types of transformations are translations, reflections, rotations, and dilations.

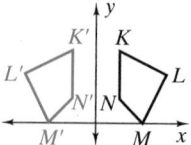

EXAMPLE $K'L'M'N'$ is a reflection of $KLMN$ across the y-axis.

Transformación (p. 501)   Una transformación es un cambio de posición o tamaño de una figura. Una transformación puede ser una traslacion, una reflexión, una rotación o una dilatación.

Translation (p. 501)   A translation is a transformation that moves points the same distance and in the same direction.

EXAMPLE $A'B'C'D'$ is the translation image of $ABCD$.

Traslación (p. 501)   Una traslación es una transformación que mueve puntos la misma distancia y en la misma dirección.

Transversal (p. 470)   A transversal is a line that intersects two other lines in different points.

EXAMPLE $\overleftrightarrow{RI}$ is a transversal of $\overleftrightarrow{QS}$ and $\overleftrightarrow{HJ}$.

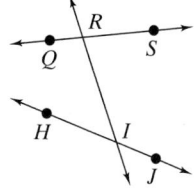

Transversal (p. 470)   Transversal es una recta que interseca a otras dos rectas en puntos distintos.

Trapezoid (p. 475)   A trapezoid is a quadrilateral with exactly one pair of parallel sides.

EXAMPLE $UVYW$ is a trapezoid.
$$\overleftrightarrow{UV} \parallel \overleftrightarrow{WY}$$

Trapecio (p. 475)   Un trapecio es un cuadrilátero que tiene exactamente un par de lados paralelos.

Tree diagram (p. 657)   A tree diagram is a diagram that displays all the possible outcomes of an event.

EXAMPLE There are for 4 possible outcomes for tossing 2 coins: HH, HT, TH, and TT.

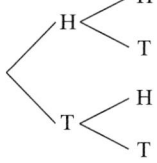

Diagrama de árbol (p. 657)   Un diagrama de árbol presenta todos los resultados posibles de un suceso.

Trend line (p. 434)   A trend line is a line that closely fits the data points in a scatter plot.

Línea de tendencia (p. 434)   Una línea de tendencia es la recta que más corresponde con los puntos de los datos en una diagrama de dispersión.

Triangle (p. 476)   A triangle is a polygon with three sides.

Triángulo (p. 476)   Un triángulo es un polígono con tres lados.

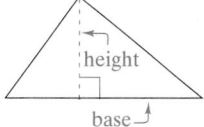

EXAMPLES

Trigonometric ratios (p. 614) Trigonometric ratios are the sine, cosine, and tangent. In $\triangle ABC$ with right $\angle C$,

$$\text{sine } \angle A = \frac{\text{length of leg opposite } \angle A}{\text{length of hypotenuse}} = \frac{a}{c},$$

$$\text{cosine } \angle A = \frac{\text{length of leg adjacent to } \angle A}{\text{length of hypotenuse}} = \frac{b}{c},$$

$$\text{tangent } \angle A = \frac{\text{length of leg opposite } \angle A}{\text{length of leg adjacent to } \angle A} = \frac{a}{b}.$$

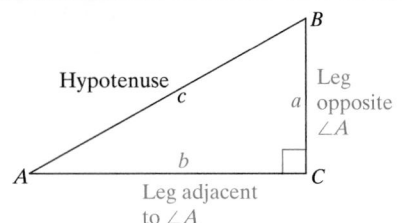

Razones trigonométricas (p. 614) Las razones trigonoméricas son seno, coseno y tangente. En $\triangle ABC$, con ángulo recto C,

$$\text{seno } \angle A = \frac{\text{longitud del cateto opuesto a } \angle A}{\text{longitud de la hipotenusa}} = \frac{a}{c},$$

$$\text{coseno } \angle A = \frac{\text{longitud del cateto adyacente a } \angle A}{\text{longitud de la hipotenusa}} = \frac{b}{c},$$

$$\text{tangente } \angle A = \frac{\text{longitud del cateto opuesto a } \angle A}{\text{longitud del cateto adyacente a } \angle A} = \frac{a}{b}.$$

Trigonometry (p. 614) Trigonometry is a branch of mathematics involving triangle measures.

Trigonometría (p. 614) La trigonometría es la rama de las matemáticas que se relaciona con la medida de triángulos.

Trinomial (p. 712) A trinomial is a polynomial with three terms. $x^2 - 5x + 6$ is a trinomial.

Trinomio (p. 712) Un trinomio es un polinomio compuesto de tres términos.

Unit rate (p. 293) A unit rate is a rate that has denominator 1.   If you drive 165 mi in 3 h, your unit rate of travel is 55 mi in 1 h or 55 mi/h.

Tasa unitaria (p. 293) Una tasa unitaria es la tasa cuyo denominador es 1.

Upper quartile (p. 641) The upper quartile is the median of the upper half of a data set.   See *Quartile*.

Cuartil superior (p. 641) El cuartil superior es la mediana de la mitad superior de un conjunto de datos.

Variable (p. 4) A variable is a letter that stands for a number. x is a variable in the equation $9 - x = 3$.

Variable (p. 4) Una variable es una letra que representa a un número.

844   Glossary

Variable expression (p. 4) A variable expression is a mathematical phrase that uses variables, numbers, and operation symbols.

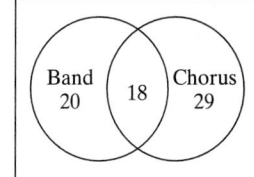

$7 + x, 2y - 4, \frac{3}{5}g$, and $\frac{7}{k}$ are variable expressions.

Expresión algebraica (p. 4) Una expresión algebraica es una expresión en la que se usan variables, números y símbolos de operaciones.

Venn diagram (p. 195) A Venn diagram is a diagram that illustrates the relationships among collections of objects or numbers. The intersection, or overlap, of two circles indicates what is common to both collections.

EXAMPLE The Venn diagram shows the activities of 67 music students.

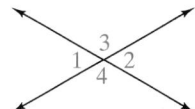

Diagrama Venn (p. 195) Un diagrama Venn es un diagrama que muestra la relación entre dos conjuntos de objectos o números. La intersección o sobreposición de dos círculos indica lo que tienen en común ambos conjuntos.

Vertex (pp. 468, 475) See *Angle* and *Polygon*.

Vértice (pp. 468, 475) Ver *Angle* y *Polygon*.

Vertical angles (p. 469) Vertical angles are angles formed by two intersecting lines, and are opposite each other. Vertical angles are congruent.

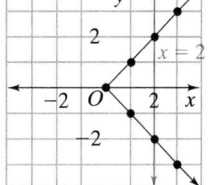

$\angle 1$ and $\angle 2$ are vertical angles, as are $\angle 3$ and $\angle 4$.

Ángulos verticales (p. 469) Ángulos verticales son aquellos formados por dos rectas que se intersecan y que son opuestos entre sí. Los ángulos verticales son congruentes.

Vertical-line test (p. 405) The vertical-line test is a test that allows you to describe graphically whether a relation is a function.

EXAMPLE Since the vertical line $x = 2$ passes through two points of the graph, the relation is not a function.

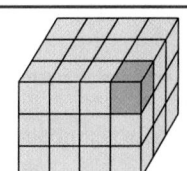

Prueba de la línea vertical (p. 405) Método que permite determinar gráficamente si una relación es o no es una función.

Volume (p. 563) The volume of a space figure is the number of cubic units needed to fill it.

EXAMPLE The volume of the rectangular prism is 36 in.^{3}.

Each cube is 1 in.^{3}.

Volumen (p. 563) El volumen de una figura tridimensional es el número de unidades cúbicas necesarias para llenar el espacio interior de dicha figura.

English/Spanish Glossary

x-axis (p. 52)   The *x*-axis is the horizontal number line that, together with the *y*-axis, establishes the coordinate plane.

See *Coordinate plane.*

Eje de *x* (p. 52)   El eje de *x* es la recta numérica horizontal que, junto al eje de *y*, forma el plano de coordenadas.

x-coordinate (p. 52)   The *x*-coordinate is the horizontal position of a point in the coordinate plane.

See *Coordinates.*

Coordenada *x* (p. 52)   La coordenada *x* muestra la ubicación horizontal de un punto en el plano de coordenadas.

x-intercept (p. 413)   The *x*-intercept of a line is the *x*-coordinate of the point where the line crosses the *x*-axis.

EXAMPLE The *x*-intercept is 2. The *y*-intercept is -3.

Intercepto *x* (p. 413)   El intercepto *x* de una recta es la coordenada *x* del punto de intercepción de la recta con el eje de *x*.

y-axis (p. 52)   The *y*-axis is the vertical number line that, together with the *x*-axis, forms the coordinate plane.

See *Coordinate plane.*

Eje de *y* (p. 52)   El eje de *y* es la recta numérica vertical que, junto al eje de *x*, forma el plano de coordenadas.

y-coordinate (p. 52)   The *y*-coordinate is the vertical position of a point in the coordinate plane.

See *Coordinates.*

Coordenada *y* (p. 52)   La coordenada *y* muestra la ubicación vertical de un punto en el plano de coordenadas.

y-intercept (pp. 413, 417)   The *y*-intercept of a line is the *y*-coordinate of the point where the line crosses the *y*-axis.

See *x-intercept.*

Intercepto *y* (pp. 413, 417)   El intercepto *y* de una recta es la coordenada *y* del punto de intercepción de la recta con el eje de *y*.

Zero pair (p. 23)   A zero pair is a positive algebra tile paired with a negative algebra tile.

◻◼◄——— A zero pair

Par cero (p. 23)   Un par cero es un ficha de álgebra positiva que se empareja con una ficha de álgebra negativa.

Answers to Instant Check System™

Chapter 1

Check Your Readiness   p. 2

1. 1 **2.** 11 **3.** 11 **4.** 19 **5.** 13 **6.** 40 **7.** 17 **8.** 44
9. 176 **10.** 28 **11.** 166 **12.** 75 **13.** > **14.** >
15. < **16.** < **17.** < **18.** = **19.** 12 **20.** 30 **21.** 28
22. 5 **23.** 96 **24.** 5 **25.** 200 **26.** 80 **27.** 31
28. 13 **29.** 480 **30.** 12 **31.** 1 **32.** 4 **33.** 7 **34.** 10

Lesson 1-1   pp. 4–7

Check Skills You'll Need 1. 7 **2.** 12 **3.** 5 **4.** 4 **5.** 3

Quick Check 1a. Variable expression; *x* is the
variable. **b.** numerical expression **c.** Variable
expression.; *d* is the variable **2a.** 0.50*b* **b.** $\frac{m}{60}$

Lesson 1-2   pp. 8–12

Check Skills You'll Need 1. 82 **2.** 43 **3.** 71 **4.** 19 **5.** 14
6. 26

Quick Check 1a. 17 **b.** 3 **c.** 3 **2a.** 4 **b.** 12 **3.** 3

Lesson 1-3   pp. 14–17

Check Skills You'll Need 1. 60 **2.** 18 **3.** 29 **4.** 32

Quick Check 1a. 28 **b.** 45 **2a.** 90 **b.** 23 **c.** 12
3. 29*c*; $145 **4.** $146

Lesson 1-4   pp. 18–22

Check Skills You'll Need 1. −7 **2.** 9 **3.** 8 **4.** 3 **5.** −5

Quick Check 1. −2

2.

−6, 0, 2 **3.** the absolute value of negative ten; 10

Checkpoint Quiz 1 1. *f* + 23 **2.** $\frac{g}{34}$ **3.** 9*p* **4.** 20 **5.** 2
6. 19 **7.** 0 **8.** 54 **9.** 15

10a.

b. Tuesday, Wednesday, Monday, Thursday

Lesson 1-5   pp. 24–29

Check Skills You'll Need 1. < **2.** > **3.** < **4.** = **5.** > **6.** >

Quick Check 1a. 3 **b.** 4 **c.** −4 **2a.** −4 **b.** 5
c. −6 **3a.** −38 **b.** 47 **c.** −90 **4.** 1,280 m **5a.** −10
b. 70

Lesson 1-6   pp. 30–34

Check Skills You'll Need 1. −1 **2.** −29 **3.** −10 **4.** 11
5. 0 **6.** −23

Quick Check 1a. −5 **b.** −1 **c.** −3 **2a.** −4
b. −6 **c.** 5 **3a.** 35 **b.** −106 **c.** −46 **3d.** −81°C

Lesson 1-7   pp. 35–39

Check Skills You'll Need 1. −7 **2.** −11 **3.** −15 **4.** −19

Quick Check 1. A six-sided figure with all vertices
on a circle. **2a.** Start with 4 and add 5 repeatedly.
b. Start with 3 and multiply by 3 repeatedly
c. Start with 1, 1. Then each number is the sum
of the previous two numbers. **3.** Start with 1 and
add 2 repeatedly; 9, 11. **4.** No; if the coin is fair,
the coin can come up tails on any toss.
5a. correct **b.** Incorrect; 8 and |8| are not
opposites. **c.** correct

Lesson 1-8   pp. 40–43

Check Skills You'll Need 1. Start with 8 and add 3
repeatedly; 20, 23, 26 **2.** Start with 1, then
alternately add 4 and subtract 1; 11, 10, 14
3. Start with 3, then alternately add 2 and multiply
by 2; 26, 52, 54 **4.** Start with 1, then add 3
repeatedly; 13, 16, 19

Quick Check 8. 127 students

Lesson 1-9   pp. 44–49

Check Skills You'll Need 1. 20 **2.** 24 **3.** 25 **4.** 28 **5.** 30
6. 140

Quick Check 1a. −12 **b.** −12 **c.** −14 **2.** 12 **3a.** 64
b. −90 **c.** 0 **4a.** −4 **b.** 8 **c.** 14 **d.** −2

Checkpoint Quiz 2 1. −8 **2.** 20 **3.** −45 **4.** 8 **5.** −12
6. 72 **7–9.** Answers may vary. Samples are given.
7. 3 + (−10) = −7 **8.** 2 − (−20) = 22
9. 8 · (−5) = −40 **10.** 13, 18, 23 **11.** 81, 243, 729

Lesson 1-10   pp. 52–56

Check Skills You'll Need

1.

2.

3.

4.

Quick Check 1a. (2, −3); (3, 3) **b.** Quadrant IV; Quadrant I

2a–b.

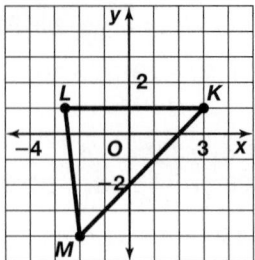

b. a triangle

Chapter 2

Check Your Readiness   **p. 66**

1. 1.1, 1.1 **2.** 0.3, 0.3 **3.** 0.7, 0.7 **4.** 5.8, 5.8
5. 2.5, 2.5 **6.** 6, 6 **7.** 0.6, 0.6 **8.** 0.07, 0.07 **9.** <
10. > **11.** < **12.** > **13.** < **14.** = **15.** = **16.** <
17. > **18.** < **19.** < **20.** > **21.** 25 **22.** 28 **23.** 15
24. −110 **25.** 36 **26.** 16 **27.** −24 **28.** 45
29. −20 **30.** −27 **31.** −5 **32.** −45

Lesson 2-1   **pp. 68–72**

Check Skills You'll Need 1. −25 **2.** 35 **3.** −7 **4.** −46

Quick Check
1. $18; 6 + 8 + 4
$= 6 + (8 + 4)$ Assoc. Prop. of Add.
$= 6 + (4 + 8)$ Comm. Prop. of Add.
$= (6 + 4) + 8$ Assoc. Prop. of Add.
$= 10 + 8$ Add within parentheses.
$= 18$ Add.
2a. Comm. Prop. of Add **b.** Ident. Prop of Mult.
c. Assoc. Prop. of Mult. **3a.** 27 **b.** 3 **c.** 40 **d.** 10
4. $6.30 **5a.** 300 **b.** −120 **c.** 240 **d.** 540

Lesson 2-2   **pp. 73–77**

Check Skills You'll Need 1. 12 **2.** 24 **3.** 20 **4.** 6 **5.** 8
6. 4

Quick Check 1. 1,791 **2.** $1,428 **3a.** 210 **b.** −120
c. 35 **4a.** $8x − 12$ **b.** $3x + 12$ **c.** $6x + 2$ **5a.** $14 − 6d$
b. $18m + 3$ **c.** $−15t + 6$

Lesson 2-3   **pp. 78–81**

Check Skills You'll Need 1. $5b + 20$ **2.** $−6x − 15$
3. $−32 − 12q$ **4.** $−12b + 42$

Quick Check 1a. 2, 4; 2s, 4s; 6 **b.** −4; none; none
c. 9, 2, −2, 1; 9m and −2m, 2r and r; none
2. $7a + 1$ **3a.** $2b$ **b.** $−13m$ **c.** $3p$ **4a.** $−y + 5m$
b. $2x − 7$

Checkpoint Quiz 1 1. Comm. Prop of Mult.
2. Assoc. Prop. of Mult. **3.** Ident. Prop. of Mult.
4. Comm. Prop. of Add. **5.** Comm. Prop. of Mult.
6. Dist. Prop. **7.** 9a **8.** 18y **9.** 16w − 6

Lesson 2-4   **pp. 82–85**

Check Skills You'll Need 1. $x + 46$ **2.** $g − 4$ **3.** $t − 5$
4. $\frac{z}{26}$

Quick Check 1a. false; $2 \neq 3$ **b.** open; has a variable
c. true; $20 = 20$ **2.** $20 − x = 3$; open because
there is a variable **3a.** no **b.** yes
4. $b + 6 = 33$; $27 + 6 = 33$; Yes, the backpack
weighs 27 lb.

Lesson 2-5   **pp. 88–92**

Check Skills You'll Need 1. 3 **2.** 9 **3.** 8 **4.** 6

Quick Check 1a. −5 **b.** 4 **c.** −1 **2.** $123 = r + 55$;
68 beats/min **3a.** 13 **b.** 72 **c.** 112 **4.** $17 ≈ $15;
$9 ≈ $10; 10 ≈ n − 15; $25

Lesson 2-6   **pp. 94–97**

Check Skills You'll Need 1. 1 **2.** −1 **3.** −1 **4.** 1

Quick Check 1a. 21 **b.** 13 **c.** 9 **2a.** −8
b. −12 **c.** 14 **3a.** −50 **b.** 324 **c.** −600

Lesson 2-7   **pp. 98–101**

Check Skills You'll Need 1. 178 **2.** 188 **3.** 183 **4.** 180
5. 180 (Ex. 4)

Quick Check 6. 53 adult tickets, 80 student tickets

Lesson 2-8   **pp. 104–107**

Check Skills You'll Need

1. −9, −3, 7
2. −10, −8, −2
3. −5, 0, 3
4. −6, 3, 10

Quick Check
1a.
b.
c.
d.

2. $x \geq 3$ **3.** $n < 5$

Lesson 2-9   pp. 108–111

Check Skills You'll Need **1.** −2 **2.** 19 **3.** 9 **4.** 29

Quick Check **1a.** $m > 3$

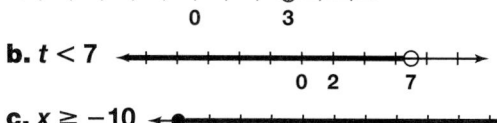

b. $t < 7$

c. $x \geq -10$

2. ≤ 28 lb **3a.** $m > 42$ **b.** $v \leq 11$ **c.** $t \geq 16$

Checkpoint Quiz 2 **1.** true; 19 = 19 **2.** open; variable
3. false; 1 ≠ −1 **4.** −4 **5.** 4 **6.** 6 **7.** −32 **8.** −9
9. $a \geq 6$ **10.** $r < 19$ **11.** $m > -19$
12. 1 quarter, 5 dimes, 2 pennies

Lesson 2-10   pp. 112–116

Check Skills You'll Need **1.** 4 **2.** −9 **3.** −20 **4.** 288

Quick Check **1a.** $x > 10$ **b.** $m < -7$
c. $t > -4$ **2a.** $m \geq 8$ **b.** $t > -21$ **c.** $r > 35$

Chapter 3

Check Your Readiness   p. 126

1. 40 **2.** 10 **3.** 0 **4.** 600 **5.** 830 **6.** 6,010 **7.** <
8. > **9.** < **10.** < **11.** > **12.** > **13.** 8,349, 8.35,
8.351, 9.25 **14.** 0.017, 0.02, 0.0201, 0.201
15. −14.1, −1.401, −1.4, −1.04 **16.** −3.2, −3.19,
−2.8, −2.3 **17.** 11.49 **18.** 3.07 **19.** 3.65 **20.** 1.206
21. 6.7067 **22.** 6.9 **23.** 55.12 **24.** 10.6 **25.** 98.7
26. 532 **27.** 300 **28.** 154,070 **29.** 0.08 **30.** 0.0842
31. 0.0161 **32.** 0.001209

Lesson 3-1   pp. 129–133

Check Skills You'll Need **1.** 2 tens **2.** 3 tenths
3. 8 hundredths **4.** 6 thousandths

Quick Check **1a.** tenths; 38.4 **b.** ones; 1
c. tenths; 7,098.6 **d.** thousandths; 274.943
e. tenths; 5.0 **f.** hundredths; 9.85 **2a.** about 560
b. about 220 **3a.** about 18.6 **b.** about $11
4a. about $15 **b.** about 125

Lesson 3-2   pp. 134–137

Check Skills You'll Need **1.** 146 **2.** 199 **3.** 101 **4.** 28

Quick Check **1a.** about 10 **b.** about 68
c. about 160 **2.** about $40 **3a.** about 20
b. about 6 **c.** about 20 **4a.** Yes; 0.68 is close to
an estimate of 0.8. **b.** No; 52.3 is not close to an
estimate of 5.

Lesson 3-3   pp. 139–143

Check Skills You'll Need **1.** 3, 4, 5, 6, 6, 8, 9
2. 68, 69, 71, 72, 72 **3.** 98, 101, 101, 112, 120
4. 3, 3.3, 3.7, 3.74, 37

Quick Check **1.** 2.95, 2.8, 2.3, 2 **2a.** 3 modes
b. 1 mode **3a.** 31; raises the mean by 2.6
b. 1; lowers the mean by 2.8 **4a.** $25.25, $23.50,
$20 **b.** Answers may vary. Sample: Median; the
mode is equal to two of the smaller data values,
and the outlier ($42) affects the mean too much.

Lesson 3-4   pp. 145–148

Check Skills You'll Need **1.** 14 **2.** 10 **3.** 14 **4.** 3.5

Quick Check **1a.** $r = 28$ mi/h **b.** $t = 51.5$ yr
2a. 61°F **b.** 59°F **c.** 53.5°F **3a.** 88.2 cm **b.** 52 in.

Checkpoint Quiz 1 **1.** 15.66 **2.** 0.891 **3.** 7,023 **4.** 345.7
5. about 32 **6.** about 24 **7.** about −1 **8.** about 6
9. 56, 57, no mode **10.** 2, 2, 1 **11.** 8.5 h

Lesson 3-5   pp. 150–153

Check Skills You'll Need **1.** 9.86 **2.** 2.45 **3.** 2.04 **4.** 3.08

Quick Check **1a.** 13.9 **b.** 38.96
2. $35.48 + m = 70$; $34.52 **3a.** 21.1 **b.** −7.4
4. $x - 14.95 = 12.48$; $27.43

Lesson 3-6   pp. 154–157

Check Skills You'll Need **1.** 11.7 **2.** 0.48 **3.** 6.618
4. 4.8018

Quick Check **1a.** −2 **b.** 0.5 **c.** 90.9
2. $5.5p = 7.70$; $1.40 **3a.** −3 **b.** 12.5 **c.** −360
4. 12 hits

Lesson 3-7   pp. 158–163

Check Skills You'll Need **1.** 500 **2.** 0.01406 **3.** 2.94
4. 0.009

Quick Check **1a.** Centimeter; a meter is too large
unless you use fractional parts of a meter;
millimeters are too small. **b.** Gram; an energy bar
has a mass of several grams, but it is much less
than 1 kilogram. **c.** Kilogram; a horse is very
heavy, so grams are too small. **d.** Liter; a gas tank
holds several liters, so milliliters are too small.
2a. 50 km; millimeters are used to measure very
small lengths. **b.** 10 mL; the eyedropper holds
several drops of water but much less than a quart.
3a. 0.035 **b.** 250,000 **c.** 6,000 **4a.** 3,800 m
b. 250 mL

Checkpoint Quiz 2 1. 0.25 **2.** 8.55 **3.** 130 **4.** 3.05
5. 6.5 **6.** 129.6 **7.** 1.5 m; 1.5 cm is a little wider
than the width of a thumbnail. **8.** 500 mL; 500 L
would be about 500 qt. **9.** 0.095 **10.** 7,650,000 **11.**
0.675 **12.** 7,100 **13.** 9,100 g

Lesson 3-8   pp. 166–169

Check Skills You'll Need 1. Start with 0 and add 6
repeatedly; 24, 30, 36 **2.** Start with −18 and add 9
repeatedly; 18, 27, 36 **3.** Start with 0. Alternately
add 2 and subtract 1; 5, 4, 6 **4.** Start with 7.
Alternately subtract 1 and add 2; 9, 11, 10

Quick Check

5.

Chapter 4

Check Your Readiness   p. 178

1. 1,728 **2.** −64 **3.** 6,561 **4.** 15,625 **5.** 512 **6.** 64
7–12. Answers may vary. Samples are given.
7. 2, 6 **8.** 9, 5 **9.** 3, 6 **10.** 9, 7 **11.** 6, 4 **12.** 2, 25
13. 16, 2 **14.** 9, 9 **15.** 6, 9 **16.** 6, 10 **17.** 4, 7
18. 7, 8 **19.** 4, 11 **20.** 9, 4 **21.** 8, 9 **22.** 90 **23.** 900
24. 22 **25.** 49 **26.** 21 **27.** 45 **28.** 212 **29.** 140
30. 23 **31.** 27 **32.** 91 **33.** 130

Lesson 4-1   pp. 180–183

Check Skills You'll Need 1. 160 **2.** 73 **3.** 51 **4.** 48
5. 177 **6.** 118

Quick Check 1a. Yes; 160 ends in 0. **b.** No; 56 does
not end in 0. **c.** No; 53 does no end in 0, 2, 4, 6, or
8. **d.** Yes; 1,118 ends in 8. **2a.** No; the sum of the
digits, 10, is not divisible by 9. **b.** No; the sum of
the digits, 13, is not divisible by 3.
c. Yes; the sum of the digits, 12, is divisible by 3.
d. Yes; the sum of the digits, 18, is divisible by 9.
3a. 1, 2, 5, 10 **b.** 1, 3, 7, 21 **c.** 1, 2, 3, 4, 6, 8, 12, 24
d. 1, 31 **e.** 1 row of 36 students, 2 rows of
18 students, 3 rows of 12 students, 4 rows of
9 students, or 6 rows of 6 students

Lesson 4-2   pp. 186–189

Check Skills You'll Need 1. 81 **2.** 144 **3.** −64 **4.** 10,000

Quick Check 1a. 6^3 **b.** $4xy^2$ **c.** $(-3)^4$ **2a.** 49
b. −16, 16 **3a.** −58 **b.** 81

Lesson 4-3   pp. 190–194

Check Skills You'll Need 1. 1, 3, 5, 15 **2.** 1, 5, 7, 35
3. 1, 7 **4.** 1, 2, 4, 5, 10, 20 **5.** 1, 2, 4, 5, 10, 20, 25,
50, 100 **6.** 1, 11, 121

Quick Check 1a. 11, 13, 17, 19 **b.** 10, 12, 14, 15, 16,
18, 20 **2a.** $2^3 \cdot 3^2$ **b.** 11^2 **c.** $3^2 \cdot 5^2$
b. $2^2 \cdot 59$ **3a.** 4 **b.** 3 **c.** $4r$ **d.** $15m$

Lesson 4-4   pp. 196–199

Check Skills You'll Need 1. 7 **2.** 12 **3.** $5mn$ **4.** 3

Quick Check 1a–c. Answers may vary. Samples are
given. **1a.** $\frac{1}{3}, \frac{10}{30}$ **b.** $\frac{5}{6}, \frac{20}{24}$ **c.** $\frac{7}{10}, \frac{28}{40}$
2a. $\frac{3}{4}$ **b.** $\frac{3}{4}$ **c.** $\frac{4}{5}$ **3a.** $\frac{1}{ac}$ **b.** $\frac{n}{3}$ **c.** $3x$

Checkpoint Quiz 1 1. 2, 3, 5, 10 **2.** 2, 3, 9 **3.** 2, 3
4. none **5.** 3, 9 **6.** 64 **7.** 125 **8.** −18 **9.** $\frac{1}{2}$ **10.** $\frac{2}{3}$ **11.** $\frac{4}{7}$
12. $\frac{1}{4}$ **13.** $2y$ **14.** Answers may vary.
Samples: $5a^2$, $10a^2$; $25a^3b$, $30a^2$

Lesson 4-5   pp. 201–204

Check Skills You'll Need 1. > **2.** > **3.** < **4.** <

Quick Check 6. 45 pictures

Lesson 4-6   pp. 205–208

Check Skills You'll Need 1. $\frac{1}{5}$ **2.** $\frac{2}{3}$ **3.** $\frac{4}{5}$ **4.** $\frac{3}{4}$

Quick Check 1a–d. Answers may vary. Samples are
given. **1a.** $\frac{2}{6}, \frac{-2}{-6}, \frac{-1}{-3}$ **b.** $-\frac{8}{10}, \frac{-4}{5}, \frac{4}{-5}$
c. $\frac{10}{16}, \frac{-10}{-16}, \frac{-5}{-8}$ **d.** $-\frac{2}{4}, \frac{-1}{2}, \frac{1}{-2}$

2a–d.

$$\begin{array}{c} \bullet \quad \quad \quad \bullet \bullet \quad \quad \quad \bullet \\ -2 \quad \quad -\frac{1}{2} \quad 0 \quad 0.9 \quad 2 \\ -\frac{4}{10} \end{array}$$

3a. $-\frac{1}{3}$ **b.** $\frac{2}{3}$ **c.** −3

Lesson 4-7   pp. 209–212

Check Skills You'll Need 1. k^4 **2.** m^2n^2 **3.** 2^4 **4.** 5^3

Quick Check 1a. 32 **b.** m^{12} **c.** x^5y^5
2a. $18a^4$ **b.** $15c^9$ **c.** $12x^6$ **3a.** 256 **b.** c^{20} **c.** m^6

Lesson 4-8   pp. 214–218

Check Skills You'll Need 1. x **2.** $\frac{1}{y}$ **3.** $\frac{2x}{3}$ **4.** $\frac{ab}{4}$

Quick Check 1a. 1,000 **b.** x^7 **c.** $4m^4$ **2a.** 1 **b.** 5 **c.** y^3
d. 5 **3a.** $\frac{1}{16}$ **b.** $\frac{1}{a^2}$ **c.** $\frac{1}{3y^4}$ **4a.** b^{-6} **b.** $m^{-3}n^{-6}$
c. $x^{-4}y^2$

Checkpoint Quiz 2 1–5. Answers may vary. Samples are given. 1. $\frac{1}{4}, \frac{-1}{-4}, \frac{2}{8}$ **2.** $\frac{1}{3}, \frac{-1}{-3}, \frac{2}{6}$ **3.** $\frac{7}{10}, \frac{-7}{-10}, \frac{14}{20}$
4. $\frac{9}{14}, \frac{-9}{-14}, \frac{-18}{-28}$ **5.** $\frac{8}{10}, \frac{-8}{-10}, \frac{-4}{-5}$ **6.** $-\frac{1}{3}$ **7.** $-\frac{1}{2}$ **8.** $\frac{2}{3}$
9. $-\frac{5}{8}$ **10.** $\frac{1}{4}$

11–15.

16. 128 **17.** x^{50} **18.** $6a^2$ **19.** $\frac{1}{x^5}$ **20.** $\frac{1}{a^6}$ **21.** $\frac{3}{4}$

Lesson 4-9 — pp. 219–224

Check Skills You'll Need 1. 10^8 **2.** 10^{16} **3.** 10^2 **4.** 10^{-3}

Quick Check 1a. 5.45×10^7 **b.** 7.23×10^5
2a. 2.1×10^{-4} **b.** 5×10^{-8} **3a.** 32,100,000
b. 0.000000059 **c.** 10,060,000,000 **4a.** 1.6×10^6
b. 2.03×10^5 **c.** 7.243×10^{15} **5a.** 18.3×10^6,
0.098×10^9, 526×10^7 **b.** 0.22×10^{-10}, 8×10^{-9},
14.7×10^{-7} **6a.** 2.4×10^{11} **b.** 5.68×10^{-3}
7. 1.002×10^{-23} kg

Chapter 5

Check Your Readiness — p. 234

1. 1.2 **2.** 60 **3.** -45 **4.** -40 **5.** 1.5 **6.** 74 **7.** 8
8. -1.78 **9.** 3 **10.** 4 **11.** 12 **12.** 1 **13.** 10 **14.** 5
15. 9 **16.** 1 **17.** 10 **18.** 14 **19–21. Answers may vary. Samples are given. 19.** $\frac{1}{2}, \frac{3}{6}$ **20.** $\frac{8}{12}, \frac{2}{3}$ **21.** $\frac{3}{4}, \frac{6}{8}$
22. $\frac{5}{6}$ **23.** $\frac{2}{5}$ **24.** -2 **25.** $\frac{1}{4}$ **26.** $-\frac{24}{25}$ **27.** $\frac{1}{3}$ **28.** $\frac{4}{15}$
29. $\frac{4}{31}$ **30.** $-\frac{2}{9}$ **31.** $-\frac{2}{13}$ **32.** $\frac{1}{6}$ **33.** $\frac{5}{7}$ **34.** 5.4
35. 0.6 **36.** 0.625 **37.** 0.75 **38.** 0.375

Lesson 5-1 — pp. 236–240

Check Skills You'll Need 1. $2^2 \cdot 5$ **2.** 5^3 **3.** $3^2 \cdot 5$
4. $2 \cdot 3 \cdot 31$ **5.** $3^3 \cdot 23$ **6.** $3^2 \cdot 5^2 \cdot 7$

Quick Check 1a. 12 **b.** 20 **c.** 60 **2a.** 48 **b.** 45 **c.** 180
3a. $60xy$ **b.** $56m^4$ **c.** $75xy^2$ **4a.** $\frac{4}{9} > \frac{2}{9}$
b. $-\frac{4}{9} < -\frac{2}{9}$ **c.** $-\frac{4}{9} < \frac{2}{9}$ **5a.** $\frac{6}{7} > \frac{4}{5}$ **b.** $\frac{2}{3} < \frac{3}{4}$
c. $-\frac{3}{4} < -\frac{7}{10}$ **6a.** $\frac{1}{6} < \frac{5}{12} < \frac{2}{3} < 1$
b. $-1 < \frac{-7}{12} < \frac{-3}{10} < \frac{1}{5} < \frac{1}{2}$

Lesson 5-2 — pp. 241–245

Check Skills You'll Need 1. 0.241, 2.41, 12.4, 24.1
2. 1.003, 1.030, 1.300, 13.03 **3.** -0.1, -0.01, 0.01, 0.1

Quick Check 1a. 0.25 **b.** 1.875 **c.** 3.3 **d.** 0.6 **2a.** $0.\overline{7}$;
repeating 7 **b.** $0.9\overline{54}$; repeating; 54
c. 1.375; terminating **d.** $0.\overline{72}$; repeating; 72
3a. 0.2, 0.5, $\frac{7}{10}$, $\frac{4}{5}$ **b.** -0.75, -0.375, $-\frac{1}{4}$, $-\frac{1}{8}$
4a. $1\frac{3}{4}$ **b.** $2\frac{8}{25}$ **c.** $\frac{13}{20}$ **5a.** $\frac{7}{9}$ **b.** $\frac{6}{11}$ **c.** $\frac{71}{333}$

Lesson 5-3 — pp. 247–251

Check Skills You'll Need 1. 8 **2.** 18 **3.** $10n$ **4.** 18 **5.** 40
6. $10n$

Quick Check 1a. $\frac{4}{7}$ **b.** $\frac{5}{k}$ **c.** $\frac{2}{5}$ **d.** $\frac{6}{y}$ **2a.** $-\frac{1}{8}$ **b.** $\frac{3m-14}{7m}$
3a. $6\frac{5}{8}$ **b.** $2\frac{1}{2}$ **c.** $3\frac{1}{4}$ **d.** $3\frac{1}{2}$ qt

Checkpoint Quiz 1 1. $>$ **2.** $=$ **3.** $<$ **4.** $<$ **5.** 0.51 **6.** $\frac{3}{250}$
7. 1.25 **8.** $\frac{1}{3}$ **9.** $0.8\overline{3}$ **10.** $\frac{17}{33}$ **11.** $\frac{11}{13}$ **12.** $\frac{5}{36}$ **13.** $4\frac{19}{40}$
14. $\frac{2}{3}$

Lesson 5-4 — pp. 252–256

Check Skills You'll Need 1. $\frac{7}{3}$ **2.** $\frac{33}{10}$ **3.** $\frac{13}{9}$ **4.** $\frac{24}{5}$ **5.** $\frac{63}{8}$
6. $\frac{36}{7}$

Quick Check 1a. $\frac{2}{15}$ **b.** $-\frac{5}{9}$ **c.** $\frac{35}{72}$ **d.** $\frac{3}{32}$ **2a.** $\frac{4}{7}$
b. $-\frac{7}{25}$ **c.** $\frac{x}{6}$ **3a.** $1\frac{1}{2}$ **b.** $\frac{6}{7}$ **c.** $-4\frac{8}{15}$ **4a.** $-\frac{1}{2}$ **b.** $\frac{15a}{16}$ **c.** $\frac{b}{2}$
5a. $1\frac{3}{5}$ **b.** $-1\frac{1}{3}$ **c.** $7\frac{1}{2}$

Lesson 5-5 — pp. 257–261

Check Skills You'll Need 1. $\frac{1}{3}$ **2.** 52 **3.** 10 **4.** $1\frac{1}{2}$

Quick Check 1a. Feet or yards; inches are too small and miles are too large. **b.** Pounds; the weight is too great to measure in ounces. **c.** Inches; the length is too small to measure in feet. **d.** Fluid ounces; the capacity of a cup is too large. **2a.** $\frac{7}{8}$
b. $1\frac{1}{6}$ **c.** 7 **3a.** 56 **b.** $10\frac{1}{2}$ **c.** 7

Lesson 5-6 — pp. 263–266

Check Skills You'll Need 1. $\frac{1}{10}, \frac{1}{5}, \frac{1}{4}, \frac{1}{3}, \frac{1}{2}$ **2.** $\frac{3}{3}, \frac{5}{3}, \frac{7}{3}, \frac{13}{3}$
3. $\frac{3}{13}, \frac{3}{7}, \frac{3}{5}, \frac{3}{3}$ **4.** $-\frac{3}{3}, -\frac{3}{5}, -\frac{3}{7}, -\frac{3}{13}$

Quick Check 7. 3 h 55 min

Lesson 5-7 — pp. 268–271

Check Skills You'll Need 1. $-1\frac{1}{8}$ **2.** $8\frac{5}{24}$ **3.** $2\frac{5}{8}$ **4.** $-7\frac{7}{18}$
Quick Check 1a. $-\frac{1}{3}$ **b.** $\frac{1}{15}$ **c.** $\frac{13}{30}$ **2.** $1\frac{1}{7}$ **3a.** $2\frac{1}{18}$
b. Answers may vary. Sample: I subtracted the mixed number $1\frac{1}{3}$ from both sides of the equation to solve for z.

Lesson 5-8 — pp. 272–276

Check Skills You'll Need 1. $\frac{5}{14}$ **2.** $-1\frac{1}{2}$ **3.** $6\frac{1}{4}$ **4.** 3

Quick Check 1a. $\frac{5}{56}$ **b.** $\frac{7}{18}$ **c.** $\frac{4}{15}$ **2a.** $3\frac{3}{4}$ **b.** $1\frac{5}{27}$
c. 1 **3a.** $-\frac{7}{8}$ **b.** $\frac{13}{15}$ **c.** $-\frac{1}{14}$ **4a.** 8 **b.** $-\frac{3}{10}$ **c.** $4\frac{6}{11}$

Instant Check System™ Answers

Answers to Instant Check System™ **851**

Checkpoint Quiz 2 **1.** 14 **2.** $\frac{1}{2}$ **3.** $-\frac{4}{27}$ **4.** $1\frac{1}{3}$ **5.** -2
6. 34 **7.** $2\frac{1}{4}$ **8.** 90 **9.** $1\frac{1}{2}$ **10.** $\frac{1}{3}$ **11.** $\frac{1}{5}$ **12.** $1\frac{5}{8}$ **13.** $11\frac{1}{4}$
14. $\frac{6}{35}$ **15.** $\frac{7}{15}$ **16.** $-17\frac{1}{3}$ **17.** $-\frac{27}{40}$ **18.** $3\frac{3}{5}$ **19.** $\frac{5}{33}$
20. 6 miles **21.** 55 mi/h **22.** \$12 **23.** Answers
may vary. Sample: A desktop can be measured
in inches; 48 inches.

Lesson 5-9   pp. 278–281

Check Skills You'll Need **1.** 64 **2.** 81 **3.** 1 **4.** x^{18} **5.** b^{10}
6. a^{28}

Quick Check **1a.** 216 **b.** $16p^4$ **c.** x^5y^{10} **d.** $25x^6$
2a. $16y^4$ **b.** $-16y^4$ **c.** $-125a^6b^3$ **3a.** $\frac{1}{8}$ **b.** $\frac{16}{81}$ **c.** $\frac{8x^6}{27}$

Chapter 6

Check Your Readiness   p. 290

1. 16 **2.** 13.5 **3.** $\frac{7}{8}$ **4.** 2.5 **5.** $1\frac{1}{4}$ **6.** 27.5
7–12. Answers may vary. Samples are given.
7. $\frac{2}{8}, \frac{4}{16}$ **8.** $\frac{2}{5}, \frac{8}{20}$ **9.** $\frac{3}{7}, \frac{12}{28}$ **10.** $\frac{4}{18}, \frac{6}{27}$ **11.** $\frac{6}{16}, \frac{9}{24}$
12. $\frac{10}{12}, \frac{15}{18}$ **13.** $\frac{1}{4}$ **14.** $\frac{1}{4}$ **15.** $\frac{4}{5}$ **16.** $\frac{3}{8}$ **17.** $\frac{3}{7}$ **18.** $\frac{1}{8}$ **19.** $\frac{5}{6}$
20. $\frac{1}{25}$ **21.** 0.35 **22.** $\frac{3}{50}$ **23.** 3.75 **24.** $\frac{7}{20}$ **25.** $\frac{7}{8}$
26. 3.6 **27.** $1\frac{7}{100}$ **28.** $0.\overline{6}$ **29.** $11.\overline{1}$ **30.** $\frac{1}{3}$ **31.** 6.25
32. $3\frac{49}{50}$

Lesson 6-1   pp. 292–295

Check Skills You'll Need **1.** $\frac{6}{7}$ **2.** $\frac{3}{5}$ **3.** $\frac{9}{10}$ **4.** $\frac{4}{5}$ **5.** $\frac{1}{3}$ **6.** $\frac{5}{3}$, or $1\frac{2}{3}$
Quick Check **1a.** $\frac{2}{5}$ **b.** $\frac{3}{2}$ **2a.** \$.99/L **b.** 34 mi/gal
3a. 52.5 **b.** 432

Lesson 6-2   pp. 298–302

Check Skills You'll Need **1.** 13 **2.** 6 **3.** 15 **4.** 3

Quick Check **1a.** 6 **b.** 44 **c.** 77 **2a.** yes, cross
products equal **b.** no, cross products not equal
c. yes, cross products equal **3.** 87 nautical miles

Lesson 6-3   pp. 303–307

Check Skills You'll Need **1.** 14 **2.** 133.3 **3.** 6.7 **4.** 3.6

Quick Check **1.** 15.8
2. 28 ft

3. $1\frac{7}{8}$ in.

Lesson 6-4   pp. 309–313

Check Skills You'll Need **1.** $\frac{5}{8}$ **2.** $\frac{3}{20}$ **3.** $\frac{5}{11}$ **4.** $\frac{11}{12}$

Quick Check **1a.** $\frac{3}{6}$, or $\frac{1}{2}$ **b.** $\frac{1}{6}$ **c.** $\frac{2}{6}$, or $\frac{1}{3}$ **2a.** $\frac{5}{6}$
b. a certain event **3a.** 1 to 4 **b.** 4 to 1 **ci.** 2 to 3
cii. 3 to 2

Checkpoint Quiz 1 **1.** 4 mi/h **2.** 6 gal/min **3.** 48 ft/s
4. 4.5 **5.** 42 times **6.** $\frac{2}{6}$, or $\frac{1}{3}$

Lesson 6-5   pp. 314–318

Check Skills You'll Need **1.** 0.625 **2.** 0.45 **3.** 0.75
4. $0.8\overline{3}$ **5.** $0.\overline{6}$ **6.** $0.\overline{72}$

Quick Check **1a.** $\frac{29}{50}$ **b.** $\frac{18}{25}$ **c.** $1\frac{11}{25}$ **2a.** 0.625 **b.** 0.45, $\frac{9}{20}$
3a. 40% **b.** 2.3% **c.** 175% **4a.** $\frac{1}{4}$, 0.26, $\frac{2}{7}$, 31%
b. 0.71, $\frac{5}{6}$, 88%, 91% **c.** $1\frac{1}{5}$, 129%, 1.34, 1.41

Lesson 6-6   pp. 319–323

Check Skills You'll Need **1.** 7 **2.** 230 **3.** 25 **4.** 18

Quick Check

1a. $\frac{25}{100} = \frac{n}{124}$; 31

b. 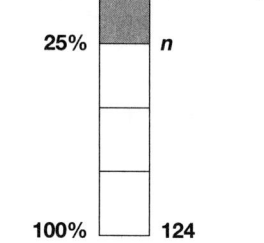 $\frac{43}{100} = \frac{n}{230}$; 98.9

c. 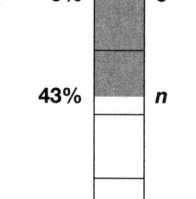 $\frac{12.5}{100} = \frac{n}{80}$; 10

2a. 55.2% **b.** 93.3% **3a.** 25.3 **b.** 313.1
4. about 3,567 screens

Lesson 6-7   pp. 324–327

Check Skills You'll Need **1.** 0.48 **2.** 0.05 **3.** 0.238
4. 0.7225 **5.** 1.36 **6.** 1.785

Quick Check **1a.** $0.96 = n \cdot 10$; 9.6%
b. $19.2 = 0.32 \cdot n$; 60 **2a.** $n = 1.455 \cdot 20$; 29.1
b. $380 = 1.25n$; 304 **3.** $.85 **4.** 1,400 people

Lesson 6-8   pp. 329–332

Check Skills You'll Need **1.** 46% **2.** 247% **3.** 3%
4. 523.6%

Quick Check **1a.** 14% **b.** 60% **c.** 112.5%
2. 26% **3a.** 50% **b.** 5.0% **c.** 92.9%

Lesson 6-9   pp. 333–336

Check Skills You'll Need **1.** $61.50 **2.** $71.40 **3.** $1.32
4. $12.79

Quick Check **1.** $42 **2.** $8.50 **3.** $3.30

Checkpoint Quiz 2 **1.** = **2.** < **3.** > **4.** $0.33 \cdot 120 = n$;
39.6 **5.** $1.25 \cdot 42 = n$; 52.5 **6.** $n \cdot 5.6 = 1.4$; 25%
7. $0.15 \cdot q = 9.75$; 65 **8.** $9,600

Lesson 6-10   pp. 338–341

Check Skills You'll Need **1.** $163.83

Quick Check **11.** about 299 million people

Chapter 7

Check Your Readiness   p. 350

1. $p + 3$ **2.** $q - 6$ **3.** $12y$ **4.** $10d$ **5.** $2b$ **6.** $n - 8$
7. $4n$ **8.** $-3b + 10$ **9.** $19c + 13$ **10.** $-7x - 5y$
11. $2a + 6$ **12.** $9m - 35$ **13.** 11 **14.** -21 **15.** -98
16. 5 **17.** 8 **18.** 9 **19.** -32 **20.** -8 **21.** $c \geq 1$
22. $y < 2$ **23.** $b < 4$ **24.** $x > 0$ **25.** $x \geq -6$
26. $x \leq 15$ **27.** $b \leq 19$ **28.** $m \geq 80$

Lesson 7-1   pp. 352–355

Check Skills You'll Need **1.** 8 **2.** 11 **3.** 1 **4.** -12 **5.** -10

Quick Check **1a.** 3 **b.** 16 **c.** -6 **d.** -1 **2a.** -2
b. 21 **c.** -3 **3.** $11

Lesson 7-2   pp. 356–360

Check Skills You'll Need **1.** $5x + 4$ **2.** $6y$ **3.** $3a$ **4.** $2 + c$
5. $2x - 7$

Quick Check **1.** 92 points **2a.** 88, 89, 90, 91 **b.** 32, 34
3a. $4\frac{2}{3}$ **b.** -14

Lesson 7-3   pp. 361–365

Check Skills You'll Need **1.** -3 **2.** $2\frac{1}{4}$ **3.** -4 **4.** $\frac{2}{3}$

Quick Check **1a.** 50 **b.** $10\frac{1}{2}$ **2a.** $\frac{3}{4}$ **b.** $5\frac{1}{2}$
3a. 4 **b.** 3.5

Lesson 7-4   pp. 366–369

Check Skills You'll Need **1.** $p - 21 = 48$ **2.** $b + 6 = 33$
3. $140 + d = 192$

Quick Check **5a.** $2 \cdot 29.95 + 0.12m = 76.34$
5b. 137 mi **c.** $29.95 \approx 30$; $0.12 \approx 0.1$; $137 \approx 140$;
$2 \cdot 30 + 0.1 \cdot 140 = 60 + 14 = 74$; Since $74 \approx$
76.34, 137 mi is a reasonable answer. **6.** 122 mi

Checkpoint Quiz 1 **1.** 20 **2.** 11 **3.** -18 **4.** 4 **5.** 28
6. -48 **7.** 2 **8.** 1.3 **9.** -6 **10.** 0 **11.** 1 **12.** 6
13. $p - 0.25p = 82.50$; $110
14. $n + (n + 1) + (n + 2) = 132$; 43, 44, 45

Lesson 7-5   pp. 371–375

Check Skills You'll Need **1.** 5 **2.** 7 **3.** -10 **4.** 8

Quick Check **1a.** 16 **b.** 2 **2.** 6 h

Lesson 7-6   pp. 377–380

Check Skills You'll Need

1. $w \geq -9$
$-10\ -9\ -8\ -7\ -6\ -5\ -4\ -3\ -2\ -1\ \ 0$

2. $z > 10$
$4\ \ 5\ \ 6\ \ 7\ \ 8\ \ 9\ \ 10\ 11\ 12\ 13\ 14$

3. $a < -2$
$-5\ -4\ -3\ -2\ -1\ \ 0\ \ 1\ \ 2\ \ 3\ \ 4\ \ 5$

4. $x \leq -1$
$-5\ -4\ -3\ -2\ -1\ \ 0\ \ 1\ \ 2\ \ 3\ \ 4\ \ 5$

Quick Check

1a. $a > 4$
$-4\ \ \ -2\ \ \ \ 0\ \ \ \ 2\ \ \ \ 4$

1b. $x \leq -8$
$-10\ \ \ -8\ \ \ -8\ \ \ -4\ \ \ -2$

1c. $c < -6$
$-12\ \ \ -6\ \ \ \ 0\ \ \ \ 6\ \ \ \ 12$

2a. $m \geq -15$
$-15\ \ \ -10\ \ \ -5\ \ \ \ 0\ \ \ \ 5\ \ \ 10$

2b. $x < 3$
$-1\ \ \ \ 0\ \ \ \ 1\ \ \ \ 2\ \ \ \ 3\ \ \ \ 4$

2c. $b < -22$
$-55\ \ \ -44\ \ \ -33\ \ \ -22\ \ \ -11\ \ \ \ 0$

3. $\geq$ $7,500

Lesson 7-7   pp. 382–385

Check Skills You'll Need **1.** 320 km **2.** 32 m **3.** 48 ft^2

Quick Check **1a.** $s = p + c$ **b.** $k = hj$
c. $p = \frac{l}{rt}$ **2a.** $a = \frac{1}{5}b - \frac{7}{5}$ **b.** $w = \frac{1}{2}P - \ell$
c. $x = 3(y - 8)$ **3.** $r = \frac{d}{t}$ **4.** $h = an$; 11 hits

Checkpoint Quiz 2 1. −2 2. −6 3. $\frac{2}{9}$ 4. 4 5. 3 6. 5
7. $y > -\frac{9}{10}$ 8. $x > -56$ 9. $x > 5$ 10. $h = s - g$
11. $r = \frac{1}{3}k - \frac{4}{3}$ 12. $t = \frac{I}{pr}$

Lesson 7-8   **pp. 386–390**

Check Skills You'll Need 1. $24 **2.** $1,100 **3.** $31.50
4. $17.88

Quick Check 1a. $30 **b.** $4.38

2a.

Bal. at Yr Start	Interest	Bal. at Yr End
$500.00	$15.00	$515.00
$515.00	$15.45	$530.45

2b.

Bal. at Yr Start	Interest	Bal. at Yr End
$625.00	$12.50	$637.50
$637.50	$12.75	$650.25
$650.25	$13.01	$663.26
$663.26	$13.27	$676.53

3a. $955.09 **b.** $955.37

Chapter 8

Check Your Readiness   **p. 400**

1. −4, −7 **2.** 19, 13 **3.** 10.5, 12 **4.** −11, −13
5. (5, 2) **6.** (−3, 4) **7.** (4, 0) **8.** (6, −3) **9.** (−4, −3)
10. (0, 3)   **11–16.**
17. $-\frac{1}{18}$ **18.** 3 **19.** 1 **20.** $\frac{1}{3}$
21. $y = -4x + 3$
22. $y = -2x + 4$
23. $y = 2x - 6$
24. $y = -6x - 8$
25. $y = -x + 12$
26. $y = -\frac{1}{2}x + \frac{5}{2}$
27. $y = \frac{1}{5}x + 4$
28. $y = -\frac{3}{4}x + 3$

Lesson 8-1   **pp. 404–408**

Check Skills You'll Need 1–6.

Quick Check 1a. No; there are two range values for
the domain value 2. **b.** Yes; there is one range
value for each domain value.
2a. No; a specific postage cost (domain value)
can mail packages of different weights (range
values). **b.** Yes; for each package weight (domain
value) there is one postage cost to the same zip
code (range value).

3a. A function; no
vertical line passes
through two graphed
points.

b. Not a function; a
vertical line passes
through both (−1, −1)
and (−1, 3).

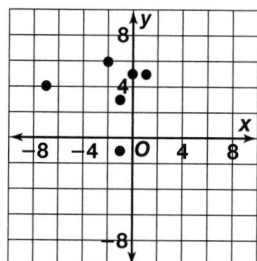

c. A function; no vertical
line passes through two
graphed points.

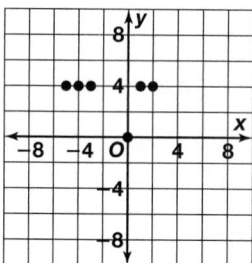

Lesson 8-2   **pp. 409–413**

Check Skills You'll Need 1. 4 **2.** −10 **3.** 3 **4.** 6

Quick Check 1a. (−3, −5) **b.** (−3, 15)
c. (−3, −4) **2.** 14°C
3a.

b.

c.

4a.
no

b.
yes

c.
no

5a.

$y = -2x + 3$

b.

$y = x + 5$

c.

$y = \frac{3}{2}x + 3$

Lesson 8-3   pp. 415–420

Check Skills You'll Need 1. -9 **2.** 5 **3.** -3 **4.** 0

Quick Check 1. $-\frac{3}{4}$ **2a.** $\frac{3}{4}$ **b.** -1
3a. undefined **b.** 0
4a.

b.

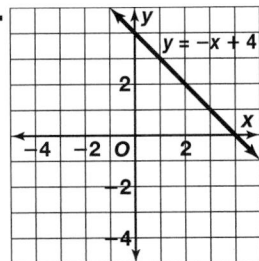

Lesson 8-4   pp. 422–426

Check Skills You'll Need 1. 0 **2.** 1 **3.** undefined **4.** $-\frac{1}{3}$

Quick Check 1. $c(p) = 3p + 4$; $19 **2a.** $f(x) = 2x$
b. $f(x) = -2x$ **c.** $y = 2x + 1$ **3.** $y = -x + 2$

Checkpoint Quiz 1 1. Answers may vary. Sample:
$(0, -9)$, $(2, 0)$, $(1, -4\frac{1}{2})$ **2.**
3. Yes; there is one range
value for each domain
value.
4. Answers may vary.
Sample: If every vertical
line passes through just
one graphed point, then
the relation is a function.
5. 5 **6.** -1 **7.** undefined
8. $-2, 5$ **9.** $p(n) = 2,000n$

Lesson 8-5   pp. 427–432

Check Skills You'll Need 1. $(-2, 2)$ **2.** $(0, 3)$ **3.** $(-3, 0)$
4. $(2, 3)$

Quick Check 1a. This person has 12 years of
education and earns $20,000 in a year. **1b.** The
person has 14 years of education and earns
$90,000 in a year. **c.** 4 people
2a.

2b.

3a. Positive correlation; as time goes by, the
winning distances have tended to increase.

Lesson 8-6   pp. 434–437

Check Skills You'll Need 1. $y = 2x + 2$ **2.** $y = -\frac{1}{4}x - 3$

Quick Check 3a–d. Answers may vary. Samples are
given. **a.** about 2,175 **b.** about -55 **c.** $y = -55x + 2,175$ **d.** 1,185

Lesson 8-7   pp. 439–444

Check Skills You'll Need
1. **2.**

3.

4.

2. $(-2, 8)$

3. $(-3, -4)$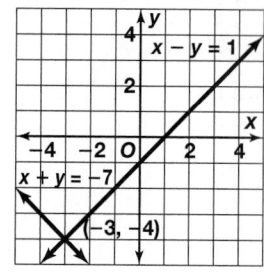

Quick Check

1a. $(2, -4)$

b. $(1, 0)$

4. $(1, 3)$

5. $g(c) = \frac{c}{231}$ **6.** $3, -7$

2a. infinitely many solutions

b. no solutions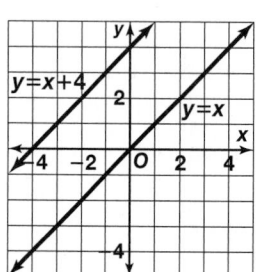

Check Skills You'll Need 1. yes; $-5 + 3 \geq -2$
2. no; $5 - 1 \not< 4$ **3.** yes; $-2 - 2(-4) \leq 6$
4. no; $4(-2) + 1 \not> -7$

Quick Check

1a.

b.

c.

2.

$2x + 4y \geq 30$

3. $-3, -5$

Checkpoint Quiz 2

1a.

Daily Newspaper Circulation (millions)

1b. Negative correlation; as the number of television sets increases, the newspaper circulation decreases.
1c. Trend lines may vary. Sample: See scatterplot; 250 million television sets.

3a.

b.

Chapter 9

1. 25 cm **2.** 14.4 in. **3.** 100.8 m **4.** 6.4 ft **5.** 6 cm
6. $\frac{1}{2}$ in. **7.** 2.8 cm **8.** 7.5 ft

9–18.

Lesson 9-1
pp. 462–467

Check Skills You'll Need 1. The graph is a line that starts at 3 and extends to the right without end. **2.** The graph is a line that starts at 0 and extends to the left without end. **3.** The graph is a line that starts at 5 and extends to the left without end. **4.** The graph is a line that starts at -2 and extends to the right without end.

Quick Check 1a. C, N, V **b.** $\overline{NC}$, $\overline{NV}$
c. $\overrightarrow{NC}$, $\overrightarrow{NV}$ **2a.** $\overline{EH}$, $\overline{FG}$, $\overline{AE}$, $\overline{BF}$
b. $\overline{HG}$, $\overline{DC}$, $\overline{AB}$ **c.** $\overline{DH}$, $\overline{CG}$, $\overline{AD}$, $\overline{BC}$

3a.

b.

c.

d.

e.

Lesson 9-2
pp. 469–473

Check Skills You'll Need 1. 135 **2.** 15 **3.** 90 **4.** 30

Quick Check 1. 160°, 20°, 160° **2.** $\angle 1 \cong \angle 5$, $\angle 2 \cong \angle 6$, $\angle 3 \cong \angle 7$, $\angle 4 \cong \angle 8$; $\angle 3 \cong \angle 5$, $\angle 4 \cong \angle 6$

Lesson 9-3
pp. 474–478

Check Skills You'll Need 1. acute **2.** obtuse **3.** obtuse **4.** right **5.** acute **6.** obtuse

Quick Check 1a. scalene right triangle
b. isosceles obtuse triangle **c.** scalene obtuse triangle **2.** rectangles and squares **3a.** $P = 6x$
b. 96 cm

Lesson 9-4
pp. 480–483

Check Skills You'll Need 1. **2.**

3. **4.** **5.**

Quick Check 5. 35

Lesson 9-5
pp. 484–488

Check Skills You'll Need 1. $\angle X$ **2.** $\angle Z$ **3.** $\overline{XY}$ **4.** $\overline{ZX}$

Quick Check 1. $\overline{AB} \cong \overline{DE}$, $\overline{BC} \cong \overline{EC}$, $\overline{AC} \cong \overline{DC}$, $\angle A \cong \angle D$, $\angle B \cong \angle E$, $\angle BCA \cong \angle ECD$, $AC = 50$ m
2. $\overline{FJ} \cong \overline{FG}$, $\overline{JI} \cong \overline{GH}$, $\overline{FI} \cong \overline{FH}$, $\triangle JFI \cong \triangle GFH$ by SSS

Checkpoint Quiz 1 1. ray **2.** line **3.** $\overline{LN}$ **4.** angle
5a. $6x + 16 + 2x + 12 = 180$, $x = 19$ **b.** 50°
c. 130° **d.** 130° **6.**

Lesson 9-6
pp. 490–494

Check Skills You'll Need 1. 36 **2.** 270 **3.** 54 **4.** 109

Quick Check 1a. about $8\frac{4}{5}$ in.
b. about 188.4 mm **c.** about 628 mi

2. Blood Types of Population

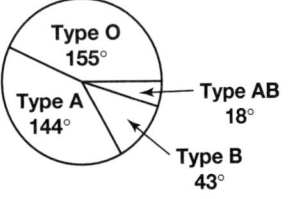

3. Student Jobs at Western High School

Instant Check System™ Answers

Lesson 9-7   pp. 495–499

Check Skills You'll Need **1.** point *B* **2.** a line segment with endpoints *A* and *B* **3.** a ray with endpoint *A* and containing *B* **4.** a line containing point *A* and point *B*

Quick Check

1.

2.

3.

4.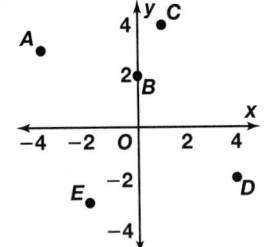

Lesson 9-8   pp. 501–505

Check Skills You'll Need 1–5.

Quick Check 1a.

b. **c.**

2. $B(-1, 5) \rightarrow B'(3, 1)$ **3.** $(x, y) \rightarrow (x + 5, y - 1)$

Checkpoint Quiz 2 **1.** A is chicken, B is fish, and C is vegetarian. **2.** The central angle for A is 180°, B is 126°, and C is 54°.

3. **4.**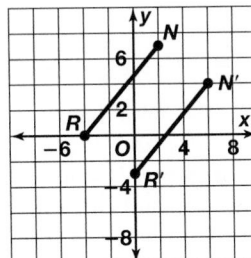

Lesson 9-9   pp. 507–510

Check Skills You'll Need

1. **2.**

3. **4.**

5. **6.**

Quick Check

1a. **b.**

2. **3a.**

b.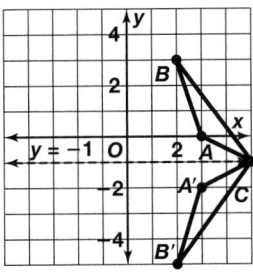

Lesson 9-10 pp. 511–514

Check Skills You'll Need

1. **2.**

3.

Quick Check

1.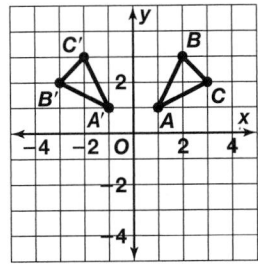

2a. no **b.** yes, 180°
c. yes, 180°

The vertices of the image are $A'(-1, 1)$, $B'(-3, 2)$, and $C'(-2, 3)$.

Chapter 10

Check Your Readiness p. 524
---

1. 36 m² **2.** 20 in.² **3.** 45 cm² **4.** 45 **5.** 78.5
6. 864 **7.** 48 **8.** 300 **9.** 452.16 **10.** 6 **11.** $19\frac{1}{2}$
12. 9 **13.** $10x$ **14.** $5x^2$ **15.** 55 **16.** 1,364 **17.** 500
18. 8 **19.** 157 yd **20.** 628 m **21.** 17.27 in.

Lesson 10-1 pp. 526–530

Check Skills You'll Need 1. $\ell = 9$ in. **2.** $A = 245$ m²
3. $w = 10$ cm **4.** $A = 51.84$ ft²

Quick Check 1a. 1,000 cm², or 0.1 m²
b. 12 ft², or $1\frac{1}{3}$ yd² **2a.** 6 m² **b.** 24 in.² **c.** The area
of the larger parallelogram is 4 times the area of
the smaller parallelogram.

Lesson 10-2 pp. 533–537

Check Skills You'll Need 1. 8 **2.** 42 **3.** $37\frac{1}{2}$ **4.** 10

Quick Check 1a. 7.38 ft² **b.** 5 m² **2.** 24 yd²
3. 13 ft² **b.** 342 mm²

Lesson 10-3 pp. 538–543

Check Skills You'll Need 1. 50.24 **2.** 78.5 **3.** 254.34
4. 0.785

Quick Check 1. $2,500\pi$ in.² **2.** about
113 mi² **3.** 40.2 cm²

Checkpoint Quiz 1 1. 100 in.² **2.** 50 in.² **3.** 300 in.²
4. 300 yd² **5.** 2,100 cm² **6.** 150 m² **7.** 100π yd²;
314 yd² **8.** 64π ft²; 201 ft² **9.** $(800 + 50\pi)$ cm²;
957 cm²

Lesson 10-4 pp. 545–549

Check Skills You'll Need 1. triangle **2.** square
3. rectangle **4.** hexagon

Quick Check 1a. cylinder **b.** cone **2a.** With a
triangular base and three faces that are triangles,
you can form a triangular pyramid. **b.** With two
square bases and 4 faces that are squares, you
can form a cube.

Lesson 10-5
pp. 551–556

Check Skills You'll Need

1. 31.4 in.
2. 26.4 cm
3. 25.1 ft
4. 21.4 in.

Quick Check **1a.** 84 yd^2 **b.** 336 yd^2 **c.** The surface area of the larger prism is 4 times the surface area of the smaller prism. **2.** 108 m^2 **3.** about 785 cm^2

Lesson 10-6
pp. 558–562

Check Skills You'll Need **1.** 10π **2.** 15π **3.** 5π **4.** 22π

Quick Check **1.** 720 ft^2 **2.** about 1,011 ft^2 **3.** about 452 cm^2

Lesson 10-7
pp. 563–566

Check Skills You'll Need **1.** about 201 cm^2 **2.** about 452 cm^2 **3.** about 314 cm^2

Quick Check **1.** 216 ft^3 **2a.** 1,900 ft^3 **b.** The volume of the larger cylinder is 8 times the volume of the smaller cylinder.

Lesson 10-8
pp. 568–571

Check Skills You'll Need

1. **2.**

3.

Quick Check **8a.** 66 in.^{3}; 52.5 in.^{3}; 21 in.^{3}
b. Yes; 5$\frac{1}{2}$ in. by 8 in. by 1$\frac{1}{2}$ in.

Checkpoint Quiz 2 **1.** square prism, 56 cm^2
2. cylinder, 207 in.^{2} **3.** square pyramid,
85 cm^2 **4.** 78.1 cm^3 **5.** 169.6 in.^{3}
6. Check students' work.

Lesson 10-9
pp. 572–575

Check Skills You'll Need

1. 20.9$\overline{3}$ **2.** 32 **3.** 33.49$\overline{3}$ **4.** 0.52$\overline{3}$

Quick Check **1.** 21 cm^3 **2.** 167 ft^3
3a. 14,130 m^3 **b.** 180 mi^3

Chapter 11

Check Your Readiness
p. 586

1. *G* **2.** *K* **3.** *H* **4.** *D* **5.** *B* **6.** *F* **7.** (−5, 4) **8.** (2, 1)
9. (7, 0) **10.** (−7, 1) **11.** (4, −2) **12.** (−6, −3)
13. 100 **14.** 36 **15.** 4 **16.** 81 **17.** 121 **18.** 0.04
19. 49 **20.** 5.29 **21.** 16 **22.** 25 **23.** 4 **24.** 4 **25.** 1
26. 10 **27.** 2 **28.** 60 **29.** 77 **30.** 26 **31.** 10 **32.** 32
33. 17 **34.** 8

Lesson 11-1
pp. 588–591

Check Skills You'll Need **1.** 1, 4, 9, 16, 25, 36, 49, 64, 81,
100, 121, 144 **2.** 100; 400; 900; 1,600; 2,500; 3,600;
4,900; 6,400; 8,100; 10,000; 12,100; 14,400

Quick Check **1a.** 10 **b.** −10 **c.** 4 **d.** −4 **2a.** 5 **b.** −8
c. 7 **d.** −5 **3a.** irrational; because 2 is not a
perfect square **b.** rational; because 81 is a perfect
square **c.** rational; because it is a terminating
decimal **d.** irrational; because 42 is not a perfect
square

Lesson 11-2
pp. 592–597

Check Skills You'll Need **1.** 52 **2.** 89 **3.** 130 **4.** 90

Quick Check **1a.** 5 ft **b.** 9 m **2.** 12.7 m
3. 8.7 ft **4a.** Yes, 7^2 + 8^2 = 113.
b. No, 5^2 + 6^2 ≠ 10^2.

Lesson 11-3
pp. 598–602

Check Skills You'll Need **1.** (−3, 4) **2.** (0, 3) **3.** (−4, −2)
4. (3, −1)

Quick Check **1a.** 4.1 **b.** 9.5 **2.** 17.5
3a. (4, 3) **b.** (−1, 0.5)

Checkpoint Quiz 1 **1.** −2 **2.** 4 **3.** 5 **4.** 9 **5.** −7 **6.** 10
7. 10 ft **8.** 16.1 m **9.** 25 yd **10.** 7.1 cm **11.** 9.2;
(−3, −5.5) **12.** 15.8; (1.5, 6.5) **13.** Answers may
vary.

Sample: $\sqrt{120}$, $\sqrt{299}$, 15.010010001 . . .

Lesson 11-4
pp. 604–607

Check Skills You'll Need **1.** 4 **2.** 4 **3.** 32 **4.** 10

Quick Check **3.** $\overline{RQ}$ and $\overline{RP}$, $\overline{ST}$ and $\overline{SP}$
4. It allows you to draw the entire 40 + *x* side to
complete the larger triangle.

Lesson 11-5
pp. 608–612

Check Skills You'll Need **1.** 10 m **2.** 12 m **3.** 45 m
4. 36 m

Quick Check **1.** 5.9 cm **2.** 17 m
3a. *a* ≈ 6.9 cm, *b* = 8 cm **b.** *e* = 6 in., *f* ≈ 10.4 in.

Lesson 11-6   pp. 614–618

Check Skills You'll Need 1. 15 ft **2.** $25\frac{2}{3}$ ft

Quick Check 1. $\sin Y = \frac{12}{13}$, $\cos Y = \frac{5}{13}$,
$\tan Y = \frac{12}{5}$ **2a.** 0.1736 **b.** 0.2588 **c.** 1.3270
d. 0.9272 **3.** about 14.3 ft

Checkpoint Quiz 2 1. 45°-45°-90° **2.** 30°-60°-90°
3. 30°-60°-90° **4.** 0.4848 **5.** 0.5774 **6.** 0.5299
7. 0.9986

Lesson 11-7   pp. 620–624

Check Skills You'll Need 1. 0.7071 **2.** 0.8480 **3.** 0.3249
4. 0.9272 **5.** 0.0349 **6.** 9.5144

Quick Check 1. about 141 m **2.** 16.1 m
3. about 22.7 m

Chapter 12

Check Your Readiness   p. 634

1. 12 **2.** 52 **3.** 101 **4.** 0.225 **5.** $\frac{1}{3}$ **6.** $\frac{3}{4}$ **7.** $\frac{4}{5}$ **8.** $\frac{2}{3}$
9. $\frac{1}{2}$ **10.** $\frac{5}{8}$ **11.** $\frac{1}{6}$ **12.** $\frac{1}{6}$ **13.** $\frac{2}{6}$ or $\frac{1}{3}$ **14.** 0 **15.** $\frac{3}{6}$, or $\frac{1}{2}$
16. 0 **17.** $\frac{5}{6}$ **18.** $\frac{2}{6}$, or $\frac{1}{3}$ **19.** $\frac{18}{33}$, or $\frac{6}{11}$ **20.** $\frac{15}{33}$, or $\frac{5}{11}$
21. $\frac{15}{33}$, or $\frac{5}{11}$ **22.** $\frac{18}{33}$, or $\frac{6}{11}$ **23.** 0.50 **24.** 0.36 **25.** 0.20
26. 0.05 **27.** 20% **28.** 87.5% **29.** 28% **30.** 30%

Lesson 12-1   pp. 636–639

Check Skills You'll Need 1. 9; 9 **2.** 77; 73 **3.** 200; 300
4. 5; 3

Quick Check
1.

Number	Frequency
10	5
11	3
12	2
13	2
14	1
15	2

2a.

Hours of Battery Life

7

b. 14; the hours of battery life are the data, so the range is 23 − 9 = 14.

Lesson 12-2   pp. 641–645

Check Skills You'll Need 1. 9.5 **2.** 4.9 **3.** 52 **4.** 101

Quick Check

1.

Migrations of Birds (thousands of miles)

2.

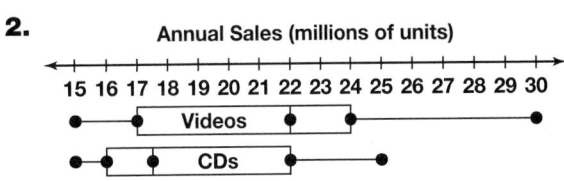

Annual Sales (millions of units)

3a. The highest value is 50 and the lowest is 10.
The median is 22.5. At least half of the values are
within 2.5 units of the median. **b.** The highest
value is 45 and the lowest is 15. The median is 35.
At least half of the values are within 10 units of
the median. **4.** The women's heights have a
median of 71 in. and a range of 10 in. The men's
heights have a median of 79 in. and a range of
12 in. Most of the men are taller than the
tallest woman.

Lesson 12-3   pp. 648–653

Check Skills You'll Need 1. $\frac{1}{2}$ **2.** $\frac{1}{2}$

Quick Check
1.

Populations of Chicago
and Los Angeles

2a. Answers may vary. Sample:

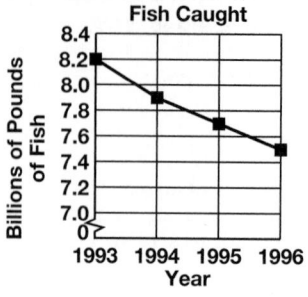

b. Answers may vary. Sample:

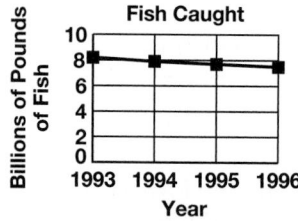

c. Answers may vary. Sample: They would use the graph from part (a) to show that the supply of fish is decreasing rapidly. Using this graph emphasizes the need for the limit.

3a. Answers may vary. Sample:

b. Answers may vary. Sample:

Check Skills You'll Need **1.** $\frac{4}{12}$, or $\frac{1}{3}$ **2.** $\frac{8}{12}$, or $\frac{2}{3}$ **3.** $\frac{5}{12}$ **4.** $\frac{9}{12}$, or $\frac{3}{4}$ **5.** $\frac{3}{12}$, or $\frac{1}{4}$ **6.** $\frac{8}{12}$, or $\frac{2}{3}$

Quick Check

1. 12 choices;

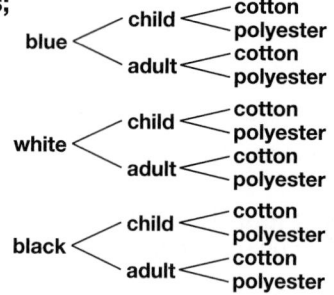

2a. 17,576 three-letter monograms **b.** 7,962,624 license plates **3.** $\frac{1}{2}$ **4.** $\frac{1}{100,000}$

Checkpoint Quiz 1

1.

Number	Frequency
47	2
48	2
49	1
50	3
51	2
52	2

2.

3a. Hourly Minimum Wage

A break in the graph makes it look like there is a significant increase in minimum wage.

3b. Hourly Minimum Wage

4. $\frac{1}{4}$

Check Skills You'll Need   **1.** $\frac{3}{25}$ **2.** $\frac{1}{8}$ **3.** $\frac{2}{25}$ **4.** $\frac{5}{18}$ **5.** $\frac{2}{7}$ **6.** $\frac{4}{5}$

Quick Check   **1.** $\frac{1}{4}$ **2.** 9% **3a.** $\frac{3}{10}$ **b.** $\frac{3}{10}$

Check Skills You'll Need   **1.** 36 outcomes **2.** 15,600 outcomes **3.** 84 outcomes **4.** 16 outcomes

Quick Check   **1.** 120 **2a.** 20 **b.** 60 **c.** 120
d. 120 **3.** 20 ways **4a.** 28 **b.** 56 **c.** 70 **d.** 56
5a. Combinations; the order in which the teacher selects the students does not matter.
b. Permutations; the order in which students are chosen matters.

Check Skills You'll Need   **1.** 80% **2.** 53% **3.** 62.5%
4. 60% **5.** 58.$\overline{3}$% **6.** 62.5%

Quick Check   **1.** 52%; 2340 people **2a.** The experimental probability is less than the theoretical probability. **b.** The experimental probability is likely to get closer to the theoretical probability of $\frac{1}{2}$.

Check Skills You'll Need   **1.** 112.5 **2.** 6,720 **3.** 400
4. 5,760

Quick Check   **1a.** Not a good sample; these students would be most interested in racing bikes. **b.** Not a good sample; this sample would not include teens who do not rent videos. **c.** This is a good sample, because there is little built-in bias for or against any cereal. **2a.** 200 calculators **b.** Less accurate; a larger sample is likely to be more representative of the population. **c.** The entire population might be too large to be surveyed. Also, the testing might be destructive, as would occur in testing light-bulb life.

Checkpoint Quiz 2   **1.** $\frac{2}{9}$ **2a.** 380 outcomes
b. 190 committees **3.** $\frac{2}{15}$; 3 goals **4.** 9,444 premium oranges

Check Skills You'll Need

1.

letter	tally	frequency
a	⊬⊬⊬	5
c	‖	1
d	‖	1
e	⊬⊬⊬ ‖	6
f	‖	1
i	‖‖‖	4
l	‖‖	3
m	‖	2
n	‖	2
o	‖‖	3
p	‖	1
r	‖	2
s	‖	2
t	‖	1
u	‖	1
x	‖	1

Chapter 13

1. 40 **2.** −32 **3.** 17 **4.** 28 **5.** 0.64 **6.** 25 **7.** 2 **8.** 7
9. $3d - 12$ **10.** $15x + 5$ **11.** $3u - 24$ **12.** $8y + 28$
13. $-12d + 4$ **14.** $50 - 30s$ **15.** $-21 + 6w$
16. $27 - 6b$ **17.** $11a - 4$ **18.** 5 **19.** $-g + 4$
20. $10t + 5s$ **21.** $7b + 4d$ **22.** $-45c$
23. −10, −4, 2 **24.** 6, 0, −6
25. −10, −2, 6 **26.** $-6\frac{1}{5}$, −5, $-3\frac{4}{5}$ **27.** 10, 6, 2
28. $-7\frac{1}{2}$, −8, $-8\frac{1}{2}$ **29.** −1, 0, 1 **30.** 5, −1, −7

Check Skills You'll Need   **1.** Start with 60 and subtract 12 repeatedly.
2. Start with 7 and add 5 repeatedly.
3. Start with 6 and multiply by 3 repeatedly.
4. Start with 60 and divide by 2 repeatedly.

Quick Check   **1a.** 5 **b.** −3 **2a.** 7, 3, −1; start with 23 and add −4 repeatedly. **b.** $-\frac{2}{3}$, $\frac{2}{3}$, 2; start with −6 and add $1\frac{1}{3}$ repeatedly. **3a.** 3; 324, 972, 2,916; start with 4 and multiply by 3 repeatedly. **b.** 0.5; 0.25, 0.125, 0.0625; start with 4 and multiply by 0.5 repeatedly. **4a.** geometric; 243, 729, 2,187
b. neither; 34, 45, 58 **c.** geometric; −12, 12, −12
d. arithmetic; 650, 800, 950

Lesson 13-2 — pp. 702–705

Check Skills You'll Need **1.** −11, −1, 9 **2.** 2, 3, 4
3. −4, 2, 8 **4.** −5$\frac{1}{2}$, −5, −4$\frac{1}{2}$

Quick Check

1a.

x	$-2x^2 = y$	(x, y)
−2	$-2(-2)^2 = -8$	(−2, −8)
−1	$-2(-1)^2 = -2$	(−1, −2)
0	$-2(0)^2 = 0$	(0, 0)
1	$-2(1)^2 = -2$	(1, −2)
2	$-2(2)^2 = -8$	(2, −8)

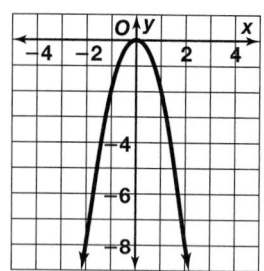

b.

x	$-x^2 + 3 = y$	(x, y)
−2	$-(-2)^2 + 3 = -1$	(−2, −1)
−1	$-(-1)^2 + 3 = 2$	(−1, 2)
0	$-0^2 + 3 = 3$	(0, 3)
1	$-1^2 + 3 = 2$	(1, 2)
2	$-2^2 + 3 = -1$	(2, −1)

2a.

b.

3a.

b.

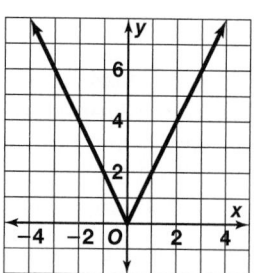

Lesson 13-3 — pp. 707–710

Check Skills You'll Need **1.** 25 **2.** 64 **3.** 243 **4.** 256

Quick Check

1.

x	3^x	y	(x, y)
1	3^1	3	(1, 3)
2	3^2	9	(2, 9)
3	3^3	27	(3, 27)
4	3^4	81	(4, 81)

2.

x	$0.5(2)^x$	y	(x, y)
0	$0.5(2)^0$	0.5	(0, 0.5)
1	$0.5(2)^1$	1	(1, 1)
2	$0.5(2)^2$	2	(2, 2)
3	$0.5(2)^3$	4	(3, 4)
4	$0.5(2)^4$	8	(4, 8)
5	$0.5(2)^5$	16	(5, 16)

3.

x	$90(\frac{1}{3})^x$	y	(x, y)
0	$90(\frac{1}{3})^0$	90	(0, 90)
1	$90(\frac{1}{3})^1$	30	(1, 30)
2	$90(\frac{1}{3})^2$	10	(2, 10)
3	$90(\frac{1}{3})^3$	$3\frac{1}{3}$	(3, 3$\frac{1}{3}$)
4	$90(\frac{1}{3})^4$	$1\frac{1}{9}$	(4, 1$\frac{1}{9}$)
5	$90(\frac{1}{3})^5$	$\frac{10}{27}$	(5, $\frac{10}{27}$)

Checkpoint Quiz 1 **1.** 40, 25, 10; start with 100 and add −15 repeatedly. **2.** 45, 52, 59; start with 17 and add 7 repeatedly. **3.** 208, 416, 832; start with 13 and multiply by 2 repeatedly. **4.** 3, 6, 12, 24, 48

5.

x	$\frac{1}{4}x^2$	y	(x, y)
-2	$\frac{1}{4} \cdot (-2)^2$	1	$(-2, 1)$
-1	$\frac{1}{4} \cdot (-1)^2$	$\frac{1}{4}$	$(-1, \frac{1}{4})$
0	$\frac{1}{4} \cdot 0^2$	0	$(0, 0)$
1	$\frac{1}{4} \cdot 1^2$	$\frac{1}{4}$	$(1, \frac{1}{4})$
2	$\frac{1}{4} \cdot 2^2$	1	$(2, 1)$

6.

x	$\frac{1}{4}|x|$	y	(x, y)
-2	$\frac{1}{4} \cdot |-2|$	$\frac{1}{2}$	$(-2, \frac{1}{2})$
-1	$\frac{1}{4} \cdot |-1|$	$\frac{1}{4}$	$(-1, \frac{1}{4})$
0	$\frac{1}{4} \cdot |2|$	0	$(0, 0)$
1	$\frac{1}{4} \cdot |1|$	$\frac{1}{4}$	$(1, \frac{1}{4})$
2	$\frac{1}{4} \cdot |2|$	$\frac{1}{2}$	$(2, \frac{1}{2})$

7.

x	$0.5(3)^x$	y	(x, y)
0	$0.5(3)^0$	0.5	$(0, 0.5)$
1	$0.5(3)^1$	1.5	$(1, 1.5)$
2	$0.5(3)^2$	4.5	$(2, 4.5)$
3	$0.5(3)^3$	13.5	$(3, 13.5)$
4	$0.5(3)^4$	40.5	$(4, 40.5)$

Lesson 13-4   pp. 712–715

Check Skills You'll Need 1. -40 **2.** -24 **3.** -2 **4.** 28

Quick Check 1a. No; the denominator contains a variable. **b.** Yes; it is the product of the variable m and the real number $\frac{1}{6}$. **c.** Yes, it is a real number. **d.** No, it is a sum. **2a.** monomial **b.** binomial **c.** binomial **d.** trinomial **3a.** -50 **b.** 13 **c.** 13 **4.** 264 ft

Lesson 13-5   pp. 718–722

Check Skills You'll Need 1. $2x - 7$ **2.** $5a - 4b$ **3.** $m - 12n$ **4.** $-6x + 3y - 5$

Quick Check 1a. $9d^2 + 10d$ **b.** $4x^2 + 3x + 17$ **2a.** $7x + 4y$ **b.** $9a^2 - 2a - 4$ **c.** $6g^2 - 2g - 1$ **d.** $-2t^2 + 3t + 9$ **3a.** $2a^2 - 5a$ **b.** $9z^2 + 14z - 2$ **c.** $-2w^2 + 11 + 8v$

Lesson 13-6   pp. 723–726

Check Skills You'll Need 1. $7v + 21$ **2.** $3u - 24$ **3.** $-30 + 15t$ **4.** $9p + 72$

Quick Check 1a. $3x^2 + 12x$ **b.** $-2x^2 + 3x$ **2a.** $x^3 + 2x^2 + 4x$ **b.** $4a^5 - 6a^4 + 6a^2$ **3a.** $x(2x + 1)$ **b.** $2b(b^2 + 3b - 6)$

Lesson 13-7   pp. 727–730

Check Skills You'll Need 1. $-4x - 2$ **2.** $21 + 12y$ **3.** $10a - 5b$ **4.** $12m - 8n$

Quick Check 1a. $x^2 + 5x + 6$ **b.** $y^2 + 5y + 4$ **2a.** $x^2 - 3x - 10 + 4x$ **b.** $2m^2 + 7m + 6$

Checkpoint Quiz 2 1. monomial **2.** binomial **3.** monomial **4.** trinomial **5.** -8 **6.** 8 **7.** 10 **8.** 9 **9.** $7a - 6b$ **10.** $2x^2 + 7x + 5$ **11.** $g^2 + 10g + 24$ **12.** $-18m^2 - 6m^3p - 30mp$ **13.** Answers may vary. Sample: $x + 3$; $x^2 + 6x + 9$

Lesson 13-8   pp. 732–735

Check Skills You'll Need 1. $7(-12) = -84$ **2.** $11x = 132$ **3.** $\frac{x}{45} = 3$ **4.** $x^2 = 64$

Quick Check 1. the length of the kite and the length of the tail **2.** The tail is 12 ft plus twice the length of the kite. Together, the two lengths total 21 ft. **3.** $18 = 12 + 2 \cdot 3$ **4.** $3 + 18 = 21$

Selected Answers

Chapter 1

Lesson 1-1   pp. 6–7

EXERCISES 3. Variable expression; n is the variable. **5.** Variable expression; x is the variable. **11.** $3b$ **15.** $2 - x$ **17.** $2 \cdot 12$ **21.** $4 \cdot 3$
23. Variable expression; d is the variable.
25. Variable expression; g is the variable.
29. $\frac{160}{16}$ **31.** $\frac{100}{12}$ **35.** $70a + 100b$ **37.** C **39.** A

Lesson 1-2   pp. 11–12

EXERCISES 15. 49 **23.** We must agree on an order of operations to ensure that everyone gets the same value for an expression. **25.** 24 **31.** 22 **33.** > **37.** > **39.** $(7 + 4) \cdot 6 = 66$ **41.** $(3 + 8 - 2) \cdot 5 = 45$ **43.** $4 \cdot 9 + 5$; 41 **45.** $17 - (25 \div 5)$; 12

Lesson 1-3   pp. 16–17

EXERCISES 1. 35 **5.** 1 **9.** 4 **13.** 14 **15a.** $55m$ **b.** 1,100 words **23.** 99 **29.** Answers may vary. Sample: You did not work within the grouping symbols first.

Lesson 1-4   pp. 20–22

EXERCISES 3. -45 **5.** -50 **11.** 5 **13.** $-9, -2, 8$ **15.** $-6, 0, 6$ **17.** 2, 2 **21.** 4, 4 **23.** 9 **27.** 2 **29.** Answers may vary. Sample: 28 golf strokes over par **31.** 6 **33.** 2 **37.** -13 **39.** -23 **43.** < **45.** < **47.** C **49.** $r + n$ **51.** Answers may vary. Sample: My friend did not take into account the signs of the numbers. **53.** negative **55.** negative

Lesson 1-5   pp. 27–29

EXERCISES 1. $-4 + 7$; 3 **3.** $-4 + (-2)$; -6 **7.** 3 **11.** -1 **15.** -13 **19.** 100 **23.** 23 **25.** -61 **27.** Negative; both numbers are negative. **29.** Zero; the numbers are opposites. **31.** 15 **35.** B **39.** > **41.** > **43.** -8 **45.** $-20 + 18$; -2 **47.** $120 + (-25)$; 95 **49.** 1 **53.** $158

Lesson 1-6   pp. 32–34

EXERCISES 1. $-9 - (-2) = -7$ **5.** 1 **13.** -6 **21.** $2 + (-6)$; -4 **31.** -15 **35.** 170 **39.** -68 **41.** -30 **43.** 10 **45–47.** Answers may vary. Samples are given. **45.** $3 - 3 = 0$; $(-4) - (-4) = 0$ **47.** $1 - 7 = -6$; $-10 - (-4) = -6$ **51.** It decreases. **53.** C **55.** -60 **59.** 66 **61.** -40

Lesson 1-7   pp. 38–39

EXERCISES 1. a square with four shaded corners

5. Start with 2 and add 5 repeatedly; 22, 27
7. Start with 1 and add 3 repeatedly; 13, 16
11. correct **13.** an eight-sided figure with bottom right eighth shaded

15. Start with 1 and add 0.5 repeatedly; 3.5, 4, 4.5
17. Start with 6 and add -2 repeatedly; $-2, -4, -6$ **19.** Incorrect; $8 + (-6)$ is 2, $2 < 8$.

Lesson 1-8   pp. 42–43

EXERCISES 1. 36 laps/day **3.** $10.23 **5.** 11 pieces; 16 pieces **7a.** $59; $21 **b.** 10 people

Lesson 1-9   pp. 47–49

EXERCISES 1. $5 \cdot (-2) = -10$ **3.** $5(-5)$; -25 **9.** -18 **17.** -360 **23.** -7 **27.** -12 **29.** $-2°C$ **31.** 0 **33.** Positive; the integers have the same sign. **35.** Negative; the integers have opposite signs. **37.** A **39.** C **43.** 4,661 **47.** -76 **53.** > **55.** = **57.** 12 **59.** -27

Lesson 1-10   pp. 54–56

EXERCISES 1. III **5.** II **9.** $(-2, 4)$ **11.** $(-8, 3)$
15, 18.

33. P **37.** $(6, 6)$ **39.** $(0, -4)$ **41.** IV **43.** II
47. III **49.** y-axis
51. triangle   **53.** parallelogram

55. (0, −5) **57.** about 90° W, 32° N
59. Frankfort, Kentucky **61.**

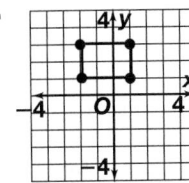

63. Answers may vary.
Sample: 62a flips the figure
across the y-axis. 62b flips the figure across the
x-axis. 62c flips the figure across one axis and then
the other. 62d doubles the lengths of the sides.

| Chapter 1 Review | pp. 59–61 |

1. origin **2.** variable **3.** y-axis **4.** quadrants
5. integers **6.** x-coordinate **7.** absolute value
8. $x - 25$ **9.** $3n$ **10.** $10 - t$ **11.** $\frac{x}{4}$ **12.** $n + 5$
13. $y + 2$ **14.** 24 **15.** 12 **16.** 37 **17.** 19 **18.** 17
19. 20 **20.** 40 **21.** 450 **22.** 16 **23.** −17
24. 1,000 **25.** 9 **26.** −12 **27.** > **28.** > **29.** <
30. = **31.** −30 **32.** −7 **33.** 12 **34.** 14 **35.** −15
36. −27 **37.** −11 **38.** −1 **39.** −20 ft **40.** Start
with 0 and add 6 repeatedly; 24, 30, 36 **41.** Start
with −18 and add 9 repeatedly; 18, 27, 36
42. Start with $\frac{1}{2}$ and add $\frac{1}{2}$ repeatedly; $2\frac{1}{2}$, 3, $3\frac{1}{2}$
43. 8 weeks **44.** $112 **45.** −42 **46.** −5 **47.** 72
48. 7 **49.** −3 **50.** −165 **51.** −8 **52.** 35 **53.** 102
54. (1, −3) **55.** (−2, 1) **56.** (−3, −3) **57.** (2, 2)

Chapter 2

| Lesson 2-1 | pp. 71–72 |

EXERCISES 1. (1 + 3) + 25; 1 + (3 + 25)
3. $215; Answers may vary.
Sample: 120 + 15 + 80
= 120 + (15 + 80) Assoc. Prop. of Add.
= 120 + (80 + 15) Comm. Prop. of Add.
= (120 + 80) + 15 Assoc. Prop. of Add.
= 200 + 15 Add within parentheses.
= 215 Add.
5. Ident. Prop. of Add. **9.** Comm. Prop. of Mult.
15. 3 **19.** 7.88 **23.** 90 **25.** 800 **27.** Assoc. Prop.
of Mult. **31.** Ident. Prop. of Add. **35.** −10,000
37. $24.20

| Lesson 2-2 | pp. 76–77 |

EXERCISES 7. 784 **9.** 1,176 people **11.** −9
13. 21 **17.** 3(3x − 1); 9x − 3 **19.** 4v − 12
21. −14z − 6 **23.** 12a + 36 **27.** −7t + 28
31. −55 **35.** −104 **37.** 1,792 miles
43. −15y − 24 **45.** My friend didn't distribute
the 7 to the t.

| Lesson 2-3 | pp. 80–81 |

EXERCISES 1. 3, 5; none; −3 **5.** −3; none;
none **7.** 7x + 10 **9.** 4x + 2 **13.** −b **15.** 8r − 5
17. 5g + 15 **19.** −m + 4d **25.** −5a − 12
33. Answers may vary. Sample: My friend added
x + y to get xy.

| Lesson 2-4 | pp. 84–85 |

EXERCISES 5. false; 7 ≠ 8 **7.** true; 20 = 20
11. 25 = v + 15; open; variable **15.** yes **19.** no
21. 140 + d = 192; yes **23.** True; for example
3 + 2 = 7. **25.** True; by definition, an open
sentence is one that contains a variable.
29. open; variable **31.** true; 12 = 12
33. (−20)(9) = −11; false; −180 ≠ −11
35. 48 ÷ 12 = 3; false; 4 ≠ 3 **37.** yes; −9 = −9
39. no; −6 ≠ 6

| Lesson 2-5 | pp. 91–92 |

EXERCISES 5. 28 **11.** 5,200 = s + 2,520;
2,680 m/s **13.** 54 **21.** 108 = d − 42;
150 million km **23.** 86; 86; −236 **31.** 23
35. Answers may vary. Sample: This year the
Tigers won 22 games in all. **37.** 100 **39.** The
student subtracted (rather than added) 6 on the
right side.

| Lesson 2-6 | pp. 96–97 |

EXERCISES 17. 23 **19.** 36 h **23.** 105 **27.** 40
33. 300 **37.** Dividing by 0 would result in 4 = 5,
which is not a true statement. **39.** no; $\frac{-18}{-3} \neq -6$
41. −20y = 100; −5 **43.** 7k = −168; −24
49. −15,000

| Lesson 2-7 | pp. 100–101 |

EXERCISES 1. Answers may vary. Samples:
14 dimes, 2 nickels; 2 quarters, 6 dimes, 8 nickels
3. 11 years and 12 years **5.** 16 ft² **11.** 2 CDs,
3 books

| Lesson 2-8 | pp. 106–107 |

EXERCISES 1.

3.

13. x ≤ −2

15. x < 0 **17.** t ≤ 3 **23.** t > 7 **27.** Use a solid dot
for ≥ and ≤; use an open dot for > and <.
29. x ≤ −10 **31.** x < −$\frac{1}{2}$

Lesson 2-9

EXERCISES **3.** $x \geq 1$

0 1

9. 64,000 lb **15.** $c > 14$ **19.** $y \leq 8$ **21.** Add 3 to each side.
23. $y > -13$

−13   0 5

29. $b > 5$

0 1   5

31. $13 + n > 15$; $n > 2$ **33.** $\leq \$49$

Lesson 2-10

EXERCISES **7.** $k \leq -8$ **11.** $f \geq -3$ **19.** $q > -18$
25. $h < 80$ **27.** unchanged **29.** reverses

31. $r \leq -21$ **37.** $x \geq 4$ **41.** $7t \leq 21$; $t \leq 3$
45. You have to divide by -4 instead of 4. The direction of each inequality sign is different when you solve each inequality.

Chapter 2 Review

1. d **2.** b **3.** e **4.** a **5.** c **6.** h **7.** j **8.** f **9.** g **10.** i
11. 80 **12.** 700 **13.** 547 **14.** 6,500 **15.** 300
16. 105 **17.** 864 **18.** 496 **19.** 387 **20.** $4w + 36$
21. $24 + 48a$ **22.** $-42 + 14m$ **23.** You can write 15 as $5 \cdot 3$. $5x + 5 \cdot 3 = 5(x + 3)$ by the Distributive Property. **24.** $-3a + 7$ **25.** $7w + 9$
26. $9 - 3x$ **27.** $15 - 24n$ **28.** k **29.** $-17r + 31$
30. They have the same variable or no variable and are separated by addition or subtraction signs. **31.** $32 + 5 = 6 \cdot 6$; false **32.** $\frac{t}{17} = -3$; open **33.** $4 \cdot 20 = 80$; true **34.** $p + 1.75 = 6.50$
35. 11 **36.** 8 **37.** -5 **38.** 27 **39.** 128 **40.** -8
41. $6.50 **42.**

−13   0 5

43.

−2   0

44.

0   2

45.

0   6

46. $t < 0$ **47.** $h > 12$ **48.** $n > 14$ **49.** $k \geq 2$
50. $s \leq 3$ **51.** $m < -6$ **52.** $d < -14$ **53.** $c \leq 36$

Chapter 3

Lesson 3-1

EXERCISES **1.** hundredths; 27.39 **3.** ones; 1,046
5. 345.7 **7.** 215 **11.** about 40 **13.** about $30
15. about $13.90 **19.** about 7.10 miles **21.** about $27 **23.** about 80 **27.** about 400 **33.** about 22,000 mi^2 **37, 39.** Answers may vary. Samples are given. **37.** about 30; rounding **39.** about 90.5; front-end

Lesson 3-2

EXERCISES **1.** about 35 **5.** about 180
7. about $18 **9.** about 2 **15.** about $2.00 per pound **19.** about 380 **23.** about $6 **25.** Answers may vary. Samples: elem. school teacher: about $45.50/h in Detroit, about $32.50/h in Lincoln; secretary: about $18/h in Detroit, about $12.75/h in Lincoln; truck driver: about $17.50 in Detroit, about $15.75 in Lincoln **27.** about $5
29. reasonable; $72 \div 12 = 6$

Lesson 3-3

EXERCISES **1.** 58.9, 56, 56, 45 **5.** 1.8 h, 1.8 h, 1.5 h
7. 1 mode **9.** 1 mode **11.** 115; lowers mean by about 1.9 **13.** Mean; there likely are no outliers.
15. Mean; there likely are no outliers. **17.** Mean, median, or mode since they are all about equal.
19. 5.8, 6.5, 6.5, 6.7; median (or mode); the outlier (1.2) affects the mean too much. **21.** 7.8, 8, none, 14; there is no mode and the mean and median are nearly the same. **23.** Mode; the data are not numerical. **25.** Median; there could easily be outliers.

Lesson 3-4

EXERCISES **1.** $d = 481.25$ m **3.** $t = 259.3$ s
5. 67°F **7.** 60°F **9.** 55.4 mm **11.** 136.4°F
13. 161.6°F **17.** 74 cm; 288.96 cm^2

Lesson 3-5

EXERCISES **3.** 26.1 **7.** $s + 599.01 = 686.98$; 87.97 days **9.** 23.7 **15.** $x - 13.50 = 26.50$; $40
17. 1.2, 1.2; 13.8 **19.** $r - 23.86 = 19.32$; 43.18 s
21. 7.285 **25.** -10.5 **27.** 1.2 **31.** Add -1.8 to each side.

Lesson 3-6

EXERCISES **5.** -25.1 **11.** $2.5m = 5.30$; $2.12
13. -1.94 **21.** 179 hits **23.** 2.3 **27.** -5.4
29. $-7.3n = 30.66$; -4.2 **31.** $\frac{n}{-2.35} = 400.9$; -942.115

Lesson 3-7

EXERCISES **1.** C **5.** A **7.** 5 kg; the mass of a dog is much greater than the mass of 5 paper clips.
9. 350 g; 350 mg is less than the mass of a paper clip. **13.** 3,010 **19.** 5.18 m **23.** Centimeter; the length is much less than a meter and much more than a millimeter, so meters are too large and millimeters are too small. **27.** Camille multiplied 6,392 g by 1,000, so she changed grams to milligrams. To change grams to kilograms she should have *divided* 6,392 by 1,000 to get 6.392 kg.

29. mm **31.** cm **33.** 150 cm; 150 m is greater than the length of a football field. **35.** 1 g; 1 mg is closer to the mass of a speck of sawdust. **43.** 301,000,000 **45.** 3.068 kg **51.** A
53a. 33,580 mm **b.** 0.03358 km

Extension   p. 165

1. 5.2 m **3.** 8.7 m **5.** Answers may vary. Sample: You ignored the units of length. **7.** 14.6 kg **9.** 7 cm **11.** 4 significant digits **13.** 5 significant digits **15.** 15.9 ft^2 **17.** 5,720 cm^2

Lesson 3-8   pp. 168–169

EXERCISES 1. 66 matches **3.** 12 ways **5.** 3.25 ft **7.** 80 sketches

Chapter 3 Review   pp. 171–173

1. mean **2.** compatible numbers **3.** mode **4.** outlier **5.** median **6.** formula **7.** measures of central tendency **8.** perimeter **9–18.** Answers may vary. Samples are given. **9.** about 10; front-end **10.** about 4; rounding **11.** about 24; rounding **12.** about 10; rounding **13.** about 60; clustering **14.** about 7; rounding **15.** about 11.7; front-end **16.** about 6; rounding **17.** about 18; clustering **18.** about 6; rounding **19.** Answers may vary. Sample: You use rounding when only a rough answer is needed and the numbers are not clustered. You use front-end estimation when you need a better estimate of a sum. You use clustering when there are 3 or more numbers and there is one number that they are all close to. **20.** about 40 feet **21.** about 48 **22.** about 4 **23.** about 10 **24.** about 5 **25.** about 12 **26.** about 5 **27.** about −8 **28.** about −6 **29.** about 12 **30.** 5.4, 5, 2 and 5; no outliers **31.** 16.1, 16.2, 16.3; no outliers **32.** 36, 33, none; outlier: 57 **33.** 1.0, 0.2, 0.1; outlier: 7.9 **34–36.** Answers may vary. Samples are given. **34.** Mode; the data are not numerical. **35.** Median; there could easily be outliers. **36.** Mean; there likely are no outliers. **37.** 70 mi **38.** 384 mm^2 **39.** 37.68 in. **40.** 52 cm **41.** 7.1 **42.** 9.25 **43.** −2.01 **44.** 26.2 **45.** −9.1 **46.** 10.6 **47.** 2.5 **48.** 40.817 **49.** 11.3 **50.** 968.75 **51.** −19.4 **52.** −185.0125 **53a.** 3.2 + x = 2.64 **b.** −$.56 **54.** Meter; a kilometer is too large unless you use fractional parts of a kilometer; centimeters are too small. **55.** Kilogram; a bicycle is heavy, so grams are too small. **56.** Milliliter; a liter is about the same as a quart, so liters are too large. **57.** 85 **58.** 0.16 **59.** 230 **60.** 1,600 **61.** 620 **62.** 0.08 **63.** A mature oak tree would be a number of meters tall. Centimeters is too small a unit. **64.** 24 **65.** 24

Chapter 4

Lesson 4-1   pp. 182–183

EXERCISES 1. yes; ends in 0 **2.** no; does not end in 0, 2, 4, 6, 8 **17.** 1, 2, 4 **21.** 1 row of 32; 2 rows of 16; 4 rows of 8 **23.** none **27.** 3, 9; 8 + 9 + 1 = 18; 18 is divisible by 3 and 9 **33.** 1 · 32, 2 · 16, 4 · 8 **37.** 1 · 53 **39.** 7 **43.** Explanations may vary. Sample: Yes; a number divisible by 9 has 3 as a factor.

Lesson 4-2   pp. 188–189

EXERCISES 1. 8^3 **5.** 9^5 **9.** 64 **13.** 1,000,000 **15.** −15 **19.** 42 **21.** −212 **23.** 22 **25.** d^3 **27.** The student didn't multiply a · a · a. **29.** −16 and 16 **31.** −288 **37.** 243

Lesson 4-3   pp. 193–194

EXERCISES 3. Prime; it has only two factors, 1 and 31. **7.** Composite; it has more than two factors, 1, 3, 29, and 87. **11.** 2 · 17 **15.** 2 · 3 · 31 **19.** 25 **23.** 6c^3 **25.** prime **29.** 8 groups **33.** 4 **43.** Answers may vary. Sample: 6, 30

Lesson 4-4   pp. 198–199

EXERCISES 1, 5, 25. Answers may vary. Samples are given. **1.** $\frac{1}{4}$, $\frac{4}{16}$ **5.** $\frac{1}{3}$, $\frac{12}{36}$ **9.** $\frac{1}{4}$ **13.** $\frac{1}{3}$ **17.** $\frac{3x}{2}$ **21.** 8b **25.** $\frac{5}{8}$, $\frac{20}{32}$ **31.** $\frac{3}{4}$ **41.** Answers may vary. Sample: $\frac{6x}{10}$, $\frac{3xy}{5y}$

Lesson 4-5   pp. 203–204

EXERCISES
1. 107 digits **3.** 15 pizzas **5.** 6 gardens **7.** B

Lesson 4-6   pp. 207–208

EXERCISES 1. $\frac{4}{8}$, $\frac{5}{10}$, $\frac{6}{12}$ **5, 7.** Answers may vary. Samples are given. **5.** $-\frac{10}{18}$, $\frac{-5}{9}$, $\frac{5}{-9}$ **7.** $\frac{-4}{6}$, $\frac{-2}{3}$, $\frac{2}{-3}$

9, 13.

15. $\frac{2}{3}$ **21.** 44 ft/s^2 **25, 27, 29.** Answers may vary. Samples are given. **25.** $-\frac{4}{9}$, $\frac{-12}{27}$, $\frac{12}{-27}$ **27.** $\frac{-10}{26}$, $\frac{-5}{13}$, $\frac{10}{-26}$ **29.** $\frac{8}{8}$ **33.** $-\frac{1}{4}$ **37.** D

Lesson 4-7   pp. 211–212

EXERCISES 9. x^{6}y^5 **21.** m^{24} **29.** 7 **33.** 3 **35.** < **39.** 2x^4; the two terms are being added, not multiplied.

Lesson 4-8
pp. 217–218

EXERCISES 3. $\frac{5y^5}{3}$ **23.** $\frac{1}{1,296}$ **25.** y^{-3}
27. $m^{-2}n^{-2}$ **31.** 5 **35.** 900 times as much
39. x^{-2} **41.** $m^7 n^{-7}$

Lesson 4-9
pp. 223–224

EXERCISES 5. 2.09×10^{-1} **7.** 5×10^9 km
9. 0.00000002104 **13.** 0.0060502 **15.** 7.2×10^{-5}
17. 3.508×10^{-4} **19.** 3.7×10^{-8}, 253×10^{-9},
12.9×10^{-7} **21.** 3×10^9 **25.** 2×10^{10} lb
27. 8,430,000 **29.** 5,880,000,000,000 mi
31. 10^{-8}, 10^{-6}, 10^0, 10^5, 10^9

Chapter 4 Review
pp. 227–229

1. factor **2.** simplest form **3.** rational number
4. scientific notation **5.** exponents **6.** prime
number **7.** 1, 2, 3, 4, 6, 12 **8.** 1, 2, 3, 5, 6, 10, 15,
30 **9.** 1, 2, 3, 6, 7, 14, 21, 42 **10.** 1, 2, 3, 4, 6, 8, 9,
12, 18, 24, 36, 72 **11.** 1, 3, 37, 111 **12.** 1, 2, 3, 4, 6,
7, 9, 12, 14, 18, 21, 28, 36, 42, 63, 84, 126, 252
13. 8 **14.** 27 **15.** 172 **16.** −25 **17.** 121 **18.** 58
19. 49 **20.** 16 **21.** prime **22.** composite; $2^2 \cdot 5$
23. prime **24.** composite; $2 \cdot 5 \cdot 11$
25. composite; $3 \cdot 29$ **26.** 4 **27.** 9 **28.** 1 **29.** $3x^2$
30. $2ab$ **31.** $3cd$ **32.** No factor of a positive
integer is greater than the integer. **33.** $\frac{1}{5}$ **34.** $\frac{1}{2}$
35. $\frac{4}{13}$ **36.** $\frac{7}{10}$ **37.** $\frac{7}{11}$ **38.** $\frac{1}{6}$ **39.** x **40.** 5 **41.** $\frac{1}{4}$
42. $\frac{2}{5}$ **43.** $\frac{x}{3}$ **44.** $4b$
45. 1, 4, 9, 16, 25, 36, 49, 64, 81, 100
46–49. **50.** $\frac{2}{5}$
51. $\frac{7}{8}$ **52.** −1 **53.** $-\frac{4}{5}$ **54.** 128 **55.** $21a^6$ **56.** b^7c^4
57. x^{15} **58.** y^{20} **59.** 4,096 **60.** $\frac{1}{b^2}$ **61.** $\frac{7}{8y^5}$
62. 2×10^6 **63.** 4.58×10^8 **64.** 7×10^{-7}
65. 5.9×10^{-9} **66.** 800,000,000,000
67. 0.0000032 **68.** 11,190,000
69. 0.000000000005 **70.** 4.3×10^{10}, 12×10^{11},
$3,644 \times 10^9$ **71.** 8×10^{-10}, 58×10^{-10},
716×10^{-10} **72.** 2.4×10^{16} **73.** 1.8×10^{11}

Chapter 5

Lesson 5-1
pp. 239–240

EXERCISES 1. 90 **9.** in 21 days **13.** 60 **17.** $24a^3$
19. $\frac{-2}{3} < -\frac{1}{3}$

21. $\frac{11}{12} > \frac{7}{12}$

23. < **25.** > **27.** $\frac{3}{9} < \frac{5}{9} < \frac{7}{9}$ **29.** $\frac{2}{7} < \frac{2}{5} < \frac{2}{3} < 2$
35. = **39.** C **41.** 1,800 **45.** $72xy$ **49.** =

Lesson 5-2
pp. 244–245

EXERCISES 1. 0.28 **5.** Yes,
$\frac{5}{16} = 5 \div 16 = 0.3125$, so $10\frac{5}{16} = 10.3125$.
7. $-0.1\overline{6}$; repeating; 6 **9.** $0.\overline{81}$ repeating; 81
13. 0.06, $\frac{2}{5}$, $\frac{6}{5}$, $\frac{3}{2}$ **15.** $\frac{22}{11}$, 2.01, 2.1, $\frac{22}{10}$ **21.** $6\frac{37}{100}$
27. $-\frac{1}{3}$ **29.** = **31.** < **33.** 5.375 **37.** −0.31
39. $\frac{7}{20}$ **43a.** Sarah: 0.286; Lizzie: 0.302 **b.** Lizzie;
$0.302 > 0.286$

Lesson 5-3
pp. 250–251

EXERCISES 3. $\frac{7}{q}$ **7.** $-\frac{2}{5}$ **9.** $\frac{1}{12}$ **11.** $-\frac{7}{20}$ **15.** $13\frac{7}{8}$
21. $3\frac{13}{20}$ h **23.** Sample answer: 15 **27.** $1\frac{7}{8}$ in.
29. $\frac{30-3n}{10n}$ **31.** $1\frac{11}{18}$ **33.** $7\frac{2}{5}$ **35.** $20\frac{3}{4}$ in.

Lesson 5-4
pp. 255–256

EXERCISES 5. $\frac{7}{10}$ **13.** $1\frac{1}{4}$ hours **17.** $-1\frac{1}{21}$ **25.** $1\frac{1}{2}$
31. $-\frac{3}{5}$ **37.** $\frac{35}{72}$ **41.** $-1\frac{7}{8}$ **45.** $\frac{2}{3w}$ **49.** $2\frac{1}{2}$
57. 4 mi; $2\frac{2}{15}$ mi

Lesson 5-5
pp. 259–261

EXERCISES 1. Ounces; it is closest to the weight
of a paper clip. **3.** Miles; distances to continents
would be measured in miles. **7.** $\frac{1}{2}$ **9.** $1\frac{1}{2}$ **13.** C
17. E **21.** 78 **25.** 7 **31.** C **37.** 9,560 ft **39.** weight
43. capacity **45.** Pounds or ounces; tons are too
large. **49a.** mile; about 3,740 mi **51.** yes
55. no; 1 lb **59.** 10,000 **67.** $3\frac{1}{8}$

Lesson 5-6
pp. 265–266

EXERCISES 1. 8:30 A.M. **3.** the 12:15 P.M. bus
5. 6 different amounts; $.40, $.45, $.50, $.55, $.60,
and $.65 **7.** $30

Lesson 5-7
pp. 270–271

EXERCISES 5. $\frac{1}{8}$ **7.** $\frac{1}{6}$ of the book **11.** $1\frac{1}{8}$ **15.** $2\frac{3}{4}$
21. Negative; $\frac{9}{10} > \frac{1}{2}$, so $\frac{1}{2} - \frac{9}{10} < 0$. **23b.** $60\frac{7}{8}$ in.
27. $-\frac{7}{9}$ **33.** $13\frac{3}{8}$ lb.

Lesson 5-8 — pp. 274–275

EXERCISES **13.** $\frac{1}{2}$ **21.** $\frac{3}{4}s = 9$; 12 sheets **25.** $\frac{7}{15}$
29. $7\frac{7}{15}$ **31.** Positive; a positive product means
the two factors have the same sign. **35.** 20 weeks
39. $3\frac{9}{13}$ **47.** 4

Lesson 5-9 — pp. 280–281

EXERCISES **7.** $8x^6$ **21a.** $25s^4$ cm^2 **b.** Yes; The
area of the tablecloth is $25s^4$ cm^2, which is
greater than $20s^4$ cm^2. **25.** $\frac{81x^8}{10,000}$ **31.** $\frac{9t^4}{25}$ **33.** 1
37. 3 **39.** $-\frac{1}{27}$ **43.** $(3x^2)^2 = 9x^4$ ft^2 **49.** $-\frac{125}{512}$
55. $-\frac{1}{32y^{15}}$

Chapter 5 Review — pp. 283–285

1. f **2.** c **3.** a **4.** b **5.** g **6.** d **7.** e **8.** 36 **9.** $56m^2$
10. 105 **11.** $30xy$ **12.** > **13.** < **14.** > **15.** =
16. 0.6 **17.** $0.1\overline{6}$ **18.** 0.625 **19.** $0.\overline{3}$ **20.** 0.07
21. $\frac{1}{4}$ **22.** $\frac{5}{6}$ **23.** $5\frac{3}{5}$ **24.** $2\frac{4}{99}$ **25.** $3\frac{1}{12}$ **26.** $7\frac{2}{15}$
27. $\frac{30 + 3x}{5x}$ **28.** $\frac{7}{8}$ **29.** $\frac{7}{12}$ ft, or 7 in. **30.** $\frac{7}{40}$ **31.** $-\frac{4}{5}$
32. $1\frac{1}{5}$ **33.** $3\frac{3}{4}$ **34.** $\frac{1}{2}$ **35.** $2\frac{1}{2}$ **36.** $3\frac{3}{8}$ **37.** 60
38. 24 **39.** 96 **40.** 5,500 **41.** 2:30 P.M.
42. 15 buses **43.** $45.50 **44.** $2\frac{3}{8}$ **45.** $1\frac{2}{15}$ **46.** $1\frac{1}{3}$
47. $\frac{1}{54}$ **48.** $-\frac{8}{21}$ **49.** $\frac{2}{9}$ **50.** $16d^4$ **51.** 36 **52.** $a^{10}b^5$
53. $-\frac{1}{8}$ **54.** $\frac{x^2}{9}$ **55.** $\frac{16a^4}{c^8}$

Chapter 6

Lesson 6-1 — pp. 294–295

EXERCISES **5.** $\frac{1}{10}$ **11.** $\frac{14}{25}$ **13.** 48 ft/s **15.** 52 mi/h
17. $\frac{1}{2}$ **21.** $117\frac{1}{3}$ **25.** $\frac{4}{3}$ **27.** Anna; $\frac{3}{8}$ mi/h
31. class A

Extension — p. 297

1. 20.3 **3.** 12.4 **5.** 47.2 **7.** 15.9 **9.** 20 **11.** 100
13. 39.4 **15.** 16.1 **17.** England to Paris; about
11.5 km or about 7 mi

Lesson 6-2 — pp. 300–302

EXERCISES **5.** 8 **11.** 20 **17.** no, cross products
not equal **23.** 15 posters **25.** no, cross products
not equal **27.** no, cross products not equal
29. 10 **31.** 72 **35.** 19.2 **39.** 17.5 **47.** 1
51. 40 defective chips **55.** $\frac{3}{1.65} = \frac{5}{x}$; $2.75
57. $\frac{25}{2.5} = \frac{100}{x}$; 10 s

Lesson 6-3 — pp. 305–307

EXERCISES **1.** $2\frac{2}{5}$ ft **3.** $3\frac{1}{3}$ ft **7.** 5.6 **9.** 51 cm
11. 144 km **13.** 99.6 cm **15.** 4 in. **19.** 1.2 m
21. 45 km **23.** 7.5 km **25.** HO model; N model
27. 4.5 in. **29.** 2 in. **31.** $1\frac{3}{4}$ in. **35.** 1 in. : 350 mi
37. 1 in. : 10 ft **39.** 2.5 ft

Lesson 6-4 — pp. 312–313

EXERCISES **3.** $\frac{3}{6}$, or $\frac{1}{2}$ **5.** $\frac{2}{6}$, or $\frac{1}{3}$ **9.** $\frac{2}{8}$, or $\frac{1}{4}$ **13a.** $\frac{2}{3}$
b. not choosing green **15.** 3 to 2; 2 to 3 **17.** 0
21. $\frac{6}{11}$ **23.** $\frac{7}{11}$ **27.** 1 to 2; 2 to 1 **31.** 1 to 3; 3 to 1

Lesson 6-5 — pp. 316–318

EXERCISES **5.** $\frac{1}{5}$ **9.** $2\frac{1}{5}$ **17.** 3.5 **21.** 0.4; $\frac{2}{5}$
23. 36% **29.** 35% **33.** 0.63, 69%, 0.72, $\frac{3}{4}$
43. 240% **45.** Sample answer: about 30%
47. 50% **51.** $\frac{1}{10}$, 10% **55.** $\frac{1}{4}$, 25% **61.** -0.09,
-0.72, 0.63, 69%, 78%

Lesson 6-6 — pp. 322–323

EXERCISES **5.** 37.1 **13.** 52 **23.** 627,000 people
25. 150 **31.** 80%

Lesson 6-7 — pp. 326–327

EXERCISES **9.** $n = 1.5 \cdot 90$; 135 **17.** $.96
19. about 83 million households
25. $n \cdot 8 = 20$; 250% **29.** $120 **31.** 50% **35.** 48

Lesson 6-8 — pp. 331–332

EXERCISES **5.** 137.5% **9.** 20% **13.** 40%
21. 43.7% **27.** 20.8% decrease
31. Eva should compare $8 - 7$ to 7, not 8.
33. 20% increase **37.** 50% decrease

Lesson 6-9 — pp. 335–336

EXERCISES **3.** $55.50 **5.** $8.55 **7.** $3.99
9. $73.92 **11.** $27; $73 **15.** $37.50; $87.50
19. $17.25 **21.** store B; $.11

Lesson 6-10 — pp. 340–341

EXERCISES **1.** about 8,934 people **3.** 24 orders
5. 16 outfits **7.** 8 and 26

Chapter 6 Review
pp. 343–345

1. c **2.** b **3.** a **4.** d **5.** g **6.** e **7.** f **8.** $\frac{3}{8}$ **9.** $\frac{4}{7}$ **10.** $\frac{3}{4}$
11. $\frac{10}{13}$ **12.** 50 mi/h **13.** $1.89/lb **14.** 90 words/min
15. 35 **16.** 0.7 **17.** 49 **18.** 126 **19.** 45 **20.** 35
21. 0.5 cm **22.** $\frac{1}{8}$; 1 to 7 **23.** $\frac{2}{8}$, or $\frac{1}{4}$; 1 to 3
24. $\frac{3}{8}$; 3 to 5 **25.** $\frac{6}{25}$; 0.24 **26.** $\frac{18}{25}$; 0.72 **27.** $\frac{2}{25}$; 0.08
28. $\frac{1}{200}$; 0.005 **29.** 30% **30.** 33% **31.** 33.3%
32. 35% **33.** 88.9% **34.** 2.1% **35.** 240%
36. 0.6% **37.** $\frac{15}{100} = \frac{n}{48}$; 7.2 **38.** $\frac{20}{100} = \frac{30}{x}$; 150
39. $\frac{n}{100} = \frac{90}{300}$; 30% **40.** $\frac{125}{100} = \frac{100}{y}$; 80
41. $0.35 \cdot a = 70$; 200 **42.** $n = 0.68 \cdot 300$; 204
43. $n \cdot 180 = 9$; 5% **44.** $n \cdot 56 = 3.5$; 6.25%
45. 25% decrease **46.** 75% decrease
47. 20% increase **48.** 75% decrease **49.** $8.75
50. $1.70/lb **51.** 30 mi

Chapter 7

Lesson 7-1
pp. 354–355

EXERCISES 1. Subtract 9 from each side.
3. Add 6 to each side. **7.** –3 **13.** 16 weeks
19. 6 **21.** $4.45 **23.** –60 **25.** 15 **31.** 2 **33.** 14

Lesson 7-2
pp. 359–360

EXERCISES 1. 12 **7.** Jasmine: 30 marbles, Bill:
64 marbles **9.** 18, 20, 22 **11.** 10 **15.** 1 **19.** −12
21. 18 **25.** −15, −14, −13, −12, −11

Lesson 7-3
pp. 364–365

EXERCISES 1. Subtract 3 from each side or
multiply each side by 4. **3.** Multiply each side by
2. **5.** 10 **7.** 8 **9.** 10 **11.** 74 **15.** 6.5 **19.** 6 pencils
21. $\frac{1}{2}$ **25.** −7

Lesson 7-4
pp. 368–369

EXERCISES 1. $60 **3.** 20 cm by 12 cm
7. 28 posts **9.** 8 quarters and 8 dimes

Lesson 7-5
pp. 373–375

EXERCISES 1. a, $-3a$, $-3a$, $-3a$, $\frac{-3a}{-3}$, 5 **9.** 3
17. 3 h **19.** −2 **23.** 2.9 **27.** The student
subtracted 4x from the left side of the equation
instead of adding 4x; $x = -\frac{2}{3}$

Lesson 7-6
pp. 379–380

EXERCISES 1. Add 2 to each side, simplify,
divide each side by 4, and simplify.
3. $a < -4$

7. $a \geq 9$

15. $8t \geq 420$; $t \geq 52.5$; at least 52.5 mi/h
17. $c \leq 72$ **19.** $y > 4\frac{4}{5}$

Lesson 7-7
pp. 384–385

EXERCISES 1. 3; 3; 6, 6; 6, c **3.** $w = \frac{V}{\ell h}$
9. $4,900 **11.** $h = \frac{2V}{\pi r^2}$

Lesson 7-8
pp. 389–390

EXERCISES 1. $16; $216 **3.** $120.00 $3,120.00
$3,120.00 $124.80 $3,244.80 $3,244.80
$129.79 $3,374.59 **7.** $2081.21 **9a.** 2%,
b. 12 periods, **c.** $760.95 **13.** $11,117.91
17. Answers may vary. Sample: $10,000 at 6%;
$13,000; $13,382.26

Chapter 7 Review
pp. 393–394

EXERCISES 1. compound interest **2.** principal
3. balance **4.** consecutive integers **5.** interest
rate **6.** simple interest **7.** interest **8.** −4 **9.** 2
10. 48 **11.** 3 **12.** 21 **13.** $1\frac{2}{3}$ **14.** $\frac{4}{5}$ **15.** −2
16. $-6\frac{3}{8}$ **17.** 39 **18.** 3.5 **19.** 8 **20.** −18, −17,
−16, −15 **21.** $p - 0.15p = 29.74$; $34.99
22. $10n + 20n + 147 = 1,167$; 34 tens, 34 twenties
23. $a + 0.08a = 1,296$; $1,200 **24.** 3 **25.** −4
26. $1\frac{1}{5}$ **27.** 4 **28.** −7 **29.** $\frac{2}{3}$ **30.** 2 h
31. $a > 7$

32. $y \leq -3$

33. $c \leq \frac{2}{3}$

34. $x < -4$

35. $x < -9$

36. $b < 2$

37. $x < 6$

38. $x \geq -\frac{3}{5}$

39. $799 + 25 \left(\frac{c}{8}\right) \leq 1,000$; about 64 megabytes
40. $m = \frac{r}{6k}$ **41.** $y = \frac{4}{3}x$ **42.** $g = \frac{Q}{P}$ **43.** $b = a + 2c$
44. $a = \frac{1}{3}w - \frac{5}{3}n$ **45.** $h = 6e - 66$ **46.** $13.50

47. $252.50 **48.** $90.00 **49.** $8,489.66
50. $22,464.38 **51.** $27,917.68 **52.** $40,203.22
53. Answers may vary. Sample: Yes; with more interest periods, the interest would start earning interest earlier.

Chapter 8

Lesson 8-1   pp. 407–408

EXERCISES 1a. Yes; there is one range value for each domain value. **7.** No; subscribers of a specific age (domain value) may pay different subscription prices (range values).

11.

13.

A function; no vertical line passes through two graphed points.

Not a function; a vertical line passes through both (−1, 3) and (−1, 2).

15.

21.

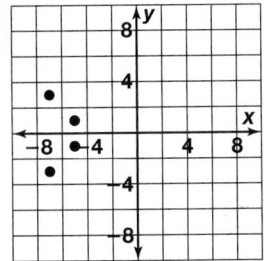

A function; there is only one range value for each domain value.

Not a function; a vertical line passes through both (−7, 3) and (−7, −3).

Lesson 8-2   pp. 412–413

EXERCISES 1. (−5, −18) **3.** (−5, −40) **5.** −2
9. −6 **11.** about 1,064 km

13. yes;

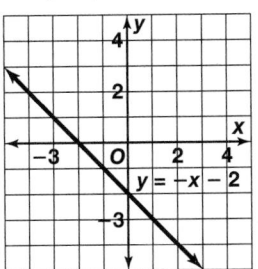

23. $y = \frac{1}{2}x - 3$

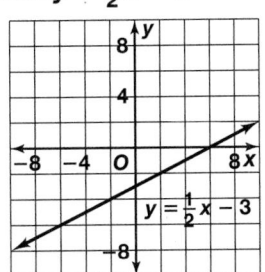

29. no; $-12 + 6 \neq 6$ **31.** no; $8 - 0 \neq 6$
33. $(-2, 5\frac{1}{2})$, $(1, 6\frac{1}{4})$, $(4, 7)$ **35.** The student forgot to divide $-3x$ by 4.

Lesson 8-3   pp. 418–420

EXERCISES 1. $\frac{3}{4}$ **3.** $-\frac{5}{6}$ **5.** −1 **9.** undefined
11. 7; 3

21. The student could have calculated
difference in x-coordinates / difference in y-coordinates.

23. $-\frac{1}{3}$ **25.** The upper roof has the steeper pitch because it has the greater slope. **27.** 0
29. undefined **41.** yes;
$2(-4) - 6(-2) = 4$

Lesson 8-4   pp. 424–426

EXERCISES 1. $a(c) = 20 - c$; $15.50
3. $m(w) = 0.4w$; 6 lb **5.** $f(x) = -x$ **11a.** $n(d) = 36d$
13. $y = 2x - 4$ **19.** D

Lesson 8-5   pp. 430–432

EXERCISES 1. averaged 4 h watching television and 2 h of physical activity daily **3.** 2 students
5.

7. No correlation; there is no apparent relationship. **11.** Negative; as one set of values increases, the other set tends to decrease.
13. 10 min **15.** A **17.** Negative; the lower the temperature, the more layers of clothing you wear. **21.** No correlation; the sets of data are not related.

Lesson 8-6 pp. 436–437

EXERCISES 1a–b. Trend lines may vary. Sample is given.

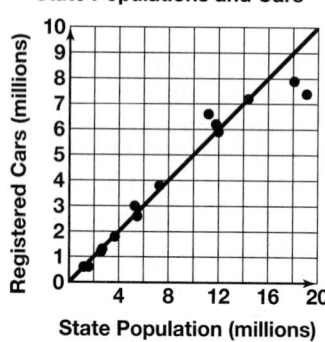

State Populations and Cars

c. about 16 million cars **d.** $y = 0.5x$; about 3.6 million cars **3.** Answers may vary. Sample: 8.4 gal **5.** Answers may vary. Sample: $1.55; (16, 1.55) is on the line through the two points (12, 1.17) and (20, 1.89). **7.** 45 ft

Lesson 8-7 pp. 442–444

EXERCISES 1. no **3.** yes **5.** (1, 7) **9.** (4, 6) **17.** no **19a.** $x + y = 4$, $x = 3y$ **b.** (3, 1); 3 ft, 1 ft **21.** infinitely many solutions

Lesson 8-8 pp. 448–450

EXERCISES 1. dashed **3.** solid
5.

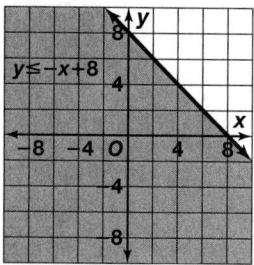

11. $y \geq -2x$
15. $10x + 5y < 100$

19.

25.

31. $y = x - 7$; solid **35.** $y = 2x - 5$; dashed
41.

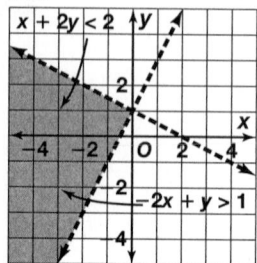

Chapter 8 Review pp. 453–455

1. slope **2.** vertical-line test **3.** negative correlation **4.** function **5.** linear equation **6.** domain **7.** range **8.** solution **9.** Yes; there is one range value for each domain value. **10.** Yes; there is one range value for each domain value. **11.** No; there are domain values for which there is more than one range value. **12.** No; one length of time (for different distances) could result in different costs. **13.** (−3, 2), (0, 5), (2, 7) **14.** (−3, 12), (0, 0), (2, −8) **15.** $(-3, 1\frac{1}{2})$, (0, 3), (2, 4) **16.** (−3, 12), (0, 6), (2, 2)
17. −1, 7

18. 1, 2

19. $-\frac{2}{5}$, 2

20. $\frac{3}{2}$, −6

21. −2 **22.** 3 **23.** $-\frac{1}{2}$ **24.** $f(x) = -x$
25. $y = 2x + 1$ **26.** $y = -x + 4$ **27.** $c(t) = 14t + 2$
28. 30 min **29.** about 620 calories **30.** Positive correlation; as the time bicycling increases, the calories used increases.
31. about 800 calories

32.

33.

34.

35.

36. $(4, -1)$

37. $(4, -3)$

38. $(2, -3)$

39. infinitely many solutions

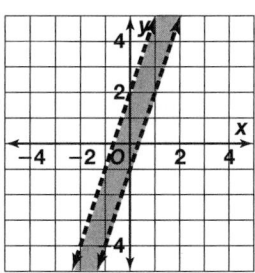

40. The graphs could be parallel lines, so there is no common solution.

Chapter 9

Lesson 9-1   pp. 465–467

EXERCISES 1. A, B, C **3.** $\overrightarrow{AC}, \overrightarrow{BC}, \overrightarrow{BA}, \overrightarrow{CA}$
13. $\overline{GF}, \overline{JI}, \overline{KH}$ **17.** $\overleftrightarrow{PS}, \overleftrightarrow{RQ}, \overleftrightarrow{PK}, \overleftrightarrow{QL}$
19. $\overline{BF}, \overline{CG}, \overline{DH}$
23.

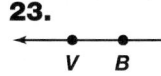

25. Answers may vary.
Sample:

27. Answers may vary.

Sample:

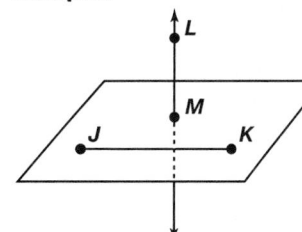

29. $6 + 5x + 4x + 1 = 12x + 1; 6, 10, 9, 25$
31. $\overline{WX}$ **33.** $\overline{TU}$
35. sometimes
37. always
41. Answers may vary.
Sample: $\overrightarrow{AB}$ and $\overrightarrow{BA}$
have different
endpoints.

Lesson 9-2   pp. 472–473

EXERCISES 1. supplementary **3.** $m\angle 1 = 80°$, $m\angle 2 = 100°$, $m\angle 3 = 80°$ **5.** $\angle 3$ is vertical to $\angle 1$. $\angle 2$ is adjacent to $\angle 1$. $m\angle 1 = 110°$ **7.** $\angle 2$ and $\angle 8$, $\angle 3$ and $\angle 5$ **9a.** $\angle 5, \angle 3, \angle 7$ **b.** $m\angle 6 = 135°$, $m\angle 7 = 45°, m\angle 8 = 135°, m\angle 3 = 45°$, $m\angle 2 = 135°, m\angle 1 = 45°, m\angle 4 = 135°$

11. complementary **15.** 5

Lesson 9-3   pp. 477–478

EXERCISES 1. equilateral acute triangle
3. scalene acute triangle **5.** trapezoid
9. rectangle, parallelogram, square, rhombus
11. $P = 4x$; 50 in. **13.** $P = 5x$; 4,605 ft

15.

19.

23. 19.5 in. **25.** trapezoid, parallelogram, rhombus

Lesson 9-4   pp. 482–483

EXERCISES **1.** 4 mi **5.** 8 students **7.** 5 cm
11. the dog

Lesson 9-5   pp. 486–488

EXERCISES **1.** $\angle D$ **5.** $m\angle D$, or 53°
15. $\overline{EB} \cong \overline{JF} \cong \overline{IL} \cong \overline{DH}$, $\overline{BD} \cong \overline{FE} \cong \overline{LJ} \cong \overline{HI}$,
$\overline{DE} \cong \overline{EJ} \cong \overline{JI} \cong \overline{ID}$ **17.** $\overline{BC} \cong \overline{HG}$, $\overline{AB} \cong \overline{KH}$,
$\angle B \cong \angle H$, $\triangle ABC \cong \triangle KHG$ by SAS **19.** $\overline{ON} \cong \overline{RQ}$,
$\overline{OM} \cong \overline{RP}$, $\overline{NM} \cong \overline{QP}$, $\triangle ONM \cong \triangle RQP$ by SSS
21. $\overline{AB} \cong \overline{XY}$, $\overline{BC} \cong \overline{YZ}$, $\overline{AC} \cong \overline{XZ}$ **23.** $\overline{NL} \cong \overline{QR}$,
$\overline{NM} \cong \overline{QP}$, $\angle N \cong \angle Q$, $\triangle LNM \cong \triangle RQP$ by SAS
25. $\overline{KM} \cong \overline{JM}$, $\overline{ML} \cong \overline{ML}$, $\angle KML \cong \angle JML$,
$\triangle KML \cong \triangle JML$ by SAS **27.** Incorrect; $\angle R$ does
not correspond with $\angle N$. **31.** Incorrect; $\angle V$ and
$\angle C$ are not corresponding angles.

Lesson 9-6   pp. 493–494

EXERCISES **1.** about 314 in. **3.** about 19.8 cm
5. about $29\frac{1}{3}$ ft **7.** about 113 in. **11.** 180°
15. 270° **19.** about 14.4 yd

Lesson 9-7   pp. 498–499

EXERCISES
1.

5.

9.   **11.**

13.
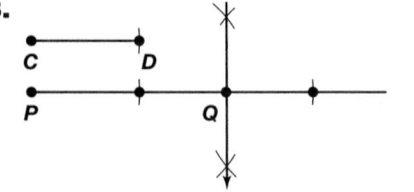

17. Answers may vary. Sample: In both
constructions, you use the compass to draw
intersecting arcs, and then use the points of
intersection to draw the bisectors.

Lesson 9-8   pp. 503–505

EXERCISES
3.   **7.**

11. $A(1, 5) \rightarrow A'(2, 7)$ **13.** $S(3, 3) \rightarrow S'(11, 1)$
15. $(x, y) \rightarrow (x + 4, y + 3)$ **17.** $(x, y) \rightarrow (x - 4, y + 1)$
19. translation 11 units to the left and 4 units up
21. translation 6 units to the left and 3 units down
23. vertical
25.   **31.** $(x, y) \rightarrow (x, y + 4)$
                  35.
 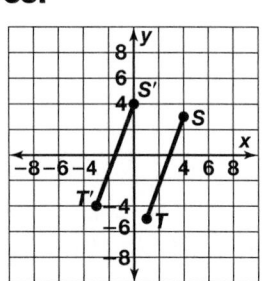

Lesson 9-9   pp. 509–510

EXERCISES

1. no line of symmetry **3.**
because no half is a
mirror reflection of
the other half

7.   **9.**

          11.

15. $V'(-9, 0)$

19. D

Lesson 9-10 pp. 513–514

EXERCISES

3a.

3b.

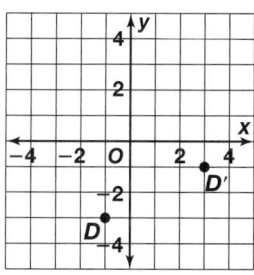

9. yes, 90° **11.** yes, 60° **15.** yes, 120° **17.** yes, 72°
21. 270°

Chapter 9 Review pp. 517–519

1. e **2.** c **3.** b **4.** a **5.** d **6.** g **7.** h **8.** f
9. ∠RPD, ∠DPL, ∠RPL **10.** $\overrightarrow{PR}$, $\overrightarrow{PD}$, $\overrightarrow{PL}$
11. Answers may vary. Sample: $\overleftrightarrow{RL}$ **12.** R, P, D, L
13. $\overline{RP}$, $\overline{PD}$, $\overline{PL}$, $\overline{RL}$ **14.** ∠3, ∠5, ∠7 **15.** Answers
may vary. Samples: ∠2 and ∠3, ∠5 and ∠6
16. ∠1 and ∠5, ∠2 and ∠6, ∠3 and ∠7, ∠4 and
∠8 **17.** ∠4 and ∠6, ∠3 and ∠5 **18.** $m\angle 1 = 105°$,
$m\angle 3 = 105°$, $m\angle 4 = 75°$, $m\angle 5 = 105°$, $m\angle 6 = 75°$,
$m\angle 7 = 105°$, $m\angle 8 = 75°$ **19.** equilateral triangle
20. square **21.** isosceles acute triangle
22. trapezoid **23.** $\angle T \cong \angle P$, $\overline{ST} \cong \overline{SP}$,
$\angle RST \cong \angle QSP$, $\triangle RST \cong \triangle QSP$ by ASA
24. $\overline{DE} \cong \overline{FE}$, $\overline{CE} \cong \overline{GE}$, $\angle DEC \cong \angle FEG$,
$\triangle CDE \cong \triangle GFE$ by SAS **25.** 50 ft wide by
55 ft long **26.** about 43.96 cm
27. Television Programming

28–29. Drawings may vary. Samples:

28.

29.

30. $A'(11, 1)$ **31.** $A'(-7, -2)$ **32.** $A'(2, 7)$
33. $A'(7, 0)$ **34.** They have no effect on size or
shape. In each case the image is congruent to the
original figure.

Chapter 10

Lesson 10-1 pp. 528–529

EXERCISES 3. 12 ft², or $1\frac{1}{3}$ yd² **11.** 48,000 ft²

13. 1,400 mm², or 14 cm² **15.** 1,694 in.²
17.

12 square units

Lesson 10-2 pp. 536–537

EXERCISES 1. 8 in.² **3.** 60 m² **5.** 130 m²
7. 77 ft² **9.** 63 ft² **13.** 5 in. **15.** 34 cm²

Lesson 10-3 pp. 541–543

EXERCISES 3. 900π cm²; 2,826 cm² **5.** 50 in.²
7. 2,856 yd² **9.** 357 mi² **11.** about 191 pieces
13. A **17a.** about 392.5 ft² **b.** about $880
21. 17.64π mm²; 55.4 mm² **23.** The circle with
radius 4 m has greater area because the four
circles have a total area of 4π m², but the circle
with radius 4 m has an area of 16π m².
25. 19 cm² **27.** 56 m²

Lesson 10-4 pp. 547–549

EXERCISES 3. The bases are pentagons. The figure is a pentagonal prism. **5.** The base is a hexagon. The figure is a hexagonal pyramid. **7.** square prism **11.** rectangular prism **13.** pyramid **15.** cone **17.** **19.** B **21.** C

25.

Lesson 10-5 pp. 554–556

EXERCISES 1. 1,008 m²

3a. |←11 in.→| 5 in.   3 in.

3b. 206 in.²
3c. 1,854 in.²
3d. The surface area of the larger prism is 9 times the surface area of the smaller prism.

5. 11,988 in.² **9.** 168 in.² **11.** 175.8 cm² **13.** 904 cm² **19a.** 5 sides **b.** 3,600 ft² **c.** $600

Lesson 10-6 pp. 561–562

EXERCISES 3. 1,017 cm² **7.** 105 cm² **11.** 28 m² **13.** C **15.** 216 m²

Lesson 10-7 pp. 565–566

EXERCISES 1. 54 cm³ **3.** 24 m³ **5.** 6,029 m³ **9.** 14,158 cm³ **11.** 10 in. **13.** 11 m

Lesson 10-8 pp. 570–571

EXERCISES 1. 10 in. by 14 in. by 3 in. **3.** 30 cm, 15 cm **5.** 50 ft by 50 ft

Lesson 10-9 pp. 574–575

EXERCISES 1. 25 yd³ **3.** 5,539 cm³ **5.** 216 in.³ **7.** 20.48 cm³ **11.** 7,235 cm³ **13.** 113,040 yd³ **15.** 4 cups **19.** about 33.5 cm³ **21.** 3 cm **23.** 5 m

Chapter 10 Review pp. 579–581

EXERCISES 1. lateral area **2.** cone **3.** altitude **4.** volume **5.** sphere **6.** cylinder **7.** area **8.** 189 m² **9.** 14 cm² **10.** 6.25 yd² **11.** 79 m² **12.** 201 mm² **13.** 57 m² **14.** 31 in.² **15.** triangular prism **16.** square pyramid **17.** cylinder **18.** 164 cm² **19.** 205,513 m² **20.** 84 cm² **21.** 63 in.² **22.** 84 cm² **23.** 85 cm² **24.** 314 ft² **25.** 27 ft² **26.** Sample answer: 24 in. by 18 in. **27.** Find the area of the walk and garden, and then subtract the area of the garden. **28.** 384 units³ **29.** 18 units³ **30.** 311 units³ **31.** 268 units³

Chapter 11

Lesson 11-1 pp. 590–591

EXERCISES 3. 1 **7.** −3 **9.** 3 **13.** 27 mi **17.** rational; because it is a repeating decimal **21.** irrational; it neither terminates nor repeats **23.** $\frac{2}{3}$ **25.** $\frac{3}{4}$ **31.** −10 **33.** 10 **35.** rational; repeating decimal **37.** x **41.** 5, −5 **43.** 2, −2

Lesson 11-2 pp. 595–597

EXERCISES 1. 13 cm **3.** 8 in. **5.** 20 in. **7.** 14 ft **9.** about 15.2 ft; about 30.4 ft **11.** 6.7 km **15.** yes; $6^2 + 7^2 = 85$ **17.** yes; $5^2 + 12^2 = 13^2$ **19.** 3.1 m **21.** 2.1 km **23.** yes; $3^2 + 4^2 = 5^2$ **25.** no; $10^2 + 24^2 \neq 25^2$ **29.** yes; $\left(\sqrt{2}\right)^2 + \left(\sqrt{3}\right)^2 = \left(\sqrt{5}\right)^2$ **31.** about 131.9 in.

Lesson 11-3 pp. 601–602

EXERCISES 1. 5 **5.** 17.7 **7.** 19.3 **9.** (1.5, 2) **11.** 30; (0, 0) **13a.** (−0.5, 3) **b.** $AM = \sqrt{(-3 - (-0.5))^2 + (5 - 3)^2} = \sqrt{10.25}$
$MB = \sqrt{(2 - (-0.5))^2 + (1 - 3)^2} = \sqrt{10.25}$

Lesson 11-4 pp. 606–607

EXERCISES 1. $\frac{20}{x + 20} = \frac{13}{21}$; 12.3 m **3.** 1.2 mi **7.** $20

Lesson 11-5 pp. 611–612

EXERCISES 3. 7.6 in. **7.** 17 in. **11.** $x \approx 18.4$ cm, $y = 13$ cm **13.** Answers may vary. Sample: The hypotenuse is twice the shorter leg. Since the shorter leg is 10 ft, the hypotenuse is 20 ft. The longer leg is $\sqrt{3}$ times the shorter leg, which is $10\sqrt{3}$, or about 17.3 ft. **15.** 9

Lesson 11-6   pp. 617–618

EXERCISES 1. 4 **3.** 5 **5.** $\frac{9}{15}$ or $\frac{3}{5}$, $\frac{12}{15}$ or $\frac{4}{5}$, $\frac{9}{12}$ or $\frac{3}{4}$
9. 0.9703 **15.** 19.3 ft
17. 1

Lesson 11-7   pp. 623–624

EXERCISES 1. about 30 yd **3.** 26.7 m
5. about 71.6 mi **7.** angle of elevation = $\angle ADC$,
angle of depression = $\angle BAD$ **13.** about 1,293.8 m

Chapter 11 Review   pp. 627–629

EXERCISES 1. c **2.** f **3.** d **4.** e **5.** a **6.** b **7.** 1
8. −4 **9.** 7 **10.** 8 **11.** −6 **12.** 2 **13.** 3 **14.** 6
15. 8 **16.** 10 **17.** rational; because it is a
terminating decimal **18.** rational; because 64
is a perfect square **19.** rational; because it is a
repeating decimal **20.** irrational; because 15 is
not a perfect square **21.** rational; because it is a
repeating decimal **22.** It is irrational because the
decimal neither terminates nor repeats. **23.** no;
$1^2 + 3^2 \neq 3^2$ **24.** yes; $8^2 + 15^2 = 17^2$ **25.** yes;
$(\sqrt{6})^2 + (\sqrt{10})^2 = 4^2$ **26.** yes; $30^2 + 40^2 = 50^2$
27. 3.6 **28.** 5 **29.** 12.6 **30.** 2.2 **31.** 9.2 **32.** 13.4
33. (2, 4) **34.** (3, 4) **35.** (−2, 2) **36.** (4.5, 10)
37. (−12, −8) **38.** (2.5, −0.5) **39.** about 337.5 ft
40. $a = 6$ in., $b \approx 10.4$ in. **41.** $y \approx 9.9$ m
42. $f = 4$ ft, $c \approx 3.5$ ft **43.** $g \approx 10.6$ mm
44. 0.2756 **45.** 7.1154 **46.** 0.9063 **47.** 0.0524
48. 0.9986 **49.** 0.2924 **50.** 0.6947 **51.** 1.0000
52. 0.9816 **53.** 0.2309 **54.** 8 ft **55.** 99 ft

Chapter 12

Lesson 12-1   pp. 638–639

EXERCISES
1.

Number	Frequency
0	2
1	2
2	2
3	2
4	2

X X X X X
X X X X X
0 1 2 3 4

5. Rolls of a Number Cube

Number	Frequency
1	4
2	3
3	3
4	2
5	3
6	2

X
X X X   X
X X X X X X
X X X X X X
1 2 3 4 5 6

7.

15. 28; 28 **17.** 70; 77.5

Lesson 12-2   pp. 644–645

EXERCISES 1.   Maximum Speeds of Animals (mi/h)

0 10 20 30 40 50 60 70 80 90 100

3.

0 1 2 3 4 5 6 7 8 9 10 11 12 13 14 15 16
set A
set B

5. \$60; \$70; \$85 **7.** Answers may vary. Sample:
The orca weights have a median of 3,000 lb and
a range of 2,000 lb. The hippopotamus weights
have a median of 2,500 lb and a range of 1,800 lb.
A significant number of the orcas and hippos fall
within the same weight range.
9. The acreages vary considerably, from about 25
acres to about 650 acres. However, about half of the
parks are between 50 and 250 acres, with a median
of 125 acres. **11.** Answers may vary. Sample: The
student assumed that the lower value, the upper
value, and the quartiles are equally spaced.

Lesson 12-3   pp. 651–653

EXERCISES 1. *American Ampersand* **3.** You might
compare the lengths of the bars without noticing
the break in the scale. **5.** It suggests that the
percent is rising rapidly, by putting 1989 and 1993
very close together.
7.   Percent of Students
    Using Computers at School

11a.

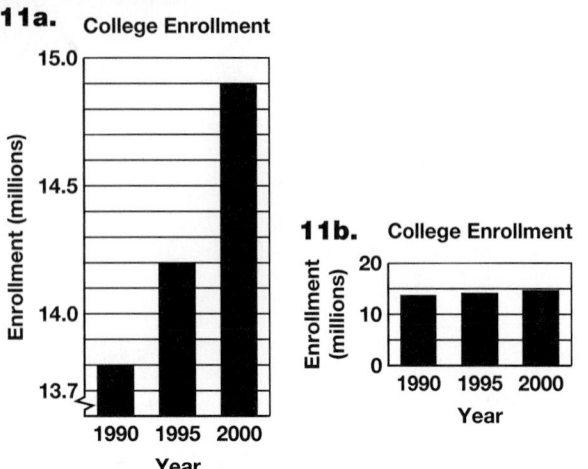

College Enrollment

13. nearly 2 to 1; about 1.14 to 1

Lesson 12-4   pp. 660–601

EXERCISES
1. 10 choices

```
                  beef              beef
               chicken          chicken
flour <       bean      corn < bean
             cheese          cheese
            vegetable       vegetable
```

3. 28 routes   **5.** $\frac{1}{8}$ **7.** $\frac{7}{8}$ **9.** $\frac{1}{125,000}$
11. 15 sweaters   **13.** $\frac{5}{15}$, or $\frac{1}{3}$ **15.** $\frac{5}{104}$

Lesson 12-5   pp. 665–666

EXERCISES 3. $\frac{2}{36}$, or $\frac{1}{18}$ **7.** about 83%   **11.** $\frac{4}{90}$, or $\frac{2}{45}$
13. $\frac{24}{90}$, or $\frac{4}{15}$ **15.** Independent; the possibilities on
the second roll are the same as on the first.
17. $\frac{8}{100}$, or $\frac{2}{25}$ **19.** $\frac{12}{100}$, or $\frac{3}{25}$ **21.** $\frac{20}{72}$, or $\frac{5}{18}$
23. $\frac{12}{72}$, or $\frac{1}{6}$

Lesson 12-6   pp. 670–671

EXERCISES 1. 6   **3.** 120   **5.** 360   **7.** 1,814,400
9. 3; CA, CT, AT   **11.** 10; VA, VL, VU, VE, AL, AU,
AE, LU, LE, UE   **15.** 45   **17.** 20 sandwiches
19. Combinations; the order of the shirts selected
does not matter.   **21.** 720   **27.** 2   **31.** 20

Lesson 12-7   pp. 675–676

EXERCISES 3. 13.2%   **5.** 77.9%   **9.** $\frac{1}{2}$ **11.** $\frac{3}{8}$

Lesson 12-8   pp. 679–680

EXERCISES 3. Not a good sample; it excludes
students not interested in basketball.
5. 2,240 pairs   **7.** Not a good sample; it excludes
people who dislike that particular restaurant.
9a. The cold virus may be passed from student to
student in that class so that more of them have
colds than in the total school population.

9b. Answers may vary. Sample: Survey
students as they enter the school cafeteria.

Lesson 12-9   pp. 684–685

EXERCISES 1. Answers may vary. Sample:
Simulate the problem by tossing a coin. Let
heads be a girl and tails be a boy. Toss the coin
100 times and organize the results into 20 groups
of five. Count the number of groups with exactly
three tails. Divide this number by 20 to get the
experimental probability. **5.** $67.50   **9.** $\frac{1}{10,000}$

Chapter 12 Review   pp. 687–689

EXERCISES 1. combination   **2.** sample
3. theoretical probability   **4.** permutation
5. range   **6.** frequency table   **7.** dependent events
8. random sample
9.

Number	Frequency
9	1
10	3
11	3
12	4
13	1

10.

Number	Frequency
45	1
46	3
47	2
48	3
49	2
50	1

11.

12.

13.

14.

15 20 25 30 35 40 45 50 55 60

15. It increased gradually.   **16.** Answers may
vary. Sample: Break the vertical axis and mark
a scale from 50 to 60 above the break.

17a. 15 types **b.** $\frac{4}{15}$ **18.** $\frac{2}{25}$ **19.** $\frac{1}{20}$

20. permutation, since order is important; 120 ways **21.** combination, since order does not matter; 220 groups **22.** $\frac{9}{20}$ **23.** $\frac{1}{2}$ **24.** Answers may vary. Sample: Simulate the problem by making a spinner with 3 congruent sections. Make one section red, to represent a correct answer. Spin 60 times and organize the results into 20 groups of 3. Count the number of groups with exactly 2 red spins. Divide this number by 20 to get the experimental probability. **25.** Not a good sample; it includes people not in the town's skating population. **26.** Not a good sample; it includes people not in the town's skating population.

Chapter 13

Lesson 13-1   pp. 699–700

EXERCISES **1.** −1 **3.** −6 **7.** 20, 25, 30; start with 0 and add 5 repeatedly. **9.** 1, 4, 7; Start with −11 and add 3 repeatedly. **11.** 2; 48, 96, 192; start with 3 and multiply by 2 repeatedly. **13.** 2; 720, 1440, 2880; start with 45 and multiply by 2 repeatedly. **17.** geometric; 81, 243, 729 **21.** geometric; −81, 243, −729 **23.** B **25.** geometric; 5 **31.** −5, −7, −9; start with 3 and add −2 repeatedly **33.** 144, 288, 576; start with 9 and multiply by 2 repeatedly **37.** neither; 3, 30, 4 **39.** arithmetic; 7.12, 7.15, 7.18

Lesson 13-2   pp. 704–705

EXERCISES

1.

x	$4(x)^2$	y	(x, y)
−2	$4(-2)^2$	16	(−2, 16)
−1	$4(-1)^2$	4	(−1, 4)
0	$4(0)^2$	0	(0, 0)
1	$4(1)^2$	4	(1, 4)
2	$4(2)^2$	16	(2, 16)

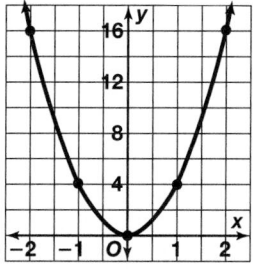

7.

x	$x^2 + 4$	y	(x, y)
−2	$(-2)^2 + 4$	8	(−2, 8)
−1	$(-1)^2 + 4$	5	(−1, 5)
0	$0^2 + 4$	4	(0, 4)
1	$1^2 + 4$	5	(1, 5)
2	$2^2 + 4$	8	(2, 8)

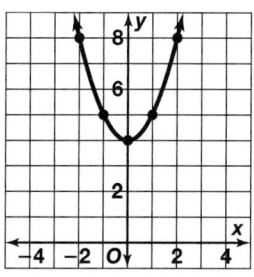

15.

x	$\lvert x \rvert + 3$	y	(x, y)
−2	$\lvert -2 \rvert + 3$	5	(−2, 5)
−1	$\lvert -1 \rvert + 3$	4	(−1, 4)
0	$\lvert 0 \rvert + 3$	3	(0, 3)
1	$\lvert 1 \rvert + 3$	4	(1, 4)
2	$\lvert 2 \rvert + 3$	5	(2, 5)

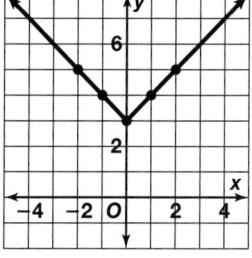

21. U shape

x	$x^2 - 8$	y	(x, y)
−2	$(-2)^2 - 8$	−4	(−2, −4)
−1	$(-1)^2 - 8$	−7	(−1, −7)
0	$(0)^2 - 8$	−8	(0, −8)
1	$(1)^2 - 8$	−7	(1, −7)
2	$(2)^2 - 8$	−4	(2, −4)

Lesson 13-3   pp. 709–710

EXERCISES

1.

x	4^x	y	(x, y)
0	4^0	1	(0, 1)
1	4^1	4	(1, 4)
2	4^2	16	(2, 16)
3	4^3	64	(3, 64)
4	4^4	256	(4, 256)

11. B **13.** C

15.

x	$\frac{1}{5} \cdot 5^x$	y	(x, y)
0	$\frac{1}{5} \cdot 5^0$	$\frac{1}{5}$	$(0, \frac{1}{5})$
1	$\frac{1}{5} \cdot 5^1$	1	(1, 1)
2	$\frac{1}{5} \cdot 5^2$	5	(2, 5)
3	$\frac{1}{5} \cdot 5^3$	25	(3, 25)
4	$\frac{1}{5} \cdot 5^4$	125	(4, 125)

9.

x	$30(\frac{1}{3})^x$	y	(x, y)
0	$30(\frac{1}{3})^0$	30	(0, 30)
1	$30(\frac{1}{3})^1$	10	(1, 10)
2	$30(\frac{1}{3})^2$	$3\frac{1}{3}$	$(2, 3\frac{1}{3})$
3	$30(\frac{1}{3})^3$	$1\frac{1}{9}$	$(3, 1\frac{1}{9})$
4	$30(\frac{1}{3})^4$	$\frac{10}{27}$	$(4, \frac{10}{27})$
5	$30(\frac{1}{3})^5$	$\frac{10}{81}$	$(5, \frac{10}{81})$

21. yes; $2^4 = 16$
23. no; $\left(\frac{1}{2}\right)^4 \neq 16$

Lesson 13-4 pp. 714–715

EXERCISES 1. No; it is a sum. **3.** Yes; it is a product of the real number $\frac{1}{3}$ and the variable a. **9.** binomial **15.** monomial **19.** 32 **23.** 37 **29.** Yes; it is a real number. **31.** No; it is a sum. **33.** binomial **37.** binomial **43.** -4 **47.** 12

Lesson 13-5 pp. 720–722

EXERCISES 1. $(2x^2 + x + 2) + (x^2 + 4) =$ $3x^2 + x + 6$ **3.** $2x^2 + 4x + 7$ **5.** $-x + 5$ **7.** $2a + 9b$ **11.** $2x^3 + 5x^2 + x + 4$ **13.** $3x + 8$ **17.** $-2ab + 2$ **19.** $x^2 - 8x - 5$ **23.** $w^2 + 7w - 6$ **29.** $m^2 + 5m$ **33.** $5y - 2$ **35.** $4b - 1$ **37.** $2a + 2$

Lesson 13-6 pp. 725–726

EXERCISES 1. $3x^2 + 3x$ **5.** $6x^2 + 2x$ **13.** $5x^3 + x^2 - 4x$ **15.** $6b^3 - 3b^2 + 12b$ **21.** $d^2(3d^2 + 1)$ **25.** $7(2a^2 + a - 1)$ **31.** $a^3 + 3a$ **35.** $6y^4 - 12y^3 - 2y^2$ **41.** D **43.** $4x^2(x^3 - x^2 + 2)$ **45.** $2a(a^2 - 3a - 2)$

Lesson 13-7 pp. 729–730

EXERCISES 1. $x^2 + 3x + 2$ **5.** $x^2 + 9x + 20$ **11.** $c^2 + 16c + 63$ **17.** $x^2 + x - 6$ **19.** C **21.** $9x^2 - 9$ **23.** $n^2 + 4n - 320$ **25.** $b^2 + 2b + 1$

Lesson 13-8 pp. 732–735

EXERCISES 1a. 4:30 P.M. **b.** 180 mi **3.** 30 ft **7.** Sandy 101 g, White Ears 108 g, Sport 115 g **9.** 64 choices

Chapter 13 Review pp. 737–739

EXERCISES 1. d **2.** e **3.** a **4.** f **5.** b **6.** h **7.** g **8.** i **9.** c **10.** 17, 21, 25; start with 1 and add 4 repeatedly. **11.** $-3.75, -1.875, -0.9375$; start with -60 and multiply by 0.5 repeatedly. **12.** 128, 135, 142; start with 100 and add 7 repeatedly. **13.** $-20, -25, -30$; start with 0 and add -5 repeatedly. **14.** $-18, -29, -40$; start with 26 and add -11 repeatedly. **15.** $62\frac{1}{2}, 312\frac{1}{2}, 1{,}562\frac{1}{2}$; start with $\frac{1}{10}$ and multiply by 5 repeatedly. **16.** arithmetic; 25, 29, 33 **17.** geometric; $-\frac{1}{2}, -\frac{1}{4}, -\frac{1}{8}$ **18.** arithmetic; 7, 8, 9 **19.** arithmetic; 22, 33, 44 **20.** neither; 30, 3, 40 **21.** geometric; $\frac{2}{25}, \frac{4}{25}, \frac{8}{25}$ **22.** Sample: A club starts with 10 members and adds 1 new member every week; 10, 11, 12, . . .; 1

23.

x	$\frac{1}{2}x^2$	y	(x, y)
-2	$\frac{1}{2} \cdot (-2)^2$	2	$(-2, 2)$
-1	$\frac{1}{2} \cdot (-1)^2$	$\frac{1}{2}$	$(-1, \frac{1}{2})$
0	$\frac{1}{2} \cdot (0)^2$	0	$(0, 0)$
1	$\frac{1}{2} \cdot (1)^2$	$\frac{1}{2}$	$(1, \frac{1}{2})$
2	$\frac{1}{2} \cdot (2)^2$	2	$(2, 2)$

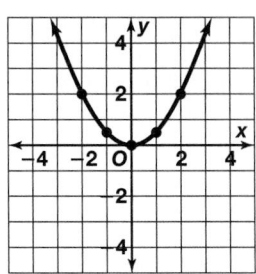

24.

x	$2|x|$	y	(x, y)
-2	$2|-2|$	4	$(-2, 4)$
-1	$2|-1|$	2	$(-1, 2)$
0	$2|0|$	0	$(0, 0)$
1	$2|1|$	2	$(1, 2)$
2	$2|2|$	4	$(2, 4)$

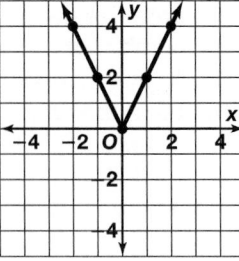

25.

x	$|x| + 1$	y	(x, y)
-2	$|-2| + 1$	3	$(-2, 3)$
-1	$|-1| + 1$	2	$(-1, 2)$
0	$|0| + 1$	1	$(0, 1)$
1	$|1| + 1$	2	$(1, 2)$
2	$|2| + 1$	3	$(2, 3)$

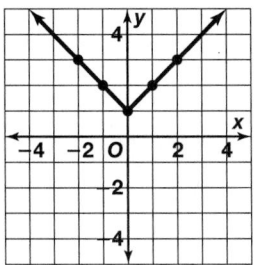

26.

x	$x^2 + 5$	y	(x, y)
-2	$(-2)^2 + 5$	9	$(-2, 9)$
-1	$(-1)^2 + 5$	6	$(-1, 6)$
0	$0^2 + 5$	5	$(0, 5)$
1	$1^2 + 5$	6	$(1, 6)$
2	$2^2 + 5$	9	$(2, 9)$

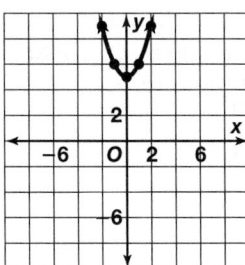

27.

x	$-|x|$	y	(x, y)
-2	$-|-2|$	-2	$(-2, -2)$
-1	$-|-1|$	-1	$(-1, -1)$
0	$-|0|$	0	$(0, 0)$
1	$-|1|$	-1	$(1, -1)$
2	$-|2|$	-2	$(2, -2)$

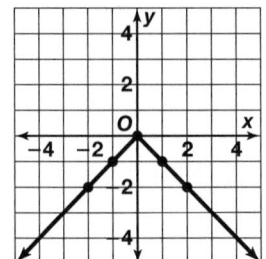

28.

x	$\frac{1}{2}|x|$	y	(x, y)
-2	$\frac{1}{2}|-2|$	1	$(-2, 1)$
-1	$\frac{1}{2}|-1|$	$\frac{1}{2}$	$(-1, \frac{1}{2})$
0	$\frac{1}{2}|0|$	0	$(0, 0)$
1	$\frac{1}{2}|1|$	$\frac{1}{2}$	$(1, \frac{1}{2})$
2	$\frac{1}{2}|2|$	1	$(2, 1)$

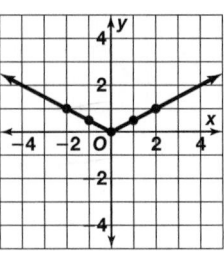

29.

x	$-x^2 - 3$	y	(x, y)
-2	$-(-2)^2 - 3$	-7	$(-2, -7)$
-1	$-(-1)^2 - 3$	-4	$(-1, -4)$
0	$-(0)^2 - 3$	-3	$(0, -3)$
1	$-(1)^2 - 3$	-4	$(1, -4)$
2	$-(2)^2 - 3$	-7	$(2, -7)$

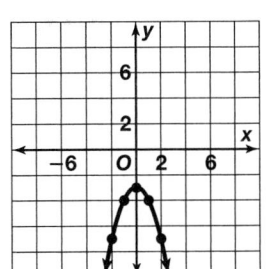

30.

x	$-x^2 + 4$	y	(x, y)
-2	$-(-2)^2 + 4$	0	$(-2, 0)$
-1	$-(-1)^2 + 4$	3	$(-1, 3)$
0	$-(0)^2 + 4$	4	$(0, 4)$
1	$-(1)^2 + 4$	3	$(1, 3)$
2	$-(2)^2 + 4$	0	$(2, 0)$

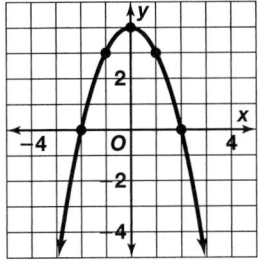

31.

x	$\left(\frac{1}{4}\right)^x$	y	(x, y)
0	$\left(\frac{1}{4}\right)^0$	1	$(0, 1)$
1	$\left(\frac{1}{4}\right)^1$	$\frac{1}{4}$	$(1, \frac{1}{4})$
2	$\left(\frac{1}{4}\right)^2$	$\frac{1}{16}$	$(2, \frac{1}{16})$
3	$\left(\frac{1}{4}\right)^3$	$\frac{1}{64}$	$(3, \frac{1}{64})$
4	$\left(\frac{1}{4}\right)^4$	$\frac{1}{256}$	$(4, \frac{1}{256})$

32.

x	$\frac{1}{2} \cdot 2^x$	y	(x, y)
0	$\frac{1}{2} \cdot 2^0$	$\frac{1}{2}$	$(0, \frac{1}{2})$
1	$\frac{1}{2} \cdot 2^1$	1	$(1, 1)$
2	$\frac{1}{2} \cdot 2^2$	2	$(2, 2)$
3	$\frac{1}{2} \cdot 2^3$	4	$(3, 4)$
4	$\frac{1}{2} \cdot 2^4$	8	$(4, 8)$

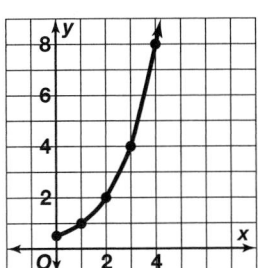

33.

x	3^x	y	(x, y)
0	3^0	1	$(0, 1)$
1	3^1	3	$(1, 3)$
2	3^2	9	$(2, 9)$
3	3^3	27	$(3, 27)$
4	3^4	81	$(4, 81)$

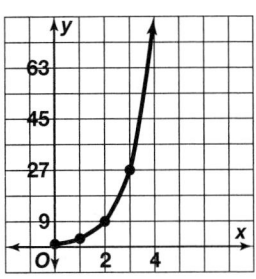

34.

x	$\left(\frac{1}{2}\right)^x$	y	(x, y)
0	$\left(\frac{1}{2}\right)^0$	1	$(0, 1)$
1	$\left(\frac{1}{2}\right)^1$	$\frac{1}{2}$	$(1, \frac{1}{2})$
2	$\left(\frac{1}{2}\right)^2$	$\frac{1}{4}$	$(2, \frac{1}{4})$
3	$\left(\frac{1}{2}\right)^3$	$\frac{1}{8}$	$(3, \frac{1}{8})$
4	$\left(\frac{1}{2}\right)^4$	$\frac{1}{16}$	$(4, \frac{1}{16})$

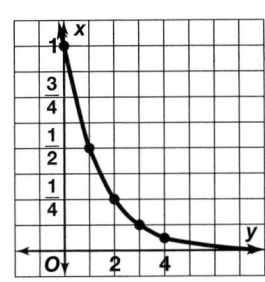

35. monomial **36.** binomial **37.** monomial
38. trinomial **39.** monomial **40.** monomial
41. binomial **42.** binomial **43.** binomial
44. trinomial **45.** 32 **46.** 7 **47.** 6 **48.** -12 **49.** 9
50. $3a^2 + 2a + 8$ **51.** $4m^2 - 2m - 12$
52. $4x^2 - 2x + 2$ **53.** $4p - 7q - 2$
54. $3w^2 + 9w - 5$ **55.** $6x + 6y$ **56.** $2a^2 + 5a$
57. $12c^2 - 28c$ **58.** $-30y^2 - 18y$
59. $3x^3 - 3x^2 - 15x$ **60.** $x^3 + 7x^2$
61. $2x^4 - 6x^3 - 12x^2$ **62.** $x^2 + 7x + 12$
63. $x^2 - 4x - 5$ **64.** $x^2 - 6x + 8$ **65.** $x(x - 1)$
66. $9(p^2 + 3)$ **67.** $3x(x^2 - 3x + 2)$
68. $5(b^5 + 4b^3 - 6)$ **69.** $2x(4x^2 + x + 2)$
70. $4a(7a - b)$ **71.** 2,401 ft^2 **72.** Answers may
vary. Sample: A diagram gives a visual picture
of the problem. A table organizes possible
dimensions and their related areas. Looking
for a pattern leads to the answer.

Extra Practice

Chapter 1   pp. 752–753

1. $x - 6$ **5.** $8p$ **9.** 9 **11.** 5 **13.** 42 **15.** 11
19. = **21.** > **23.** -7 **27.** -32 **31.** Start with -12,
and add 9 to the previous term. 33, 42, 51
33. Add the two previous terms. 21, 34, 55 **37.** 24
41. 9   **42–50.**
51. $g - 8$
53. $28 \div 7 - 2 = 2$
55. $3 + 10p = 33$
57. $t - 4$
59. $1000 - 450 = 550$
61. incorrect; $-5 + 2 = -3$
63. 12
65. $(-3, -6)$

Chapter 2   pp. 754–755

1. $99 + (-99) + 45 + (-46)$
Commutative Property of Addition
$0 + 45 + (-46)$
additive inverse
-1
5. $2 \cdot 50 \cdot 58$
Commutative Property of Multiplication
$100 \cdot 58$
Multiply from left to right.
5,800

7. 20 **13.** $-17y + 38$ **17.** $\frac{-3}{-1} = 3$; true **21.** -24
25. 24 **33.**

35.

39. $x > -13$ **43.** $c \le -15$
49. Commutative Prop. of Add.
51. 116,800 people **53.** $4d + 7 + 3 = 4d + 10$
55. $15w = 105$; $15(6) = 90$; no
57. $15p = 165$; 11 cans **59.** 10 and 12
61. $7p > 42$; $p > 6$
63. $s + 37 \ge 100$; $s \ge 63$

Chapter 3   pp. 756–757

1. about 13; rounding **5.** about 120; clustering
7. about 120 **11.** about 18 **13.** mean: 12.9;
median: 12; modes: 10 and 12; outlier: 19
15. mean: \$27.30; median: \$29; mode: \$30; outlier:
\$15 **17.** 130 yd **19.** 175 mi **25.** 63.6 **33.** 3
37. 0.25 **45.** 0.036 **49.** about \$21 **51.** about \$27
53. \$31.20; \$30; \$25; \$17; mean **55.** about 0.65
mi/min **57.** 52.5 mi **59.** $1.5c = 5.64$; \$3.76/lb
61. 10,000 m

Chapter 4   pp. 758–759

3. 1, 2, 4, 8, 16, 32, 64 **5.** 1, 2, 3, 4, 6, 9, 12, 18, 36
7. 64 **11.** 48 **13.** composite; 5^2 **15.** prime **19.** 10
21. $5x$ **25.** $\frac{7}{16}$ **31.** $\frac{x}{15}$

35–39.

41. $-\frac{2}{5}$ **43.** $\frac{4}{25}$ **45.** $6y^5$ **49.** $3t^{15}$ **53.** 6.6×10^{16}
55. a group of 1, 2, 3, 4, 6, or 12 **57.** $(7 - j)(j + 4)$
59. No; 6 is not a factor of 5. **61.** $\frac{5}{6}$ **63.** 53 digits
65. 3 ft/s² **67.** $\frac{4y^4}{y^2}$

Chapter 5   pp. 760–761

1. 30 **3.** $24xy$ **5.** > **7.** = **11.** $0.\overline{27}$ **13.** -0.7
15. $1\frac{3}{10}$ **19.** $\frac{7}{20}$ **23.** $-\frac{3}{8}$ **27.** $\frac{20 + 3t}{4t}$ **31.** -1
37. -2 **39.** 5 ft **41.** 64 oz **43.** $8\frac{1}{2}$ **47.** $1\frac{13}{24}$
51. $a^5 b^5 c^{15}$ **55.** $\frac{4c^2}{d^6}$ **59.** Pietro **61.** $\frac{7}{20}$
63. $1\frac{3}{4} - 1\frac{1}{2} = \frac{1}{4}$; $\frac{1}{4}$ ft **65.** $4c$ **67.** \$18.20
69. $h = \frac{3}{5}(60)$; 36 ft

Chapter 6   pp. 762–763

1. $\frac{1}{2}$ **3.** $\frac{1}{4}$ **5.** $58.\overline{6}$ ft/s **7.** 82.5 gal/h **9.** 84 **13.** 26.7
17. 34.4 mi **19.** 18.8 mi **21.** 0; 0 to 6 **23.** $\frac{2}{6}$, or $\frac{1}{3}$;
1 to 2 **25.** $\frac{2}{1}$; 2 **27.** $\frac{7}{400}$; 0.0175 **29.** 15% **31.** 41.7%
35. 40 **37.** 36.3 **39.** 150% increase **41.** 12.5%
decrease **43.** \$45 **45.** 3 ft/s **47.** 22.5 km **49.** $\frac{1}{5}$
51. 12% **53.** $\frac{40}{100} = \frac{n}{120}$; 48 people
55. $p = 1.06(25)$; \$26.50
57. 15% decrease **59.** \$52

Chapter 7   pp. 764–765

9. $-5\frac{1}{3}$ **17.** -5
23. $a \ge -3$

27. $t \le 50$

31. $p = s - c$ **33.** $a = c + b$
37. \$4,500 **41.** \$1,480.24
45. $-3n + 4 = 2n - 6$; 2
47. $n = 85 + 8(6 - 2)$; 117 coins
49. $70 + 20w = 250$; 9 wk
51. $4(t + 0.25) = 8t$; 15 min **53.** 42 mi/h
55. \$1,904.25

Chapter 8   pp. 766–767

1. No; there are two range values for the domain
value 4. **3.** Yes; there is one range value for each
domain value. **5.** $(-3, -11)$, $(0, -2)$, $(2, 4)$
9. $(-3, -4)$, $(0, -4)$, $(2, -4)$ **13.** 5, -4 **17.** $\frac{3}{5}$, -1

21.

23.

27. $y = 3x - 1$ **29.** $y = 5x + y$ **31.** $y = 2x + 3$
34. Positive correlation; as you move to the right,
most scores increase. **35.** (2, 5)

37.

39. No; speed and type of car can affect the amount of gasoline used. **41.** 95°F **43.** $\frac{5}{132}$
45. positive correlation **47.** about 5.4 gal
49. $b + 20 = r$; $2b = r$; 60 marbles

Chapter 9   pp. 768–769

1. $\overleftrightarrow{AB}$, $\overleftrightarrow{AC}$, $\overleftrightarrow{BC}$ **3.** $\overline{RS}$, $\overline{MQ}$, $\overline{MN}$, $\overline{UR}$ **5.** $\overleftrightarrow{UT}$, $\overleftrightarrow{NP}$, $\overleftrightarrow{ST}$ **7.** $m\angle 7 = 67°$; $m\angle 4 = 67°$; $m\angle 1 = 67°$; $m\angle 8 = 113°$; $m\angle 6 = 113°$; $m\angle 2 = 113°$; $m\angle 3 = 113°$ **9.** rectangle **11.** A **13.** 78.5 ft **15.** 314 m

17.

19.
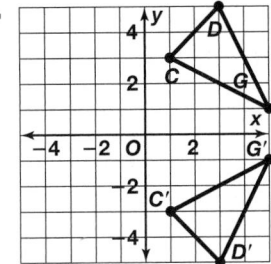

21. always **23.** 115° **25.** 60 yd
27. Yes; the triangles are ≅ by SSS.
31. Always; only the x-coordinate would change.

Chapter 10   pp. 770–771

3. 75 m² **5.** 20 ft² **7.** 676π m², 2,122.6 m²
9. 75π yd², 235.5 yd² **13.** 803.8 cm², 2,143.6 cm³
17. 452.2 cm², 904.3 cm³ **21.** 360 yd² **23.** 150 m²
25. 36π m² **27.** sphere **29.** about 87.92 in.²
31. 254 yd² **33.** 44,509.5 ft² **35.** 7.07 m³
37. Answers may vary. Sample: Yes, cut off 5 in. by 5 in. corners.

Chapter 11   pp. 772–773

3. −6 **5.** 5 **7.** 3 **9.** 10 **11.** rational
15. irrational **17.** 7.5 yd **19.** 5.7 **21.** 10.4
23. $\left(\frac{1}{2}, -\frac{3}{2}\right)$ **25.** $x = 32\sqrt{2}$ cm   45.3 cm,
$y = 32$ cm **27.** $x = 15$ mi, $y = 15\sqrt{2}$ mi   21.2 mi
29. 11.4301 **33.** 0.4226 **39.** 37.7 mi
41. No; $10^2 + 24^2 \neq 29^2$ **43.** 21.5 m
45. $5\sqrt{3}$ in., 10 in. **47.** 314.4 ft

Chapter 12   pp. 774–775

1. range = 3

Number	Frequency
20	2
21	5
22	2
23	1

3.
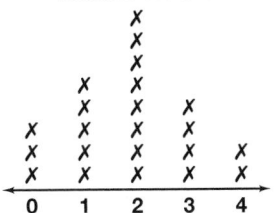

7. $\frac{4}{121}$ **9.** 3
13. 120 **15.** $\frac{1}{6}$

17.

19.
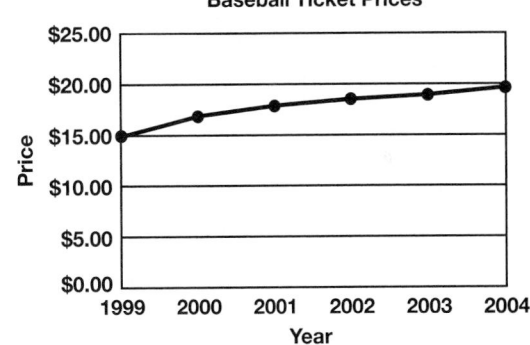

21.

Average Major League Baseball Ticket Prices

23. independent, $\frac{1}{4}$ **25.** 20 possibilities **27.** $\frac{1}{12}$
29. 450 students

1. 20, 0, −20; start with 100 and add −20 repeatedly **5.** −3,125, 15,625, −78,125; start with −5 and multiply by −5 repeatedly.

9.

13.

15.

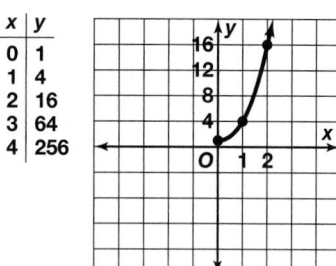

x	y
0	1
1	4
2	16
3	64
4	256

17.

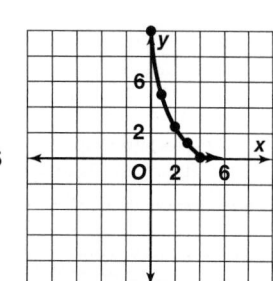

x	y
0	10
1	5
2	2.5
3	1.25
4	0.625

19. trinomial **23.** monomial **27.** $7y - 2$
31. $6x^2 + 5x - 12$ **35.** $10x^3 + 12x$
39. $2y^2 + 16y + 24$ **43.** $2(a^2b - 2a + 3b)$
45. $x(6y + 2 + 3xy)$ **47.** 25, 30, 35 **49.** 6 ft
51.

Number of Cells in a Bacteria Culture

53. 144 m^2
55. $(8x^2 + 48x)$ m^2
57. $(50.24c^2 - 50.24c + 12.56)$ ft^2

Skills Handbook

PAGE 779 1. > **3.** > **11.** 3,347; 3,474; 3,734; 3,747; 3,774 **13.** 30,256,403; 30,265,403; 32,056,403; 302,056,403

PAGE 780 3. 670 **5.** 7,030 **15.** 82,000 **17.** 35,000 **23.** 71,230,000 **25.** 400,000

PAGE 781 17. 9,214 **19.** 492

PAGE 782 37. 26 R 8 **39.** 7 R 32

PAGE 783 1. 9 hundred-thousandths **3.** 5 hundredths **9.** 0.000008 **11.** 0.013 **15.** eleven hundred-thousandths **17.** twelve thousandths

PAGE 784 1. < **3.** > **13.** 0.23, 0.231, 2.31, 3.21, 23.1 **15.** 0.002, 0.02, 0.22, 0.222, 2.22

PAGE 785 1. 105,000 **5.** 4,312,000 **7.** 3 **9.** 101 **11.** 82.0 **13.** 20.4 **17.** 96.40 **19.** 4.23 **33.** 2.58 **35.** 19

PAGE 786 41. 12.403 **43.** 747.1109

PAGE 787 9. 1.1424 **11.** 2.07828

PAGE 788 31. 0.01812 **33.** 0.007

PAGE 789 23. 2.551 **25.** 3.9

PAGE 790 15. 0.47 **17.** 0.236

PAGE 791 15. 16 **17.** 44

PAGE 792 1. 0.046 **3.** 0.075

PAGE 793 9. 3 **11.** 16 **17.** $\frac{5}{6}$ **19.** $\frac{3}{4}$

PAGE 794 9. $3\frac{2}{5}$ **11.** $4\frac{1}{4}$ **39.** $\frac{24}{7}$ **41.** $\frac{31}{10}$

PAGE 795 7. $\frac{3}{8}$ **9.** $\frac{3}{5}$

PAGE 796 13. $7\frac{1}{2}$ **15.** $43\frac{3}{4}$ **19.** $\frac{7}{8}$ **21.** $1\frac{3}{8}$

PAGE 797 5. 3 **7.** 12 **11.** < **15.** >

Index

of polynomial, 724
prime factorization, 190–192, 228, 236–237
scale, 308

Factor tree, 191

Fahrenheit-Celsius formula, 383

Fair game, 676

Favorable outcomes, 309

Fibonacci sequence, 700

Flip (reflection), 508, 519

FOIL method, 736

Formulas
for acceleration, 206
for area, 382, 802
for area of circle, 538, 540, 580
for area of parallelogram, 526, 538
for area of rectangle, 526, 540
for area of trapezoid, 534–535
for compound interest, 388, 395
defined, 145, 172
for distance, 145, 380, 383, 598–599, 628
Einstein's, 366
for lateral area of prism, 552
for midpoint of a segment, 600, 628
for perimeter, 146, 172, 382, 802
problem solving with, 383
reading, 557
for simple interest, 386, 395
solving for a given variable, 382
for surface area of cylinder, 553, 560, 580
for surface area of prism, 552, 580
transforming, 382–383, 395
using, 145–146
for volume of cone, 572, 581
for volume of cylinder, 581
for volume of prism, 581
for volume of pyramid, 573, 581
for volume of sphere, 573, 581

45°-45°-90° triangles, 608–609, 629

Four-step plan. *See* Problem-Solving Strategies

Fraction(s). *See also* Decimals; Percent; Rational numbers
adding, 247–248, 268, 284, 795
applying, 288–289
choosing to solve a problem, 277
comparing, 237–238
denominator of. *See* Denominator
dividing, 254, 284, 796
equivalent, 196, 205, 228
estimating with, 246
evaluating, 206
improper, 248, 284, 794
least common denominator (LCD) of, 238, 283
mixed numbers and, 246, 248, 284
modeling, 196, 247, 252
multiplying, 252–253, 272–273, 284, 796
numerator of, 196–197, 206, 246, 252–254
ordering, 238, 242
reciprocal of, 254, 284
rounding, 246

simplest form of, 196–197, 228
simplifying, 196–197, 206, 247, 248, 253, 272
solving equations with, 268–269, 272–273, 285, 361–362, 393
subtracting, 247–248, 268, 284, 795
with unlike denominators, 248
writing as decimals, 241–242
writing as percents, 315
writing decimals as, 243
writing percents as, 314

Fraction bar, 9, 46, 206, 216

Frequency tables, 636, 637, 683, 687

Front-end estimate, 130, 131, 171, 218

Function(s). *See also* Equations; Graph(s)
absolute value, 703, 738
cubing, 704
defined, 404, 453
domain of, 404, 405, 453
graphing, 405–406, 702–703, 711
identifying, 404–405
linear, 410, 411, 415–417, 422–423
nonlinear, 702–703, 711
quadratic, 702–703, 738
range of, 404, 405, 453
trigonometric. *See* Trigonometric ratios
vertical-line test for, 405–406

Function notation, 422

Function rules, 422–423, 454

G

Games
fair, 676
probability in, 662
schedules for, 482

GCF (greatest common factor), 191–192, 228

Geometric figures, naming, 463

Geometric formulas, table of, 802. *See also* Formulas

Geometric sequences, 697–698, 737

Geometry. *See also* Linear functions
angles. *See* Angle(s)
area. *See* Area
base. *See* Base
circle. *See* Circle(s)
cone. *See* Cones
constructions, 495–497
coordinate geometry, 528
coordinate plane. *See* Coordinate plane
coordinates. *See* Coordinate(s)
cylinder. *See* Cylinders
dilations, 308, 506
early, 631
exercises that use, 42, 53, 55, 100, 147, 149, 189, 203, 204, 211, 240, 253, 265, 279, 280, 281, 301, 313, 340, 360, 365, 368, 408, 424, 442, 443, 482, 506, 591, 596, 601, 602, 612, 618, 653, 676, 680, 684, 685, 704, 714, 715, 721, 722, 726, 729, 734, 735
face, 545, 551, 558

flip (reflection), 508, 519
formulas. *See* Formulas
height. *See* Height
line. *See* Line(s)
net. *See* Net
parallelogram. *See* Parallelograms
perimeter. *See* Perimeter
pi (π), 490
prism. *See* Prisms
pyramids. *See* Pyramids
radius. *See* Radius
rectangle. *See* Rectangles
reflection, 508, 519
right triangle. *See* Right triangles
rotations, 511–512, 519
similar figures. *See* Similar figures
similarity. *See* Similarity
slide. *See* Translations
solid, 544, 576–577. *See also* Space figures
space figure. *See* Space figures
square. *See* Square(s)
surface area. *See* Surface area (S.A.)
symbols. *See* Symbols
symmetry, 507–508, 512
three-dimensional figure. *See* Space figures
transformations, 308, 501–502, 519
triangle. *See* Triangles
turn (rotation), 511–512, 519
vertex. *See* Vertex
volume. *See* Volume

Golden ratio, 632–633

Golden rectangle, 632–633

Gram (g), 158, 159

Graph(s)
of absolute value functions, 703
Activity Lab, 51, 57, 102–103, 402–403, 421, 451, 458–459, 655–656
bar, 51, 94, 103, 139, 648, 650, 655–656
choosing the best, 655–656
circle, 491–492, 655–656
coordinates. *See* Coordinate(s); Coordinate plane
of data, 94, 102–103, 139, 491–492, 648–650, 655–656, 702
of equations with two variables, 410–411
of exponential decay, 708, 738
of exponential growth, 708, 738
of functions, 405–406, 702–703, 711
of inequalities, 104–105, 121, 377, 379, 380, 451
line, 51, 102, 410–411, 421, 648–650, 655–656
of linear equations, 410–411, 417, 421, 454
of linear functions, 410, 411
of linear inequalities, 445–447, 455
misleading, 648, 649, 650, 688
of negative numbers, 19
of nonlinear functions, 702–703, 711
of points, 53
in problem solving, 434–435, 455, 703
of quadratic functions, 702–703
of rational numbers, 206
reading, 51, 433

Index

modeling, 23, 24–25, 30–31, 75
multiplying, 44–45, 47, 61, 75
negative, 18, 45, 46
on number line, 44–45, 47
opposite, 24
order of operations and, 26
ordering, 18–19
positive, 18, 45, 46
as rational numbers, 205
rules to add, 25–26
rules to multiply, 45
significant digits and, 164, 165
signs of, 25, 45, 46, 60, 61
subtracting, 30–31, 60
writing, 18–19

Interdisciplinary Connections
algebra, 101, 224, 406, 437, 466, 472, 473, 476, 477, 478, 488, 591, 607, 734
architecture, 306, 307, 390, 418, 464, 477, 562, 607
art, 364
astronomy, 91, 150, 152, 223, 274, 332, 413, 624
biology, 100, 152, 161, 274, 314, 340, 539, 642, 644, 646, 707, 709
botany, 512, 663, 664
earth science, 26, 162
economics, 331, 384
engineering, 113, 417, 437, 561, 628
geography, 27, 55, 132, 140, 160, 161, 174, 245, 260, 306, 562, 597, 668
geometry, 42, 53, 55, 100, 147, 149, 189, 203, 204, 211, 240, 253, 265, 279, 280, 281, 301, 313, 340, 360, 365, 368, 408, 424, 442, 443, 506, 591, 596, 601, 602, 612, 618, 653, 676, 680, 684, 685, 704, 714, 715, 721, 722, 726, 729, 734, 735
history, 240, 260
language arts, 85, 189, 413
marine biology, 16, 162, 275
medical science, 673
meteorology, 31, 33, 43, 47, 98, 101, 116, 133, 171, 250, 623, 665
natural science, 513
physics, 91, 93, 368, 424, 437, 574
science, 5, 39, 187, 188, 207, 295, 424
social studies, 643
weather, 31, 33, 43, 47, 98, 101, 116, 133, 171, 250, 623, 665
zoology, 162, 223, 332

Interest
compound, 387–388, 395
on credit cards, 391
defined, 386
simple, 386–387, 395

Interest period, 387

Interest rate, 386, 395

Interior angles, alternate, 470, 471, 518

Internet Links. *See* Active Math Online; Homework Video Tutor; Lesson Quiz Online; Video Tutor Help Online; Vocabulary Quiz Online

Intersecting lines, 463

Intersection of two circles, 195

Inverse, additive, 24

Inverse operations, 88–90, 94–95, 121, 173

Inverse Properties
Additive, 24, 803
Multiplicative, 803

Irrational numbers, 589, 627

Irregular figures, area of, 10, 12, 540

Isometric dot paper, 544

Isometric view, 544

Isosceles triangle, 474

J

Justifying steps. *See* Reasoning

K

Kilogram (kg), 158, 159
Kilometer (km), 158, 159

L

Lateral area (L.A.)
of cylinder, 550, 553, 580
defined, 552, 580
of prism, 552
of pyramid, 558, 581

Lateral faces or surfaces, 545, 552

Latitude, 53

LCD (least common denominator), 238, 283

LCM (least common multiple), 236–237, 283, 362

Leaf, 646

Least common denominator (LCD), 238, 283

Least common multiple (LCM), 236–237, 283, 362

Legs, of right triangle, 592, 628, 629

Length
approximate, 593
customary units of, 257
of hypotenuse, 609, 610, 616, 628, 629
measures of, 798
metric units of, 158, 159
rafter, 594
of similar figures, 303, 304, 604–605, 614, 628
in 30°-60°-90° triangles, 610

Lesson Quiz Online, 7, 11, 17, 21, 27, 33, 39, 43, 49, 55, 71, 77, 81, 85, 91, 97, 101, 107, 111, 115, 133, 137, 143, 147, 153, 157, 163, 169, 183, 189, 193, 199, 203, 207, 211, 217, 223, 239, 245, 251, 255, 259, 265, 271, 275, 281, 295, 301, 307, 313, 317, 323, 327, 331, 335, 339, 355, 359, 365, 369, 373, 379, 385, 389, 407, 413, 419, 425, 431, 437, 443, 449, 467, 473, 477, 483, 487, 493, 499, 505, 509, 513, 529, 537, 543, 549, 555, 561, 565, 571, 575, 591, 595, 601, 607, 611, 617, 623, 639, 645, 653, 661, 669, 675, 679, 685, 699, 703, 709, 715, 721, 725

Like denominators, 247, 795

Like terms
aligning, 719

combining, 79, 356–357, 393, 718
defined, 78

Line(s). *See also* Linear equations; Linear inequalities; Systems of linear equations
defined, 462, 517
drawing, 464
graphing, 410–411, 421
horizon, 548
intersecting, 463
parallel, 463, 464, 470–471
perpendicular, 496
of reflection, 508
of sight, 620–621
skewing, 463
slope of, 415–417, 454
of symmetry, 507
trend, 429, 434–435
vanishing, 548
y-intercept of, 417

Line graph, 51, 102, 410–411, 421, 648–650, 655–656

Line plot, 636, 687

Linear equations
defined, 410, 454
graphing, 410–411, 417, 421, 454
systems of, 439–441, 455

Linear functions, 415–417
graphing, 410, 411
rules for, 422–423, 454

Linear inequalities. *See also* Inequality(ies)
defined, 445
graphing, 445–447, 455
systems of, 447, 455

Liter (L), 158, 159

Longitude, 53

***Look for a Pattern* problem-solving strategy,** 40–41, 61

Lowest (least) common denominator, 238, 283

M

Make a Conjecture, 185

***Make a Model* problem-solving strategy,** 568–569, 581

***Make a Table* problem-solving strategy,** 338–339, 345

Manipulatives. *See also* Algebra tiles; Calculator; Graphing calculator; Mathematical modeling
centimeter ruler, 164, 262
coins, 311, 659, 672, 673, 674
compass, 495, 496, 497, 612
graph paper, 544, 592
grid paper, 516, 531
isometric dot paper, 544
marbles, 665
number cubes, 309–310, 636, 661, 663, 665, 672, 676
protractor, 468
ruler, 495
straightedge, 495, 612
tape measure, 164, 262, 304

Mapping, of a figure, 502

Mapping diagram, 404

Markup, 151, 333, 345

Mass, 798
customary units of, 257
metric units of, 158, 159

Math at Work
air-traffic controller, 597
caterer, 341
choreographer, 467
city planner, 375
geophysicist, 212
movie-camera operator, 420
nurse, 101
pharmacist, 530
systems analyst, 705
technical artist, 261
weaver, 29
wildlife statistician, 671
woodworker, 169

MATH feature, of graphing calculator, 591

Math Strategies in Action, 40, 98, 166, 201, 263, 338, 366, 434, 480, 568, 604, 682, 732

Math symbols, 799

Mathematical modeling. *See also* Simulations
adding fractions, 247
adding integers, 24–25
area, 181, 723
of equations, 86–87, 120, 352, 356, 371
exercises that use, 7, 27, 32, 465, 720
expressions, 7, 24, 27, 30–31, 75, 79, 86–87, 352, 371
of fractions, 196, 247, 252
of integers, 23
multiplying binomials, 727, 739
multiplying fractions, 252
multiplying integers, 75
of multi-step equations, 356
nets, 546, 551–553
number line. *See* Number line
percents, 319–320, 322
as problem-solving strategy, 568–569, 581
relating graphs to events, 402–403
scale models, 304, 344
solving equations with, 86–87, 371
subtracting integers, 30–31
of trinomials, 731
of two-step equations, 352
writing a proportion, 319

Mean
on calculator, 144
defined, 139, 172
finding, 139–141
outlier effect on, 140, 141
on stem-and-leaf plot, 646

Measurement. *See also* Metric system
of angles, 468, 470, 619
customary units of, 257–258, 285, 296–297
exercises that use, 5, 6, 135, 157, 360, 424, 426, 444, 482, 484, 639
historical, 260

indirect, 304, 305, 604, 606, 621, 628
metric units of, 158, 159, 173
precise, 164–165
with scientific notation, 222
significant digits in, 164–165

Measures of central tendency, 139–141, 172. *See also* Mean; Median; Mode

Median
on calculator, 144
defined, 139, 172
finding, 139–141
on stem-and-leaf plot, 646, 647

Mental Math, 8, 27, 33, 47, 54, 69, 70, 71, 72, 74, 76, 77, 81, 92, 96, 97, 120, 152, 160, 161, 162, 173, 189, 239, 244, 250, 255, 300, 327, 331, 354, 364, 374, 736

Meter (m), 158, 159

Metric system, 158–160, 173
converting metric units, 159–160, 296–297
defined, 173
estimating with, 159
identifying appropriate measures, 158–159
prefixes in, 159
table of, 798
units of measure in, 158, 159, 173

Midpoint, 600, 628

Milligram (mg), 158, 159

Milliliter (mL), 158, 159

Millimeter (mm), 158, 159

Misleading graphs, 648, 649, 650, 688

Mixed numbers
adding, 248–249, 284
changing to improper fractions, 248, 284
dividing, 254
estimating with, 246
multiplying, 246, 253, 273
solving equations with, 273, 281, 284
subtracting, 248–249, 284
writing decimals as, 243
writing percents as, 314

Mixed Review, 7, 12, 17, 22, 29, 34, 39, 43, 49, 56, 72, 77, 81, 85, 92, 97, 101, 107, 111, 116, 133, 137, 143, 148, 153, 157, 163, 169, 183, 189, 194, 199, 204, 208, 212, 218, 224, 240, 245, 251, 256, 261, 266, 271, 276, 281, 295, 302, 307, 313, 318, 323, 327, 332, 336, 341, 355, 360, 365, 369, 375, 380, 385, 390, 408, 413, 420, 426, 432, 437, 444, 450, 467, 473, 478, 483, 488, 494, 499, 505, 510, 514, 530, 537, 543, 549, 556, 562, 566, 571, 575, 591, 597, 602, 607, 612, 618, 624, 639, 645, 653, 661, 666, 671, 676, 680, 685, 700, 705, 710, 715, 722, 726, 730, 735

Mode
defined, 139, 172
finding, 139–141
identifying, 140
on stem-and-leaf plot, 646, 647

Modeling. *See* Mathematical modeling; Simulations

Monomials
defined, 712, 738
multiplying polynomials by, 723–724, 739

More Than One Way, 10, 114, 131, 192, 249, 334, 363, 441, 471, 560, 616, 674, 728

Multiple(s)
common, 236, 283
defined, 236, 283
least common (LCM), 236–237, 283, 362

Multiple choice examples, 9, 45, 74, 146, 155, 220, 248, 273, 293, 299, 383, 387, 422, 427, 492, 564, 594, 600, 659, 723

Multiple choice exercises, 7, 11, 12, 17, 21, 22, 27, 28–29, 33, 34, 39, 43, 49, 54, 56, 72, 77, 81, 85, 91, 96, 97, 101, 107, 111, 115, 116, 123, 133, 137, 143, 147, 148, 153, 157, 161, 169, 183, 189, 193, 194, 199, 203, 204, 207, 208, 212, 218, 223, 224, 231, 239, 240, 245, 251, 256, 266, 271, 275, 281, 295, 302, 307, 313, 318, 327, 332, 336, 341, 347, 355, 359, 360, 369, 373, 375, 379, 380, 385, 389, 390, 408, 413, 422, 425, 426, 431, 432, 437, 443, 449, 450, 457, 467, 473, 477, 478, 483, 486, 488, 493, 499, 505, 509, 510, 514, 529, 537, 542, 547, 549, 550, 555, 556, 561, 562, 565, 566, 571, 578, 591, 597, 607, 612, 618, 624, 639, 645, 653, 656, 661, 666, 671, 675, 679–680, 685, 691, 699, 700, 705, 709, 715, 722, 725, 726, 729, 730, 735, 741–743, 779

Multiplication
algebra tiles for, 75, 723, 727, 739
Associative Property of, 68, 119, 186, 278, 803
of binomials, 727–728, 736
Commutative Property of, 68, 119, 186, 210, 278, 803
of decimals, 155, 787
Distributive Property of, 73–74, 723, 727
estimating products, 134, 172
exponents and, 209–210, 229
of fractions, 252–253, 272–273, 284, 796
Identity Property of, 69, 78, 803
of integers, 44–45, 47, 61, 75
Inverse Property of, 803
mental math with, 70
of mixed numbers, 246, 253, 273
order of operations and, 8–10
of polynomials by monomials, 723–724, 739
by powers of ten, 790
of powers with same base, 209–210, 220, 229
of rational numbers, 252–253
by a reciprocal, 272, 273, 284, 361

repeated, 186–187
with scientific notation, 222
solving equations with, 95, 155, 272–273
solving inequalities with, 113–114, 121, 377–378
solving proportions with, 298–299
of square roots, 608
symbols for, 45
of whole numbers, 781
zeros in product, 788

Multiplication Counting Principle, 658, 659, 667, 688

Multiplication Property
of Equality, 95, 362, 803
of Inequality, 113, 803

Multiplicative identity, 69

Multi-step equations
combining like terms in, 356–357, 393
Distributive Property for, 358
finding consecutive integers in, 357
least common multiple and, 362
modeling, 356
solving with decimals, 362–363, 393
solving with fractions, 361–362, 393

N

Negative coefficients, 353
Negative correlation, 429
Negative exponents, 216, 803
Negative integers, 18, 45, 46
Negative numbers, 18, 19
Negative reciprocal, 273
Negative sign, 279
Negative slope, 429
Negative trend, 429, 444

Net
defined, 546, 580
finding surface area using, 551
modeling, 546, 551–553
naming space figures from, 546

New Vocabulary, 4, 8, 14, 18, 35, 52, 68, 73, 78, 82, 88, 134, 139, 145, 180, 186, 190, 196, 205, 219, 236, 241, 252, 257, 292, 298, 303, 309, 314, 324, 329, 333, 356, 386, 404, 409, 415, 422, 427, 434, 439, 445, 462, 469, 474, 484, 490, 495, 501, 507, 511, 526, 533, 545, 551, 558, 563, 588, 592, 598, 614, 620, 636, 641, 657, 662, 667, 673, 677, 696, 702, 712

No correlation, 429

Nonlinear functions, graphing, 702–703, 711

Nonzero digits (1–9), 164

Notation
arrow, 502
combination, 668–669
function, 422
permutation, 667–668
prime, 501
scientific, 219–222, 225, 229
standard, 220–221

Number(s). *See also* Integers; Mixed numbers
classifying, 589
compatible, 135, 172
composite, 190, 228
even, 180
factoring, 181, 227
irrational, 589, 627
negative, 18–19
odd, 180
ordering, 221, 779
positive, 18–19
prime, 190–191, 228
properties of, 68–70
random, 677, 681
rational, 205, 229, 236–238, 252–253, 627. *See also* Fraction(s)
real, 589
rounding. *See* Rounding
whole. *See* Whole numbers

Number line
absolute value on, 19
adding integers, 25, 44
box-and-whisker plots on, 641–643, 688
comparing on, 18–19, 237–238
graphing inequalities on, 104–105, 377, 379, 380
graphing integers on, 18–19
horizontal and vertical, 52
multiplying integers on, 44–45, 47
opposites on, 641–643
rational numbers on, 206
repeated addition on, 44

Number patterns, 35, 36, 40–41, 61

Number Sense, 12, 42, 48, 87, 107, 135, 136, 157, 160, 162, 244, 245, 259, 270, 274, 280, 340, 357, 359, 360, 368, 369, 373, 379, 396, 399, 499, 514, 541, 606

Number square, 34

Number theory, 100
divisibility tests and, 180–181
factors and common factors in, 191, 227
multiples and common multiples in, 236–237, 283
prime and composite numbers in, 190–191, 228

Numerator, 206
comparing to denominator, 246
multiplying and dividing, 252–254
simplest form of, 196–197

Numerical expressions, 4–5, 73–74

O

Oblique cylinder, 551
Oblique prism, 551
Obtuse angle, 468, 496
Obtuse triangle, 474
Octagons, 476, 480
Odd number, 180
Odds, 311, 344
One-point perspective, 548

One-step inequalities
solving by adding, 109
solving by dividing, 112–113, 121
solving by multiplying, 113–114, 121
solving by subtracting, 108–109

Online Active Math. *See* Active Math Online

Online Homework Help. *See* Homework Video Tutor

Open-Ended, 12, 20, 21, 32, 34, 48, 49, 56, 80, 87, 92, 97, 116, 122, 124, 133, 183, 193, 198, 199, 207, 211, 217, 256, 276, 306, 312, 318, 323, 373, 389, 408, 418, 443, 449, 456, 477, 488, 499, 505, 515, 520, 529, 536, 542, 547, 555, 571, 582, 602, 645, 661, 676, 679, 704, 711, 714, 725, 730, 738, 740

Open sentence, 82, 120

Operations. *See also* Order of operations
with fractions, 236–285
undoing, 352

Opposite(s)
addition of, 24
defined, 19, 60
on number line, 641–643

Opposite integers, 24

Order of operations
in addition, 8–10, 26, 59
in division, 8–10, 46
with exponents, 187
grouping symbols, 9–10
in multiplication, 8–10
in subtraction, 8–19
using, 8–9, 26, 59, 60

Ordered pair, 52, 57, 61, 404, 703

Ordering
decimals, 242, 784
exponents, 221, 229
fractions, 238, 242
integers, 18–19
numbers, 221, 779
whole numbers, 2, 779

Origin, 52, 511

Outcomes
counting, 309–311, 657–659
defined, 309, 344
exploring possible, 657
favorable, 309
in sample space, 658

Outlier
defined, 140, 172
effect on mean, 140, 141

P

Pairs of angles, 469–471
Parabolas, 702–703, 738
Parallel lines, 463, 464, 470–471

Parallelograms
altitude of, 527
area of, 526–527, 532, 538, 579
defined, 475
formula for, 802
similar, 303

Index

simulating problems, 672–674, 681, 682–683

theoretical, 658–659, 688

tree diagrams in, 657, 659

Problem(s)

simplifying, 166–167, 173

simulating, 672–674, 681, 682–683

solving a simpler problem, 201–202, 228

Problem Solving

choosing fractions or decimals for, 277

with formulas, 383

Guided, 10, 13, 93, 149, 200, 267, 337, 370, 433, 489, 557, 603, 625, 654, 706

with trigonometric ratios, 615–616

with two-step equations, 353, 394

using proportions, 299, 604–605, 628

Problem-Solving Hints, 15, 75, 130, 205, 209, 210, 253, 377, 378, 423, 424, 464, 604, 724

Problem-Solving Strategies

Act It Out, 166–167, 173

Draw a Diagram, 480–481, 519

Guess, Check, Revise, 98–99, 121

Look for a Pattern, 40–41, 61

Make a Model, 568–569, 581

Make a Table, 338–339, 345

Simulate the Problem, 682–683

Solve a Simpler Problem, 201–202, 228

Solve by Graphing, 434–435, 455, 703

Use Multiple Strategies, 732–733, 739

Work Backward, 263–264, 285

Write a Proportion, 604–605, 628

Write an Equation, 366–367, 394

Products. *See also* Multiplication

cross, 298, 299, 803

estimating, 134, 172

finding, 94–95

of integers with different signs, 45

of integers with same sign, 45

of negative and positive integers, 45

powers of, 278–279

raising to a power, 278, 285

simplifying, 278, 724, 727–728

writing polynomials as, 724

zeros in, 788

Proof

area of parallelogram, 527

area of trapezoid, 535

area of triangle, 533

distance formula, 598

dividing powers with same base, 214

finding a power of a power, 210

formula for area of circle, 538

45°-45°-90° triangle, 608

midpoint formula, 600

multiplying powers with same base, 209

negative exponents, 216

Pythagorean Theorem, 592

raising a quotient to a power, 279

rule for raising a product to a power, 278

surface area of cone, 559

surface area of cylinder, 553

surface area of prism, 552

surface area of pyramid, 558

surface area of sphere, 559

30°-60°-90° triangles, 610

volume of cone, 572

volume of cylinder, 564

volume of prism, 563–564, 581, 780

volume of pyramid, 572, 573

volume of sphere, 573

zero as exponent, 215

Properties

Addition Property of Equality, 90, 151, 803

Addition Property of Inequality, 109, 803

Associative Property of Addition, 68, 119, 718, 803

Associative Property of Additive Inverse, 803

Associative Property of Multiplication, 68, 119, 186, 278, 803

closure, 803

Commutative Property of Addition, 68, 119, 716, 718, 803

Commutative Property of Multiplication, 68, 119, 186, 210, 278, 803

Comparison Property of Inequality, 803

cross product, 803

density, 295, 803

Distributive. *See* Distributive Property

Division Property of Equality, 94, 803

Division Property of Inequality, 112, 803

identifying, 68–69

Identity Property of Addition, 69, 803

Identity Property of Multiplication, 69, 78, 803

Inverse Property of Addition and Multiplication, 24, 803

Multiplication Property of Equality, 95, 362, 803

Multiplication Property of Inequality, 113, 803

negative exponent, 216, 803

of numbers, 68–70

quotient of powers, 803

Reflexive Property of Equality, 803

solving equations with, 352–353

Substitution Property of Equality, 803

Subtraction Property of Equality, 88, 803

Subtraction Property of Inequality, 108–109, 803

Symmetric Property of Equality, 803

Symmetric Property of Inequality, 803

Transitive Property of Equality, 803

Transitive Property of Inequality, 803

zero exponent, 803

zero product, 803

Proportional Relationships, 414

Proportions

cross products, 298, 299

defined, 298, 343

estimating, 300

finding measures of central angles, 491–492

finding part of a whole, 319

finding percent, 319–320

finding whole amount, 320–321, 324

indirect measurement and, 304, 604, 628

modeling, 319

multiplying to solve, 298–299

as problem-solving strategy, 299, 604–605, 628

in scale drawings, 304, 344

in similar figures, 303, 304, 344, 604–605

solving, 298, 319

testing for, 299

Protractor, 468

Pyramids

base of, 546

defined, 545

height of, 572, 573

hexagonal, 546

lateral area of, 558, 581

net of, 546

regular, 558

slant height of, 558, 581

square, 558, 573, 580

surface area of, 558, 581, 802

volume of, 572, 573, 581, 802

Pythagoras, 631

Pythagorean Theorem, 592–594

converse of, 594

finding distance with, 598–599

with special right triangles, 592–594, 608–610, 628

statement of, 592

using, 593–594, 628

Pythagorean triple, 596

Q

Quadrant, 52–53, 61

Quadratic functions, 702–703, 738

Quadrilaterals, 475, 518

Quartiles, 641, 688

Quick Check. *See* Assessment; Instant Check System

Quotients. *See also* Division

estimating, 135, 172

of integers with different signs, 46

of integers with same sign, 46

of negative and positive integers, 46

patterns in, 256

powers of, 279

raising to a power, 279, 285

R

Radical symbol, 588

Radius

of circle, 490

of cone, 559, 572

of cylinder, 564

defined, 490

of sphere, 560, 573

Rafter length, 594

RandInt feature, of graphing calculator, 681

Random numbers, 677, 681

Random samples, 677, 689

Range
    of data, 637, 687
    defined, 139, 687
    finding, 139
    of function, 404, 405, 453
    of relation, 404, 405, 453

Rates
    converting, 293
    defined, 293, 343
    finding, 293
    unit, 293, 343

Ratio
    applying, 632–633
    of circumference to diameter,
      490–491
    common, 697–698, 737
    cosine, 614–615, 629
    defined, 292, 343
    golden, 632–633
    proportions and, 298–299
    right triangles, 614–616, 629
    scales and scale factors, 304
    similarity and, 576, 577
    simplest form of, 292
    sine, 614–616, 629
    tangent, 614–615, 629
    trigonometric, 614–616, 629, 801
    writing, 292

Rational numbers, 236–238. *See also*
      Decimals; Fraction(s); Mixed
      numbers; Whole numbers
    absolute value of, 208
    comparing, 205
    defined, 205, 229
    dividing, 254, 284
    evaluating fractions containing
      variables, 206
    graphing, 206
    identifying, 205, 627
    integers as, 205
    multiplying, 252–253
    simplest form of, 196–197, 228
    solving equations with, 268–269

Ray, 462, 468, 517

Reading Comprehension, 63, 175, 226,
    287, 397, 521, 631

Real numbers, 589

Real-World Connections. *See also*
      Interdisciplinary Connections;
      Math at Work
    academic competitions, 238
    acceleration, 206
    account balances, 32
    aeronautics, 624
    amusement parks, 106
    aviation, 275, 373
    baking, 624
    ballet, 611
    banking, 322, 340, 408, 726
    baseball, 301, 609, 638
    basketball, 357, 560, 682
    batting averages, 155, 156, 157
    beach gear, 335
    bicycling, 372
    bird watching, 623, 625

birdhouses, 360
boat building, 274
boat races, 207
bone scans, 708
bookshelf, 273
bookstore, 194
borrowing, 380, 390
budgeting, 110, 115, 368, 385, 491
business, 436, 437
can lids, 542
car rental, 482
car sales, 152
carbon dating, 744–745
carpentry, 262, 270, 594, 595
cases, 15
cell phones, 362, 374, 398–399
charity, 722
checking accounts, 151, 152
chess, 502, 734
city planning, 466
city property, 725
climate, 428
clothing, 335
coin collections, 100, 396, 448
collections, 100, 133, 250, 359, 368,
    375, 396, 448
commissions, 325, 326, 378, 384, 396
commuting, 365
comparison shopping, 141
computers, 109, 111, 395, 651
concerts, 181
construction, 168, 255, 274, 354, 384,
    419, 476, 534, 556, 566
consumer issues, 241, 258, 542, 671
containers, 487
cooking, 336, 405, 541, 556
cost of living, 649
crafts, 250
creative writing, 327
culinary arts, 541
culture, 120
currency, 46, 100
cycling, 294
day care, 116
deep-sea exploration, 44
drill team, 182
earnings, 96, 115, 422
earthquakes, 217
education, 316, 427
elections, 168, 436
endangered animals, 450
environment, 271
Erie Canal, 535
exchange rates, 300
exercising, 699
family, 323
famous ships, 21
farming, 368
fencing, 122, 168
Ferris wheel, 522–523
finance, 28, 152, 173, 256, 302, 354,
    394, 432, 493
fireworks, 713
flooring, 611
food, 136, 270, 437
food service, 651
football, 25, 28, 584–585

footwear, 335
fundraising, 139, 607
furniture, 280
game schedules, 482
gardening, 71, 281, 723
gas mileage, 4, 137, 307
gift wrapping, 555
goat pen, 703
golf, 68
grades, 142, 317, 318
grocery shopping, 130, 183, 446
growth, 270
health, 89, 137, 198, 224
hiking, 97, 248, 260, 378, 595
hobbies, 732–733
home economics, 297
homework, 250, 255, 316
horses, 163
hot-air balloons, 617, 625
hummingbirds, 216
income, 84, 427, 449, 493
income tax, 397
indirect measurement, 304, 305, 604,
    606, 621
inductive reasoning, 44, 48, 466
information, 40
insects, 145, 232–233
interior design, 536
investing, 48, 388, 390
jobs, 12, 271
jogging, 735
kites, 442, 620, 626
knot tying, 163
landscaping, 529, 540, 596, 606
latitude and longitude, 53
lawn care, 265, 541, 549
life spans, 331
lifeguarding, 589
literature, 638, 670
lottery, 660
manufacturing, 156
maps, 304, 305, 317
marathon training, 85
markup, 151
measurement, 6, 135, 157, 222, 304,
    305, 360, 424, 426, 444, 482, 484,
    604, 606, 621
mechanics, 174
medical science, 673
meteorology, 31, 33, 43, 47, 98, 101,
    116, 133, 171, 250, 623, 665
model airplanes, 356
modeling, 7, 86, 87, 252, 465
money, 176–177, 424, 566
monograms, 658
Mount Rushmore, 409
moving vans, 366–367
music sales, 333
nautical miles, 299
navigation, 622, 623, 630, 715
number patterns, 35, 36
number sense, 12, 42
numbers in nature, 63
nutrition, 7, 105, 107, 143, 162, 355,
    430
oil spills, 199
Olympics, 644

online shopping, 15, 16
organization, 193
packaging, 465, 555, 568–569, 570, 574
painting, 555, 595, 734
pancake breakfast, 74
parades, 478, 526
party planning, 212
patterns, 33, 35, 36, 49, 92, 112, 408, 486
personal finance, 152, 256, 302, 432, 493
petroleum, 154, 199
pets, 80, 132, 315, 570, 734
photocopies, 300
photography, 134, 201–202, 379
physical fitness, 132, 142, 162, 494
plants, 574
pool design, 541
population, 168, 316, 322, 338–339, 340, 648, 678, 689, 700
postage, 156
prices, 684
probability, 317, 341, 355, 426, 444
profit, 323
projection, 305
publishing, 570
purchasing, 7, 15, 16, 90, 300, 322
quality control, 301, 678, 679, 685
quilting, 134, 288–289, 486, 596
ramps, 616, 617
reading, 270
recipes, 336, 556
recreation, 72, 334, 492, 541
recycling, 268, 275, 677
relay races, 100
remodeling, 244
renting, 384
repairs, 29
reptiles, 174
research, 348
retail delivery, 482
retail sales, 143, 333
rock climbing, 81
routes, 204
royalties, 325, 326
running, 152, 697, 735
salaries, 735
sales, 76, 98–99, 107, 143, 152, 313, 333, 335, 340, 364, 420, 431, 483
sales tax, 323, 380
savings, 42, 96, 100, 354, 386, 389, 700
scale drawings, 317
scatter plots, 427
schedules, 239
school, 173, 715
school coaches, 195
school supplies, 70, 121
scores, 32
scuba diving, 83
seafood, 270
seating arrangements, 168, 193
sewing, 407
shipping, 536
shopping, 15, 16, 100, 110, 130, 141, 174, 183, 246, 335, 337, 446, 710
sightseeing, 380
snacks, 276, 574, 660
snails, 166–167
snow spheres, 573

soccer, 692–693
softball, 204, 261
solar system, 223
sports, 168, 236, 326, 426, 429, 528, 679, 714, 725
sports equipment, 136
statistics, 36, 94, 197, 224, 292, 430, 433, 436, 444, 520, 641, 652, 705
Statue of Liberty, 220
storage, 565
submarines, 56
surveying, 604–605, 612, 624
surveys, 292, 325, 636, 637, 680, 700
telephone service, 131, 362, 363, 374, 398–399
television programming, 519
temperature, 18, 22, 383
test scores, 169, 317, 318
theaters, 321
ticket sales, 76, 98–99, 107, 313, 340, 420, 431, 483
time, 263
track and field, 239, 259
transportation, 110, 265, 294
travel, 71, 72, 137, 145, 265, 297, 353, 379, 383, 394, 396, 666, 734
typesetting, 168
unit cost, 293
unit pricing, 136
urban planning, 10
utilities, 157
vacation, 295
video rental, 374
video sales, 335
viewing distance, 589, 590
vital statistics, 31
walking, 407
waste management, 330
water resources, 340
water slides, 60
waterskiing, 617
weather, 31, 33, 43, 47, 98, 101, 116, 133, 171, 250, 623, 665
weight, 84
white-water rafting, 364
wildlife, 60, 434–435
wings or wheels, 63
woodworking, 269
word processing, 16

Reasonableness
checking problem solutions for, 41, 99, 167, 202, 264, 356, 367
of estimation, 130, 135, 159, 246, 321
Reasoning, 8, 21, 23, 27, 28, 33, 39, 42, 48, 49, 56, 72, 79, 96, 106, 107, 110, 115, 116, 141, 153, 157, 182, 183, 185, 188, 189, 198, 207, 208, 211, 228, 233, 245, 247, 256, 260, 263, 275, 301, 306, 308, 310, 312, 317, 318, 323, 326, 327, 332, 336, 374, 390, 391, 403, 419, 427, 431, 449, 458, 472, 479, 487, 494, 509, 514, 515, 529, 531, 536, 537, 550, 555, 556, 562, 566, 570, 590, 595, 601, 611, 639, 645, 646, 649, 650, 657, 660, 662, 672, 678, 679, 684, 704, 710, 715, 721, 731.
See also Conjectures; Deductive reasoning; Error Analysis; Inductive reasoning

Reciprocals
defined, 254
multiplying by, 272, 273, 284, 361
negative, 273
Rectangles
area of, 10, 12, 73–74, 211, 253, 382, 526–527, 531, 534, 540
classifying, 475
defined, 475
formulas for, 802
golden, 632–633
modeling factors, 181, 190, 252
perimeter of, 531
Rectangular graph paper, 544
Rectangular prism, 563, 576, 802
Reductions (dilations), 308, 506
Reflection(s), 508, 519
Reflectional symmetry, 507–508
Reflexive Property of Equality, 803
Regular polygon
defined, 476
diagonals in, 480–481
Regular pyramid, 558
Relations
defined, 404, 453
graphing, 405–406
range of, 404, 405, 453
vertical-line test of, 405–406
Relatively prime numbers, 194
Repeated addition, 44
Repeated multiplication, 186–187
Repeating decimal, 242, 243, 245, 284
Research, 64, 348
Review. *See* Assessment; Mixed Review; Skills Handbook
Rhombus, 475
Right angle, 468
Right cylinder, 551
Right prism, 551
Right triangles, 474
angles of, 619
finding, 594
45°-45°-90° triangles, 608–609, 629
hypotenuse of, 592, 609, 610, 616, 628, 629
identifying, 594
legs of, 592, 628, 629
Pythagorean Theorem and, 592–594, 608–610, 628
ratios in, 614–615, 629
special, 608–610, 629
30°-60°-90° triangles, 609–610, 629
trigonometric ratios in, 614–616, 629, 801
Rise, 415, 594
Roots
cube, 591
square. *See* Square roots
Rotation(s)
angle of, 511
center of, 511
defined, 511, 519
graphing, 511–512

Index

Acknowledgments

Staff Credits

The people who made up the Pre-Algebra team—representing design services, editorial, editorial services, education technology, image services, marketing, market research, production services, publishing processes, and strategic markets—are listed below. Bold type denotes the core team members.

Leora Adler, **Scott Andrews,** Carolyn Artin, Peter Brooks, Judith D. Buice, Justin Collins, Patrick Culleton, Sheila DeFazio, Marian DeLollis, Kathleen Dempsey, Emily Ellen, Paul Frisoli, **Patti Fromkin,** Paul Gagnon, **Ellen Granter,** Jayne Holman, Karen Holtzman, Kate House, Lisa LaVallee, **Elizabeth Lehnertz,** James Lonergan, Catherine Maglio, **Cheryl Mahan,** Constance McCarty, Eve Melnechuk, Terri Mitchell, Janet Morris, Cindy Noftle, **Michael Oster,** Rashid Ross, Suzanne Schineller, Siri Schwartzman, Dennis Slattery, Nancy Smith, Lisa Smith-Ruvalcaba, Deborah Sommer, Kara Stokes, Mark Tricca, **Paula Vergith,** Merce Wilczek, **Joe Will,** Mathew Wilson, Mary Jane Wolfe, Helen Young

Additional Credits: J. J. Andrews, Sarah Aubry, Jonathan Kier, Lucinda O'Neill, Sara Shelton, Ted Smykal, Michael Torocsik

Cover Design

Brainworx Studio

Cover Image

Peacock, Charles Philip/Corbis; Ferris wheel, PhotoDisc, Inc./Getty Images, Inc.

Technical Illustration

Nesbitt Graphics, Inc.

Illustration

DLF Group: 619
Ortelius Design, Inc.: 31, 55, 147, 160, 222, 245, 248, 253, 304b, 353, 383, 535, 604t

Photo Research

Sharon Donahue

Photography

Picture Research: Toni Michaels
Front Matter: Page vii, Royal Tyrrell Museum of Palaeontology/ Alberta CommunityDevelopment; **viii,** Jose L. Palaez/Corbis; **ix,** Doug Armand/Getty Images, Inc.; **x,** Russell C. Hansen/Peter Arnold, Inc.; **xi,** Jason Hawkes/Getty Images, Inc.; **xii,** Renee Lynn/Getty Images, Inc.; **xiii,** Jose Carrillo /PhotoEdit; **xiv,** Joe Sohm/The Image Works; **xv,** Alfred Pasteka/Science Photo Library/Photo Researchers, Inc.; **xvi,** "rendering © dbox, inc. www.dbox.com"; **xvii,** Hideo Kurihara/ Getty Images, Inc.; **xviii,** Marilyn Kazmers/Peter Arnold, Inc.; **xix,** Bob Burch/Bruce Coleman, Inc.

Chapter One: Pages 2-3, Stephen Frink/Index Stock Imagery Inc.; **5,** Royal Tyrrell Museum of Palaeontology/Alberta Community Development; **6,** PhotoDisc, Inc./Getty Images, Inc.; **10 tl,** Minnesota Dept. of Natural Resources; **10 mr,** Richard Haynes; **10 bl,** Richard Haynes; **15,** Russ Lappa; **16,** Stuart Westmorland/Getty Images, Inc.; **26,** Albuquerque Seismological Lab, USGS; **29,** Patrick Somelet/DIAF/Corbis Stock Market; **31,** Sowers/Penn State University; **33,** Index Stock Imagery, Inc.; **40,** Michael Simpsonl/Getty Images, Inc.; **42 t,** PhotoDisc, Inc./Getty Images, Inc.; **42 b,** Russ Lappa; **44,** OAR/National Undersea Research Program (NURP); **53,** Tom Van Sant/Corbis; **64 tr,** Corbis; **64 bl,** Dorling Kindersley/ Charlestown Shipwreck Heritage Centre; **64 br,** EyeWire/Getty Images, Inc.; **65 tl,** AP/Wide World Photos; **65 r,** Stephen Frink/ Getty Images, Inc.

Chapter Two: Pages 66-67, Mark Richards/PhotoEdit; **70,** Russ Lappa; **72,** Mark Kelley/Stock Boston; **74,** Tony Freeman/ PhotoEdit; **83,** Chris Simpson/Getty Images, Inc.; **86 all,** Ken O'Donoghue; **88 both,** Anthony Neste; **89,** David R. Frazier Photolibrary; **98,** SuperStock, Inc.; **101,** Jose Luis Pelaez, Inc./ Corbis; **106 ml,** SuperStock, Inc.; **106 mr,** Spencer Grant/ PhotoEdit; **106 bl,** D. & J. Heaton/Stock Boston; **109,** Russ Lappa; **113,** Andrew Yates/Image Bank/Getty Images, Inc.; **114 both,** Richard Haynes; **124 t,** Dennis Galante/Getty Images, Inc.; **124 m,** Davies & Starr/Getty Images, Inc.; **124 bl,** Arthur Tilley/Getty Images, Inc.; **125 t,** www.Merlin-Net.com; **125 b,** Doug Menuez/Getty Images, Inc.

Chapter Three: Pages 126-127, Alan Goldsmith/Corbis; **130,** Russ Lappa; **131 both,** Richard Haynes; **134,** Russ Lappa; **135,** G. Cigolini/Image Bank/Getty Images, Inc.; **145,** Alvin Staffan/ Photo Researchers, Inc.; **150,** Corel Corp.; **152,** Kevin Schafer/ Peter Arnold, Inc.; **153,** DILBERT reprinted by permission of United Feature Syndicate, Inc.; **155,** Corbis; **160,** Ed Simpson/ Getty Images, Inc.; **162,** Doug Armand/Getty Images, Inc.; **164 both,** Russ Lappa; **166,** Dana White/PhotoEdit; **169,** Bob Daemmrich/Stock Boston; **176 tl,** Smithsonian Institution/ National Numismatic Collection/Douglas Mudd; **176 tr,** Prentice Hall; **176 ml,** Equity Management, Inc.; **176 mr,** U.S. Postal Service; **176 b,** Stamp from the private collection of Professor C.M. Lang, photography by Gary J. Shulfer, University of Wisconsin, Stevens Point; **176-177,** Eric Meola/Getty Images, Inc.; **177 tl,** Getty Images Inc.-Hulton Archive Photos; **177 mr,** Phil Banko/Getty Images, Inc.

Chapter Four: Pages 178-179, John Mitchell/Photo Researchers, Inc.; **181,** Russ Lappa; **187 all,** Bruce Iverson; **190,** Russ Lappa; **192 both,** Richard Haynes; **197,** Bob Daemmrich/Stock Boston; **201,** I. Burgum/P. Boorman/Getty Images, Inc.; **206,** AP/Dusan Vranic/Wide World Photos; **212,** Peggy Yoram Kahana/Peter Arnold; **216,** Russell C. Hansen/Peter Arnold, Inc.; **220,** Tim Barnwell/Stock Boston; **222,** K & G Photo/Getty Images, Inc.; **232 t,** Breck P Kent/Animals Animals/Earth Scenes; **232 b,** Colin Keates/Dorling Kindersley; **233 br,** Gary C. Will/Visuals Unlimited.

Chapter Five: Pages 234-235, Gary Noland/Seeley Swan/ Pathfinder; **238,** Monkmeyer/Grant Pix; **241 both,** Ken Karp; **248,** Mark Gibson/Corbis; **249 both,** Richard Haynes; **253,** Alan Schen/Corbis; **254,** Russ Lappa; **261,** Photri/Corbis; **262,** Russ Lappa; **263,** Jason Hawkes/Getty Images, Inc.; **264 all,** Russ Lappa; **270,** Jim Corwim/Photo Researchers, Inc.; **274,** Daniel Lyons/Bruce Coleman, Inc.; **279,** Dirk Weisheit/DDB Stock Photo; **288 t,** Robert Kirkham/Buffalo News; **288 b,** New England Quilt Museum. Gift of The Brinney Family, 1995.20.

Photo by Greg Heins.; **289 br,** Pilgrim/Roy Quilt Collection Warner, NH.

Chapter Six: Pages 290-291, Michael Paras/Image State; **293,** Russ Lappa; **295,** Kindra Clineff/Getty Images, Inc.; **299,** NASA; **301,** REAL LIFE ADVENTURES ©1999 GarLanco. Reprinted with permission of Universal Press Syndicate. All rights reserved.; **304,** Russ Lappa; **306,** Richard Haynes; **308, 309,** Russ Lappa; **311 all,** The United States Mint; **315,** Renee Lynn/Getty Images, Inc.; **317,** Jay Syverson/Stock Boston; **332,** Cincinnati Zoo; **334 both,** Richard Haynes; **338,** Joseph Sohm/Stock Boston; **340,** Tek Image/Science Photo Library/ Photo Researchers, Inc.; **341,** Spencer Grant/Stock Boston; **348,** Rafael Macia/Photo Researchers, Inc.; **348-349 b,** 1997 ChromoSohm/Sohm.; **349 tr,** Charles Thatcher/Getty Images, Inc.; **349 m,** Bruno Joachim/Index Stock Imagery, Inc.

Chapter Seven: Pages 350-351 t, Elizabeth Crews/The Image Works; **353,** Mark Lewis/Getty Images, Inc.; **363 both,** Richard Haynes; **364,** Tim Barnell/Stock Boston; **366,** The Granger Collection, NY; **372,** James Frank/Stock Connection/Picture Quest; **375,** Michael Heron/Corbis; **378,** Jose Carrillo/PhotoEdit; **383,** David Schultz/Getty Images, Inc.; **398 tl,** Russ Lappa; **398 tr,** Bob Mitchell/Corbis; **398 bl,** Dieceland Technologies Corp; **398 br,** Dieceland Technologies Corp; **399 both,** The Boston Globe via www.Merlin-Net.com.

Chapter Eight: Pages 400-401, Dana White/PhotoEdit; **405,** David Young-Wolff/Getty Images, Inc.; **406,** Corel Corp.; **409,** Lester Lefkowitz/Corbis; **415,** Jess Stock/Getty Images, Inc.; **419 t,** Bob Daemmrich/The Image Works; **419 b,** Donald Dietz/ Stock Boston; **420,** Don Smetzer/Getty Images, Inc.; **430,** Russ Lappa; **434,** Erwin & Peggy Bauer/Bruce Coleman, Inc.; **438,** Terry Oakley/Alamy; **441 both,** Richard Haynes; **446,** Joe Sohm/The Image Works; **458 t,** Haruyoshi Yamaguchi/Corbis; **458-459 b,** Raoul Minsart/Corbis; **459 tl,** Yoshida-Fujifotos/The Image Works; **459 tr,** Lester Lefkowitz/Getty Images, Inc.

Chapter Nine: Pages 460-461, Jim Corwin/Stock Boston; **462,** Photo Researchers, Inc.; **464,** James Marshall/Corbis; **467,** AP/ Paul Warner/Wide World Photos; **468,** Jon Chomitz; **471 tl,** Richard Haynes; **471 tr,** Courtesy, J.C. Guillois/Santa Fe Stained Glass; **471 b,** Richard Haynes; **476,** Peter Gridley/Getty Images, Inc.; **477,** Gianalberto Cigolini/Image Bank/Getty Images, Inc.; **480,** Alfred Pasteka/Science Photo Library/Photo Researchers, Inc.; **484,** George Gerster/Photo Researchers, Inc.; **485,** John Heiney/Sportschrome; **487,** R Wahhlstrom/Image Bank/Getty Images, Inc.; **490,** Russ Lappa; 495 t, Russ Lappa; **496 b,** Jon Chomitz; **502,** Russ Lappa; **507 both top,** Russ Lappa; **507 bl,** Patti Murray/Animals Animals/Earth Scenes; **507 br,** C. Zeiss/ Bruce Coleman, Inc.; **512 t,** Russ Lappa; **512 b,** Danilo G.

Donadoni/Bruce Coleman, Inc.; **513 l,** Steve Solum/Bruce Coleman; **513 ml,** Adam Peiperl/Corbis; **513 mr,** Larry West/ Bruce Coleman, Inc.; **513 r,** John Gerlach/Tom Stack & Associates, Inc.; **522-523 b,** Ray Juno/Corbis; **522 tl,** B.W. Kilburn/Corbis; **522 tr,** C. Kropp, Publ. Milwaukee No **331; 523 tr,** Kyodo News International, Inc.

Chapter Ten: Pages 524-525, Barth Falkenberg/Stock Boston; **526,** Leslye Borden/PhotoEdit; **530,** Ken Chernus/PictureQuest; **534,** Pascal Quittemelle/Stock Boston; **535,** Corbis; **539,** Alan Carey/Photo Researchers Inc.; **546,** Ellis Herwig/Stock Boston; **548 all,** Russ Lappa; **550, 553,** Russ Lappa; **560 t,** Russ Lappa; **560 ml,** J. Sapinsky/Corbist; **560 mr,** Richard Haynes; **560 b,** Richard Haynes; **562,** Sara Krulwich/NYT Pictures; **564, 566,** Russ Lappa; **568,** Steven Peters/Getty Images, Inc.; **573,** Jeff Foott/Bruce Coleman, Inc.; **584-585 b,** Eyewire/Getty Images, Inc.; **584 l,** Jim Cummins/Getty Images, Inc.; **585 tl,** Bill Sikes/ AP Wide World Photo; **585 tm,** Steve Lipofsky/Index Stock Imagery, Inc.;**585 tr,** Jamie Squire/Getty Images, Inc.

Chapter Eleven: Pages 578-579, Steve Casimiro/Getty Images, Inc.; **589,** Alese/Mort Pechter/Corbis; **590,** Telegraph Colour Library/Getty Images, Inc.; **597,** Chad Slattery/Getty Images, Inc.; **604,** Hideo Kurihara/Getty Images, Inc.; **607,** H.P. Merten/ Corbis; **609,** Landslides; **616 both,** Richard Haynes; **618,** Lance Nelson/Corbis; **632 b,** Ping Amranand/Superstock, Inc.; **633 tl,** Sydney McGinley credit: Collection of the Artist; **633 tr,** ARS, NY Anthony Scibilia/Art Resource, NY

Chapter Twelve: Pages 634-635, Zoran Milich/Getty Images, Inc.; **641,** Getty Images, Inc.; **642 t,** Marilyn Kazmers/Peter Arnold, Inc.; **642 b,** David Madison/Bruce Coleman, Inc.; **648 l,** Brent Jones/Stock Boston; **648 r,** Nik Wheeler/Corbis; **649,** Gerard Lacz/Peter Arnold, Inc.; **658,** Russ Lappa; **663,** John Lemker/Animals Animals/Earth Scenes; **668,** Corel Corp.; **671,** Lynn Rogers/Peter Arnold, Inc.; **674 both,** Richard Haynes; **682,** Greg Pease/Getty Images, Inc.; **692 tr,** AFP/Corbis; **692 b,** Al Bello/Getty Images News & Sport; **693 tl,** AP/Wide World Photos/FIFA; **693 tm,** Andy Crawford/Dorling Kindersley; **693 tr,** AFP/Corbis

Chapter Thirteen: Pages 694-695, Tannen Maury/The Image Works; **697,** Marc Romanelli/Image Bank/Getty Images, Inc.; **703,** Sydney Thompson/Animals Animals/Earth Scenes; **705,** Bob Daemmrich/Stock Boston; **707,** Andrew Henley/Auscape; **708,** Peter Berndt, M.D., P.A.; **713,** Bob Burch/Bruce Coleman, Inc.; **728 both,** Richard Haynes; **732,** John Davenport/Getty Images, Inc.; **744 tr,** SuperStock, Inc.; **744 m,** James King-Holmes/Photo Researchers, Inc.; **744 bl,** Dorling Kindersley/ Royal British Columbia Museum; **745,** Malcolm Macgregor/ Dorling Kindersley

Acknowledgments